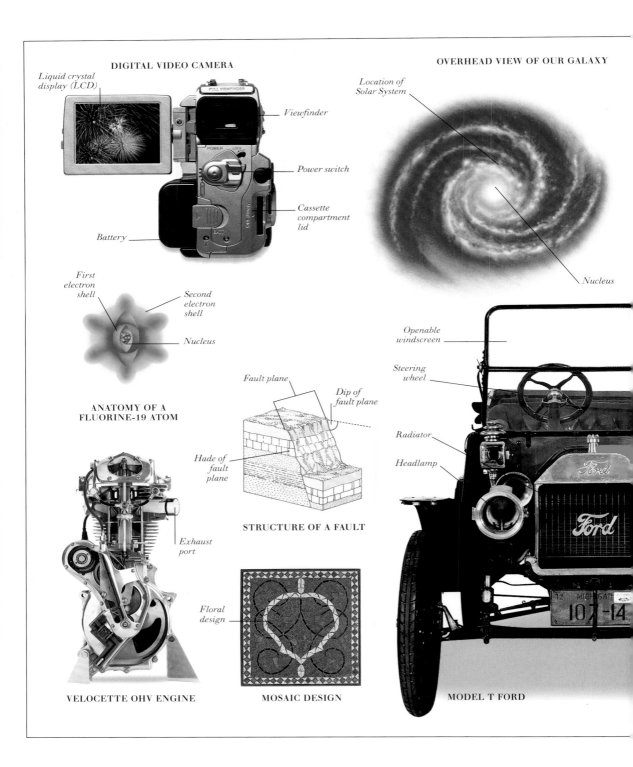

DIGITAL VIDEO CAMERA

Liquid crystal
display (LCD)

Viewfinder

Power switch

Cassette
compartment
lid

Battery

OVERHEAD VIEW OF OUR GALAXY

Location of
Solar System

Nucleus

First
electron
shell

Second
electron
shell

Nucleus

ANATOMY OF A
FLUORINE-19 ATOM

Fault plane

Dip of
fault plane

Hade of
fault
plane

STRUCTURE OF A FAULT

Openable
windscreen

Steering
wheel

Radiator

Headlamp

Exhaust
port

Floral
design

VELOCETTE OHV ENGINE

MOSAIC DESIGN

MODEL T FORD

ULTIMATE FAMILY
VISUAL
dictionary

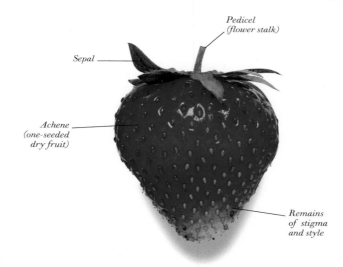

Pedicel
(flower stalk)

Sepal

Achene
(one-seeded
dry fruit)

Remains
of stigma
and style

STRAWBERRY

THIS EDITION

DK LONDON

Editorial Consultants Ian Graham, Darren Naish, Carole Stott
Picture Researcher Karen VanRoss
Jacket Designer Silke Spingies
Digital Conversion Coordinator Linda Zacharia
Production Editor Joanna Byrne
Production Controller Linda Dare
Managing Editor Julie Ferris
Managing Art Editor Owen Peyton Jones
Art Director Philip Ormerod
Associate Publishing Director Liz Wheeler
Publishing Director Jonathan Metcalf

DK DELHI

Managing Art Editor Arunesh Talapatra
Managing Editor Saloni Talwar
Deputy Managing Art Editor Priyabrata Roy Chowdhury
Senior Art Editor Rajnish Kashyap
Senior Editor Neha Gupta
Art Editors Arijit Ganguly, Pooja Pipil
Assistant Art Editor Pooja Pawwar
DTP Manager Balwant Singh
DTP Designer Jaypal Singh Chauhan
Managing Director Aparna Sharma

Anatomical And Botanical Models Supplied By Somso Modelle, Coburg, Germany

ORIGINAL EDITION (*Ultimate Visual Dictionary*)

Project Art Editors Heather McCarry, Johnny Pau, Chris Walker, Kevin Williams
Designer Simon Murrell
Project Editors Luisa Caruso, Peter Jones, Jane Mason, Geoffrey Stalker
Editor Jo Evans
DTP Designer Zirrinia Austin
Picture Researcher Charlotte Bush
Managing Art Editor Toni Kay
Senior Editor Roger Tritton
Managing Editor Sean Moore
Production Manager Hilary Stephens

THIS EDITION PUBLISHED IN 2016
FIRST PUBLISHED IN GREAT BRITAIN IN 1994
UNDER THE TITLE *ULTIMATE VISUAL DICTIONARY* BY
DORLING KINDERSLEY LIMITED
80 STRAND, LONDON WC2R 0RL
A PENGUIN RANDOM HOUSE COMPANY

2 4 6 8 10 9 7 5 3 1
001–178144–Mar/16
REVISED EDITIONS IN 1996, 1997, 1998, 1999, 2000, 2002, 2006, 2011, 2016

A CIP CATALOGUE RECORD FOR THIS BOOK IS AVAILABLE FROM THE BRITISH LIBRARY

ISBN 978-0-2412-7919-9

PRINTED AND BOUND IN CHINA

A WORLD OF IDEAS:
SEE ALL THERE IS TO KNOW
www.dk.com

Prosoma
(cephalothorax)

Spinneret

Leg

**EXTERNAL FEATURES
OF A SPIDER**

Canopy

Fin

G-BNHB

Main landing
gear

SIDE VIEW OF ARV SUPER 2 AEROPLANE

Barrel

Permanent
black ink

FOUNTAIN PEN AND INK

CONTENTS

INTRODUCTION 6

THE UNIVERSE 8

PREHISTORIC EARTH 54

PLANTS 110

ANIMALS 164

THE HUMAN BODY 208

GEOLOGY, GEOGRAPHY,
AND METEOROLOGY 262

PHYSICS AND CHEMISTRY 304

RAIL AND ROAD 322

SEA AND AIR 370

THE VISUAL ARTS 428

ARCHITECTURE 456

MUSIC 500

SPORTS 522

THE MODERN WORLD 564

APPENDIX 616

INDEX 624

Heat shield

Third
stage
motor

Delta II
launch
vehicle
second
stage

MARS PATHFINDER

Face light
emitting
diodes
(LEDs)

Movable
tail

**SONY AIBO
ROBOT DOG**

Low pressure
gases

Central
electrode

**BALL CONTAINING HIGH
TEMPERATURE GAS (PLASMA)**

Parallel
bands

ONYX

Non-breakable
plastic

Shock
absorber

**AMERICAN FOOTBALL
HELMET**

Introduction

THE VISUAL DICTIONARY is a completely new kind of reference book. It provides a link between pictures and words in a way that no ordinary dictionary ever has. Most dictionaries simply tell you what a word means, but the *VISUAL DICTIONARY* shows you – through a combination of detailed annotations, explicit photographs, and illustrations. In the *VISUAL DICTIONARY*, pictures define the annotations around them. You do not read definitions of the annotated words, you see them. The highly accessible format of the *VISUAL DICTIONARY*, the thoroughness of its annotations, and the range of its subject matter make it a unique and helpful reference tool.

How to use the VISUAL DICTIONARY

You will find the *VISUAL DICTIONARY* simple to use. Instead of being organized alphabetically, it is divided by subject into 14 sections – THE UNIVERSE, PREHISTORIC EARTH, PLANTS, ANIMALS, THE HUMAN BODY, etc. Each section begins with a table of contents listing the major entries within that section. For example, The Visual Arts section has entries on *Drawing, Tempera, Fresco, Oils, Watercolour, Pastels, Acrylics, Calligraphy, Printmaking, Mosaic,* and *Sculpture.* Every entry has a short introduction explaining the purpose of the photographs and illustrations, and the significance of the annotations.

If you know what something looks like, but don't know its name, find the term you need by turning to the annotations surrounding the pictures; if you know a word, but don't know what it refers to, use the comprehensive index to direct you to the appropriate page.

Suppose that you want to know what the bone at the end of your little finger is called. With a standard dictionary, you wouldn't know where to begin. But with the *VISUAL DICTIONARY* you simply turn to the entry called *Hands* – within THE HUMAN BODY section – where you will find four fully annotated, colour photographs showing the skin, muscles, and bones of the human hand. In this entry you will quickly find that the bone you are searching for is called the distal phalanx, and for good measure you will discover that it is attached to the middle phalanx by the distal interphalangeal joint.

Perhaps you want to know what a catalytic converter looks like. If you look up "catalytic converter" in an ordinary dictionary, you will be told what it is and possibly what it does – but you will not be able to tell what shape it is or what it is made of. However, if you look up "catalytic converter" in the index of the *VISUAL DICTIONARY*, you will be directed to the *Modern engines* entry on page 344 – where the introduction gives you basic information about what a catalytic converter is – and to page 350 – where there is a spectacular exploded-view photograph of the mechanics of a Renault Clio. From these pages you will find out not only what a catalytic converter looks like, but also that it is attached at one end to an exhaust downpipe and at the other to a silencer.

Whatever it is that you want to find a name for, or whatever name you want to find a picture for, you will find it quickly and easily in the *VISUAL DICTIONARY*. Perhaps you need to know where the vamp on a shoe is; or how to tell obovate and lanceolate leaves apart; or what a spiral galaxy looks like; or whether birds have nostrils. With the *VISUAL DICTIONARY* at hand, the answers to each of these questions, and thousands more, are readily available.

The *VISUAL DICTIONARY* does not just tell you what the names of the different parts of an object are. The photographs, illustrations, and annotations are all specially arranged to help you understand which parts relate to one another and how objects function.

With the *VISUAL DICTIONARY* you can find in seconds the words or pictures that you are looking for; or you can simply browse through the pages of the book for your own pleasure. The *VISUAL DICTIONARY* is not intended to replace a standard dictionary or conventional encyclopedia, but is instead a stimulating and valuable companion to ordinary reference volumes. Giving you instant access to the language that is used by astronomers and architects, musicians and mechanics, scientists and sportspeople, it is the ideal reference book for specialists and generalists of all ages.

Sections of the VISUAL DICTIONARY

The 14 sections of the *Visual Dictionary* contain a total of more than 30,000 terms, encompassing a wide range of topics:

• In the first section, THE UNIVERSE, spectacular photographs and illustrations are used to show the names of the stars and planets and to explain the structure of solar systems, galaxies, nebulae, comets, and black holes.

• PREHISTORIC EARTH tells the story in annotations of how our own planet has evolved since its formation. It includes examples of prehistoric flora and fauna, and fascinating dinosaur models – some with parts of the body stripped away to show anatomical sections.

• PLANTS covers a huge range of species – from the familiar to the exotic. In addition to the colour photographs of plants included in this section, there is a series of micrographic photographs illustrating plant details – such as pollen grains, spores, and cross-sections of stems and roots – in close-up.

• In the ANIMALS section, skeletons, anatomical diagrams, and different parts of animals' bodies have been meticulously annotated. This section provides a comprehensive guide to the vocabulary of zoological classification and animal physiology.

• The structure of the human body, its parts, and its systems are presented in THE HUMAN BODY. The section includes lifelike, three-dimensional models and the latest false-colour images. Clear and authoritative annotations indicate the correct anatomical terms.

• GEOLOGY, GEOGRAPHY, AND METEOROLOGY describes the structure of the Earth – from the inner core to the exosphere – and the physical phenomena – such as volcanoes, rivers, glaciers, and climate – that shape its surface.

• PHYSICS AND CHEMISTRY is a visual journey through the fundamental principles underlying the physical universe, and provides the essential vocabulary of these sciences.

• In RAIL AND ROAD, a wide range of trains, trams and buses, cars, bicycles, and motorcycles are described. Exploded-view photographs show mechanical details with striking clarity.

• SEA AND AIR gives the names for hundreds of parts of ships and aeroplanes. The section includes civil and fighting craft, both historical and modern.

• THE VISUAL ARTS shows the equipment and materials used by painters, sculptors, printers, and other artists. Well-known compositions have been chosen to illustrate specific artistic techniques and effects.

• ARCHITECTURE includes photographs of exemplary architectural models and illustrates dozens of additional features such as columns, domes, and arches.

• MUSIC provides a visual introduction to the special language of music and musical instruments. It includes clearly annotated photographs of each of the major groups of traditional instruments – brass, woodwind, strings, and percussion – together with modern electronic instruments.

• The SPORTS section is a guide to the playing areas, formations, equipment, and techniques needed for many of today's most popular sports.

• In THE MODERN WORLD, items that are a familiar part of our daily lives are taken apart to reveal their inner workings and give access to the language used by their manufacturers. It also includes systems and concepts, such as the Internet, that increasingly influence our 21st century world.

THE UNIVERSE

ANATOMY OF THE UNIVERSE ·········· 10
GALAXIES ·········· 12
THE MILKY WAY ·········· 14
NEBULAE AND STAR CLUSTERS ·········· 16
STARS OF NORTHERN SKIES ·········· 18
STARS OF SOUTHERN SKIES ·········· 20
STARS ·········· 22
SMALL STARS ·········· 24
MASSIVE STARS ·········· 26
NEUTRON STARS AND BLACK HOLES ·········· 28
THE SOLAR SYSTEM ·········· 30
THE SUN ·········· 32
MERCURY ·········· 34
VENUS ·········· 36
THE EARTH ·········· 38
THE MOON ·········· 40
MARS ·········· 42
JUPITER ·········· 44
SATURN ·········· 46
URANUS ·········· 48
NEPTUNE AND PLUTO ·········· 50
ASTEROIDS, COMETS, AND METEOROIDS ·········· 52

Anatomy of the Universe

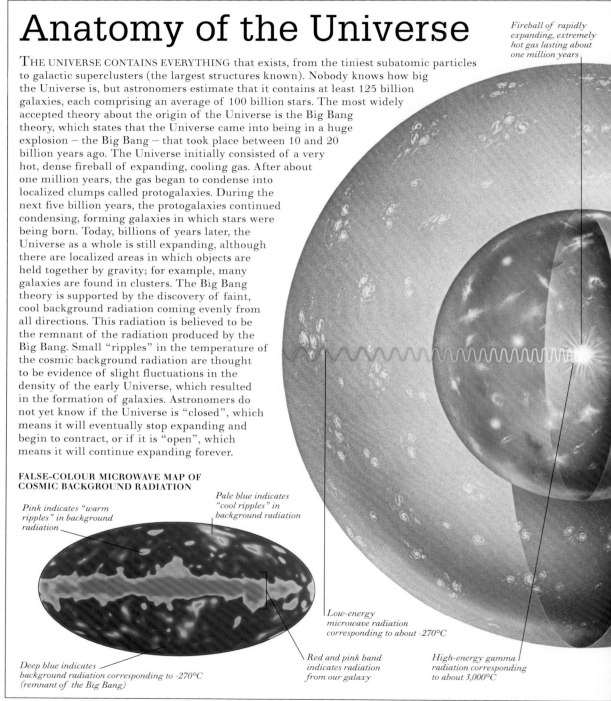

THE UNIVERSE CONTAINS EVERYTHING that exists, from the tiniest subatomic particles to galactic superclusters (the largest structures known). Nobody knows how big the Universe is, but astronomers estimate that it contains at least 125 billion galaxies, each comprising an average of 100 billion stars. The most widely accepted theory about the origin of the Universe is the Big Bang theory, which states that the Universe came into being in a huge explosion – the Big Bang – that took place between 10 and 20 billion years ago. The Universe initially consisted of a very hot, dense fireball of expanding, cooling gas. After about one million years, the gas began to condense into localized clumps called protogalaxies. During the next five billion years, the protogalaxies continued condensing, forming galaxies in which stars were being born. Today, billions of years later, the Universe as a whole is still expanding, although there are localized areas in which objects are held together by gravity; for example, many galaxies are found in clusters. The Big Bang theory is supported by the discovery of faint, cool background radiation coming evenly from all directions. This radiation is believed to be the remnant of the radiation produced by the Big Bang. Small "ripples" in the temperature of the cosmic background radiation are thought to be evidence of slight fluctuations in the density of the early Universe, which resulted in the formation of galaxies. Astronomers do not yet know if the Universe is "closed", which means it will eventually stop expanding and begin to contract, or if it is "open", which means it will continue expanding forever.

Fireball of rapidly expanding, extremely hot gas lasting about one million years

FALSE-COLOUR MICROWAVE MAP OF COSMIC BACKGROUND RADIATION

Pink indicates "warm ripples" in background radiation

Pale blue indicates "cool ripples" in background radiation

Deep blue indicates background radiation corresponding to -270°C (remnant of the Big Bang)

Red and pink band indicates radiation from our galaxy

Low-energy microwave radiation corresponding to about -270°C

High-energy gamma radiation corresponding to about 3,000°C

ORIGIN AND EXPANSION OF THE UNIVERSE

OBJECTS IN THE UNIVERSE

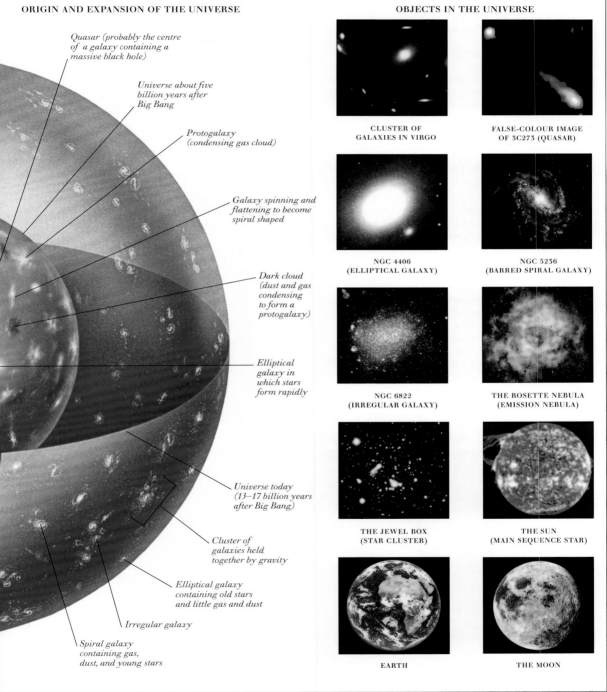

Quasar (probably the centre
of a galaxy containing a
massive black hole)

Universe about five
billion years after
Big Bang

Protogalaxy
(condensing gas cloud)

Galaxy spinning and
flattening to become
spiral shaped

Dark cloud
(dust and gas
condensing
to form a
protogalaxy)

Elliptical
galaxy in
which stars
form rapidly

Universe today
(13–17 billion years
after Big Bang)

Cluster of
galaxies held
together by gravity

Elliptical galaxy
containing old stars
and little gas and dust

Irregular galaxy

Spiral galaxy
containing gas,
dust, and young stars

CLUSTER OF
GALAXIES IN VIRGO

FALSE-COLOUR IMAGE
OF 3C273 (QUASAR)

NGC 4406
(ELLIPTICAL GALAXY)

NGC 5236
(BARRED SPIRAL GALAXY)

NGC 6822
(IRREGULAR GALAXY)

THE ROSETTE NEBULA
(EMISSION NEBULA)

THE JEWEL BOX
(STAR CLUSTER)

THE SUN
(MAIN SEQUENCE STAR)

EARTH

THE MOON

Galaxies

SOMBRERO,
A SPIRAL GALAXY

A GALAXY IS A HUGE MASS OF STARS, nebulae, and interstellar material. The smallest galaxies contain about 100,000 stars, while the largest contain up to 3,000 billion stars. There are three main types of galaxy, classified according to their shape: elliptical, which are oval shaped; spiral, which have arms spiralling outwards from a central bulge (those whose arms spiral from a bar-shaped bulge are called spirals); and irregular, which have no obvious shape. Sometimes, the shape of a galaxy is distorted by a collision with another galaxy. Quasars (quasi-stellar objects) are thought to be galactic nuclei but are so far away that their exact nature is still uncertain. They are compact, highly luminous objects in the outer reaches of the known Universe: while the furthest known "ordinary" galaxies are about 12 billion light years away, the furthest known quasar is about 13 billion light years away. Active galaxies, such as Seyfert galaxies and radio galaxies, emit intense radiation. In a Seyfert galaxy, this radiation comes from the galactic nucleus; in a radio galaxy, it also comes from huge lobes on either side of the galaxy. The radiation from active galaxies and quasars is thought to be caused by material falling into central black holes (see pp. 28-29).

OPTICAL IMAGE OF NGC 4486
(ELLIPTICAL GALAXY)

Globular cluster containing very old red giants

Central region containing old red giants

Less densely populated region

Neighbouring galaxy

OPTICAL IMAGE OF LARGE MAGELLANIC CLOUD (IRREGULAR GALAXY)

Tarantula Nebula

Dust cloud obscuring light from stars

Emission nebula

Light from stars

OPTICAL IMAGE OF NGC 2997 (SPIRAL GALAXY)

Glowing nebula in spiral arm

Spiral arm containing young stars

Galactic nucleus containing old stars

Dust in spiral arm reflecting blue light from hot young stars

Hot, ionized hydrogen gas emitting red light

Dust lane

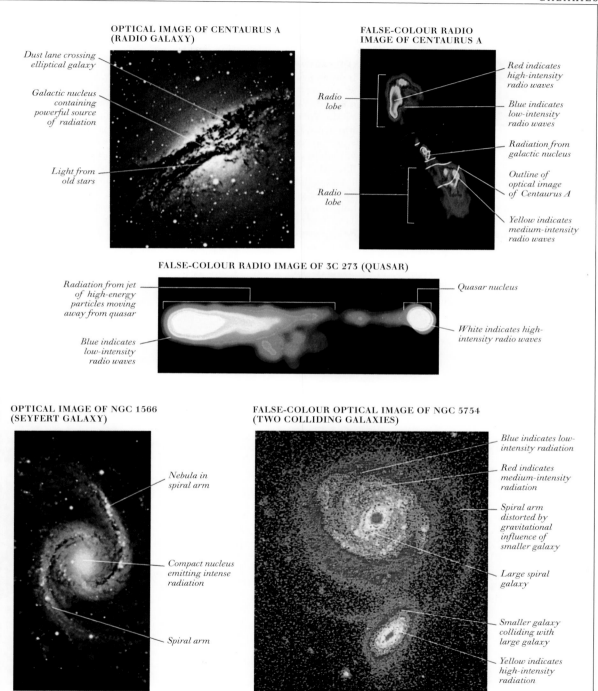

**OPTICAL IMAGE OF CENTAURUS A
(RADIO GALAXY)**

Dust lane crossing
elliptical galaxy

Galactic nucleus
containing
powerful source
of radiation

Light from
old stars

**FALSE-COLOUR RADIO
IMAGE OF CENTAURUS A**

Radio
lobe

Radio
lobe

Red indicates
high-intensity
radio waves

Blue indicates
low-intensity
radio waves

Radiation from
galactic nucleus

Outline of
optical image
of Centaurus A

Yellow indicates
medium-intensity
radio waves

FALSE-COLOUR RADIO IMAGE OF 3C 273 (QUASAR)

Radiation from jet
of high-energy
particles moving
away from quasar

Blue indicates
low-intensity
radio waves

Quasar nucleus

White indicates high-
intensity radio waves

**OPTICAL IMAGE OF NGC 1566
(SEYFERT GALAXY)**

Nebula in
spiral arm

Compact nucleus
emitting intense
radiation

Spiral arm

**FALSE-COLOUR OPTICAL IMAGE OF NGC 5754
(TWO COLLIDING GALAXIES)**

Blue indicates low-
intensity radiation

Red indicates
medium-intensity
radiation

Spiral arm
distorted by
gravitational
influence of
smaller galaxy

Large spiral
galaxy

Smaller galaxy
colliding with
large galaxy

Yellow indicates
high-intensity
radiation

13

The Milky Way

VIEW TOWARDS
GALACTIC CENTRE

THE MILKY WAY IS THE NAME GIVEN TO THE FAINT BAND OF LIGHT that stretches across the night sky. This light comes from stars and nebulae in our galaxy, known as the Milky Way Galaxy or simply as "the Galaxy". The Galaxy is believed to be a barred spiral, with a dense central bar of stars encircled by four arms spiralling outwards and surrounded by a less dense halo. We cannot see the spiral shape because the Solar System is in one of the spiral arms, the Orion Arm (also called the Local Arm). From our position, the centre of the Galaxy is completely obscured by dust clouds; as a result, optical maps give only a limited view of the Galaxy. However, a more complete picture can be obtained by studying radio, infra-red, and other radiation. The central part of the Galaxy is relatively small and dense and contains mainly older red and yellow stars. The halo is a less dense region in which the oldest stars are situated; some of these stars are as old as the Galaxy itself (possibly 13 billion years). The spiral arms contain main sequence stars and hot, young, blue stars, as well as nebulae (clouds of dust and gas inside which stars are born). The Galaxy is vast, about 100,000 light years across (a light year is about 9,460 billion kilometres); in comparison, the Solar System seems small, at about 12 light hours across (about 13 billion kilometres). The entire Galaxy is rotating in space, although the inner stars travel faster than those further out. The Sun, which is about two-thirds out from the centre, completes one lap of the Galaxy about every 220 million years.

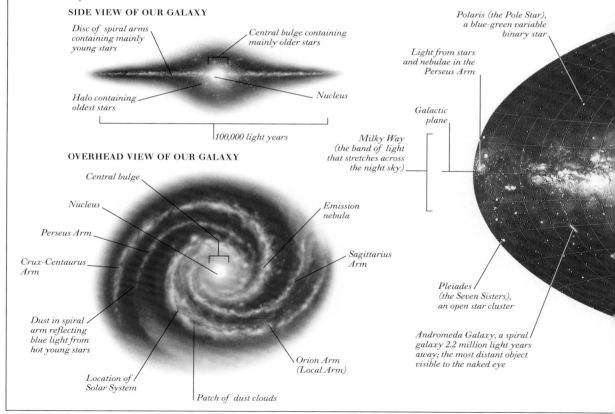

SIDE VIEW OF OUR GALAXY

Disc of spiral arms containing mainly young stars

Central bulge containing mainly older stars

Halo containing oldest stars

Nucleus

100,000 light years

OVERHEAD VIEW OF OUR GALAXY

Central bulge

Nucleus

Perseus Arm

Crux-Centaurus Arm

Emission nebula

Sagittarius Arm

Dust in spiral arm reflecting blue light from hot young stars

Location of Solar System

Patch of dust clouds

Orion Arm (Local Arm)

PANORAMIC OPTICAL MAP OF OUR GALAXY AND NEARBY GALAXIES

Polaris (the Pole Star), a blue-green variable binary star

Light from stars and nebulae in the Perseus Arm

Galactic plane

Milky Way (the band of light that stretches across the night sky)

Pleiades (the Seven Sisters), an open star cluster

Andromeda Galaxy, a spiral galaxy 2.2 million light years away; the most distant object visible to the naked eye

PANORAMIC RADIO MAP OF OUR GALAXY

PANORAMIC INFRA-RED MAP OF OUR GALAXY

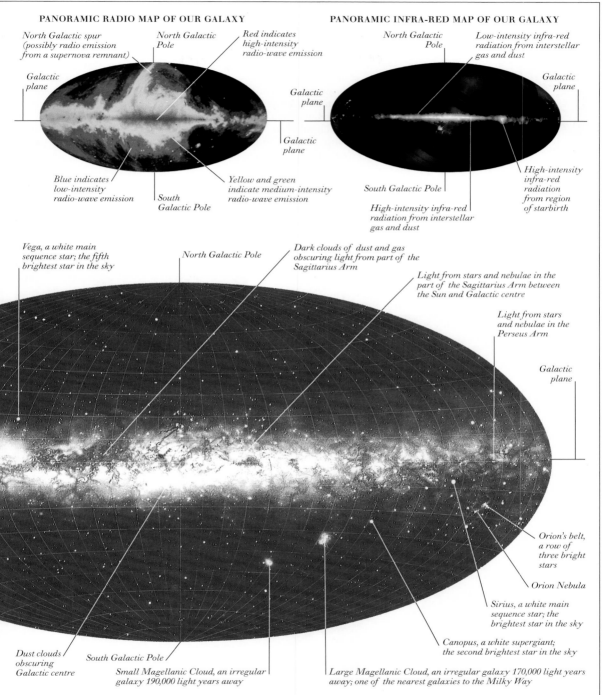

North Galactic spur
(possibly radio emission
from a supernova remnant)

North Galactic
Pole

Red indicates
high-intensity
radio-wave emission

Galactic
plane

North Galactic
Pole

Low-intensity infra-red
radiation from interstellar
gas and dust

Galactic
plane

Galactic
plane

Galactic
plane

Blue indicates
low-intensity
radio-wave emission

South
Galactic Pole

Yellow and green
indicate medium-intensity
radio-wave emission

South Galactic Pole

High-intensity infra-red
radiation from interstellar
gas and dust

High-intensity
infra-red
radiation
from region
of starbirth

Vega, a white main
sequence star; the fifth
brightest star in the sky

North Galactic Pole

Dark clouds of dust and gas
obscuring light from part of the
Sagittarius Arm

Light from stars and nebulae in the
part of the Sagittarius Arm between
the Sun and Galactic centre

Light from stars
and nebulae in the
Perseus Arm

Galactic
plane

Orion's belt,
a row of
three bright
stars

Orion Nebula

Sirius, a white main
sequence star; the
brightest star in the sky

Canopus, a white supergiant;
the second brightest star in the sky

Dust clouds
obscuring
Galactic centre

South Galactic Pole

Small Magellanic Cloud, an irregular
galaxy 190,000 light years away

Large Magellanic Cloud, an irregular galaxy 170,000 light years
away; one of the nearest galaxies to the Milky Way

Nebulae and star clusters

**HODGE 11, A
GLOBULAR CLUSTER**

A NEBULA IS A CLOUD OF DUST AND GAS inside a galaxy. Nebulae become visible if the gas glows, or if the cloud reflects starlight or obscures light from more distant objects. Emission nebulae shine because their gas emits light when it is stimulated by radiation from hot young stars. Reflection nebulae shine because their dust reflects light from stars in or around the nebula. Dark nebulae appear as silhouettes because they block out light from shining nebulae or stars behind them. Two types of nebula are associated with dying stars: planetary nebulae and supernova remnants. Both consist of expanding shells of gas that were once the outer layers of a star. A planetary nebula is a gas shell drifting away from a dying stellar core. A supernova remnant is a gas shell moving away from a stellar core at great speed following a violent explosion called a supernova (see pp. 26-27). Stars are often found in groups known as clusters. Open clusters are loose groups of a few thousand young stars that were born from the same cloud and are drifting apart. Globular clusters are densely packed, roughly spherical groups of hundreds of thousands of older stars.

TRIFID NEBULA (EMISSION NEBULA)

Reflection nebula

Emission nebula

Dust lane

Starbirth region
(area in which
dust and gas
clump together
to form stars)

**PLEIADES (OPEN STAR CLUSTER)
WITH A REFLECTION NEBULA**

Wisps of dust and
hydrogen gas. The
cluster is passing
through a region of
inter-stellar
material

Young star in an
open cluster of more
than 1,000 stars

Reflection nebula

HORSEHEAD NEBULA (DARK NEBULA)

Glowing filament
of hot, ionized
hydrogen gas

Alnitak (star in
Orion's belt)

Dust lane

Emission nebula

Star near southern
end of Orion's belt

Emission nebula

Horsehead Nebula

Reflection nebula

Dark nebula
obscuring light
from distant stars

ORION NEBULA (DIFFUSE EMISSION NEBULA)

Glowing cloud of dust and hydrogen gas forming part of Orion Nebula

Dust cloud

Trapezium (group of four young stars)

Red light from hot, ionized hydrogen gas

Gas cloud emitting light due to ultraviolet radiation from the four young Trapezium stars

Green light from hot, ionized oxygen gas

Glowing filament of hot, ionized hydrogen gas

VELA SUPERNOVA REMNANT

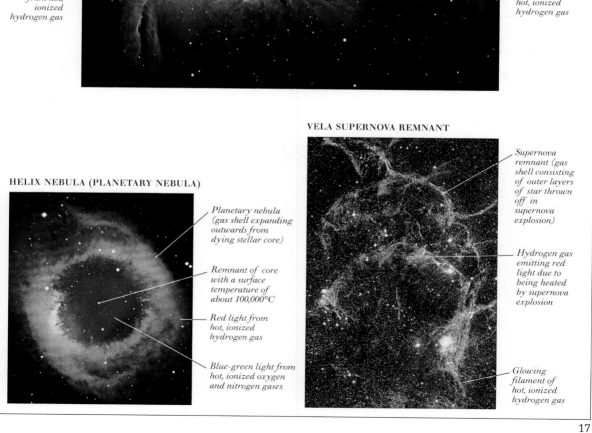

Supernova remnant (gas shell consisting of outer layers of star thrown off in supernova explosion)

Hydrogen gas emitting red light due to being heated by supernova explosion

Glowing filament of hot, ionized hydrogen gas

HELIX NEBULA (PLANETARY NEBULA)

Planetary nebula (gas shell expanding outwards from dying stellar core)

Remnant of core with a surface temperature of about 100,000°C

Red light from hot, ionized hydrogen gas

Blue-green light from hot, ionized oxygen and nitrogen gases

Stars of northern skies

WHEN YOU LOOK AT THE NORTHERN SKY, you look away from the densely populated Galactic centre, so the northern sky generally appears less bright than the southern sky (see pp. 20-21). Among the best-known sights in the northern sky are the constellations Ursa Major (the Great Bear) and Orion. Some ancient civilizations believed that the stars were fixed to a celestial sphere surrounding the Earth, and modern maps of the sky are based on a similar idea. The North and South Poles of this imaginary celestial sphere are directly above the North and South Poles of the Earth, at the points where the Earth's axis of rotation intersects the sphere. The celestial North Pole is at the centre of the map shown here, and Polaris (the Pole Star) lies very close to it. The celestial equator marks a projection of the Earth's equator on the sphere. The ecliptic marks the path of the Sun across the sky as the Earth orbits the Sun. The Moon and planets move against the background of the stars because the stars are much more distant; the nearest star outside the Solar System (Proxima Centauri) is more than 50,000 times further away than the planet Jupiter.

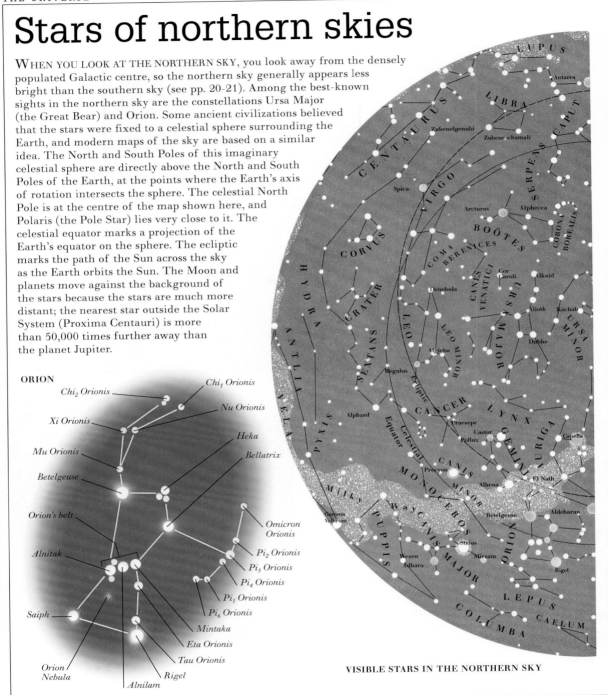

ORION

- Chi₂ Orionis
- Chi₁ Orionis
- Nu Orionis
- Xi Orionis
- Heka
- Mu Orionis
- Bellatrix
- Betelgeuse
- Orion's belt
- Omicron Orionis
- Alnitak
- Pi₂ Orionis
- Pi₃ Orionis
- Pi₄ Orionis
- Pi₅ Orionis
- Pi₆ Orionis
- Saiph
- Mintaka
- Eta Orionis
- Tau Orionis
- Orion Nebula
- Rigel
- Alnilam

VISIBLE STARS IN THE NORTHERN SKY

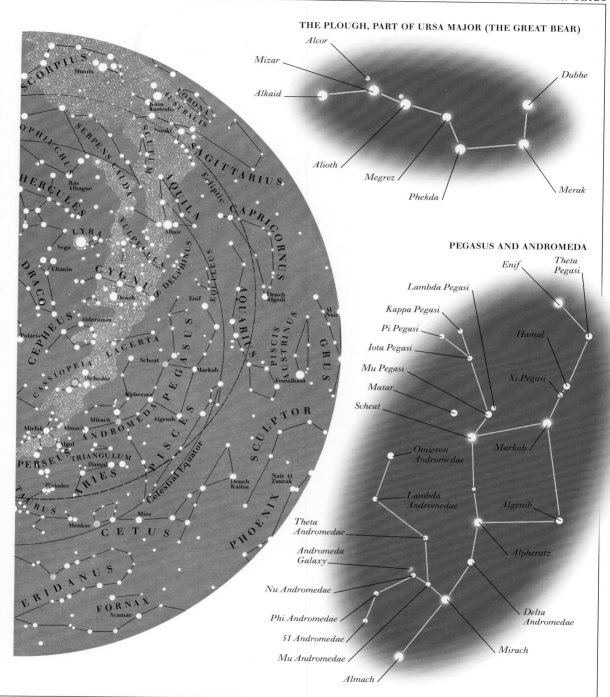

THE PLOUGH, PART OF URSA MAJOR (THE GREAT BEAR)

Alcor
Mizar
Alkaid
Dubhe
Alioth
Megrez
Phekda
Merak

PEGASUS AND ANDROMEDA

Enif
Theta Pegasi
Lambda Pegasi
Kappa Pegasi
Pi Pegasi
Iota Pegasi
Mu Pegasi
Matar
Scheat
Hamal
Xi Pegasi
Markab
Omicron Andromedae
Lambda Andromedae
Algenib
Theta Andromedae
Andromeda Galaxy
Alpheratz
Nu Andromedae
Phi Andromedae
51 Andromedae
Delta Andromedae
Mu Andromedae
Mirach
Almach

SCORPIUS
Shaula
CORONA AUSTRALIS
Kaus Australis
Nunki
OPHIUCHUS
SERPENS CAUDA
SCUTUM
SAGITTARIUS
AQUILA
Ecliptic
CAPRICORNUS
HERCULES
Ras Alhague
Altair
VULPECULA
LYRA
Vega
DELPHINUS
Enif
EQUULEUS
AQUARIUS
Deneb Algedi
Al Nair
DRACO
Eltanin
CYGNUS
Deneb
PISCIS AUSTRINUS
GRUS
CEPHEUS
Alderamin
LACERTA
Scheat
Markab
Fomalhaut
Polaris
PEGASUS
CASSIOPEIA
Schedar
Alpheratz
ANDROMEDA
Algenib
PISCES
SCULPTOR
Mirfak
Almach
Mirach
Nair Al Zaurak
Algol
TRIANGULUM
Hamal
Celestial Equator
Deneb Kaitos
PERSEUS
ARIES
Pleiades
Mira
PHOENIX
TAURUS
Menkar
CETUS
ERIDANUS
FORNAX
Acamar

19

Stars of southern skies

WHEN YOU LOOK AT THE SOUTHERN SKY, you look towards the Galactic centre, which has a huge population of stars. As a result, the Milky Way appears brighter in the southern sky than in the northern sky (see pp. 18-19). The southern sky is rich in nebulae and star clusters. It contains the Large and Small Magellanic Clouds, which are two of the nearest galaxies to our own. Stars make fixed patterns in the sky called constellations. However, the constellations are only apparent groupings of stars, since the distances to the stars in a constellation may vary enormously. The shapes of constellations may change over many thousands of years due to the relative motions of stars. The movement of the constellations across the sky is due to the Earth's motion in space. The daily rotation of the Earth causes the constellations to move across the sky from east to west, and the orbit of the Earth around the Sun causes different areas of sky to be visible in different seasons. The visibility of areas of sky also depends on the location of the observer. For instance, stars near the celestial equator may be seen from either hemisphere at some time during the year, whereas stars close to the celestial poles (the celestial South Pole is at the centre of the map shown here) can never be seen from the opposite hemisphere.

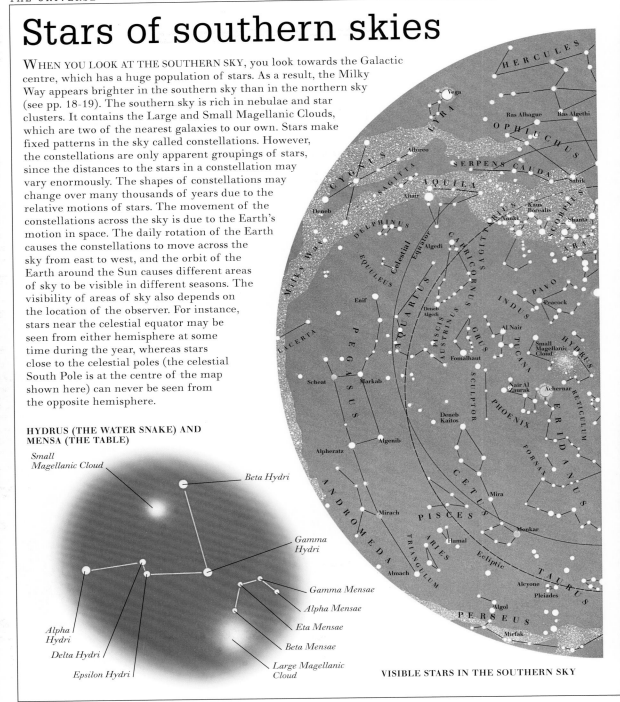

HYDRUS (THE WATER SNAKE) AND MENSA (THE TABLE)

Small Magellanic Cloud
Beta Hydri
Gamma Hydri
Gamma Mensae
Alpha Mensae
Eta Mensae
Beta Mensae
Large Magellanic Cloud
Alpha Hydri
Delta Hydri
Epsilon Hydri

VISIBLE STARS IN THE SOUTHERN SKY

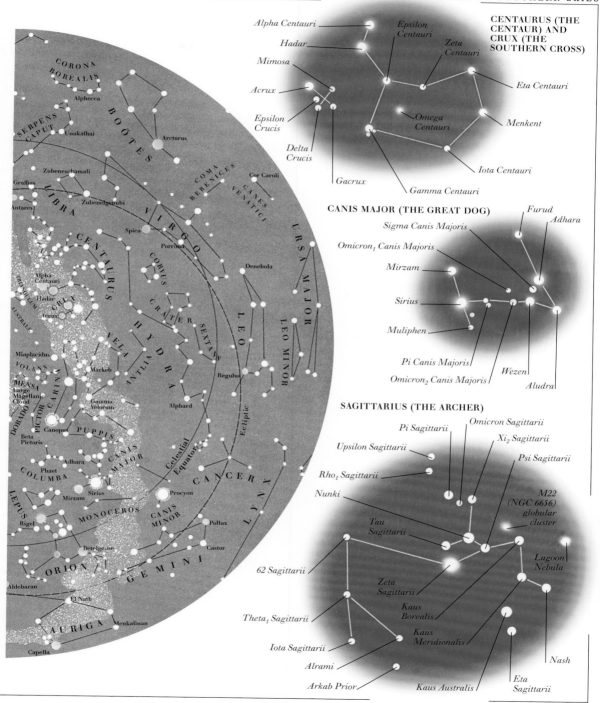

CENTAURUS (THE CENTAUR) AND CRUX (THE SOUTHERN CROSS)

Alpha Centauri

Epsilon Centauri

Hadar

Zeta Centauri

Mimosa

Acrux

Eta Centauri

Epsilon Crucis

Omega Centauri

Menkent

Delta Crucis

Gacrux

Iota Centauri

Gamma Centauri

CANIS MAJOR (THE GREAT DOG)

Furud

Sigma Canis Majoris

Adhara

Omicron₁ Canis Majoris

Mirzam

Sirius

Muliphen

Pi Canis Majoris

Wezen

Omicron₂ Canis Majoris

Aludra

SAGITTARIUS (THE ARCHER)

Pi Sagittarii

Omicron Sagittarii

Upsilon Sagittarii

Xi₂ Sagittarii

Rho₁ Sagittarii

Psi Sagittarii

Nunki

M22 (NGC 6656) globular cluster

Tau Sagittarii

Lagoon Nebula

62 Sagittarii

Zeta Sagittarii

Kaus Borealis

Theta₁ Sagittarii

Kaus Meridionalis

Iota Sagittarii

Nash

Alrami

Arkab Prior

Kaus Australis

Eta Sagittarii

CORONA BOREALIS

Alphecca

SERPENS CAPUT

Unukalhai

Arcturus

BOÖTES

Graffias

Zubeneschamali

COMA BERENICES

CANES VENATICI

Cor Caroli

Antares

LIBRA

Zubenelgenubi

VIRGO

URSA MAJOR

Spica

Porrima

Denebola

CENTAURUS

Alpha Centauri

CORVUS

CRATER

SEXTANS

LEO

LEO MINOR

Hadar

CRUX

Acrux

HYDRA

Miaplacidus

VELA

ANTLIA

Regulus

Alphard

VOLANS

Markeb

MENSA

Large Magellanic Cloud

PICTOR

CARINA

Gamma Velorum

Ecliptic

Canopus

PUPPIS

CANCER

LYNX

DORADO

Beta Pictoris

CANIS MAJOR

Celestial Equator

Phact

Adhara

COLUMBA

Mirzam Sirius

MONOCEROS

Procyon

CANIS MINOR

LEPUS

Rigel

Pollux

Castor

ORION

Betelgeuse

GEMINI

Aldebaran

El Nath

Menkalinan

AURIGA

Capella

21

Stars

OPEN STAR CLUSTER
AND DUST CLOUD

STARS ARE BODIES of hot, glowing gas that are born in nebulae (see pp. 24-27). They vary enormously in size, mass, and temperature: diameters range from about 450 times smaller to over 1,000 times bigger than that of the Sun; masses range from about a twentieth to over 50 solar masses; and surface temperatures range from about 3,000°C to over 50,000°C. The colour of a star is determined by its temperature: the hottest stars are blue and the coolest are red. The Sun, with a surface temperature of 5,500°C, is between these extremes and appears yellow. The energy emitted by a shining star is usually produced by nuclear fusion in the star's core. The brightness of a star is measured in magnitudes – the brighter the star, the lower its magnitude. There are two types of magnitude: apparent magnitude, which is the brightness seen from Earth, and absolute magnitude, which is the brightness that would be seen from a standard distance of 10 parsecs (32.6 light years). The light emitted by a star may be split to form a spectrum containing a series of dark lines (absorption lines). The patterns of lines indicate the presence of particular chemical elements, enabling astronomers to deduce the composition of the star's atmosphere. The magnitude and spectral type (colour) of stars may be plotted on a graph called a Hertzsprung-Russell diagram, which shows that stars tend to fall into several well-defined groups. The principal groups are main sequence stars (those which are fusing hydrogen to form helium), giants, supergiants, and white dwarfs.

STAR SIZES

Red giant (diameters between about 15 million and 150 million km)

The Sun (main sequence star with diameter about 1.4 million km)

White dwarf (diameters between about 3,000 and 50,000 km)

ENERGY EMISSION FROM THE SUN

Nuclear fusion in core produces gamma rays and neutrinos

Neutrinos travel to Earth directly from Sun's core in about 8 minutes

Lower-energy radiation travels to Earth in about 8 minutes

Earth

Sun

Lower-energy radiation (mainly ultraviolet, infra-red, and light rays) leaves surface

High-energy radiation (gamma rays) loses energy while travelling to surface over 2 million years

STAR MAGNITUDES

APPARENT MAGNITUDE

ABSOLUTE MAGNITUDE

Brighter stars

Sirius: apparent magnitude of -1.46

Rigel: apparent magnitude of +0.12

Objects of magnitude higher than about +6.0 cannot be seen by the naked eye

Rigel: absolute magnitude of -7.1

Sirius: absolute magnitude of +1.4

Fainter stars

NUCLEAR FUSION IN MAIN SEQUENCE STARS LIKE THE SUN

Positron

Deuterium nucleus

Proton

Neutron

Proton (hydrogen nucleus)

Neutrino

Gamma rays

Helium-3 nucleus

Helium-4 nucleus

HERTZSPRUNG-RUSSELL DIAGRAM

Hotter stars   TEMPERATURE (°C)   Cooler stars

50,000   10,000   5,000   5,500   3,000

More luminous stars

-7
-6
-5
-4
-3
-2
-1
0
+1
+2
+3
+4
+5
+6
+7
+8
+9
+10
+11
+12
+13
+14
+15
+16

Less luminous stars

ABSOLUTE
VISUAL
MAGNITUDE

Deneb (blue supergiant)

Sirius A (massive
main sequence star)

Sirius B (white dwarf)

SUPERGIANTS

GIANTS

MAIN SEQUENCE STARS

WRITE DWARFS

Betelgeuse (red supergiant)

Arcturus (red giant)

The Sun (yellow main
sequence dwarf)

Barnard's Star (main
sequence red dwarf)

O5   B0   A0   F0   G0   K0   M0   M5

SPECTRAL TYPE

STELLAR SPECTRAL ABSORPTION LINES

Calcium line   Hydrogen
gamma line

Hydrogen
beta line

Helium line

Sodium
lines

Hydrogen
alpha line

STAR OF SPECTRAL
TYPE A (e.g., SIRIUS)

STAR OF SPECTRAL
TYPE G (e.g., THE SUN)

Hydrogen
beta line

Magnesium
lines

Sodium
lines

Hydrogen
alpha line

23

Small stars

**REGION OF
STAR FORMATION
IN ORION**

SMALL STARS HAVE A MASS of up to about one and a half
times that of the Sun. They begin to form when a region of
higher density in a nebula condenses into a huge globule
of gas and dust that contracts under its own gravity.
Within a globule, regions of condensing matter heat
up and begin to glow, forming protostars. If a
protostar contains enough matter, the central
temperature reaches about 8 million °C. At this
temperature, nuclear reactions in which hydrogen
fuses to form helium can start. This process releases
energy, which prevents the star from contracting
further and also causes it to shine; it is now a main
sequence star. A star of about one solar mass remains
on the main sequence for about 10 billion years, until much of the hydrogen in
the star's core has been converted into helium. The helium core then contracts,
and nuclear reactions continue in a shell around the core. The core becomes hot
enough for helium to fuse to form carbon, while the outer
layers of the star expand and cool. The expanding
star is known as a red giant. When the
helium in the core runs out, the outer
layers of the star may be blown
away as an expanding gas shell
called a planetary nebula. The
remaining core (about 80
per cent of the original
star) is now in its final
stages. It becomes
a white dwarf star
that gradually cools
and dims. When it
finally stops shining
altogether, the dead
star will become
a black dwarf.

**STRUCTURE OF A
MAIN SEQUENCE STAR**

*Core containing hydrogen
fusing to form helium*

*Radiative
zone*

*Convective
zone*

*Surface temperature
about 5,500°C*

*Core temperature
about 15 million °C*

STRUCTURE OF A NEBULA

*Young main
sequence star*

*Dense region of dust and
gas (mainly hydrogen)
condensing under gravity
to form globules*

*Hot, ionized hydrogen
gas emitting red light
due to being stimulated
by radiation from hot
young stars*

*Dark globule of dust and
gas (mainly hydrogen)
contracting to form protostars*

LIFE OF A SMALL STAR OF ABOUT ONE SOLAR MASS

*Cool cloud of
gas (mainly
hydrogen)
and dust*

*Dense globule
condensing to
form protostars*

NEBULA

*Glowing
ball of gas
(mainly
hydrogen)*

*Natal cocoon
(shell of dust
blown away by
radiation from
protostar)*

PROTOSTAR
Duration: 50 million years

About 1.4 million km

*Star
producing
energy by
nuclear fusion
in core*

MAIN SEQUENCE STAR
Duration: 10 billion years

STRUCTURE OF A RED GIANT

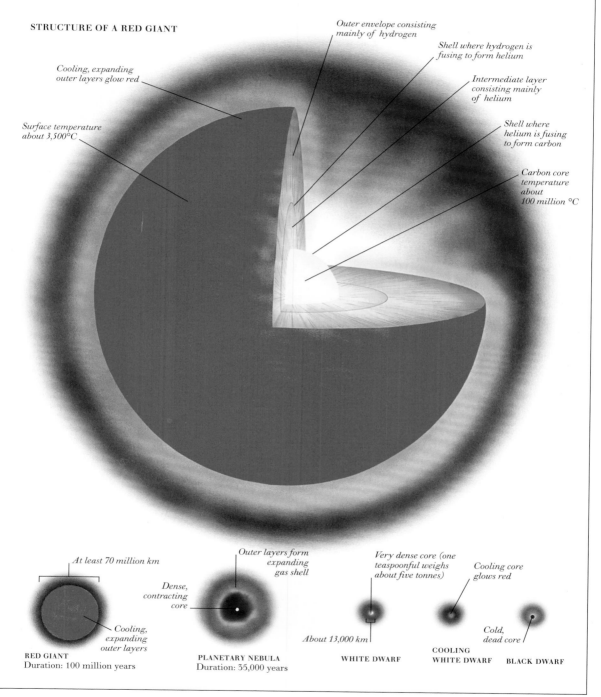

Outer envelope consisting mainly of hydrogen

Shell where hydrogen is fusing to form helium

Cooling, expanding outer layers glow red

Intermediate layer consisting mainly of helium

Shell where helium is fusing to form carbon

Surface temperature about 3,500°C

Carbon core temperature about 100 million °C

At least 70 million km

Cooling, expanding outer layers

RED GIANT
Duration: 100 million years

Outer layers form expanding gas shell

Dense, contracting core

PLANETARY NEBULA
Duration: 35,000 years

Very dense core (one teaspoonful weighs about five tonnes)

About 13,000 km

WHITE DWARF

Cooling core glows red

Cold, dead core

COOLING WHITE DWARF

BLACK DWARF

Massive stars

MASSIVE STARS HAVE A MASS AT LEAST THREE TIMES that of the Sun, and some stars are as massive as about 50 Suns. A massive star evolves in a similar way to a small star until it reaches the main sequence stage (see pp. 24-25). During its life as a main sequence star, it shines steadily until the hydrogen in its core has fused to form helium. This process takes billions of years in a small star, but only millions of years in a massive star. A massive star then becomes a red supergiant, which initially consists of a helium core surrounded by outer layers of cooling, expanding gas. Over the next few million years, a series of nuclear reactions form different elements in shells around an iron core. The core eventually collapses in less than a second, causing a massive explosion called a supernova, in which a shock wave blows away the outer layers of the star. Supernovae shine brighter than an entire galaxy for a short time. Sometimes, the core survives the supernova explosion. If the surviving core is between about one and a half and three solar masses, it contracts to become a tiny, dense neutron star. If the core is greater than three solar masses, it contracts to become a black hole (see pp. 28-29).

SUPERNOVA

TARANTULA NEBULA BEFORE SUPERNOVA

STRUCTURE OF A RED SUPERGIANT

Outer envelope consisting mainly of hydrogen

Layer consisting mainly of helium

Layer consisting mainly of carbon

Layer consisting mainly of oxygen

Layer consisting mainly of silicon

Shell of hydrogen fusing to form helium

Shell of helium fusing to form carbon

Shell of carbon fusing to form oxygen

Shell of oxygen fusing to form silicon

Shell of silicon fusing to form iron core

Surface temperature about 3,000°C

Cooling, expanding outer layers glow red

Core of mainly iron at a temperature of 3-5 billion °C

LIFE OF A MASSIVE STAR OF ABOUT 10 SOLAR MASSES

Dense globule condensing to form protostars

Cool cloud of gas (mainly hydrogen) and dust

NEBULA

Glowing ball of gas (mainly hydrogen)

About 3 million km

Star producing energy by nuclear fusion in core

Natal cocoon (shell of dust blown away by radiation from protostar)

PROTOSTAR
Duration: a few hundred thousand years

MAIN SEQUENCE STAR
Duration: 10 million years

FEATURES OF A SUPERNOVA

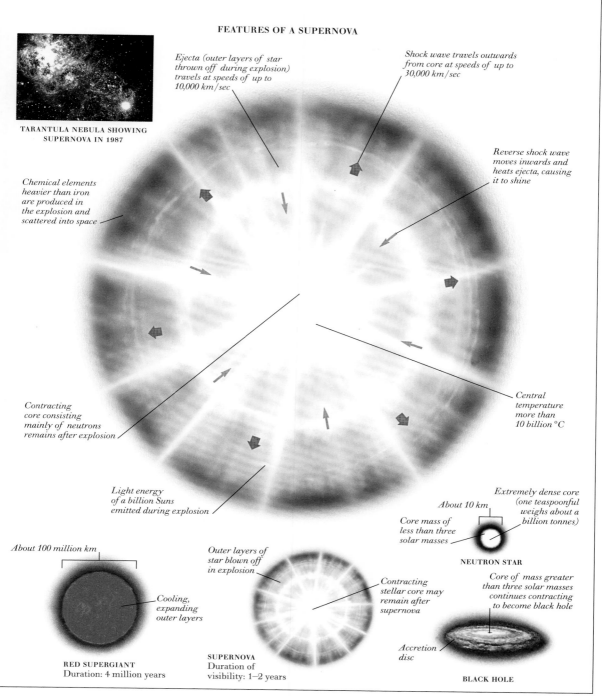

TARANTULA NEBULA SHOWING SUPERNOVA IN 1987

Ejecta (outer layers of star thrown off during explosion) travels at speeds of up to 10,000 km/sec

Shock wave travels outwards from core at speeds of up to 30,000 km/sec

Reverse shock wave moves inwards and heats ejecta, causing it to shine

Chemical elements heavier than iron are produced in the explosion and scattered into space

Contracting core consisting mainly of neutrons remains after explosion

Central temperature more than 10 billion °C

Light energy of a billion Suns emitted during explosion

About 100 million km

Cooling, expanding outer layers

RED SUPERGIANT
Duration: 4 million years

Outer layers of star blown off in explosion

Contracting stellar core may remain after supernova

SUPERNOVA
Duration of visibility: 1–2 years

About 10 km

Core mass of less than three solar masses

Extremely dense core (one teaspoonful weighs about a billion tonnes)

NEUTRON STAR

Core of mass greater than three solar masses continues contracting to become black hole

Accretion disc

BLACK HOLE

27

Neutron stars and black holes

NEUTRON STARS AND BLACK HOLES form from the stellar cores that remain after stars have exploded as supernovae (see pp. 26-27). If the remaining core is between about one and a half and three solar masses, it contracts to form a neutron star. If the remaining core is greater than about three solar masses, it contracts to form a black hole. Neutron stars are typically only about 10 kilometres in diameter and consist almost entirely of subatomic particles called neutrons. Such stars are so dense that a teaspoonful would weigh about a billion tonnes. Neutron stars are observed as pulsars, so-called because they rotate rapidly and emit two beams of radio waves, which sweep across the sky and are detected as short pulses. Black holes are characterized by their extremely strong gravity, which is so powerful that not even light can escape; as a result, black holes are invisible. However, they can be detected if they have a close companion star. The gravity of the black hole pulls gas from the other star, forming an accretion disc that spirals around the black hole at high speed, heating up and emitting radiation. Eventually, the matter spirals in to cross the event horizon (the boundary of the black hole), thereby disappearing from the visible Universe.

Nebula of gas and dust surrounds pulsar

Rapidly rotating pulsar

Beam of radiation from pulsar

X-RAY IMAGE OF PULSAR AND CENTRAL REGION OF CRAB NEBULA (SUPERNOVA REMNANT)

PULSAR (ROTATING NEUTRON STAR)

Rotational axis of neutron star

Beam of radio waves possibly produced by rapid rotation of magnetic field

Path of beam of radio waves

Magnetic axis

North Pole

North magnetic polar region

Solid, crystalline external crust

Magnetic field line

Solid, neutron-rich internal crust

Layer of superfluid neutrons

Solid core

Magnetic axis

Beam of radio waves possibly produced by rapid rotation of magnetic field

South Pole

South magnetic polar region

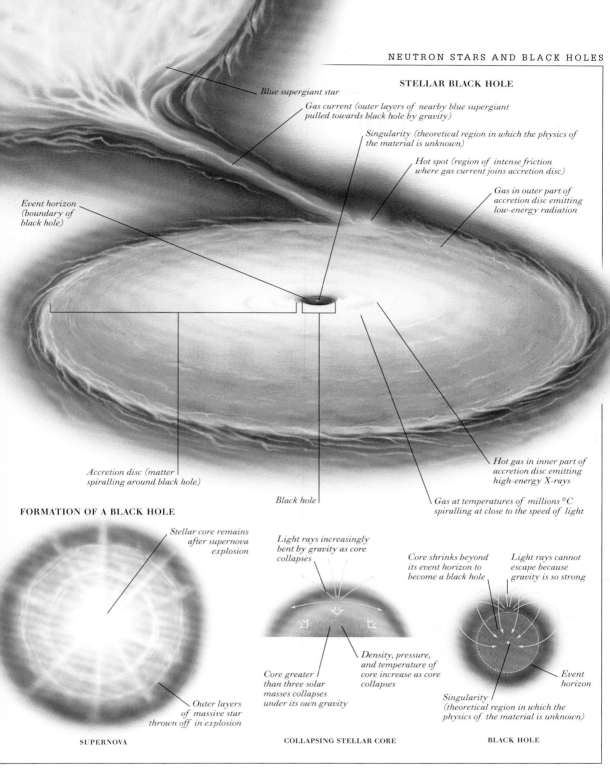

STELLAR BLACK HOLE

Blue supergiant star

Gas current (outer layers of nearby blue supergiant pulled towards black hole by gravity)

Singularity (theoretical region in which the physics of the material is unknown)

Hot spot (region of intense friction where gas current joins accretion disc)

Gas in outer part of accretion disc emitting low-energy radiation

Event horizon (boundary of black hole)

Accretion disc (matter spiralling around black hole)

Hot gas in inner part of accretion disc emitting high-energy X-rays

Black hole

Gas at temperatures of millions °C spiralling at close to the speed of light

FORMATION OF A BLACK HOLE

Stellar core remains after supernova explosion

Light rays increasingly bent by gravity as core collapses

Core shrinks beyond its event horizon to become a black hole

Light rays cannot escape because gravity is so strong

Outer layers of massive star thrown off in explosion

Core greater than three solar masses collapses under its own gravity

Density, pressure, and temperature of core increase as core collapses

Event horizon

Singularity (theoretical region in which the physics of the material is unknown)

SUPERNOVA

COLLAPSING STELLAR CORE

BLACK HOLE

The Solar System

THE SUN

THE SOLAR SYSTEM consists of a central star (the Sun) and the bodies that orbit it. These bodies include eight planets and their more than 160 known moons; dwarf planets; Kuiper Belt objects; asteroids; comets; and meteoroids. The Solar System also contains interplanetary gas and dust. The planets fall into two groups: four small rocky planets near the Sun (Mercury, Venus, Earth, and Mars); and four planets further out, the giants (Jupiter, Saturn, Uranus, and Neptune). Between the rocky planets and giants is the asteroid belt, which contains thousands of chunks of rock orbiting the Sun. Beyond Neptune is the Kuiper Belt and, more distant, the Oort Cloud. Most of the bodies in the planetary part of the Solar System move around the Sun in elliptical orbits located in a thin disc around the Sun's equator. All the planets orbit the Sun in the same direction (anticlockwise when viewed from above) and all but Venus and Uranus also spin about their axes in this direction. Moons also spin as they, in turn, orbit their planets. The entire Solar System orbits the centre of our galaxy, the Milky Way (see pp. 14-15).

PLANETARY ORBIT (EXAGGERATED)

Perihelion (orbital point closest to Sun)

Sun

Elliptical orbit

Planet orbiting Sun

Direction of planetary rotation

Aphelion (orbital point furthest from Sun)

Aphelion of Neptune: 4,545 million km

ORBITS OF INNER PLANETS

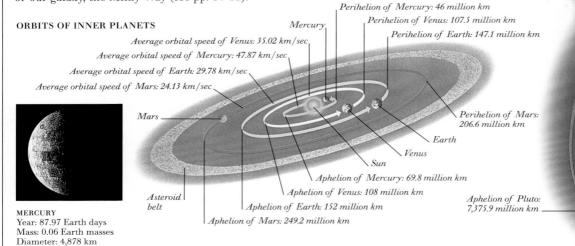

Perihelion of Mercury: 46 million km

Mercury

Perihelion of Venus: 107.5 million km

Average orbital speed of Venus: 35.02 km/sec

Perihelion of Earth: 147.1 million km

Average orbital speed of Mercury: 47.87 km/sec

Average orbital speed of Earth: 29.78 km/sec

Average orbital speed of Mars: 24.13 km/sec

Mars

Perihelion of Mars: 206.6 million km

Earth

Venus

Sun

Aphelion of Mercury: 69.8 million km

Asteroid belt

Aphelion of Venus: 108 million km

Aphelion of Earth: 152 million km

Aphelion of Pluto: 7,375.9 million km

Aphelion of Mars: 249.2 million km

MERCURY
Year: 87.97 Earth days
Mass: 0.06 Earth masses
Diameter: 4,878 km

VENUS
Year: 224.7 Earth days
Mass: 0.81 Earth masses
Diameter: 12,103 km

EARTH
Year: 365.26 days
Mass: 1 Earth mass
Diameter: 12,756 km

MARS
Year: 1.88 Earth years
Mass: 0.11 Earth masses
Diameter: 6,786 km

JUPITER
Year: 11.87 Earth years
Mass: 317.83 Earth masses
Diameter: 142,984 km

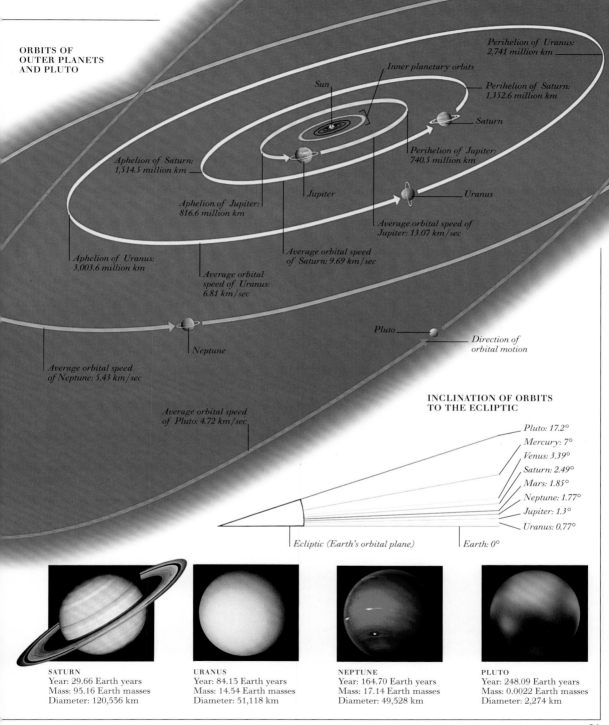

ORBITS OF
OUTER PLANETS
AND PLUTO

Inner planetary orbits

Sun

*Perihelion of Uranus:
2,741 million km*

*Perihelion of Saturn:
1,352.6 million km*

Saturn

*Perihelion of Jupiter:
740.5 million km*

*Aphelion of Saturn:
1,514.5 million km*

Uranus

*Aphelion of Jupiter:
816.6 million km*

Jupiter

*Average orbital speed of
Jupiter: 13.07 km/sec*

*Aphelion of Uranus:
3,003.6 million km*

*Average orbital
speed of Uranus:
6.81 km/sec*

*Average orbital speed
of Saturn: 9.69 km/sec*

Pluto

*Direction of
orbital motion*

Neptune

*Average orbital speed
of Neptune: 5.43 km/sec*

*Average orbital speed
of Pluto: 4.72 km/sec*

INCLINATION OF ORBITS
TO THE ECLIPTIC

Pluto: 17.2°
Mercury: 7°
Venus: 3.39°
Saturn: 2.49°
Mars: 1.85°
Neptune: 1.77°
Jupiter: 1.3°
Uranus: 0.77°

Ecliptic (Earth's orbital plane)   *Earth: 0°*

SATURN
Year: 29.66 Earth years
Mass: 95.16 Earth masses
Diameter: 120,536 km

URANUS
Year: 84.13 Earth years
Mass: 14.54 Earth masses
Diameter: 51,118 km

NEPTUNE
Year: 164.70 Earth years
Mass: 17.14 Earth masses
Diameter: 49,528 km

PLUTO
Year: 248.09 Earth years
Mass: 0.0022 Earth masses
Diameter: 2,274 km

The Sun

**SOLAR
PHOTOSPHERE**

THE SUN IS THE STAR AT THE CENTRE of the Solar System. It is about five billion years old and will continue to shine as it does now for about another five billion years. The Sun is a yellow main sequence star (see pp. 22-23) about 1.4 million kilometres in diameter. It consists almost entirely of hydrogen and helium. In the Sun's core, hydrogen is converted to helium by nuclear fusion, releasing energy in the process. The energy travels from the core, through the radiative and convective zones, to the photosphere (visible surface), where it leaves the Sun in the form of heat and light. On the photosphere there are often dark, relatively cool areas called sunspots, which usually appear in pairs or groups and are caused by the cooling effect of the magnetic field. Other types of solar activity are flares, which are usually associated with sunspots, and prominences. Flares are sudden discharges of high-energy radiation and atomic particles. Prominences are huge loops or filaments of gas extending into the solar atmosphere; some last for hours, others for months. Beyond the photosphere is the chromosphere (inner atmosphere) and the extremely rarified corona (outer atmosphere), which extends millions of kilometres into space. Tiny particles that escape from the corona give rise to the solar wind, which streams through space at hundreds of kilometres per second. The chromosphere and corona can be seen from Earth when the Sun is totally eclipsed by the Moon.

Sun

*Moon passes
between Sun
and Earth*

*Umbra
(inner, total
shadow) of
Moon*

*Region of
Earth from
which total
eclipse is visible*

*Penumbra
(outer,
partial
shadow)
of Moon*

*Region of Earth
from which partial
eclipse is visible*

Earth

*Umbra (inner, total
shadow) of Earth*

*Penumbra (outer,
partial shadow)
of Earth*

SURFACE FEATURES

*Gas loop (looped
prominence)*

*Prominence (jet of gas at
edge of Sun's disc up to
hundreds of thousands of
kilometres high)*

*Spicule
(vertical
jet of gas)*

*Photosphere
(visible surface)*

*Chromosphere
(inner atmosphere)*

TOTAL SOLAR ECLIPSE

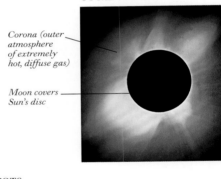

*Corona (outer
atmosphere
of extremely
hot, diffuse gas)*

*Moon covers
Sun's disc*

SUNSPOTS

*Granulated surface
of Sun*

*Penumbra
(lighter, outer region)
containing radial fibrils*

*Umbra (darker, inner
region) temperature
about 2,700°C*

*Photosphere
temperature
about 5,500°C*

EXTERNAL FEATURES AND
INTERNAL STRUCTURE OF THE SUN

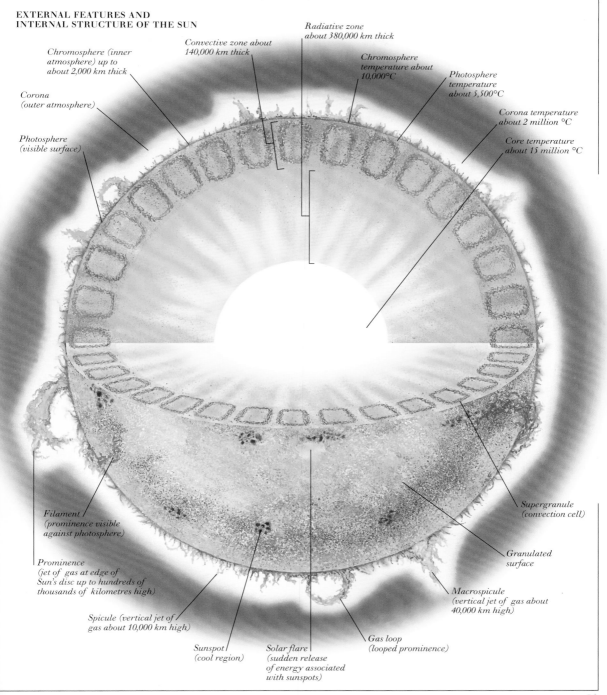

*Radiative zone
about 380,000 km thick*

*Convective zone about
140,000 km thick*

*Chromosphere (inner
atmosphere) up to
about 2,000 km thick*

*Chromosphere
temperature about
10,000°C*

*Photosphere
temperature
about 5,500°C*

*Corona
(outer atmosphere)*

*Corona temperature
about 2 million °C*

*Photosphere
(visible surface)*

*Core temperature
about 15 million °C*

*Filament
(prominence visible
against photosphere)*

*Supergranule
(convection cell)*

*Prominence
(jet of gas at edge of
Sun's disc up to hundreds of
thousands of kilometres high)*

*Granulated
surface*

*Spicule (vertical jet of
gas about 10,000 km high)*

*Macrospicule
(vertical jet of gas about
40,000 km high)*

*Sunspot
(cool region)*

*Solar flare
(sudden release
of energy associated
with sunspots)*

*Gas loop
(looped prominence)*

Mercury

MERCURY

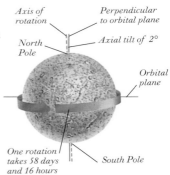

Axis of rotation

Perpendicular to orbital plane

North Pole

Axial tilt of 2°

Orbital plane

One rotation takes 58 days and 16 hours

South Pole

MERCURY IS THE NEAREST PLANET to the Sun, orbiting at an average distance of about 58 million kilometres. Because Mercury is the closest planet to the Sun, it moves faster than any other planet, travelling at an average speed of nearly 48 kilometres per second and completing an orbit in just under 88 days. Mercury is very small (only 40 per cent bigger than the Moon) and rocky. Most of the surface has been heavily cratered by the impact of meteorites, although there are also smooth, sparsely cratered lava-covered plains. The Caloris Basin is the largest crater, measuring about 1,300 kilometres across. It is thought to have been formed when a 60-kilometre-diameter asteroid hit the planet, and is surrounded by concentric rings of mountains thrown up by the impact. The surface also has many cliff-like ridges (called rupes) that are thought to have been formed when the hot core of the young planet cooled and shrank about four billion years ago, buckling the planet's surface in the process. The planet rotates about its axis very slowly, taking nearly 59 Earth days to complete one rotation. As a result, a solar day (sunrise to sunrise) on Mercury is about 176 Earth days — twice as long as the 88-day Mercurian year. Mercury has extreme surface temperatures, ranging from a maximum of 430°C on the sunlit side to -170°C on the dark side. At nightfall, the temperature drops very quickly because the planet's atmosphere is almost non-existent. It consists only of minute amounts of helium and hydrogen captured from the solar wind, plus traces of other gases.

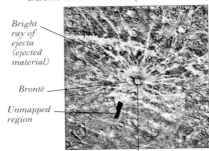

Bright ray of ejecta (ejected material)

Brontë

Unmapped region

Degas with central peak

FORMATION OF A RAY CRATER

Debris thrown out by impact

Path of meteorite colliding with planet

Wall of rock thrown up around crater

Impact forms saucer-shaped crater

Fractured rock

METEORITE IMPACT

Path of rocky ejecta (ejected material)

Ejecta forms secondary craters

Loose debris on crater floor

SECONDARY CRATERING

Wall of rock forms ring of mountains

Ray of ejecta (ejected material)

Small secondary crater

Loose ejected rock

Central mountain rings form if floor of large crater recoils from meteorite impact

Falling debris forms ridges on side of wall

RAY CRATER

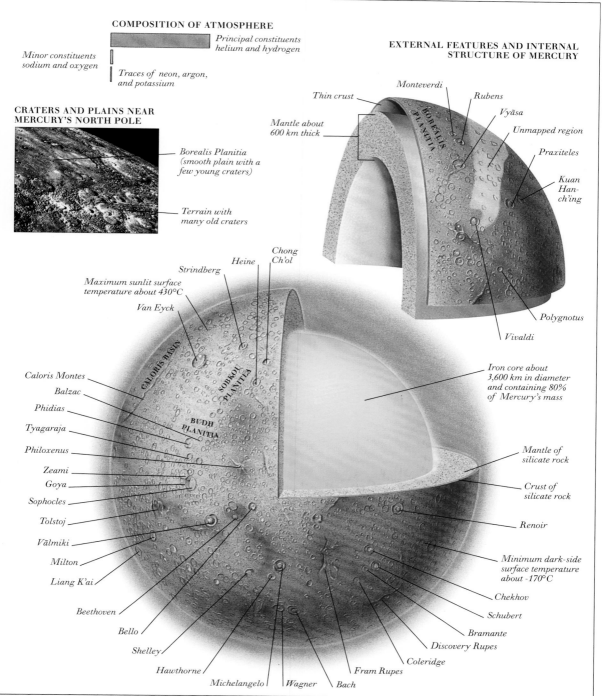

COMPOSITION OF ATMOSPHERE

Principal constituents helium and hydrogen

Minor constituents sodium and oxygen

Traces of neon, argon, and potassium

CRATERS AND PLAINS NEAR MERCURY'S NORTH POLE

Borealis Planitia (smooth plain with a few young craters)

Terrain with many old craters

EXTERNAL FEATURES AND INTERNAL STRUCTURE OF MERCURY

Thin crust

Mantle about 600 km thick

Monteverdi

Rubens

Vyāsa

Unmapped region

Praxiteles

Kuan Han-ch'ing

BOREALIS PLANITIA

Polygnotus

Vivaldi

Chong Ch'ol

Heine

Strindberg

Maximum sunlit surface temperature about 430°C

Van Eyck

CALORIS BASIN

SOBKOU PLANITIA

BUDH PLANITIA

Caloris Montes

Balzac

Phidias

Tyagaraja

Philoxenus

Zeami

Goya

Sophocles

Tolstoj

Vālmiki

Milton

Liang K'ai

Beethoven

Bello

Shelley

Hawthorne

Michelangelo

Wagner

Bach

Fram Rupes

Coleridge

Discovery Rupes

Bramante

Schubert

Chekhov

Minimum dark-side surface temperature about -170°C

Renoir

Crust of silicate rock

Mantle of silicate rock

Iron core about 3,600 km in diameter and containing 80% of Mercury's mass

35

Venus

RADAR IMAGE OF
VENUS

VENUS IS A ROCKY PLANET and the second planet from
the Sun. Venus spins slowly backwards as it orbits the Sun,
causing its rotational period to be the longest in the Solar
System, at about 243 Earth days. It is slightly smaller
than Earth and probably has a similar internal structure,
consisting of a semi-solid metal core, surrounded by a
rocky mantle and crust. Venus is the brightest object in
the sky after the Sun and Moon because its clouds reflect
sunlight strongly. The main component of the atmosphere is carbon
dioxide, which traps heat in a greenhouse effect far stronger than that
on Earth. As a result, Venus is the hottest planet, with a maximum surface
temperature of about 480°C. The thick cloud layers contain droplets of
sulphuric acid and are driven around the planet by winds at speeds of up to
360 kilometres per hour. Although the planet takes 243 Earth days to rotate
once, the high-speed winds cause the clouds to circle the planet in only
four Earth days. The high temperature, acidic clouds, and enormous
atmospheric pressure (about 90 times greater at the surface than that
on Earth) make the environment extremely hostile. However, space
probes have managed to land on Venus and photograph its dry, dusty
surface. The Venusian surface has also been mapped by probes with
radar equipment that can "see" through the cloud layers. Such radar
maps reveal a terrain with craters, mountains, volcanoes, and areas
where craters have been covered by plains of solidified volcanic
lava. There are two large highland regions called Aphrodite Terra
and Ishtar Terra.

TILT AND ROTATION OF VENUS

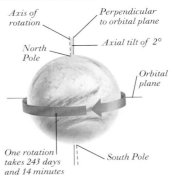

Axis of
rotation

Perpendicular
to orbital plane

North
Pole

Axial tilt of 2°

Orbital
plane

One rotation
takes 243 days
and 14 minutes

South Pole

CLOUD FEATURES

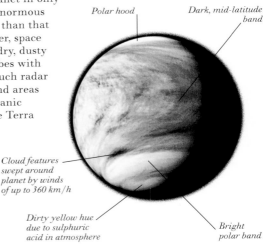

Polar hood

Dark, mid-latitude
band

Cloud features
swept around
planet by winds
of up to 360 km/h

Dirty yellow hue
due to sulphuric
acid in atmosphere

Bright
polar band

VENUSIAN CRATERS

Danilova

Ejecta (ejected
material)

Central peak

Howe

FALSE-COLOUR RADAR MAP
OF THE SURFACE OF VENUS

Metis Regio

Maxwell Montes

Bell Regio

Tethus Regio

Atalanta Planitia

Leda Planitia

Sedna Planitia

ISHTAR TERRA

Tellus Regio

Eisila Regio

Niobe Planitia

Guinevere Planitia

Phoebe Regio

Ovda Regio

Alpha Regio

Thetis Regio

Themis Regio

APHRODITE TERRA

Lavinia Planitia

Aino Planitia

Helen Planitia

Lada Terra

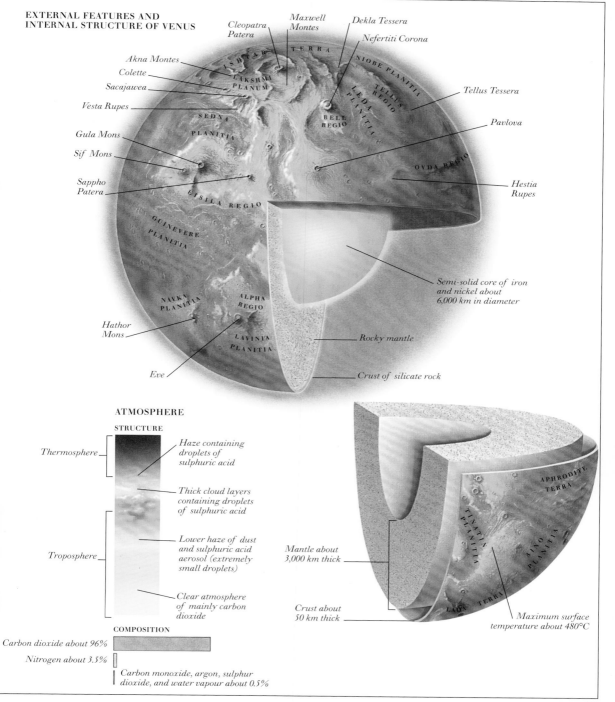

EXTERNAL FEATURES AND
INTERNAL STRUCTURE OF VENUS

Cleopatra
Patera

Maxwell
Montes

Dekla Tessera

Nefertiti Corona

Akna Montes

Colette

Sacajawea

Vesta Rupes

Gula Mons

Sif Mons

Sappho
Patera

ISHTAR
TERRA

LAKSHMI
PLANUM

SEDNA
PLANITIA

EISILA REGIO

GUINEVERE
PLANITIA

NAVKA
PLANITIA

NIOBE PLANITIA

TELLUS
REGIO

LEDA
PLANITIA

BELL
REGIO

OVDA REGIO

ALPHA
REGIO

Tellus Tessera

Pavlova

Hestia
Rupes

Hathor
Mons

LAVINIA
PLANITIA

Eve

Semi-solid core of iron
and nickel about
6,000 km in diameter

Rocky mantle

Crust of silicate rock

ATMOSPHERE

STRUCTURE

Thermosphere

Troposphere

Haze containing
droplets of
sulphuric acid

Thick cloud layers
containing droplets
of sulphuric acid

Lower haze of dust
and sulphuric acid
aerosol (extremely
small droplets)

Clear atmosphere
of mainly carbon
dioxide

COMPOSITION

Carbon dioxide about 96%

Nitrogen about 3.5%

Carbon monoxide, argon, sulphur
dioxide, and water vapour about 0.5%

Mantle about
3,000 km thick

Crust about
50 km thick

APHRODITE
TERRA

TINATIN
PLANITIA

AINO
PLANITIA

LADA TERRA

Maximum surface
temperature about 480°C

The Earth

Axis of rotation

Axial tilt of 23.4°

North Pole

Orbital plane

THE EARTH

THE EARTH IS THE THIRD of the eight planets that orbit the Sun. It is the largest and densest rocky planet, and the only one known to support life. About 70 per cent of the Earth's surface is covered by water, which is not found in liquid form on the surface of any other planet. There are four main layers: the inner core, the outer core, the mantle, and the crust. At the heart of the planet the solid inner core has a temperature of about 6,600°C. The heat from this inner core causes material in the molten outer core and mantle to circulate in convection currents. It is thought that these convection currents generate the Earth's magnetic field, which extends into space as the magnetosphere. The Earth's atmosphere helps screen out some of the harmful radiation from the Sun, stops most meteoroids from reaching the planet's surface, and traps enough heat to prevent extremes of cold. The Earth has one natural satellite, the Moon, which is thought to have formed when a huge asteroid impacted Earth in the distant past.

South Pole

One rotation takes 23 hours and 56 minutes

Perpendicular to orbital plane

THE FORMATION OF THE EARTH

Micro-organisms began to photosynthesize, creating a build up of oxygen

The heat of the collisions caused the planet to glow red

The cloud formed a disc of material around the young Sun's equator. The disc material stuck together to form planets

4,600 MILLION YEARS AGO, THE SOLAR SYSTEM FORMED FROM A CLOUD OF ROCK, ICE, AND GAS

THE EARTH WAS FORMED FROM COLLIDING ROCKS

4,500 MILLION YEARS AGO THE SURFACE COOLED TO FORM THE CRUST

THE CONTINENTS BROKE UP AND REFORMED, GRADUALLY MOVING TO THEIR PRESENT POSITIONS

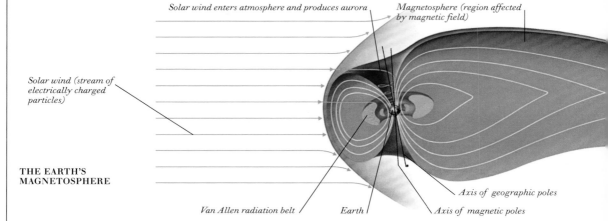

Solar wind enters atmosphere and produces aurora

Magnetosphere (region affected by magnetic field)

Solar wind (stream of electrically charged particles)

THE EARTH'S MAGNETOSPHERE

Van Allen radiation belt

Earth

Axis of geographic poles

Axis of magnetic poles

EXTERNAL FEATURES AND
INTERNAL STRUCTURE
OF THE EARTH

COMPOSITION OF THE EARTH

Greenland

*Atmosphere about
500 km deep*

Crust 6–40 km thick

*Mantle about
2,800 km
thick*

*Outer core
about 2,300 km
thick*

NORTH ATLANTIC
OCEAN

*Cyclonic
storm*

Other elements less than 1 %

Aluminium 0.4%

Calcium 0.6%

Sulphur 2.7%

Nickel 2.7%

Silicon 13%

Magnesium 17%

Oxygen 28%

Iron 35%

*Surface temperature
between about -88°C
and 58°C*

Core temperature about 6,600°C

*Molten core of iron
and nickel*

*Solid inner core
of iron and nickel
about 2,400 km
in diameter*

*Gutenberg discontinuity
(boundary between outer
core and mantle)*

*Mantle of mostly solid
silicate material*

*Mohorovicic
discontinuity
(boundary
between mantle
and crust)*

Crust of silicate rock

*Amazon Basin (tropical
rain-forest region)*

*Andes (mountain range
near crustal plate
boundary)*

*Earthquake region along
crustal plate boundary*

EUROPE

AFRICA

SOUTH
PACIFIC
OCEAN

SOUTH
AMERICA

SOUTH ATLANTIC
OCEAN

Atlas Mountains

*Sahara (desert
region)*

*Congo Basin
(tropical
rain-forest)*

*Land forms about
30% of surface*

*Cloud typically covers about
70% of surface*

*Oceans cover about
70% of surface*

The Moon

THE MOON FROM EARTH

THE MOON IS THE EARTH'S only natural satellite. It is relatively large for a moon, with a diameter of about 3,470 kilometres — just over a quarter that of the Earth. The Moon takes the same time to rotate on its axis as it takes to orbit the Earth (27.3 days), and so the same side (the near side) always faces us. However, the amount of the surface we can see — the phase of the Moon — depends on how much of the near side is in sunlight. The Moon is dry and barren, with negligible atmosphere and water. It consists mainly of solid rock, although its core may contain molten rock or iron. The surface is dusty, with highlands covered in craters caused by meteorite impacts, and lowlands in which large craters have been filled by solidified lava to form dark areas called maria or "seas". Maria occur mainly on the near side, which has a thinner crust than the far side. Many of the craters are rimmed by mountain ranges that form the crater walls and can be thousands of metres high.

TILT AND ROTATION OF THE MOON

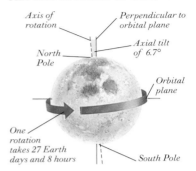

Axis of rotation

Perpendicular to orbital plane

Axial tilt of 6.7°

North Pole

Orbital plane

One rotation takes 27 Earth days and 8 hours

South Pole

CRATERS ON OCEANUS PROCELLARUM

Aristarchus

Cobra Head (head of Schröter's Valley)

Herodotus

NEAR SIDE OF THE MOON

Aristoteles

De la Rue

Aristillus

Hercules

Plato

Atlas

Archimedes

Montes Apenninus

Montes Jura

Cleomedes

Sinus Iridum

Macrobius

Julius Caesar

Bright rays of ejected material

Copernicus

Aristarchus

Langrenus

Kepler

Vendelinus

Encke

Cyrillus

Flamsteed

Petavius

Fra Mauro

Fracastorius

Grimaldi

Furnerius

Letronne

Catharina

Gassendi

Rupes Altai

Mersenius

Albategnius

Ptolemaeus

Arzachel

Walter

Pitatus

Stöfler

Schickard

Deslandres

Alphonsus

Bailly

Tycho

Clavius

Maginus

MARE FRIGORIS

MARE IMBRIUM

MARE SERENITATIS

MARE VAPORUM

MARE TRANQUILLITATIS

MARE CRISIUM

MARE FECUNDITATIS

OCEANUS PROCELLARUM

MARE NECTARIS

MARE NUBIUM

MARE HUMORUM

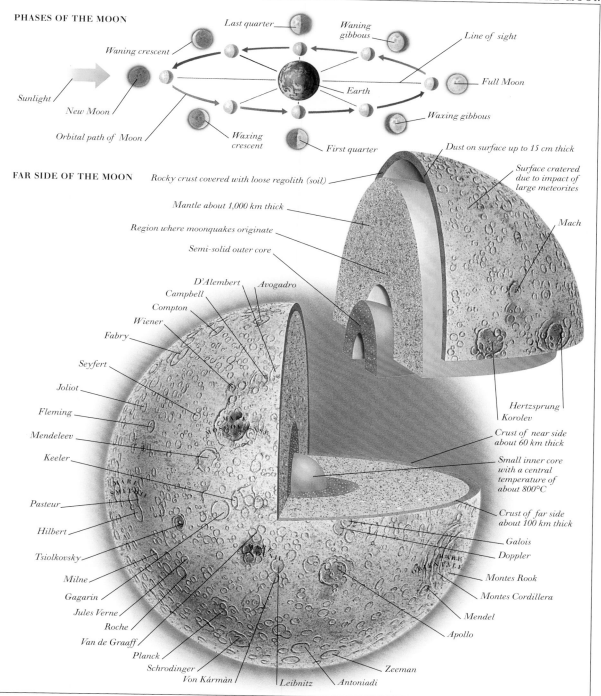

PHASES OF THE MOON

Last quarter

Waning gibbous

Waning crescent

Line of sight

Sunlight

New Moon

Earth

Full Moon

Orbital path of Moon

Waxing crescent

First quarter

Waxing gibbous

FAR SIDE OF THE MOON

Rocky crust covered with loose regolith (soil)

Mantle about 1,000 km thick

Region where moonquakes originate

Semi-solid outer core

Dust on surface up to 15 cm thick

Surface cratered due to impact of large meteorites

Mach

D'Alembert

Avogadro

Campbell

Compton

Wiener

Fabry

Seyfert

Joliot

Fleming

Mendeleev

Keeler

Pasteur

Hilbert

Tsiolkovsky

Milne

Gagarin

Jules Verne

Roche

Van de Graaff

Planck

Schrodinger

Von Kármàn

Leibnitz

Antoniadi

Zeeman

MARE MOSCOVIENSE

MARE SMITH

MARE INGENII

MARE ORIENTALE

Hertzsprung

Korolev

Crust of near side about 60 km thick

Small inner core with a central temperature of about 800°C

Crust of far side about 100 km thick

Galois

Doppler

Montes Rook

Montes Cordillera

Mendel

Apollo

41

Mars

MARS

MARS, KNOWN AS THE RED PLANET, is the fourth planet from the Sun and the outermost rocky planet. In the 19th century, astronomers first observed what were thought to be signs of life on Mars. These signs included apparent canal-like lines on the surface, and dark patches that were thought to be vegetation. It is now known that the "canals" are an optical illusion, and the dark patches are areas where the red dust that covers most of the planet has been blown away. The fine dust particles are often whipped up by winds into dust storms that occasionally obscure almost all the surface. Residual fine dust in the atmosphere gives the Martian sky a pinkish hue. The northern hemisphere of Mars has many large plains formed of solidified volcanic lava, whereas the southern hemisphere has many craters and large impact basins. There are also several huge, extinct volcanoes, including Olympus Mons, which, at 600 kilometres across and 25 kilometres high, is the largest known volcano in the Solar System. The surface also has many canyons and branching channels. The canyons were formed by movements of the surface crust, but the channels are thought to have been formed by flowing water that has now dried up. The Martian atmosphere is much thinner than Earth's, with only a few clouds and morning mists. Mars has two tiny, irregularly shaped moons called Phobos and Deimos. Their small size indicates that they may be asteroids that have been captured by the gravity of Mars.

TILT AND ROTATION OF MARS

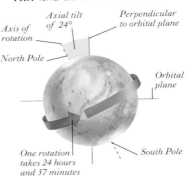

Axis of rotation

Axial tilt of 24°

Perpendicular to orbital plane

North Pole

Orbital plane

One rotation takes 24 hours and 37 minutes

South Pole

SURFACE FEATURES OF MARS

Bright water-ice fog

Fog in canyon about 20 km wide at end of Valles Marineris

Syria Planum

NOCTIS LABYRINTHUS (CANYON SYSTEM)

Summit caldera consisting of overlapping collapsed volcanic craters

Gentle slope produced by lava flow

Cloud formation

OLYMPUS MONS (EXTINCT SHIELD VOLCANO)

THE SURFACE OF MARS

Dark area where dust has been blown away by wind

South polar ice-cap

Surface covered with red-coloured iron oxide dust

MOONS OF MARS

PHOBOS
Average diameter: 22 km
Average distance from planet: 9,400 km

DEIMOS
Average diameter: 13 km
Average distance from planet: 23,500 km

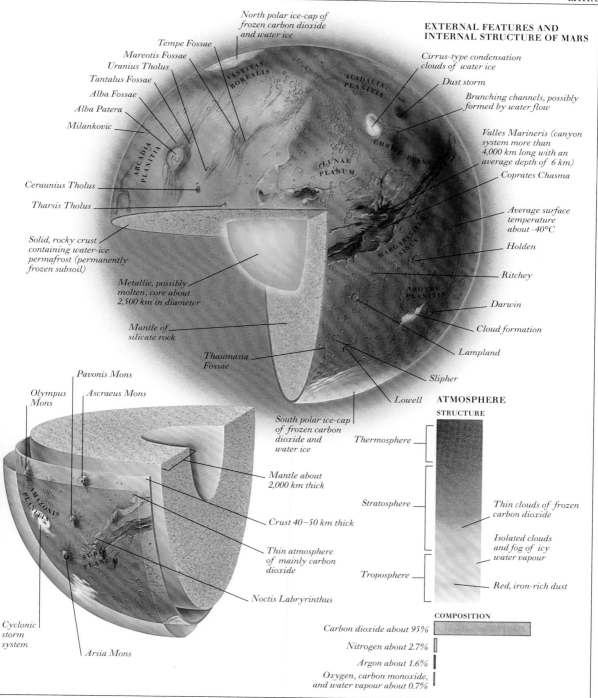

EXTERNAL FEATURES AND
INTERNAL STRUCTURE OF MARS

North polar ice-cap of
frozen carbon dioxide
and water ice

Tempe Fossae

Mareotis Fossae

Uranius Tholus

Tantalus Fossae

Alba Fossae

Alba Patera

Milankovic

Ceraunius Tholus

Tharsis Tholus

Solid, rocky crust
containing water-ice
permafrost (permanently
frozen subsoil)

Metallic, possibly
molten, core about
2,500 km in diameter

Mantle of
silicate rock

Thaumasia
Fossae

VASTITAS BOREALIS

ACIDALIA PLANITIA

ARCADIA PLANITIA

CLUNAE PLANUM

CHRISE PLANITIA

MARGARITIFER SINUS

ARGYRE PLANITIA

Cirrus-type condensation
clouds of water ice

Dust storm

Branching channels, possibly
formed by water flow

Valles Marineris (canyon
system more than
4,000 km long with an
average depth of 6 km)

Coprates Chasma

Average surface
temperature
about -40°C

Holden

Ritchey

Darwin

Cloud formation

Lampland

Slipher

Lowell

Olympus Mons

Pavonis Mons

Ascraeus Mons

AMAZONIS PLANITIA

SYRTIS PLANUM

Cyclonic storm system

Arsia Mons

South polar ice-cap
of frozen carbon
dioxide and
water ice

Mantle about
2,000 km thick

Crust 40–50 km thick

Thin atmosphere
of mainly carbon
dioxide

Noctis Labryrinthus

ATMOSPHERE

STRUCTURE

Thermosphere

Stratosphere

Troposphere

Thin clouds of frozen
carbon dioxide

Isolated clouds
and fog of icy
water vapour

Red, iron-rich dust

COMPOSITION

Carbon dioxide about 95%

Nitrogen about 2.7%

Argon about 1.6%

Oxygen, carbon monoxide,
and water vapour about 0.7%

Jupiter

JUPITER

JUPITER IS THE FIFTH PLANET from the Sun and the innermost of the four giant planets. It is the largest and the most massive planet, with a diameter about 11 times that of the Earth and a mass about 2.5 times the combined mass of the seven other planets. Jupiter is thought to have a small rocky core surrounded by an inner mantle of metallic hydrogen (liquid hydrogen that acts like a metal). Outside the inner mantle is an outer mantle of liquid hydrogen and helium that merges into the gaseous atmosphere. Jupiter's rapid rate of rotation causes the clouds in its atmosphere to form belts and zones that encircle the planet parallel to the equator. Belts are dark, low-lying, relatively warm cloud layers, and zones are bright, high-altitude, cooler cloud layers. Within the belts and zones, turbulence causes the formation of cloud features such as white ovals and red spots, both of which are huge storm systems. The most prominent cloud feature is a storm called the Great Red Spot, which consists of a spiralling column of clouds three times wider than the Earth that rises about eight kilometres above the upper cloud layer. Jupiter has a thin, faint, main ring, inside which is a tenuous halo ring of tiny particles. Beyond the main ring's outer edge is a broad and faint two-part gossamer ring. There are 63 known Jovian moons. The four largest moons (called the Galileans) are Ganymede, Callisto, Io, and Europa. Ganymede and Callisto are cratered and icy. Europa is smooth and icy and is thought to have a subsurface water ocean. Io is covered in bright red, orange, and yellow splotches. This colouring is caused by sulphurous material from active volcanoes that shoot plumes of lava hundreds of kilometres above the surface.

TILT AND ROTATION OF JUPITER

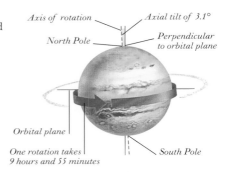

Axis of rotation

Axial tilt of 3.1°

North Pole

Perpendicular to orbital plane

Orbital plane

One rotation takes 9 hours and 55 minutes

South Pole

GREAT RED SPOT AND WHITE OVAL

Great Red Spot (anticyclonic storm system)

Red colour probably due to phosphorus

White oval (temporary anticyclonic storm system)

GALILEAN MOONS OF JUPITER

EUROPA
Diameter: 3,130 km
Average distance from planet: 670,900 km

CALLISTO
Diameter: 4,806 km
Average distance from planet: 1,883,000 km

GANYMEDE
Diameter: 5,268 km
Average distance from planet: 1,070,000 km

IO
Diameter: 3,642 km
Average distance from planet: 421,800 km

INNER RINGS OF JUPITER

Main ring

Halo ring

ATMOSPHERE

STRUCTURE

EXTERNAL FEATURES AND INTERNAL STRUCTURE OF JUPITER

Stratosphere

Troposphere

White clouds of
ammonia crystals

Dark orange
clouds of ammonium
hydrosulphide crystals

Bluish clouds of water
ice and water droplets

COMPOSITION

Hydrogen about 90%

Helium about 10%

Traces of ammonia,
methane, and water
vapour

Atmosphere of mainly
hydrogen and helium

Outer mantle
merging into
atmosphere

Inner mantle about
30,000 km thick

Zone (high-pressure
region of rising gases)

Red-coloured
storm

Plume
(trailing
cloud)

High-altitude
white cloud

North polar
aurora

North Temperate Zone

North Temperate Belt

North Tropical
Zone

North Equatorial
Belt

Equatorial Zone

South
Equatorial Belt

South
Tropical Zone

South
Temperate Belt

South
Temperate Zone

Flash of lightning

Great Red Spot
(anticyclonic
storm system)

Cloud-top
temperature
about -120°C

White oval
(temporary
anticyclonic
storm system)

Belt (low-pressure
region of sinking
gases)

Outer mantle of liquid
hydrogen and helium

Inner mantle of
metallic hydrogen

Rocky core about
28,000 km in diameter

Core temperature
about 30,000°C

Saturn

SATURN IS THE SIXTH PLANET from the Sun. It is a gas giant almost as big as Jupiter, with an equatorial diameter of about 120,500 kilometres. Saturn is thought to consist of a small core of rock and ice surrounded by an inner mantle of metallic hydrogen (liquid hydrogen that acts like a metal). Outside the inner mantle is an outer mantle of liquid hydrogen that merges into a gaseous atmosphere. Saturn's clouds form belts and zones similar to those on Jupiter, but obscured by overlying haze. Storms and eddies, seen as red or white ovals, occur in the clouds. Saturn has an extremely thin but wide system of rings that is less than one kilometre thick but extends outwards to about 420,000 kilometres from the planet's surface. The main rings comprise thousands of narrow ringlets, each made of icy rock lumps that range in size from tiny particles to chunks several metres across. The D, E, and G rings are very faint, the F ring is brighter, and the A, B, and C rings are bright enough to be seen from Earth with binoculars. In 2009, a huge dust ring was discovered 6 kilometres (4 million miles) beyond the main system. Saturn has more than 60 known moons, some of which orbit inside the rings and are thought to exert a gravitational influence on the shapes of the rings. Unusually, seven of the moons are co-orbital — they share an orbit with another moon. Astronomers believe that such co-orbital moons may have originated from a single satellite that broke up.

FALSE-COLOUR IMAGE OF SATURN

TILT AND ROTATION OF SATURN

Axial tilt of 26.7°

One rotation takes 10 hours and 40 minutes

North Pole

Orbital plane

South Pole

Perpendicular to orbital plane

Axis of rotation

FALSE-COLOUR IMAGE OF SATURN'S CLOUD FEATURES

Ribbon-shaped striation caused by winds of up to 540 km/h

Oval (rotating storm system)

INNER RINGS OF SATURN

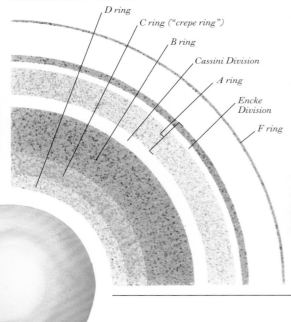

D ring

C ring ("crepe ring")

B ring

Cassini Division

A ring

Encke Division

F ring

MOONS OF SATURN

ENCELADUS
Diameter: 498 km
Average distance from
planet: 238,000 km

TETHYS
Diameter: 1,066 km
Average distance from
planet: 295,000 km

DIONE
Diameter: 1,123 km
Average distance from
planet: 377,000 km

MIMAS
Diameter: 397 km
Average distance from
planet: 186,000 km

ATMOSPHERE

EXTERNAL FEATURES AND INTERNAL STRUCTURE OF SATURN

COMPOSITION

Hydrogen about 96.3%

Helium about 3.3%

Traces of ammonia, methane, and water vapour

STRUCTURE

Stratosphere

Troposphere

Haze of ammonia crystals

White clouds of ammonia crystals

Dark orange clouds of ammonium hydrosulphide crystals

Blue clouds of water ice and water vapour

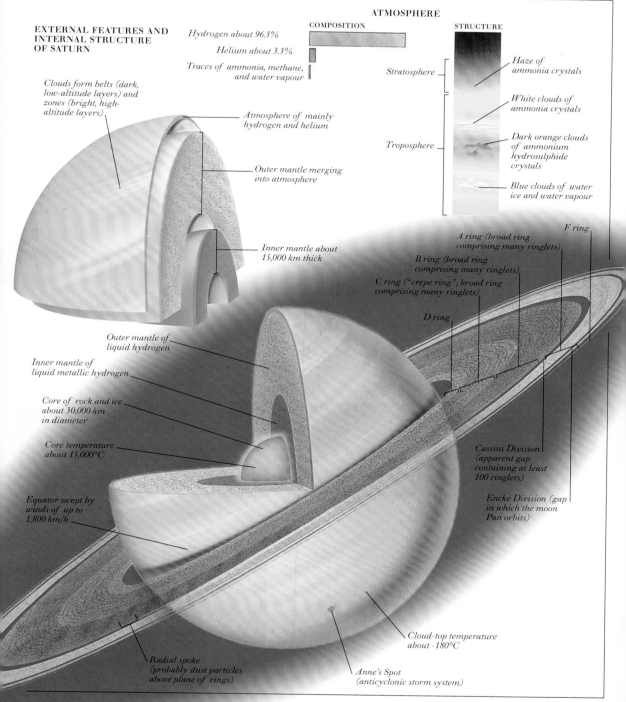

Clouds form belts (dark, low-altitude layers) and zones (bright, high-altitude layers)

Atmosphere of mainly hydrogen and helium

Outer mantle merging into atmosphere

Inner mantle about 15,000 km thick

Outer mantle of liquid hydrogen

Inner mantle of liquid metallic hydrogen

Core of rock and ice about 30,000 km in diameter

Core temperature about 15,000°C

Equator swept by winds of up to 1,800 km/h

Radial spoke (probably dust particles above plane of rings)

A ring (broad ring comprising many ringlets)

B ring (broad ring comprising many ringlets)

C ring ("crepe ring"; broad ring comprising many ringlets)

D ring

F ring

Cassini Division (apparent gap containing at least 100 ringlets)

Encke Division (gap in which the moon Pan orbits)

Cloud-top temperature about -180°C

Anne's Spot (anticyclonic storm system)

47

Uranus

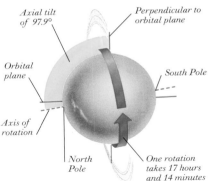

Axial tilt of 97.9°

Perpendicular to orbital plane

Orbital plane

South Pole

Axis of rotation

North Pole

One rotation takes 17 hours and 14 minutes

URANUS IS THE SEVENTH PLANET from the Sun and the third largest, with a diameter of about 51,000 kilometres. It is thought to consist of a dense mixture of different types of ice and gas around a solid core. Its atmosphere contains traces of methane, giving the planet a blue-green hue, and the temperature at the cloud tops is about -210°C. Uranus is the most featureless planet to have been closely observed: only a few icy clouds of methane have been seen so far. Uranus is unique among the planets in that its axis of rotation lies close to its orbital plane. As a result of its strongly tilted rotational axis, Uranus rolls on its side along its orbital path around the Sun, whereas other planets spin more or less upright. Uranus is encircled by main rings that consist of rocks interspersed with dust lanes and too distant outer rings made of dust. The rings contain some of the darkest matter in the Solar System and are extremely narrow, making them difficult to detect: most of them are less than 10 kilometres wide, whereas most of Saturn's rings are thousands of kilometres in width. There are 27 known Uranian moons, all of which are icy and most of which are further out than the rings. The 13 inner moons are small and dark, with diameters of less than 160 kilometres, and the five major moons are between about 470 and 1,600 kilometres in diameter. The major moons have a wide variety of surface features. Miranda has the most varied surface, with cratered areas broken up by huge ridges and cliffs 20 kilometres high. Beyond these are nine much more distant moons with diameters less than 150 km.

FALSE-COLOUR IMAGE OF URANUS

MAJOR MOONS

MIRANDA
Diameter: 470 km
Average distance from planet: 129,800 km

RINGS OF URANUS

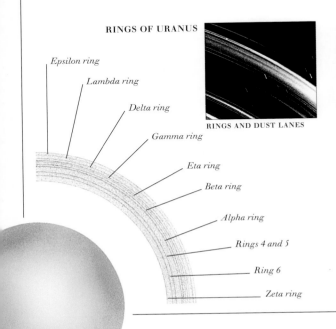

RINGS AND DUST LANES

Epsilon ring

Lambda ring

Delta ring

Gamma ring

Eta ring

Beta ring

Alpha ring

Rings 4 and 5

Ring 6

Zeta ring

ARIEL
Diameter: 1,158 km
Average distance from planet: 191,200 km

TITANIA
Diameter: 1,578 km
Average distance from planet: 435,800 km

UMBRIEL
Diameter: 1,170 km
Average distance from planet: 266,000 km

OBERON
Diameter: 1,523 km
Average distance from planet: 583,600 km

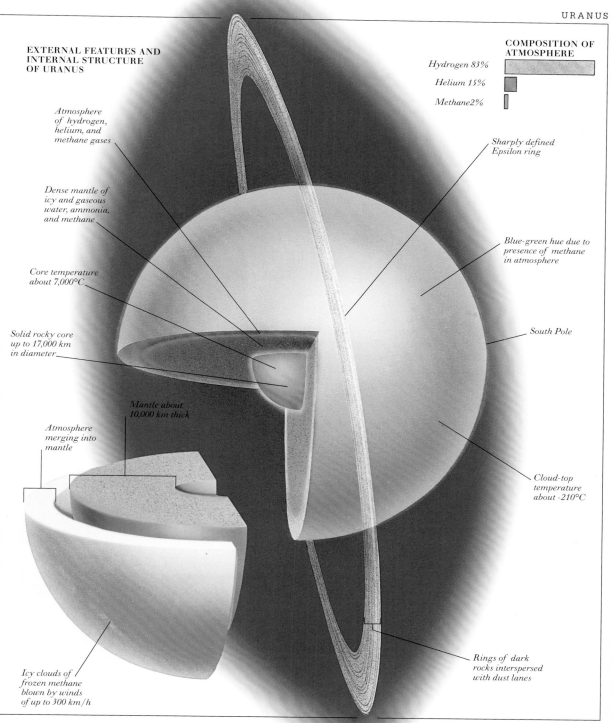

EXTERNAL FEATURES AND
INTERNAL STRUCTURE
OF URANUS

COMPOSITION OF
ATMOSPHERE

Hydrogen 83%

Helium 15%

Methane 2%

*Atmosphere
of hydrogen,
helium, and
methane gases*

*Dense mantle of
icy and gaseous
water, ammonia,
and methane*

*Core temperature
about 7,000°C*

*Solid rocky core
up to 17,000 km
in diameter*

*Mantle about
10,000 km thick*

*Atmosphere
merging into
mantle*

*Icy clouds of
frozen methane
blown by winds
of up to 300 km/h*

*Sharply defined
Epsilon ring*

*Blue-green hue due to
presence of methane
in atmosphere*

South Pole

*Cloud-top
temperature
about -210°C*

*Rings of dark
rocks interspersed
with dust lanes*

49

Neptune and Pluto

FALSE-COLOUR
IMAGE OF NEPTUNE

NEPTUNE IS the furthest planet from the Sun, at an average distance of about 4,500 million kilometres. Neptune is the smallest of the giant planets and is thought to consist of a small rocky core surrounded by a mixture of liquids and gases. Several transient cloud features have been observed in its atmosphere. The largest of these were the Great Dark Spot, which was as wide as the Earth, the Small Dark Spot, and the Scooter. The Great and Small Dark Spots were huge storms that were swept around the planet by winds of about 2,000 kilometres per hour. The Scooter was a large area of cirrus cloud. Neptune has six tenuous rings and 13 known moons. Triton is the largest Neptunian moon and the coldest object in the Solar System, with a temperature of -240°C. Unlike most moons in the Solar System, Triton orbits its mother planet in the opposite direction to the planet's rotation. The region extending out from Neptune's orbit is populated by Kuiper Belt objects and dwarf planets. They make a dough-nut shaped belt called the Kuiper Belt. The Kuiper Belt objects are a mix of rock and ice, irregular in shape, and less than 1,000 kilometres across. The larger dwarf planets, which include Pluto, are almost round bodies. Pluto was the first object discovered beyond Neptune and was considered a planet until the dwarf planet category was introduced in 2006. It is made of rock and ice and is 2,274 kilometres across. It has three known moons. The largest, Charon, is about half Pluto's size and the two probably had a common origin.

TILT AND ROTATION OF NEPTUNE

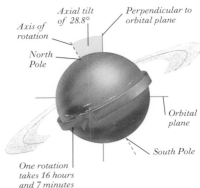

Axial tilt of 28.8°

Perpendicular to orbital plane

Axis of rotation

North Pole

Orbital plane

South Pole

One rotation takes 16 hours and 7 minutes

CLOUD FEATURES OF NEPTUNE

Great Dark Spot (anticyclonic wind storm)

Scooter (cirrus cloud)

Small Dark Spot (cyclonic wind storm)

RINGS OF NEPTUNE

Adams ring and unnamed ring on its inner edge

Arago ring

Lassell ring

Le Verrier ring

Galle ring

HIGH-ALTITUDE CLOUDS

Methane cirrus clouds 40 km above main cloud deck

Cloud shadow

Main cloud deck blown by winds at speeds of about 2,000 km/h

MOONS OF NEPTUNE

TRITON
Diameter: 2,705 km
Average distance from planet: 354,800 km

PROTEUS
Diameter: 416 km
Average distance from planet: 117,600 km

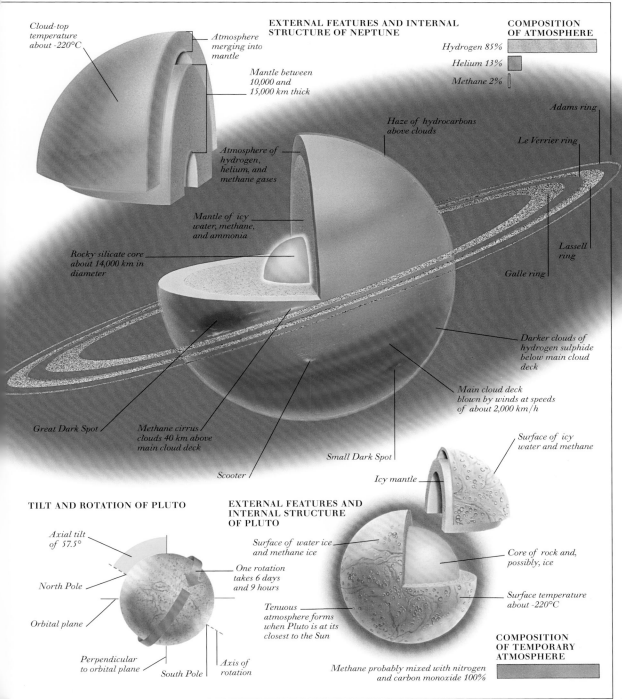

EXTERNAL FEATURES AND INTERNAL STRUCTURE OF NEPTUNE

COMPOSITION OF ATMOSPHERE

Hydrogen 85%

Helium 13%

Methane 2%

Cloud-top temperature about -220°C

Atmosphere merging into mantle

Mantle between 10,000 and 15,000 km thick

Haze of hydrocarbons above clouds

Adams ring

Le Verrier ring

Atmosphere of hydrogen, helium, and methane gases

Mantle of icy water, methane, and ammonia

Lassell ring

Rocky silicate core about 14,000 km in diameter

Galle ring

Darker clouds of hydrogen sulphide below main cloud deck

Main cloud deck blown by winds at speeds of about 2,000 km/h

Great Dark Spot

Methane cirrus clouds 40 km above main cloud deck

Small Dark Spot

Scooter

Surface of icy water and methane

Icy mantle

TILT AND ROTATION OF PLUTO

EXTERNAL FEATURES AND INTERNAL STRUCTURE OF PLUTO

Axial tilt of 57.5°

Surface of water ice and methane ice

Core of rock and, possibly, ice

North Pole

One rotation takes 6 days and 9 hours

Orbital plane

Surface temperature about -220°C

Tenuous atmosphere forms when Pluto is at its closest to the Sun

Perpendicular to orbital plane

South Pole

Axis of rotation

COMPOSITION OF TEMPORARY ATMOSPHERE

Methane probably mixed with nitrogen and carbon monoxide 100%

Asteroids, comets, and meteoroids

ASTEROID 951 GASPRA

ASTEROIDS, COMETS, AND METEOROIDS are all debris remaining from the nebula from which the Solar System formed 4.6 billion years ago. Asteroids are rocky bodies up to about 1,000 kilometres in diameter, although most are much smaller. Most of them orbit the Sun in the asteroid belt, which lies between the orbits of Mars and Jupiter. Cometary nuclei exist in a huge cloud (called the Oort Cloud) that surrounds the planetary part of the Solar System. They are made of frozen water and dust, and are a few kilometres in diameter. Occasionally, a comet is deflected from the Oort Cloud on to a long, elliptical path that brings it much closer to the Sun. As the comet approaches the Sun, the cometary nucleus starts to vaporize in the heat, producing both a brightly shining coma (a huge sphere of gas and dust around the nucleus), and a gas tail, and a dust tail. Meteoroids are small chunks of stone or stone and iron, which are fragments of asteroids or comets. Meteoroids range in size from tiny dust particles to objects tens of metres across. If a meteoroid enters the Earth's atmosphere, it is heated by friction and appears as a glowing streak of light called a meteor (also known as a shooting star). Meteor showers occur when the Earth passes through the trail of dust particles left by a comet. Most meteoroids burn up in the atmosphere. The remnants of the few that are large enough to reach the Earth's surface are termed meteorites.

OPTICAL IMAGE OF HALLEY'S COMET

FALSE-COLOUR IMAGE OF HALLEY'S COMET

High-intensity light emission

Nucleus

Medium-intensity light emission

Low-intensity light emission

FALSE-COLOUR IMAGE OF A LEONID METEOR SHOWER

METEORITES

STONY METEORITE

Fusion crust formed when passing through atmosphere

Olivine and pyroxene mineral interior

STONY-IRON METEORITE

Iron

Stone (olivine)

DEVELOPMENT OF COMET TAILS

Dust tail deflected by photons in sunlight and curved due to comet's motion

Gas tail pushed away from Sun by charged particles in solar wind

Tails lengthen as comet nears Sun

Direction of comet's orbital motion

Coma surrounding nucleus

Sun

Tails behind nucleus

Tails in front of nucleus

Nucleus vaporized by Sun's heat, forming a coma with two tails

Gas tail

Dust tail

Coma and tails fade as comet moves away from Sun

FEATURES OF A COMET

Comet tails up to
100 million km long

Gas molecules excited by
Sun and emitting light

Thin, straight
gas tail

Thin, straight
gas tail blown by
solar wind

Head
(coma and
nucleus)

Broad, curved
dust tail

Coma
surrounding
nucleus

Nucleus a few
kilometres
across

**STRUCTURE OF
A COMET**

Glowing coma up
to 1 million km
across surrounding
nucleus

Dust layer
with active
areas emitting
jets of gas
and dust

Jet of gas and
dust produced by
vaporization
on sunlit side
of nucleus

Ices, mainly water ice, but
also frozen carbon dioxide,
methane, and ammonia

Broad curved
dust tail

Dust particles
reflecting sunlight

PREHISTORIC EARTH

THE CHANGING EARTH ·········· 56
THE EARTH'S CRUST ·········· 58
FAULTS AND FOLDS ·········· 60
MOUNTAIN BUILDING ·········· 62
PRECAMBRIAN TO DEVONIAN PERIOD ·········· 64
CARBONIFEROUS TO PERMIAN PERIOD ·········· 66
TRIASSIC PERIOD ·········· 68
JURASSIC PERIOD ·········· 70
CRETACEOUS PERIOD ·········· 72
TERTIARY PERIOD ·········· 74
QUATERNARY PERIOD ·········· 76
EARLY SIGNS OF LIFE ·········· 78
AMPHIBIANS AND REPTILES ·········· 80
THE DINOSAURS ·········· 82
THEROPODS 1 ·········· 84
THEROPODS 2 ·········· 86
SAUROPODOMORPHS 1 ·········· 88
SAUROPODOMORPHS 2 ·········· 90
THYREOPHORANS 1 ·········· 92
THYREOPHORANS 2 ·········· 94
ORNITHOPODS 1 ·········· 96
ORNITHOPODS 2 ·········· 98
MARGINOCEPHALIANS 1 ·········· 100
MARGINOCEPHALIANS 2 ·········· 102
MAMMALS 1 ·········· 104
MAMMALS 2 ·········· 106
THE FIRST HUMANS ·········· 108

The changing Earth

THE EARTH FORMED FROM A CLOUD OF DUST and gas drifting through space about 4,600 million years ago. Dense minerals sank to the centre while lighter ones formed a thin rocky crust. However, the first known life-forms – bacteria and blue-green algae – did not appear until about 3,400 million years ago, and it was only about 700 million years ago that more complex plants and animals began to develop. Since then, thousands of animal and plant species have evolved; some, such as the dinosaurs, survived for many millions of years, while others died out quickly. The Earth itself is continually changing. Although continents neared their present locations about 50 million years ago, they are still drifting slowly over the planet's surface, and mountain ranges such as the Himalayas – which began to form 40 million years ago – are continually being built up and worn away. Climate is also subject to change: the Earth has undergone a series of ice ages interspersed with warmer periods (the most recent glacial period was at its height about 20,000 years ago).

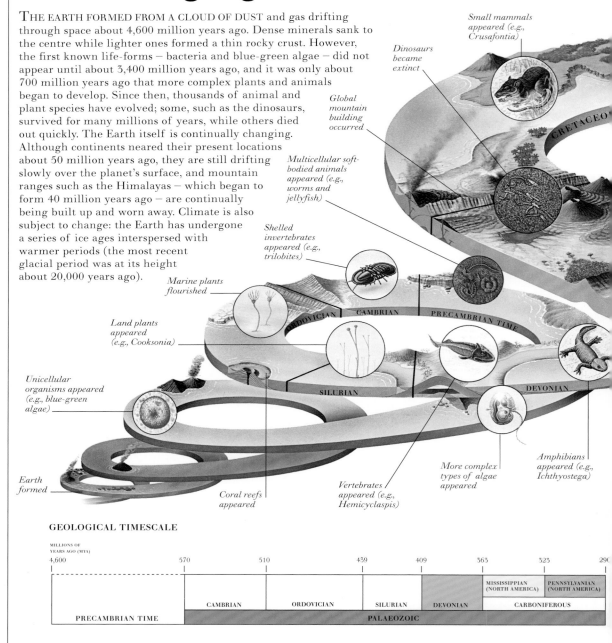

Small mammals appeared (e.g., Crusafontia)

Dinosaurs became extinct

Global mountain building occurred

Multicellular soft-bodied animals appeared (e.g., worms and jellyfish)

Shelled invertebrates appeared (e.g., trilobites)

Marine plants flourished

Land plants appeared (e.g., Cooksonia)

Unicellular organisms appeared (e.g., blue-green algae)

Earth formed

Coral reefs appeared

Vertebrates appeared (e.g., Hemicyclaspis)

More complex types of algae appeared

Amphibians appeared (e.g., Ichthyostega)

CRETACEO

ORDOVICIAN   CAMBRIAN   PRECAMBRIAN TIME

SILURIAN

DEVONIAN

GEOLOGICAL TIMESCALE

MILLIONS OF YEARS AGO (MYA)

4,600	570	510	439	409	363	323	290

PRECAMBRIAN TIME	CAMBRIAN	ORDOVICIAN	SILURIAN	DEVONIAN	MISSISSIPPIAN (NORTH AMERICA)	PENNSYLVANIAN (NORTH AMERICA)
					CARBONIFEROUS	

	PALAEOZOIC

EVOLUTION OF THE EARTH

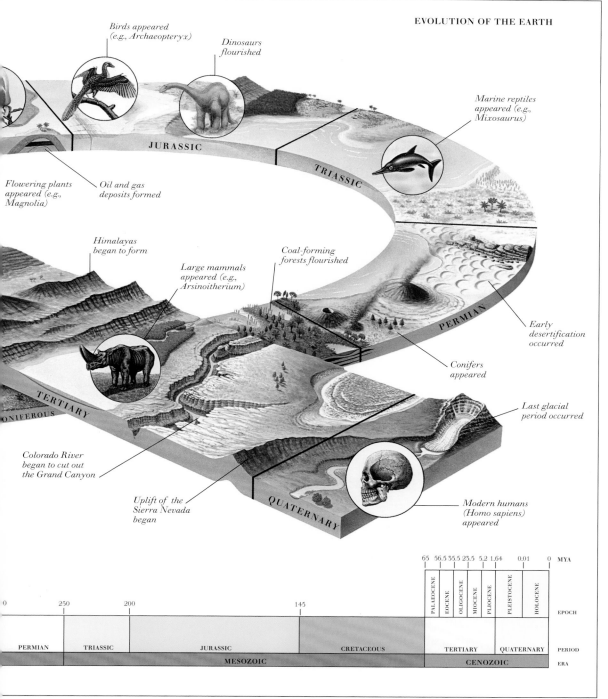

*Birds appeared
(e.g., Archaeopteryx)*

*Dinosaurs
flourished*

*Marine reptiles
appeared (e.g.,
Mixosaurus)*

JURASSIC

TRIASSIC

*Flowering plants
appeared (e.g.,
Magnolia)*

*Oil and gas
deposits formed*

*Himalayas
began to form*

*Coal-forming
forests flourished*

*Large mammals
appeared (e.g.,
Arsinoitherium)*

*Early
desertification
occurred*

PERMIAN

*Conifers
appeared*

*Last glacial
period occurred*

TERTIARY

CONIFEROUS

*Colorado River
began to cut out
the Grand Canyon*

*Uplift of the
Sierra Nevada
began*

QUATERNARY

*Modern humans
(Homo sapiens)
appeared*

		65	56.5	35.5	23.5	5.2	1.64		0.01	0	MYA
		PALAEOCENE	EOCENE	OLIGOCENE	MIOCENE	PLIOCENE		PLEISTOCENE		HOLOCENE	EPOCH
0	250	200					145				
PERMIAN	TRIASSIC	JURASSIC				CRETACEOUS		TERTIARY		QUATERNARY	PERIOD
		MESOZOIC						CENOZOIC			ERA

The Earth's crust

THE EARTH'S CRUST IS THE SOLID outer shell of the Earth. It includes
continental crust (about 40 kilometres thick) and oceanic crust (about
six kilometres thick). The crust and the topmost layer of the mantle
form the lithosphere. The lithosphere consists of semi-rigid plates
that move relative to each other on the underlying asthenosphere
(a partly molten layer of the mantle). This process is known as plate
tectonics and helps explain continental drift. Where two plates move
apart, there are rifts in the crust. In mid-ocean, this movement results
in sea-floor spreading and the formation of ocean ridges; on continents,
crustal spreading can form rift valleys. When plates move towards each other,
one may be subducted beneath (forced under) the other. In mid-ocean, this causes
ocean trenches, seismic activity, and arcs of volcanic islands. Where oceanic crust
is subducted beneath continental crust or where continents collide, land may be
uplifted and mountains formed (see pp. 62–65). Plates may also slide past each
other – along the San Andreas fault, for example. Crustal movement on continents
may result in earthquakes, while movement under the seabed can lead to tidal waves.

ELEMENTS IN THE EARTH'S CRUST

Other elements 2%

Potassium 2.6%
Calcium 3.6%
Aluminium 8%

Magnesium 2%
Sodium 2.8%
Iron 5%
Silicon 28%

Oxygen 46%

FEATURES OF PLATE MOVEMENTS

*Ridge where magma
is rising to form new
oceanic crust*

*Region of
sea-floor
spreading*

*Ocean trench formed where oceanic
crust is forced under continental crust*

Subduction zone

*Rift formed where
two plates are
moving apart*

*Magma (molten rock)
erupts at rift*

*Magma rises to
form a hot spot*

*Volcano develops
over hot spot and
builds up to form
an island*

*Volcanic island
that originally
formed over
hot spot*

*Oceanic
crust melts*

*Magma rises
to form a
volcano*

MAJOR PLATES OF THE EARTH'S CRUST

North American plate

Plates sliding past each other

Cocos plate

Caribbean plate

Nazca plate

Hellenic plate

Eurasian plate

Pacific plate

Philippine plate

Plates converging

South American plate

Plates moving apart

African plate

Indo-Australian plate

Boundary along which two plates slide past each other

Mountain range uplifted where subducting oceanic crust compresses and deforms edge of continental crust

Lithosphere (crust and topmost layer of mantle)

Asthenosphere (upper part of mantle)

MOVEMENT OF LAND ALONG OCEANIC RIDGES

Land moves apart at a constant rate, perpendicular to ridge

STRAIGHT OCEANIC RIDGE

Land moves apart at a constant rate, perpendicular to curve

CURVED OCEANIC RIDGE

Staggered parallel ridge sections take shape of curve

Transform fault

STRESSES RESOLVE INTO SECTIONS

Faults and folds

THE CONTINUOUS MOVEMENT of the Earth's crustal plates (see pp. 58–59) can squeeze, stretch, or break rock strata, deforming them and producing faults and folds. A fault is a fracture in a rock along which there is movement of one side relative to the other. The movement can be vertical, horizontal, or oblique (vertical and horizontal). Faults develop when rocks are subjected to compression or tension. They tend to occur in hard, rigid rocks, which are more likely to break than bend. The smallest faults occur in single mineral crystals and are microscopically small, whereas the largest – the Great Rift Valley in Africa, which formed between 5 million and 100,000 years ago – is more than 9,000 kilometres long. A fold is a bend in a rock layer caused by compression. Folds occur in elastic rocks, which tend to bend rather than break. The two main types of fold are anticlines (upfolds) and synclines (downfolds). Folds vary in size from a few millimetres long to folded mountain ranges hundreds of kilometres long, such as the Himalayas (see pp. 62–63) and the Alps, which are repeatedly folding. In addition to faults and folds, other features associated with rock deformations include boudins, mullions, and *en échelon* fractures.

STRUCTURE OF A FOLD

Axial plane

Crest

Limb

Angle of plunge

Hingeline

STRUCTURE OF A FAULT

Fault plane

Dip of fault plane (angle from horizontal)

Upthrow

Throw (vertical displacement of fault)

Downthrow

Hade of fault plane (angle from vertical)

FOLDED ROCK

Crest of anticline

Steeply dipping limbs

Plunge

STRUCTURE OF A SLOPE

Strike

Angle of dip

Strike and dip are at right angles to each other

Direction of dip

SECTION THROUGH FOLDED ROCK STRATA THAT HAVE BEEN ERODED

Dipping bed

Anticlinal fold

Monoclinal fold

Mineral-filled fault

Upper Carboniferous Millstone Grit

Lower Carboniferous Limestone

EXAMPLES OF FOLDS

Anticlinorium

Monocline

Syncline

Overturned fold

Overthrust fold

Chevron fold

Synclinorium

Anticline

Isocline

Recumbent fold

Fan fold

Box fold

Cuspate fold

EXAMPLES OF FAULTS

Sinistral strike-slip (lateral) fault

Dextral strike-slip (lateral) fault

Horst

Tear fault

Normal dip-slip fault

Reverse dip-slip fault

Thrust fault

Oblique-slip fault

Graben

Cylindrical fault

SMALL-SCALE ROCK DEFORMATIONS

Competent bed (rocks that break)

Tension

Incompetent bed

Tension

Tension

Tension

Masses of rock shear past each other

En échelon fracture

Tension

Tension

Incompetent bed (rocks that bend)

Competent bed breaks into sections

Competent bed

Competent bed splits into prisms

Tension

Joint opened by stress

BOUDIN

MULLION

EN ECHELON FRACTURE

Mineral-filled fault

Dipping bed

Gently folded bed

Horizontal bed

Mineral-filled fault

Dipping bed

Upper Carboniferous Millstone Grit

Upper Carboniferous Coal Measures

61

Mountain building

THE PROCESSES INVOLVED in mountain building – termed orogenesis – occur as a result of the movement of the Earth's crustal plates (see pp. 58–59). There are three main types of mountains: volcanic mountains, fold mountains, and block mountains. Most volcanic mountains have been formed along plate boundaries where plates have come together or moved apart and lava and other debris have been ejected onto the Earth's surface. The lava and debris may have built up to form a dome around the vent of a volcano. Fold mountains are formed where plates push together and cause the rock to buckle upwards. Where oceanic crust meets less dense continental crust, the oceanic crust is forced under the continental crust. The continental crust is buckled by the impact. This is how folded mountain ranges, such as the Appalachian Mountains in North America, were formed. Fold mountains are also formed where two areas of continental crust meet. The Himalayas, for example, began to form when India collided with Asia, buckling the sediments and parts of the oceanic crust between them. Block mountains are formed when a block of land is uplifted between two faults as a result of compression or tension in the Earth's crust (see pp. 60–61). Often, the movement along faults has taken place gradually over millions of years. However, two plates may cause an earthquake by suddenly sliding past each other along a faultline.

BHAGIRATHI PARBAT,
HIMALAYAS

FORMATION OF THE HIMALAYAS

Asia

Himalayas formed by buckling of sediment and part of the oceanic crust between two colliding continents

India moves north

India collides with Asia about 40 million years ago

EXAMPLES OF MOUNTAINS

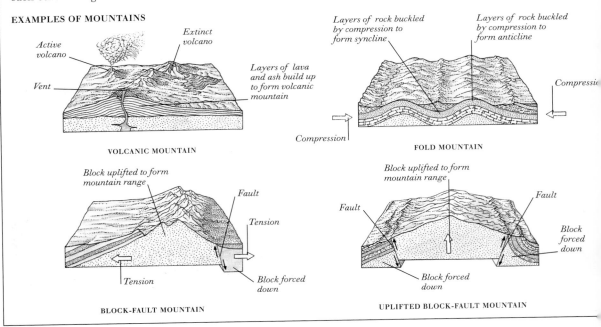

Active volcano

Extinct volcano

Vent

Layers of lava and ash build up to form volcanic mountain

VOLCANIC MOUNTAIN

Layers of rock buckled by compression to form syncline

Layers of rock buckled by compression to form anticline

Compression

Compression

FOLD MOUNTAIN

Block uplifted to form mountain range

Fault

Tension

Tension

Block forced down

BLOCK-FAULT MOUNTAIN

Block uplifted to form mountain range

Fault

Fault

Block forced down

Block forced down

UPLIFTED BLOCK-FAULT MOUNTAIN

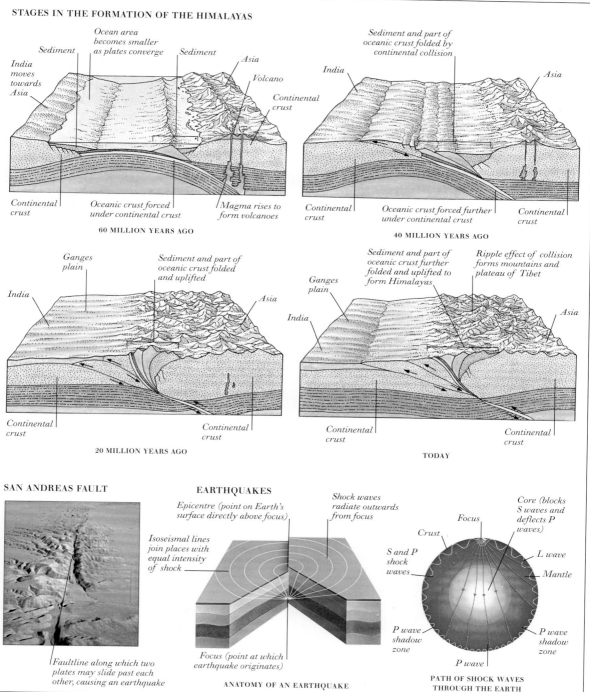

STAGES IN THE FORMATION OF THE HIMALAYAS

India moves towards Asia

Sediment

Ocean area becomes smaller as plates converge

Sediment

Asia

Volcano

Continental crust

Continental crust

Oceanic crust forced under continental crust

Magma rises to form volcanoes

60 MILLION YEARS AGO

Sediment and part of oceanic crust folded by continental collision

India

Asia

Continental crust

Oceanic crust forced further under continental crust

Continental crust

40 MILLION YEARS AGO

Ganges plain

Sediment and part of oceanic crust folded and uplifted

India

Asia

Continental crust

Continental crust

20 MILLION YEARS AGO

Sediment and part of oceanic crust further folded and uplifted to form Himalayas

Ripple effect of collision forms mountains and plateau of Tibet

Ganges plain

India

Asia

Continental crust

Continental crust

TODAY

SAN ANDREAS FAULT

Faultline along which two plates may slide past each other, causing an earthquake

EARTHQUAKES

Epicentre (point on Earth's surface directly above focus)

Shock waves radiate outwards from focus

Isoseismal lines join places with equal intensity of shock

Focus (point at which earthquake originates)

ANATOMY OF AN EARTHQUAKE

Focus

Crust

Core (blocks S waves and deflects P waves)

S and P shock waves

L wave

Mantle

P wave shadow zone

P wave shadow zone

P wave

PATH OF SHOCK WAVES THROUGH THE EARTH

63

Precambrian to Devonian periods

WHEN THE EARTH FORMED about 4,600 million years ago, its atmosphere consisted of volcanic gases with little oxygen, making it hostile to most forms of life. One large supercontinent, Gondwana, was situated over the southern polar region, while other smaller continents were spread over the rest of the world. Constant movement of the earth's crustal plates carried continents across the earth's surface. The first primitive life-forms emerged around 3,400 million years ago in shallow, warm seas. The build up of oxygen began to form a shield of ozone around the earth, protecting living organisms from the sun's harmful rays and helping to establish an atmosphere in which life could sustain itself. The first vertebrates appeared about 470 million years ago, during the Ordovician period (510–439 million years ago), the first land plants appeared around 400 million years ago during the Devonian period (409–363 million years ago), and the first land animals about 30 million years later.

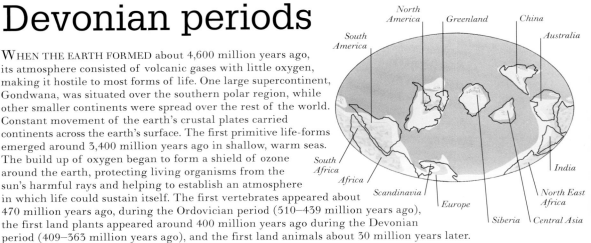

MIDDLE ORDOVICIAN POSITIONS
OF PRESENT-DAY LAND-MASSES

North America
Greenland
China
South America
Australia
South Africa
India
Africa
Scandinavia
North East Africa
Europe
Siberia
Central Asia

EXAMPLES OF PRECAMBRIAN TO DEVONIAN PLANT GROUPS

A PRESENT-DAY CLUBMOSS
(*Lycopodium sp.*)

A PRESENT-DAY
LAND PLANT
(*Asparagus setaceous*)

FOSSIL OF AN EXTINCT LAND PLANT
(*Cooksonia hemisphaerica*)

FOSSIL OF AN EXTINCT SWAMP PLANT
(*Zosterophyllum llanoveranum*)

EXAMPLES OF PRECAMBRIAN TO DEVONIAN TRILOBITES

ACADAGNOSTUS
Group: Agnostidae
Length: 8 mm (⅓ in)

PHACOPS
Group: Phacopidae
Length: 4.5 cm (1¾ in)

OLENELLUS
Group: Olenellidae
Length: 6 cm (2½ in)

ELRATHIA
Group: Ptychopariidae
Length: 2 cm (¾ in)

THE EARTH DURING THE MIDDLE ORDOVICIAN PERIOD

Siberia

Laurentia

China

Kazakstania

Gondwana

Baltica

EXAMPLES OF EARLY MARINE INVERTEBRATES

FOSSIL NAUTILOID
(*Estonioceras perforatum*)

FOSSIL BRACHIOPOD
(*Dicoelosia bilobata*)

TRACE FOSSIL
(*Mawsonites spriggi*)

FOSSIL GRAPTOLITE
(*Monograptus convolutus*)

EXAMPLES OF DEVONIAN FISH

RHAMPHODOPSIS
Group: Ptyctodontidae
Length: 15 cm (6 in)

PTERASPIS
Group: Pteraspidae
Length: 25 cm (10 in)

COCCOSTEUS
Group: Coccosteidae
Length: 35 cm (14 in)

BOTHRIOLEPIS
Group: Bothriolepididae
Length: 40 cm (16 in)

CHEIRACANTHUS
Group: Acanthodidae
Length: 30 cm (12 in)

PTERICHTHYODES
Group: Asterolepididae
Length: 15 cm (6 in)

CHEIROLEPIS
Group: Cheirolepidae
Length: 17 cm (6¾ in)

CEPHALASPIS
Group: Cephalaspidae
Length: 22 cm (8¾ in)

Carboniferous to Permian periods

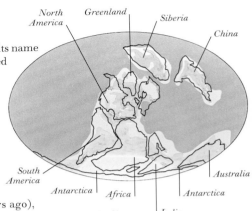

THE CARBONIFEROUS PERIOD (363–290 million years ago) takes its name from the thick, carbon-rich layers – now coal – that were produced during this period as swampy tropical forests were repeatedly drowned by shallow seas. The humid climate across northern and equatorial continents throughout Carboniferous times produced the first dense plant cover on Earth. During the early part of this period, the first reptiles appeared. Their development of a waterproof egg with a protective internal structure ended animal life's dependence on an aquatic environment. Towards the end of Carboniferous times, the earth's continents Laurasia and Gondwana collided, resulting in the huge land-mass of Pangaea. Glaciers smothered much of the southern hemisphere during the Permian period (290–245 million years ago), covering Antarctica, parts of Australia, and much of South America, Africa, and India. Ice locked up much of the world's water and large areas of the northern hemisphere experienced a drop in sea-level. Away from the poles, deserts and a hot dry climate predominated. As a result of these conditions, the Permian period ended with the greatest mass extinction of life on earth ever.

EXAMPLES OF CARBONIFEROUS AND PERMIAN PLANT GROUPS

A PRESENT-DAY FIR
(Abies concolor)

FOSSIL OF AN EXTINCT FERN
(Zeilleria frenzlii)

**FOSSIL OF AN
EXTINCT HORSETAIL**
(Equisetites sp.)

**FOSSIL OF AN
EXTINCT CLUBMOSS**
(Lepidodendron sp.)

EXAMPLES OF CARBONIFEROUS AND PERMIAN TREES

PECOPTERIS
Group: Marattiaceae
Height: 4 m (13 ft)

PARIPTERIS
Group: Medullosaceae
Height: 5 m (16 ft 6 in)

MARIOPTERIS
Group: Lyginopteridales
Height: 5 m (16 ft 6 in)

MEDULLOSA
Group: Medullosaceae
Height: 5 m (16 ft 6 in)

THE EARTH DURING THE LATE CARBONIFEROUS PERIOD

Siberia

Laurussia

China

Ural
Mountains

Caledonian
Mountains

Appalachian
Mountains

Gondwana

SKULL OF AN EXTINCT SYNAPSID
(*Dimetrodon loomisi*)

**FOSSIL TEETH OF
AN EXTINCT SHARK**
(*Helicoprion bessonowi*)

**MODEL OF AN EXTINCT EARLY
REPTILE-LIKE ANIMAL**
(*Westlothiana lizziae*)

LEPIDODENDRON
Group: Lepidodendraceae
Height: 30 m (100 ft)

CORDAITES
Group: Cordaitacea
Height: 10 m (33 ft)

GLOSSOPTERIS
Group: Glossopteridaceae
Height: 8 m (26 ft)

ALETHOPTERIS
Group: Medullosaceae
Height: 5 m (16 ft 6 in)

Triassic period

THE TRIASSIC PERIOD (250–200 million years ago) marked the beginning of what is known as the Age of the Dinosaurs (the Mesozoic era). During this period, the present-day continents were massed together, forming one huge continent known as Pangaea. This land-mass experienced extremes of climate, with lush green areas around the coast or by lakes and rivers, and arid deserts in the interior. The only forms of plant life were non-flowering plants, such as conifers, ferns, cycads, and ginkgos; flowering plants had not yet evolved. The principal forms of animal life included diverse, often gigantic, amphibians, rhynchosaurs ("beaked lizards"), and primitive crocodilians. Dinosaurs first appeared about 230 million years ago, at the beginning of the Late Triassic period. Among the earliest dinosaurs were the carnivorous (flesh-eating) herrerasaurids, such as *Herrerasaurus* and *Staurikosaurus*. Early herbivorous (plant-eating) dinosaurs first appeared in Late Triassic times and included *Plateosaurus* and *Technosaurus*. By the end of the Triassic period, dinosaurs dominated Pangaea, possibly contributing to the extinction of many other reptiles.

TRIASSIC POSITIONS OF PRESENT-DAY LAND-MASSES

North America

Europe

Asia

South America

Africa

Antarctica

India

Australia

EXAMPLES OF TRIASSIC PLANT GROUPS

A PRESENT-DAY CYCAD
(*Cycas revoluta*)

A PRESENT-DAY GINKGO
(*Ginkgo biloba*)

A PRESENT-DAY CONIFER
(*Araucaria araucana*)

FOSSIL OF AN EXTINCT FERN
(*Pachypteris sp.*)

FOSSIL LEAF OF AN EXTINCT CYCAD
(*Cycas sp.*)

EXAMPLES OF TRIASSIC DINOSAURS

MELANOROSAURUS
Group: Melanorosauridae
Length: 12.2 m (40 ft)

MUSSAURUS
Group: Sauropodomorpha
Length: 2–3 m (6 ft 6 in–10 ft)

HERRERASAURUS
Group: Herrerasauridae
Length: 3 m (10 ft)

PISANOSAURUS
Group: Ornithischia
Length: 90 cm (3 ft)

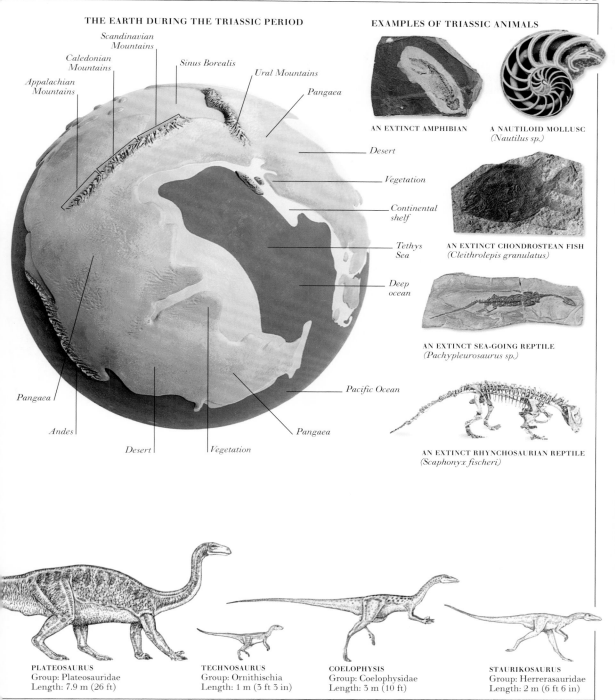

THE EARTH DURING THE TRIASSIC PERIOD

Scandinavian Mountains

Caledonian Mountains

Sinus Borealis

Ural Mountains

Appalachian Mountains

Pangaea

Desert

Vegetation

Continental shelf

Tethys Sea

Deep ocean

Pangaea

Pacific Ocean

Andes

Pangaea

Desert

Vegetation

EXAMPLES OF TRIASSIC ANIMALS

AN EXTINCT AMPHIBIAN

A NAUTILOID MOLLUSC
(Nautilus sp.)

AN EXTINCT CHONDROSTEAN FISH
(Cleithrolepis granulatus)

AN EXTINCT SEA-GOING REPTILE
(Pachypleurosaurus sp.)

AN EXTINCT RHYNCHOSAURIAN REPTILE
(Scaphonyx fischeri)

PLATEOSAURUS
Group: Plateosauridae
Length: 7.9 m (26 ft)

TECHNOSAURUS
Group: Ornithischia
Length: 1 m (3 ft 3 in)

COELOPHYSIS
Group: Coelophysidae
Length: 3 m (10 ft)

STAURIKOSAURUS
Group: Herrerasauridae
Length: 2 m (6 ft 6 in)

Jurassic period

THE JURASSIC PERIOD, the middle part of the Mesozoic era, lasted from 199 to 145 million years ago. During Jurassic times, the land-mass of Pangaea broke up into the continents of Gondwana and Laurasia, and sea-levels rose, flooding areas of lower land. The Jurassic climate was warm and moist. Plants such as ginkgos, horsetails, and conifers thrived, and giant redwood trees appeared, as did the first flowering plants. The abundance of plant food coincided with the proliferation of herbivorous (plant-eating) dinosaurs, such as the large sauropods (e.g., *Diplodocus*) and stegosaurs (e.g., *Stegosaurus*). Carnivorous (flesheating) dinosaurs, such as *Compsognathus* and *Allosaurus*, also flourished by hunting the many animals that existed – among them other dinosaurs. Further Jurassic animals included shrew-like mammals, and pterosaurs (flying reptiles), as well as plesiosaurs and ichthyosaurs (both marine reptiles).

JURASSIC POSITIONS OF PRESENT-DAY LAND-MASSES

North America

Europe

Arabia

Asia

South America

Africa

Antarctica

India

Australia

EXAMPLES OF JURASSIC PLANT GROUPS

A PRESENT-DAY FERN
(*Dicksonia antarctica*)

A PRESENT-DAY HORSETAIL
(*Equisetum arvense*)

A PRESENT-DAY CONIFER
(*Taxus baccata*)

FOSSIL LEAF OF AN EXTINCT CONIFER
(*Taxus sp.*)

FOSSIL LEAF OF AN EXTINCT REDWOOD
(*Sequoiadendron affinis*)

EXAMPLES OF JURASSIC DINOSAURS

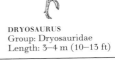

DIPLODOCUS
Group: Diplodocidae
Length: 26.8 m (88 ft)

CAMPTOSAURUS
Group: Iguanodontia
Length: 4.9–7 m (16–23 ft)

DRYOSAURUS
Group: Dryosauridae
Length: 3–4 m (10–13 ft)

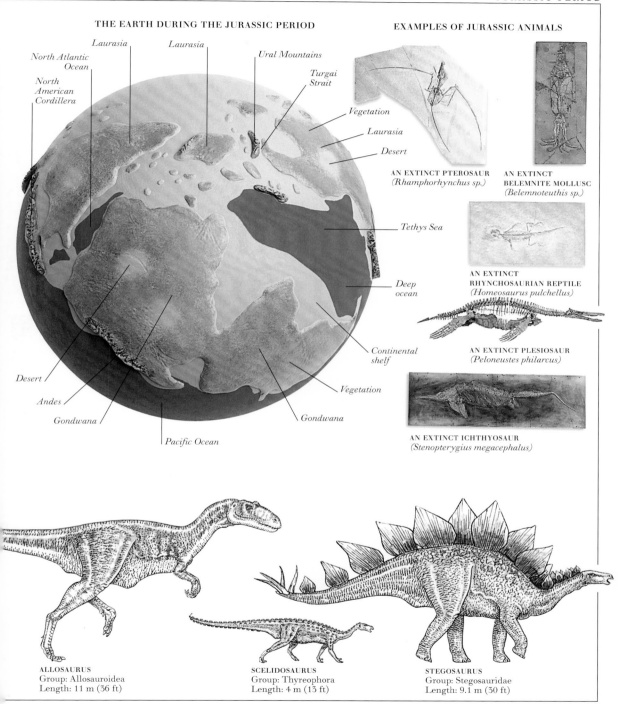

THE EARTH DURING THE JURASSIC PERIOD

North Atlantic Ocean

Laurasia

Laurasia

Ural Mountains

North American Cordillera

Turgai Strait

Vegetation

Laurasia

Desert

Tethys Sea

Deep ocean

Continental shelf

Desert

Andes

Gondwana

Vegetation

Gondwana

Pacific Ocean

EXAMPLES OF JURASSIC ANIMALS

AN EXTINCT PTEROSAUR
(*Rhamphorhynchus sp.*)

AN EXTINCT BELEMNITE MOLLUSC
(*Belemnoteuthis sp.*)

AN EXTINCT RHYNCHOSAURIAN REPTILE
(*Homeosaurus pulchellus*)

AN EXTINCT PLESIOSAUR
(*Peloneustes philarcus*)

AN EXTINCT ICHTHYOSAUR
(*Stenopterygius megacephalus*)

ALLOSAURUS
Group: Allosauroidea
Length: 11 m (36 ft)

SCELIDOSAURUS
Group: Thyreophora
Length: 4 m (13 ft)

STEGOSAURUS
Group: Stegosauridae
Length: 9.1 m (30 ft)

Cretaceous period

THE MESOZOIC ERA ENDED WITH the Cretaceous period, which lasted from 146 to 65 million years ago. During this period, Gondwana and Laurasia were breaking up into smaller land-masses that more closely resembled the modern continents. The climate remained mild and moist but the seasons became more marked. Flowering plants, including deciduous trees, replaced many cycads, seed ferns, and conifers. Animal species became more varied, with the evolution of new mammals, insects, fish, crustaceans, and turtles. Dinosaurs evolved into a wide variety of species during Cretaceous times; more than half of all known dinosaurs – including *Iguanodon*, *Deinonychus*, *Tyrannosaurus*, and *Hypsilophodon* – lived during this period. At the end of the Cretaceous period, however, most dinosaurs became extinct. The reason for this mass extinction is unknown but it is thought to have been caused by climatic changes due to either a catastrophic meteor impact with the Earth or extensive volcanic eruptions.

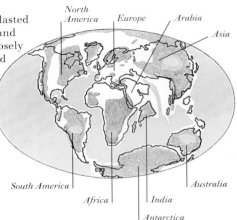

CRETACEOUS POSITIONS OF PRESENT-DAY LAND-MASSES

North America · Europe · Arabia · Asia · South America · Africa · India · Antarctica · Australia

EXAMPLES OF CRETACEOUS PLANT GROUPS

A PRESENT-DAY CONIFER
(*Pinus muricata*)

A PRESENT-DAY DECIDUOUS TREE
(*Magnolia sp.*)

FOSSIL OF AN EXTINCT FERN
(*Sphenopteris latiloba*)

FOSSIL OF AN EXTINCT GINKGO
(*Ginkgo pluripartita*)

FOSSIL LEAVES OF AN EXTINCT DECIDUOUS TREE
(*Cercidyphyllum sp.*)

EXAMPLES OF CRETACEOUS DINOSAURS

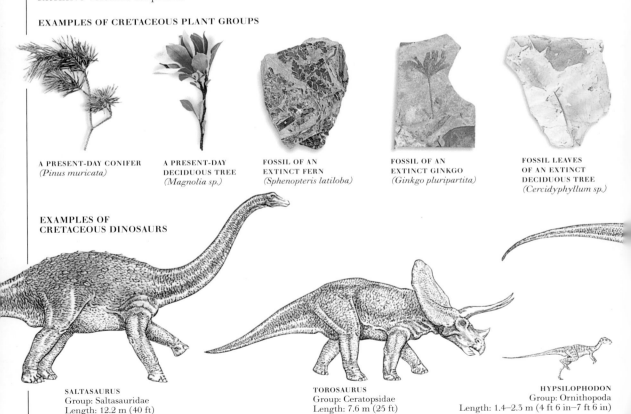

SALTASAURUS
Group: Saltasauridae
Length: 12.2 m (40 ft)

TOROSAURUS
Group: Ceratopsidae
Length: 7.6 m (25 ft)

HYPSILOPHODON
Group: Ornithopoda
Length: 1.4–2.3 m (4 ft 6 in–7 ft 6 in)

THE EARTH DURING THE CRETACEOUS PERIOD

West Africa

Africa

Greenland

Europe

Continental Sea

North America

Rocky Mountains

Ural Mountains

Desert

Tethys Sea

Asia

India

Indian Ocean

Australia

Pacific Ocean

North Atlantic Ocean

Andes

South America

South Atlantic Ocean

Antarctica

Vegetation

EXAMPLES OF CRETACEOUS ANIMALS

AN EXTINCT INSECT
(*Libellulium longialatum*)

AN EXTINCT MARINE TURTLE
(*Plesiochelys latiscutata*)

AN EXTINCT CRUSTACEAN
(*Homarus sp.*)

AN EXTINCT CROCODILIAN

AN EXTINCT HOLOSTEAN FISH
(*Lepidotes maximus*)

TYRANNOSAURUS
Group: Tyrannosauridae
Length: 12.2 m (40 ft)

DEINONYCHUS
Group: Dromaeosauridae
Length: 2.4–3.4 m (8–11 ft)

IGUANODON
Group: Iguanodontia
Length: 9.1 m (30 ft)

73

Tertiary period

FOLLOWING THE DEMISE OF THE DINOSAURS at the end of the Cretaceous period, the Tertiary period (65–1.6 million years ago), which formed the first part of the Cenozoic era (65 million years ago–present), was characterized by a huge expansion of mammal life. Placental mammals nourish and maintain the young in the mother's uterus; only a few groups of placental mammals existed during Cretaceous times, compared with several tens of groups during the Tertiary period. One of these tens included the early human (see pp.108–109), *Ardipithecus*, which appeared in Africa. By the beginning of the Tertiary period, the continents had almost reached their present position. The Tethys Sea, which had separated the northern continents from Africa and India, began to close up, forming the Mediterranean Sea and allowing the migration of terrestrial animals between Africa and western Europe. India's collision with Asia led to the formation of the Himalayas. During the middle part of the Tertiary period, the forest-dwelling and browsing mammals were replaced by mammals such as the horses, better suited to grazing the open savannahs that began to dominate. Repeated cool periods throughout the Tertiary period established the Antarctic as an icy island continent.

North America Europe Asia

South America Africa Australia

Antarctica

EXAMPLES OF TERTIARY PLANT GROUPS

A PRESENT-DAY OAK
(*Quercus palustris*)

A PRESENT-DAY BIRCH
(*Betula grossa*)

FOSSIL LEAF OF AN
EXTINCT BIRCH
(*Betulites sp.*)

FOSSILIZED STEM OF
AN EXTINCT PALM
(*Palmoxylon sp.*)

EXAMPLES OF TERTIARY ANIMAL GROUPS

HYAENODON
Group: Hyaenodontidae
Length: 2 m (6 ft 6 in)

TITANOHYRAX
Group: Pliohyracidae
Length: 2 m (6 ft 6 in)

PHORUSRHACOS
Group: Phorusrhacidae
Length: 1.5 m (5 ft)

SAMOTHERIUM
Group: Giraffidae
Length: 3 m (10 ft)

THE EARTH DURING THE TERTIARY PERIOD

North America
Appalachian Mountains
Rocky Mountains
Pyrenees
Europe
Alps
Sierra Nevada
Asia
Continental sea
Zagros Mountains
Himalayas
Tethys Sea
Australia
India
Indian Ocean
Andes
South America
Atlantic Ocean
Atlas Mountains
Africa
Antarctica
Vegetation

EXAMPLES OF TERTIARY ANIMALS

AN EXTINCT MAMMAL
(*Arsinoitherium*)

AN EXTINCT MAMMAL
(*Merycoidodon culbertsonii*)

AN EXTINCT PRIMATE
(*Aegyptopithecus sp.*)

AN EXTINCT GASTROPOD MOLLUSC
(*Ecphora quadricostata*)

MAMMUT
Group: Mammutidae
Length: 2.5 m (8 ft)

TETRALOPHODON
Group: Gomphotheriidae
Length: 2.5 m (8 ft)

Quaternary period

THE QUATERNARY PERIOD (1.6 million years ago–present) forms the second part of the Cenozoic era (65 million years ago–present): it has been characterized by alternating cold (glacial) and warm (interglacial) periods. During cold periods, ice sheets and glaciers have formed repeatedly on northern and southern continents. The cold environments in North America and Eurasia, and to a lesser extent in southern South America and parts of Australia, have caused the migration of many life forms towards the Equator. Only the specialized ice age mammals such as *Mammuthus* and *Coelodonta*, with their thick wool and fat insulation, were suited to life in very cold climates. Humans developed throughout the Pleistocene period (1.6 million–10,000 years ago) in Africa and migrated northward into Europe and Asia. Modern humans, *Homo sapiens*, lived on the cold European continent 30,000 years ago and hunted other mammals. The end of the last ice age and the climatic changes that occurred about 10,000 years ago brought extinction to many Pleistocene mammals, but enabled humans to flourish.

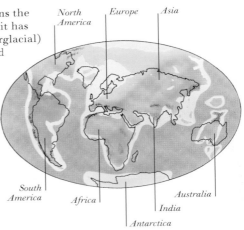

North America Europe Asia

South America Africa Australia
India
Antarctica

EXAMPLES OF QUATERNARY PLANT GROUPS

A PRESENT-DAY BIRCH
(*Betula lenta*)

A PRESENT-DAY SWEETGUM
(*Liquidambar styraciflua*)

FOSSIL LEAF OF A SWEETGUM
(*Liquidambar europeanum*)

FOSSIL LEAF OF A BIRCH
(*Betula sp.*)

EXAMPLES OF QUATERNARY ANIMAL GROUPS

PROCOPTODON
Group: Macropodidae
Length: 3 m (10 ft)

DIPROTODON
Group: Diprotodontidae
Length: 3 m (10 ft)

TOXODON
Group: Toxodontidae
Length: 3 m (10 ft)

MAMMUTHUS
Group: Elephantidae
Length: 3 m (10 ft)

THE EARTH DURING THE QUATERNARY PERIOD

EXAMPLES OF QUATERNARY ANIMALS

Pyrenees

Alps

Appalachian
Mountains

Ice sheet

Rocky
Mountains

Asia

North
America

Vegetation

Carpathian
Mountains

Taurus
Mountains

Himalayas

India

Australia

Andes

South
America

Desert

Atlantic
Ocean

Indian
Ocean

Atlas
Mountains

Africa

Antarctica

Ice cap

A MAMMAL SKELETON
(*Hippopotamus
amphibius*)

**SKULL OF AN EXTINCT
CAVE BEAR**
(*Ursus spelaeus*)

**SKULL OF AN
EXTINCT TORTOISE**
(*Meiolania platyceps*)

A MAMMOTH TOOTH
(*Mammuthus
primigenius*)

DEINOTHERIUM
Group: Deinotheriidae
Length: 4 m (13 ft)

COELODONTA
Group: Rhinocerotidae
Length: 4 m (13 ft)

AUSTRALOPITHECUS
Group: Hominidae
Length: 1.2 m (4 ft)

Early signs of life

FOR ALMOST A THOUSAND MILLION YEARS after its formation, there was no known life on Earth. The first simple, sea-dwelling organic structures appeared about 3,500 million years ago; they may have formed when certain chemical molecules joined together. Prokaryotes, single-celled micro-organisms such as blue-green algae, were able to photosynthesize (see pp. 138–139), and thus produce oxygen. A thousand million years later, sufficient oxygen had built up in the earth's atmosphere to allow multicellular organisms to proliferate in the Precambrian seas (before 570 million years ago). Soft-bodied jellyfish, corals, and seaworms flourished about 700 million years ago. Trilobites, the first animals with hard body frames, developed during the Cambrian period (570–510 million years ago). However, it was not until the beginning of the Devonian period (409–363 million years ago) that early land plants, such as *Asteroxylon*, formed a water-retaining cuticle, which ended their dependence on an aquatic environment. About 360 million years ago, the first amphibians (see pp. 80–81) crawled onto the land, although they probably still returned to the water to lay their soft eggs. By the time the first reptiles and synapsids appeared late in the Carboniferous, animals with backbones had become fully independent of water.

STROMATOLITIC LIMESTONE

Alternate layers of mud and sand

Layers bound by algae

Layered structure

Limestone

Long, beak-like snout

Growth line

Dorsal plate

Dorsal spine base

Fixed lateral plate

Bony dorsal shield

FOSSILIZED JAWLESS FISH

Glabella

Eye

Thoracic pleurae

Tail shield

Tail area

FOSSILIZED TRILOBITE

Ambulacral groove

Small ossicles of upper surface

Central disc

Iron pyrites

FOSSILIZED STARFISH

Row of ossicles

Broad disc

UPPER SURFACE OF FOSSILIZED STARFISH

Row of ossicles

Short arm

LOWER SURFACE OF FOSSILIZED STARFISH

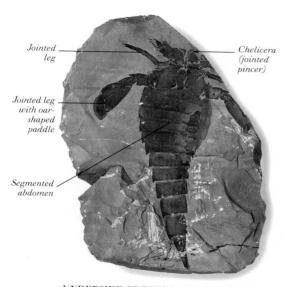

Jointed leg

Chelicera (jointed pincer)

Jointed leg with oar-shaped paddle

Segmented abdomen

UNDERSIDE OF FOSSILIZED EURYPTERID

Telson (tail spine)

Shell contains eight somites (thoracic segments)

Abdominal segments

Hingeless, bivalved shell

FOSSIL OF AN EXTINCT SHRIMP

Growing tip

Disc-shaped sporangium (spore-case)

Leaf-like scale

Stem

RECONSTRUCTION OF ASTEROXYLON

Amphibians and reptiles

THE EARLIEST KNOWN AMPHIBIANS, such as *Acanthostega* and *Ichthyostega*, lived about 363 million years ago at the end of the Devonian period (409–363 million years ago). Their limbs may have evolved from the muscular fins of lungfish-like creatures. These fish can use their fins to push themselves along the bottom of lakes and some can breathe at the water's surface. While amphibians (see pp. 182–183) can exist on land, they are dependent on a wet environment because their skin does not retain moisture and most species must return to the water to lay their eggs. Evolving from amphibians, reptiles (see pp. 184–187) first appeared during the Carboniferous period (363–290 million years ago): *Westlothiana*, a possible early reptile, lived on land 338 million years ago. The development of the amniotic egg, with an embryo enclosed in its own wet environment (the amnion) and protected by a waterproof shell, freed reptiles from the amphibian's dependence on a wet habitat. A scaly skin protected the reptile from desiccation on land and enabled it to exploit ways of life closed to its amphibian ancestors. Reptiles include the dinosaurs, which came to dominate life on land during the Mesozoic era (245–65 million years ago).

Orbit

Pocket enclosing nostril

Sculpted or pitted bone surface

Spiracle to draw in water

Mandible

Small tooth

FOSSIL SKULL OF ACANTHOSTEGA

Muscular back

Shoulder girdle

Scaly skin

Finned tail

Hip girdle

MODEL OF ICHTHYOSTEGA

Dorsal vertebra

Scapula

Cleithrum

Cervical vertebra

Cranium

Orbit

Maxilla

Naris

Rib

Glenoid cavity

Humerus

Elbow joint

Mandible

Clavicle

Radius

Ulna

Sharp tooth

Phalanges

Metacarpals

SKELETON OF ERYOPS

FOSSIL SKELETON OF WESTLOTHIANA

Pelvis

Rib

Vertebra

Flattened
skull bones

Leg

Rear foot

Caudal
vertebra

FOSSIL SKELETON OF A PAREIASAUR

Scapula

Humerus

Radius

Ulna

Rib

Dorsal
vertebra

Femur

Tail

Waterproof,
scaly skin

Eye

Mouth

Five-toed
foot

Semi-sprawling
stance

MODEL OF WESTLOTHIANA

Neural spine

Sacral vertebra

Ilium

Tri-lobed tail

Fleshy,
lobed
pelvic fin

Fleshy,
lobed
pectoral
fin

FOSSILIZED LUNGFISH

Caudal vertebra

Pubis

Acetabulum

Femur

Ischium

Tibia

Metatarsals

Phalanges

Fibula

Chevron

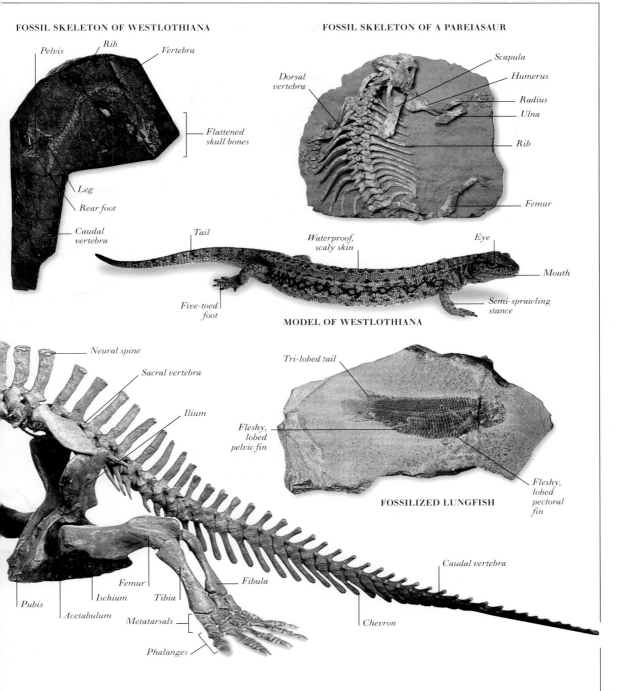

The dinosaurs

THE DINOSAURS WERE A LARGE GROUP of reptiles that were the dominant land vertebrates (animals with backbones) for most of the Mesozoic era (245–65 million years ago). They appeared some 230 million years ago and were distinguished from other scaly, egg-laying reptiles by an important feature: dinosaurs had an erect limb stance. This enabled them to keep their bodies well above the ground, unlike the sprawling and semi-sprawling stance of other reptiles. The head of the dinosaur's femur (thigh-bone) fitted into a socket in its pelvis (hip-bone), producing efficient and mobile locomotion. Dinosaurs are categorized into two groups according to the structure of their pelvis: saurischian (lizard-hipped) and ornithischian (bird-hipped) dinosaurs. In the case of most saurischians, the pubis (part of the pelvis) jutted forward, while in ornithischians it slanted back, parallel to the ischium (another part of the pelvis). Dinosaurs ranged in size from smaller than a domestic cat to the biggest land animals ever known. The Dinosauria were the most successful land vertebrates ever, and survived for 165 million years, until most became extinct 65 million years ago.

STRUCTURE OF SAURISCHIAN PELVIS

Ilium
Postacetabular process
Ilio-ischial joint
Ischium
Hook of preacetabular process
Ilio-pubic joint
Acetabulum
Pubis
Pubic foot

GALLIMIMUS
A saurischian dinosaur

POSITION OF PELVIS IN A SAURISCHIAN DINOSAUR

STRUCTURE OF ORNTHISCHIAN PELVIS

Ilium
Postacetabular process
Ilio-ischial joint
Preacetabular process
Ilio-pubic joint
Prepubis
Acetabulum
Pubis
Ischium

HYPSILOPHODON
An ornithischian dinosaur

POSITION OF PELVIS IN AN ORNITHISCHIAN DINOSAUR

BAROSAURUS
A saurischian dinosaur

COMPARISON OF ANIMAL STANCES

SPRAWLING STANCE
The thighs and upper arms project straight out from the body so that the knees and elbows are bent at right angles.

COMMON IGUANA
(*Iguana iguana*)
A present-day reptile

ERECT STANCE
The thighs and upper arms project straight down from the body so that the knees and elbows are straight.

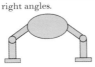

SEMI-SPRAWLING STANCE
The thighs and upper arms project downwards and outwards so that the knees and elbows are slightly bent.

DWARF CROCODILE
(*Osteolaemus tetraspis*)
A present-day reptile

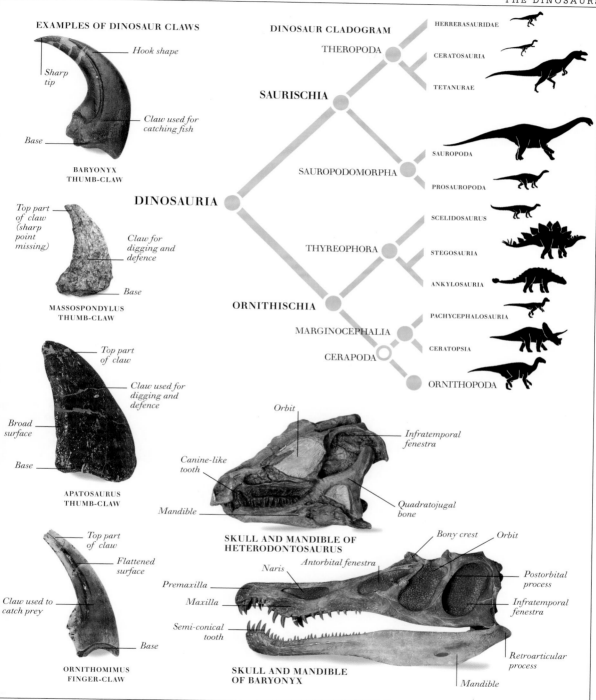

EXAMPLES OF DINOSAUR CLAWS

Hook shape

Sharp tip

Claw used for catching fish

Base

BARYONYX THUMB-CLAW

Top part of claw (sharp point missing)

Claw for digging and defence

Base

MASSOSPONDYLUS THUMB-CLAW

Top part of claw

Claw used for digging and defence

Broad surface

Base

APATOSAURUS THUMB-CLAW

Top part of claw

Flattened surface

Claw used to catch prey

Base

ORNITHOMIMUS FINGER-CLAW

DINOSAUR CLADOGRAM

HERRERASAURIDAE

THEROPODA

CERATOSAURIA

TETANURAE

SAURISCHIA

SAUROPODA

SAUROPODOMORPHA

PROSAUROPODA

DINOSAURIA

SCELIDOSAURUS

THYREOPHORA

STEGOSAURIA

ANKYLOSAURIA

ORNITHISCHIA

PACHYCEPHALOSAURIA

MARGINOCEPHALIA

CERATOPSIA

CERAPODA

ORNITHOPODA

Orbit

Infratemporal fenestra

Canine-like tooth

Quadratojugal bone

Mandible

SKULL AND MANDIBLE OF HETERODONTOSAURUS

Bony crest   Orbit

Antorbital fenestra

Naris

Postorbital process

Premaxilla

Infratemporal fenestra

Maxilla

Semi-conical tooth

Retroarticular process

SKULL AND MANDIBLE OF BARYONYX

Mandible

83

Theropods 1

AN ENORMOUSLY SUCCESSFUL SUBGROUP of the Saurischia, the bipedal (two-footed) theropods ("beast-feet") emerged 230 million years ago in Late Triassic times; the oldest known example comes from South America. Theropods spanned the age of most dinosaurs (230–65 million years ago) and beyond, and included most of the known predatory dinosaurs. The typical theropod had smallish arms with sharp, clawed fingers; powerful jaws lined with sharp teeth; an S-shaped neck; long, muscular hind limbs; and clawed, usually four-toed feet. Many theropods may have been warm-blooded; most were exclusively carnivorous. Theropods ranged from animals no larger than a chicken to huge creatures, such as *Tyrannosaurus* and *Baryonyx*. The group also included ostrich-like omnivores and herbivores with toothless beaks, such as *Struthiomimus* and *Gallimimus*. Birds are dinosaurs and evolved from within a group of tetanuran theropods called maniraptorans. *Archaeopteryx*, small and feathered, was the first known bird and lived alongside other dinosaurs.

INTERNAL ANATOMY OF ALBERTOSAURUS LEG

Ilio-tibial muscle
Ilio-femoral muscle
Femoro-tibial muscle
Internal tibial flexor muscle
Femur
Ilio-fibular muscle
Gastrocnemius muscle
Digital flexor muscle
Fibula
Tarsal
Metatarsal
Ambiens muscle
Femoro-tibial muscle
Anterior tibial muscle
Common digital extensor muscle
Toe
Claw

Cranium
Orbit
Naris
Supraoccipital crest
Cervical vertebrae
Dorsal vertebrae
Ilium
Cervical rib
Scapula
Shoulder joint
Ulna
Phalanges
Metacarpals
Wrist joint
Elbow joint
Humerus
Coracoid
Rib
Femur
Ischium
Hip joint
Knee joint
Mandible
Serrated tooth
Naris
Eye
Thigh
Scaly skin
Tail
Pubis
Forelimb
Hand
Knee
Ankle
Toe
Claw
Foot
Hind limb
Metatarsals
Phalanges
Tibia
Fibula
Ankle joint
Hallux (first toe)

SKELETON OF TYRANNOSAURUS

EXTERNAL FEATURES OF TYRANNOSAURUS

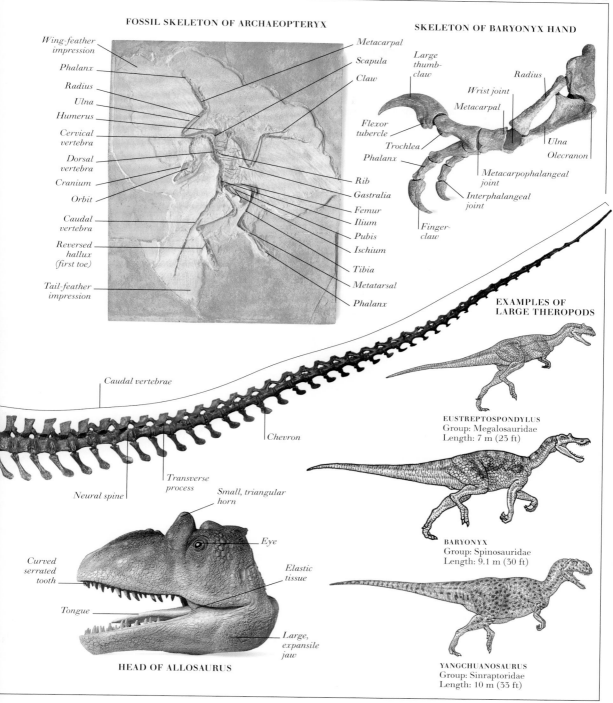

FOSSIL SKELETON OF ARCHAEOPTERYX

Wing-feather impression
Phalanx
Radius
Ulna
Humerus
Cervical vertebra
Dorsal vertebra
Cranium
Orbit
Caudal vertebra
Reversed hallux (first toe)
Tail-feather impression

Metacarpal
Scapula
Claw
Rib
Gastralia
Femur
Ilium
Pubis
Ischium
Tibia
Metatarsal
Phalanx

SKELETON OF BARYONYX HAND

Large thumb-claw
Wrist joint
Radius
Metacarpal
Flexor tubercle
Trochlea
Ulna
Olecranon
Phalanx
Metacarpophalangeal joint
Interphalangeal joint
Finger-claw

Caudal vertebrae
Chevron
Transverse process
Neural spine

EXAMPLES OF LARGE THEROPODS

EUSTREPTOSPONDYLUS
Group: Megalosauridae
Length: 7 m (23 ft)

BARYONYX
Group: Spinosauridae
Length: 9.1 m (30 ft)

YANGCHUANOSAURUS
Group: Sinraptoridae
Length: 10 m (33 ft)

Small, triangular horn
Eye
Curved serrated tooth
Elastic tissue
Tongue
Large, expansile jaw

HEAD OF ALLOSAURUS

Theropods 2

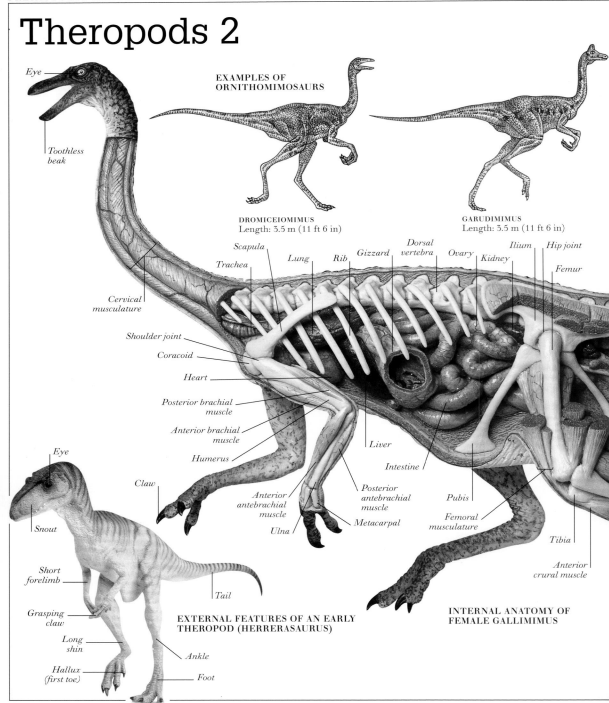

Eye

Toothless beak

Cervical musculature

EXAMPLES OF ORNITHOMIMOSAURS

DROMICEIOMIMUS
Length: 3.5 m (11 ft 6 in)

GARUDIMIMUS
Length: 3.5 m (11 ft 6 in)

Scapula

Trachea

Lung

Rib

Gizzard

Dorsal vertebra

Ovary

Kidney

Ilium

Hip joint

Femur

Shoulder joint

Coracoid

Heart

Posterior brachial muscle

Anterior brachial muscle

Humerus

Liver

Intestine

Anterior antebrachial muscle

Posterior antebrachial muscle

Metacarpal

Ulna

Pubis

Femoral musculature

Tibia

Anterior crural muscle

Eye

Snout

Claw

Short forelimb

Grasping claw

Tail

Long shin

Ankle

Hallux (first toe)

Foot

EXTERNAL FEATURES OF AN EARLY THEROPOD (HERRERASAURUS)

INTERNAL ANATOMY OF FEMALE GALLIMIMUS

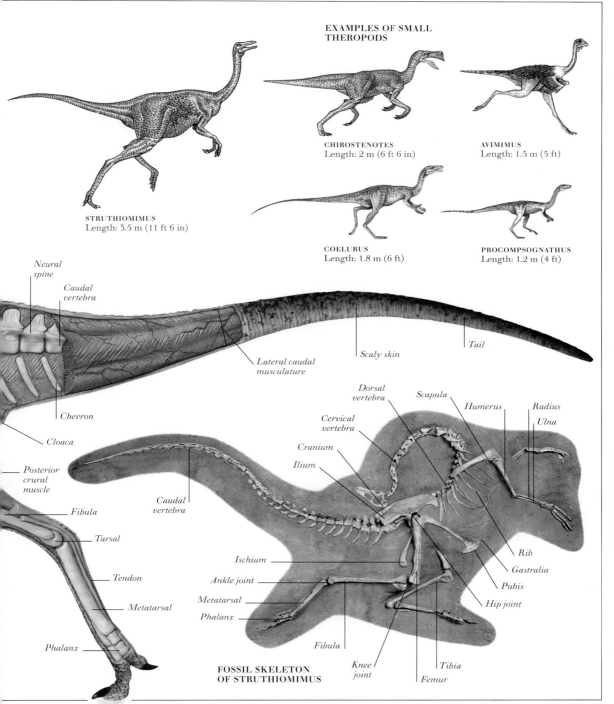

EXAMPLES OF SMALL THEROPODS

CHIROSTENOTES
Length: 2 m (6 ft 6 in)

AVIMIMUS
Length: 1.5 m (5 ft)

STRUTHIOMIMUS
Length: 3.5 m (11 ft 6 in)

COELURUS
Length: 1.8 m (6 ft)

PROCOMPSOGNATHUS
Length: 1.2 m (4 ft)

Neural spine

Caudal vertebra

Chevron

Cloaca

Posterior crural muscle

Fibula

Tarsal

Tendon

Metatarsal

Phalanx

Lateral caudal musculature

Scaly skin

Tail

Caudal vertebra

Dorsal vertebra

Scapula

Humerus

Radius

Ulna

Cervical vertebra

Cranium

Ilium

Ischium

Ankle joint

Metatarsal

Phalanx

Fibula

Rib

Gastralia

Pubis

Hip joint

Knee joint

Femur

Tibia

FOSSIL SKELETON OF STRUTHIOMIMUS

87

Sauropodomorphs 1

THECODONTOSAURUS

THE SAUROPODOMORPHA ("lizard-feet forms") were herbivorous, usually quadrupedal (four-footed) dinosaurs. A clade within Saurischia, they were characterized by small heads, bulky bodies, and long necks and tails. Sauropodomorphs have often been split into two groups: prosauropods and sauropods. Prosauropods lived from Late Triassic to Early Jurassic times (225–180 million years ago) and included beasts such as the small *Anchisaurus* and one of the first very large dinosaurs, *Plateosaurus*. By Middle Jurassic times (about 165 million years ago), sauropods had replaced prosauropods and spread worldwide. They included the heaviest and longest land animals ever, such as *Diplodocus* and *Brachiosaurus*. Sauropods persisted to the end of the Cretaceous period (65 million years ago). Many of these dinosaurs moved in herds, protected from predatory theropods by their huge bulk and powerful tails, which they could use to lash out at attackers. Sauropodomorphs were the most common large herbivores until Late Jurassic times (about 145 million years ago), and appear to have survived in both southern and northern continents until the end of the Cretaceous period.

SKULL AND MANDIBLE OF PLATEOSAURUS

Naris
Antorbital fenestra
Orbit
Mandible
Infratemporal fenestra
Paroccipital process
Serrated, leaf-shaped tooth
Mandibular fenestra

SKELETON OF PLATEOSAURUS

Dorsal vertebrae
Sacral vertebrae
Cervical vertebrae
Ilium
Humerus
Scapula
Pubis
Femur
Hip joint
Ischium
Thumb-claw
Shoulder joint
Rib
Knee joint
Tail
Elbow joint
Tibia
Radius
Fibula
Wrist joint
Ulna
Ankle joint
Metacarpal
Metatarsals
Cranium
Phalanx
Orbit
Mandible
Phalanges
Naris

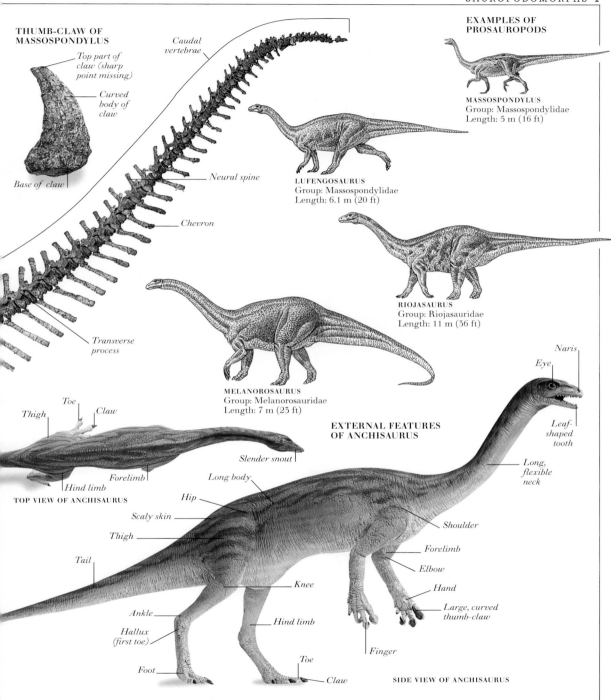

THUMB-CLAW OF MASSOSPONDYLUS

Top part of claw (sharp point missing)

Curved body of claw

Base of claw

Caudal vertebrae

Neural spine

Chevron

Transverse process

EXAMPLES OF PROSAUROPODS

MASSOSPONDYLUS
Group: Massospondylidae
Length: 5 m (16 ft)

LUFENGOSAURUS
Group: Massospondylidae
Length: 6.1 m (20 ft)

RIOJASAURUS
Group: Riojasauridae
Length: 11 m (36 ft)

MELANOROSAURUS
Group: Melanorosauridae
Length: 7 m (23 ft)

EXTERNAL FEATURES OF ANCHISAURUS

Toe

Claw

Thigh

Forelimb

Hind limb

TOP VIEW OF ANCHISAURUS

Slender snout

Long body

Hip

Scaly skin

Thigh

Tail

Knee

Ankle

Hallux (first toe)

Foot

Hind limb

Toe

Claw

Finger

Hand

Large, curved thumb-claw

Elbow

Forelimb

Shoulder

Long, flexible neck

Leaf-shaped tooth

Eye

Naris

SIDE VIEW OF ANCHISAURUS

Sauropodomorphs 2

Orbit

Cranium

Antorbital fenestra

Maxillary fenestra

Maxilla

Peg-shaped tooth

Sclerotic ring

Infratemporal fenestra

Mandible

SKULL AND MANDIBLE OF DIPLODOCUS

FOREFOOT OF ELEPHANT

Wrist

Nail

FOREFOOT BONES OF ELEPHANT

Radius

Ulna

Carpals

Metacarpals

Phalanges

COMPARISON OF THE FOREFEET OF AN ELEPHANT AND DIPLODOCUS

FOREFOOT BONES OF DIPLODOCUS

Radius

Ulna

Carpals

Metacarpals

Phalanges

Coracoid

Scapula

Dorsal vertebra

Sacral vertebra

Ilium

Caudal vertebra

Ischium

Hip joint

Femur

Humerus

Rib

Elbow joint

Ulna

Radius

Wrist joint

Metacarpals

Knee joint

Tibia

Fibula

Phalanges

Ankle joint

MIDDLE SECTION OF DIPLODOCUS SKELETON

Neural spine

Small intestine

Dorsal vertebra

Ovary

Kidney

Rib

Large intestine

Hip joint

Caecum

Pubis

Femur

Oviduct

Cloaca

Thigh musculature

Caudal musculature

Posterior crural musculature

Fibula

Ankle joint

Metatarsal

Anterior crural muscle

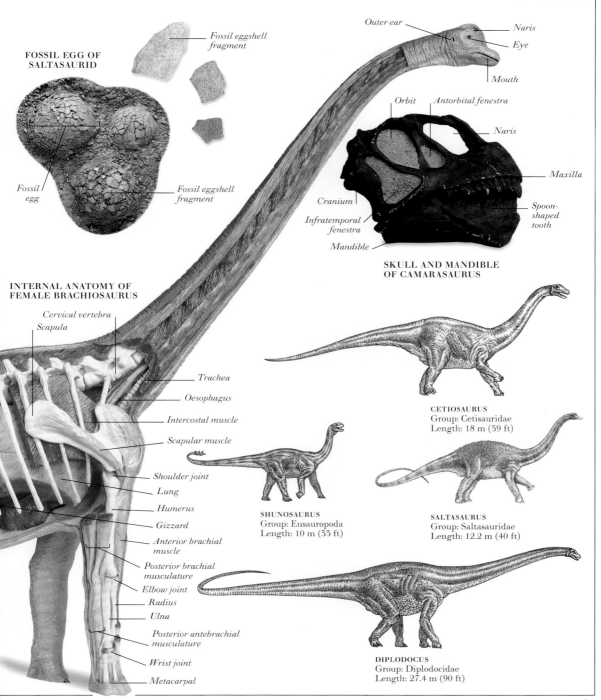

**FOSSIL EGG OF
SALTASAURID**

Fossil eggshell
fragment

Fossil
egg

Fossil eggshell
fragment

Outer ear

Naris

Eye

Mouth

Orbit

Antorbital fenestra

Naris

Cranium

Maxilla

Infratemporal
fenestra

Spoon-
shaped
tooth

Mandible

**SKULL AND MANDIBLE
OF CAMARASAURUS**

**INTERNAL ANATOMY OF
FEMALE BRACHIOSAURUS**

Cervical vertebra

Scapula

Trachea

Oesophagus

Intercostal muscle

Scapular muscle

Shoulder joint

Lung

Humerus

Gizzard

Anterior brachial
muscle

Posterior brachial
musculature

Elbow joint

Radius

Ulna

Posterior antebrachial
musculature

Wrist joint

Metacarpal

CETIOSAURUS
Group: Cetisauridae
Length: 18 m (59 ft)

SHUNOSAURUS
Group: Eusauropoda
Length: 10 m (33 ft)

SALTASAURUS
Group: Saltasauridae
Length: 12.2 m (40 ft)

DIPLODOCUS
Group: Diplodocidae
Length: 27.4 m (90 ft)

Thyreophorans 1

THYREOPHORANS ("SHIELD BEARERS") were a group of quadrupedal armoured dinosaurs. They were one clade among several within the Ornithischia (bird-hipped dinosaurs), they were characterized by rows of bony studs, plates, or spikes along the back, which protected some from predators and may have helped others regulate body temperature. Up to 9 m (30 ft) long, with a small head and small cheek teeth, thyreophorans had shorter forelimbs than hind limbs and probably browsed on low-level vegetation. The earliest thyreophorans were small and lived in Early Jurassic times (about 200 million years ago) in Europe, North America, and China. Stegosaurs, such as *Stegosaurus* and *Kentrosaurus*, replaced these older forms. The earliest stegosaur remains come mainly from China. Several genera of stegosaurs survived into the Early Cretaceous period (145–100 million years ago). Ankylosaurs, with a combination of beak and teeth in close proximity, and cheek teeth adapted for cropping vegetation, appeared at the same time as stegosaurs. They originated in the Late Jurassic period (155 million years ago) and in North America survived until 65 million years ago.

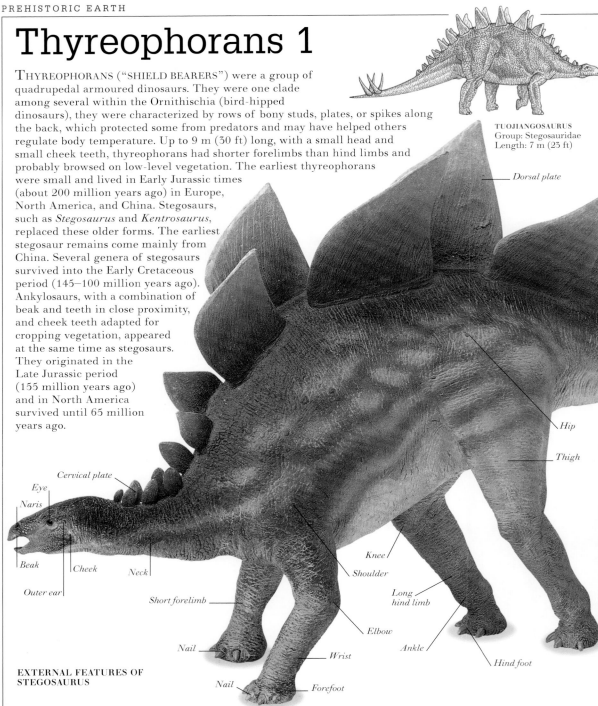

TUOJIANGOSAURUS
Group: Stegosauridae
Length: 7 m (23 ft)

Dorsal plate

Hip

Thigh

Cervical plate

Eye

Naris

Beak

Cheek

Neck

Outer ear

Short forelimb

Knee

Shoulder

Long hind limb

Elbow

Ankle

Nail

Wrist

Hind foot

Nail

Forefoot

EXTERNAL FEATURES OF STEGOSAURUS

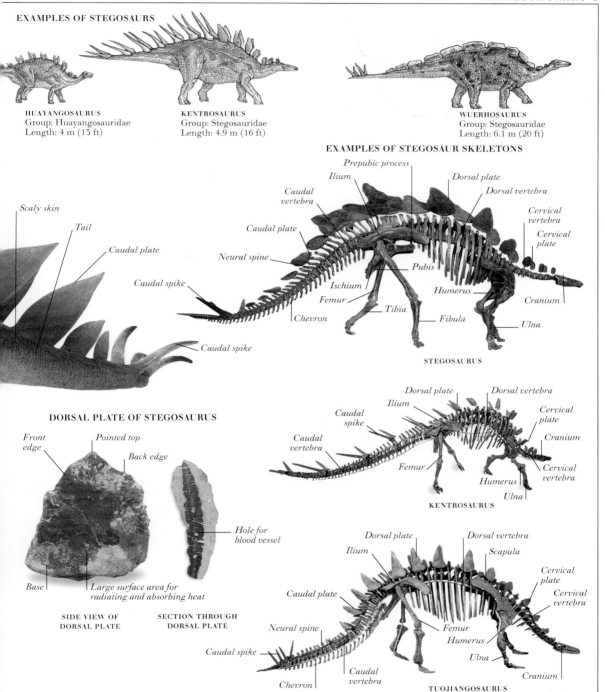

EXAMPLES OF STEGOSAURS

HUAYANGOSAURUS
Group: Huayangosauridae
Length: 4 m (13 ft)

KENTROSAURUS
Group: Stegosauridae
Length: 4.9 m (16 ft)

WUERHOSAURUS
Group: Stegosauridae
Length: 6.1 m (20 ft)

EXAMPLES OF STEGOSAUR SKELETONS

Scaly skin
Tail
Caudal plate
Caudal spike
Caudal spike

Prepubic process
Ilium
Caudal vertebra
Caudal plate
Neural spine
Dorsal plate
Dorsal vertebra
Cervical vertebra
Cervical plate
Pubis
Ischium
Femur
Humerus
Tibia
Fibula
Cranium
Chevron
Ulna

STEGOSAURUS

DORSAL PLATE OF STEGOSAURUS

Front edge
Pointed top
Back edge
Base
Large surface area for radiating and absorbing heat
Hole for blood vessel

SIDE VIEW OF DORSAL PLATE

SECTION THROUGH DORSAL PLATE

Dorsal plate
Ilium
Caudal spike
Caudal vertebra
Dorsal vertebra
Cervical plate
Cranium
Cervical vertebra
Femur
Humerus
Ulna

KENTROSAURUS

Dorsal plate
Ilium
Caudal plate
Neural spine
Caudal spike
Chevron
Caudal vertebra
Dorsal vertebra
Scapula
Femur
Humerus
Cervical plate
Cervical vertebra
Ulna
Cranium

TUOJIANGOSAURUS

93

Thyreophorans 2

EXAMPLES OF ANKYLOSAUR SKULLS

Maxilla

Orbit

Posterolateral horn

Naris

Cranium

Beak

Tooth

Mandible

Jugal plate

SKULL AND MANDIBLE OF EUOPLOCEPHALUS

Nasal bone

Maxilla

Posterolateral horn

Orbit

Cranium

Naris

Beak

Tooth

Mandible

SKULL AND MANDIBLE OF ANKYLOSAURUS

Orbit

Nasal bone

Beak

Cranium

Naris

Infratemporal fenestra

Mandible

SKULL AND MANDIBLE OF PANOPLOSAURUS

Dorsal vertebra

Small intestine

Ilio-tibial muscle

Rib

Gizzard

Scapula

Lung

Ilium

Reproductive canal

Ischium

Shoulder spike

Coracoid

Cervical musculature

Head horn

Humerus

Radius

Wrist joint

Heart

Ilio-tibial muscle

Femur

Liver

Knee joint

Toothless beak

Fibula

Gastrocnemius muscle

Metacarpal

Large intestine

Digital extensor muscle

Ankle joint

Ventral antebrachial muscle

Ulna

Elbow joint

Metatarsal

INTERNAL ANATOMY OF FEMALE EUOPLOCEPHALUS

EXTERNAL FEATURES OF EDMONTONIA

EXAMPLES OF ANKYLOSAURS

Flank spike

Dorsal scute

Dermal armour

Scaly skin

Nuchal ring

Shoulder spike

Broad, flat snout

Naris

Hind limb

Elbow

Forelimb

Ankle

Forefoot

Blunt nail

Caudal vertebra

Neural spine

Ureter

Terminal plate

PINACOSAURUS
Group: Ankylosauridae
Length: 16 ft 6 in (5 m)

MINMI
Group: Ankylosauria
Length: 8 ft (2.4 m)

POLACANTHUS
Group: Polacanthidae
Length: 13 ft (4 m)

Ossified caudal vertebra

FOSSIL OF ANKYLOSAURUS TAIL CLUB

Chevron

Cloaca

Lateral plate

Lateral caudal musculature

Tail club

95

Ornithopods 1

IGUANODON TOOTH

ORNITHOPODS ("BIRD FEET") were a group of ornithischian ("bird-hipped") dinosaurs. These bipedal and quadrupedal herbivores had a horny beak, plant-cutting or grinding cheek teeth, and a pelvic and tail region stiffened by bony tendons. They evolved teeth and jaws adapted to pulping vegetation and flourished from the Middle Jurassic to the Late Cretaceous period (165–65 million years ago) in North America, Europe, Africa, China, Australia, and Antarctica. Some ornithopods were no larger than a dog, while others were immense creatures up to 15 m (49 ft) long. Iguanodonts, an ornithopod group, had a broad, toothless beak at the end of a long snout, large jaws with long rows of ridged, closely packed teeth for grinding vegetation, a bulky body, and a heavy tail. *Iguanodon* and some other iguanodonts had large thumb-spikes that were strong enough to stab attackers. Another group, the hadrosaurs, such as *Gryposaurus* and *Hadrosaurus*, lived in Late Cretaceous times (97–65 million years ago) and with their broad beaks are sometimes known as "duckbills". They were characterized by their deep skulls and closely packed rows of teeth, while some, such as *Corythosaurus* and *Lambeosaurus*, had tall, hollow, bony head crests.

SKELETON OF IGUANODON

Orbit
Cranium
Naris
Mandible
Cervical vertebra
Cervical rib
Scapula
Dorsal vertebra
Humerus
Sternal bone
Sacral vertebra
Radius
Ulna
Caudal vertebra
Prepubic process
Femur
Neural spine
Pubis
Tibia
Ilium
Chevron
Fibula
Ischium
Metatarsal
Thigh

EXTERNAL FEATURES OF MANTELLISAURUS

Heavy, stiff tail

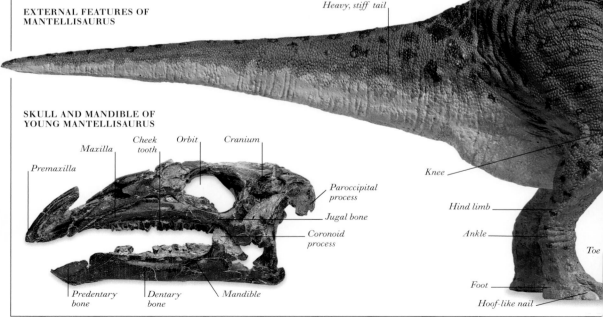

SKULL AND MANDIBLE OF YOUNG MANTELLISAURUS

Cheek tooth
Maxilla
Orbit
Cranium
Premaxilla
Paroccipital process
Knee
Jugal bone
Hind limb
Coronoid process
Ankle
Toe
Predentary bone
Dentary bone
Mandible
Foot
Hoof-like nail

EXAMPLES OF IGUANODONTS

OURANOSAURUS
Group: Iguanodontia
Length: 7 m (23 ft)

CAMPTOSAURUS
Group: Camptosauridae
Length: 4.9–7 m (16–23 ft)

MUTTABURRASAURUS
Group: Iguanodontia
Length: 7 m (23 ft)

PROBACTROSAURUS
Group: Hadrosauroidea
Length: 6.1 m (20 ft)

INTERNAL ANATOMY OF HIND LEG OF IGUANODON

Eye

Naris

Shoulder

Neck

Ilium

Ilio-femoral muscle

Ilio-tibial muscle

Ambiens muscle

Tongue

Beak

Short caudo-femoral muscle

External pubo-ischio-femoral muscle

Tibial flexor muscle

Femur

Ilio-fibular muscle

Scaly skin

Common digital extensor muscle

Gastrocnemius muscle

Anterior tibial muscle

Forelimb

Tibia

Elbow

Fibula

Wrist

Thumb-spike

Tarsal

Hand

Metatarsal

Finger

Toe

Hoof-like nail

Hoof-like nail

Ornithopods 2

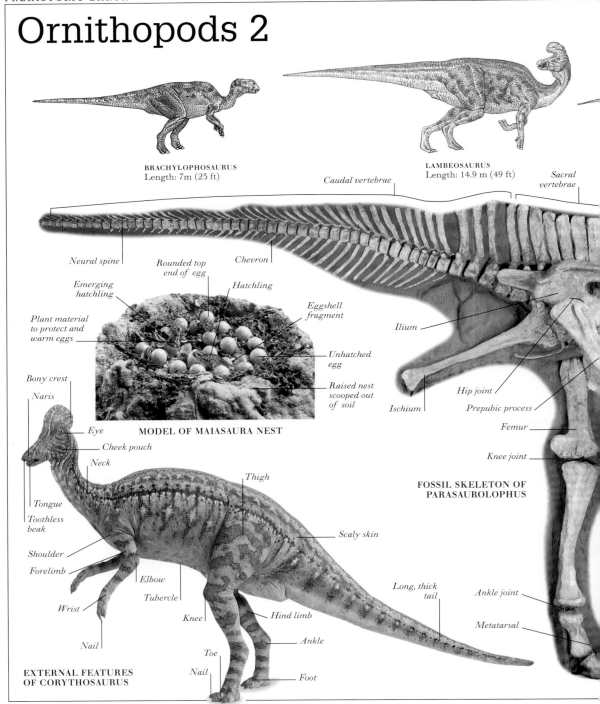

BRACHYLOPHOSAURUS
Length: 7m (23 ft)

LAMBEOSAURUS
Length: 14.9 m (49 ft)

Caudal vertebrae

Sacral vertebrae

Neural spine

Rounded top end of egg

Chevron

Emerging hatchling

Hatchling

Eggshell fragment

Plant material to protect and warm eggs

Ilium

Unhatched egg

Bony crest

Raised nest scooped out of soil

Hip joint

Naris

Ischium

Prepubic process

Eye

MODEL OF MAIASAURA NEST

Femur

Cheek pouch

Neck

Knee joint

Thigh

**FOSSIL SKELETON OF
PARASAUROLOPHUS**

Tongue

Toothless beak

Scaly skin

Shoulder

Forelimb

Elbow

Long, thick tail

Ankle joint

Tubercle

Wrist

Knee

Hind limb

Metatarsal

Nail

Ankle

Toe

**EXTERNAL FEATURES
OF CORYTHOSAURUS**

Nail

Foot

EXAMPLES OF HADROSAURS

HYPACROSAURUS
Length: 9.1 m (30 ft)

HADROSAURUS
Length: 7.9–10 m (26–33 ft)

GRYPOSAURUS
Length: 7.9–10 m (26–33 ft)

Dorsal vertebrae

Bony crest

Air passage

Cranium

Infratemporal fenestra

Orbit

Cervical vertebrae

Mandible

Naris

Scapula

Shoulder joint

Tibia

Rib

Fibula

Humerus

Elbow joint

Radius

Ulna

Wrist joint

Phalanges

Metacarpal

Phalanges

Orbit

Infratemporal fenestra

Air passage

Naris

Mandible

Tooth

**SKULL AND MANDIBLE
OF JUVENILE
LAMBEOSAURUS**

Sclerotic ring

Bony crest

Cranium

Orbit

Naris

Infratemporal fenestra

Mandible

Premaxilla

**SKULL AND MANDIBLE OF
ADULT LAMBEOSAURUS**

Marginocephalians 1

Thick, high-domed cranium
Supraorbital ridge
Orbit
Naris
Mandible
Neural spine
Cervical rib
Humerus
Ulna
Radius
Wrist joint
Metacarpal
Phalanx
Pubis
Ilium
Ischium
Metatarsals
Phalanges

HEAD-BUTTING PRENOCEPHALES

MARGINOCEPHALIA ("margined heads") were a group of bipedal and quadrupedal ornithischian dinosaurs with a narrow shelf or deep, bony frill at the back of the skull. Marginocephalians were probably descended from the same ancestor as the ornithopods and lived in what are now North America, Africa, Asia, and Europe during the Cretaceous period (145–65 million years ago). They were divided into two groups: Pachycephalosauria ("thickheaded lizards"), such as *Pachycephalosaurus* and *Stegoceras*, and Ceratopsia ("horned faces"), such as *Triceratops* and *Psittacosaurus*. The thick skulls of Pachycephalosauria may have protected their brains during possible head-butting contests fought to win territory and mates; their hips and spines may also have been strengthened to withstand the shock. The bony frill of Ceratopsia would have added to their frightening appearance when charging; the neck was strengthened for impact and to support the huge head, with its snipping beak and powerful slicing toothed jaws. A charging ceratopsian would have been a formidable opponent for even the largest predators. Ceratopsians were among the most abundant herbivorous dinosaurs of the Late Cretaceous period (97–65 million years ago).

EXAMPLES OF SKULLS OF PACHYCEPHALOSAURS

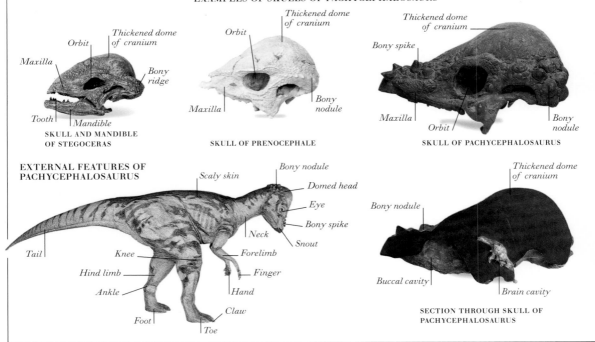

Orbit
Thickened dome of cranium
Maxilla
Bony ridge
Tooth
Mandible
SKULL AND MANDIBLE OF STEGOCERAS

Thickened dome of cranium
Orbit
Maxilla
Bony nodule
SKULL OF PRENOCEPHALE

Thickened dome of cranium
Bony spike
Maxilla
Orbit
Bony nodule
SKULL OF PACHYCEPHALOSAURUS

EXTERNAL FEATURES OF PACHYCEPHALOSAURUS

Bony nodule
Scaly skin
Domed head
Eye
Bony spike
Neck
Snout
Forelimb
Finger
Hand
Claw
Toe
Foot
Ankle
Hind limb
Knee
Tail

Thickened dome of cranium
Bony nodule
Buccal cavity
Brain cavity
SECTION THROUGH SKULL OF PACHYCEPHALOSAURUS

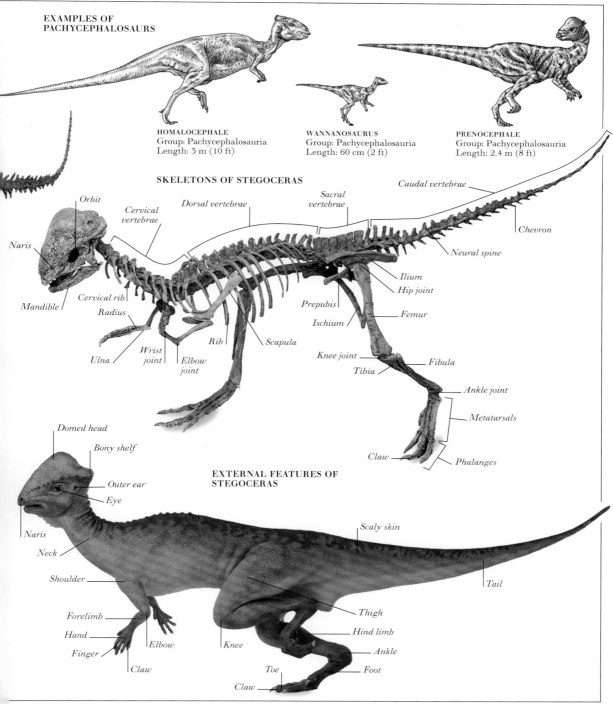

EXAMPLES OF PACHYCEPHALOSAURS

HOMALOCEPHALE
Group: Pachycephalosauria
Length: 3 m (10 ft)

WANNANOSAURUS
Group: Pachycephalosauria
Length: 60 cm (2 ft)

PRENOCEPHALE
Group: Pachycephalosauria
Length: 2.4 m (8 ft)

SKELETONS OF STEGOCERAS

Caudal vertebrae

Sacral vertebrae

Dorsal vertebrae

Orbit

Cervical vertebrae

Chevron

Naris

Neural spine

Ilium

Hip joint

Mandible

Cervical rib

Prepubis

Femur

Radius

Ischium

Rib

Scapula

Wrist joint

Elbow joint

Ulna

Knee joint

Fibula

Tibia

Ankle joint

Metatarsals

Claw

Phalanges

EXTERNAL FEATURES OF STEGOCERAS

Domed head

Bony shelf

Outer ear

Eye

Scaly skin

Naris

Neck

Shoulder

Tail

Forelimb

Thigh

Hand

Hind limb

Finger

Elbow

Knee

Ankle

Claw

Toe

Foot

Claw

Marginocephalians 2

Parietal fenestra

Epoccipital bone

Parietosquamosal frill

Nose horn core

Supraorbital ridge

Naris

Orbit

Cranium

Mandible

SKULL AND MANDIBLE OF STYRACOSAURUS

Parietosquamosal frill

Epoccipital bone

Brow horn

Nose horn

Thick, scaly skin

Thigh

Tail

Ankle

Hind limb

Elbow

Nail

Forelimb

Wrist

Eye

Naris

Toothless beak

EXTERNAL FEATURES OF TRICERATOPS

Parietosquamosal frill

Cranium

Postorbital bone

Nasal bone

Orbit

Lacrimal bone

Naris

Parietal fenestra

Beak

Infratemporal fenestra

Rostral bone

Jugal bone

Predentary bone

Surangular bone

Dentary bone

Tooth

Angular bone

Mandible

SKULL AND MANDIBLE OF PROTOCERATOPS

Hip joint

Ilium

Pubis

Dorsal vertebrae

Ischium

Femur

Knee joint

Fibula

Tibia

Ankle joint

Rib

Scapula

Humerus

Elbow joint

Sternal bone

Caudal vertebra

Neural spine

Ulna

Coracoid

Metatarsals

Chevron

Shoulder joint

Phalanges

Radius

SKELETON OF TRICERATOPS

**EXTERNAL FEATURES
OF PSITTACOSAURUS**

Eye

Cheek horn

Beak

Claw

Finger

Forelimb

Scaly skin

Thigh

Elbow

Knee

Claw

Toe

Ankle

Hind limb

Parietosquamosal
frill

Tail

Cranium

Orbit

Brow horn
core

Nose horn
core

Naris

Cervical
rib

Infratemporal
fenestra

Jugal bone

Tooth

Metacarpals

Mandible

Phalanges

Predentary
bone

Rostral bone

EXAMPLES OF CERATOPSIA

PROTOCERATOPS
Group: Protoceratopsidae
Length: 2.7 m (9 ft)

STYRACOSAURUS
Group: Centrosaurinae
Length: 5.5 m (18 ft)

TRICERATOPS
Group: Chasmosaurinae
Length: 9.1 m (30 ft)

PACHYRHINOSAURUS
Group: Centrosaurinae
Length: 5.5 m (18 ft)

LEPTOCERATOPS
Group: Leptoceratopsidae
Length: 2.1 m (7 ft)

Mammals 1

**TETRALOPHODON
CHEEK TEETH**

SINCE THE EXTINCTION of most of the dinosaurs 65 million years
ago, mammals (along with birds) have been the dominant vertebrates
on land. This class includes terrestrial, aerial, and aquatic forms.
Having developed from the therapsids, the first true mammals –
small, nocturnal, shrew-like creatures, such as *Megazostrodon*-
appeared over 200 million years ago during the Triassic period
(250–200 million years ago). Mammals had several
features that differed from those of their ancestors: an efficient
four-chambered heart allowed these warm-blooded animals
to sustain high levels of activity; a covering of hair helped them
maintain a constant body temperature; an improved limb
structure gave them more efficient locomotion; and the birth of live
young and the immediate supply of food from the mother's milk aided their
rapid growth. Since the end of the Mesozoic era (65 million years ago), the
number of major mammal groups and the abundance of species in each
have varied dramatically. For example, the Perissodactyla (the group
that includes *Coelodonta* and modern horses) was a common group
during the Early Tertiary period (about 54 million years ago).
Today, the mammalian groups with the most species include the
Rodentia (rats and mice), the Chiroptera (bats), the Primates
(monkeys and apes), the Carnivora (bears, cats, and dogs),
and the Artiodactyla (cattle, deer, and pigs), while the
Proboscidea group, which formerly included many genera,
such as *Phiomia*, *Moeritherium*, *Tetralophodon*, and
Mammuthus, now has only three species of elephant.
In Australia and South America, millions of years
of continental isolation led to increased diversity
of the marsupials, a group of mammals
distinct from the placentals (see p. 74)
that existed elsewhere.

*Long tail aids
balance*

*Insulating
hair*

*Neural
spine*

Scapula

*Cervical
vertebra*

Humerus

Nasal horn

Naris

Orbit

Radius

Premaxilla bone

Mandible

Ulna

*Chisel-edged
molar*

Metacarpal

Phalanx

UPPER JAWBONE
(MAXILLA) OF A HORSE

Molars

Premolars

HOOFBONE (THIRD
PHALANX) OF A HORSE

Articular
surface

Tendon insertion

Naris

Cranium

Premaxilla
bone

Molar
tooth

SKULL AND MANDIBLE
OF A MOERITHERIUM

Upper jaw tusk

Molar
tooth

Shovel-
shaped
tusk

SKULL AND MANDIBLE
OF A PHIOMIA

Trunk

Thick hide

Short tusk used
for rooting up
plants

MODEL OF A PHIOMIA

Dorsal vertebra

Ilium

Ball and
socket
joint

Pubis

Rib

Caudal
vertebra

Femur

Tibia

Fibula

Metatarsal

Phalanx

SKELETON OF AN ARSINOITHERIUM

Cranium

Mandible

Teeth

Elongated
digit

Humerus

Hind limb
bone

FOSSIL SKELETON OF A BAT

Mammals 2

LOWER JAW OF A BEAR

Articulation
with skull

Large
canine

Diastema

Low cusp

Molar

Premolar

SKELETON OF A TOXODON

Scapula

Neural
spine

Cervical
vertebra

Zygomatic
arch

Cranium

Orbit

Maxilla

Nasal bone

Incisor

Mandible

Molar

Occipital region

Incisor

Humerus

Radius

Ulna

Large
breastbone

Metacarpals

Phalanx

SKULL OF AN OPOSSUM

Orbit

Cranium

Naris

Canine

Infraorbital
foramen

Molar

Occipital
region

**FOSSIL SKULL OF
AN HYAENODON**

Orbit

Naris

Sagittal crest

Cranium

Canine

Neck
insertion

Infraorbital
foramen

Mandible

Molar

**LOWER JAW OF AN
AUSTRALOPITHECUS**

Expanded
occlusal
surface

Premolar

Molar

Ilium

Rib

Femur

Knee
joint

Tibia

Fibula

Metatarsals

Phalanx

SKULL OF A SMILODON

Orbit

Muscle scar

Naris

Infraorbital
foramen

Sagittal crest

Occipital
condyle

Canine

Dentary
bone

Slicing
tooth

Zygomatic
arch

Thick,
insulating
coat

Ivory tusk

Woolly
underhair

Hairy trunk

RECONSTRUCTION OF A MAMMOTH

The first humans

MODERN HUMANS BELONG TO THE MAMMALIAN order of primates (see pp. 202–203), which originated about 55 million years ago; primates included the only extant hominid species. The earliest members of the human clade include *Ardipithecus* ("ground ape") and *Australopithecus* ("southern ape"), both small-brained intermediates between apes and humans that were capable of standing and walking upright. *Homo habilis*, the earliest member of the genus Homo, appeared at least 2 million years ago. This larger-brained "handy man" began making tools for hunting. *Homo ergaster* first appeared in Africa about 1.8 million years ago and spread into Asia about 800,000 years later. Smaller-toothed than *Homo habilis*, H. ergaster – followed by Homo erectus – developed fire as a tool, which enabled it to cook food. Neanderthals, a near relative of modern humans, originated about 200,000 years ago, and *Homo sapiens* (modern humans) appeared in Africa about 100,000 years later. The two co-existed for thousands of years, but by 30,000 years ago, *Homo sapiens* had become dominant and the Neanderthals had died out. Classification of *Homo sapiens* in relation to its ancestors is enormously problematic: modern humans must be classified not only by bone structure, but also by specific behaviour – the ability to plan future action; to follow traditions; and to use symbolic communication, including complex language and the ability to use and recognize symbols.

JAWBONE OF AUSTRALOPITHECUS (SOUTHERN APE)

Larger jawbone than modern human

Large back tooth

Cranium

Jutting brow ridge

Orbit

Naris

Jutting jawbone

SKULL OF AUSTRALOPITHECUS (SOUTHERN APE)

Orbit

Naris

SKULL OF HOMO HABILIS (FIRST MEMBER OF HOMO GENUS)

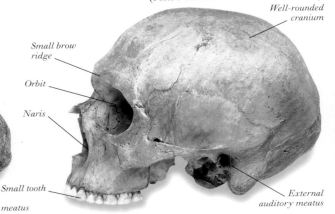

Larger braincase than Australopithecus

Orbit

Naris

External auditory meatus

SKULL OF HOMO ERECTUS (UPRIGHT MAN)

Well-rounded cranium

Small brow ridge

Orbit

Naris

Small tooth

External auditory meatus

SKULL OF HOMO SAPIENS (MODERN HUMAN)

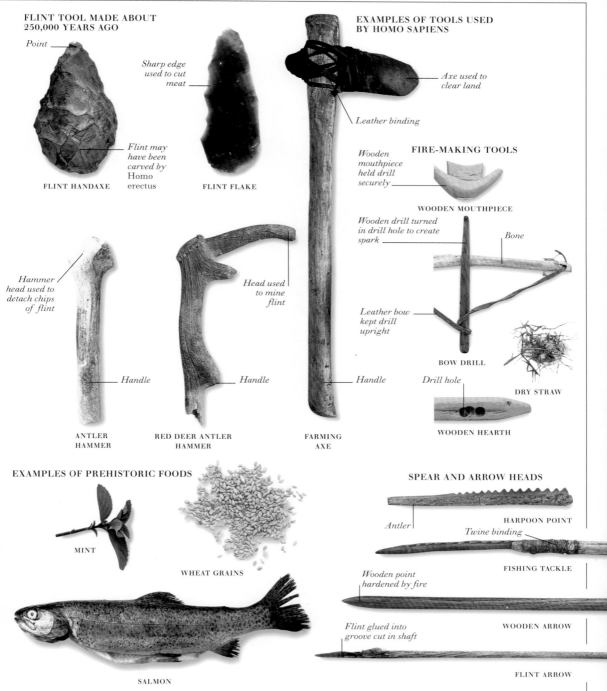

FLINT TOOL MADE ABOUT 250,000 YEARS AGO

Point

Sharp edge used to cut meat

Flint may have been carved by Homo erectus

FLINT HANDAXE

FLINT FLAKE

Hammer head used to detach chips of flint

Handle

Handle

Head used to mine flint

Handle

ANTLER HAMMER

RED DEER ANTLER HAMMER

FARMING AXE

EXAMPLES OF TOOLS USED BY HOMO SAPIENS

Axe used to clear land

Leather binding

FIRE-MAKING TOOLS

Wooden mouthpiece held drill securely

WOODEN MOUTHPIECE

Wooden drill turned in drill hole to create spark

Bone

Leather bow kept drill upright

BOW DRILL

Drill hole

DRY STRAW

WOODEN HEARTH

EXAMPLES OF PREHISTORIC FOODS

MINT

WHEAT GRAINS

SALMON

SPEAR AND ARROW HEADS

Antler

HARPOON POINT

Twine binding

FISHING TACKLE

Wooden point hardened by fire

WOODEN ARROW

Flint glued into groove cut in shaft

FLINT ARROW

Plants

PLANT VARIETY··· 112
FUNGI AND LICHENS··· 114
ALGAE AND SEAWEEDS·· 116
LIVERWORTS AND MOSSES·· 118
HORSETAILS, CLUBMOSSES, AND FERNS·················· 120
GYMNOSPERMS 1·· 122
GYMNOSPERMS 2·· 124
MONOCOTYLEDONS AND DICOTYLEDONS················ 126
HERBACEOUS FLOWERING PLANTS························· 128
WOODY FLOWERING PLANTS································· 130
ROOTS··· 132
STEMS·· 134
LEAVES·· 136
PHOTOSYNTHESIS·· 138
FLOWERS 1··· 140
FLOWERS 2··· 142
POLLINATION··· 144
FERTILIZATION··· 146
SUCCULENT FRUITS·· 148
DRY FRUITS··· 150
GERMINATION·· 152
VEGETATIVE REPRODUCTION··································· 154
DRYLAND PLANTS··· 156
WETLAND PLANTS··· 158
CARNIVOROUS PLANTS··· 160
EPIPHYTIC AND PARASITIC PLANTS························· 162

Plant variety

THERE ARE MORE THAN 300,000 SPECIES of plants.
They show a wide diversity of forms and life-styles, ranging, for example,
from delicate liverworts, adapted for life in a damp habitat, to cacti, capable of surviving
in the desert, and from herbaceous plants, such as corn, which completes its life-cycle in one year,
to the giant redwood tree, which can live for thousands of years. This diversity reflects the adaptations
of plants to survive in a wide range of habitats. This is seen most clearly in the flowering plants (phylum
Angiospermophyta), which are the most numerous, with over 250,000 species, and the most widespread,
being found from the tropics to the poles. Despite their diversity, plants share certain characteristics: typically,
plants are green, and make their food by photosynthesis; and most plants live in or on a substrate, such as
soil, and do not actively move. Algae (kingdom Protista) and fungi (kingdom Fungi) have
some plant-like characteristics and are often studied alongside plants, although they
are not true plants.

FLOWERING PLANT
Bromeliad
(*Acanthostachys strobilacea*)

Leaf

GREEN ALGA
Micrograph of desmid
(*Micrasterias sp.*)

Pyrenoid
(*small protein
body*)

Chloroplast

Sinus
(*division between
two halves of cell*)

Cell wall

FERN
Tree fern
(*Dicksonia antarctica*)

Rachis
(*main axis
of pinnate leaf*)

Petiole
(*leaf stalk*)

Ramentum
(*brown scale*)

Base of dead
frond (leaf)

Trunk

Adventitious
root

Epiphytic
fern growing
at base

BRYOPHYTE
Moss
(*Bryum sp.*)

Seta
(*stalk*)

Immature capsule

Sporophyte
(*spore-
producing
plant*)

Capsule
(*site of spore
production*)

"Leaf"

Gametophyte
(*gamete-producing
plant*)

FLOWERING PLANT
Succulent
(*Kedrostis africana*)

Petiole
(leaf stalk)

FLOWERING PLANT
Micrograph of cross-section
through leaf of marram grass
(*Ammophila arenaria*)

Leaf

Spine

Flower

Bract
(leaf-like structure)

Inflorescence

Sclerenchyma
(strengthening
tissue)

Cuticle
(waterproof
covering)

Stem

Stem

Xylem

Phloem

Vascular
tissue

Stiff trichome
(hair)

Interlocked
trichomes (hairs)

Epidermis
(outer layer
of cells)

Caudex
(swollen
stem
base)

Hinge cells
(cause curling of leaf to
reduce water loss)

Mesophyll
(photosynthetic
tissue)

Root

Pinna
(leaflet)

FLOWERING PLANT
Couch grass
(*Agropyron repens*)

FLOWERING PLANT
Pitcher plant
(*Sarracenia purpurea*)

Caryopsis
(type of
dry fruit)

Sepal

Fruit
surrounded
by floral parts

Rachis
(main axis of
grass inflorescence)

Umbrella
of style

Pitcher (leaf
modified to trap
insects)

Frond (leaf)

Pedicel
(flower
stalk)

Node

Hood

Downward-pointing
hair (encourages
insect prey into
pitcher)

Midrib of
pinna (leaflet)

Wing

Lamina
(blade)

Round, hollow
stem

Sheathing
leaf base

Immature
pitcher

Adventitious
root

113

Fungi and lichens

FUNGI WERE ONCE THOUGHT OF AS PLANTS but are now classified as a separate kingdom. This kingdom includes not only the familiar mushrooms, puffballs, stinkhorns, and moulds, but also yeasts, smuts, rusts, and lichens. Most fungi are multicellular, consisting of a mass of thread-like hyphae that together form a mycelium. However, the simpler fungi (e.g., yeasts) are microscopic, single-celled organisms. Typically, fungi reproduce by means of spores. Most fungi feed on dead or decaying matter, or on living organisms. A few fungi obtain their food from plants or algae, with which they have a symbiotic (mutually advantageous) relationship. Lichens are a symbiotic partnership between algae and fungi. Of the six types of lichens the three most common are crustose (flat and crusty), foliose (leafy), and fruticose (shrub-like). Some lichens (e.g., *Cladonia floerkeana*) are a combination of types. Lichens reproduce by means of spores or soredia (powdery vegetative fragments).

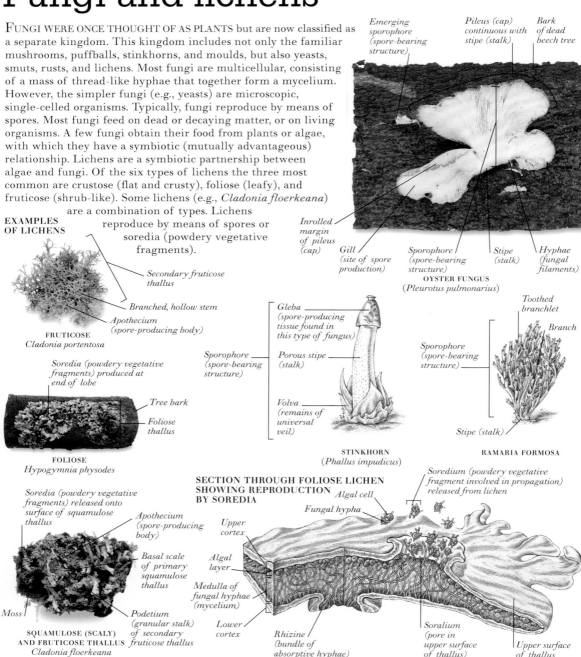

EXAMPLES OF LICHENS

Emerging sporophore (spore-bearing structure)

Pileus (cap) continuous with stipe (stalk)

Bark of dead beech tree

Inrolled margin of pileus (cap)

Gill (site of spore production)

Sporophore (spore-bearing structure)

Stipe (stalk)

Hyphae (fungal filaments)

OYSTER FUNGUS
(*Pleurotus pulmonarius*)

Secondary fruticose thallus

Branched, hollow stem

Apothecium (spore-producing body)

FRUTICOSE
Cladonia portentosa

Soredia (powdery vegetative fragments) produced at end of lobe

Tree bark

Foliose thallus

FOLIOSE
Hypogymnia physodes

Gleba (spore-producing tissue found in this type of fungus)

Sporophore (spore-bearing structure)

Porous stipe (stalk)

Volva (remains of universal veil)

STINKHORN
(*Phallus impudicus*)

Toothed branchlet

Branch

Sporophore (spore-bearing structure)

Stipe (stalk)

RAMARIA FORMOSA

Soredia (powdery vegetative fragments) released onto surface of squamulose thallus

Apothecium (spore-producing body)

Basal scale of primary squamulose thallus

Moss

Podetium (granular stalk) of secondary fruticose thallus

SQUAMULOSE (SCALY) AND FRUTICOSE THALLUS
Cladonia floerkeana

SECTION THROUGH FOLIOSE LICHEN SHOWING REPRODUCTION BY SOREDIA

Algal cell

Fungal hypha

Upper cortex

Algal layer

Medulla of fungal hyphae (mycelium)

Lower cortex

Rhizine (bundle of absorptive hyphae)

Soredium (powdery vegetative fragment involved in propagation) released from lichen

Soralium (pore in upper surface of thallus)

Upper surface of thallus

Gleba (spore-producing tissue found in this type of fungus)

Exoperidium

Endoperidium

Peridium (wall surrounding spore-producing tissue)

Scale on exoperidium (outer part of peridium)

Sporophore (spore-bearing structure)

Stipe (stalk)

Underground mycelium (mass of hyphae)

Substratum of woodland soil and leaf litter

COMMON EARTH-BALL (Scleroderma citrinum)

Fan-shaped pileus (cap)

Sporophore (spore-bearing structure)

Stipe (stalk)

Gill (site of spore production)

HOHENBUEHELIA PETALOIDES

Sporophore (spore-bearing structure)

Pileus (cap)

Stipe (stalk)

Substratum of woodland soil and leaf litter

FRINGED CRUMBLE CAP (Psathyrella candolleana)

Hyphae (fungal filaments)

LIFE-CYCLE OF A MUSHROOM

Velar scale (remains of universal veil)

Pileus (cap)

Gill (site of spore production)

Annulus (ring)

Stipe (stalk)

Underground mycelium

MATURE SPOROPHORE (SPORE-BEARING STRUCTURE)

Basidium (spore-producing structure)

Discharged spore

SECTION OF GILL

Primary mycelium develops from spore

Spore

Primary mycelia fuse to produce secondary mycelium

Septum (cross wall)

Hypha

Nucleus

SPORES GERMINATE AND PRODUCE MYCELIUM

Immature sporophore

Mycelium

MYCELIUM FORMS SPOROPHORE

Universal veil (membrane enclosing developing sporophore)

Pileus (cap)

Gill

Underground mycelium

Stipe (stalk)

SPOROPHORE GROWS ABOVE GROUND

Expanding pileus (cap)

Partial veil (joins pileus to stipe)

Annulus (ring) being formed as partial veil breaks

Stipe (stalk)

Underground mycelium

Volva (remains of universal veil)

UNIVERSAL VEIL BREAKS

Algae and seaweeds

ALGAE ARE NOT TRUE PLANTS. They form a diverse group
of plant-like organisms that belong to the kingdom Protista.
Like plants, algae possess the green pigment chlorophyll
and make their own food by photosynthesis (see pp. 138-139).
Many algae also possess other pigments by which they can be
classified; for example, the brown pigment fucoxanthin is
found in the brown algae. Some of the ten phyla of algae are
exclusively unicellular (single-celled); others also contain
aggregates of cells in filaments or colonies. Three phyla –
the Chlorophyta (green algae), Rhodophyta (red algae),
and Phaeophyta (brown algae) – contain larger, multicellular,
thalloid (flat), marine organisms commonly known as seaweeds.

Most algae can reproduce sexually. For
example, in the brown seaweed
Fucus vesiculosus, gametes
(sex cells) are produced in
conceptacles (chambers) in
the receptacles (fertile tips
of fronds); after their release
into the sea, antherozoids
(male gametes) and oospheres
(female gametes) fuse; the
resulting zygote settles on a rock
and develops into a new seaweed.

EXAMPLES OF ALGAE

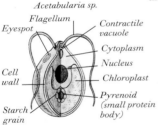

Reproductive chamber

Cap

Sterile whorl

Cell wall

Stalk

Rhizoid

GREEN ALGA
Acetabularia sp.

Flagellum
Eyespot
Contractile vacuole
Cytoplasm
Nucleus
Cell wall
Chloroplast
Pyrenoid (small protein body)
Starch grain

GREEN ALGA
Chlamydomonas sp.

Coenobium (colony of cells)
Daughter coenobium
Gelatinous sheath
Nucleus
Biflagellate cell

GREEN ALGA
Volvox sp.

Spine
Cytoplasm
Girdle
Vacuole
Plastid (photosynthetic organelle)

DIATOM
Thalassiosira sp.

BROWN SEAWEED
Oarweed
(*Laminaria digitata*)

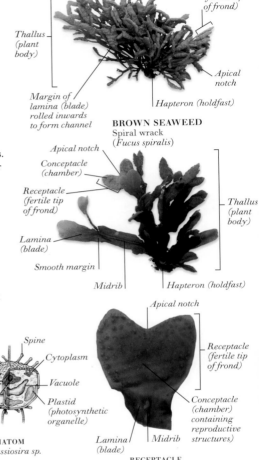

BROWN SEAWEED
Channelled wrack
(*Pelvetia canaliculata*)

Receptacle (fertile tip of frond)

Thallus (plant body)

Apical notch

Margin of lamina (blade) rolled inwards to form channel

Hapteron (holdfast)

BROWN SEAWEED
Spiral wrack
(*Fucus spiralis*)

Apical notch
Conceptacle (chamber)
Receptacle (fertile tip of frond)
Lamina (blade)
Smooth margin
Midrib
Thallus (plant body)
Hapteron (holdfast)

Apical notch
Receptacle (fertile tip of frond)
Conceptacle (chamber) containing reproductive structures
Lamina (blade)
Midrib

RECEPTACLE
Spiral wrack
(*Fucus spiralis*)

Thallus (plant body)

Lamina (blade) palmately divided

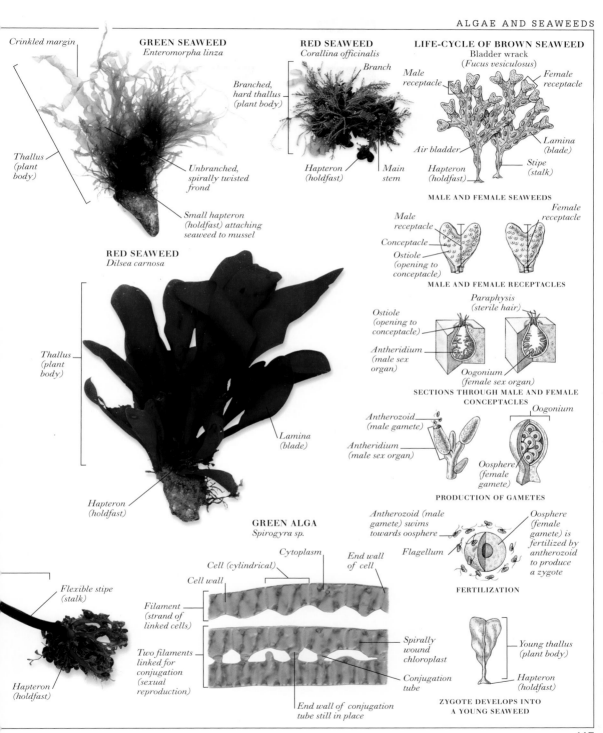

GREEN SEAWEED
Enteromorpha linza

Crinkled margin

Thallus
(plant
body)

Unbranched,
spirally twisted
frond

Small hapteron
(holdfast) attaching
seaweed to mussel

RED SEAWEED
Corallina officinalis

Branch

Branched,
hard thallus
(plant body)

Hapteron
(holdfast)

Main
stem

LIFE-CYCLE OF BROWN SEAWEED
Bladder wrack
(*Fucus vesiculosus*)

Male
receptacle

Female
receptacle

Air bladder

Lamina
(blade)

Stipe
(stalk)

Hapteron
(holdfast)

MALE AND FEMALE SEAWEEDS

Male
receptacle

Female
receptacle

Conceptacle

Ostiole
(opening to
conceptacle)

MALE AND FEMALE RECEPTACLES

Paraphysis
(sterile hair)

Ostiole
(opening to
conceptacle)

Antheridium
(male sex
organ)

Oogonium
(female sex organ)

**SECTIONS THROUGH MALE AND FEMALE
CONCEPTACLES**

Antherozoid
(male gamete)

Oogonium

Antheridium
(male sex organ)

Oosphere
(female
gamete)

PRODUCTION OF GAMETES

RED SEAWEED
Dilsea carnosa

Thallus
(plant
body)

Lamina
(blade)

Hapteron
(holdfast)

GREEN ALGA
Spirogyra sp.

Antherozoid (male
gamete) swims
towards oosphere

Flagellum

Oosphere
(female
gamete) is
fertilized by
antherozoid
to produce
a zygote

FERTILIZATION

Cell (cylindrical)

Cytoplasm

End wall
of cell

Cell wall

Filament
(strand of
linked cells)

Two filaments
linked for
conjugation
(sexual
reproduction)

Spirally
wound
chloroplast

Conjugation
tube

End wall of conjugation
tube still in place

Young thallus
(plant body)

Hapteron
(holdfast)

**ZYGOTE DEVELOPS INTO
A YOUNG SEAWEED**

Flexible stipe
(stalk)

Hapteron
(holdfast)

Liverworts and mosses

LIVERWORTS AND MOSSES ARE SMALL, LOW-GROWING PLANTS that belong to the phylum Bryophyta. Bryophytes do not have true stems, leaves, or roots (they are anchored to the ground by rhizoids), nor do they have the vascular tissues (xylem and phloem) that transport water and nutrients in higher plants. With no outer, waterproof cuticle, bryophytes are susceptible to drying out, and most grow in moist habitats. The bryophyte life-cycle has two stages. In stage one, the green plant (gametophyte) produces male and female gametes (sex cells), which fuse to form a zygote. In stage two, the zygote develops into a sporophyte that remains attached to the gametophyte. The sporophyte produces spores, which are released and germinate into new green plants. Liverworts (class Hepaticae) grow horizontally and may be thalloid (flat and ribbon-like) or "leafy". Mosses (class Musci) typically have an upright "stem" with spirally arranged "leaves".

A LEAFY LIVERWORT
Scapania undulata

"Stem"

"Leaf"

Rhizoid

A THALLOID LIVERWORT
Marchantia polymorpha

Gemma cup

Gemma (detachable tissue that produces new plants)

Thallus (plant body)

Toothed margin of cup

DETAIL OF GEMMA CUP

Disc

Archegoniophore (stalked structure carrying archegonia)

Lobe

Stalk

Thallus (plant body)

Apical notch

Rhizoid

Disc

Lobe

Stalk

FEMALE GAMETOPHYTE

Lobe

Disc

Ray (radial groove)

Stalk

ARCHEGONIOPHORE FROM BELOW

SIDE VIEW OF ARCHEGONIOPHORE

Pore

Ray (radial groove)

MICROGRAPH OF LOBE

Gemma cup

Thallus (plant body)

Midrib

Archegoniophore (stalked structure carrying archegonia)

MICROGRAPH OF THALLUS
Conocephalum conicum

Position of air chamber

Pore for exchange of gases

Upper surface

Rhizoid

A COMMON MOSS
Polytrichum commune

"Stem"

Branch of
conducting
tissue to "leaf"

Cortex

Epidermis
(outer layer
of cells)

Central strand
of conducting
tissue

"Leaf"

Midrib

**MICROGRAPH OF CROSS-SECTION
THROUGH STEM AND LEAF**

MICROGRAPH OF MOSS SPORE
Funaria hygrometrica

Epidermis
of capsule

Spore-containing
space

Columella
(central tissue
of capsule)

Remains of
spore-forming
tissue

**CROSS-SECTION
THROUGH CAPSULE**

LIFE-CYCLE OF MOSS
Funaria sp.

Male rosette
("leaves" around
antheridia)

Main "stem"

Rhizoid

Female rosette
("leaves"
around
archegonia)

Lateral
branch
of "stem"

Archegonium
(female sex
organ)

GAMETOPHYTE

Antherozoids
(male gametes)
released from
antheridium

Antheridium
(male sex organ)

**SECTION THROUGH
MATURE MALE APEX**

Archegonium
(female sex
organ)

**SECTION THROUGH
MATURE FEMALE APEX**

Flagellum

Antherozoid
(male gamete)
swims to
oosphere

Oosphere (female
gamete) fertilized
by antherozoid

FERTILIZATION

Capsule

Apophysis
(swollen area between
seta and capsule)

Columella
(central tissue
of capsule)

Operculum
(lid)

Beak

Calyptra
(hood
covering
capsule)

Seta
(stalk)

"Leaf"

Male apex
("leaves"
surrounding
antheridia)

Young
aerial
"stem"

"Leaf"

"Stem"

"Stem"

**EXTERNAL VIEW
OF MOSS**

Capsule

Seta
(stalk)

Sporophyte
grows from
fertilized
oosphere

Gametophyte

SPOROPHYTE

Capsule

Operculum
(lid)

Peristome
tooth opens

Apophysis

Seta
(stalk)

Air space

Spores
dispersed

RIPE CAPSULE

Young
gametophyte

Protonema
(branched
green filament)

Rhizoid

Bud

Spore

**DEVELOPING
GAMETOPHYTE**

119

Horsetails, clubmosses, and ferns

HORSETAILS, CLUBMOSSES, AND FERNS are primitive land plants, which, like higher plants, have stems, roots, and leaves, and vascular systems that transport water, minerals, and food. However, unlike higher plants, they do not produce seeds when reproducing. Their life-cycles involve two stages. In stage one, the sporophyte (green plant) produces spores in sporangia. In stage two, the spores germinate, developing into small, short-lived gametophyte plants that produce male and female gametes (sex cells); the gametes fuse to form a zygote from which a new sporophyte plant develops. Horsetails (phylum Sphenophyta) have erect, green stems with branches arranged in whorls; some stems are fertile and have a single spore-producing strobilus (group of sporangia) at the tip. Clubmosses (phylum Lycopodophyta) typically have small leaves arranged spirally around the stem, with spore-producing strobili at the tip of some stems. Ferns (phylum Filicinophyta) typically have large, pinnate fronds (leaves); sporangia, grouped together in sori, develop on the underside of fertile fronds.

FROND
Male fern
(*Dryopteris filix-mas*)

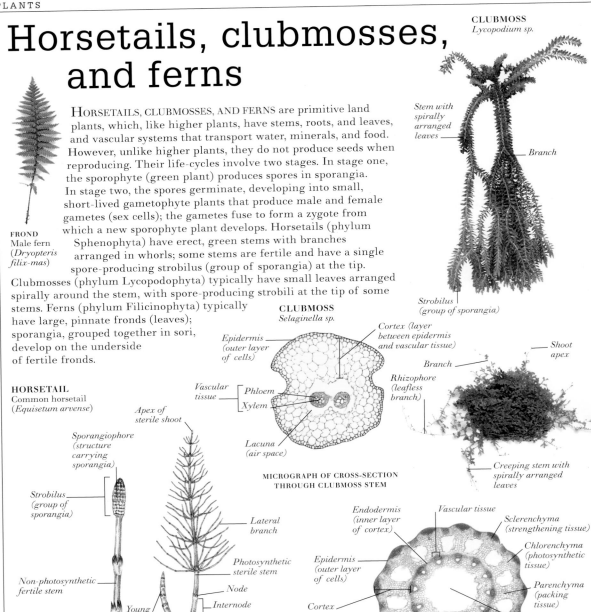

CLUBMOSS
Lycopodium sp.

Stem with spirally arranged leaves

Branch

Strobilus (group of sporangia)

CLUBMOSS
Selaginella sp.

Epidermis (outer layer of cells)

Cortex (layer between epidermis and vascular tissue)

Vascular tissue — Phloem / Xylem

Lacuna (air space)

Shoot apex

Branch

Rhizophore (leafless branch)

Creeping stem with spirally arranged leaves

MICROGRAPH OF CROSS-SECTION THROUGH CLUBMOSS STEM

HORSETAIL
Common horsetail
(*Equisetum arvense*)

Apex of sterile shoot

Sporangiophore (structure carrying sporangia)

Strobilus (group of sporangia)

Non-photosynthetic fertile stem

Collar of small brown leaves

Young shoot

Lateral branch

Photosynthetic sterile stem

Node

Internode

Node

Tuber

Rhizome

Adventitious root

Endodermis (inner layer of cortex)

Vascular tissue

Sclerenchyma (strengthening tissue)

Chlorenchyma (photosynthetic tissue)

Epidermis (outer layer of cells)

Cortex (layer between epidermis and vascular tissue)

Parenchyma (packing tissue)

Hollow pith cavity

Vallecular canal (longitudinal channel)

Carinal canal (longitudinal channel)

MICROGRAPH OF CROSS-SECTION THROUGH HORSETAIL STEM

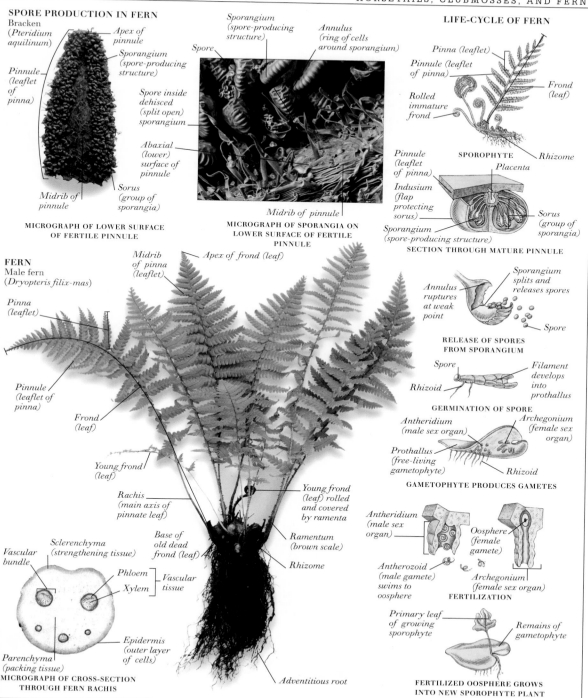

SPORE PRODUCTION IN FERN

Bracken
(*Pteridium aquilinum*)

Apex of pinnule

Sporangium (spore-producing structure)

Pinnule (leaflet of pinna)

Spore inside dehisced (split open) sporangium

Abaxial (lower) surface of pinnule

Midrib of pinnule

Sorus (group of sporangia)

MICROGRAPH OF LOWER SURFACE OF FERTILE PINNULE

Sporangium (spore-producing structure)

Spore

Annulus (ring of cells around sporangium)

Midrib of pinnule

MICROGRAPH OF SPORANGIA ON LOWER SURFACE OF FERTILE PINNULE

LIFE-CYCLE OF FERN

Pinna (leaflet)

Pinnule (leaflet of pinna)

Rolled immature frond

Frond (leaf)

SPOROPHYTE

Rhizome

Pinnule (leaflet of pinna)

Indusium (flap protecting sorus)

Sporangium (spore-producing structure)

Placenta

Sorus (group of sporangia)

SECTION THROUGH MATURE PINNULE

Annulus ruptures at weak point

Sporangium splits and releases spores

Spore

RELEASE OF SPORES FROM SPORANGIUM

Spore

Rhizoid

Filament develops into prothallus

GERMINATION OF SPORE

Antheridium (male sex organ)

Archegonium (female sex organ)

Prothallus (free-living gametophyte)

Rhizoid

GAMETOPHYTE PRODUCES GAMETES

FERN

Male fern
(*Dryopteris filix-mas*)

Pinna (leaflet)

Midrib of pinna (leaflet)

Apex of frond (leaf)

Pinnule (leaflet of pinna)

Frond (leaf)

Young frond (leaf)

Rachis (main axis of pinnate leaf)

Base of old dead frond (leaf)

Young frond (leaf) rolled and covered by ramenta

Ramentum (brown scale)

Rhizome

Vascular bundle

Sclerenchyma (strengthening tissue)

Phloem

Xylem

Vascular tissue

Epidermis (outer layer of cells)

Parenchyma (packing tissue)

MICROGRAPH OF CROSS-SECTION THROUGH FERN RACHIS

Adventitious root

Antheridium (male sex organ)

Oosphere (female gamete)

Antherozoid (male gamete) swims to oosphere

Archegonium (female sex organ)

FERTILIZATION

Primary leaf of growing sporophyte

Remains of gametophyte

FERTILIZED OOSPHERE GROWS INTO NEW SPOROPHYTE PLANT

Gymnosperms 1

THE GYMNOSPERMS ARE FOUR RELATED PHYLA of seed-producing plants; their seeds, however, lack the protective, outer covering which surrounds the seeds of flowering plants. Typically, gymnosperms are woody, perennial shrubs or trees, with stems, leaves, and roots, and a well-developed vascular (transport) system. The reproductive structures in most gymnosperms are cones: male cones produce microspores in which male gametes (sex cells) develop; female cones produce megaspores in which female gametes develop. Microspores are blown by the wind to female cones, male and female gametes fuse during fertilization, and a seed develops. The four gymnosperm phyla are the conifers (phylum Coniferophyta), mostly tall trees; cycads (phylum Cycadophyta), small palm-like trees; the ginkgo or maidenhair tree (phylum Ginkgophyta), a tall tree with bilobed leaves; and gnetophytes (phylum Gnetophyta), a diverse group of plants, mainly shrubs, but also including the horizontally growing welwitschia.

LIFE-CYCLE OF SCOTS PINE
(*Pinus sylvestris*)

Needle (*foliage leaf*)

Cone

Ovuliferous scale (*ovule- then seed-bearing structure*)

MALE CONES

YOUNG FEMALE CONE

Pollen grain in micropyle (*entrance to ovule*)

Ovuliferous scale

Pollen grain

Ovule (*contains female gamete*)

Nucleus

Air sac

POLLINATION

Integument (*outer part of ovule*)

Archegonium (*containing female gamete*)

Pollen tube (*carries male gamete from pollen grain to ovum*)

FERTILIZATION

SCALE AND SEEDS
Pine
(*Pinus sp.*)

Ovuliferous scale (*ovule- then seed-bearing structure*)

Wing scar

Wing of seed derived from ovuliferous scale

Seed

Seed

Seed scar

Point of attachment to axis of cone

OVULIFEROUS SCALE FROM THIRD-YEAR FEMALE CONE

Seed

Ovuliferous scale (*ovule- then seed-bearing structure*)

Seed

Wing

MATURE FEMALE CONE AND WINGED SEED

Microsporangium (*structure in which pollen grains are formed*)

Microsporophyll (*modified leaf carrying microsporangia*)

Ovule (*contains female gametes*)

Plumule (*embryonic shoot*)

Cotyledon (*seed leaf*)

Root

GERMINATION OF PINE SEEDLING

Axis of cone

Scale leaf

Ovuliferous scale (*ovule- then seed-bearing structure*)

Bract scale

Axis of cone

WELWITSCHIA
(*Welwitschia mirabilis*)

MICROGRAPH OF LONGITUDINAL SECTION THROUGH YOUNG MALE CONE

MICROGRAPH OF LONGITUDINAL SECTION THROUGH SECOND-YEAR FEMALE CONE

Frayed end of leaf

SMOOTH CYPRESS
(*Cupressus glabra*)

Immature female cone

Ovuliferous scale

Ovule (contains female gamete)

CROSS-SECTION THROUGH IMMATURE CONE

Ovuliferous scale (ovule- then seed-bearing structure)

Mature female cone

Scale-like leaf

Seed

Ovuliferous scale (ovule- then seed-bearing structure)

CROSS-SECTION THROUGH MATURE CONE

Immature male cone

Woody scale

Opening between woody scales through which seeds are released

DISCARDED CONE

Stem

YEW
(*Taxus baccata*)

Single ovule (contains female gamete)

Scale

Female "cone"

Scale

Developing seed

Scale

Seed

Aril (fleshy outgrowth from seed)

Stem

FEMALE "CONES" AT VARIOUS STAGES OF DEVELOPMENT

Needle (foliage leaf)

CYCAD
Sago palm
(*Cycas revoluta*)

Pinna (leaflet)

Pinnate leaf

Scale leaf

Old leaf base

Stem covered by scale leaves

Continuously growing leaf

Immature cone

Site of cone growth

Stalk scar

Woody stem

Adaxial (upper) surface of leaf

Abaxial (lower) surface of leaf

MAIDENHAIR TREE
(*Ginkgo biloba*)

Girdle scar

Stem

Petiole (leaf stalk)

Bilobed leaf

Frayed end of leaf

Gymnosperms 2

BRANCH OF BISHOP PINE
(*Pinus muricata*)

Second-year female cone

Ovuliferous scale
(ovule- then seed-bearing
structure)

Needle
(foliage leaf)

Ovuliferous scale
(ovule- then seed-
bearing structure)

Bud
scale

Cone

Cone stalk

Stem

Scale leaf scar

Dwarf shoot

**FEMALE CONE
(FIRST YEAR)**

Apical bud

Stem

Male cone

Dwarf shoot

Needle (foliage leaf)

Scar of
dwarf shoot

Upper surface
of needle
(foliage leaf)

Margin
of needle
(foliage leaf)

Needle
(foliage leaf)

Apical bud

Stem

Dwarf shoot

TERMINAL ZONE OF BRANCH

Stoma
(pore)

Female
cone

Woody ovuliferous
scale (ovule- then
seed-bearing structure)

**FEMALE CONE
(THIRD YEAR)**

Vascular tissue

Phloem   Xylem

Mesophyll
(photosynthetic tissue)

Epidermis
(outer
layer of
cells)

Stoma
(pore)

Endodermis
(inner layer
of cortex)

Resin canal

Cuticle
(waterproof
covering)

**MICROGRAPH OF CROSS-SECTION
THROUGH NEEDLE (FOLIAGE LEAF)**

**MICROGRAPH OF NEEDLE
(FOLIAGE LEAF) OF PINE**
(*Pinus sp.*)

Apical bud scale

Apical bud

Shoot apex

Needle (foliage leaf) bud

Bud scale

Scale leaf

CROSS-SECTION THROUGH MATURE STEM OF BISHOP PINE
(*Pinus muricata*)

Annual ring

Immature needle (foliage leaf)

Heartwood (supportive, inactive secondary xylem)

Branch trace (vascular bundle supplying branch)

Pith

MICROGRAPH OF LONGITUDINAL SECTION
THROUGH SHOOT APEX OF PINE
(*Pinus sp.*)

Medullary ray (extension of pith)

Pith

Hypodermis (cell layer below epidermis)

Cortex (layer between epidermis and vascular tissue)

Base of dwarf shoot

Dwarf shoot trace (vascular bundle supplying dwarf shoot)

Secondary xylem

Vascular tissue

Phloem

Primary xylem

Epidermis (outer layer of cells)

Resin canal

Sapwood (active secondary xylem)

Bark

Phloem

Periderm (outer layer of bark)

MICROGRAPH OF CROSS-SECTION
THROUGH YOUNG STEM OF PINE
(*Pinus sp.*)

Cortex (layer between phellem and vascular tissue)

Resin canal

Endodermis (inner layer of cortex)

Phloem

Phellem (protective outer layer)

Secondary xylem

Primary xylem

MICROGRAPH OF CROSS-SECTION
THROUGH YOUNG ROOT OF PINE
(*Pinus sp.*)

Cortex (layer between phellem and vascular tissue)

Secondary xylem

Phellem (protective outer layer)

Primary xylem

Phloem

Resin canal

MICROGRAPH OF CROSS-SECTION
THROUGH MATURE ROOT OF PINE
(*Pinus sp.*)

125

Monocotyledons and dicotyledons

FLOWERING PLANTS (PHYLUM ANGIOSPERMOPHYTA) are divided into two classes: monocotyledons (class Monocotyledoneae) and dicotyledons (class Dicotyledoneae). Typically, monocotyledons have seeds with one cotyledon (seed leaf); their foliage leaves are narrow with parallel veins; the flower components occur in multiples of three; sepals and petals are indistinguishable and are known as tepals; vascular (transport) tissues are scattered in random bundles throughout the stem; and, since they lack stem cambium (actively dividing cells that produce wood), most monocotyledons are herbaceous (see pp. 128-129). Dicotyledons have seeds with two cotyledons; leaves are broad with a central midrib and branched veins; flower parts occur in multiples of four or five; sepals are generally small and green; petals are large and colourful; vascular bundles are arranged in a ring around the edge of the stem; and, because many dicotyledons possess wood-producing stem cambium, there are woody forms (see pp. 130-131) as well as herbaceous ones.

CROSS-SECTION
THROUGH
MONOCOTYLEDONOUS
LEAF BASES

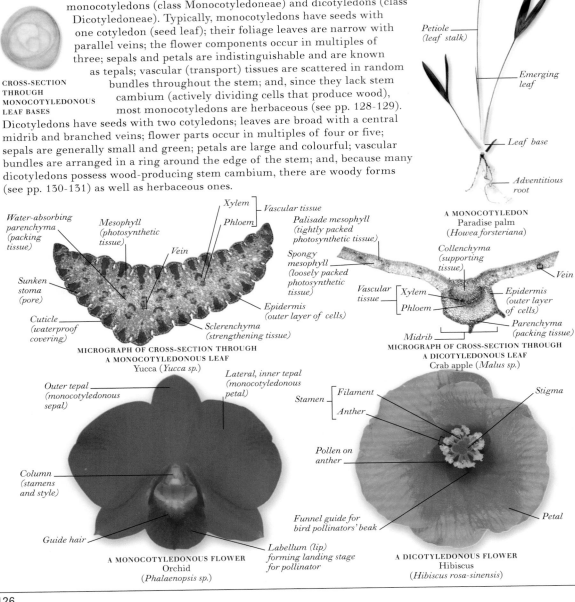

Vein (parallel venation)

Leaflet

Petiole (leaf stalk)

Emerging leaf

Leaf base

Adventitious root

A MONOCOTYLEDON
Paradise palm
(Howea forsteriana)

Water-absorbing parenchyma (packing tissue)

Mesophyll (photosynthetic tissue)

Xylem ⎤ Vascular tissue
Phloem ⎦

Vein

Sunken stoma (pore)

Cuticle (waterproof covering)

Sclerenchyma (strengthening tissue)

Epidermis (outer layer of cells)

MICROGRAPH OF CROSS-SECTION THROUGH
A MONOCOTYLEDONOUS LEAF
Yucca (Yucca sp.)

Palisade mesophyll (tightly packed photosynthetic tissue)

Spongy mesophyll (loosely packed photosynthetic tissue)

Vascular tissue ⎡ Xylem
⎣ Phloem

Collenchyma (supporting tissue)

Vein

Epidermis (outer layer of cells)

Parenchyma (packing tissue)

Midrib

MICROGRAPH OF CROSS-SECTION THROUGH
A DICOTYLEDONOUS LEAF
Crab apple (Malus sp.)

Outer tepal (monocotyledonous sepal)

Lateral, inner tepal (monocotyledonous petal)

Stamen ⎡ Filament
⎣ Anther

Stigma

Pollen on anther

Column (stamens and style)

Guide hair

Labellum (lip) forming landing stage for pollinator

A MONOCOTYLEDONOUS FLOWER
Orchid
(Phalaenopsis sp.)

Funnel guide for bird pollinators' beak

Petal

A DICOTYLEDONOUS FLOWER
Hibiscus
(Hibiscus rosa-sinensis)

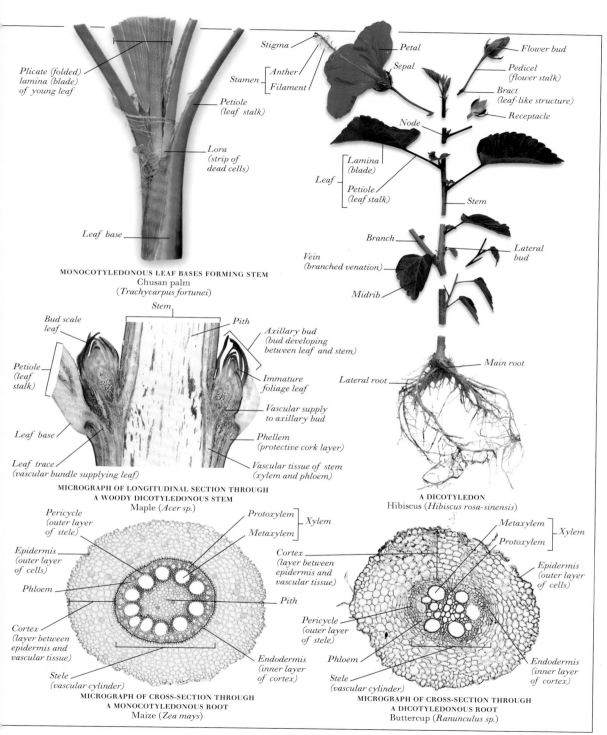

Plicate (folded)
lamina (blade)
of young leaf

Petiole
(leaf stalk)

Lora
(strip of
dead cells)

Leaf base

Stigma

Stamen — Anther
Filament

Petal

Sepal

Flower bud

Pedicel
(flower stalk)

Bract
(leaf-like structure)

Receptacle

Node

Leaf — Lamina
(blade)

Petiole
(leaf stalk)

Stem

Branch

Vein
(branched venation)

Midrib

Lateral
bud

MONOCOTYLEDONOUS LEAF BASES FORMING STEM
Chusan palm
(*Trachycarpus fortunei*)

Bud scale
leaf

Petiole
(leaf
stalk)

Leaf base

Leaf trace
(vascular bundle supplying leaf)

Stem

Pith

Axillary bud
(bud developing
between leaf and stem)

Immature
foliage leaf

Vascular supply
to axillary bud

Phellem
(protective cork layer)

Vascular tissue of stem
(xylem and phloem)

Main root

Lateral root

**MICROGRAPH OF LONGITUDINAL SECTION THROUGH
A WOODY DICOTYLEDONOUS STEM**
Maple (*Acer sp.*)

A DICOTYLEDON
Hibiscus (*Hibiscus rosa-sinensis*)

Pericycle
(outer layer
of stele)

Epidermis
(outer layer
of cells)

Phloem

Cortex
(layer between
epidermis and
vascular tissue)

Stele
(vascular cylinder)

Protoxylem
Metaxylem — Xylem

Cortex
(layer between
epidermis and
vascular tissue)

Pith

Endodermis
(inner layer
of cortex)

Metaxylem
Protoxylem — Xylem

Epidermis
(outer layer
of cells)

Pericycle
(outer layer
of stele)

Phloem

Stele
(vascular cylinder)

Endodermis
(inner layer
of cortex)

**MICROGRAPH OF CROSS-SECTION THROUGH
A MONOCOTYLEDONOUS ROOT**
Maize (*Zea mays*)

**MICROGRAPH OF CROSS-SECTION THROUGH
A DICOTYLEDONOUS ROOT**
Buttercup (*Ranunculus sp.*)

127

Herbaceous flowering plants

HERBACEOUS FLOWERING PLANTS TYPICALLY HAVE GREEN, NON-WOODY STEMS, and tend to be relatively short-lived. Many herbaceous plants live for only one or two years. Annuals (e.g., sweet peas) grow from seed, produce flowers and then seeds, and die within a single year. Biennials (e.g., carrots) have a two-year life cycle. In the first year, seeds grow into plants, which produce leaves and store food in underground storage organs; the stems and foliage then die back in winter. In the second year, new stems grow from the storage organs, produce leaves, flowers, and seeds, and then die. Some herbaceous plants (e.g., potatoes) are perennial. They grow back year after year, producing shoots and flowers in spring, storing food in underground tubers or rhizomes during summer, dying back in autumn, and surviving underground during winter.

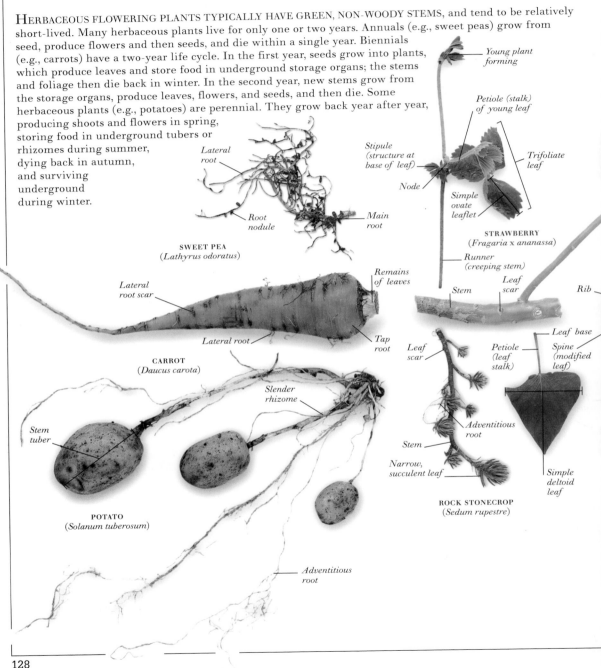

Young plant forming

Petiole (stalk) of young leaf

Lateral root

Stipule (structure at base of leaf)

Node

Trifoliate leaf

Simple ovate leaflet

Root nodule

Main root

SWEET PEA
(*Lathyrus odoratus*)

STRAWBERRY
(*Fragaria x ananassa*)

Runner (creeping stem)

Lateral root scar

Remains of leaves

Stem

Leaf scar

Rib

Lateral root

Tap root

Leaf scar

Petiole (leaf stalk)

Leaf base

Spine (modified leaf)

CARROT
(*Daucus carota*)

Slender rhizome

Stem tuber

Adventitious root

Stem

Narrow, succulent leaf

Simple deltoid leaf

POTATO
(*Solanum tuberosum*)

ROCK STONECROP
(*Sedum rupestre*)

Adventitious root

PARTS OF HERBACEOUS FLOWERING PLANTS

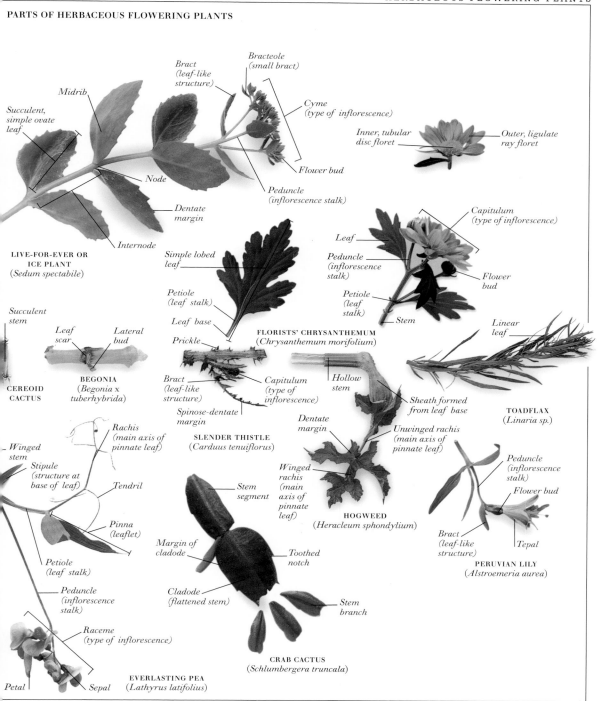

Bract (leaf-like structure)

Bracteole (small bract)

Midrib

Cyme (type of inflorescence)

Succulent, simple ovate leaf

Inner, tubular disc floret

Outer, ligulate ray floret

Flower bud

Node

Peduncle (inflorescence stalk)

Dentate margin

Internode

LIVE-FOR-EVER OR ICE PLANT
(Sedum spectabile)

Simple lobed leaf

Capitulum (type of inflorescence)

Leaf

Peduncle (inflorescence stalk)

Flower bud

Petiole (leaf stalk)

Petiole (leaf stalk)

Leaf base

Stem

FLORISTS' CHRYSANTHEMUM
(Chrysanthemum morifolium)

Linear leaf

Succulent stem

Leaf scar

Lateral bud

Prickle

Hollow stem

CEREOID CACTUS

BEGONIA
(Begonia x tuberhybrida)

Bract (leaf-like structure)

Capitulum (type of inflorescence)

Sheath formed from leaf base

TOADFLAX
(Linaria sp.)

Spinose-dentate margin

Dentate margin

SLENDER THISTLE
(Carduus tenuiflorus)

Unwinged rachis (main axis of pinnate leaf)

Peduncle (inflorescence stalk)

Rachis (main axis of pinnate leaf)

Winged stem

Stipule (structure at base of leaf)

Tendril

Stem segment

Winged rachis (main axis of pinnate leaf)

Flower bud

Pinna (leaflet)

HOGWEED
(Heracleum sphondylium)

Bract (leaf-like structure)

Tepal

Petiole (leaf stalk)

Margin of cladode

Toothed notch

PERUVIAN LILY
(Alstroemeria aurea)

Peduncle (inflorescence stalk)

Cladode (flattened stem)

Stem branch

Raceme (type of inflorescence)

CRAB CACTUS
(Schlumbergera truncata)

Petal

Sepal

EVERLASTING PEA
(Lathyrus latifolius)

Woody flowering plants

WOODY FLOWERING PLANTS ARE PERENNIAL, that is, they continue to grow and reproduce for many years. They have one or more permanent stems above ground, and numerous smaller branches. The stems and branches have a strong woody core that supports the plant and contains vascular tissue for transporting water and nutrients. Outside the woody core is a layer of tough, protective bark, which has lenticels (tiny pores) in it to enable gases to pass through. Woody flowering plants may be shrubs, which have several stems arising from the soil; bushes, which are shrubs with dense branching and foliage; or trees, which typically have a single upright stem (the trunk) that bears branches. Deciduous woody plants (e.g., roses) shed all their leaves once a year and remain leafless during winter. Evergreen woody plants (e.g., ivy) shed their leaves gradually, so retaining full leaf cover throughout the year.

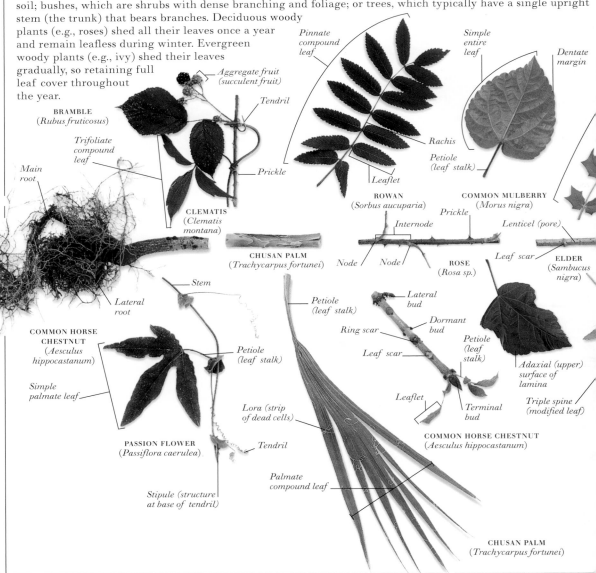

Aggregate fruit (succulent fruit)

Tendril

BRAMBLE
(*Rubus fruticosus*)

Trifoliate compound leaf

Prickle

Main root

CLEMATIS
(*Clematis montana*)

Lateral root

Stem

COMMON HORSE CHESTNUT
(*Aesculus hippocastanum*)

Simple palmate leaf

Petiole (leaf stalk)

PASSION FLOWER
(*Passiflora caerulea*)

Tendril

Stipule (structure at base of tendril)

Pinnate compound leaf

Simple entire leaf

Dentate margin

Rachis

Petiole (leaf stalk)

Leaflet

ROWAN
(*Sorbus aucuparia*)

COMMON MULBERRY
(*Morus nigra*)

Prickle

Internode

Lenticel (pore)

Node   Node

ROSE
(*Rosa sp.*)

Leaf scar

ELDER
(*Sambucus nigra*)

CHUSAN PALM
(*Trachycarpus fortunei*)

Petiole (leaf stalk)

Lateral bud

Dormant bud

Ring scar

Petiole (leaf stalk)

Leaf scar

Adaxial (upper) surface of lamina

Leaflet

Triple spine (modified leaf)

Terminal bud

COMMON HORSE CHESTNUT
(*Aesculus hippocastanum*)

Lora (strip of dead cells)

Palmate compound leaf

CHUSAN PALM
(*Trachycarpus fortunei*)

PARTS OF WOODY FLOWERING PLANTS

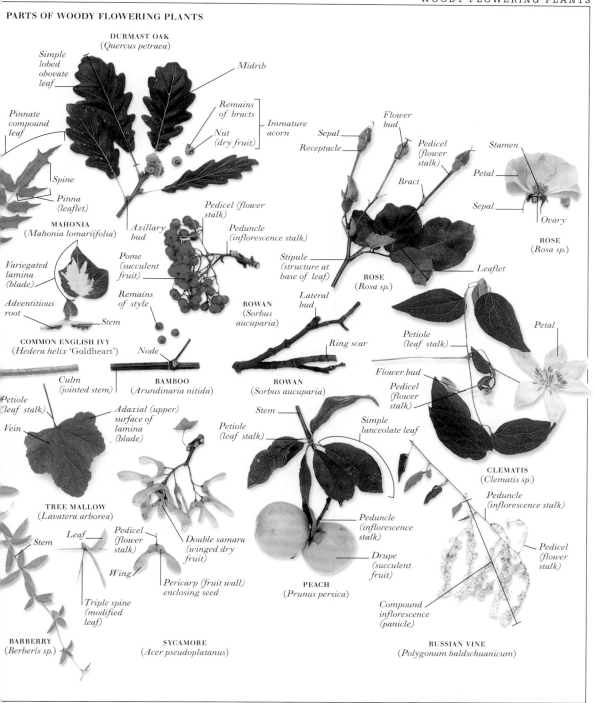

DURMAST OAK
(*Quercus petraea*)

Simple lobed obovate leaf

Midrib

Remains of bracts

Immature acorn

Nut (dry fruit)

Pinnate compound leaf

Spine

Pinna (leaflet)

MAHONIA
(*Mahonia lomariifolia*)

Axillary bud

Pome (succulent fruit)

Variegated lamina (blade)

Pedicel (flower stalk)

Peduncle (inflorescence stalk)

Adventitious root

Stem

Remains of style

COMMON ENGLISH IVY
(*Hedera helix* 'Goldheart')

Node

ROWAN
(*Sorbus aucuparia*)

Culm (jointed stem)

BAMBOO
(*Arundinaria nitida*)

Petiole (leaf stalk)

Vein

Adaxial (upper) surface of lamina (blade)

ROWAN
(*Sorbus aucuparia*)

Lateral bud

Ring scar

TREE MALLOW
(*Lavatera arborea*)

Stem

Leaf

Pedicel (flower stalk)

Wing

Double samara (winged dry fruit)

Pericarp (fruit wall) enclosing seed

Triple spine (modified leaf)

BARBERRY
(*Berberis sp.*)

SYCAMORE
(*Acer pseudoplatanus*)

Sepal

Receptacle

Flower bud

Pedicel (flower stalk)

Bract

Stipule (structure at base of leaf)

ROSE
(*Rosa sp.*)

Leaflet

Stamen

Petal

Sepal

Ovary

ROSE
(*Rosa sp.*)

Petiole (leaf stalk)

Flower bud

Pedicel (flower stalk)

Petal

CLEMATIS
(*Clematis sp.*)

Stem

Petiole (leaf stalk)

Simple lanceolate leaf

Peduncle (inflorescence stalk)

Drupe (succulent fruit)

PEACH
(*Prunus persica*)

Peduncle (inflorescence stalk)

Pedicel (flower stalk)

Compound inflorescence (panicle)

RUSSIAN VINE
(*Polygonum baldschuanicum*)

Roots

ROOTS ARE THE UNDERGROUND PARTS OF PLANTS. They have three main functions. First, they anchor the plant in the soil. Second, they absorb water and minerals from the spaces between soil particles; the roots' absorptive properties are increased by root hairs, which grow behind the root tip, allowing maximum uptake of vital substances. Third, the root is part of the plant's transport system: xylem carries water and minerals from the roots to the stem and leaves, and phloem carries nutrients from the leaves to all parts of the root system. In addition, some roots (e.g., carrots) are food stores. Roots have an outer epidermis covering a cortex of parenchyma (packing tissue), and a central cylinder of vascular tissue. This arrangement helps the roots resist the forces of compression as they grow through the soil.

Split in testa
as seed
germinates

Cotyledon
(seed leaf)

Primary root

Testa
(seed coat)

Root hair

CARROT
(*Daucus carota*)

FEATURES OF A TYPICAL ROOT
Buttercup
(*Ranunculus sp.*)

Stele
(vascular cylinder)

Phloem sieve tube
(through which
nutrients are
transported)

Root tip
(region of
cell division)

Pericycle
(outer layer
of stele)

Root hair

Air space
(allowing gas
diffusion in
the root)

Companion cell
(cell associated
with phloem
sieve tube)

Cortex
(layer between
epidermis and
vascular tissue)

Root hair

Epidermis
(outer layer
of cells)

Xylem vessel
(through which water
and minerals are transported)

Endodermis
(inner layer
of cortex)

Cell wall

Nucleus

Cytoplasm

Parenchyma
(packing) cell

PRIMARY ROOT AND MICROGRAPHS OF SECTIONS THROUGH ROOTS

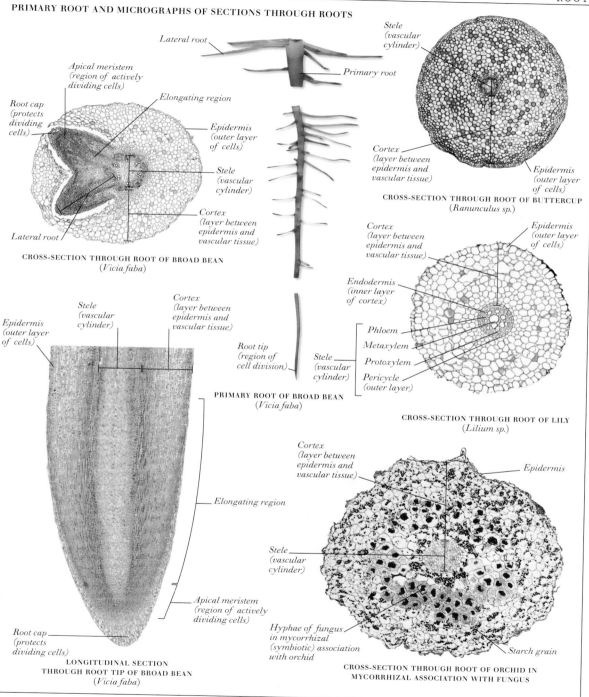

Lateral root

Primary root

Stele (vascular cylinder)

Apical meristem (region of actively dividing cells)

Elongating region

Root cap (protects dividing cells)

Epidermis (outer layer of cells)

Stele (vascular cylinder)

Cortex (layer between epidermis and vascular tissue)

Epidermis (outer layer of cells)

Lateral root

CROSS-SECTION THROUGH ROOT OF BROAD BEAN
(*Vicia faba*)

CROSS-SECTION THROUGH ROOT OF BUTTERCUP
(*Ranunculus sp.*)

Cortex (layer between epidermis and vascular tissue)

Epidermis (outer layer of cells)

Stele (vascular cylinder)

Cortex (layer between epidermis and vascular tissue)

Root tip (region of cell division)

Endodermis (inner layer of cortex)

Epidermis (outer layer of cells)

Phloem

Metaxylem

Protoxylem

Stele (vascular cylinder)

Pericycle (outer layer)

PRIMARY ROOT OF BROAD BEAN
(*Vicia faba*)

CROSS-SECTION THROUGH ROOT OF LILY
(*Lilium sp.*)

Epidermis (outer layer of cells)

Elongating region

Cortex (layer between epidermis and vascular tissue)

Epidermis

Apical meristem (region of actively dividing cells)

Stele (vascular cylinder)

Root cap (protects dividing cells)

Hyphae of fungus in mycorrhizal (symbiotic) association with orchid

Starch grain

LONGITUDINAL SECTION THROUGH ROOT TIP OF BROAD BEAN
(*Vicia faba*)

CROSS-SECTION THROUGH ROOT OF ORCHID IN MYCORRHIZAL ASSOCIATION WITH FUNGUS

Stems

THE STEM IS THE MAIN SUPPORTIVE PART OF A PLANT that grows above ground. Stems bear leaves (organs of photosynthesis), which grow at nodes; buds (shoots covered by protective scales), which grow at the stem tip (apical or terminal buds) and in the angle between a leaf and the stem (axillary or lateral buds); and flowers (reproductive structures). The stem forms part of the plant's transport system: xylem tissue in the stem transports water and minerals from the roots to the aerial parts of the plant, and phloem tissue transports nutrients manufactured in the leaves to other parts of the plant. Stem tissues are also used for storing water and food. Herbaceous (non-woody) stems have an outer protective epidermis covering a cortex that consists mainly of parenchyma (packing tissue) but also has some collenchyma (supporting tissue). The vascular tissue of such stems is arranged in bundles, each of which consists of xylem, phloem, and sclerenchyma (strengthening tissue). Woody stems have an outer protective layer of tough bark, which is perforated with lenticels (pores) to allow gas exchange. Inside the bark is a ring of secondary phloem, which surrounds an inner core of secondary xylem.

MICROGRAPH OF LONGITUDINAL SECTION THROUGH APEX OF STEM
Coleus sp.

Apical meristem (region of actively dividing cells)

Procambial strand (cells that produce vascular tissue)

Leaf primordium (developing leaf)

Developing bud

Cortex (layer between epidermis and vascular tissue)

Vascular tissue

Epidermis (outer layer of cells)

Pith

YOUNG WOODY STEM
Lime
(Tilia sp.)

Secondary phloem

Pith

Phellem (protective cork layer)

Cortex (layer between phellem and vascular tissue)

Xylem vessel (through which water and minerals are transported)

Xylem fibre (supporting tissue)

Ray (parenchyma cells)

Phloem sieve tube (through which nutrients are transported)

Phloem fibre (supporting tissue)

Lenticel (pore)

Vascular cambium (actively dividing cells that produce xylem and phloem)

Autumn wood

Secondary xylem

Spring wood

Companion cell (cell associated with phloem sieve tube)

EMERGENT BUDS
London plane
(Platanus x acerifolia)

Young leaves emerging

Terminal bud

Lateral bud

Node

Internode

Inner bud scale

Secondary xylem

Outer bud scale

Node

Leaf scar

Lenticel (pore)

Woody stem

MICROGRAPHS OF CROSS-SECTIONS THROUGH VARIOUS STEMS

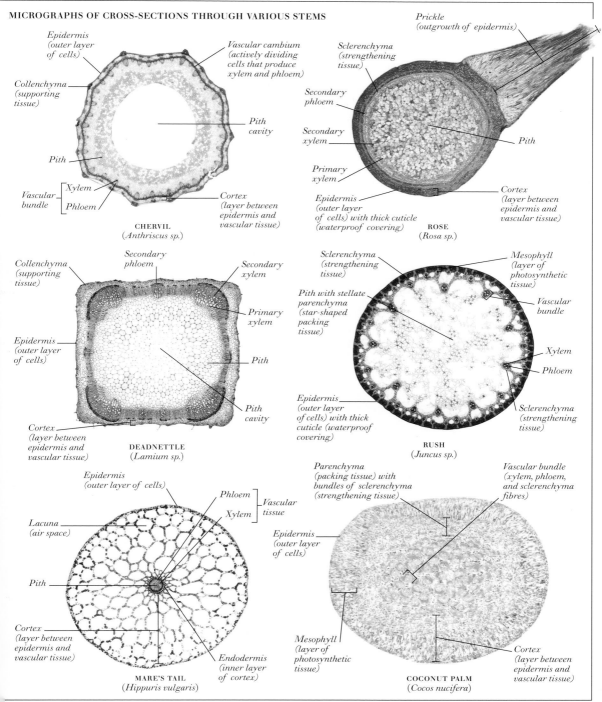

Epidermis (outer layer of cells)

Vascular cambium (actively dividing cells that produce xylem and phloem)

Collenchyma (supporting tissue)

Pith cavity

Pith

Vascular bundle — Xylem / Phloem

Cortex (layer between epidermis and vascular tissue)

CHERVIL
(Anthriscus sp.)

Prickle (outgrowth of epidermis)

Sclerenchyma (strengthening tissue)

Secondary phloem

Secondary xylem

Primary xylem

Pith

Epidermis (outer layer of cells) with thick cuticle (waterproof covering)

Cortex (layer between epidermis and vascular tissue)

ROSE
(Rosa sp.)

Collenchyma (supporting tissue)

Secondary phloem

Secondary xylem

Primary xylem

Pith

Epidermis (outer layer of cells)

Pith cavity

Cortex (layer between epidermis and vascular tissue)

DEADNETTLE
(Lamium sp.)

Sclerenchyma (strengthening tissue)

Mesophyll (layer of photosynthetic tissue)

Pith with stellate parenchyma (star-shaped packing tissue)

Vascular bundle

Xylem

Phloem

Sclerenchyma (strengthening tissue)

Epidermis (outer layer of cells) with thick cuticle (waterproof covering)

RUSH
(Juncus sp.)

Epidermis (outer layer of cells)

Phloem / Xylem — Vascular tissue

Lacuna (air space)

Pith

Cortex (layer between epidermis and vascular tissue)

Endodermis (inner layer of cortex)

MARE'S TAIL
(Hippuris vulgaris)

Parenchyma (packing tissue) with bundles of sclerenchyma (strengthening tissue)

Vascular bundle (xylem, phloem, and sclerenchyma fibres)

Epidermis (outer layer of cells)

Mesophyll (layer of photosynthetic tissue)

Cortex (layer between epidermis and vascular tissue)

COCONUT PALM
(Cocos nucifera)

Leaves

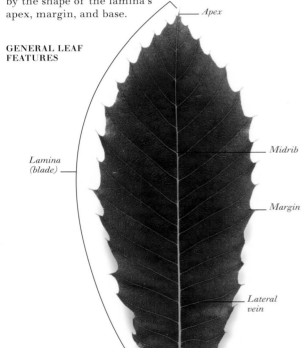

LEAVES ARE THE MAIN SITES OF PHOTOSYNTHESIS (see pp. 138-139) and transpiration (water loss by evaporation) in plants. A typical leaf consists of a thin, flat lamina (blade) supported by a network of veins; a petiole (leaf stalk); and a leaf base, where the petiole joins the stem. Leaves can be classified as simple, in which the lamina is a single unit, or compound, in which the lamina is divided into separate leaflets. Compound leaves may be pinnate, with pinnae (leaflets) on both sides of a rachis (main axis), or palmate, with leaflets arising from a single point at the tip of the petiole. Leaves can be classified further by the overall shape of the lamina, and by the shape of the lamina's apex, margin, and base.

CHECKERBLOOM
(*Sidalcea malviflora*)

SIMPLE LEAF SHAPES

Subacute apex

Acuminate apex

Entire margin

Entire margin

Cuneate base

Cordate base

PANDURIFORM
Croton
(*Codiaeum variegatum*)

LANCEOLATE
Sea buckthorn
(*Hippophae rhamnoides*)

GENERAL LEAF FEATURES

Apex

Midrib

Lamina (blade)

Margin

Lateral vein

Lamina base

Petiole (leaf stalk)

Leaf base

Sweet chestnut
(*Castanea sativa*)

COMPOUND LEAF SHAPES

Terminal pinna (leaflet)

Emarginate apex

Rachis (main axis of pinnate leaf)

Pinna (leaflet)

Petiolule (leaflet stalk)

Petiole (leaf stalk)

ODD PINNATE
False acacia
(*Robinia pseudoacacia*)

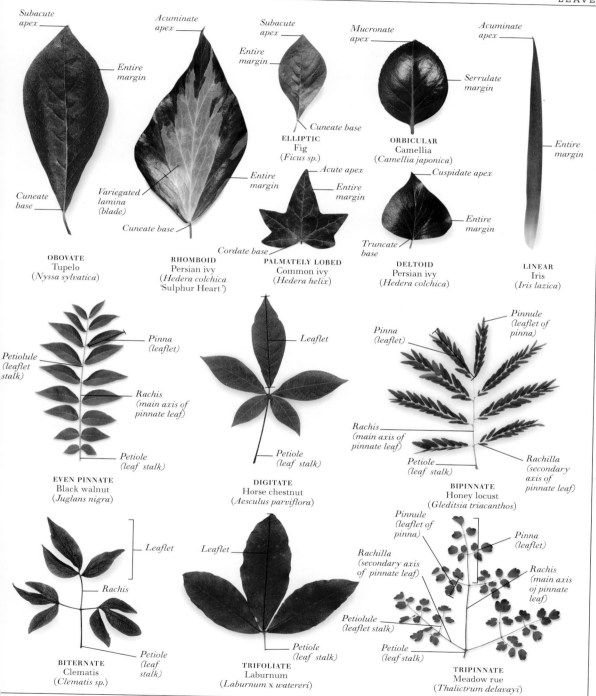

Subacute apex

Entire margin

Cuneate base

OBOVATE
Tupelo
(*Nyssa sylvatica*)

Acuminate apex

Entire margin

Variegated lamina (blade)

Cuneate base

RHOMBOID
Persian ivy
(*Hedera colchica* 'Sulphur Heart')

Subacute apex

Entire margin

Cuneate base

ELLIPTIC
Fig
(*Ficus sp.*)

Acute apex

Entire margin

Cordate base

PALMATELY LOBED
Common ivy
(*Hedera helix*)

Mucronate apex

Serrulate margin

ORBICULAR
Camellia
(*Camellia japonica*)

Cuspidate apex

Entire margin

Truncate base

DELTOID
Persian ivy
(*Hedera colchica*)

Acuminate apex

Entire margin

LINEAR
Iris
(*Iris lazica*)

Pinna (leaflet)

Petiolule (leaflet stalk)

Rachis (main axis of pinnate leaf)

Petiole (leaf stalk)

EVEN PINNATE
Black walnut
(*Juglans nigra*)

Leaflet

Petiole (leaf stalk)

DIGITATE
Horse chestnut
(*Aesculus parviflora*)

Pinnule (leaflet of pinna)

Pinna (leaflet)

Rachis (main axis of pinnate leaf)

Petiole (leaf stalk)

Rachilla (secondary axis of pinnate leaf)

BIPINNATE
Honey locust
(*Gleditsia triacanthos*)

Leaflet

Rachis

Petiole (leaf stalk)

BITERNATE
Clematis
(*Clematis sp.*)

Leaflet

Petiole (leaf stalk)

TRIFOLIATE
Laburnum
(*Laburnum x watereri*)

Pinnule (leaflet of pinna)

Pinna (leaflet)

Rachilla (secondary axis of pinnate leaf)

Rachis (main axis of pinnate leaf)

Petiolule (leaflet stalk)

Petiole (leaf stalk)

TRIPINNATE
Meadow rue
(*Thalictrum delavayi*)

Photosynthesis

PHOTOSYNTHESIS IS THE PROCESS by which plants make their food using sunlight, water, and carbon dioxide. It takes place inside special structures in leaf cells called chloroplasts. The chloroplasts contain chlorophyll, a green pigment that absorbs energy from sunlight. During photosynthesis, the absorbed energy is used to join together carbon dioxide and water to form the sugar glucose, which is the energy source for the whole plant; oxygen, a waste product, is released into the air. Leaves are the main sites of photosynthesis, and have various adaptations for that purpose: flat laminae (blades) provide a large surface for absorbing sunlight; stomata (pores) in the lower surface of the laminae allow gases (carbon dioxide and oxygen) to pass into and out of the leaves; and an extensive network of veins brings water into the leaves and transports the glucose produced by photosynthesis to the rest of the plant.

MICROGRAPH OF LEAF
Lily (*Lilium sp.*)

Stoma (pore)   Guard cell (controls opening and closing of stoma)   Lower surface of lamina (blade)

THE PROCESS OF PHOTOSYNTHESIS

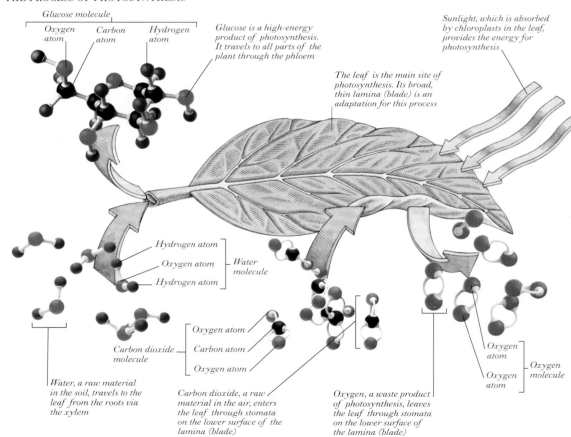

Glucose molecule

Oxygen atom   Carbon atom   Hydrogen atom

Glucose is a high-energy product of photosynthesis. It travels to all parts of the plant through the phloem

Sunlight, which is absorbed by chloroplasts in the leaf, provides the energy for photosynthesis

The leaf is the main site of photosynthesis. Its broad, thin lamina (blade) is an adaptation for this process

Hydrogen atom
Oxygen atom   — Water molecule
Hydrogen atom

Carbon dioxide molecule

Oxygen atom
Carbon atom
Oxygen atom

Oxygen atom

Oxygen atom   — Oxygen molecule

Water, a raw material in the soil, travels to the leaf from the roots via the xylem

Carbon dioxide, a raw material in the air, enters the leaf through stomata on the lower surface of the lamina (blade)

Oxygen, a waste product of photosynthesis, leaves the leaf through stomata on the lower surface of the lamina (blade)

CROSS-SECTION THROUGH LEAF
Christmas rose
(*Helleborus niger*)

Cuticle (*waterproof covering*)

Upper (*adaxial*) epidermis (*outer layer of cells*)

Cell wall

Cytoplasm

Vacuole

Palisade mesophyll (*tightly packed layer of photosynthetic tissue*)

Chloroplast (*photosynthetic organelle*)

Nucleus

Intercellular space

Sclerenchyma (*strengthening tissue*)

Xylem (*tissue that transports water and mineral salts*)

Spongy mesophyll (*loosely packed layer of photosynthetic tissue*)

Phloem (*tissue that transports sugars and other nutrients*)

Vein

Lower (*abaxial*) epidermis (*outer layer of cells*)

Guard cell (*controls opening and closing of stoma*)

Stoma (*pore*)

Substomatal chamber

Parenchyma (*packing tissue*)

INTERNAL VIEW OF CHLOROPLAST

Granum (*stack of thylakoids that hold chlorophyll molecules in position*)

Lamella (*membrane of thylakoid*)

Thylakoid (*flat sac of granum*)

Stroma (*watery matrix*)

Deoxyribonucleic acid (*DNA*) strand

Chloroplast envelope

Outer membrane

Inner membrane

Starch grain

Ribosome (*site of protein synthesis*)

Stroma thylakoid (*link between grana*)

Flowers 1

FLOWERS ARE THE SITES OF SEXUAL REPRODUCTION in flowering plants. Their component parts are arranged in whorls around the receptacle (tip of the flower stalk). The sepals (collectively called the calyx) are outermost; typically small and green, they protect the developing flower. The petals (collectively called the corolla) are typically large and brightly coloured; they are found inside the sepals. In monocotyledonous flowers (see pp. 126-127), sepals and petals are indistinguishable; individually they are called tepals (collectively called the perianth). The petals surround the male and female reproductive structures (androecium and gynoecium). The androecium consists of stamens (male organs); each stamen is made up of a filament (stalk) and anther. The gynoecium has one or more carpels (female organs); each carpel consists of an ovary, style, and stigma. Some flowers (e.g., lily) occur singly on a pedicel (flower stalk); others (e.g., elder, sunflower) are arranged in a group (inflorescence) on a peduncle (inflorescence stalk).

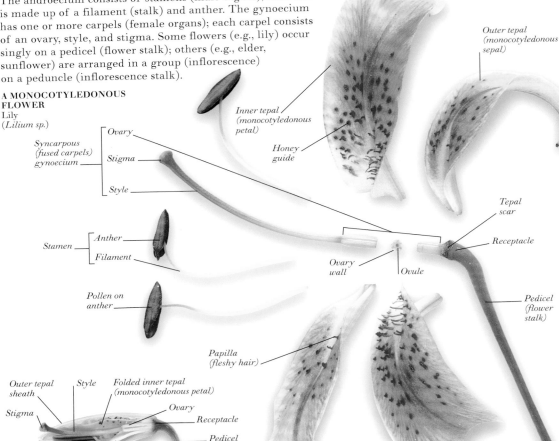

EXTERNAL VIEW

Inner tepal (monocotyledonous petal)

Honey guide

Groove secreting nectar

Style

Filament

Outer tepal (monocotyledonous sepal)

Stigma

Anther

Outer tepal (monocotyledonous sepal)

Inner tepal (monocotyledonous petal)

Honey guide

Tepal scar

Receptacle

Ovary wall

Ovule

Pedicel (flower stalk)

Papilla (fleshy hair)

A MONOCOTYLEDONOUS FLOWER
Lily
(*Lilium sp.*)

Syncarpous (fused carpels) gynoecium

Ovary

Stigma

Style

Stamen

Anther

Filament

Pollen on anther

Outer tepal sheath

Style

Folded inner tepal (monocotyledonous petal)

Stigma

Ovary

Receptacle

Anther

Pedicel (flower stalk)

Filament

LONGITUDINAL SECTION THROUGH FLOWER BUD

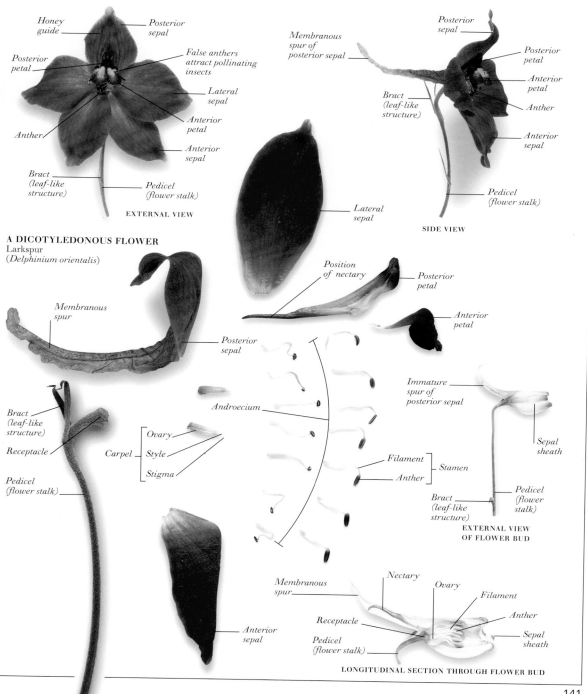

Honey guide

Posterior sepal

Posterior petal

False anthers attract pollinating insects

Lateral sepal

Anterior petal

Anther

Anterior sepal

Bract (leaf-like structure)

Pedicel (flower stalk)

EXTERNAL VIEW

Posterior sepal

Membranous spur of posterior sepal

Posterior petal

Anterior petal

Anther

Bract (leaf-like structure)

Anterior sepal

Pedicel (flower stalk)

SIDE VIEW

A DICOTYLEDONOUS FLOWER
Larkspur
(*Delphinium orientalis*)

Membranous spur

Lateral sepal

Position of nectary

Posterior petal

Anterior petal

Posterior sepal

Immature spur of posterior sepal

Androecium

Sepal sheath

Bract (leaf-like structure)

Receptacle

Carpel — Ovary / Style / Stigma

Filament

Anther

Stamen

Bract (leaf-like structure)

Pedicel (flower stalk)

EXTERNAL VIEW OF FLOWER BUD

Pedicel (flower stalk)

Anterior sepal

Membranous spur

Nectary

Ovary

Filament

Anther

Sepal sheath

Receptacle

Pedicel (flower stalk)

LONGITUDINAL SECTION THROUGH FLOWER BUD

Flowers 2

COMPOUND INFLORESCENCE
(CAPITULUM)
Sunflower
(*Helianthus annulus*)

Disc florets

Ray floret

Florets (small
flowers) are grouped
together to resemble
a single large flower

Sterile ray floret to
attract pollinating
insects

Outer
fertilized
floret

Two-lobed
stigma

Florets with
anthers ready
to shed pollen

Style

Pollen

Anther

Inner, immature
florets

Corolla
tube
(fused
petals)

Pappus
(modified
sepal)

Ovary

Corolla tube (fused petals)

Ovary

FLORETS FROM SUNFLOWER

Pollen

Anther

Nectar

Disc floret

Ray floret

Stigma

Style

Ovary

Corolla tube
(fused petals)

Pappus
(modified
sepal)

Bract
(leaf-like structure)

Hair

Domed receptacle
(flattened top of
inflorescence stalk)

Pith

LONGITUDINAL SECTION THROUGH
SUNFLOWER INFLORESCENCE

Epidermis
(outer layer
of cells)
of peduncle
(inflorescence
stalk)

Peduncle
(inflorescence
stalk)

142

ARRANGEMENT OF FLOWERS ON STEM

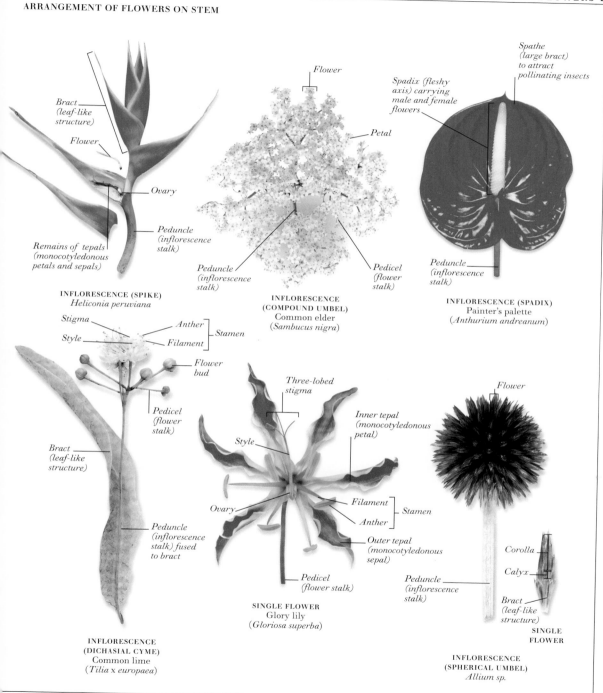

Bract
(leaf-like
structure)

Flower

Ovary

Peduncle
(inflorescence
stalk)

Remains of tepals
(monocotyledonous
petals and sepals)

INFLORESCENCE (SPIKE)
Heliconia peruviana

Flower

Petal

Peduncle
(inflorescence
stalk)

Pedicel
(flower
stalk)

**INFLORESCENCE
(COMPOUND UMBEL)**
Common elder
(*Sambucus nigra*)

Spadix (fleshy
axis) carrying
male and female
flowers

Spathe
(large bract)
to attract
pollinating insects

Peduncle
(inflorescence
stalk)

INFLORESCENCE (SPADIX)
Painter's palette
(*Anthurium andreanum*)

Stigma

Style

Anther

Filament

Stamen

Flower
bud

Pedicel
(flower
stalk)

Bract
(leaf-like
structure)

Peduncle
(inflorescence
stalk) fused
to bract

**INFLORESCENCE
(DICHASIAL CYME)**
Common lime
(*Tilia* x *europaea*)

Three-lobed
stigma

Style

Ovary

Inner tepal
(monocotyledonous
petal)

Filament

Anther

Stamen

Outer tepal
(monocotyledonous
sepal)

Pedicel
(flower stalk)

SINGLE FLOWER
Glory lily
(*Gloriosa superba*)

Flower

Corolla

Calyx

Bract
(leaf-like
structure)

**SINGLE
FLOWER**

Peduncle
(inflorescence
stalk)

**INFLORESCENCE
(SPHERICAL UMBEL)**
Allium sp.

Pollination

POLLINATION IS THE TRANSFER OF POLLEN (which contains the male sex cells) from an anther (part of the male reproductive organ) to a stigma (part of the female reproductive organ). This process precedes fertilization (see pp. 146-147). Pollination may occur within the same flower (self-pollination), or between flowers on separate plants of the same species (cross-pollination). In most plants, pollination is carried out either by insects (entomophilous pollination) or by the wind (anemophilous pollination). Less commonly, birds, bats, or water are the agents of pollination. Insect-pollinated flowers are typically brightly coloured, scented, and produce nectar, on which insects feed. Such flowers also tend to have patterns that are visible only in ultraviolet light, which many insects can see but which humans cannot. These features attract insects, which become covered with the sticky or hooked pollen grains when they visit one flower, and then transfer the pollen to the next flower they visit. Wind-pollinated flowers are generally small, relatively inconspicuous, and unscented. They produce large quantities of light pollen grains that are easily blown by the wind to other flowers.

REPRODUCTIVE STRUCTURES IN WIND-POLLINATED PLANT
Sweet chestnut
(*Castanea saliva*)

Flower bud
Prominent stigma protrudes from flower
Female flower
Petiole (leaf stalk)
Bract (leaf-like structure)
Peduncle (inflorescence stalk)
FEMALE

Male flower
Peduncle (inflorescence stalk)
Part of male catkin (inflorescence adapted for wind pollination)
Filament
Anther
MALE

REPRODUCTIVE STRUCTURES IN INSECT-POLLINATED PLANTS

Stigma
Style
Dehisced (split open) pollen sac
Boundary between two fused carpels (each carpel consists of a stigma, style, and ovary)
Ovary

Endothecium (pollen sac wall)
Pollen grain
Anther
Filament
Stamen
Calyx (whorl of sepals)

MICROGRAPHS OF POLLEN GRAINS

Exine (outer coat of pollen grain)
Pore
EUROPEAN FIELD ELM
(*Ulmus minor*)

MICROGRAPH OF CARPELS (FEMALE ORGANS)
Yellow-wort
(*Blackstonia perfoliata*)

Colpus (furrow-shaped aperture)
Exine (outer coat of pollen grain)
JUSTICIA AUREA

Exine (outer coat of pollen grain)
Pore
Baculum (rod-shaped structure)
MEADOW CRANESBILL
(*Geranium pratense*)

MICROGRAPH OF STAMENS (MALE ORGANS)
Common centaury
(*Centaurium erythraea*)

Colpus (furrow-shaped aperture)
Exine (outer coat of pollen grain)
Equator
furrow
BOX-LEAVED MILKWORT
(*Polygala chamaebuxus*)

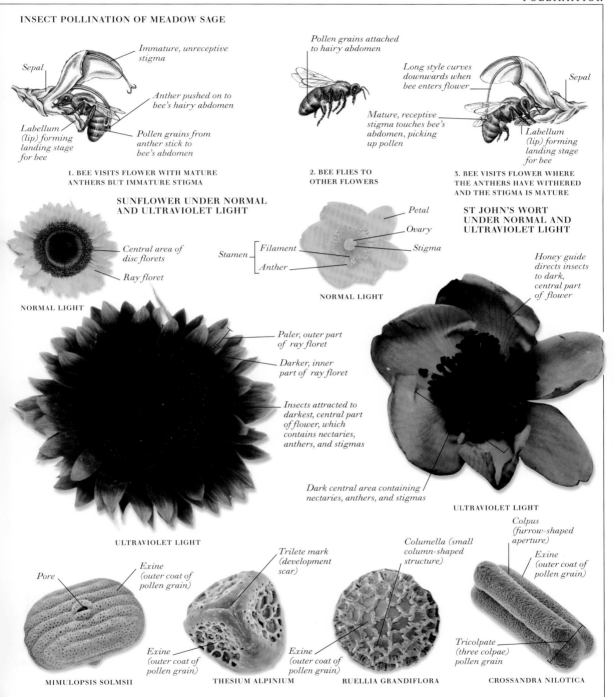

INSECT POLLINATION OF MEADOW SAGE

Sepal

Immature, unreceptive stigma

Anther pushed on to bee's hairy abdomen

Labellum (lip) forming landing stage for bee

Pollen grains from anther stick to bee's abdomen

1. BEE VISITS FLOWER WITH MATURE ANTHERS BUT IMMATURE STIGMA

Pollen grains attached to hairy abdomen

2. BEE FLIES TO OTHER FLOWERS

Long style curves downwards when bee enters flower

Sepal

Mature, receptive stigma touches bee's abdomen, picking up pollen

Labellum (lip) forming landing stage for bee

3. BEE VISITS FLOWER WHERE THE ANTHERS HAVE WITHERED AND THE STIGMA IS MATURE

SUNFLOWER UNDER NORMAL AND ULTRAVIOLET LIGHT

Central area of disc florets

Ray floret

NORMAL LIGHT

Paler, outer part of ray floret

Darker, inner part of ray floret

Insects attracted to darkest, central part of flower, which contains nectaries, anthers, and stigmas

ULTRAVIOLET LIGHT

Petal

Ovary

Stigma

Stamen [Filament / Anther]

NORMAL LIGHT

ST JOHN'S WORT UNDER NORMAL AND ULTRAVIOLET LIGHT

Honey guide directs insects to dark, central part of flower

Dark central area containing nectaries, anthers, and stigmas

ULTRAVIOLET LIGHT

Pore

Exine (outer coat of pollen grain)

Exine (outer coat of pollen grain)

MIMULOPSIS SOLMSII

Trilete mark (development scar)

Exine (outer coat of pollen grain)

THESIUM ALPINIUM

Columella (small column-shaped structure)

Exine (outer coat of pollen grain)

RUELLIA GRANDIFLORA

Colpus (furrow-shaped aperture)

Exine (outer coat of pollen grain)

Tricolpate (three colpae) pollen grain

CROSSANDRA NILOTICA

Fertilization

FERTILIZATION IS THE FUSION of male and female gametes (sex cells) to produce a zygote (embryo). Following pollination (see pp. 144-145), the pollen grains that contain the male gametes are on the stigma, some distance from the female gamete (ovum) inside the ovule. To enable the gametes to meet, the pollen grain germinates and produces a pollen tube, which grows down and enters the embryo sac (the inner part of the ovule that contains the ovum). Two male gametes, travelling at the tip of the pollen tube, enter the embryo sac. One gamete fuses with the ovum to produce a zygote that will develop into an embryo plant. The other male gamete fuses with two polar nuclei to produce the endosperm, which acts as a food store for the developing embryo. Fertilization also initiates other changes: the integument (outer part of ovule) forms a testa (seed coat) around the embryo and endosperm; the petals fall off; the stigma and style wither; and the ovary wall forms a layer (called the pericarp) around the seed. Together, the pericarp and seed form the fruit, which may be succulent (see pp. 148-149) or dry (see pp. 150-151). In some species (e.g., blackberry), apomixis can occur: the seed develops without fertilization of the ovum by a male gamete but endosperm formation and fruit development take place as in other species.

BANANA
(*Musa 'lacatan'*)

DEVELOPMENT OF A SUCCULENT FRUIT
Blackberry
(*Rubus fruticosus*)

Petal

Stamen
- Filament
- Anther

Carpel
- Ovary
- Stigma
- Style

**1. FLOWER IN FULL BLOOM
ATTRACTS POLLINATORS**

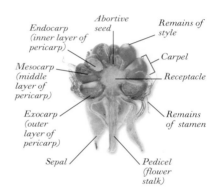

Endocarp
(inner layer of
pericarp)

Abortive
seed

Remains of
style

Mesocarp
(middle
layer of
pericarp)

Carpel

Receptacle

Exocarp
(outer
layer of
pericarp)

Remains
of stamen

Sepal

Pedicel
(flower
stalk)

**4. PERICARP FORMS
FLESH, SKIN, AND A HARD INNER
LAYER (SHOWN IN CROSS-SECTION)**

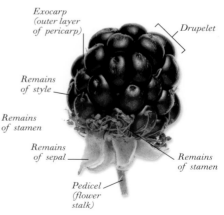

Exocarp
(outer layer of
pericarp)

Carpel

Remains
of style

Remains
of stamen

Remains
of sepal

Pedicel
(flower
stalk)

**7. MESOCARP (FLESHY PART OF PERICARP)
OF EACH CARPEL STARTS TO
CHANGE COLOUR**

Exocarp
(outer layer of
pericarp)

Drupelet

Remains
of style

Remains
of stamen

Remains
of sepal

Pedicel
(flower
stalk)

**8. CARPELS MATURE INTO DRUPELETS
(SMALL FLESHY FRUITS WITH SINGLE SEEDS
SURROUNDED BY HARD ENDOCARP)**

Exocarp
(outer layer
of pericarp)

Drupelet

Remains
of style

Remains
of sepal

Remains
of stamen

Pedicel
(flower
stalk)

**9. MESOCARP OF DRUPELET BECOMES
DARKER AND SWEETER**

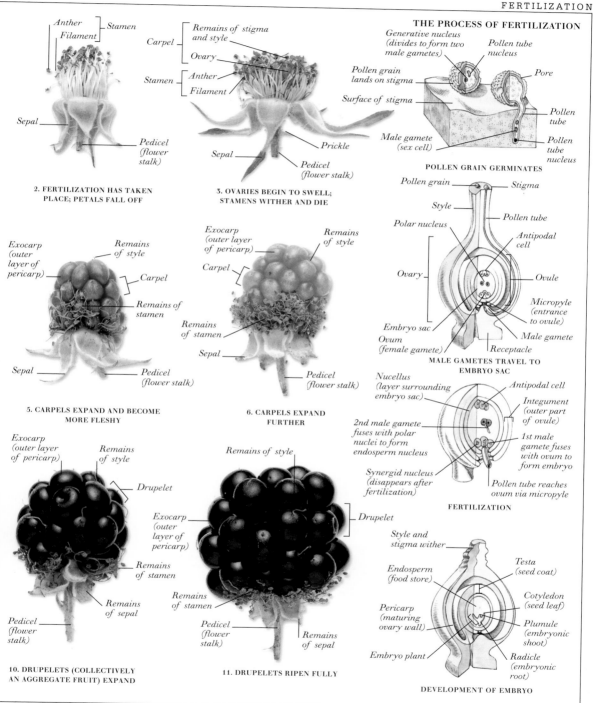

Anther
Filament] **Stamen**

Sepal

Pedicel *(flower stalk)*

2. FERTILIZATION HAS TAKEN PLACE; PETALS FALL OFF

Carpel
Remains of stigma and style
Ovary
Stamen [**Anther**
Filament
Sepal
Prickle
Pedicel *(flower stalk)*

3. OVARIES BEGIN TO SWELL; STAMENS WITHER AND DIE

THE PROCESS OF FERTILIZATION

Generative nucleus *(divides to form two male gametes)*
Pollen tube nucleus
Pollen grain lands on stigma
Pore
Surface of stigma
Pollen tube
Male gamete *(sex cell)*
Pollen tube nucleus

POLLEN GRAIN GERMINATES

Exocarp *(outer layer of pericarp)*
Remains of style
Carpel
Remains of stamen
Sepal
Pedicel *(flower stalk)*

5. CARPELS EXPAND AND BECOME MORE FLESHY

Exocarp *(outer layer of pericarp)*
Remains of style
Carpel
Remains of stamen
Sepal
Pedicel *(flower stalk)*

6. CARPELS EXPAND FURTHER

Pollen grain
Stigma
Style
Polar nucleus
Pollen tube
Antipodal cell
Ovary
Ovule
Micropyle *(entrance to ovule)*
Embryo sac
Male gamete
Ovum *(female gamete)*
Receptacle

MALE GAMETES TRAVEL TO EMBRYO SAC

Exocarp *(outer layer of pericarp)*
Remains of style
Drupelet
Exocarp *(outer layer of pericarp)*
Remains of stamen
Remains of sepal
Pedicel *(flower stalk)*

10. DRUPELETS (COLLECTIVELY AN AGGREGATE FRUIT) EXPAND

Remains of style
Drupelet
Remains of stamen
Pedicel *(flower stalk)*
Remains of sepal

11. DRUPELETS RIPEN FULLY

Nucellus *(layer surrounding embryo sac)*
Antipodal cell
Integument *(outer part of ovule)*
2nd male gamete fuses with polar nuclei to form endosperm nucleus
1st male gamete fuses with ovum to form embryo
Synergid nucleus *(disappears after fertilization)*
Pollen tube reaches ovum via micropyle

FERTILIZATION

Style and stigma wither
Testa *(seed coat)*
Endosperm *(food store)*
Cotyledon *(seed leaf)*
Pericarp *(maturing ovary wall)*
Plumule *(embryonic shoot)*
Embryo plant
Radicle *(embryonic root)*

DEVELOPMENT OF EMBRYO

Succulent fruits

A FRUIT IS A FULLY DEVELOPED and ripened ovary (seed-producing part of a plant's female reproductive organs). Fruits may be succulent or dry (see pp. 150-151). Succulent fruits are fleshy and brightly coloured, making them attractive to animals, which eat them and so disperse the seeds away from the parent plant. The wall (pericarp) of a succulent fruit has three layers: an outer exocarp, a middle mesocarp, and an inner endocarp. These three layers vary in thickness and texture in different types of fruits and may blend into each other. Succulent fruits can be classed as simple (derived from one ovary) or compound (derived from several ovaries). Simple succulent fruits include berries, which typically have many seeds, and drupes, which typically have a single stone or pip (e.g., cherry and peach). Compound succulent fruits include aggregate fruits, which are formed from many ovaries in one flower, and multiple fruits, which develop from the ovaries of many flowers. Some fruits, known as false fruits or pseudocarps, develop from parts of the flower in addition to the ovaries. For example, the flesh of the apple is formed from the receptacle (the upper end of the flower stalk).

BERRY
Cocoa
(*Theobroma cacao*)

HESPERIDIUM (A TYPE OF BERRY)
Lemon
(*Citrus limon*)

Pedicel
(flower
stalk)

Leathery
exocarp

Remains
of style

Endocarp

Mesocarp

Oil
gland

Remains
of style

Pedicel
(flower stalk)

Exocarp

Seed

Vesicle
(juice
sac)

Placenta

**EXTERNAL VIEW
OF FRUIT**

**LONGITUDINAL SECTION
THROUGH FRUIT**

Hilum
(point of
attachment
to ovary)

Testa
(seed
coat)

Embryo

Cotyledon
(seed leaf)

Seed

Carpel
wall

Carpel

Placenta

**EXTERNAL VIEW AND
SECTION THROUGH SEED**

**CROSS-SECTION
THROUGH FRUIT**

SYCONIUM (A TYPE OF FALSE FRUIT)
Fig
(*Ficus carica*)

Peduncle
(inflorescence
stalk)

Skin

Remains
of female
flowers

Pip (seed
surrounded
by endocarp)

Pore closed
by scales

Fleshy infolded
receptacle

Rer
of
flo

Ren
of r
flou

**EXTERNAL VIEW
OF FRUIT**

**LONGITUDINAL SECTION
THROUGH FRUIT**

FRUIT WITH FLESHY ARIL
Lychee
(*Litchi chinensis*)

Pedicel
(flower stalk)

Pericarp
(fruit wall)

Pedicel
(flower stalk)

Seed

Aril (fleshy
outgrowth
from seed
stalk)

Pericarp
(fruit wall)

**EXTERNAL VIEW
OF FRUIT**

**LONGITUDINAL SECTION
THROUGH FRUIT**

Remains
of style

Drupelet

Pedicel
(flower
stalk)

Endocarp

Pip

Endocarp

Embryo

**EXTERNAL VIEW AN►
SECTION THROUGH I**

Cotyledon
(seed leaf)

Testa
(seed coat)

**REMAINS OF A SINGLE
FEMALE FLOWER**

BERRY
Cape gooseberry
(*Physalis peruviana*)

Calyx (whorl of sepals)

Calyx (whorl of sepals) surrounding berry

Pedicel (flower stalk)

Pedicel (flower stalk)

Exocarp of berry

EXTERNAL VIEW OF FRUIT

INTERNAL VIEW OF FRUIT

Seed

Placenta

Pericarp

Testa (seed coat)

CROSS-SECTION THROUGH FRUIT

EXTERNAL VIEW OF SEED

AGGREGATE FRUIT
Raspberry
(*Rubus idaeus*)

Remains of stamen

Drupelet

Remains of style

Pedicel (flower stalk)

Mesocarp and exocarp

Pip (seed surrounded by endocarp)

Receptacle

Drupelet

EXTERNAL VIEW OF FRUIT

LONGITUDINAL SECTION THROUGH FRUIT

Hard endocarp

Hard endocarp

Cotyledon (seed leaf)

Pip

Testa (seed coat)

Seed

EXTERNAL VIEW AND SECTION THROUGH PIP

POME (A TYPE OF FALSE FRUIT)
Apple
(*Malus sylvestris*)

Pedicel (flower stalk)

seed

Mesocarp and exocarp

Swollen receptacle

Waxy skin

Endocarp

Vascular strand

EXTERNAL VIEW OF FRUIT

CROSS-SECTION THROUGH FRUIT

Hilum (point of attachment to ovary)

Testa (seed coat)

Embryo

Cotyledon (seed leaf)

Testa (seed coat)

EXTERNAL VIEW AND SECTION THROUGH SEED

PEPO (A TYPE OF BERRY)
Charentais melon
(*Cucumis melo*)

Pedicel (flower stalk)

Rind (fused receptacle and exocarp)

Seed

Rind (fused receptacle and exocarp)

Mesocarp and endocarp

EXTERNAL VIEW OF FRUIT

CROSS-SECTION THROUGH FRUIT

Testa (seed coat)

Embryo

Testa (seed coat)

Cotyledon (seed leaf)

EXTERNAL VIEW AND SECTION THROUGH SEED

Dry fruits

DRY FRUITS HAVE A HARD, DRY PERICARP (fruit wall)
around their seeds unlike succulent fruits, which have fleshy
pericarps (see pp. 148-149). Dry fruits are divided into three types:
dehiscent, in which the pericarp splits open to
release the seeds; indehiscent, which do not split
open; and schizocarpic, in which the fruit splits
but the seeds are not exposed. Dehiscent dry
fruits include capsules (e.g., love-in-a-mist),
follicles (e.g., delphinium), legumes (e.g., pea),
and siliquas (e.g., honesty). Typically, the
seeds of dehiscent fruits are dispersed by
the wind. Indehiscent dry fruits include nuts
(e.g., sweet chestnut), nutlets (e.g., goosegrass),
achenes (e.g., strawberry), caryopses
(e.g., wheat), samaras (e.g., elm), and cypselas (e.g., dandelion).
Some indehiscent dry fruits are dispersed by the wind, assisted
by "wings" (e.g., elm) or "parachutes" (e.g., dandelion); others
(e.g., goosegrass) have hooked pericarps to aid dispersal on
animals' fur. Schizocarpic dry fruits include cremocarps
(e.g., hogweed), and double samaras (e.g., sycamore);
these are dispersed by the wind.

NUTLET
Goosegrass
(*Galium aparine*)

NUT
Sweet chestnut
(*Castanea sativa*)

Peduncle (inflorescence stalk)

Line of splitting between valves of cupule

Remains of male inflorescence

Nut (indehiscent fruit)

Spiky cupule (husk around fruit formed from bracts)

EXTERNAL VIEW OF FRUIT WITH SURROUNDING CUPULE

Remains of stigma

Remains of stigma

Remains of style

Remains of style

Nut (indehiscent fruit)

Embryo

Cotyledon (seed leaf)

Testa (seed coat)

Woody pericarp (fruit wall)

Woody pericarp (fruit wall)

EXTERNAL VIEW AND SECTION THROUGH FRUIT

LEGUME
Pea
(*Pisum sativum*)

Pedicel (flower stalk)

Pedicel (flower stalk)

Receptacle

Remains of sepal

Receptacle

Remains of sepal

Remains of stamen

Funicle (stalk attaching seed to placenta)

Placenta

Pericarp (fruit wall)

Pericarp (fruit wall)

Seed

Remains of style and stigma

Remains of style and stigma

EXTERNAL VIEW OF FRUIT

INTERNAL VIEW OF FRUIT

Funicle (stalk attaching seed to placenta)

Cotyledon (seed leaf)

Radicle (embryonic root)

Micropyle (pore for water absorption)

Testa (seed coat)

Plumule (embryonic shoot)

Testa (seed coat)

EXTERIOR VIEW AND SECTION THROUGH SEED

ACHENE
Strawberry
(*Fragaria* x *ananassa*)

Pedicel (flower stalk)

Sepal

Sepal

Pedicel (flower stalk)

Swollen receptacle

Remains of stigma and style

Achene (one-seeded dry fruit)

Swollen fleshy tissues of receptacle

EXTERNAL VIEW OF FRUIT

LONGITUDINAL SECTION THROUGH FRUIT

Pericarp (fruit wall)

Pericarp (fruit wall)

Cotyledon (seed leaf)

Testa (seed coat)

EXTERNAL VIEW AND SECTION THROUGH SEED

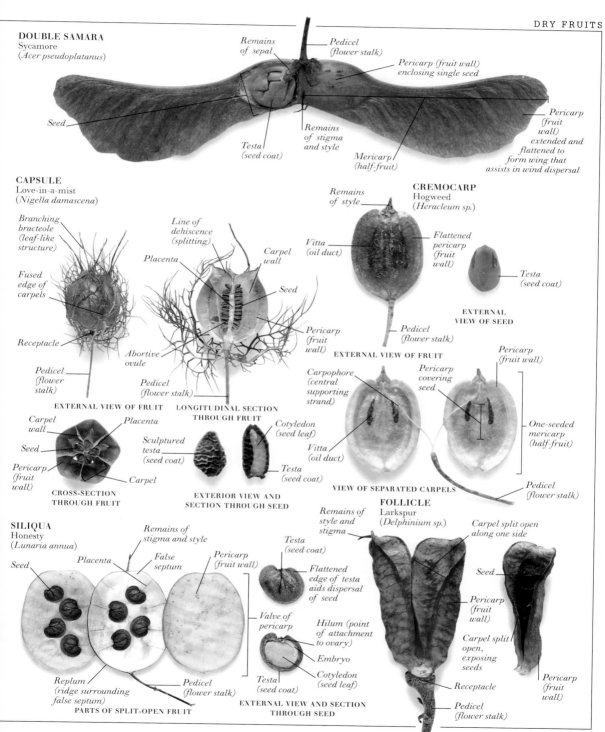

DOUBLE SAMARA
Sycamore
(*Acer pseudoplatanus*)

Remains of sepal

Pedicel (flower stalk)

Pericarp (fruit wall) enclosing single seed

Seed

Remains of stigma and style

Testa (seed coat)

Mericarp (half-fruit)

Pericarp (fruit wall) extended and flattened to form wing that assists in wind dispersal

CAPSULE
Love-in-a-mist
(*Nigella damascena*)

Branching bracteole (leaf-like structure)

Line of dehiscence (splitting)

Placenta

Carpel wall

Fused edge of carpels

Seed

Receptacle

Pericarp (fruit wall)

Pedicel (flower stalk)

Abortive ovule

Pedicel (flower stalk)

EXTERNAL VIEW OF FRUIT

LONGITUDINAL SECTION THROUGH FRUIT

CREMOCARP
Hogweed
(*Heracleum sp.*)

Remains of style

Vitta (oil duct)

Flattened pericarp (fruit wall)

Testa (seed coat)

Pedicel (flower stalk)

EXTERNAL VIEW OF SEED

EXTERNAL VIEW OF FRUIT

Carpel wall

Placenta

Seed

Pericarp (fruit wall)

Carpel

CROSS-SECTION THROUGH FRUIT

Sculptured testa (seed coat)

Cotyledon (seed leaf)

Testa (seed coat)

EXTERIOR VIEW AND SECTION THROUGH SEED

Carpophore (central supporting strand)

Pericarp covering seed

Pericarp (fruit wall)

Vitta (oil duct)

One-seeded mericarp (half-fruit)

Pedicel (flower stalk)

VIEW OF SEPARATED CARPELS

SILIQUA
Honesty
(*Lunaria annua*)

Remains of stigma and style

False septum

Pericarp (fruit wall)

Seed

Placenta

FOLLICLE
Larkspur
(*Delphinium sp.*)

Remains of style and stigma

Testa (seed coat)

Carpel split open along one side

Flattened edge of testa aids dispersal of seed

Seed

Valve of pericarp

Hilum (point of attachment to ovary)

Pericarp (fruit wall)

Embryo

Carpel split open, exposing seeds

Replum (ridge surrounding false septum)

Pedicel (flower stalk)

Testa (seed coat)

Cotyledon (seed leaf)

Receptacle

Pericarp (fruit wall)

PARTS OF SPLIT-OPEN FRUIT

EXTERNAL VIEW AND SECTION THROUGH SEED

Pedicel (flower stalk)

151

Germination

GERMINATION IS THE GROWTH OF SEEDS INTO SEEDLINGS. It starts when seeds become active below ground, and ends when the first foliage leaves appear above ground. A seed consists of an embryo and its food store, surrounded by a testa (seed coat). The embryo is made up of one or two cotyledons (seed leaves) attached to a central axis. The upper part of the axis consists of an epicotyl, which has a plumule (embryonic shoot) at its tip. The lower part of the axis consists of a hypocotyl and a radicle (embryonic root). After dispersal from the parent plant, the seeds dehydrate and enter a period of dormancy. Following this dormant period, germination begins, provided that the seeds have enough water, oxygen, warmth, and, in some cases, light. In the first stages of germination, the seed takes in water; the embryo starts to use its food store; and the radicle swells, breaks through the testa, and grows downwards. Germination then proceeds in one of two ways, depending on the type of seed. In epigeal germination, the hypocotyl lengthens, pulling the plumule and its protective cotyledons out of the soil. In hypogeal germination, the cotyledons remain below ground and the epicotyl lengthens, pushing the plumule upwards.

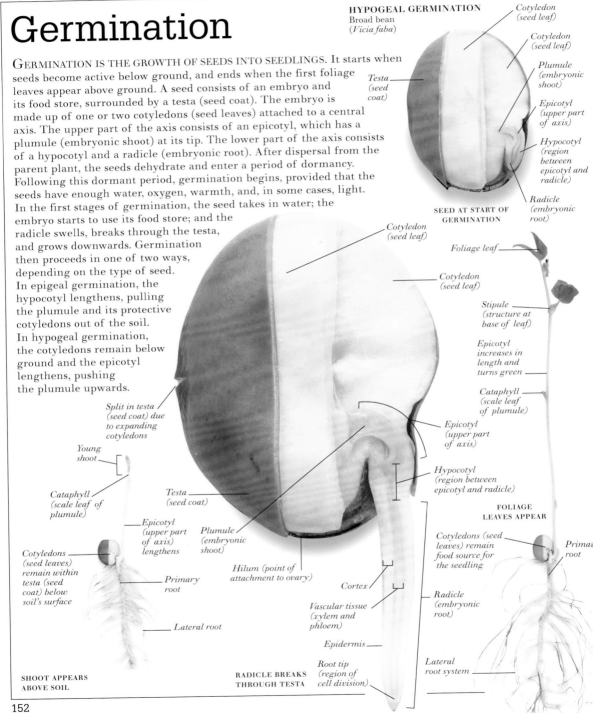

HYPOGEAL GERMINATION
Broad bean
(*Vicia faba*)

Cotyledon (seed leaf)

Cotyledon (seed leaf)

Plumule (embryonic shoot)

Epicotyl (upper part of axis)

Testa (seed coat)

Hypocotyl (region between epicotyl and radicle)

Radicle (embryonic root)

SEED AT START OF GERMINATION

Cotyledon (seed leaf)

Foliage leaf

Cotyledon (seed leaf)

Stipule (structure at base of leaf)

Epicotyl increases in length and turns green

Cataphyll (scale leaf of plumule)

Epicotyl (upper part of axis)

Hypocotyl (region between epicotyl and radicle)

FOLIAGE LEAVES APPEAR

Cotyledons (seed leaves) remain food source for the seedling

Prima[...] root

Radicle (embryonic root)

Lateral root system

Split in testa (seed coat) due to expanding cotyledons

Young shoot

Cataphyll (scale leaf of plumule)

Testa (seed coat)

Epicotyl (upper part of axis) lengthens

Cotyledons (seed leaves) remain within testa (seed coat) below soil's surface

Plumule (embryonic shoot)

Primary root

Hilum (point of attachment to ovary)

Cortex

Vascular tissue (xylem and phloem)

Epidermis

Lateral root

Root tip (region of cell division)

SHOOT APPEARS ABOVE SOIL

RADICLE BREAKS THROUGH TESTA

EPIGEAL GERMINATION
Black bean
(*Phaseolus* sp.)

Testa
(seed coat)

Raphe
(ridge)

Hilum (point
of attachment
to ovary)

Micropyle
(pore for
water
absorption)

EXTERNAL VIEW OF SEED AT
START OF GERMINATION

Epicotyl
(upper part
of axis)

Plumule
(embryonic
shoot)

Hypocotyl
(region between
epicotyl and
radicle)

Radicle
(embryonic
root)

Hilum
(point of
attachment
to ovary)

Testa
(seed coat)

Cotyledon
(seed leaf)

LONGITUDINAL SECTION
THROUGH SEED AT START OF
GERMINATION

Epicotyl
(upper part
of axis)

Testa
(seed coat)

Plumule
(embryonic
shoot)

Cotyledon
(seed leaf)

Hypocotyl
(region between
epicotyl and radicle)

First foliage
leaf fully
grown

Petiole
(leaf stalk)

Growing
point

Cotyledon (seed
leaf) withers

Lateral root

Primary root
(elongated
radicle)

First foliage leaf
protected by cotyledons
(seed leaves)

Cotyledon
(seed leaf)

Testa
(seed
coat)
splits

Hypocotyl
"hook" pushes
out of soil

Hypocotyl (region
between epicotyl and
radicle) elongates

Hypocotyl (region
between epicotyl
and radicle)
straightens
and lengthens

RADICLE BREAKS THROUGH
TESTA AND LENGTHENS

Testa (seed
coat) shed

Lateral
root

Testa (seed
coat) begins to
disintegrate

Root

Root

Primary
root

HYPOCOTYL
"HOOK" APPEARS
ABOVE SOIL

HYPOCOTYL
STRAIGHTENS,
PULLING LEAVES
AND COTYLEDONS
OUT OF SOIL

FIRST FOLIAGE
LEAVES FULLY
DEVELOPED

Root cap
(protective
covering for
root tip)

153

Vegetative reproduction

CORM
Gladiolus
(*Gladiolus sp.*)

MANY PLANTS CAN PROPAGATE THEMSELVES by vegetative reproduction. In this process, part of a plant separates off, takes root, and grows into a new plant. Vegetative reproduction is a type of asexual reproduction; that is, it involves only one parent, and there is no fusion of gametes (sex cells). Plants use various structures to reproduce vegetatively. Some plants use underground storage organs. Such organs include rhizomes (horizontal, underground stems), the branches of which produce new plants; bulbs (swollen leaf bases) and corms (swollen stems), which produce daughter bulbs or corms that separate off from the parent; and stem tubers (thickened underground stems) and root tubers (swollen adventitious roots), which also separate off from the parent. Other propagative structures include runners and stolons, creeping horizontal stems that take root and produce new plants; bulbils, small bulbs that develop on the stem or in the place of flowers, and then drop off and grow into new plants; and adventitious buds, miniature plants that form on leaf margins before dropping to the ground and growing into mature plants.

ADVENTITIOUS BUD
Mexican hat plant
(*Kalanchoe daigremontiana*)

Apex of leaf

Lamina (blade) of leaf

Leaf margin

Notch in leaf margin containing meristematic (actively dividing) cells

Adventitious bud (detachable bud with adventitious roots) drops from leaf

Petiole (leaf stalk)

BULBIL IN PLACE OF FLOWER
Orange lily
(*Lilium bulbiferum*)

Scar left by flower

Leaf

Pedicel (flower stalk)

Terminal bud

Detachable bulbil formed in place of flower

Peduncle (inflorescence stalk)

STOLON
Ground ivy
(*Glechoma hederacea*)

Internode

Parent plant

Node

Stolon (creeping stem)

Node

Adventitious root of daughter plant

Daughter plant developed from lateral bud

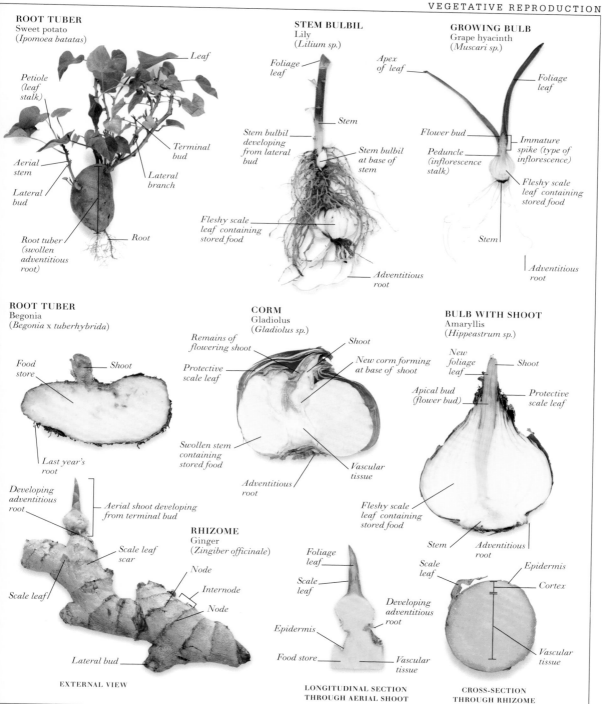

ROOT TUBER
Sweet potato
(*Ipomoea batatas*)

Leaf

Petiole
(leaf
stalk)

Terminal
bud

Aerial
stem

Lateral
branch

Lateral
bud

Root tuber
(swollen
adventitious
root)

Root

STEM BULBIL
Lily
(*Lilium sp.*)

Foliage
leaf

Stem

Stem bulbil
developing
from lateral
bud

Stem bulbil
at base of
stem

Fleshy scale
leaf containing
stored food

Adventitious
root

GROWING BULB
Grape hyacinth
(*Muscari sp.*)

Apex
of leaf

Foliage
leaf

Flower bud

Immature
spike (type of
inflorescence)

Peduncle
(inflorescence
stalk)

Fleshy scale
leaf containing
stored food

Stem

Adventitious
root

ROOT TUBER
Begonia
(*Begonia* x *tuberhybrida*)

Food
store

Shoot

Last year's
root

Developing
adventitious
root

Aerial shoot developing
from terminal bud

Scale leaf
scar

Node

Internode

Node

Scale leaf

Lateral bud

EXTERNAL VIEW

RHIZOME
Ginger
(*Zingiber officinale*)

CORM
Gladiolus
(*Gladiolus sp.*)

Remains of
flowering shoot

Shoot

Protective
scale leaf

New corm forming
at base of shoot

Swollen stem
containing
stored food

Adventitious
root

Vascular
tissue

Foliage
leaf

Scale
leaf

Developing
adventitious
root

Epidermis

Food store

Vascular
tissue

LONGITUDINAL SECTION
THROUGH AERIAL SHOOT

BULB WITH SHOOT
Amaryllis
(*Hippeastrum sp.*)

New
foliage
leaf

Shoot

Apical bud
(flower bud)

Protective
scale leaf

Fleshy scale
leaf containing
stored food

Stem

Adventitious
root

Scale
leaf

Epidermis

Cortex

Vascular
tissue

CROSS-SECTION
THROUGH RHIZOME

Dryland plants

DRYLAND PLANTS (XEROPHYTES) are able to survive in unfavourable habitats. All are found in places where little water is available; some live in high temperatures that cause excessive loss of water from the leaves. Xerophytes show a number of adaptations to dry conditions; these include reduced leaf area, rolled leaves, sunken stomata, hairs, spines, and thick cuticles. One group, succulent plants, stores water in specially enlarged spongy tissues found in leaves, roots, or stems. Leaf succulents have enlarged, fleshy, water-storing leaves. Root succulents have a large, underground water-storage organ with short-lived stems and leaves above ground. Stem succulents are represented by the cacti (family Cactaceae). Cacti stems are fleshy, green, and photosynthetic; they are typically ribbed or covered by tubercles in rows, with leaves being reduced to spines or entirely absent.

LEAF
SUCCULENT
Lithops sp.

*Areole
(modified
lateral shoot)*

*Trichome
(hair)*

*Spine
(modified
leaf)*

*Waxy cuticle
(waterproof
covering)*

*Water-storing
parenchyma
(packing tissue)*

*Tubercle
(projection
from stem
surface)*

*Vascular
cylinder
(transport
tissue)*

*Spine
(modified
leaf)*

*Sinuous
(wavy)
cell wall*

*Tubercle
(projection
from stem
surface)*

Root

*Stoma (pore)
controlling
exchange of
gases*

EXTERNAL VIEW

MICROGRAPH OF STEM SURFACE

*Spine
(modified
leaf)*

Root

*Areole
(modified
lateral shoot)*

*Tubercle
(projection from
stem surface)*

*Waxy cuticle
(waterproof
covering)*

DETAIL OF STEM SURFACE

**LONGITUDINAL SECTION
THROUGH STEM**

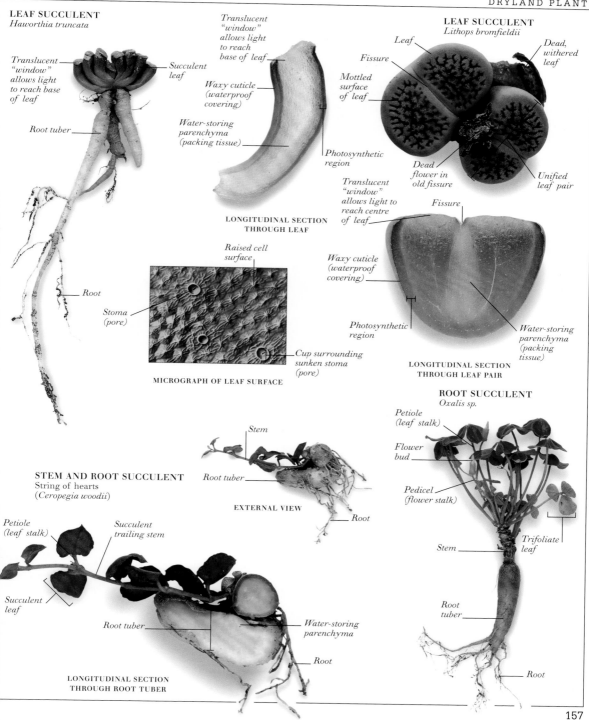

LEAF SUCCULENT
Haworthia truncata

Translucent "window" allows light to reach base of leaf

Succulent leaf

Root tuber

Root

Translucent "window" allows light to reach base of leaf

Waxy cuticle (waterproof covering)

Water-storing parenchyma (packing tissue)

Photosynthetic region

LONGITUDINAL SECTION THROUGH LEAF

Raised cell surface

Stoma (pore)

Cup surrounding sunken stoma (pore)

MICROGRAPH OF LEAF SURFACE

LEAF SUCCULENT
Lithops bromfieldii

Leaf

Fissure

Mottled surface of leaf

Dead, withered leaf

Dead flower in old fissure

Unified leaf pair

Translucent "window" allows light to reach centre of leaf

Fissure

Waxy cuticle (waterproof covering)

Photosynthetic region

Water-storing parenchyma (packing tissue)

LONGITUDINAL SECTION THROUGH LEAF PAIR

ROOT SUCCULENT
Oxalis sp.

Petiole (leaf stalk)

Flower bud

Pedicel (flower stalk)

Stem

Root tuber

Trifoliate leaf

Root

STEM AND ROOT SUCCULENT
String of hearts
(*Ceropegia woodii*)

Stem

Root tuber

Root

EXTERNAL VIEW

Petiole (leaf stalk)

Succulent trailing stem

Succulent leaf

Root tuber

Water-storing parenchyma

Root

LONGITUDINAL SECTION THROUGH ROOT TUBER

157

Wetland plants

WETLAND PLANTS GROW SUBMERGED IN WATER, either partially (e.g., water hyacinth) or completely (e.g., pond weeds), and show various adaptations to this habitat. Typically, there are numerous air spaces inside the stems, leaves, and roots; these aid gas exchange and buoyancy. Submerged parts generally have no cuticle (waterproof covering), enabling the plants to absorb minerals and gases directly from the water; in addition, being supported by the water, they need little of the supportive tissue found in land plants. Stomata, the gas exchange pores, are absent from plants that are completely submerged; in partially submerged plants with floating leaves (e.g., water lilies), stomata are found on the upper leaf surfaces, where they cannot be flooded.

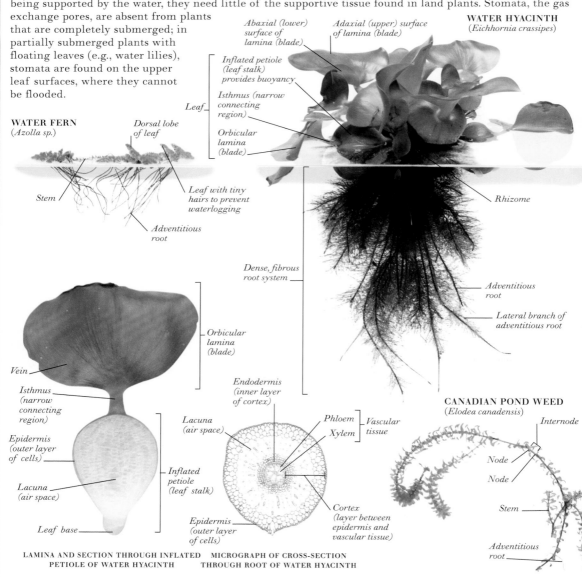

WATER FERN
(*Azolla sp.*)

Dorsal lobe of leaf

Stem

Leaf with tiny hairs to prevent waterlogging

Adventitious root

Abaxial (lower) surface of lamina (blade)

Adaxial (upper) surface of lamina (blade)

WATER HYACINTH
(*Eichhornia crassipes*)

Inflated petiole (leaf stalk) provides buoyancy

Isthmus (narrow connecting region)

Leaf

Orbicular lamina (blade)

Rhizome

Dense, fibrous root system

Adventitious root

Lateral branch of adventitious root

Orbicular lamina (blade)

Vein

Isthmus (narrow connecting region)

Epidermis (outer layer of cells)

Lacuna (air space)

Leaf base

Inflated petiole (leaf stalk)

Endodermis (inner layer of cortex)

Lacuna (air space)

Phloem | Vascular
Xylem | tissue

Epidermis (outer layer of cells)

Cortex (layer between epidermis and vascular tissue)

CANADIAN POND WEED
(*Elodea canadensis*)

Internode

Node

Node

Stem

Adventitious root

LAMINA AND SECTION THROUGH INFLATED PETIOLE OF WATER HYACINTH

MICROGRAPH OF CROSS-SECTION THROUGH ROOT OF WATER HYACINTH

WATER LILY
(*Nymphaea sp.*)

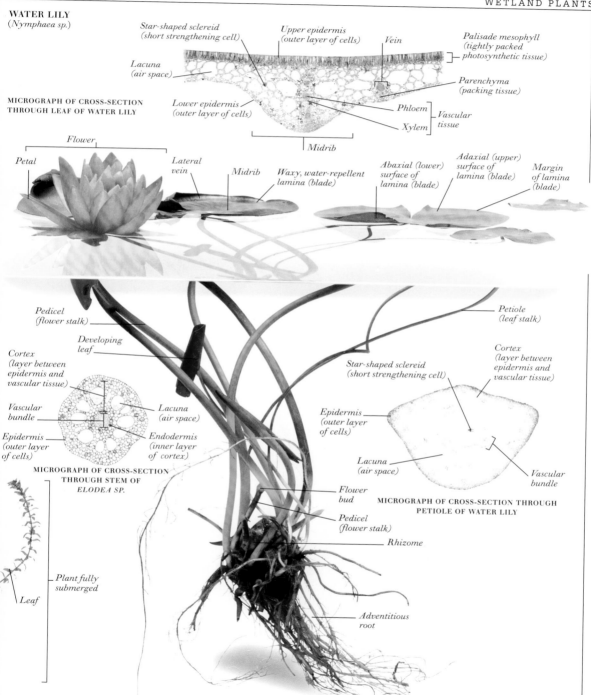

Star-shaped sclereid
(short strengthening cell)

Upper epidermis
(outer layer of cells)

Vein

Palisade mesophyll
(tightly packed
photosynthetic tissue)

Lacuna
(air space)

**MICROGRAPH OF CROSS-SECTION
THROUGH LEAF OF WATER LILY**

Lower epidermis
(outer layer of cells)

Parenchyma
(packing tissue)

Phloem ⎤
            ⎬ Vascular
Xylem ⎦   tissue

Midrib

Flower

Petal

Lateral
vein

Midrib

Waxy, water-repellent
lamina (blade)

Abaxial (lower)
surface of
lamina (blade)

Adaxial (upper)
surface of
lamina (blade)

Margin
of lamina
(blade)

Pedicel
(flower stalk)

Developing
leaf

Petiole
(leaf stalk)

Cortex
(layer between
epidermis and
vascular tissue)

Lacuna
(air space)

Star-shaped sclereid
(short strengthening cell)

Cortex
(layer between
epidermis and
vascular tissue)

Vascular
bundle

Epidermis
(outer layer
of cells)

Epidermis
(outer layer
of cells)

Endodermis
(inner layer
of cortex)

Lacuna
(air space)

Vascular
bundle

**MICROGRAPH OF CROSS-SECTION
THROUGH STEM OF
ELODEA SP.**

Flower
bud

**MICROGRAPH OF CROSS-SECTION THROUGH
PETIOLE OF WATER LILY**

Pedicel
(flower stalk)

Rhizome

Plant fully
submerged

Leaf

Adventitious
root

159

Carnivorous plants

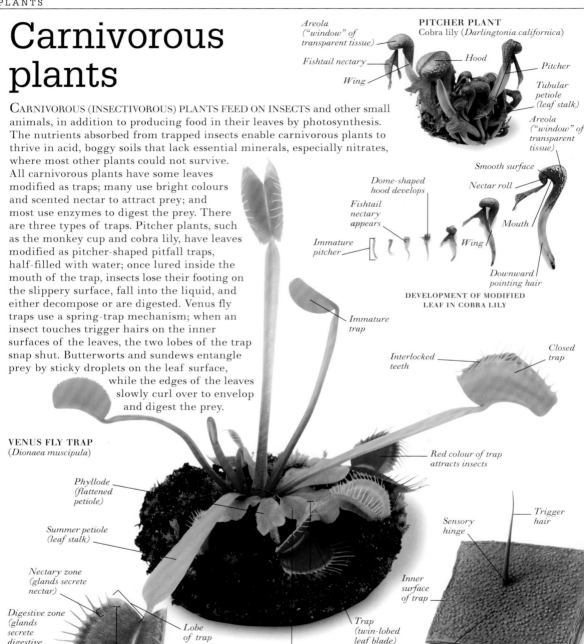

PITCHER PLANT
Cobra lily (*Darlingtonia californica*)

Areola ("window" of transparent tissue)

Fishtail nectary

Wing

Hood

Pitcher

Tubular petiole (leaf stalk)

Areola ("window" of transparent tissue)

CARNIVOROUS (INSECTIVOROUS) PLANTS FEED ON INSECTS and other small animals, in addition to producing food in their leaves by photosynthesis. The nutrients absorbed from trapped insects enable carnivorous plants to thrive in acid, boggy soils that lack essential minerals, especially nitrates, where most other plants could not survive. All carnivorous plants have some leaves modified as traps; many use bright colours and scented nectar to attract prey; and most use enzymes to digest the prey. There are three types of traps. Pitcher plants, such as the monkey cup and cobra lily, have leaves modified as pitcher-shaped pitfall traps, half-filled with water; once lured inside the mouth of the trap, insects lose their footing on the slippery surface, fall into the liquid, and either decompose or are digested. Venus fly traps use a spring-trap mechanism; when an insect touches trigger hairs on the inner surfaces of the leaves, the two lobes of the trap snap shut. Butterworts and sundews entangle prey by sticky droplets on the leaf surface, while the edges of the leaves slowly curl over to envelop and digest the prey.

Dome-shaped hood develops

Smooth surface

Nectar roll

Fishtail nectary appears

Mouth

Immature pitcher

Wing

Downward pointing hair

DEVELOPMENT OF MODIFIED LEAF IN COBRA LILY

Immature trap

Interlocked teeth

Closed trap

VENUS FLY TRAP
(*Dionaea muscipula*)

Red colour of trap attracts insects

Phyllode (flattened petiole)

Summer petiole (leaf stalk)

Nectary zone (glands secrete nectar)

Digestive zone (glands secrete digestive enzymes)

Tooth

Lobe of trap

Midrib (hinge of trap)

Trigger hair

Spring petiole (leaf stalk)

Trap (twin-lobed leaf blade)

Sensory hinge

Trigger hair

Inner surface of trap

Digestive gland

MICROGRAPH OF LOBE OF VENUS FLY TRAP

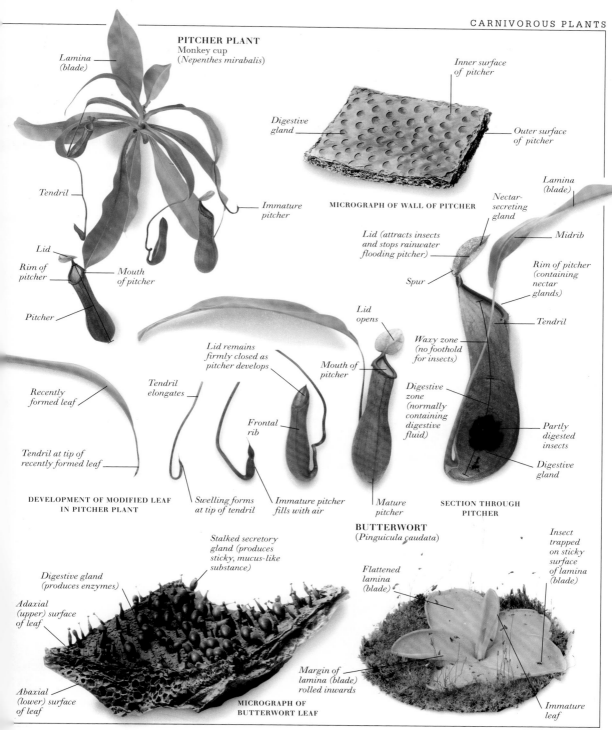

PITCHER PLANT
Monkey cup
(*Nepenthes mirabalis*)

Lamina
(blade)

Inner surface
of pitcher

Digestive
gland

Outer surface
of pitcher

MICROGRAPH OF WALL OF PITCHER

Tendril

Immature
pitcher

Lamina
(blade)

Nectar-
secreting
gland

Midrib

Lid (attracts insects
and stops rainwater
flooding pitcher)

Lid

Rim of
pitcher

Mouth
of pitcher

Spur

Rim of pitcher
(containing
nectar
glands)

Pitcher

Tendril

Lid
opens

Waxy zone
(no foothold
for insects)

Recently
formed leaf

Lid remains
firmly closed as
pitcher develops

Tendril
elongates

Mouth of
pitcher

Digestive
zone
(normally
containing
digestive
fluid)

Frontal
rib

Tendril at tip of
recently formed leaf

Partly
digested
insects

Digestive
gland

**DEVELOPMENT OF MODIFIED LEAF
IN PITCHER PLANT**

Swelling forms
at tip of tendril

Immature pitcher
fills with air

Mature
pitcher

**SECTION THROUGH
PITCHER**

BUTTERWORT
(*Pinguicula caudata*)

Stalked secretory
gland (produces
sticky, mucus-like
substance)

Insect
trapped
on sticky
surface
of lamina
(blade)

Flattened
lamina
(blade)

Digestive gland
(produces enzymes)

Adaxial
(upper) surface
of leaf

Abaxial
(lower) surface
of leaf

Margin of
lamina (blade)
rolled inwards

Immature
leaf

**MICROGRAPH OF
BUTTERWORT LEAF**

Epiphytic and parasitic plants

EPIPHYTIC AND PARASITIC PLANTS GROW ON OTHER LIVING PLANTS. Typically, epiphytic plants are not rooted in the soil; instead, they live above ground level on the stems and branches of other plants. Epiphytes obtain water from trapped rainwater and from moisture in the air, and minerals from organic matter that has accumulated on the surface of the plant on which they are growing. Like other green plants, epiphytes produce their food by photosynthesis. Epiphytes include tropical orchids and bromeliads (air plants), and some mosses that live in temperate regions. Parasitic plants obtain all their nutrient requirements from the host plants on which they grow. The parasites produce haustoria, root-like organs that penetrate the stem or roots of the host and grow inwards to merge with the host's vascular tissue, from which the parasite extracts water, minerals, and manufactured nutrients. As they have no need to produce their own food, parasitic plants lack chlorophyll, the green photosynthetic pigment, and they have no foliage leaves. Partial parasitic plants (e.g., mistletoe) obtain water and minerals from the host plant but have green leaves and stems and are therefore able to produce their own food by photosynthesis.

EPIPHYTIC ORCHID
Brassavola nodosa

Peduncle (inflorescence stalk)

Pedicel (flower stalk)

Flower

Scale leaf

Aerial root

Node

Stem

Bark of tree to which epiphyte is attached

Inflorescence (spike)

Peduncle (inflorescence stalk)

Flower bud

Strap-shaped arching leaf (part of rosette of leaves)

Leaf margin with spines

Overlapping leaf bases in which rainwater is trapped

EPIPHYTIC BROMELIAD
Aechmea miniata

Mass of adventitious roots

Stem

Bark of tree to which epiphyte is attached

Leaf

Velamen (multi-layered epidermis capable of absorbing water from rain or condensation)

Exodermis (outer layer of cortex)

Cortex (layer between epidermis and vascular tissue)

Cortex cell containing chloroplasts

Pith

Vascular tissue

Xylem

Phloem

Endodermi (inner layer of cortex)

MICROGRAPH OF CROSS-SECTION THROUGH AERIAL ROOT OF EPIPHYTIC ORCHID

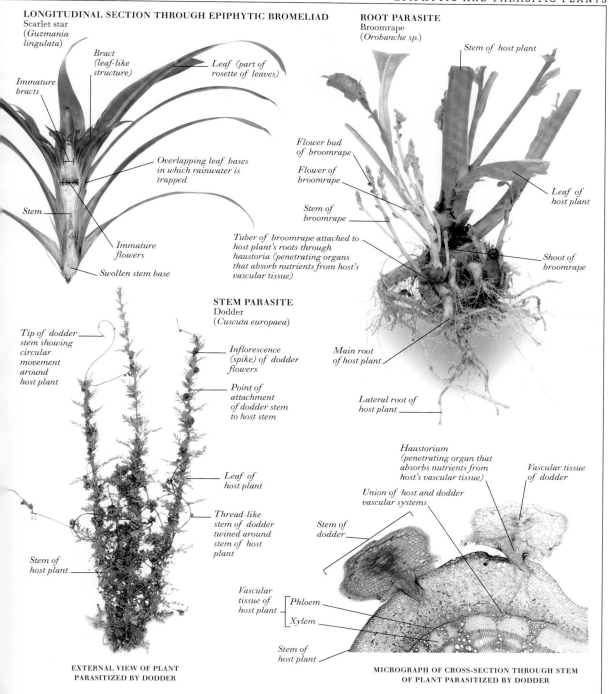

LONGITUDINAL SECTION THROUGH EPIPHYTIC BROMELIAD
Scarlet star
(*Guzmania lingulata*)

Bract
(leaf-like
structure)

Leaf (part of
rosette of leaves)

Immature
bracts

Overlapping leaf bases
in which rainwater is
trapped

Stem

Immature
flowers

Swollen stem base

ROOT PARASITE
Broomrape
(*Orobanche sp.*)

Stem of host plant

Flower bud
of broomrape

Flower of
broomrape

Stem of
broomrape

Leaf of
host plant

Shoot of
broomrape

Tuber of broomrape attached to
host plant's roots through
haustoria (penetrating organs
that absorb nutrients from host's
vascular tissue)

Main root
of host plant

Lateral root of
host plant

STEM PARASITE
Dodder
(*Cuscuta europaea*)

Tip of dodder
stem showing
circular
movement
around
host plant

Inflorescence
(spike) of dodder
flowers

Point of
attachment
of dodder stem
to host stem

Leaf of
host plant

Thread-like
stem of dodder
twined around
stem of host
plant

Stem of
host plant

Haustorium
(penetrating organ that
absorbs nutrients from
host's vascular tissue)

Vascular tissue
of dodder

Union of host and dodder
vascular systems

Stem of
dodder

Vascular
tissue of
host plant

Phloem

Xylem

Stem of
host plant

**EXTERNAL VIEW OF PLANT
PARASITIZED BY DODDER**

**MICROGRAPH OF CROSS-SECTION THROUGH STEM
OF PLANT PARASITIZED BY DODDER**

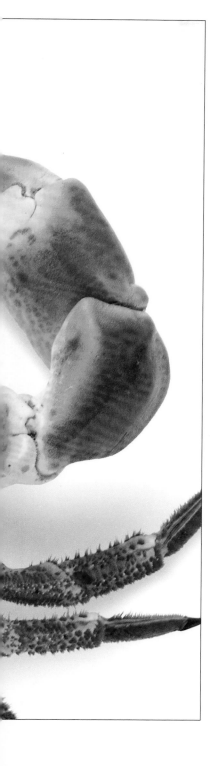

ANIMALS

SPONGES, JELLYFISH, AND SEA ANEMONES ········ 166

INSECTS ··· 168

ARACHNIDS ·· 170

CRUSTACEANS ·· 172

STARFISH AND SEA URCHINS ··························· 174

MOLLUSCS ··· 176

SHARKS AND JAWLESS FISH ···························· 178

BONY FISH ··· 180

AMPHIBIANS ·· 182

LIZARDS AND SNAKES ··································· 184

CROCODILIANS AND TURTLES ······················· 186

BIRDS 1 ·· 188

BIRDS 2 ·· 190

EGGS ··· 192

CARNIVORES ··· 194

RABBITS AND RODENTS ································ 196

UNGULATES ·· 198

ELEPHANTS ··· 200

PRIMATES ·· 202

DOPHINS, WHALES, AND SEALS ······················· 204

MARSUPIALS AND MONOTREMES ····················· 206

Sponges, jellyfish, and sea anemones

SPONGES ARE MAINLY MARINE animals that make up the phylum Porifera. They are among the simplest of all animals, having no tissues or organs. Their bodies consist of two layers of cells separated by a jelly-like layer (mesohyal) that is strengthened by mineral spicules or protein fibres. The body is perforated by a system of pores and water channels called the aquiferous system. Special cells (choanocytes) with whip-like structures (flagella) draw water through the aquiferous system, thereby bringing tiny food particles to the sponge's cells. Jellyfish (class Scyphozoa), sea anemones (class Anthozoa), and corals (also class Anthozoa) belong to the phylum Cnidaria, also known as Coelenterata. More complex than sponges, coelenterates have simple tissues, such as nervous tissue; a radially symmetrical body; and a mouth surrounded by tentacles with unique stinging cells (cnidocytes).

INTERNAL ANATOMY OF A SPONGE

Amoebocyte

Osculum (excurrent pore)

Choanocyte (collar cell)

Ostium (incurrent pore)

Porocyte (pore cell)

Mesohyal

Spongocoel (atrium; paragaster)

Spicule

Pinacocyte (epidermal cell)

Ostium (incurrent pore)

SKELETON OF A SPONGE

Protein matrix

Pore

EXTERNAL FEATURES OF A SEA ANEMONE

Tentacle

EXAMPLES OF SEA ANEMONES

PARASITIC ANEMONE
(Calliactis parasitica)

JEWEL ANEMONE
(Corynactis viridis)

PLUMOSE ANEMONE
(Metridium senile)

MEDITERRANEAN SEA ANEMONE
(Condylactis sp.)

GREEN SNAKELOCK
ANEMONE
(Anemonia viridis)

BEADLET ANEMONE
(Actinia equina)

GHOST ANEMONE
(Actinothoe
sphyrodeta)

Sagartia elegans

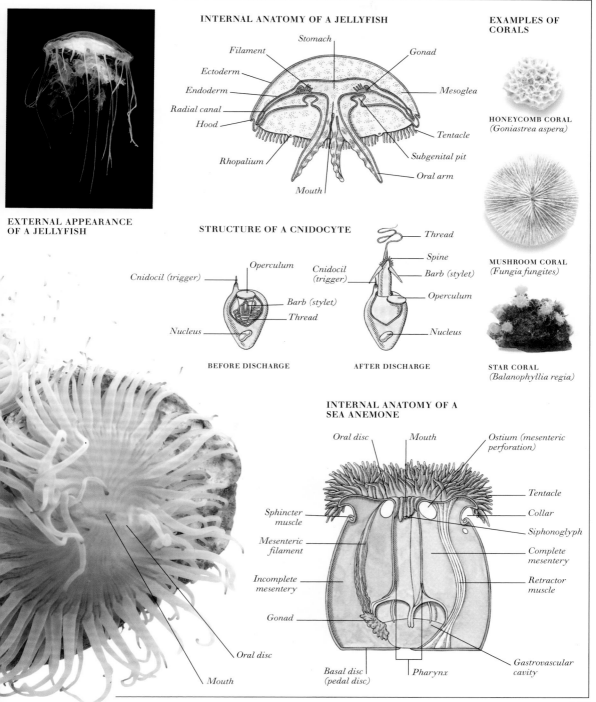

INTERNAL ANATOMY OF A JELLYFISH

Stomach

Filament

Gonad

Ectoderm

Endoderm

Mesoglea

Radial canal

Hood

Tentacle

Rhopalium

Subgenital pit

Oral arm

Mouth

EXTERNAL APPEARANCE OF A JELLYFISH

EXAMPLES OF CORALS

HONEYCOMB CORAL
(Goniastrea aspera)

MUSHROOM CORAL
(Fungia fungites)

STAR CORAL
(Balanophyllia regia)

STRUCTURE OF A CNIDOCYTE

Thread

Spine

Operculum

Cnidocil (trigger)

Cnidocil (trigger)

Barb (stylet)

Barb (stylet)

Operculum

Thread

Nucleus

Nucleus

BEFORE DISCHARGE

AFTER DISCHARGE

INTERNAL ANATOMY OF A SEA ANEMONE

Oral disc

Mouth

Ostium (mesenteric perforation)

Tentacle

Sphincter muscle

Collar

Siphonoglyph

Mesenteric filament

Complete mesentery

Incomplete mesentery

Retractor muscle

Gonad

Oral disc

Gastrovascular cavity

Basal disc (pedal disc)

Pharynx

Mouth

167

Insects

**PUPA
(CHRYSALIS)**

THE WORD INSECT REFERS to small invertebrate creatures, especially those with bodies divided into sections. Insects, including beetles, ants, bees, butterflies, and moths, belong to various orders in the class Insecta, which is a division of the phylum Arthropoda. Features common to all insects are an exoskeleton (external skeleton); three pairs of jointed legs; three body sections (head, thorax, and abdomen); and one pair of sensory antennae. Beetles (order Coleoptera) are the biggest group of insects, with about 300,000 species (about 30 per cent of all known insects). They have a pair of hard elytra (wing cases), which are modified front wings. The principal function of the elytra is to protect the hind wings, which are used for flying. Ants, together with bees and wasps, form the order Hymenoptera, which contains about 200,000 species. This group is characterized by a marked narrowing between the thorax and abdomen. Butterflies and moths form the order Lepidoptera, which has about 150,000 species. They have wings covered with tiny scales, hence the name of their order (Lepidoptera means "scale wings"). The separation of lepidopterans into butterflies and moths is largely artificial as there are no features that categorically distinguish one group from the other. In general, however, most butterflies fly by day, whereas most moths are night-flyers. Some insects, including butterflies and moths, undergo complete metamorphosis (transformation) during their life-cycle. A butterfly metamorphoses from an egg to a larva (caterpillar), then to a pupa (chrysalis), and finally to an imago (adult).

EXAMPLES OF INSECTS

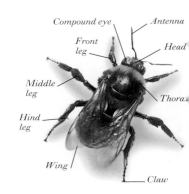

Compound eye · Antenna · Front leg · Head · Middle leg · Thorax · Hind leg · Wing · Claw

BUMBLEBEE

Compound eye · Stigma (spot) · Vein · Abdomen

DAMSELFLY

**EXTERNAL FEATURES
OF A BEETLE**

Elytron · Tarsus · Claw · Tibia · Costal margin · Pedicel · Apex · Femur · Vein · Trochanter · Wing · Flagellum · Mandible · Scape · Coxa · Labrum · Labial palp · Abdomen · Compound eye · Head · Prothorax · Mesothorax · Front leg · Scutellum · Hind leg · Metathorax · Middle leg

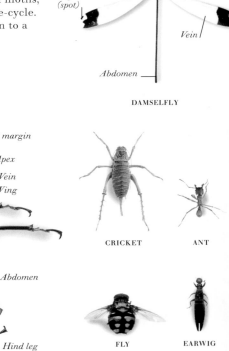

CRICKET · **ANT**

FLY · **EARWIG**

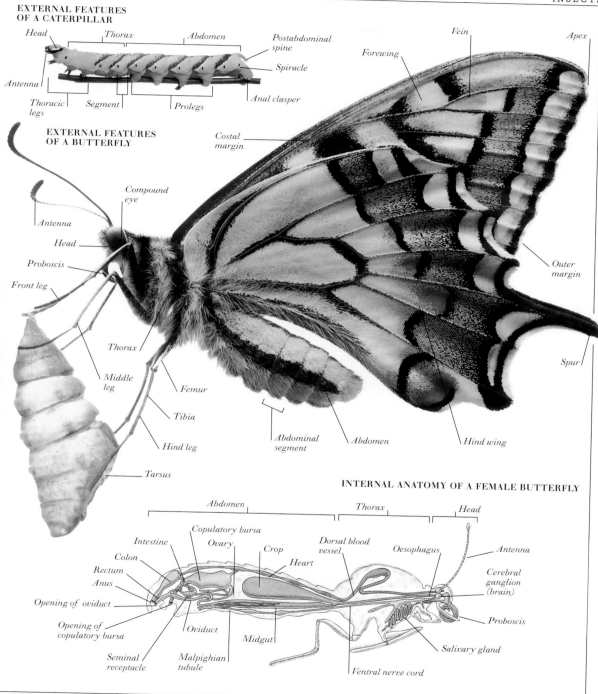

EXTERNAL FEATURES
OF A CATERPILLAR

Head
Thorax
Abdomen
Postabdominal
spine
Spiracle
Antenna
Thoracic
legs
Segment
Prolegs
Anal clasper

EXTERNAL FEATURES
OF A BUTTERFLY

Vein
Forewing
Apex

Costal
margin

Compound
eye
Antenna
Head
Proboscis
Front leg
Thorax
Middle
leg
Femur
Tibia
Hind leg
Tarsus

Outer
margin

Spur

Abdominal
segment
Abdomen
Hind wing

INTERNAL ANATOMY OF A FEMALE BUTTERFLY

Abdomen
Thorax
Head

Copulatory bursa
Intestine
Ovary
Crop
Dorsal blood
vessel
Oesophagus
Antenna
Colon
Heart
Cerebral
ganglion
(brain)
Rectum
Anus
Opening of oviduct
Opening of
copulatory bursa
Oviduct
Proboscis
Seminal
receptacle
Malpighian
tubule
Midgut
Salivary gland
Ventral nerve cord

Arachnids

THE CLASS ARACHNIDA INCLUDES SPIDERS (order Araneae) and scorpions (order Scorpiones). The class is part of the phylum Arthropoda, which also includes insects and crustaceans.
Spiders and scorpions are characterized by having four pairs of walking legs; a pair of pincer-like mouthparts called chelicerae; another pair of frontal appendages called pedipalps, which are sensory in spiders but used for grasping in scorpions; and a body divided into two sections (a combined head and thorax called a cephalothorax or prosoma, and an abdomen or opisthosoma).
Unlike other arthropods, spiders and scorpions lack antennae. Spiders and scorpions are carnivorous. Spiders poison prey by biting with the fanged chelicerae, scorpions by stinging with the end of the metasoma (tail).

MEXICAN TRUE RED-LEGGED TARANTULA
(*Euathlus emilia*)

INTERNAL ANATOMY OF A FEMALE SPIDER

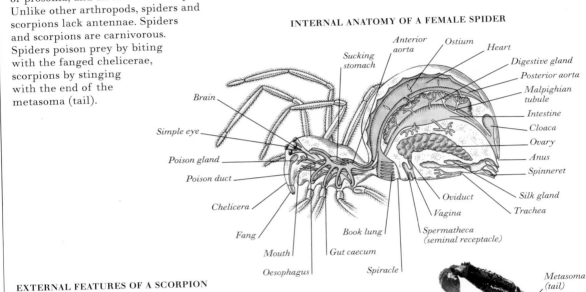

Anterior aorta
Ostium
Heart
Sucking stomach
Digestive gland
Posterior aorta
Malpighian tubule
Brain
Intestine
Simple eye
Cloaca
Ovary
Poison gland
Anus
Poison duct
Spinneret
Chelicera
Silk gland
Oviduct
Trachea
Vagina
Fang
Spermatheca (seminal receptacle)
Mouth
Book lung
Gut caecum
Oesophagus
Spiracle

EXTERNAL FEATURES OF A SCORPION

Chela (claw of pedipalp)
Pedipalp
Prosoma (cephalothorax)
Opisthosoma (abdomen)
Sting
Metasoma (tail)
Chelicera
Median eye
Patella
Tibia
Tarsus
Femur
Coxa
3rd walking leg
4th walking leg
Claw
1st walking leg
Metatarsus
Trochanter
2nd walking leg

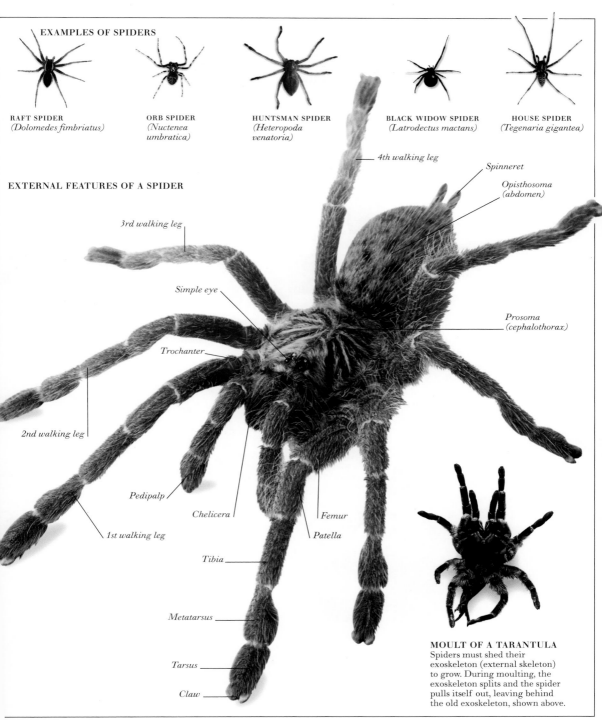

EXAMPLES OF SPIDERS

RAFT SPIDER
(Dolomedes fimbriatus)

ORB SPIDER
(Nuctenea umbratica)

HUNTSMAN SPIDER
(Heteropoda venatoria)

BLACK WIDOW SPIDER
(Latrodectus mactans)

HOUSE SPIDER
(Tegenaria gigantea)

EXTERNAL FEATURES OF A SPIDER

4th walking leg

Spinneret

Opisthosoma (abdomen)

3rd walking leg

Simple eye

Prosoma (cephalothorax)

Trochanter

2nd walking leg

Pedipalp

Chelicera

Femur

1st walking leg

Patella

Tibia

Metatarsus

Tarsus

Claw

MOULT OF A TARANTULA
Spiders must shed their exoskeleton (external skeleton) to grow. During moulting, the exoskeleton splits and the spider pulls itself out, leaving behind the old exoskeleton, shown above.

171

Crustaceans

THE SUBPHYLUM CRUSTACEA is one of the largest groups in the phylum Arthropoda. The subphylum is divided into several classes, the most important of which are Malacostraca and Cirripedia. The class Malacostraca includes crayfish, crabs, lobsters, and shrimps. Typical features of malacostracans include a body divided into two sections (a combined head and thorax called a cephalothorax, and an abdomen); an exoskeleton (external skeleton) with a large plate (carapace) covering the cephalothorax; stalked, compound eyes; and two pairs of antennae. The class Cirripedia includes barnacles, which, unlike other crustaceans, spend their adult lives attached to a surface, such as a rock. Other characteristics of cirripedes include an exoskeleton of overlapping calcareous plates; a body consisting almost entirely of thorax (the abdomen and head are minute); and six pairs of thoracic appendages (cirri) used for filter feeding.

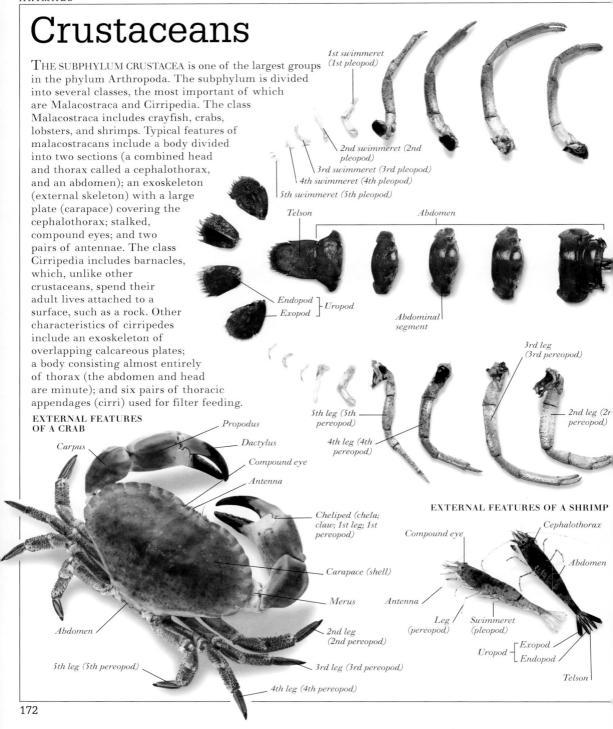

1st swimmeret (1st pleopod)

2nd swimmeret (2nd pleopod)

3rd swimmeret (3rd pleopod)

4th swimmeret (4th pleopod)

5th swimmeret (5th pleopod)

Telson

Abdomen

Endopod
Exopod } Uropod

Abdominal segment

3rd leg (3rd pereopod)

2nd leg (2nd pereopod)

5th leg (5th pereopod)

4th leg (4th pereopod)

EXTERNAL FEATURES OF A CRAB

Propodus

Carpus

Dactylus

Compound eye

Antenna

Cheliped (chela; claw; 1st leg; 1st pereopod)

Carapace (shell)

Merus

2nd leg (2nd pereopod)

3rd leg (3rd pereopod)

4th leg (4th pereopod)

5th leg (5th pereopod)

Abdomen

EXTERNAL FEATURES OF A SHRIMP

Compound eye

Cephalothorax

Abdomen

Antenna

Leg (pereopod)

Swimmeret (pleopod)

Uropod [Exopod
Endopod

Telson

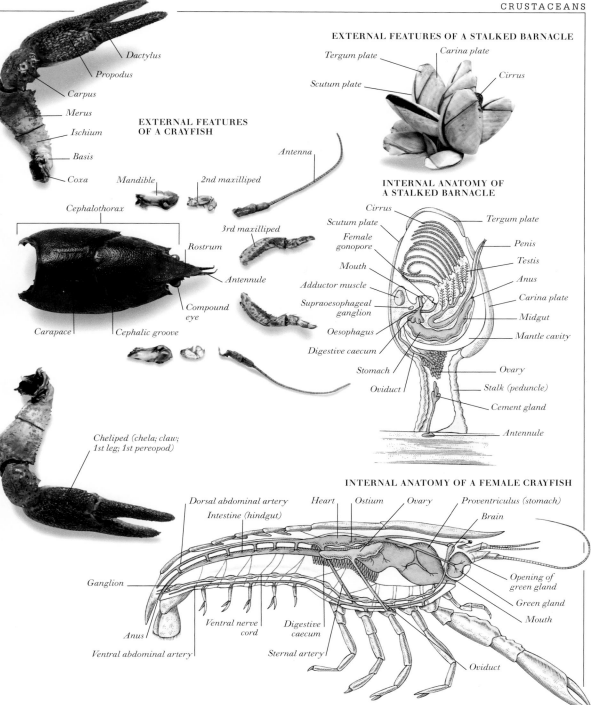

EXTERNAL FEATURES OF A STALKED BARNACLE

Tergum plate

Carina plate

Scutum plate

Cirrus

Dactylus

Propodus

Carpus

Merus

Ischium

Basis

Coxa

**EXTERNAL FEATURES
OF A CRAYFISH**

Mandible

2nd maxilliped

Antenna

**INTERNAL ANATOMY OF
A STALKED BARNACLE**

Cirrus

Scutum plate

*Female
gonopore*

Mouth

Adductor muscle

*Supraoesophageal
ganglion*

Oesophagus

Digestive caecum

Stomach

Oviduct

Tergum plate

Penis

Testis

Anus

Carina plate

Midgut

Mantle cavity

Ovary

Stalk (peduncle)

Cement gland

Antennule

Cephalothorax

Rostrum

3rd maxilliped

Antennule

*Compound
eye*

Carapace

Cephalic groove

INTERNAL ANATOMY OF A FEMALE CRAYFISH

*Cheliped (chela; claw;
1st leg; 1st pereopod)*

Dorsal abdominal artery

Intestine (hindgut)

Heart

Ostium

Ovary

Proventriculus (stomach)

Brain

Ganglion

*Opening of
green gland*

Green gland

Mouth

Anus

*Ventral nerve
cord*

*Digestive
caecum*

Ventral abdominal artery

Sternal artery

Oviduct

Starfish and sea urchins

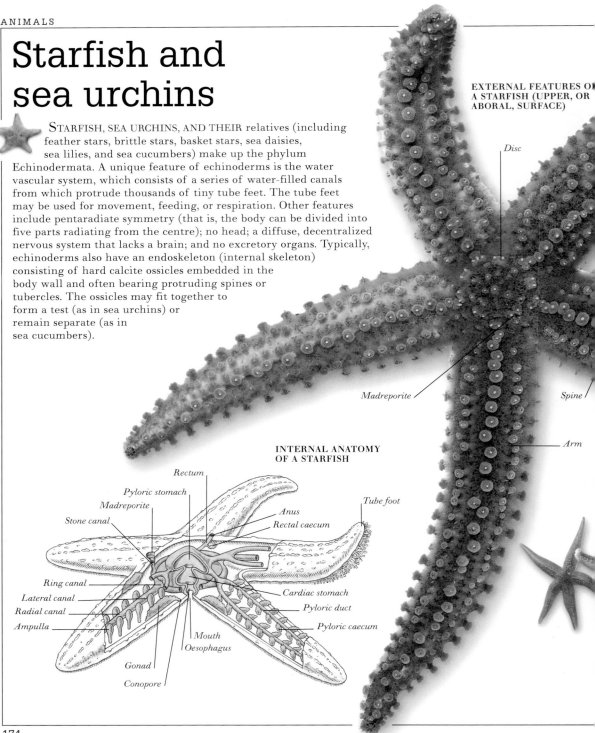

STARFISH, SEA URCHINS, AND THEIR relatives (including feather stars, brittle stars, basket stars, sea daisies, sea lilies, and sea cucumbers) make up the phylum Echinodermata. A unique feature of echinoderms is the water vascular system, which consists of a series of water-filled canals from which protrude thousands of tiny tube feet. The tube feet may be used for movement, feeding, or respiration. Other features include pentaradiate symmetry (that is, the body can be divided into five parts radiating from the centre); no head; a diffuse, decentralized nervous system that lacks a brain; and no excretory organs. Typically, echinoderms also have an endoskeleton (internal skeleton) consisting of hard calcite ossicles embedded in the body wall and often bearing protruding spines or tubercles. The ossicles may fit together to form a test (as in sea urchins) or remain separate (as in sea cucumbers).

EXTERNAL FEATURES OF A STARFISH (UPPER, OR ABORAL, SURFACE)

Disc

Madreporite

Spine

Arm

INTERNAL ANATOMY OF A STARFISH

Rectum

Pyloric stomach

Madreporite

Stone canal

Anus

Rectal caecum

Tube foot

Ring canal

Lateral canal

Radial canal

Ampulla

Cardiac stomach

Pyloric duct

Pyloric caecum

Mouth
Oesophagus

Gonad

Conopore

Tube foot

EXAMPLES OF SEA URCHINS

EDIBLE SEA URCHIN
(*Echinus escelentus*)

**CALIFORNIAN PURPLE
SEA URCHIN**
(*Strongylocentrotus
purpuratus*)

**PENCIL SLATE SEA
URCHIN**
(*Heterocentrotus
mammillatus*)

**INTERNAL ANATOMY
OF A SEA URCHIN**

Gonopore   *Anus*   *Madreporite*

Genital plate

Intestine

Stone canal

Ring canal

Polian vesicle

Pharynx

Nerve ring

Radial nerve   *Mouth*

Radial canal

Ampulla

Gonad

Axial gland

Siphon

Test

Spine

Tube foot

**EXTERNAL FEATURES OF A
SEA URCHIN (UPPER, OR
ABORAL, SURFACE)**

Anus

Spine

Tube foot

CUSHION STAR
(*Asterina gibbosa*)

COMMON BRITTLE STAR
(*Ophiothix fragilis*)

Tube foot

**EXAMPLES OF
STARFISH**

Mouth

Ambulacral groove

COMMON STARFISH
(*Asterias rubens*)

**EXTERNAL FEATURES OF A STARFISH
(LOWER, OR ORAL, SURFACE)**

Molluscs

THE PHYLUM MOLLUSCA (MOLLUSCS) is a large group of animals that includes octopuses, snails, and scallops. Octopuses and their relatives – including squid and cuttlefish – form the class Cephalopoda. Cephalopods typically have a head with a radula (a file-like feeding organ) and beak; a well-developed nervous system; sucker-bearing tentacles; a muscular mantle (part of the body wall) that can expel water through the siphon, enabling movement by jet propulsion; and a small shell or no shell. Snails and their relatives – including slugs, limpets, and abalones – make up the class Gastropoda. Gastropods typically have a coiled external shell, although some, such as slugs, have a small internal shell or no shell; a flat foot; and a head with tentacles and a radula. Scallops and their relatives – including clams, mussels, and oysters – make up the class Bivalvia (also called Pelecypoda). Features of bivalves include a shell with two halves (valves); large gills that are used for breathing and filter feeding; and no radula.

EXTERNAL FEATURES OF A SCALLOP

Upper valve (shell)   Mantle   Ocellus (eye)

Lower valve (shell)   Shell rib   Sensory tentacle

Sensory tentacle   Ventral margin of shell   Shell rib

Anterior wing of shell

Umbo   Posterior wing of shell

Dorsal margin of shell

INTERNAL ANATOMY OF AN OCTOPUS

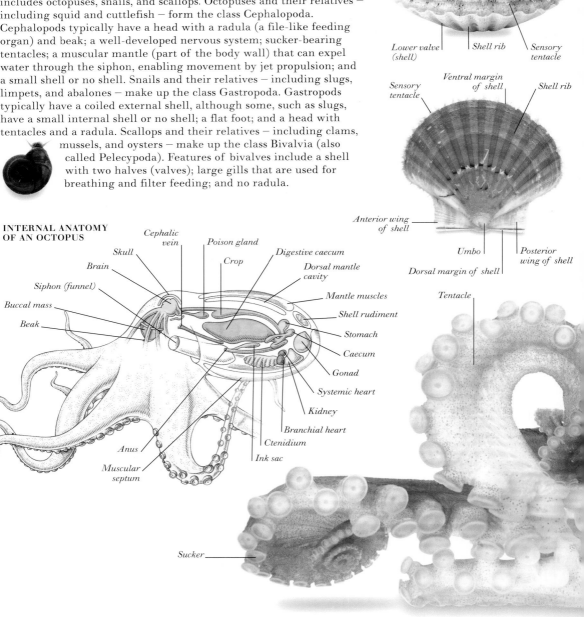

Cephalic vein
Poison gland
Skull
Crop
Digestive caecum
Brain
Dorsal mantle cavity
Siphon (funnel)
Mantle muscles
Buccal mass
Shell rudiment
Beak
Stomach
Caecum
Gonad
Systemic heart
Kidney
Branchial heart
Ctenidium
Anus
Ink sac
Muscular septum
Tentacle
Sucker

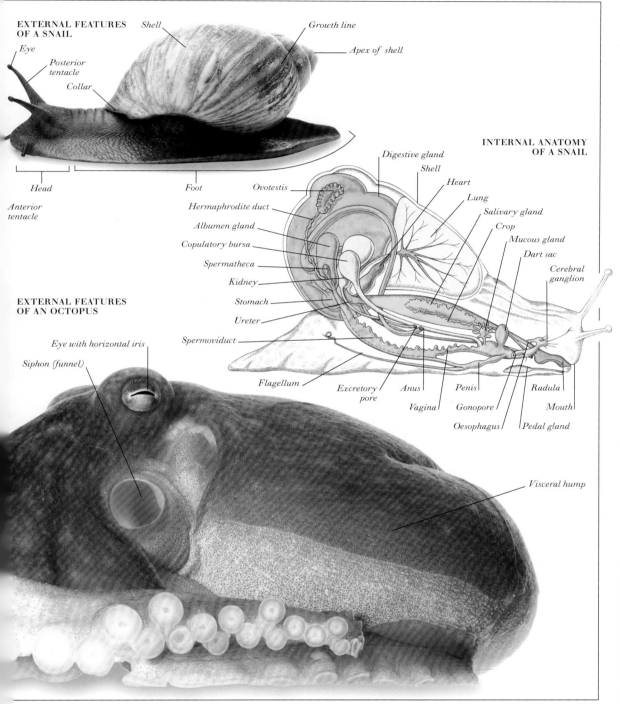

EXTERNAL FEATURES OF A SNAIL

Shell

Growth line

Apex of shell

Eye

Posterior tentacle

Collar

Head

Foot

Anterior tentacle

INTERNAL ANATOMY OF A SNAIL

Digestive gland

Shell

Heart

Lung

Salivary gland

Crop

Mucous gland

Dart sac

Cerebral ganglion

Ovotestis

Hermaphrodite duct

Albumen gland

Copulatory bursa

Spermatheca

Kidney

Stomach

Ureter

Spermoviduct

Flagellum

Excretory pore

Anus

Vagina

Penis

Gonopore

Oesophagus

Pedal gland

Radula

Mouth

EXTERNAL FEATURES OF AN OCTOPUS

Eye with horizontal iris

Siphon (funnel)

Visceral hump

177

Sharks and jawless fish

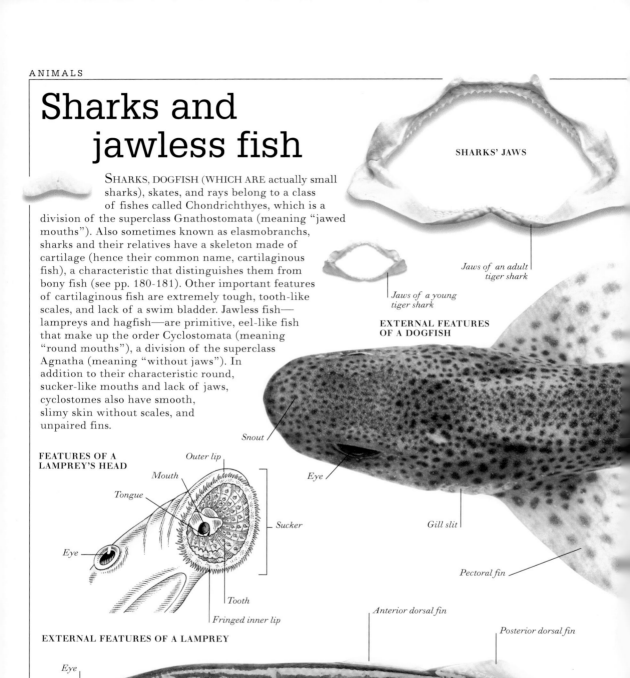

SHARKS, DOGFISH (WHICH ARE actually small sharks), skates, and rays belong to a class of fishes called Chondrichthyes, which is a division of the superclass Gnathostomata (meaning "jawed mouths"). Also sometimes known as elasmobranchs, sharks and their relatives have a skeleton made of cartilage (hence their common name, cartilaginous fish), a characteristic that distinguishes them from bony fish (see pp. 180-181). Other important features of cartilaginous fish are extremely tough, tooth-like scales, and lack of a swim bladder. Jawless fish— lampreys and hagfish—are primitive, eel-like fish that make up the order Cyclostomata (meaning "round mouths"), a division of the superclass Agnatha (meaning "without jaws"). In addition to their characteristic round, sucker-like mouths and lack of jaws, cyclostomes also have smooth, slimy skin without scales, and unpaired fins.

SHARKS' JAWS

Jaws of an adult tiger shark

Jaws of a young tiger shark

EXTERNAL FEATURES OF A DOGFISH

Snout

Eye

Gill slit

Pectoral fin

Anterior dorsal fin

Posterior dorsal fin

FEATURES OF A LAMPREY'S HEAD

Outer lip

Mouth

Tongue

Eye

Sucker

Eye

Tooth

Fringed inner lip

EXTERNAL FEATURES OF A LAMPREY

Eye

Gill opening

Sucker

Anal fin

Caudal fin

EXAMPLES OF CARTILAGINOUS FISH

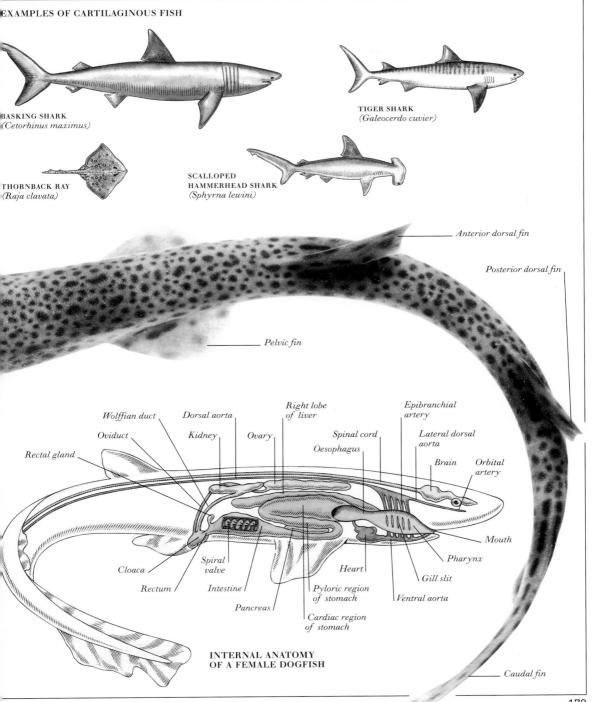

BASKING SHARK
(*Cetorhinus maximus*)

TIGER SHARK
(*Galeocerdo cuvier*)

THORNBACK RAY
(*Raja clavata*)

SCALLOPED HAMMERHEAD SHARK
(*Sphyrna lewini*)

Anterior dorsal fin

Posterior dorsal fin

Pelvic fin

Wolffian duct

Oviduct

Rectal gland

Dorsal aorta

Kidney

Ovary

Right lobe of liver

Oesophagus

Spinal cord

Epibranchial artery

Lateral dorsal aorta

Brain

Orbital artery

Mouth

Pharynx

Gill slit

Ventral aorta

Spiral valve

Cloaca

Rectum

Intestine

Pancreas

Heart

Pyloric region of stomach

Cardiac region of stomach

**INTERNAL ANATOMY
OF A FEMALE DOGFISH**

Caudal fin

Bony fish

BONY FISH, SUCH AS CARP, TROUT, SALMON, perch, and cod, are by far the best known and largest group of fish, with more than 20,000 species (over 95 per cent of all known fish). As their name suggests, bony fish have skeletons made of bone, in contrast to the cartilaginous skeletons of sharks, jawless fish, and their relatives (see pp. 178-179). Other typical features of bony fish include a swim bladder, which functions as a variable-buoyancy organ, enabling a fish to remain effortlessly at whatever depth it is swimming; relatively thin, bone-like scales; a flap (called an operculum) covering the gills; and paired pelvic and pectoral fins. Scientifically, bony fish belong to the class Osteichthyes, which is a division of the superclass Gnathostomata (meaning "jawed mouths").

HOW FISH BREATHE

Fish "breathe" by extracting oxygen from water through their gills. Water is sucked in through the mouth; simultaneously, the opercula close to prevent the water from escaping. The mouth is then closed, and muscles in the walls of the mouth, pharynx, and opercular cavity contract to pump the water inside over the gills and out through the opercula. Some fish rely on swimming with their mouths open to keep water flowing over the gills.

Pharynx
Gill raker
Water out
Gill slit
Mouth
Operculum
Water in
Gill filament

EXAMPLES OF BONY FISH

MANDARINFISH
(*Synchiropus splendidus*)

ANGLERFISH
(*Caulophryne jordani*)

OCEANIC SEAHORSE
(*Hippocampus kuda*)

LIONFISH
(*Pterois volitans*)

STURGEON
(*Acipenser sturio*)

Vertebra
Neural spine
Hypural
Haemal spine
Caudal fin ray
Radial cartilage
Anal fin ray

SNOWFLAKE MORAY EEL
(*Echidna nebulosa*)

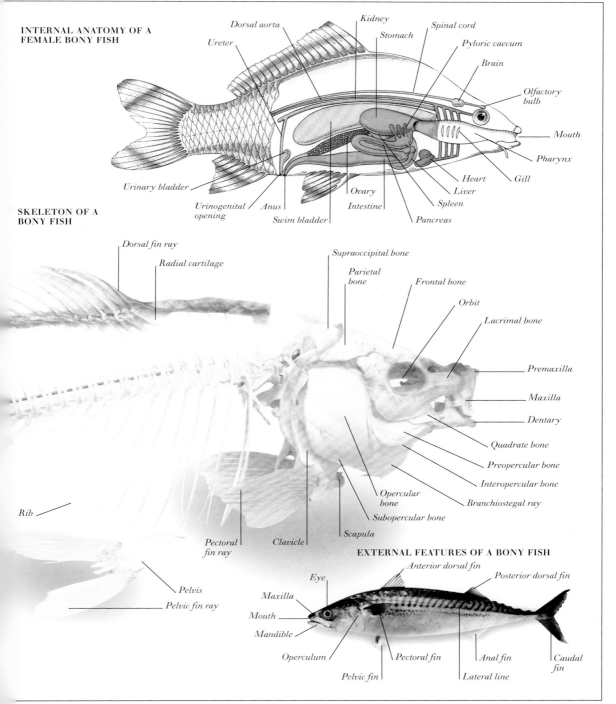

**INTERNAL ANATOMY OF A
FEMALE BONY FISH**

Ureter

Dorsal aorta

Kidney

Stomach

Spinal cord

Pyloric caecum

Brain

Olfactory
bulb

Mouth

Pharynx

Gill

Heart

Liver

Spleen

Pancreas

Urinary bladder

Urinogenital
opening

Anus

Swim bladder

Ovary

Intestine

**SKELETON OF A
BONY FISH**

Dorsal fin ray

Radial cartilage

Supraoccipital bone

Parietal
bone

Frontal bone

Orbit

Lacrimal bone

Premaxilla

Maxilla

Dentary

Quadrate bone

Preopercular bone

Interopercular bone

Branchiostegal ray

Opercular
bone

Subopercular bone

Scapula

Rib

Pectoral
fin ray

Clavicle

Pelvis

Pelvic fin ray

EXTERNAL FEATURES OF A BONY FISH

Anterior dorsal fin

Posterior dorsal fin

Eye

Maxilla

Mouth

Mandible

Operculum

Pelvic fin

Pectoral fin

Lateral line

Anal fin

Caudal
fin

Amphibians

THE CLASS AMPHIBIA INCLUDES FROGS and toads (which make up the order Anura), and newts and salamanders (which make up the order Urodela). Amphibians typically have moist, scaleless, hairless skin; lungs; and are cold-blooded. They also undergo complete metamorphosis, from eggs laid in water through various water-living larval stages (such as tadpoles) to land-living adults. Typical features of adult frogs and toads include a squat body with no tail; long, powerful hind legs; and large, often bulging, eyes. Adult newts and salamanders typically have a long body with a well-developed tail; and relatively short, equal-sized legs. However, newts and salamanders show considerable variation; for example, in some species the adults have minute legs, external gills rather than lungs, and spend their entire lives in water.

INTERNAL ANATOMY OF A FEMALE FROG

EXTERNAL FEATURES OF A FROG

EXTERNAL FEATURES OF A SALAMANDER

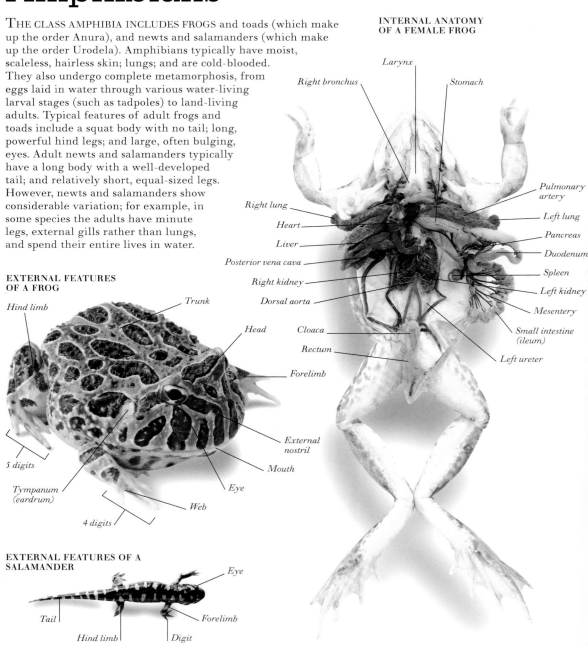

Larynx
Stomach
Right bronchus
Right lung
Heart
Liver
Posterior vena cava
Right kidney
Dorsal aorta
Cloaca
Rectum
Forelimb
External nostril
Mouth
Eye
Web
Pulmonary artery
Left lung
Pancreas
Duodenum
Spleen
Left kidney
Mesentery
Small intestine (ileum)
Left ureter

Hind limb
Trunk
Head
5 digits
Tympanum (eardrum)
4 digits

Tail
Hind limb
Digit
Eye
Forelimb

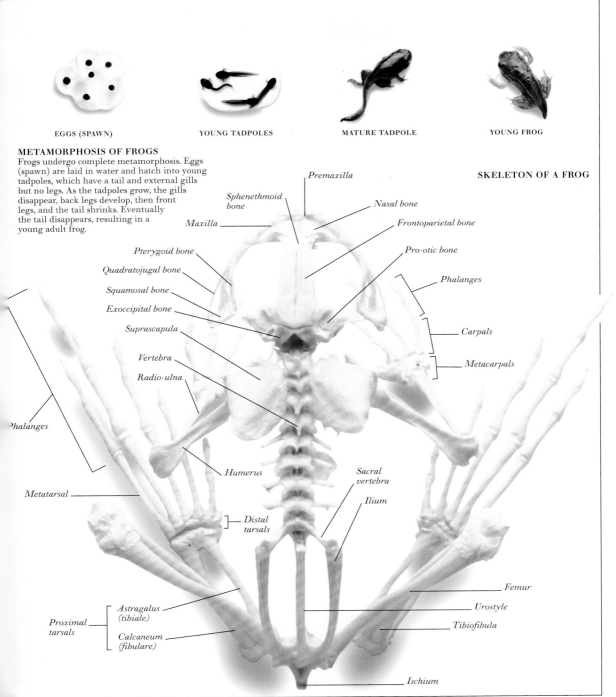

EGGS (SPAWN) YOUNG TADPOLES MATURE TADPOLE YOUNG FROG

METAMORPHOSIS OF FROGS

Frogs undergo complete metamorphosis. Eggs
(spawn) are laid in water and hatch into young
tadpoles, which have a tail and external gills
but no legs. As the tadpoles grow, the gills
disappear, back legs develop, then front
legs, and the tail shrinks. Eventually
the tail disappears, resulting in a
young adult frog.

SKELETON OF A FROG

Premaxilla

Sphenethmoid
bone

Nasal bone

Maxilla

Frontoparietal bone

Pro-otic bone

Pterygoid bone

Quadratojugal bone

Phalanges

Squamosal bone

Exoccipital bone

Carpals

Suprascapula

Metacarpals

Vertebra

Radio-ulna

Phalanges

Humerus

Sacral
vertebra

Ilium

Metatarsal

Distal
tarsals

Proximal
tarsals

Astragalus
(tibiale)

Femur

Urostyle

Calcaneum
(fibulare)

Tibiofibula

Ischium

183

Lizards and snakes

LIZARDS AND SNAKES BELONG to the order Squamata, a division of the class Reptilia. Characteristic reptilian features include scaly skin, lungs, and cold-bloodedness. Most reptiles lay leathery-shelled eggs, although some hatch the eggs inside their bodies and give birth to live young. Lizards belong to the suborder Lacertilia. Typically, they have long tails, and shed their skin in several pieces. Many lizards can regenerate a tail if it is lost; some can change colour; and some are limbless. Snakes make up the suborder Ophidia (also called Serpentes). All snakes have long, limbless bodies; can dislocate their lower jaw to swallow large prey; and have eyelids that are joined together to form a single transparent covering over the front of the eye. Most snakes shed their skin in a single piece. Constrictor snakes kill their prey by squeezing; venomous snakes poison their prey.

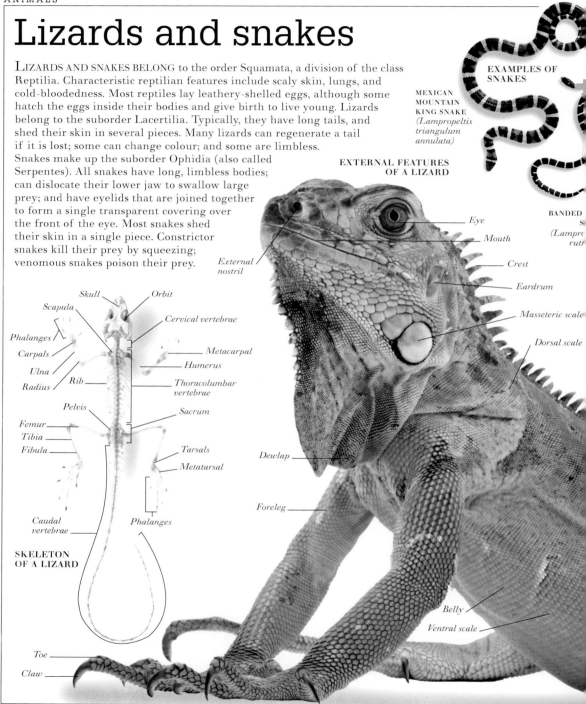

EXAMPLES OF SNAKES

MEXICAN MOUNTAIN KING SNAKE
(*Lampropeltis triangulum annulata*)

BANDED S
(*Lampro rutt*)

EXTERNAL FEATURES OF A LIZARD

Eye

Mouth

Crest

Eardrum

External nostril

Masseteric scale

Dorsal scale

Dewlap

Foreleg

Belly

Ventral scale

SKELETON OF A LIZARD

Skull

Orbit

Scapula

Cervical vertebrae

Phalanges

Carpals

Metacarpal

Ulna

Humerus

Radius

Rib

Thoracolumbar vertebrae

Pelvis

Sacrum

Femur

Tibia

Fibula

Tarsals

Metatarsal

Caudal vertebrae

Phalanges

Toe

Claw

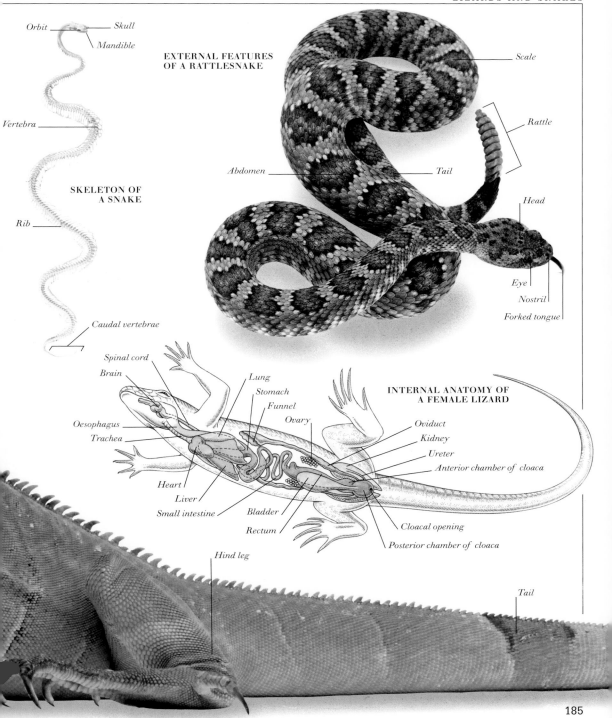

Orbit

Skull

Mandible

**EXTERNAL FEATURES
OF A RATTLESNAKE**

Scale

Vertebra

Rattle

Abdomen

Tail

Head

**SKELETON OF
A SNAKE**

Rib

Eye

Nostril

Forked tongue

Caudal vertebrae

Spinal cord

Brain

Lung

Stomach

Funnel

Ovary

**INTERNAL ANATOMY OF
A FEMALE LIZARD**

Oviduct

Kidney

Oesophagus

Trachea

Ureter

Anterior chamber of cloaca

Heart

Liver

Small intestine

Bladder

Rectum

Cloacal opening

Posterior chamber of cloaca

Hind leg

Tail

Crocodilians and turtles

CROCODILIANS AND TURTLES BELONG to different orders in the class Reptilia. The order Crocodilia includes crocodiles, alligators, caimans, and gharials. Typically, crocodilians are carnivores (flesh-eaters), and have a long snout, sharp teeth for gripping prey, and hard, square scales. All crocodilians are adapted to living on land and in water: they have four strong legs for moving on land; a powerful tail for swimming; and their eyes and nostrils are high on the head so that they stay above water while the rest of the body is submerged. The order Chelonia includes marine turtles, terrapins (freshwater turtles), and tortoises (land turtles). Characteristically, chelonians have a short, broad body encased in a bony shell with an outer horny covering, into which the head and limbs can be withdrawn; and a horny beak instead of teeth.

SKULLS OF CROCODILIAN

GHARIAL
(Gavialis gangeticus)

NILE CROCODILE
(Crocodylus niloticus)

AMERICAN ALLIGATOR
(Alligator mississippiensis)

SKELETON OF A CROCODILE

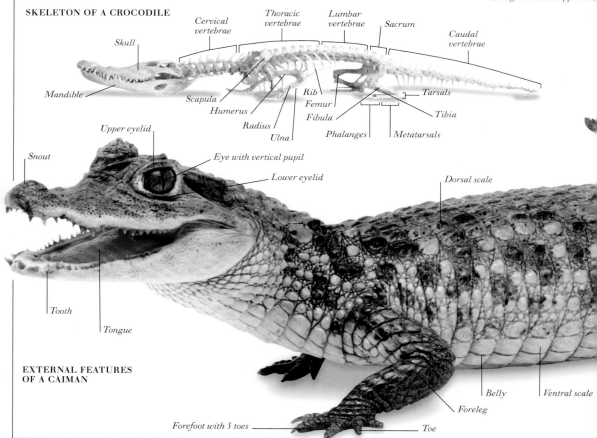

Cervical vertebrae

Thoracic vertebrae

Lumbar vertebrae

Sacrum

Caudal vertebrae

Skull

Mandible

Scapula

Humerus

Radius

Ulna

Rib

Femur

Fibula

Phalanges

Tarsals

Tibia

Metatarsals

Upper eyelid

Eye with vertical pupil

Lower eyelid

Dorsal scale

Snout

Tooth

Tongue

EXTERNAL FEATURES OF A CAIMAN

Belly

Ventral scale

Foreleg

Forefoot with 5 toes

Toe

EXTERNAL FEATURES OF A TERRAPIN

Eyelid

Eye

Nuchal shield

Claw

Foreleg

Marginal
shield

Hind leg

Lateral shield
(costal shield)

Central shield
(vertebral shield)

Pygal shield

SKELETON OF A TURTLE

Mandible

Vertebra

Skull

Scapula

Phalanges

Nuchal plate

Ulna

Radius

Humerus

Carapace
(upper shell)

Proscapular
process

Coracoid

Centrum

Femur

Fibula

Tibia

Pelvis

Tail crest

Tail

Scute

Hind leg

Hind foot with 4 toes

Claw

INTERNAL ANATOMY OF A
FEMALE TORTOISE

Buccal cavity

Lung

Trachea

Oesophagus

Heart

Stomach

Liver

Pancreas

Gallbladder

Duodenum

Small intestine

Ovary

Kidney

Bladder

Rectum

Oviduct

Cloaca

Anus

187

Birds 1

BIRDS MAKE UP THE CLASS AVES. There are more than 9,000 species, almost all of which can fly (the only flightless birds are penguins, ostriches, rheas, cassowaries, and kiwis). The ability to fly is reflected in the typical bird features: forelimbs modified as wings; a streamlined body; and hollow bones to reduce weight. All birds lay hard-shelled eggs, which the parents incubate. Birds' beaks and feet vary according to diet and way of life. Beaks range from general-purpose types suitable for a mixed diet (those of thrushes, for example), to types specialized for particular foods (such as the large, curved, sieving beaks of flamingos). Feet range from the webbed "paddles" of ducks, to the talons of birds of prey. Plumage also varies widely, and in many species the male is brightly coloured for courtship display whereas the female is drab.

EXTERNAL FEATURES OF A BIRD

Forehead

Eye

Crown

Nostril

Nape

Upper mandible

Beak

Lower mandible

Chin

Throat

EXAMPLES OF BIRDS

MALE TUFTED DUCK
(*Aythya fuligula*)

WHITE STORK
(*Ciconia ciconia*)

MALE OSTRICH
(*Struthio camelus*)

Minor coverts

Lesser wing coverts

Median wing coverts

Greater wing coverts (major coverts)

Secondary flight feathers (secondary remiges)

Primary flight feathers (primary remiges)

Breast

Belly

Flank

Thigh

Under tail coverts

Claw

Tarsus

Toe

Tail feathers (retrices)

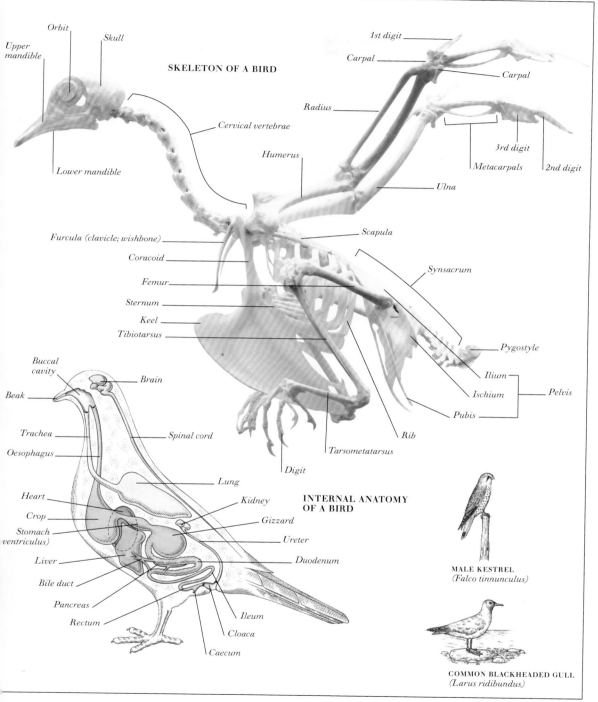

SKELETON OF A BIRD

Upper mandible

Orbit

Skull

1st digit

Carpal

Carpal

Radius

Cervical vertebrae

Humerus

3rd digit

Metacarpals

2nd digit

Lower mandible

Ulna

Furcula (clavicle; wishbone)

Scapula

Coracoid

Synsacrum

Femur

Sternum

Keel

Tibiotarsus

Pygostyle

Ilium

Ischium

Pelvis

Pubis

Rib

Tarsometatarsus

Digit

INTERNAL ANATOMY OF A BIRD

Buccal cavity

Brain

Beak

Trachea

Spinal cord

Oesophagus

Lung

Heart

Kidney

Crop

Gizzard

Stomach (ventriculus)

Ureter

Liver

Duodenum

Bile duct

Pancreas

Rectum

Ileum

Cloaca

Caecum

MALE KESTREL
(Falco tinnunculus)

COMMON BLACKHEADED GULL
(Larus ridibundus)

189

Birds 2

EXAMPLES OF BIRDS' FEET

KITTIWAKE
(Rissa tridactyla)
The webbed feet are
adapted for paddling
through water.

LITTLE GREBE
(Tachybaptus ruficollis)
The lobed, flattened feet
are adapted for swimming
underwater.

TAWNY OWL
(Strix aluco)
The clawed feet are adapted
for gripping prey.

EXAMPLES OF BIRDS' BEAKS

KING VULTURE
(Sarcorhamphus papa)
The hooked beak is adapted
for pulling apart flesh.

GREATER FLAMINGO
(Phoenicopterus ruber)
In the living bird, the large,
curved beak contains a
cartilaginous "sieve" for
filtering food particles
from water.

MISTLE THRUSH
(Turdus viscivorus)
The general-purpose beak is
suitable for a wide range of
animal and plant foods.

BLUE-AND-YELLOW MACAW
(Ara ararauna)
The broad, powerful, hooked beak
is adapted for crushing seeds and
eating fruit.

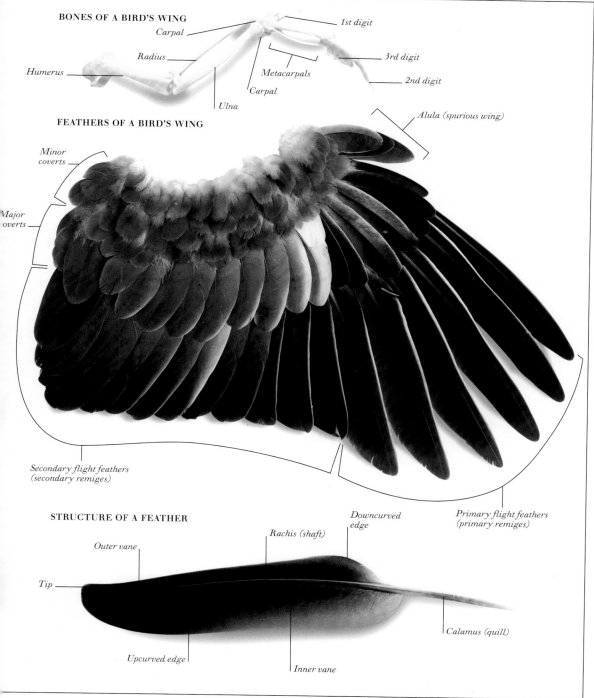

BONES OF A BIRD'S WING

Carpal

1st digit

Radius

3rd digit

Humerus

2nd digit

Metacarpals

Carpal

Ulna

FEATHERS OF A BIRD'S WING

Alula (spurious wing)

Minor coverts

Major coverts

Secondary flight feathers
(secondary remiges)

Primary flight feathers
(primary remiges)

STRUCTURE OF A FEATHER

Downcurved edge

Rachis (shaft)

Outer vane

Tip

Calamus (quill)

Upcurved edge

Inner vane

Eggs

AN EGG IS A SINGLE CELL, produced by the female, with the capacity to develop into a new individual. Development may take place inside the mother's body (as in most mammals) or outside, in which case the egg has a protective covering such as a shell. Egg yolk nourishes the growing young. Eggs developing inside the mother generally have little yolk, because the young are nourished from her body. Eggs developing outside may also have little yolk if they are produced by animals whose young go through a larval stage (such as a caterpillar) that feeds itself while developing into the adult form. The shelled eggs of birds and reptiles contain enough yolk to sustain the young until it hatches into a juvenile version of the adult.

SECTION THROUGH
A CHICKEN'S EGG

Yolk
Yolk sac
Shell
Allantoic fluid
Allantois
Chorioallantoic membrane
Air sac
Albumen (egg white)
Amnion
Amniotic fluid
Developing chick
Developing wing
Shell membrane

VARIETY OF EGGS

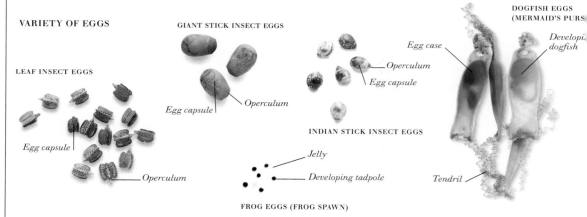

LEAF INSECT EGGS

Egg capsule
Operculum

GIANT STICK INSECT EGGS

Egg capsule
Operculum

INDIAN STICK INSECT EGGS

Operculum
Egg capsule

Jelly
Developing tadpole

FROG EGGS (FROG SPAWN)

DOGFISH EGGS
(MERMAID'S PURSE)

Egg case
Developing dogfish
Tendril

HATCHING OF A QUAIL'S EGG

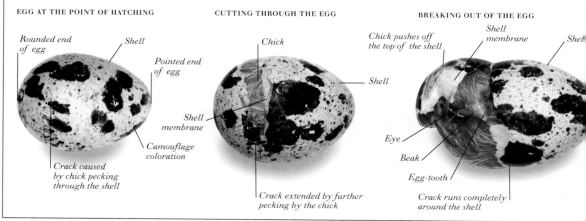

EGG AT THE POINT OF HATCHING

Rounded end of egg
Shell
Pointed end of egg
Shell membrane
Camouflage coloration
Crack caused by chick pecking through the shell

CUTTING THROUGH THE EGG

Chick
Shell
Crack extended by further pecking by the chick

BREAKING OUT OF THE EGG

Chick pushes off the top of the shell
Shell membrane
Shell
Eye
Beak
Egg-tooth
Crack runs completely around the shell

EXAMPLES OF BIRDS' EGGS

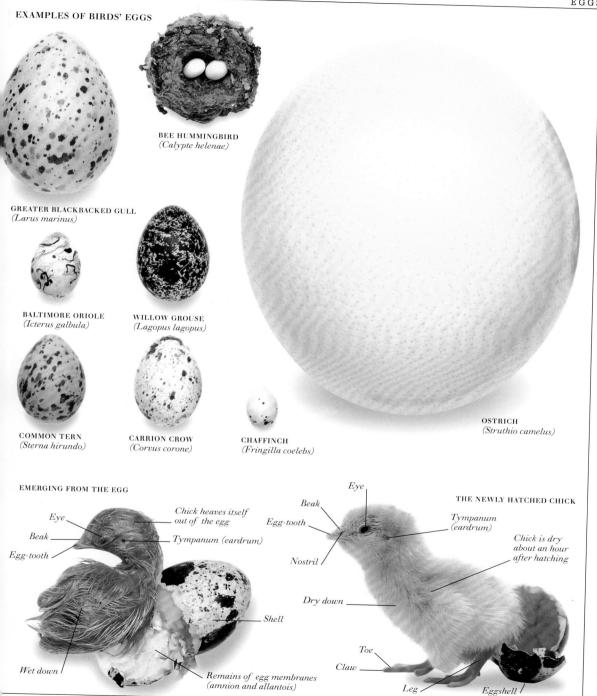

BEE HUMMINGBIRD
(Calypte helenae)

GREATER BLACKBACKED GULL
(Larus marinus)

BALTIMORE ORIOLE
(Icterus galbula)

WILLOW GROUSE
(Lagopus lagopus)

COMMON TERN
(Sterna hirundo)

CARRION CROW
(Corvus corone)

CHAFFINCH
(Fringilla coelebs)

OSTRICH
(Struthio camelus)

EMERGING FROM THE EGG

Eye

Beak

Egg-tooth

Chick heaves itself
out of the egg

Tympanum (eardrum)

Shell

Wet down

Remains of egg membranes
(amnion and allantois)

THE NEWLY HATCHED CHICK

Eye

Beak

Egg-tooth

Nostril

Tympanum
(eardrum)

Chick is dry
about an hour
after hatching

Dry down

Toe

Claw

Leg

Eggshell

Carnivores

THE MAMMALIAN ORDER CARNIVORA includes cats, dogs, bears, raccoons, pandas, weasels, badgers, skunks, otters, civets, mongooses, and hyenas. The order's name is derived from the fact that most of its members are carnivores (flesheaters). Typical carnivore features therefore reflect a hunting life-style: speed and agility; sharp claws and well-developed canine teeth for holding and killing prey; carnassial teeth (cheek teeth) for cutting flesh; and forward-facing eyes for good distance judgment. However, some members of the order – bears, badgers, and foxes, for example – have a more mixed diet, and a few are entirely herbivorous (plant-eating), notably pandas. Such animals have no carnassial teeth and tend to be slower-moving than pure flesh-eaters.

EXTERNAL FEATURES OF A MALE LION

Nose

Eye

Mane

Nostril

Vibrissa (whisker)

Tongue

Canine tooth

Incisor tooth

Chest

Elbow

Lower arm

Toe

SKULL OF A LION

Zygomatic arch

Nasal bone

Coronoid process

Maxilla

Orbit

Upper premolars

Sagittal crest

Upper canine

Lower canine

Mandible

Lower premolars

Occipital condyle

Condyle

Tympanic bulla

Angular process

Upper carnassial tooth (4th upper premolar)

SKULL OF A BEAR

Sagittal crest

Zygomatic arch

Upper molars

Occipital condyle

Orbit

Nasal bone

Upper premolars

Maxilla

Upper canine

Upper incisor

Lower incisor

Lower canine

Mandible

Tympanic bulla

Angular process

Condyle

Lower molars

Lower premolars

EXAMPLES OF CARNIVORES

ALSATIAN DOG
(Canis familiaris)

MANED WOLF
(Chrysocyon brachyurus)

RACCOON
(Procyon lotor)

AMERICAN BLACK BEAR
(Ursus americanus)

SKELETON OF A DOMESTIC CAT

Back

Rump

Hip

Rib cage

Sacrum

Lumbar vertebrae

Thoracic vertebrae

Cervical vertebrae

Skull

Caudal vertebrae

Pelvis

Femur

Scapula

Sternum

Humerus

Patella

Rib

Fibula

Ulna

Tibia

Radius

Carpals

Metacarpals

Tarsals

Metatarsals

Belly

Thigh

Knee

Phalanges

INTERNAL ANATOMY OF A MALE DOMESTIC CAT

Brain

Spinal cord

Stomach

Kidney

Diaphragm

Liver

Ureter

Large intestine

Nasal cavity

Small intestine

Buccal cavity

Anus

Nostril

Testis

Tongue

Trachea

Oesophagus

Lung

Vas deferens (sperm duct)

Hock

Tail

Urethra

Paw

Heart

Gallbladder

Bladder

Pancreas

Spleen

Rabbits and rodents

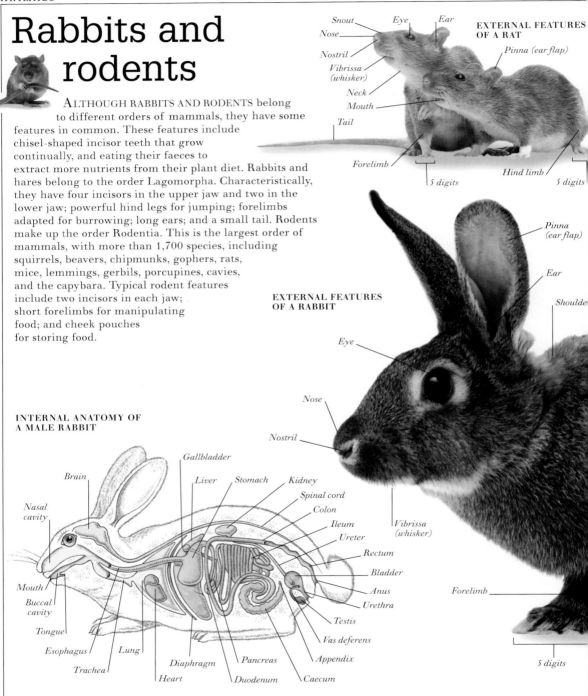

ALTHOUGH RABBITS AND RODENTS belong to different orders of mammals, they have some features in common. These features include chisel-shaped incisor teeth that grow continually, and eating their faeces to extract more nutrients from their plant diet. Rabbits and hares belong to the order Lagomorpha. Characteristically, they have four incisors in the upper jaw and two in the lower jaw; powerful hind legs for jumping; forelimbs adapted for burrowing; long ears; and a small tail. Rodents make up the order Rodentia. This is the largest order of mammals, with more than 1,700 species, including squirrels, beavers, chipmunks, gophers, rats, mice, lemmings, gerbils, porcupines, cavies, and the capybara. Typical rodent features include two incisors in each jaw; short forelimbs for manipulating food; and cheek pouches for storing food.

EXTERNAL FEATURES OF A RAT

Snout
Eye
Ear
Nose
Nostril
Vibrissa (whisker)
Neck
Mouth
Tail
Forelimb
5 digits
Pinna (ear flap)
Hind limb
5 digits

EXTERNAL FEATURES OF A RABBIT

Pinna (ear flap)
Ear
Shoulder
Eye
Nose
Nostril
Vibrissa (whisker)
Forelimb
5 digits

INTERNAL ANATOMY OF A MALE RABBIT

Brain
Gallbladder
Liver
Stomach
Kidney
Spinal cord
Colon
Ileum
Ureter
Rectum
Bladder
Anus
Urethra
Testis
Vas deferens
Appendix
Caecum
Duodenum
Pancreas
Heart
Diaphragm
Trachea
Lung
Esophagus
Tongue
Buccal cavity
Mouth
Nasal cavity

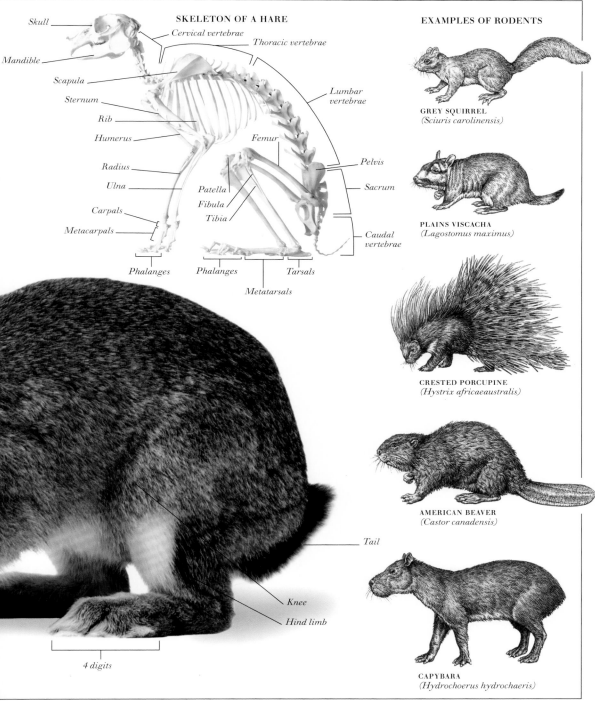

SKELETON OF A HARE

Skull

Mandible

Cervical vertebrae

Thoracic vertebrae

Scapula

Lumbar
vertebrae

Sternum

Rib

Humerus

Femur

Radius

Pelvis

Ulna

Sacrum

Patella

Carpals

Fibula

Metacarpals

Tibia

Caudal
vertebrae

Phalanges

Phalanges

Tarsals

Metatarsals

4 digits

Tail

Knee

Hind limb

EXAMPLES OF RODENTS

GREY SQUIRREL
(Sciuris carolinensis)

PLAINS VISCACHA
(Lagostomus maximus)

CRESTED PORCUPINE
(Hystrix africaeaustralis)

AMERICAN BEAVER
(Castor canadensis)

CAPYBARA
(Hydrochoerus hydrochaeris)

Ungulates

UNGULATES IS A GENERAL TERM FOR a large, varied group of mammals that includes horses, cattle, and their relatives. The ungulates are divided into two orders on the basis of the number of toes. Members of the order Perissodactyla (odd-toed ungulates) have one or three toes. Perissodactyls include horses, asses, and zebras (all of which are one-toed), and rhinoceroses and tapirs (which are three-toed). Members of the order Artiodactyla (even-toed ungulates) have two or four toes. Most artiodactyls have two toes, which are typically encased in hooves to give the so-called cloven hoof. Two-toed, cloven-hoofed artiodactyls include cows and other cattle, sheep, goats, antelopes, deer, and giraffes. The other main two-toed artiodactyls are camels and llamas. Most two-toed artiodactyls are ruminants; that is, they have a four-chambered stomach and chew the cud. The principal four-toed artiodactyls are pigs, peccaries, and hippopotamuses.

Chambers of stomach

Rumen Omasum Abomasum Reticulum

Colon

Anus

Rectum

Caecum

Small intestine

Mo

Tongt

Oesophagus

Duodenum

DIGESTIVE SYSTEM OF A COW

COMPARISON OF THE FRONT FEET OF A HORSE AND A COW

SKELETON OF THE LEFT FRONT FOOT OF A HORSE

SKELETON OF THE RIGHT FRONT FOOT OF A COW

2nd metacarpal (splint bone)

3rd metacarpal (cannon bone)

Fused 3rd and 4th metacarpals

Sesamoid bone

Sesamoid bone

Phalanges of 3rd digit

Phalanges of 3rd digit

Phalanges of 4th digit

Hoof bone

Hoof bone of 3rd digit

Hoof bone of 4th digit

E

Croup

Loin

Root of tail

Buttock

Tail

Thigh

Flank

Stifle

Belly

Gaskin

Hock

Chestnut

Shannon bone (cannon bone)

Pastern

Heel

Coronet

Hoof

**EXAMPLES OF
UNGULATES**

MALE RED DEER
(Cervus elephas)
An even-toed ungulate
(order Artiodactyla)

BACTRIAN CAMEL
(Camelus ferus)
An even-toed ungulate
(order Artiodactyla)

GIRAFFE
(Giraffa camelopardalis)
An even-toed ungulate
(order Artiodactyla)

**EXTERNAL FEATURES
OF A HORSE**

Mane
Poll
Crest
Ear
Forelock
Withers
Forehead
Eye
Muzzle
Nose
Nostril
Cheek
Mouth
Neck
Chin
groove
Shoulder

BLACK RHINOCEROS
(Diceros bicornis)
An odd-toed ungulate
(order Perissodactyla)

Breast

SKELETON OF A HORSE

Orbit
Skull
Lumbar vertebrae
Thoracic vertebrae
Atlas
Axis
Caudal
vertebrae
Sacrum
Cervical
vertebrae
Pelvis
Scapula
Mandible
ow
Femur
Forearm
Fibula
Sternum
Humerus
Tibia
Patella
Knee
Calcaneum
Tarsals
Radius
2nd metatarsal
Rib
Carpals
Cannon bone
4th metatarsal
Ulna
3rd metatarsal
3rd metacarpal
(cannon bone)
Fetlock
Phalanges of
3rd digit
Phalanges of 3rd digit
Pastern

Elephants

THE TWO SPECIES OF elephants – African and Asian – are the only members of the mammalian order Proboscidea. The bigger African elephant is the largest land animal: a fully grown male may be up to 4 m (13 ft) tall and weigh as much as 7 tonnes (6.9 tons). A fully grown male Asian elephant may be 3.3 m (11 ft) tall and weigh 5.4 tonnes (5.3 tons). The trunk – an extension of the nose and upper lip – is the elephant's other most obvious feature. It is used for manipulating and lifting, feeding, drinking and spraying water, smelling, touching, and producing trumpeting sounds. Other characteristic features include a pair of tusks, used for defence and for crushing vegetation; thick, pillar-like legs and broad feet to support the massive body; and large ear flaps that act as radiators to keep the elephant cool.

DIFFERENCES BETWEEN AFRICAN AND ASIAN ELEPHANTS

Flat forehead
Concave back
Very large ears
2 "lips" at the end of the trunk
4 toenails

AFRICAN ELEPHANT
(Loxodonta africana)
3 toenails

Twin-domed forehead
Arched back
Smaller ears
1 "lip" at the end of the trunk
5 toenails
4 toenails

ASIAN ELEPHANT
(Elephas maximus)

INTERNAL ANATOMY OF A FEMALE ELEPHANT

Spinal cord
Heart
Stomach
Duodenum
Kidney
Ureter
Rump
Brain
Uterus
Nasal cavity
Rectum
Buccal cavity
Bladder
Mouth
Anal flap
Tongue
Anus
Tusk
Vagina
Epiglottis
Oesophagus
Trachea
Hind leg
Lung
Small intestine
Diaphragm
Spleen
Vulva
Nasal passage
Toenail
Nostril

EXTERNAL FEATURES OF A FEMALE AFRICAN ELEPHANT (TUSKS REMOVED)

Flat forehead

Eye

Pinna (ear flap)

SKULL OF AN ASIAN ELEPHANT

Orbit

Cranium

Maxilla

Jugal bar

Premaxilla

Tusk (upper incisor)

Upper molars

Lower molars

Mandible

Annulus (ring) of trunk

SKELETON OF AN AFRICAN ELEPHANT (TUSKS REMOVED)

Cervical vertebrae

Thoracolumbar vertebrae

Skull

Sacrum

Caudal vertebrae

Mandible

Scapula

Sternum

Pelvis

Rib

Femur

Humerus

Patella

Radius

Ulna

Tibia

Fibula

Carpals

Metacarpals

Tarsals

Phalanx

Phalanx

Metatarsals

Belly

Foreleg

Trunk (proboscis)

Upper "lip" of trunk

Lower "lip" of trunk

Primates

THE MAMMALIAN ORDER PRIMATES consists of monkeys, apes, and their relatives (including humans). There are two suborders of primates: Prosimii, the primitive primates, which include lemurs, tarsiers, and lorises; and Anthropoidea, the advanced primates, which include monkeys, apes, and humans. The anthropoids are divided into New World monkeys, Old World monkeys, and hominids. New World monkeys typically have wide-apart nostrils that open to the side; and long tails, which are prehensile (grasping) in some species. This group of monkeys lives in South America, and includes marmosets, tamarins, and howler monkeys. Old World monkeys typically have close-set nostrils that open forwards or downwards; and non-prehensile tails. This group of monkeys lives in Africa and Asia, and includes langurs, mandrills, macaques, and baboons. Hominids typically have large brains, and no tail. This group includes the apes — chimpanzees, gibbons, gorillas, and orangutans — and humans.

INTERNAL ANATOMY OF A FEMALE CHIMPANZEE

Buccal cavity
Tongue
Trachea
Lung
Liver
Pancreas
Small intestine
Caecum
Appendix
Ovary
Uterus

Brain
Nasal cavity
Spinal cord
Oesophagus
Heart
Diaphragm
Stomach
Spleen
Large intestine
Rectum
Bladder
Urethra

Vagina

SKELETON OF A RHESUS MONKEY

Cervical vertebrae
Thoracic vertebrae
Lumbar vertebrae
Sacrum
Femur
Patella
Fibula
Pelvis
Caudal vertebrae
Tarsals
Metatarsals

Skull
Orbit
Mandible
Clavicle
Scapula
Rib
Humerus
Radius
Ulna
Carpals
Metacarpals
Tibia
Phalanges
Phalanges

SKULL OF A CHIMPANZEE

Temporal bone
Suture
Parietal bone
Occipital bone
Auditory meatus
Zygomatic arch
Mandible

Frontal bone
Supraorbital ridge
Orbit
Maxilla
Premaxilla
Incisor tooth
Canine tooth
Premolar tooth
Molar tooth

EXAMPLES OF PRIMATES

RING-TAILED LEMUR
(*Lemur catta*)
A prosimian

MALE RED HOWLER MONKEY
(*Alouatta seniculus*)
A New World monkey

MALE MANDRILL
(*Mandrillus sphinx*)
An Old World monkey

CHIMPANZEE
(*Pan troglodytes*)
An ape

EXTERNAL FEATURES OF
A YOUNG GORILLA

GOLDEN LION TAMARIN
(*Leontopithecus rosalia*)
A New World monkey

Pinna (ear flap)

Brow ridge

Shoulder

Eye

Nostril

Mouth

Upper arm

Thigh

Forearm

Chest

Knee

Elbow

Lower leg

Hand

Foot

Toe

Finger

Toenail

Dolphins, whales, and seals

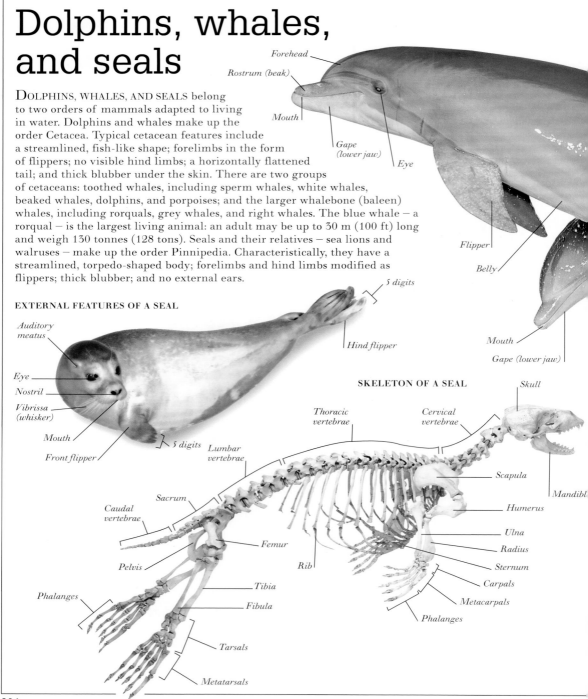

DOLPHINS, WHALES, AND SEALS belong to two orders of mammals adapted to living in water. Dolphins and whales make up the order Cetacea. Typical cetacean features include a streamlined, fish-like shape; forelimbs in the form of flippers; no visible hind limbs; a horizontally flattened tail; and thick blubber under the skin. There are two groups of cetaceans: toothed whales, including sperm whales, white whales, beaked whales, dolphins, and porpoises; and the larger whalebone (baleen) whales, including rorquals, grey whales, and right whales. The blue whale – a rorqual – is the largest living animal: an adult may be up to 30 m (100 ft) long and weigh 130 tonnes (128 tons). Seals and their relatives – sea lions and walruses – make up the order Pinnipedia. Characteristically, they have a streamlined, torpedo-shaped body; forelimbs and hind limbs modified as flippers; thick blubber; and no external ears.

Forehead

Rostrum (beak)

Mouth

Gape (lower jaw)

Eye

Flipper

Belly

Mouth

Gape (lower jaw)

EXTERNAL FEATURES OF A SEAL

5 digits

Hind flipper

Auditory meatus

Eye

Nostril

Vibrissa (whisker)

Mouth

Front flipper

5 digits

SKELETON OF A SEAL

Lumbar vertebrae

Thoracic vertebrae

Cervical vertebrae

Skull

Scapula

Mandible

Humerus

Ulna

Radius

Sternum

Carpals

Metacarpals

Phalanges

Sacrum

Caudal vertebrae

Pelvis

Femur

Rib

Tibia

Fibula

Phalanges

Tarsals

Metatarsals

EXAMPLES OF CETACEANS

BLUE WHALE
(Balaenoptera musculus)

SPERM WHALE
(Physeter catodon)

MALE BAIRD'S BEAKED WHALE
(Berardius bairdi)

MALE KILLER WHALE
(Orcinus orca)

MALE NARWHAL
(Monodon monoceros)

EXTERNAL FEATURES OF A DOLPHIN

Dorsal fin

Tail

Tail fluke

INTERNAL ANATOMY OF A MALE DOLPHIN

Spinal cord

Stomach

Kidney

Blowhole (nostril)

Brain

Aorta

Intestine

Bladder

Nasal plug

Melon

Buccal cavity

Tongue

Anus

Oesophagus

Rectum

Penis

Trachea

Liver

Testis

Heart

Lung

Urinogenital opening

205

Marsupials and Monotremes

MARSUPIALS AND MONOTREMES are two orders of mammals that differ from other mammalian groups in the ways that their young develop. The order Marsupalia, the pouched mammals, is made up of kangaroos and their relatives. Typically, marsupials give birth to their young at a very early stage of development. The young then crawls to the mother's pouch (which is on the outside of her abdomen), where it attaches itself to a nipple and remains until fully developed. Most marsupials live in Australia, although the opossums — which are classified as marsupials despite not having a pouch — live in the Americas. The order Monotremata is made up of the platypus and its relatives (the echidnas, or spiny anteaters). The monotremes are primitive mammals that lay eggs, which the mother incubates. The monotremes are found only in Australia and New Guinea.

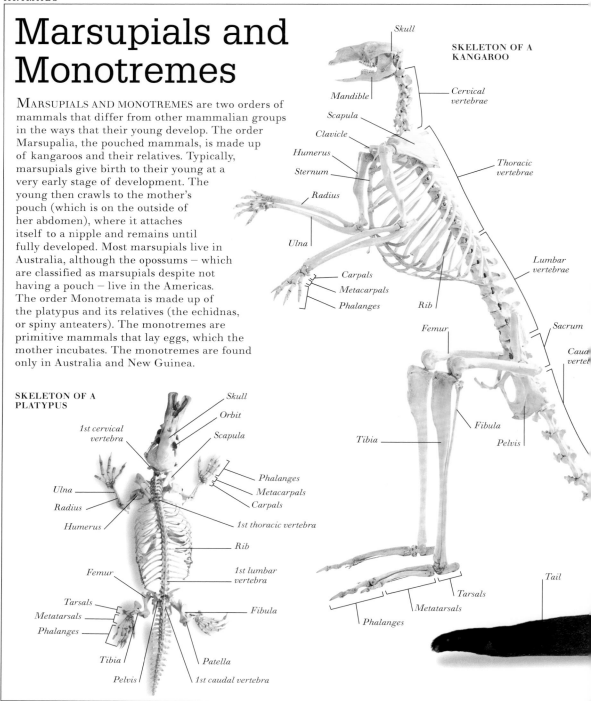

SKELETON OF A KANGAROO

Skull

Mandible

Cervical vertebrae

Scapula

Clavicle

Humerus

Sternum

Thoracic vertebrae

Radius

Ulna

Lumbar vertebrae

Carpals

Metacarpals

Phalanges

Rib

Femur

Sacrum

Caud vertel

Fibula

Tibia

Pelvis

Tarsals

Metatarsals

Phalanges

Tail

SKELETON OF A PLATYPUS

Skull

Orbit

Scapula

1st cervical vertebra

Phalanges

Metacarpals

Carpals

Ulna

Radius

Humerus

1st thoracic vertebra

Rib

1st lumbar vertebra

Femur

Tarsals

Metatarsals

Phalanges

Fibula

Tibia

Patella

Pelvis

1st caudal vertebra

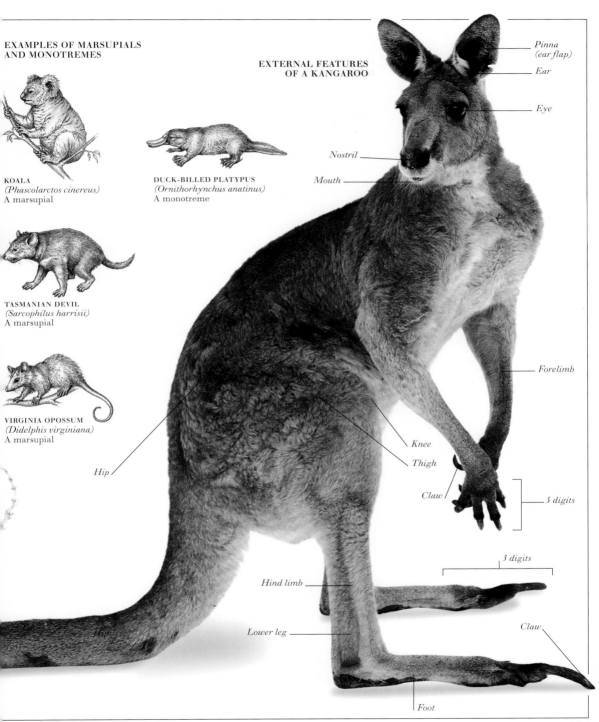

EXAMPLES OF MARSUPIALS AND MONOTREMES

EXTERNAL FEATURES OF A KANGAROO

KOALA
(Phascolarctos cinereus)
A marsupial

DUCK-BILLED PLATYPUS
(Ornithorhynchus anatinus)
A monotreme

TASMANIAN DEVIL
(Sarcophilus harrisii)
A marsupial

VIRGINIA OPOSSUM
(Didelphis virginiana)
A marsupial

Pinna
(ear flap)

Ear

Eye

Nostril

Mouth

Forelimb

Knee

Thigh

Claw

5 digits

3 digits

Hip

Hip

Hind limb

Lower leg

Claw

Foot

THE HUMAN BODY

BODY FEATURES·······210
HEAD·······212
BODY ORGANS·······214
BODY CELLS·······216
SKELETON·······218
SKULL·······220
SPINE·······222
BONES AND JOINTS·······224
MUSCLES 1·······226
MUSCLES 2·······228
HANDS·······230
FEET·······232
SKIN AND HAIR·······234
BRAIN·······236
NERVOUS SYSTEM·······238
EYE·······240
EAR·······242
NOSE, MOUTH, AND THROAT·······244
TEETH·······246
DIGESTIVE SYSTEM·······248
HEART·······250
CIRCULATORY SYSTEM·······252
RESPIRATORY SYSTEM·······254
URINARY SYSTEM·······256
REPRODUCTIVE SYSTEM·······258
DEVELOPMENT OF A BABY·······260

Body features

ALTHOUGH THERE IS enormous
variation between the external
appearances of humans, all bodies
contain the same basic features.
The outward form of the
human body depends on the
size of the skeleton, the shape
of the muscles, the thickness
of the fat layer beneath
the skin, the elasticity or
sagginess of the skin, and
the person's age and sex.
Males tend to be taller than
females, with broader
shoulders, more body hair,
and a different pattern of fat
deposits under the skin; the
female body tends to be
less muscular and has
a shallower and wider
pelvis to allow
for childbirth.

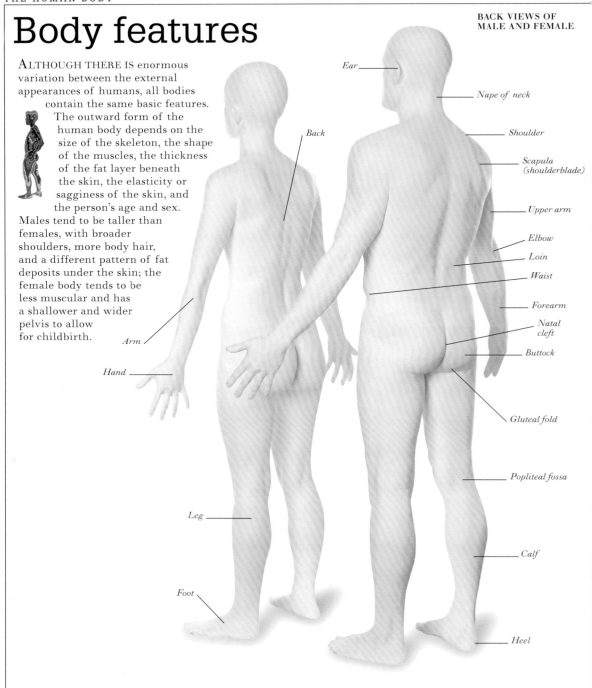

Ear

Nape of neck

Shoulder

Scapula
(shoulderblade)

Back

Upper arm

Elbow

Loin

Waist

Forearm

Natal
cleft

Buttock

Arm

Hand

Gluteal fold

Popliteal fossa

Leg

Calf

Foot

Heel

**FRONT VIEWS OF
MALE AND FEMALE**

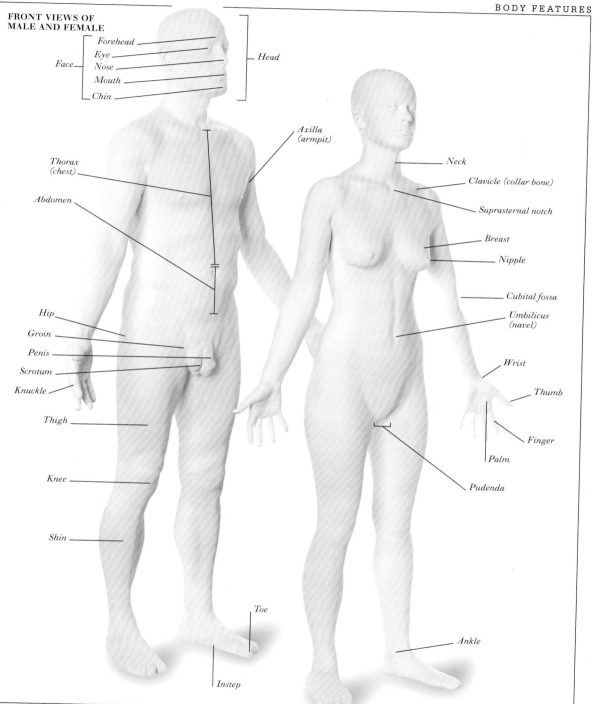

Forehead

Eye

Face — Nose

Mouth

Chin

Head

Axilla
(armpit)

Thorax
(chest)

Neck

Clavicle (collar bone)

Suprasternal notch

Abdomen

Breast

Nipple

Cubital fossa

Umbilicus
(navel)

Hip

Groin

Penis

Scrotum

Knuckle

Wrist

Thumb

Finger

Palm

Thigh

Pudenda

Knee

Shin

Toe

Ankle

Instep

Head

IN A NEWBORN BABY, the head accounts
for one-quarter of the total body length;
by adulthood, the proportion has reduced
to one-eighth. Contained in the head are
the body's main sense organs: eyes, ears,
olfactory nerves that detect smells, and the
taste buds of the tongue. Signals from these
organs pass to the body's great coordination
centre: the brain, housed in the protective,
bony dome of the skull. Hair on the head
insulates against heat loss, and adult males
also grow thick facial hair. The face has
three important openings: two nostrils
through which air passes, and the mouth,
which takes in nourishment and helps form
speech. Although all heads are basically
similar, differences in the size, shape, and
colour of features produce an infinite variety
of appearances.

SIDE VIEW OF EXTERNAL FEATURES OF HEAD

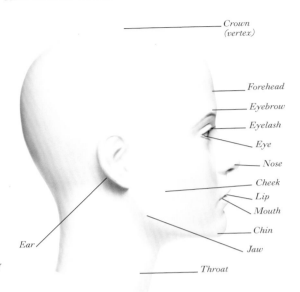

Crown
(vertex)

Forehead

Eyebrow

Eyelash

Eye

Nose

Cheek

Lip

Mouth

Chin

Jaw

Ear

Throat

SECTION THROUGH HEAD

Superior sagittal sinus

Cerebrum

Frontal sinus

Sphenoidal sinus

Superior concha

Middle concha

Inferior concha

Vestibule

Maxilla (upper jaw)

Hard palate

Soft palate

Tongue

Uvula

Mandible (lower jaw)

Palatine tonsil

Epiglottis

Trachea

Oesophagus

Skull

Pineal body

Pituitary gland

Cerebellum

Pons

Medulla oblongata

Pharynx

Cervical vertebra

Spinal cord

Intervertebral disc

**FRONT VIEW OF EXTERNAL
FEATURES OF HEAD**

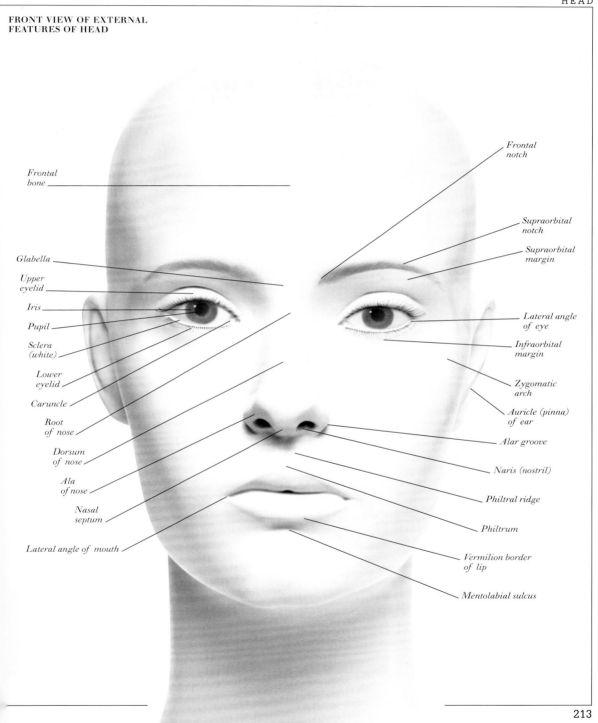

Frontal
notch

Supraorbital
notch

Supraorbital
margin

Frontal
bone

Lateral angle
of eye

Glabella

Upper
eyelid

Infraorbital
margin

Iris

Pupil

Zygomatic
arch

Sclera
(white)

Auricle (pinna)
of ear

Lower
eyelid

Alar groove

Caruncle

Naris (nostril)

Root
of nose

Philtral ridge

Dorsum
of nose

Ala
of nose

Philtrum

Nasal
septum

Vermilion border
of lip

Lateral angle of mouth

Mentolabial sulcus

Body organs

ALL THE VITAL BODY ORGANS except for the brain are enclosed within the trunk or torso (the body apart from the head and limbs). The trunk contains two large cavities separated by a muscular sheet called the diaphragm. The upper cavity, known as the thorax or chest cavity, contains the heart and lungs. The lower cavity, called the abdominal cavity, contains the stomach, intestines, liver, and pancreas, which all play a role in digesting food. Also within the trunk are the kidneys and bladder, which are part of the urinary system, and the reproductive organs, which hold the seeds of new human life. Modern imaging techniques, such as contrast X-rays and different types of scans, make it possible to see and study body organs without the need to cut through their protective coverings of skin, fat, muscle, and bone.

MAJOR INTERNAL STRUCTURES

Thyroid gland

Larynx

Heart

Right lung

Left lung

Diaphragm

Liver

Large intestine

Stomach

Small intestine

Greater omentum

IMAGING THE BODY

SCINTIGRAM OF HEART CHAMBERS

ANGIOGRAM OF RIGHT LUNG

CONTRAST X-RAY OF GALLBLADDER

SCINTIGRAM OF NERVOUS SYSTEM

DOUBLE CONTRAST X-RAY OF COLON

ULTRASOUND SCAN OF TWINS IN UTERUS

ANGIOGRAM OF KIDNEYS

ANGIOGRAM OF ARTERIES OF HEAD

CT SCAN THROUGH FEMALE CHEST

THERMOGRAM OF CHEST REGION

ANGIOGRAM OF ARTERIES OF HEART

MRI SCAN THROUGH HEAD AT EYE LEVEL

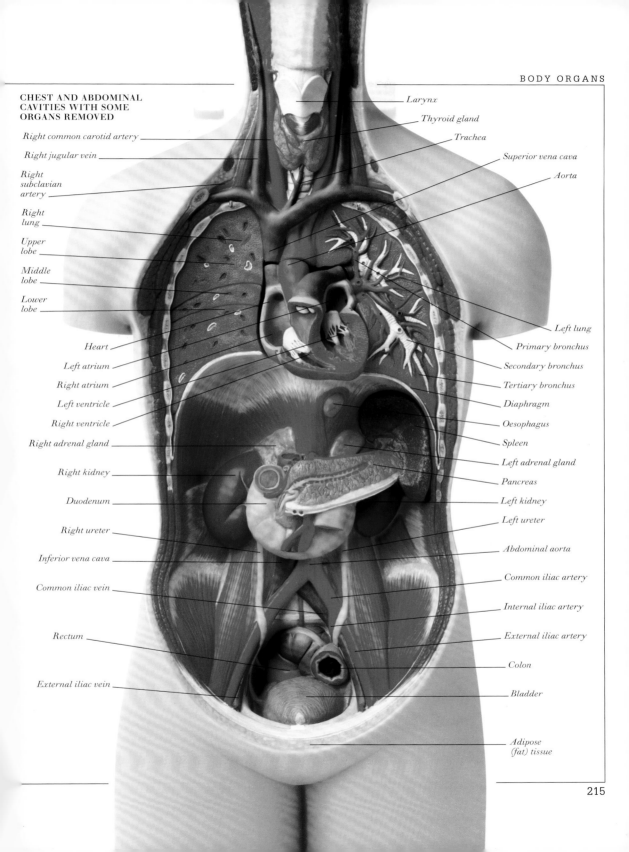

**CHEST AND ABDOMINAL
CAVITIES WITH SOME
ORGANS REMOVED**

Right common carotid artery

Right jugular vein

*Right
subclavian
artery*

*Right
lung*

*Upper
lobe*

*Middle
lobe*

*Lower
lobe*

Heart

Left atrium

Right atrium

Left ventricle

Right ventricle

Right adrenal gland

Right kidney

Duodenum

Right ureter

Inferior vena cava

Common iliac vein

Rectum

External iliac vein

Larynx

Thyroid gland

Trachea

Superior vena cava

Aorta

Left lung

Primary bronchus

Secondary bronchus

Tertiary bronchus

Diaphragm

Oesophagus

Spleen

Left adrenal gland

Pancreas

Left kidney

Left ureter

Abdominal aorta

Common iliac artery

Internal iliac artery

External iliac artery

Colon

Bladder

*Adipose
(fat) tissue*

Body cells

EVERYONE IS MADE UP OF BILLIONS OF CELLS, which are the basic structural units of the body. Bones, muscles, nerves, skin, blood, and all other body tissues are formed from different types of cells. Each cell has a specific function but works with other types of cells to perform the enormous number of tasks needed to sustain life. Most body cells have a similar basic structure. Each cell has an outer layer (called the cell membrane) and contains a fluid material (cytoplasm). Within the cytoplasm are many specialized structures (organelles). The most important organelle is the nucleus, which contains vital genetic material and acts as the cell's control centre.

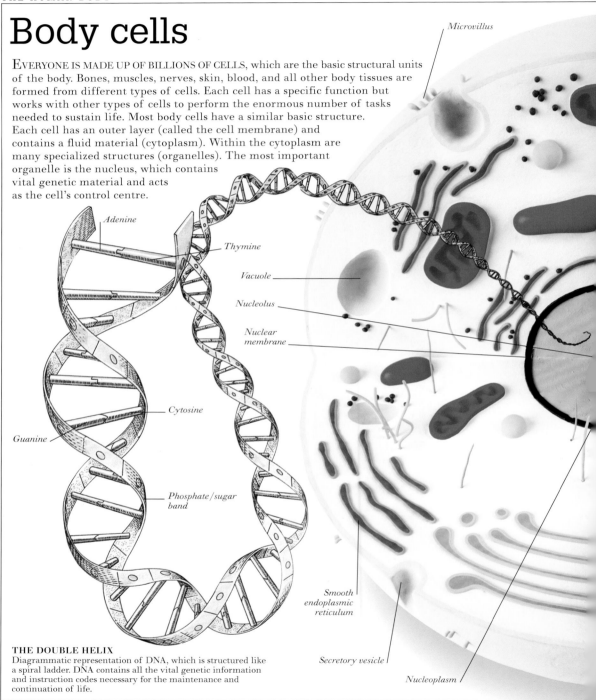

Microvillus

Adenine

Thymine

Vacuole

Nucleolus

Nuclear membrane

Cytosine

Guanine

Phosphate/sugar band

Smooth endoplasmic reticulum

Secretory vesicle

Nucleoplasm

THE DOUBLE HELIX
Diagrammatic representation of DNA, which is structured like a spiral ladder. DNA contains all the vital genetic information and instruction codes necessary for the maintenance and continuation of life.

GENERALIZED HUMAN CELL

Cytoplasm

Lysosome

Cell membrane

Mitochondrial crista

Nucleus

Rough endoplasmic reticulum

Microfilament

Pore of nuclear membrane

Ribosome

Centriole

Mitochondrion

Microtubule

Peroxisome

Pinocytotic vesicle

Golgi complex (Golgi apparatus; Golgi body)

TYPES OF CELLS

BONE-FORMING CELL

NERVE CELLS IN SPINAL CORD

SPERM CELLS IN SEMEN

SECRETORY THYROID GLAND CELLS

ACID-SECRETING STOMACH CELLS

CONNECTIVE TISSUE CELLS

MUCUS-SECRETING DUODENAL CELLS

RED AND TWO WHITE BLOOD CELLS

FAT CELLS IN ADIPOSE TISSUE

EPITHELIAL CELLS IN CHEEK

Skeleton

THE SKELETON IS A MOBILE FRAMEWORK made up of 206 bones, approximately half of which are in the hands and feet. Although individual bones are rigid, the skeleton as a whole is remarkably flexible and allows the human body a huge range of movement. The skeleton serves as an anchorage for the skeletal muscles, and as a protective cage for the body's internal organs. Female bones are usually smaller and lighter than male bones, and the female pelvis is shallower and has a wider cavity.

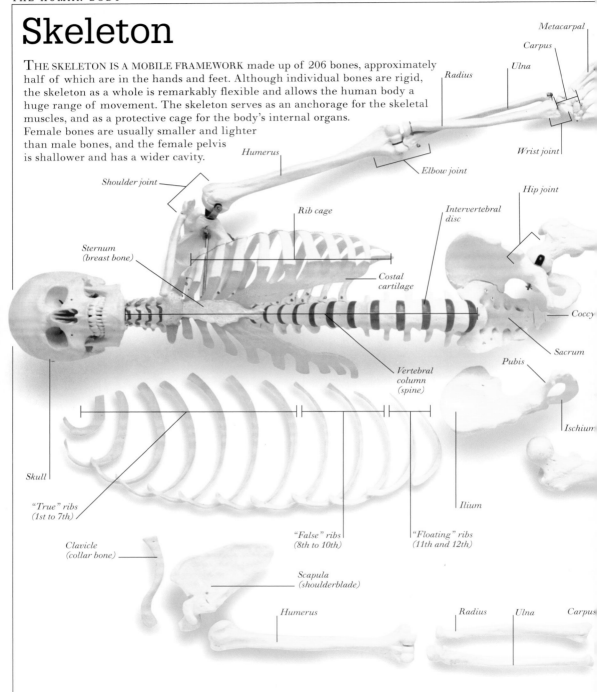

Metacarpal

Carpus

Ulna

Radius

Humerus

Elbow joint

Wrist joint

Shoulder joint

Rib cage

Hip joint

Intervertebral disc

Sternum (breast bone)

Costal cartilage

Coccy

Vertebral column (spine)

Sacrum

Pubis

Skull

Ischiur

Ilium

"True" ribs (1st to 7th)

"False" ribs (8th to 10th)

"Floating" ribs (11th and 12th)

Clavicle (collar bone)

Scapula (shoulderblade)

Humerus

Radius

Ulna

Carpus

Distal phalanx

Middle phalanx

Proximal phalanx

Femur

Patella

Tibia

Fibula

Tarsus

Proximal phalanx

Middle phalanx

Distal phalanx

Knee joint

Ankle joint

Metatarsal

Patella

Distal phalanx

Middle phalanx

Proximal phalanx

Femur

Tibia

Fibula

Tarsus

Metatarsal

Metacarpal

Proximal phalanx

Middle phalanx

Distal phalanx

Skull

THE SKULL is the most complicated bony structure of the body but every feature serves a purpose. Internally, the main hollow chamber of the skull has three levels that support the brain, with every bump and hollow corresponding to the shape of the brain. Underneath and towards the back of the skull is a large round hole, the foramen magnum, through which the spinal cord passes. To the front of this are many smaller openings through which nerves, arteries, and veins pass to and from the brain. The roof of the skull is formed from four thin, curved bones that are firmly fixed together from the age of about two years. At the front of the skull are the two orbits, which contain the eyeballs, and a central hole for the airway of the nose. The jaw bone hinges on either side at ear level.

RIGHT SIDE VIEW OF A FETAL SKULL

Anterior fontanelle

Parietal bone

Coronal suture

Frontal bone

Nasal bone

Mental symphysis

Lambdoid suture

Occipital bone

Mastoid fontanelle

External auditory meatus

Sphenoidal fontanelle

RIGHT SIDE VIEW OF SKULL

Coronal suture

Frontal bone

Greater wing of sphenoid bone

Frontozygomatic suture

Parietal bone

Supraorbital margin

Squamous suture

Orbital cavity

Nasal bone

Anterior nasal spine

Maxilla (upper jaw)

Mandible (lower jaw)

Lambdoid suture

Occipital bone

Temporal bone

External auditory meatus

Styloid process

Mastoid process

Condyle

Zygomatic arch

Zygomatic bone

Coronoid process

Posterior border of vomer

Mental foramen

Concha

Mandible (lower jaw)

VIEW OF SKULL FROM BELOW

External occipital crest

Foramen magnum

Occipital condyle

Carotid canal

Mastoid process

Pharyngeal tubercle

Pterygoid plate

Pterygoid hamulus

Greater palatine foramen

Posterior nasal aperture

FRONT VIEW OF SKULL

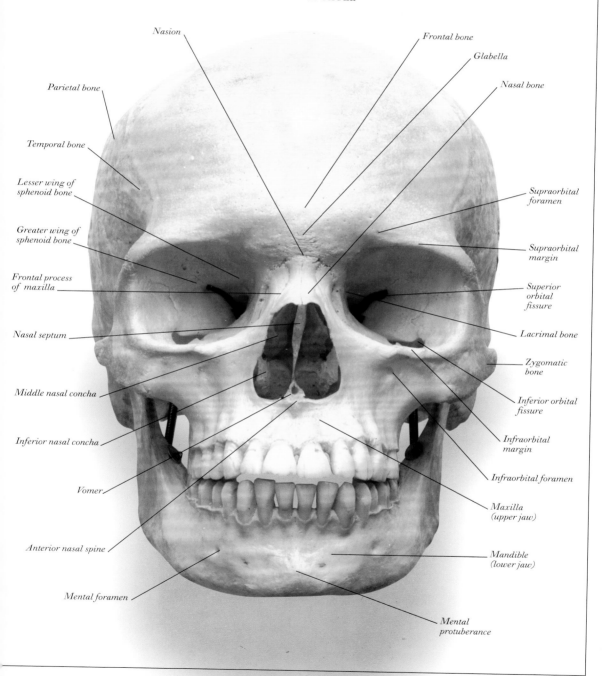

Nasion

Frontal bone

Glabella

Nasal bone

Parietal bone

Temporal bone

Lesser wing of
sphenoid bone

Greater wing of
sphenoid bone

Frontal process
of maxilla

Nasal septum

Middle nasal concha

Inferior nasal concha

Vomer

Anterior nasal spine

Mental foramen

Supraorbital
foramen

Supraorbital
margin

Superior
orbital
fissure

Lacrimal bone

Zygomatic
bone

Inferior orbital
fissure

Infraorbital
margin

Infraorbital foramen

Maxilla
(upper jaw)

Mandible
(lower jaw)

Mental
protuberance

Spine

THE SPINE (OR VERTEBRAL COLUMN) has two main functions: it serves as a protective surrounding for the delicate spinal cord and forms the supporting back bone of the skeleton. The spine consists of 24 separate differently shaped bones (vertebrae) with a curved, triangular bone (the sacrum) at the bottom. The sacrum is made up of fused vertebrae; at its lower end is a small tail-like structure made up of tiny bones collectively called the coccyx. Between each pair of vertebrae is a disc of cartilage that cushions the bones during movement. The top two vertebrae differ in appearance from the others and work as a pair: the first, called the atlas, rotates around a stout vertical peg on the second, the axis. This arrangement allows the skull to move freely up and down, and from side to side.

SPINE DIVIDED INTO VERTEBRAL SECTIONS

FRONT

Cervical vertebrae

Thoracic vertebrae

Lumbar vertebrae

Sacral vertebrae

Coccygeal vertebrae

TYPES OF VERTEBRAE (VIEWED FROM ABOVE)

ATLAS

Anterior arch
Lateral mass with superior articular facet
Posterior arch
Anterior tubercle
Posterior tubercle
Vertebral foramen
Transverse process
Transverse foramen

AXIS

Facet
Dens
Vertebral foramen
Spinous process
Lamina
Transverse process and foramen

CERVICAL VERTEBRA

Body
Superior articular process
Anterior tubercle
Spinous process
Posterior tubercle
Vertebral foramen
Transverse foramen

SKULL AND SPINE

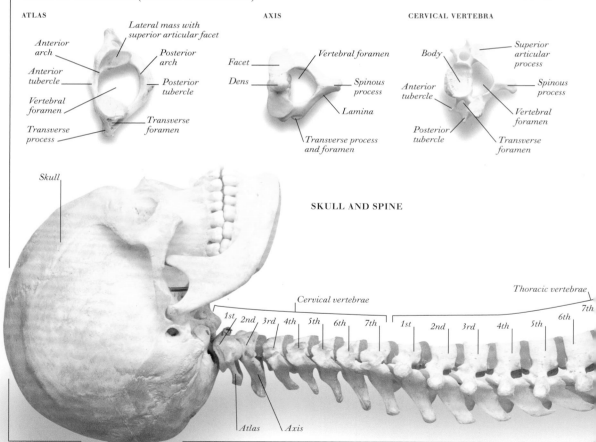

Skull

Cervical vertebrae

Thoracic vertebrae

7th

1st 2nd 3rd 4th 5th 6th 7th

1st 2nd 3rd 4th 5th 6th

Atlas   Axis

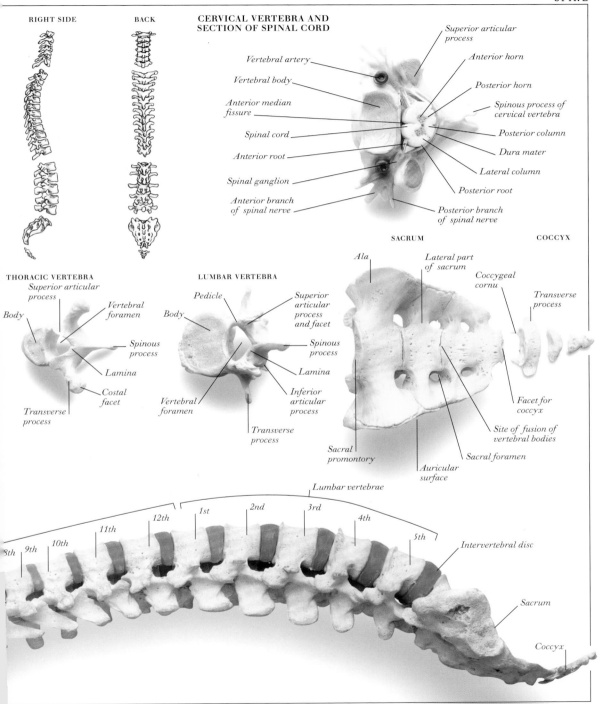

RIGHT SIDE

BACK

CERVICAL VERTEBRA AND SECTION OF SPINAL CORD

Vertebral artery

Vertebral body

Anterior median fissure

Spinal cord

Anterior root

Spinal ganglion

Anterior branch of spinal nerve

Superior articular process

Anterior horn

Posterior horn

Spinous process of cervical vertebra

Posterior column

Dura mater

Lateral column

Posterior root

Posterior branch of spinal nerve

THORACIC VERTEBRA

Superior articular process

Vertebral foramen

Body

Spinous process

Lamina

Costal facet

Transverse process

LUMBAR VERTEBRA

Pedicle

Body

Superior articular process and facet

Spinous process

Lamina

Inferior articular process

Vertebral foramen

Transverse process

SACRUM

Ala

Lateral part of sacrum

Sacral promontory

Auricular surface

Sacral foramen

Site of fusion of vertebral bodies

COCCYX

Coccygeal cornu

Transverse process

Facet for coccyx

Lumbar vertebrae

8th   9th   10th   11th   12th   1st   2nd   3rd   4th   5th

Intervertebral disc

Sacrum

Coccyx

Bones and joints

BONES FORM the body's hard, strong
skeletal framework. Each bone has a
hard, compact exterior surrounding
a spongy, lighter interior. The long
bones of the arms and legs, such as
the femur (thigh bone), have a central
cavity containing bone marrow. Bones
are composed chiefly of calcium,
phosphorus, and a fibrous substance
known as collagen. Bones meet at joints,
which are of several different types. For
example, the hip is a ball-and-socket
joint that allows the femur a wide range
of movement, whereas finger joints are
simple hinge joints that allow only
bending and straightening. Joints are
held in place by bands of tissue called
ligaments. Movement of joints is
facilitated by the smooth hyaline
cartilage that covers the bone ends
and by the synovial membrane that
lines and lubricates the joint.

LIGAMENTS SURROUNDING HIP JOINT

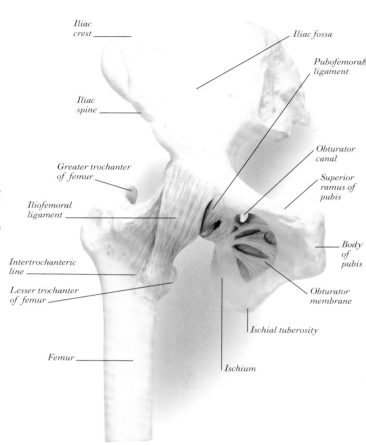

Iliac crest

Iliac fossa

Pubofemoral ligament

Iliac spine

Obturator canal

Greater trochanter of femur

Superior ramus of pubis

Iliofemoral ligament

Body of pubis

Intertrochanteric line

Obturator membrane

Lesser trochanter of femur

Ischial tuberosity

Femur

Ischium

SECTION THROUGH LEFT FEMUR

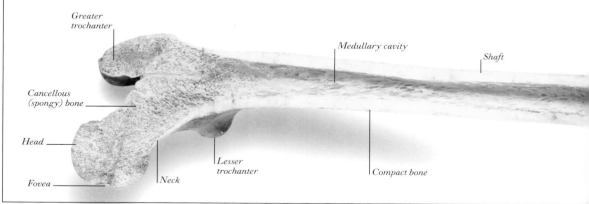

Greater trochanter

Medullary cavity

Shaft

Cancellous (spongy) bone

Head

Lesser trochanter

Compact bone

Fovea

Neck

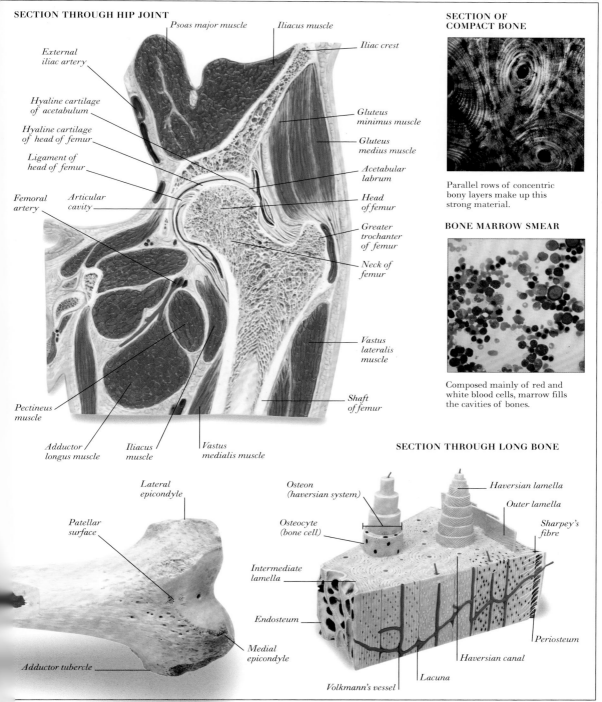

SECTION THROUGH HIP JOINT

Psoas major muscle

Iliacus muscle

Iliac crest

External iliac artery

Hyaline cartilage of acetabulum

Hyaline cartilage of head of femur

Ligament of head of femur

Femoral artery

Articular cavity

Pectineus muscle

Adductor longus muscle

Iliacus muscle

Vastus medialis muscle

Gluteus minimus muscle

Gluteus medius muscle

Acetabular labrum

Head of femur

Greater trochanter of femur

Neck of femur

Vastus lateralis muscle

Shaft of femur

SECTION OF COMPACT BONE

Parallel rows of concentric bony layers make up this strong material.

BONE MARROW SMEAR

Composed mainly of red and white blood cells, marrow fills the cavities of bones.

Lateral epicondyle

Patellar surface

Adductor tubercle

Medial epicondyle

SECTION THROUGH LONG BONE

Osteon (haversian system)

Osteocyte (bone cell)

Intermediate lamella

Endosteum

Volkmann's vessel

Lacuna

Haversian lamella

Outer lamella

Sharpey's fibre

Periosteum

Haversian canal

Muscles 1

THERE ARE THREE MAIN TYPES OF MUSCLE: skeletal muscle (also called voluntary muscle because it can be consciously controlled); smooth muscle (also called involuntary muscle because it is not under voluntary control); and the specialized muscle tissue of the heart. Humans have more than 600 skeletal muscles, which differ in size and shape according to the jobs they do. Skeletal muscles are attached either directly or indirectly (via tendons) to bones, and work in opposing pairs (one muscle in the pair contracts while the other relaxes) to produce body movements as diverse as walking, threading a needle, and an array of facial expressions. Smooth muscles occur in the walls of internal body organs and perform actions such as forcing food through the intestines, contracting the uterus (womb) in childbirth, and pumping blood through the blood vessels.

SOME OTHER MUSCLES IN THE BODY

Iris

Pupil

IRIS
The muscle fibres contract and dilate (expand) to alter pupil size.

TONGUE
Interlacing layers of muscle allow great mobility.

ILEUM
Opposing muscle layers transport semi-digested food.

SUPERFICIAL SKELETAL MUSCLES

FRONT VIEW

Brachioradialis

Flexors of forearm

Brachialis

Frontalis

Orbicularis oculi

Temporalis

Sternocleidomastoid

Trapezius

Pectoralis major

Deltoid

Serratus anterior

Biceps brachii

Rectus abdominis

Linea alba

External oblique

Tensor fasciae latae

Iliopsoas

Pectineus

Adductor longus

Rectus femoris

Sartorius

Vastus lateralis

Gracilis

Vastus medialis

Gastrocnemius

Tibialis anterior

BACK VIEW

Extensors
of hand

Flexors
of hand

Temporalis

Sternocleidomastoid

Trapezius

Deltoid

Triceps
brachii

Teres minor

Teres major

Infraspinatus

Rhomboideus major

Latissimus dorsi

Gluteus
maximus

Adductor
magnus

Gracilis

Biceps femoris

Semitendinosus

Gastrocnemius

Soleus

Peroneus
brevis

MOVEMENT OF THE FOREARM

Controlled movement of the limbs relies
on coordinated relaxation and contraction
of opposing muscles. To raise the forearm,
the biceps (two-rooted muscle) contracts
and shortens while the triceps (three-
rooted muscle) relaxes; the reverse
occurs when the forearm is lowered.

Triceps in
resting phase

Biceps in
resting phase

Forearm
at rest

Triceps
relaxes

Biceps
contracts

Forearm
half raised

Triceps fully
relaxed

Biceps fully
contracted

Forearm
fully raised

Triceps
contracts

Biceps
relaxes

Forearm
half lowered

Triceps back in
resting phase

Biceps back in
resting phase

Forearm
back at rest

Muscles 2

SKELETAL MUSCLE FIBRE

Myofibril

Sarcomere

Motor
end plate

Nucleus

Synaptic
knob

*Sarcoplasmic
reticulum*

Sarcolemma

Schwann
cell

Endomysium

Motor
neuron

Node of
Ranvier

MUSCLES OF FACIAL EXPRESSION

A single expression is the result of movement of many muscles; the main muscles of expression are shown in action below.

FRONTALIS

**CORRUGATOR
SUPERCILII**

ORBICULARIS ORIS

ZYGOMATICUS MAJOR

**DEPRESSOR ANGULI
ORIS**

TYPES OF MUSCLE

CARDIAC MUSCLE

SKELETAL MUSCLE

SMOOTH MUSCLE

CONTRACTION OF SKELETAL MUSCLE

RELAXED STATE

CONTRACTED STATE

**MUSCLES OF
HEAD AND NECK**

Frontalis

Procerus

Temporalis

Corrugator
supercilii

Orbicularis
oculi

Levator labii
superioris

Zygomaticus
major

Nasalis

Orbicularis oris

Buccinator

Masseter

Risorius

Levator anguli oris

Platysma

Depressor labii
inferioris

Mentalis

Depressor anguli oris

Thyrohyoid

Scalenus medius

Sternocleidomastoid

Sternohyoid

Omohyoid

Cricothyroid

Trapezius

Hands

THE HUMAN HAND is an extremely versatile tool, capable of delicate manipulation as well as powerful gripping actions. The arrangement of its 27 small bones, moved by 37 skeletal muscles that are connected to the bones by tendons, allows a wide range of movements. Our ability to bring the tips of our thumbs and fingers together, combined with the extraordinary sensitivity of our fingertips due to their rich supply of nerve endings, makes our hands uniquely dextrous.

X-RAY OF LEFT HAND OF A YOUNG CHILD

Area of ossification in phalanx

Area of ossification in metacarpal

Area of ossification in wrist

Epiphysis of ulna

Epiphysis of radius

Areas of cartilage in the wrist and at the ends of the finger bones are the sites of growth and have still to ossify.

BONES OF HAND

Ring finger

Middle finger

Index finger

Little finger

Distal phalanx

Middle phalanx

Proximal phalanx

2nd metacarpal

3rd metacarpal

4th metacarpal

5th metacarpal

Hamate

Pisiform

Capitate

Triquetral

Lunate

Ulna

— Head

— Shaft

— Base

Distal phalanx of thumb

Proximal phalanx of thumb

1st metacarpal

Trapezium

Trapezoid

Scaphoid

Radius

STRUCTURES UNDERLYING SKIN OF PALM OF HAND

Flexor pollicis brevis muscle

Opponens pollicis muscle

Abductor pollicis brevis muscle

Flexor retinaculum

Radial artery

Adductor pollicis muscle

2nd lumbrical muscle

Digital artery

Digital nerve

Flexor digitorum tendon

Opponens digiti minimi muscle

Abductor digiti minimi muscle

Ulnar nerve

Ulnar artery

Palmaris longus tendon

EXTERNAL FEATURES OF BACK OF HAND

Distal interphalangeal joint

Little finger

Proximal interphalangeal joint

Extensor digitorum tendon

Head of ulna

Ring finger

Middle finger

Cuticle

Lunule

Index finger

Nail

Metacarpophalangeal joint

Wrist

Distal end of radius

Thumb

231

BONES OF FOOT

Feet

THE FEET AND TOES are essential elements in body movement. They bear and propel the weight of the body during walking and running, and also help to maintain balance during changes of body position. Each foot has 26 bones, more than 100 ligaments, and 33 muscles, some of which are attached to the lower leg. The heel pad and the arch of the foot act as shock absorbers, providing a cushion against the jolts that occur with every step.

2nd toe

Hallux (big toe)

3rd toe

Distal phalanx of hallux

4th toe

5th (little) toe

Distal phalanx

Proximal phalanx of hallux

Middle phalanx

Proximal phalanx

1st metatarsal

2nd metatarsal

3rd metatarsal

4th metatarsal

1st cuneiform

5th metatarsal

2nd cuneiform

3rd cuneiform

LIGAMENTS OF FOOT

Articular capsule of interphalangeal joint

Posterior cuneonavicular ligament

Plantar calcaneonavicular ligament

Navicular

Cuboid

Articular capsule of metatarsophalangeal joint

Talus

Posterior tarsometatarsal ligament

Talonavicular ligament

Bifurcate ligament

Deltoid ligament

Calcaneus

Fibula

Tibia

Calcanean (Achilles) tendon

Interosseous ligament

STRUCTURES UNDERLYING SKIN OF FOOT

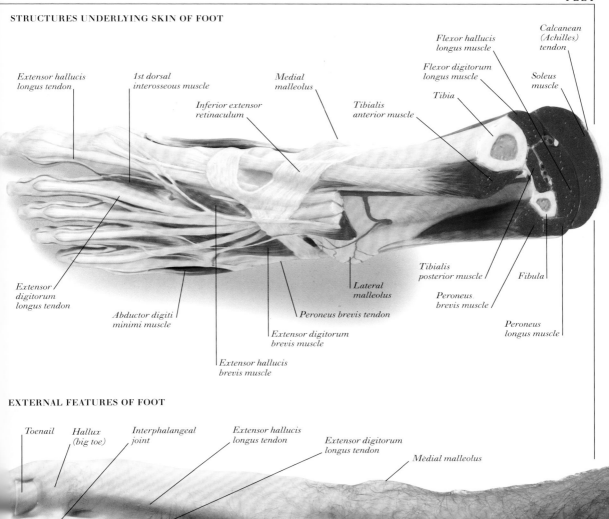

Calcanean
(Achilles)
tendon

Flexor hallucis
longus muscle

Flexor digitorum
longus muscle

Soleus
muscle

Extensor hallucis
longus tendon

1st dorsal
interosseous muscle

Medial
malleolus

Tibia

Inferior extensor
retinaculum

Tibialis
anterior muscle

Extensor
digitorum
longus tendon

Abductor digiti
minimi muscle

Extensor hallucis
brevis muscle

Extensor digitorum
brevis muscle

Lateral
malleolus

Peroneus brevis tendon

Tibialis
posterior muscle

Peroneus
brevis muscle

Fibula

Peroneus
longus muscle

EXTERNAL FEATURES OF FOOT

Toenail

Hallux
(big toe)

Interphalangeal
joint

Extensor hallucis
longus tendon

Extensor digitorum
longus tendon

Medial malleolus

2nd toe

3rd toe

4th toe

5th
(little) toe

Lateral malleolus

233

Skin and hair

SKIN IS THE BODY'S LARGEST ORGAN, a waterproof barrier that protects the internal organs against infection, injury, and harmful sun rays. The skin is also an important sensory organ and helps to control body temperature. The outer layer of the skin, known as the epidermis, is coated with keratin, a tough, horny protein that is also the chief constituent of hair and nails. Dead cells are shed from the skin's surface and are replaced by new cells from the base of the epidermis, the region that also produces the skin pigment, melanin. The dermis contains most of the skin's living structures, and includes nerve endings, blood vessels, elastic fibres, sweat glands that cool the skin, and sebaceous glands that produce oil to keep the skin supple. Beneath the dermis lies the subcutaneous tissue (hypodermis), which is rich in fat and blood vessels. Hair shafts grow from hair follicles situated in the dermis and subcutaneous tissue. Hair grows on every part of the skin apart from the palms of the hands and soles of the feet.

SECTION OF HAIR

Medulla

Cortex

Melanin granule

Cell nucleus residue

Macrofibril

Cuticle

SECTIONS OF DIFFERENT TYPES OF SKIN

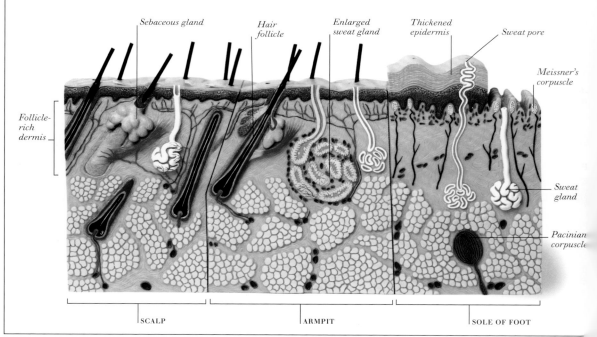

Sebaceous gland

Hair follicle

Enlarged sweat gland

Thickened epidermis

Sweat pore

Meissner's corpuscle

Follicle-rich dermis

Sweat gland

Pacinian corpuscle

SCALP

ARMPIT

SOLE OF FOOT

SECTION OF SKIN

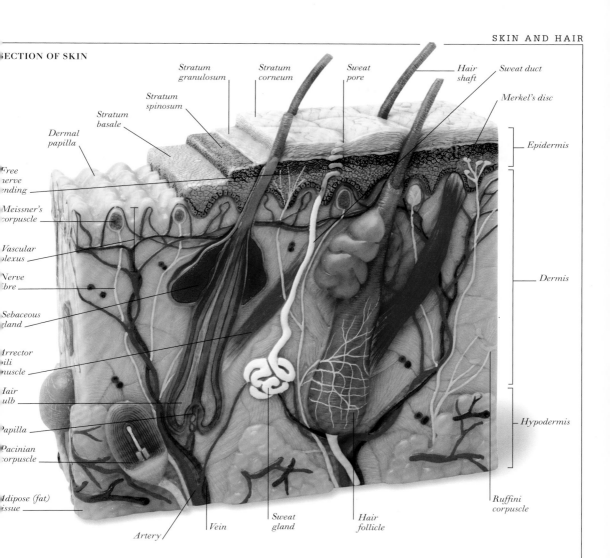

Stratum granulosum

Stratum corneum

Sweat pore

Hair shaft

Sweat duct

Stratum spinosum

Merkel's disc

Stratum basale

Dermal papilla

Epidermis

Free nerve ending

Meissner's corpuscle

Vascular plexus

Dermis

Nerve fibre

Sebaceous gland

Arrector pili muscle

Hair bulb

Hypodermis

Papilla

Pacinian corpuscle

Adipose (fat) tissue

Ruffini corpuscle

Artery

Vein

Sweat gland

Hair follicle

PHOTOMICROGRAPHS OF SKIN AND HAIR

SECTION OF SKIN
The flaky cells at the skin's surface are shed continuously.

SWEAT PORE
This allows loss of fluid as part of temperature control.

SKIN HAIR
Two hairs pushing through the outer layer of skin.

HEAD HAIR
The root and part of the shaft of a hair from the scalp.

Brain

THE BRAIN IS THE MAJOR ORGAN of the central nervous system and the control centre for all the body's voluntary and involuntary activities. It is also responsible for the complexities of thought, memory, emotion, and language. In adults, this complex organ is a mere 1.4 kg (3 lb) in weight, containing over 10 thousand million nerve cells. Three distinct regions can easily be seen – the brainstem, the cerebellum, and the large cerebrum. The brainstem controls vital body functions, such as breathing and digestion. The cerebellum's main functions are the maintenance of posture and the coordination of body movements. The cerebrum, which consists of the right and left cerebral hemispheres joined by the corpus callosum, is the site of most conscious and intelligent activities.

MRI SCAN OF TRANSVERSE SECTION THROUGH BRAIN

White matter

Grey matter

Skull

Scalp

Lateral ventricle

Longitudinal fissure

Coronal section

Sagittal section

SAGITTAL SECTION THROUGH BRAIN

Central sulcus

Fornix

Cerebrum

Parietal lobe

Corpus callosum

Parieto-occipital sulucs

Thalamus

Pineal body

Occipital lobe

Frontal lobe

Aqueduct

Hypothalamus

Cerebellum

Optic chiasma

4th ventricle

Pituitary gland

Spinal cord

Mesencephalon (midbrain)

Pons

Brainstem

Medulla oblongata

236

SECTION THROUGH SKULL AND BRAIN

- Scalp
- Epicranial aponeurosis
- Arachnoid granulation
- Pericranium
- Skull
- Lateral lacuna
- Dura mater
- Arachnoid mater
- Superior sagittal sinus
- Pia mater
- Falx cerebri
- Subarachnoid space
- Cerebral vessel
- Cerebrum
  - Grey matter
  - White matter

CORONAL SECTION THROUGH BRAIN

- Corpus callosum
- Longitudinal fissure
- Grey matter
- White matter
- Cerebrum
- Caudate nucleus
- Lateral ventricle
- Fornix
- Lentiform nucleus
- Internal capsule
- Thalamus
- Crus cerebri of midbrain
- 3rd ventricle
- Pons
- Medulla oblongata
- Cerebellum

EXTERNAL ANATOMY OF BRAIN

- Parietal lobe
- Parieto-occipital sulcus
- Precentral gyrus
- Postcentral gyrus
- Central sulcus
- Frontal lobe
- Lateral sulcus
- Temporal lobe
- Occipital lobe
- Cerebellum

SPECIFIC ROLES OF AREAS OF CEREBRUM

- Skilled movements
- Basic movements
- Sensation
- Visual recognition
- Behaviour and emotion
- Speech
- Hearing
- Vision
- Balance and muscle coordination

NERVE CELLS IN BRAIN

The dark cells are Purkinje's cells, which are among the largest nerve cells in the body.

237

Nervous system

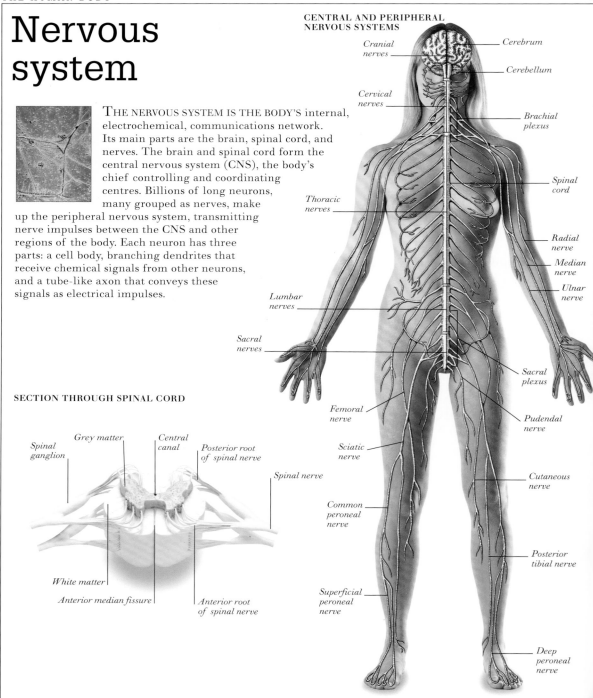

THE NERVOUS SYSTEM IS THE BODY'S internal, electrochemical, communications network. Its main parts are the brain, spinal cord, and nerves. The brain and spinal cord form the central nervous system (CNS), the body's chief controlling and coordinating centres. Billions of long neurons, many grouped as nerves, make up the peripheral nervous system, transmitting nerve impulses between the CNS and other regions of the body. Each neuron has three parts: a cell body, branching dendrites that receive chemical signals from other neurons, and a tube-like axon that conveys these signals as electrical impulses.

CENTRAL AND PERIPHERAL NERVOUS SYSTEMS

- Cranial nerves
- Cerebrum
- Cerebellum
- Cervical nerves
- Brachial plexus
- Thoracic nerves
- Spinal cord
- Radial nerve
- Median nerve
- Ulnar nerve
- Lumbar nerves
- Sacral nerves
- Sacral plexus
- Femoral nerve
- Pudendal nerve
- Sciatic nerve
- Cutaneous nerve
- Common peroneal nerve
- Posterior tibial nerve
- Superficial peroneal nerve
- Deep peroneal nerve

SECTION THROUGH SPINAL CORD

- Spinal ganglion
- Grey matter
- Central canal
- Posterior root of spinal nerve
- Spinal nerve
- White matter
- Anterior median fissure
- Anterior root of spinal nerve

238

STRUCTURE OF A MOTOR NEURON

Cell body

Nucleus

Synaptic knob

Axon hillock

Axon

Dendrite

Nucleolus

Nissl body

Schwann cell

Node of Ranvier

Mitochondrion

Myelin sheath

STRUCTURE OF A SYNAPTIC KNOB

Presynaptic axon

Microtubule

Neurofilament

Endoplasmic reticulum

Mitochondrion

Synaptic vesicle

Neurotransmitter

Presynaptic membrane

TYPES OF NEURON

MULTIPOLAR

Motor end plate

Node of Ranvier

Schwann cell

Myelin sheath

Axon

Cell body

Nucleus

Dendrite

Receptor

UNIPOLAR

Dendrite

Axon

Cell body

Nucleus

BIPOLAR

Dendrite

Axon

Cell body

Nucleus

Dendrite

TYPES OF NERVE ENDING

FREE NERVE ENDING

MEISSNER'S CORPUSCLE

MERKEL'S DISC

RUFFINI CORPUSCLE

PACINIAN CORPUSCLE

Eye

THE EYE IS THE ORGAN OF SIGHT. The two eyeballs, protected within bony sockets called orbits and on the outside by the eyelids, eyebrows, and tear film, are directly connected to the brain by the optic nerves. Each eye is moved by six muscles, which are attached around the eyeball. Light rays entering the eye through the pupil are focused by the cornea and lens to form an image on the retina. The retina contains millions of light-sensitive cells, called rods and cones, which convert the image into a pattern of nerve impulses. These impulses are transmitted along the optic nerve to the brain. Information from the two optic nerves is processed in the brain to produce a single coordinated image.

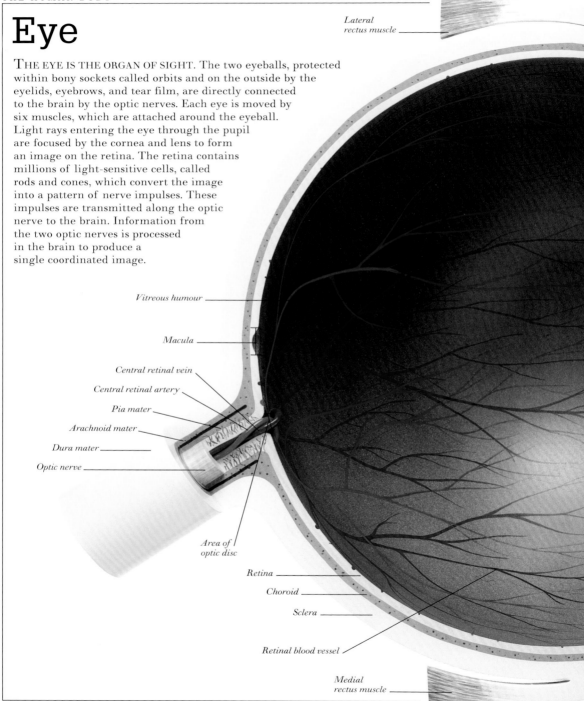

Lateral rectus muscle

Vitreous humour

Macula

Central retinal vein

Central retinal artery

Pia mater

Arachnoid mater

Dura mater

Optic nerve

Area of optic disc

Retina

Choroid

Sclera

Retinal blood vessel

Medial rectus muscle

SECTION THROUGH LEFT EYE

LACRIMAL (TEAR-PRODUCING) APPARATUS

Lacrimal sac

Lacrimal canaliculus

Lacrimal gland

Middle meatus

Middle nasal concha

Nasal septum

Inferior nasal concha

Nasolacrimal duct

Lacrimal punctum

Iris

Anterior chamber

Posterior chamber

Aqueous humour

Conjunctiva

Pupil

Cornea

Lens

Sphincter muscle

Dilator muscle

Zonular ligament

Sinus venosus sclerae

Iridocorneal angle

Ciliary body

Annular tendon

Ora serrata

OPHTHALMOSCOPIC VIEW OF RETINA

Retinal blood vessel

Optic disc

Macula

The blind spot, where the optic nerve leaves the eye, can be clearly seen as a light circular area towards the centre of the image.

MUSCLES SURROUNDING RIGHT EYE

Medial rectus

Superior oblique

Trochlea

Levator palpebrae superioris

Superior rectus

Inferior rectus

Lateral rectus

Inferior oblique

Ear

THE EAR IS THE ORGAN OF HEARING AND BALANCE. The outer ear consists of a flap called the auricle or pinna and the auditory canal. The main functional parts – the middle and inner ears – are enclosed within the skull. The middle ear consists of three tiny bones, known as auditory ossicles, and the eustachian tube, which links the ear to the back of the nose. The inner ear consists of the spiral-shaped cochlea, and also the semicircular canals and the vestibule, which are the organs of balance. Sound waves entering the ear travel through the auditory canal to the tympanic membrane (eardrum), where they are converted to vibrations that are transmitted via the ossicles to the cochlea. Here, the vibrations are converted by millions of microscopic hairs into electrical nerve signals to be interpreted by the brain.

RIGHT AURICLE (PINNA)

Upper crux of antihelix

Auricle (pinna)

Triangular fossa

Scaphoid fossa

Lower crux of antihelix

Concha

Helix

Auditory canal

Antihelix

Tragus

Antitragus

Intertragic notch

External auditory meatus

Cartilaginous part of meatus

Lobule

Lobule

Temporal bone

Cartilage of auricle

Mastoid process

OSSICLES OF MIDDLE EAR

MALLEUS (HAMMER)   INCUS (ANVIL)   STAPES (STIRRUP)

These three tiny bones connect to form a bridge between the tympanic membrane and the oval window. With a system of membranes they convey sound vibrations to the inner ear.

INTERNAL STRUCTURE OF AMPULLA

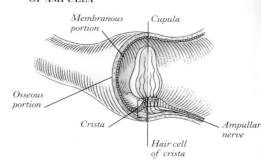

Membranous portion

Cupula

Osseous portion

Crista

Hair cell of crista

Ampullar nerve

LABYRINTH

Utricle

Saccule

Vestibular nerve

Common crus

Tympanic canal

Anterior semicircular canal

Median canal

Osseous (bony) part of meatus

Vestibular canal

Tympanic membrane (eardrum)

Lateral semicircular canal

Cochlea

Semicircular canal

Ampulla

Vestibulocochlear nerve

Cochlea

Cochlear nerve

Tensor tympani muscle

Oval window

Posterior semicircular canal

Internal carotid artery

SECTION THROUGH COCHLEA

Organ of Corti

Median canal

Vestibular canal

Eustachian tube

Vestibular membrane

Spiral ganglion

Cochlear nerve

Hair cells

Tympanic canal

Basilar membrane

Styloid process

Nose, mouth, and throat

WITH EVERY BREATH, air passes through the nasal cavity down the pharynx (throat), larynx ("voice box"), and trachea (windpipe) to the lungs. The nasal cavity warms and moistens air, and the tiny layers in its lining protect the airway against damage by foreign bodies. During swallowing, the tongue moves up and back, the larynx rises, the epiglottis closes off the entrance to the trachea, and the soft palate separates the nasal cavity from the pharynx. Saliva, secreted from three pairs of salivary glands, lubricates food to make swallowing easier; it also begins the chemical breakdown of food, and helps to produce taste. The senses of taste and smell are closely linked. Both depend on the detection of dissolved molecules by sensory receptors in the olfactory nerve endings of the nose and in the taste buds of the tongue.

STRUCTURE OF TONGUE

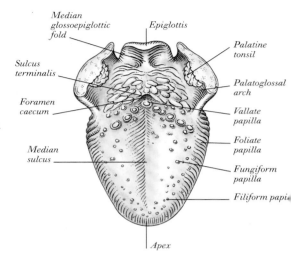

- Median glossoepiglottic fold
- Epiglottis
- Palatine tonsil
- Sulcus terminalis
- Palatoglossal arch
- Foramen caecum
- Vallate papilla
- Foliate papilla
- Median sulcus
- Fungiform papilla
- Filiform papi
- Apex

TASTE AREAS ON TONGUE

- Bitter
- Sour
- Salt
- Sweet

STRUCTURES SURROUNDING PHARYNX

- Lingual nerve
- Tongue
- Styloglossus muscle
- Hyoglossus muscle
- Sublingual gland
- Hypoglossal nerve
- Mandible (lower jaw)
- Superior laryngeal nerve
- Submandibular gland
- Superior thyroid artery
- Hyoid bone
- Laryngeal prominence (Adam's apple)
- Thyrohyoid muscle
- Thyrohyoid membrane
- Cricothyroid muscle
- Cricothyroid ligament
- Thyroid gland
- Trachea

TYPES OF PAPILLAE

FILIFORM PAPILLAE   **FUNGIFORM PAPILLAE**   **VALLATE PAPILLAE**

SECTION THROUGH NOSE, MOUTH, AND THROAT

Frontal sinus

Superior nasal concha

Sphenoidal sinus

Middle nasal concha

Inferior nasal concha

Superior meatus

Middle meatus

Nasal cavity

Vestibule

Inferior meatus

Hard palate

Maxilla (upper jaw)

Incisive canal

Orbicularis oris muscle

Superior longitudinal muscle

Incisor

Apex of tongue

Genioglossus muscle

Sublingual fold

Sublingual salivary gland

Fibrous septum

Mandible (lower jaw)

Geniohyoid muscle

Myohyoid muscle

Soft palate

Nasopharynx

Uvula

Palatine tonsil

Oropharynx

Epiglottis

Lingual tonsil

Hyoid bone

Laryngeal prominence (Adam's apple)

Thyroid cartilage

Thyroid gland

Cricothyroid muscle

Cervical vertebra

Intervertebral disc

Oesophagus

Trachea

ENDOSCOPIC VIEW OF VOCAL CORDS

Posterior part of tongue

Epiglottis

Vocal cord

Teeth

THE 20 PRIMARY TEETH (also called deciduous or milk teeth) usually begin to erupt when a baby is about six months old. They start to be replaced by the permanent teeth when the child is about six years old. By the age of 20, most adults have a full set of 32 teeth although the third molars (commonly called wisdom teeth) may never erupt. While teeth help people to speak clearly and give shape to the face, their main function is the chewing of food. Incisors and canines shear and tear the food into pieces; premolars and molars crush and grind it further. Although tooth enamel is the hardest substance in the body, it tends to be eroded and destroyed by acid produced in the mouth during the breakdown of food.

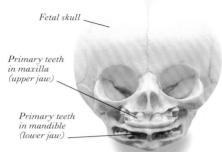

Fetal skull

Primary teeth in maxilla (upper jaw)

Primary teeth in mandible (lower jaw)

FETAL JAWS
By the sixth week of embryonic development areas of thickening occur in each jaw; these areas give rise to tooth buds. By the time the fetus is six months old, enamel has formed on the tooth buds.

DEVELOPMENT OF JAW AND TEETH

Maxilla (upper jaw)

Mandible (lower jaw)

A NEWBORN BABY'S JAWS
The primary teeth can be seen developing in the jaw bones; they begin to erupt around the age of six months.

A FIVE-YEAR-OLD CHILD'S TEETH
There is a full set of 20 erupted primary teeth; the permanent teeth can be seen developing in the upper and lower jaws.

A NINE-YEAR-OLD CHILD'S TEETH
Most of the teeth are primary teeth but the permanent incisors and first molars have now emerged.

AN ADULT'S TEETH
By the age of 20, the full set of 32 permanent teeth (including the wisdom teeth) should be in position.

THE PERMANENT TEETH

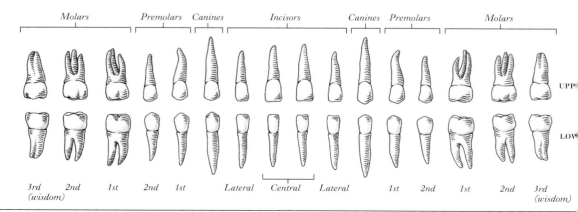

Molars | Premolars | Canines | Incisors | Canines | Premolars | Molars

UPP

LOW

3rd (wisdom) | 2nd | 1st | 2nd | 1st | Lateral | Central | Lateral | 1st | 2nd | 1st | 2nd | 3rd (wisdom)

STRUCTURE OF A TOOTH

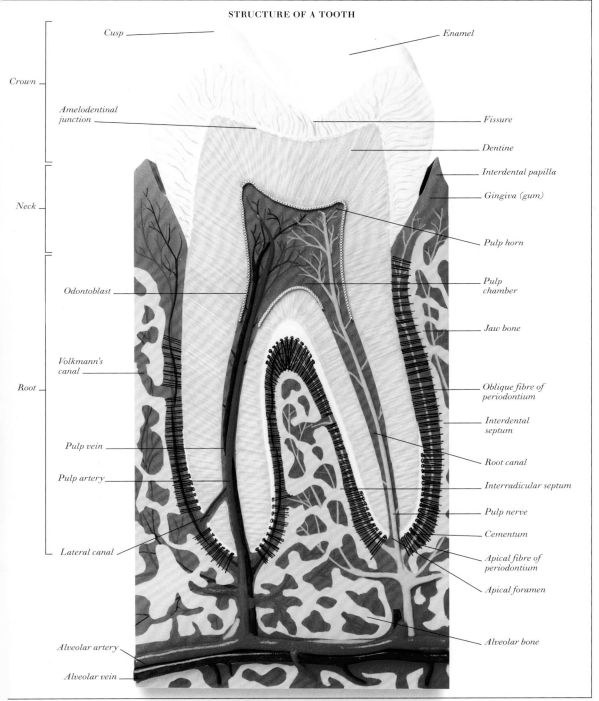

Cusp

Enamel

Crown

Amelodentinal junction

Fissure

Dentine

Neck

Interdental papilla

Gingiva (gum)

Pulp horn

Odontoblast

Pulp chamber

Jaw bone

Volkmann's canal

Oblique fibre of periodontium

Root

Interdental septum

Pulp vein

Root canal

Pulp artery

Interradicular septum

Pulp nerve

Cementum

Lateral canal

Apical fibre of periodontium

Apical foramen

Alveolar bone

Alveolar artery

Alveolar vein

Digestive system

THE DIGESTIVE SYSTEM BREAKS DOWN FOOD into particles so tiny that blood can take nourishment to all parts of the body. The system's main part is a 9 m (30 ft) tube from mouth to rectum; muscles in this alimentary canal force food along. Chewed food first travels through the oesophagus to the stomach, which churns and liquidizes food before it passes through the duodenum, jejunum, and ileum – the three parts of the long, convoluted small intestine. Here, digestive juices from the gallbladder and pancreas break down food particles; many filter out into the blood through tiny fingerlike villi that line the small intestine's inner wall. Undigested food in the colon forms faeces that leave the body through the anus.

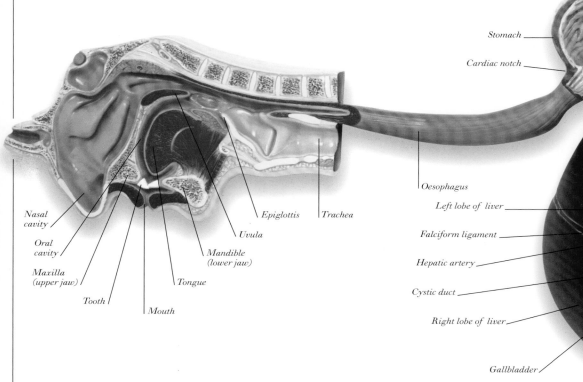

Stomach

Cardiac notch

Oesophagus

Left lobe of liver

Falciform ligament

Hepatic artery

Cystic duct

Right lobe of liver

Gallbladder

Nasal cavity

Oral cavity

Maxilla (upper jaw)

Tooth

Mouth

Tongue

Mandible (lower jaw)

Uvula

Epiglottis

Trachea

ENDOSCOPIC VIEWS INSIDE ALIMENTARY CANAL

OESOPHAGUS

Mucosa

STOMACH ENTRANCE

Cardiac orifice

STOMACH

Ruga

STOMACH EXIT

Pylorus

ALIMENTARY CANAL

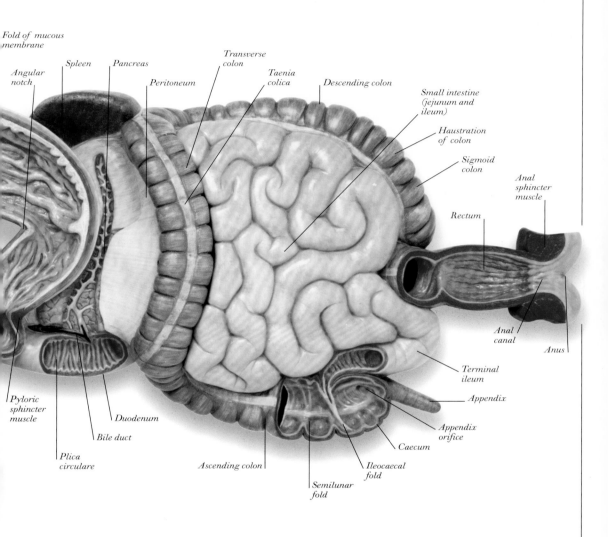

Fold of mucous
membrane

Angular
notch

Spleen

Pancreas

Peritoneum

Transverse
colon

Taenia
colica

Descending colon

Small intestine
(jejunum and
ileum)

Haustration
of colon

Sigmoid
colon

Anal
sphincter
muscle

Rectum

Anal
canal

Anus

Terminal
ileum

Appendix

Appendix
orifice

Caecum

Ileocaecal
fold

Ascending colon

Semilunar
fold

Pyloric
sphincter
muscle

Duodenum

Bile duct

Plica
circulare

DUODENUM

Plica
circulare

ILEUM

Villi of
mucosa

COLON

Semilunar
fold

Blood
vessel

RECTUM

Mucosa

Heart

THE HEART IS A HOLLOW MUSCLE in the middle of the chest that pumps blood around the body, supplying cells with oxygen and nutrients. A muscular wall, called the septum, divides the heart lengthways into left and right sides. A valve divides each side into two chambers: an upper atrium and a lower ventricle. When the heart muscle contracts, it squeezes blood through the atria and then through the ventricles. Oxygenated blood from the lungs flows from the pulmonary veins into the left atrium, through the left ventricle, and then out via the aorta to all parts of the body. Deoxygenated blood returning from the body flows from the vena cava into the right atrium, through the right ventricle, and then out via the pulmonary artery to the lungs for reoxygenation. At rest the heart beats between 60 and 80 times a minute; during exercise or at times of stress or excitement the rate may increase to 200 beats a minute.

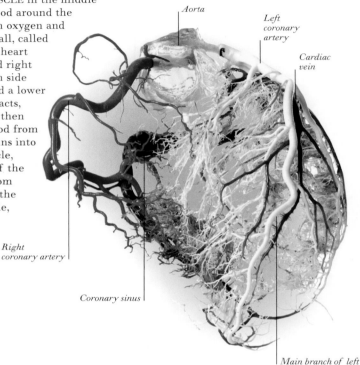

Aorta

Left coronary artery

Cardiac vein

Right coronary artery

Coronary sinus

Main branch of left coronary artery

SECTION THROUGH HEART WALL

Pericardial cavity

Trabecula

Endocardium

Myocardium

Epicardium (visceral pericardium)

Serous pericardium

Fibrous pericardium

HEARTBEAT SEQUENCE

ATRIAL DIASTOLE

Right atrium

Left atrium

Right ventricle

Left ventricle

Deoxygenated blood enters the right atrium while the left atrium receives oxygenated blood.

STRUCTURE OF HEART

Brachiocephalic trunk

Left subclavian artery

Left common carotid artery

Superior vena cava

Ascending aorta

Right pulmonary artery

Fossa ovalis

Left pulmonary vein

Right pulmonary vein

Right atrium

Opening of inferior vena cava

Branch of coronary artery

Tricuspid valve

Chordae tendineae

Right ventricle

Trabecula

Left pulmonary vein

Pulmonary trunk

Pulmonary semilunar valve

Coronary artery

Chordae tendineae

Muscular part of interventricular septum

Left ventricle

Papillary muscle

Myocardium of left ventricle

ATRIAL SYSTOLE (VENTRICULAR DIASTOLE)

Right atrium contracts

Tricuspid valve opens

Right ventricle dilates

Left atrium contracts

Mitral valve opens

Left ventricle dilates

Left and right atria contract, forcing blood into the relaxed ventricles.

VENTRICULAR SYSTOLE

Pulmonary artery

Pulmonary valve opens

Tricuspid valve closes

Right ventricle contracts

Aorta

Aortic valve opens

Mitral valve closes

Left ventricle contracts

Ventricles contract and force blood to the lungs for oxygenation and via the aorta to the rest of the body.

251

Circulatory system

THE CIRCULATORY SYSTEM consists of the heart and blood vessels, which together maintain a continuous flow of blood around the body. The heart pumps oxygen-rich blood from the lungs to all parts of the body through a network of tubes called arteries, and smaller branches called arterioles. Blood returns to the heart via small vessels called venules, which lead in turn into larger tubes called veins. Arterioles and venules are linked by a network of tiny vessels called capillaries, where the exchange of oxygen and carbon dioxide between blood and body cells takes place. Blood has four main components: red blood cells, white blood cells, platelets, and liquid plasma.

ARTERIAL SYSTEM OF BRAIN

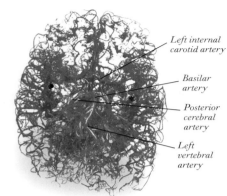

Left internal carotid artery

Basilar artery

Posterior cerebral artery

Left vertebral artery

CIRCULATORY SYSTEM OF HEART AND LUNGS

Superior vena cava

Aorta

Right ventricle

Left ventricle

CIRCULATORY SYSTEM OF LIVER

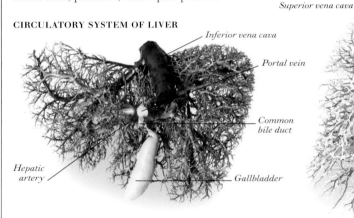

Inferior vena cava

Portal vein

Common bile duct

Hepatic artery

Gallbladder

SECTION OF MAIN ARTERY

Tunica media

Collagen and elastic fibres

External elastic lamina

Tunica adventitia

Internal elastic lamina

Tunica intima

Endothelium

Arteriole

SECTION OF MAIN VEIN

Tunica media

Collagen and elastic fibres

External elastic lamina

Tunica adventitia

Valve cusp

Internal elastic lamina

Tunica intima

Endothelium

PRINCIPAL ARTERIES AND VEINS OF CIRCULATORY SYSTEM

TYPES OF BLOOD CELLS

Common carotid artery

Subclavian artery

Arch of aorta

Axillary artery

Pulmonary artery

Coronary artery

Brachial artery

Gastric artery

Hepatic artery

Splenic artery

Superior mesenteric artery

Radial artery

Ulnar artery

Palmar arch

Digital artery

Common iliac artery

External iliac artery

Internal iliac artery

Femoral artery

Popliteal artery

Peroneal artery

Anterior tibial artery

Posterior tibial artery

Lateral plantar artery

Dorsal metatarsal artery

Internal jugular vein

Brachiocephalic vein

Subclavian vein

Axillary vein

Cephalic vein

Superior vena cava

Pulmonary vein

Basilic vein

Hepatic portal vein

Median cubital vein

Inferior vena cava

Anterior median vein

Gastroepiploic vein

Palmar vein

Digital vein

Inferior mesenteric vein

Superior mesenteric vein

Common iliac vein

External iliac vein

Internal iliac vein

Femoral vein

Great saphenous vein

Short saphenous vein

Dorsal venous arch

Digital vein

RED BLOOD CELLS
These cells are biconcave in shape to maximize their oxygen-carrying capacity.

WHITE BLOOD CELLS
Lymphocytes are the smallest white blood cells; they form antibodies against disease.

PLATELETS
Tiny cells that are activated whenever blood clotting or repair to vessels is necessary.

BLOOD CLOTTING

Filaments of fibrin enmesh red blood cells as part of the process of blood clotting.

Respiratory system

THE RESPIRATORY SYSTEM supplies the oxygen needed by body cells and carries off their carbon dioxide waste. Inhaled air passes via the trachea (windpipe) through two narrower tubes, the bronchi, to the lungs. Each lung comprises many fine, branching tubes called bronchioles that end in tiny clustered chambers called alveoli. Gases cross the thin alveolar walls to and from a network of tiny blood vessels. Intercostal (rib) muscles and the muscular diaphragm below the lungs operate the lungs like bellows, drawing air in and forcing it out at regular intervals.

BRONCHIOLE AND ALVEOLI

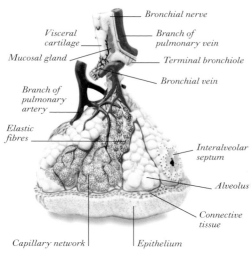

Bronchial nerve

Visceral cartilage

Branch of pulmonary vein

Mucosal gland

Terminal bronchiole

Bronchial vein

Branch of pulmonary artery

Elastic fibres

Interalveolar septum

Alveolus

Connective tissue

Capillary network

Epithelium

SEGMENTS OF BRONCHIAL TREE

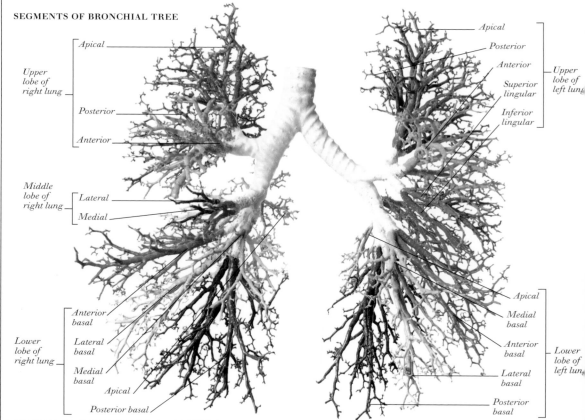

Apical

Upper lobe of right lung

Posterior

Anterior

Middle lobe of right lung

Lateral

Medial

Lower lobe of right lung

Anterior basal

Lateral basal

Medial basal

Apical

Posterior basal

Apical

Posterior

Anterior

Superior lingular

Inferior lingular

Upper lobe of left lung

Apical

Medial basal

Anterior basal

Lateral basal

Posterior basal

Lower lobe of left lung

STRUCTURES OF THORACIC CAVITY

GASEOUS EXCHANGE IN ALVEOLUS

Epiglottis

Hyoid bone

Thyroid cartilage

Thyroid gland

Apex of lung

Superior vena cava

Upper lobe of right lung

Horizontal fissure

que re

Cricoid cartilage

Trachea

Aorta

Upper lobe of left lung

Pulmonary trunk

Left pulmonary artery

Heart

Lower lobe of left lung

Secondary bronchus

Tertiary bronchus

er of lung

Middle lobe of right lung

Right crus of diaphragm

Abdominal aorta

Left crus of diaphragm

Oesophagus

Muscular wall of diaphragm

Oxygen diffuses into blood

Oxygenated blood

Alveolus

Deoxygenated blood rich in carbon dioxide

Carbon dioxide diffuses from blood into alveolus

MECHANISM OF RESPIRATION
INSPIRATION

Lung expands

Air drawn into lungs

Diaphragm contracts and flattens

Intercostal muscles contract

EXPIRATION

Lung contracts

Air forced out of lungs

Diaphragm relaxes and moves up

Intercostal muscles relax

Urinary system

THE URINARY SYSTEM FILTERS WASTE PRODUCTS from the blood and removes them from the body via a system of tubes. Blood is filtered in the two kidneys, which are fist-sized, bean-shaped organs. The renal arteries carry blood to the kidneys; the renal veins remove blood after filtering. Each kidney contains about one million tiny units called nephrons. Each nephron is made up of a tubule and a filtering unit called a glomerulus, which consists of a collection of tiny blood vessels surrounded by the hollow Bowman's capsule. The filtering process produces a watery fluid that leaves the kidney as urine. The urine is carried via two tubes called ureters to the bladder, where it is stored until its release from the body through another tube called the urethra.

ARTERIAL SYSTEM OF KIDNEYS

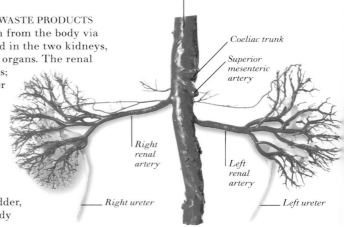

Aorta

Coeliac trunk

Superior mesenteric artery

Right renal artery

Left renal artery

Right ureter

Left ureter

SECTION THROUGH LEFT KIDNEY

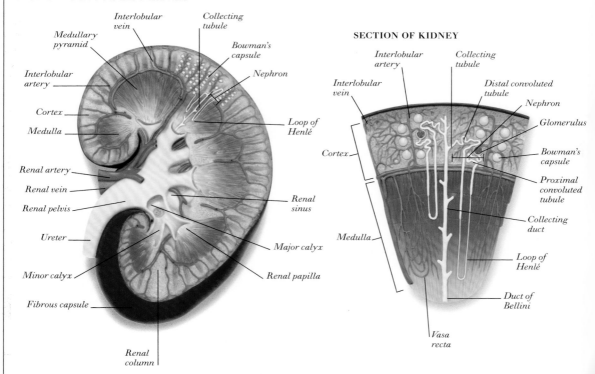

Interlobular vein

Medullary pyramid

Collecting tubule

Bowman's capsule

Nephron

Interlobular artery

Cortex

Medulla

Loop of Henlé

Renal artery

Renal vein

Renal pelvis

Renal sinus

Ureter

Major calyx

Minor calyx

Renal papilla

Fibrous capsule

Renal column

SECTION OF KIDNEY

Interlobular artery

Collecting tubule

Interlobular vein

Distal convoluted tubule

Nephron

Cortex

Glomerulus

Bowman's capsule

Proximal convoluted tubule

Collecting duct

Medulla

Loop of Henlé

Duct of Bellini

Vasa recta

MALE URINARY TRACT

Superior mesenteric artery

Celiac trunk

Left adrenal (suprarenal) gland

Right adrenal (suprarenal) gland

Inferior vena cava

Left suprarenal vein

Left renal artery

Renal artery

Left renal vein

Renal vein

Left kidney

Right kidney

Left ureter

Vertebral column

Aorta

Psoas muscle

Right ureter

Left common iliac artery

Left common iliac vein

Testicular vein and artery

Bladder

Superior pubic ramus

SECTION THROUGH BOWMAN'S CAPSULE

Distal convoluted tubule

Efferent arteriole

Afferent arteriole

Basement membrane of Bowman's capsule

Bowman's space

Bowman's capsule

Glomerulus

Proximal convoluted tubule

SECTION THROUGH MALE BLADDER

Right ureter

Peritoneum

Urachus

Left ureter

Transitional cell mucosa

Right ureteric orifice

Internal urethral orifice

Muscle layer

Left ureteric orifice

Trigone

Prostate gland

Internal urethral sphincter muscle

Urethra

257

Reproductive system

SEX ORGANS LOCATED IN THE PELVIS create new human lives. Each month a ripe egg is released from one of the female's ovaries into a fallopian tube leading to the uterus (womb), a muscular pear-sized organ. A male produces minute tadpole-like sperm in two oval glands called testes. When the male is ready to release sperm into the female's vagina, many millions pass into his urethra and leave his body through the fleshy penis. The sperm travel up through the vagina into the uterus and fallopian tubes, and one sperm may enter and fertilize an egg. The fertilized egg becomes embedded in the uterus wall and starts to grow into a new human being.

SECTION THROUGH OVARY

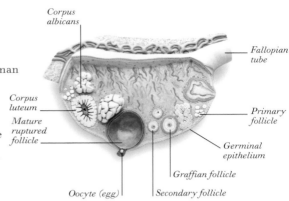

- Corpus albicans
- Fallopian tube
- Corpus luteum
- Primary follicle
- Mature ruptured follicle
- Germinal epithelium
- Graffian follicle
- Oocyte (egg)
- Secondary follicle

SECTION THROUGH FEMALE PELVIC REGION

- Ureter
- Ampulla of fallopian tube
- Fimbria of fallopian tube
- Ovary
- Isthmus of fallopian tube
- Fundus of uterus
- Uterus (womb)
- Cervix (neck of uterus)
- Bladder
- Pubic symphysis
- Os
- Urethra
- Rectum
- Clitoris
- Vagina
- External urinary meatus
- Anus
- Perineum
- Labia minora
- Labia majora
- Introitus (vaginal opening)

FEMALE REPRODUCTIVE ORGANS

Fallopian tube
Ovarian ligament
Ovary
Body of uterus (womb)
Os
Vagina
Fundus of uterus
Isthmus of fallopian tube
Ampulla of fallopian tube
Fimbria of fallopian tube
Cervix (neck of uterus)

MALE REPRODUCTIVE ORGANS

External spermatic fascia
Cremasteric fascia
Internal spermatic fascia
Epididymis
Testis (testicle)
Scrotum
Glans penis
Prostate gland
Ductus (vas) deferens
Seminal vesicle
Bulbourethral gland
Urethra
Corpus spongiosum
Corpus cavernosum
Prepuce (foreskin)
Urethral opening

SECTION THROUGH MALE PELVIC REGION

Intervertebral disc
Ureter

Colon
Sacrum
Seminal vesicle
Ejaculatory duct

Bladder
Pubis of pelvis
Prostate gland
Penis
Corpus cavernosum
Corpus spongiosum
Urethra
Epididymis
Glans penis
Testis (testicle)
Scrotum

EXTERNAL STRUCTURE OF SPERM

Acrosomal cap
Mitochondrial sheath
Tailpiece
Head
Terminal ring
Flagellum

259

Development of a baby

A FERTILIZED EGG IS NOURISHED AND PROTECTED as it develops into an embryo and then a fetus during the 40 weeks of pregnancy. The placenta, a mass of blood vessels implanted in the uterus lining, delivers nourishment and oxygen, and removes waste through the umbilical cord. Meanwhile, the fetus lies snugly in its amniotic sac, a bag of fluid that protects it against any sudden jolts. In the last weeks of the pregnancy, the rapidly growing fetus turns head-down: a baby ready to be born.

EMBRYO AT FIVE WEEKS

Rudimentary ear

Rudimentary eye

Rudimentary mouth

Heart bulge

Arm bud

Rudimentary liver

Tail bud

Leg bud

Rudimentary vertebra

Amniotic fluid

Umbilicus (navel)

Uterine wall

Fetus

SECTION THROUGH PLACENTA

Umbilical cord

Umbilical vein

Umbilical artery

Fetal blood vessels

Amnion

Chorion

Trophoblast

Chorionic villus

Chorionic plate

Pool of maternal blood

Septum

Decidual plate

Maternal blood vessel

Myometrium

SECTION THROUGH PELVIS IN NINTH MONTH OF PREGNANCY

THE DEVELOPING FETUS

Placenta

Uterine wall

Fallopian tube

Fetus

SECOND MONTH
All the internal organs have developed by this stage.

Intervertebral disc

Vertebra

Spinal cord

Umbilical cord

THIRD MONTH
The fetus is fully formed and now begins a period of rapid growth.

FIFTH MONTH
Although the fetus is here in breech (bottom down) position, it will probably turn by 180° before birth. By the fifth month the baby is moving actively and responds to sound.

Cervix

Bladder

Cervix

Rectum

Anus

SEVENTH MONTH
The internal organs are maturing in preparation for life outside the uterus. The baby has grown to such a size that there is less room for movement within the uterus.

Pubic bone

Vagina

Placenta

Urethra

261

GEOLOGY, GEOGRAPHY, AND METEOROLOGY

EARTH'S PHYSICAL FEATURES ⋯⋯⋯⋯⋯⋯ 264
THE ROCK CYCLE ⋯⋯⋯⋯⋯⋯⋯⋯ 266
MINERALS ⋯⋯⋯⋯⋯⋯⋯⋯⋯⋯ 268
MINERAL FEATURES ⋯⋯⋯⋯⋯⋯⋯ 270
VOLCANOES ⋯⋯⋯⋯⋯⋯⋯⋯⋯ 272
IGNEOUS AND METAMORPHIC ROCKS ⋯⋯ 274
SEDIMENTARY ROCKS ⋯⋯⋯⋯⋯⋯ 276
FOSSILS ⋯⋯⋯⋯⋯⋯⋯⋯⋯⋯ 278
MINERAL RESOURCES ⋯⋯⋯⋯⋯⋯ 280
WEATHERING AND EROSION ⋯⋯⋯⋯ 282
CAVES ⋯⋯⋯⋯⋯⋯⋯⋯⋯⋯ 284
GLACIERS ⋯⋯⋯⋯⋯⋯⋯⋯⋯ 286
RIVERS ⋯⋯⋯⋯⋯⋯⋯⋯⋯⋯ 288
RIVER FEATURES ⋯⋯⋯⋯⋯⋯⋯ 290
LAKES AND GROUNDWATER ⋯⋯⋯⋯ 292
COASTLINES ⋯⋯⋯⋯⋯⋯⋯⋯⋯ 294
OCEANS AND SEAS ⋯⋯⋯⋯⋯⋯⋯ 296
THE OCEAN FLOOR ⋯⋯⋯⋯⋯⋯⋯ 298
THE ATMOSPHERE ⋯⋯⋯⋯⋯⋯⋯ 300
WEATHER ⋯⋯⋯⋯⋯⋯⋯⋯⋯ 302

Earth's physical features

MOST OF THE EARTH'S SURFACE (about 70 per cent) is covered with water. The largest single body of water, the Pacific Ocean, alone covers about 30 per cent of the surface. Most of the land is distributed as seven continents; these are (from largest to smallest) Asia, Africa, North America, South America, Antarctica, Europe, and Australasia. The physical features of the land are remarkably varied. Among the most notable are mountain ranges, rivers, and deserts. The largest mountain ranges – the Himalayas in Asia and the Andes in South America – extend for thousands of kilometres. The Himalayas include the world's highest mountain, Mount Everest (8,848 metres). The longest rivers are the River Nile in Africa (6,695 kilometres) and the Amazon River in South America (6,437 kilometres). Deserts cover about 20 per cent of the total land area. The largest is the Sahara, which covers nearly a third of Africa. The Earth's surface features can be represented in various ways. Only a globe can correctly represent areas, shapes, sizes, and directions, because there is always distortion when a spherical surface – the Earth's, for example – is projected on to the flat surface of a map. Each map projection is therefore a compromise: it shows some features accurately but distorts others. Even satellite mapping does not produce completely accurate maps, although they can show physical features with great clarity.

CYLINDRICAL PROJECTION

CYLINDRICAL-PROJECTION MAP

180° 160° 120° 80°

Great Slave Lake
Great Bear Lake
Lake Superior
Gree
Mackenzie-Peace River
Bering Sea
Hudson Bay
NORTH AMERICA
Rocky Mountains
Sonoran Desert
Lake Hu
Lake Ontario
Sierra Madre
Lake Erie
Lake Michigan
Chihuahuan Desert
Gulf of Mexico
Appalachian Mountains
ATLA
OCE
Mississippi-Missouri River
Caribbean Sea
Guiana Highlands

PACIFIC OCEAN

Andes
Atacama Desert
Gran Chaco
Parana River
Pamp
Patagonia

SATELLITE MAPPING OF THE EARTH

Satellite takes photographs of the Earth

Solar panel

Earth's rotation

Antenna

Earth

Polar orbit of satellite

Area of Earth's surface on each photograph

Composite picture of Earth created from thousands of separate images

180° 160° 120° 8

WEST OF G
MERI

CONICAL PROJECTION

CONICAL- PROJECTION MAP

AZIMUTHAL PROJECTION

AZIMUTHAL- PROJECTION MAP

MODIFIED AZIMUTHAL-PROJECTION MAP

SATELLITE MAP OF THE EARTH

160°   180°

120°

80°

40°

0°

ARCTIC OCEAN

Sea of Azov

Ural Mountains

Kara Kum

River Ob-Irtysh

River Lena

Caucasus

Carpathians

Alps

ARCTIC CIRCLE (66° 32'N)

River Amur

Pyrenees

EUROPE

Black Sea

ASIA

Lake Baikal

Sea of Japan

Honshu

Mediterranean Sea

ins

Gobi Desert

TROPIC OF CANCER (23° 30 N)

Yellow River (Huang He)

Red Sea

Pamirs

Himalayas

Yangtze River (Chang Jiang)

PACIFIC OCEAN

AFRICA

Caspian Sea

Thar Desert

South China Sea

Arabian Desert

Takla Makan Desert

River Mekong

Borneo

New Guinea

EQUATOR (0°)

River Nile

River Congo (Zaire)

Lake Victoria

Sumatra

Lake Tanganyika

INDIAN OCEAN

Australian Desert

AUSTRALASIA

Madagascar

Namib Desert

TROPIC OF CAPRICORN (23° 30'S)

Lake Nyasa

Kalahari Desert

Drakensberg

New Zealand

ANTARCTIC CIRCLE (66° 32'S)

ANTARCTICA

0°

40°

80°

120°

160°

180°

The rock cycle

THE ROCK CYCLE IS A CONTINUOUS PROCESS through which old rocks are transformed into new ones. Rocks can be divided into three main groups: igneous, sedimentary, and metamorphic. Igneous rocks are formed when magma (molten rock) from the Earth's interior cools and solidifies (see pp. 274-275). Sedimentary rocks are formed when sediment (rock particles, for example) becomes compressed and cemented together in a process known as lithification (see pp. 276-277). Metamorphic rocks are formed when igneous, sedimentary, or other metamorphic rocks are changed by heat or pressure (see pp. 274-275). Rocks are added to the Earth's surface by crustal movements and volcanic activity. Once exposed on the surface, the rocks are broken down into rock particles by weathering (see pp. 282-283). The particles are then transported by glaciers, rivers, and wind, and deposited as sediment in lakes, deltas, deserts, and on the ocean floor. Some of this sediment undergoes lithification and forms sedimentary rock. This rock may be thrust back to the surface by crustal movements or forced deeper into the Earth's interior, where heat and pressure transform it into metamorphic rock. The metamorphic rock in turn may be pushed up to the surface or may be melted to form magma. Eventually, the magma cools and solidifies - below or on the surface -forming igneous rock. When the sedimentary, igneous, and metamorphic rocks are exposed once more on the Earth's surface, the cycle begins again.

HEXAGONAL BASALT
COLUMNS, ICELAND

THE ROCK CYCLE

Igneous rock

Weathering, transport, and deposition

Sediment

Cooling and solidification (crystallization)

Heat and pressure (metamorphism)

Weathering, transport, and deposition

Weathering, transport, and deposition

Compression and cementation (lithification)

Magma

Melting

Heat and pressure (metamorphism)

Metamorphic rock

Sedimentary rock

STAGES IN THE ROCK CYCLE

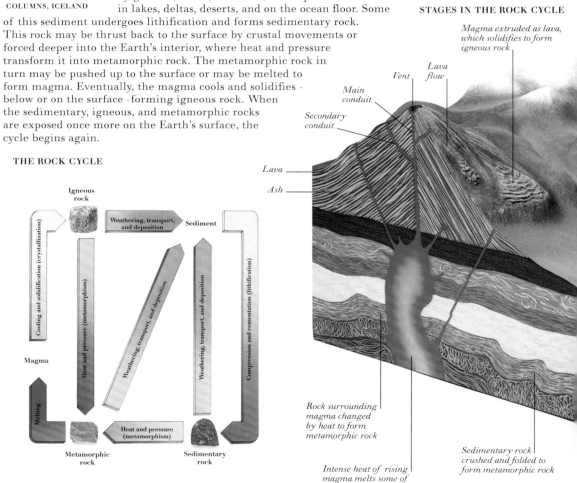

Magma extruded as lava, which solidifies to form igneous rock

Lava flow

Vent

Main conduit

Secondary conduit

Lava

Ash

Rock surrounding magma changed by heat to form metamorphic rock

Intense heat of rising magma melts some of the surrounding rock

Sedimentary rock crushed and folded to form metamorphic rock

IGNEOUS ROCK

Pyroxene crystal

Olivine crystal

Plagioclase feldspar

Coarse-grained texture

Dark pyroxene crystal

PHOTOMICROGRAPH OF GABBRO

PIECE OF GABBRO

SEDIMENTARY ROCK

Mud groundmass (matrix)

Ammonite shell

Brown colouring from iron oxides

Fine-grained texture

Ammonite shell embedded in rock

PHOTOMICROGRAPH OF SHELLY LIMESTONE

PIECE OF SHELLY LIMESTONE

METAMORPHIC ROCK

Garnet crystal (pink)

Quartz and feldspar crystals (grey)

Red garnet crystal

Wavy foliation

PHOTOMICROGRAPH OF GARNET-MICA SCHIST

PIECE OF GARNET-MICA SCHIST

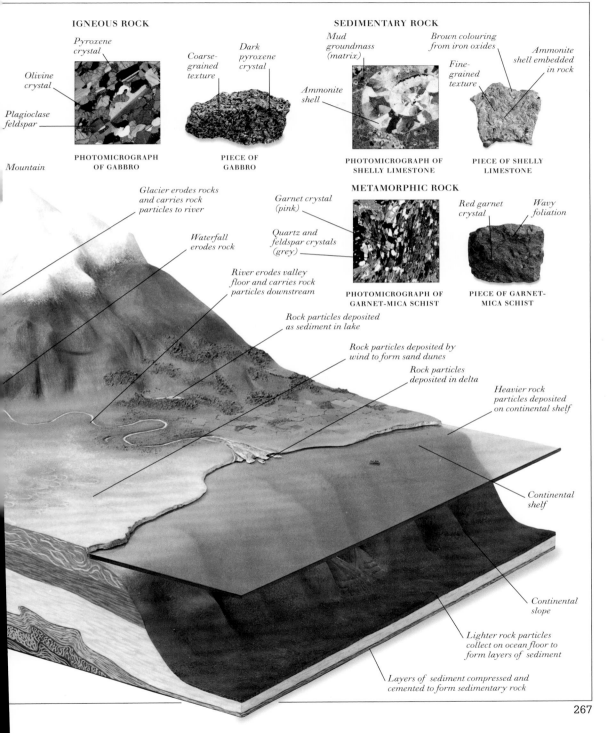

Mountain

Glacier erodes rocks and carries rock particles to river

Waterfall erodes rock

River erodes valley floor and carries rock particles downstream

Rock particles deposited as sediment in lake

Rock particles deposited by wind to form sand dunes

Rock particles deposited in delta

Heavier rock particles deposited on continental shelf

Continental shelf

Continental slope

Lighter rock particles collect on ocean floor to form layers of sediment

Layers of sediment compressed and cemented to form sedimentary rock

Minerals

A MINERAL IS A NATURALLY OCCURRING SUBSTANCE that has a characteristic chemical composition and specific physical properties, such as habit and streak (see pp. 270-271). A rock, by comparison, is an aggregate of minerals and need not have a specific chemical composition. Minerals are made up of elements (substances that cannot be broken down chemically into simpler substances), each of which can be represented by a chemical symbol. Minerals can be divided into two main groups: native elements and compounds. Native elements are made up of a pure element. Examples include gold (chemical symbol Au), silver (Ag), copper (Cu), and carbon (C); carbon occurs as a native element in two forms, diamond and graphite. Compounds are combinations of two or more elements. For example, sulphides are compounds of sulphur (S) and one or more other elements, such as lead (Pb) in the mineral galena, or antimony (Sb) in the mineral stibnite.

NATIVE ELEMENTS

Dendritic (branching) copper

COPPER
(Cu)

Limonite groundmass (matrix)

SULPHIDES

Cubic galena crystal

GALENA
(PbS)

Prismatic stibnite crystal

Quartz groundmass (matrix)

STIBNITE
(Sb_2S_3)

Perfect octahedral pyrites crystal

Quartz crystal

PYRITES
(FeS_2)

Dendritic (branching) gold

Quartz vein

GOLD
(Au)

Kimberlite groundmass (matrix)

White diamond

DIAMOND
(C)

Hexagonal graphite crystal

GRAPHITE
(C)

OXIDES/HYDROXIDES

Milky quartz groundmass (matrix)

Smoky quartz crystal

SMOKY QUARTZ
(SiO_2)

Rounded bauxite grains in groundmass (matrix)

BAUXITE
(FeO(OH) and $Al_2O_3.2H_2O$)

Mass of specular haematite crystals

SPECULAR HAEMATITE
(Fe_2O_3)

Parallel bands of onyx

ONYX
(SiO_2)

Kidney ore haematite

Specular crystals of haematite

KIDNEY ORE HAEMATITE
(Fe_2O_3)

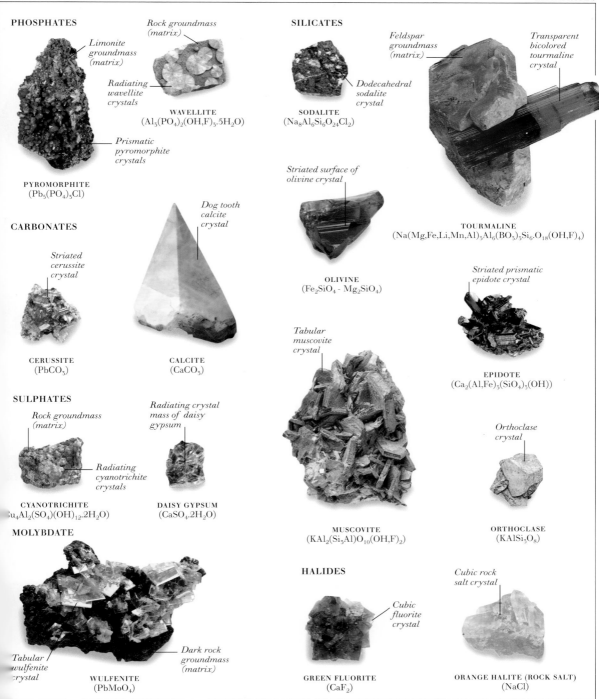

PHOSPHATES

Limonite groundmass (matrix)

Rock groundmass (matrix)

Radiating wavellite crystals

WAVELLITE
($Al_3(PO_4)_2(OH,F)_3.5H_2O$)

Prismatic pyromorphite crystals

PYROMORPHITE
($Pb_5(PO_4)_3Cl$)

CARBONATES

Striated cerussite crystal

Dog tooth calcite crystal

CERUSSITE
($PbCO_3$)

CALCITE
($CaCO_3$)

SULPHATES

Rock groundmass (matrix)

Radiating crystal mass of daisy gypsum

Radiating cyanotrichite crystals

CYANOTRICHITE
($Cu_4Al_2(SO_4)(OH)_{12}.2H_2O$)

DAISY GYPSUM
($CaSO_4.2H_2O$)

MOLYBDATE

Tabular wulfenite crystal

Dark rock groundmass (matrix)

WULFENITE
($PbMoO_4$)

SILICATES

Feldspar groundmass (matrix)

Transparent bicolored tourmaline crystal

Dodecahedral sodalite crystal

SODALITE
($Na_8Al_6Si_6O_{24}Cl_2$)

TOURMALINE
($Na(Mg,Fe,Li,Mn,Al)_3Al_6(BO_3)_3Si_6.O_{18}(OH,F)_4$)

Striated surface of olivine crystal

OLIVINE
($Fe_2SiO_4 - Mg_2SiO_4$)

Striated prismatic epidote crystal

Tabular muscovite crystal

EPIDOTE
($Ca_2(Al,Fe)_3(SiO_4)_3(OH)$)

Orthoclase crystal

MUSCOVITE
($KAl_2(Si_3Al)O_{10}(OH,F)_2$)

ORTHOCLASE
($KAlSi_3O_8$)

HALIDES

Cubic rock salt crystal

Cubic fluorite crystal

GREEN FLUORITE
(CaF_2)

ORANGE HALITE (ROCK SALT)
($NaCl$)

Mineral features

MINERALS CAN BE IDENTIFIED BY STUDYING features such as fracture, cleavage, crystal system, habit, hardness, colour, and streak. Minerals can break in different ways. If a mineral breaks in an irregular way, leaving rough surfaces, it possesses fracture. If a mineral breaks along well-defined planes of weakness, it possesses cleavage. Specific minerals have distinctive patterns of cleavage; for example, mica cleaves along one plane. Most minerals form crystals, which can be categorized into crystal systems according to their symmetry and number of faces. Within each system, several different but related forms of crystal are possible; for example, a cubic crystal can have six, eight, or twelve sides. A mineral's habit is the typical form taken by an aggregate of its crystals. Examples of habit include botryoidal (like a bunch of grapes) and massive (no definite form). The relative hardness of a mineral may be assessed by testing its resistance to scratching. This property is usually measured using Mohs scale, which increases in hardness from 1 (talc) to 10 (diamond). The colour of a mineral is not a dependable guide to its identity as some minerals have a range of colours. Streak (the colour the powdered mineral makes when rubbed across an unglazed tile) is a more reliable indicator.

CLEAVAGE

Cleavage in one direction

CLEAVAGE ALONG ONE PLANE

Cleavage in three directions, forming a block cube

CLEAVAGE ALONG THREE PLANES

Horizontal cleavage

Vertical cleavage

CLEAVAGE ALONG TWO PLANES

Cleavage in four directions, forming a double-pyramid crystal

CLEAVAGE ALONG FOUR PLANES

CRYSTAL SYSTEMS

Cubic iron pyrites crystal

Tetragonal idocrase crystal

Representation of tetragonal system

TETRAGONAL SYSTEM

CUBIC SYSTEM

Representation of cubic system

Hexagonal beryl crystal

Representation of hexagonal/trigonal system

HEXAGONAL/TRIGONAL SYSTEM

Orthorhombic barytes crystal

Representation of orthorhombic system

ORTHORHOMBIC SYSTEM

FRACTURE

Fire opal with conchoidal (shell-like) fracture

Nickel-iron with hackly (jagged) fracture

CONCHOIDAL FRACTURE

HACKLY FRACTURE

Orpiment with uneven fracture

Garnierite with splintery fracture

UNEVEN FRACTURE

SPLINTERY FRACTURE

Monoclinic selenite crystal

Representation of monoclinic system

MONOCLINIC SYSTEM

Representation of triclinic system

Triclinic axinite crystal

TRICLINIC SYSTEM

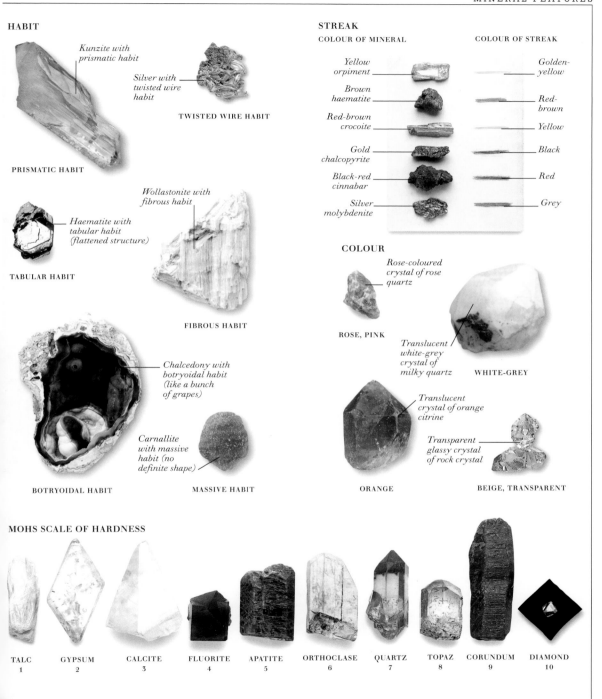

HABIT

Kunzite with prismatic habit

Silver with twisted wire habit

TWISTED WIRE HABIT

PRISMATIC HABIT

Wollastonite with fibrous habit

Haematite with tabular habit (flattened structure)

TABULAR HABIT

FIBROUS HABIT

Chalcedony with botryoidal habit (like a bunch of grapes)

Carnallite with massive habit (no definite shape)

BOTRYOIDAL HABIT

MASSIVE HABIT

STREAK

COLOUR OF MINERAL	COLOUR OF STREAK
Yellow orpiment	Golden-yellow
Brown haematite	Red-brown
Red-brown crocoite	Yellow
Gold chalcopyrite	Black
Black-red cinnabar	Red
Silver molybdenite	Grey

COLOUR

Rose-coloured crystal of rose quartz

ROSE, PINK

Translucent white-grey crystal of milky quartz

WHITE-GREY

Translucent crystal of orange citrine

Transparent glassy crystal of rock crystal

ORANGE

BEIGE, TRANSPARENT

MOHS SCALE OF HARDNESS

TALC	GYPSUM	CALCITE	FLUORITE	APATITE	ORTHOCLASE	QUARTZ	TOPAZ	CORUNDUM	DIAMOND
1	2	3	4	5	6	7	8	9	10

Volcanoes

Folded, rope-like surface

VOLCANOES ARE VENTS OR FISSURES in the Earth's crust through which magma (molten rock that originates from deep beneath the crust) is forced on to the surface as lava. They occur most commonly along the boundaries of crustal plates; most volcanoes lie in a belt called the "Ring of Fire", which runs along the edge of the Pacific Ocean. Volcanoes can be classified according to the violence and frequency of their eruptions.

Non-explosive volcanic eruptions generally occur where crustal plates pull apart. These eruptions produce runny basaltic lava that spreads quickly over a wide area to form relatively flat cones. The most violent eruptions take place where plates collide. Such eruptions produce thick rhyolitic lava and may also blast out clouds of dust and pyroclasts (lava fragments). The lava does not flow far before cooling and therefore builds up steep-sided, conical volcanoes. Some volcanoes produce lava and ash eruptions, which build up composite volcanic cones. Volcanoes that erupt frequently are described as active; those that erupt rarely are termed dormant; and those that have stopped erupting altogether are termed extinct. As well as the volcanoes themselves, other features associated with volcanic regions include geysers, hot mineral springs, solfataras, fumaroles, and bubbling mud pools.

HORU GEYSER, NEW ZEALAND

PAHOEHOE (ROPY LAVA)

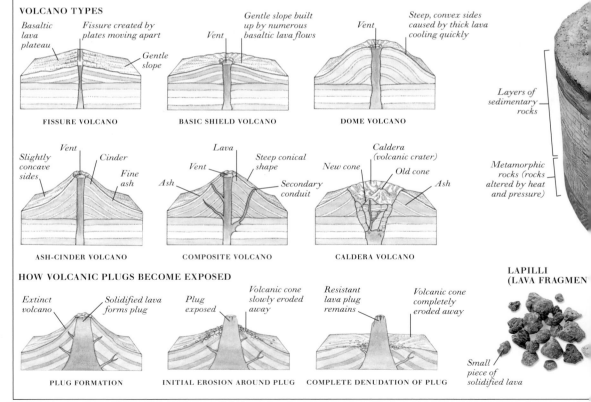

VOLCANO TYPES

Basaltic lava plateau
Fissure created by plates moving apart
Gentle slope

FISSURE VOLCANO

Gentle slope built up by numerous basaltic lava flows
Vent

BASIC SHIELD VOLCANO

Steep, convex sides caused by thick lava cooling quickly
Vent

DOME VOLCANO

Layers of sedimentary rocks

Slightly concave sides
Vent
Cinder
Fine ash

ASH-CINDER VOLCANO

Lava
Steep conical shape
Vent
Ash
Secondary conduit

COMPOSITE VOLCANO

Caldera (volcanic crater)
New cone
Old cone
Ash

CALDERA VOLCANO

Metamorphic rocks (rocks altered by heat and pressure)

HOW VOLCANIC PLUGS BECOME EXPOSED

LAPILLI (LAVA FRAGMEN

Extinct volcano
Solidified lava forms plug

PLUG FORMATION

Plug exposed
Volcanic cone slowly eroded away

INITIAL EROSION AROUND PLUG

Resistant lava plug remains
Volcanic cone completely eroded away

COMPLETE DENUDATION OF PLUG

Small piece of solidified lava

TYPES OF LAVA

Scoria (sharp, angular chunks)

Driblets of lava from roof of tunnel

AA (BLOCKY LAVA)

REMELTED LAVA

LOCATION OF VOLCANOES

▲ Volcano   ┗┼┼┼┛ Plate boundary

STRUCTURE OF A VOLCANO

Steeply sloping cone consisting of numerous layers of ash and lava

Vent

Plug (solidified lava)

Main conduit

Volcanic ash

Cinder cone

Mineral spring

Laccolith

Secondary conduit

Magma reservoir

Lava flow

Groundwater

VOLCANIC FEATURES

Sulphurous gases

Jet of hot water and steam

Water heated by hot rocks

Steam pressure builds up

Hot water

Mud and surface deposits mixed with hot water

Superheated water

Steam

SOLFATARA

GEYSER

MUD POOL

FUMAROLE

Igneous and metamorphic rocks

IGNEOUS ROCKS ARE FORMED WHEN MAGMA (molten rock that originates from deep beneath the Earth's crust) cools and solidifies. There are two main types of igneous rock: intrusive and extrusive. Intrusive rocks are formed deep underground where magma is forced into cracks or between rock layers to form structures such as sills, dykes, and batholiths. The magma cools slowly to form coarse-grained rocks such as gabbro and pegmatite. Extrusive rocks are formed above the Earth's surface from lava (magma that has been ejected in a volcanic eruption). The molten lava cools quickly, producing fine-grained rocks such as rhyolite and basalt. Metamorphic rocks are those that have been altered by intense heat (contact metamorphism) or extreme pressure (regional metamorphism). Contact metamorphism occurs when rocks are changed by heat from, for example, an igneous intrusion or lava flow. Regional metamorphism occurs when rock is crushed in the middle of a folding mountain range. Metamorphic rocks can be formed from igneous rocks, sedimentary rocks, or even from other metamorphic rocks.

BASALT COLUMNS

IGNEOUS ROCK STRUCTURES

Cinder cone
Large eroded lava flow
Cedar-tree laccolith
Butte
Plug
Cone sheet
Ring dyke
Batholith
Dyke
Sill
Dyke swarm
Lopolith

CONTACT METAMORPHISM

Metamorphic aureole (region where contact metamorphism occurs)
Hot igneous intrusion
Limestone
Shale
Marble (metamorphosed limestone)
Slate (metamorphosed shale)

REGIONAL METAMORPHISM

Mountain range
Slate, formed under low pressure and temperature
Compression
Compression
Schist, formed under medium pressure and temperature
Crust
Gneiss, formed under high pressure and temperature
Mantle
Magma

EXAMPLES OF METAMORPHIC ROCKS

Pale feldspar
Dark mica
Dark mineral band
Pale calcite

GNEISS

FOLDED SCHIST

SKARN

EXAMPLES OF EXTRUSIVE IGNEOUS ROCKS

Porphyritic texture

Fine-grained crystals

Elongated vesicles (gas cavities)

Fine-grained groundmass (matrix)

Conchoidal fracture

Glassy lustre

RHYOLITE

BASALT

PUMICE

PORPHYRITIC ANDESITE

OBSIDIAN

Mesa (flat-topped plateau)

Extinct geyser

Lake

Caldera

Sea

Lava flow

Vent

Active juvenile volcano

Parasitic volcano

Main conduit

Sagging caused by weight of volcano

Batholith

Laccolith

Eroded plug of extinct volcano

Magma reservoir

EXAMPLES OF INTRUSIVE IGNEOUS ROCKS

Dark groundmass (matrix)

KIMBERLITE

Plagioclase feldspar

OLIVINE GABBRO

Amphibole crystals

White feldspar

FELDSPAR PEGMATITE

Amphibole crystal

SYENITE

Fine groundmass (matrix)

Pyrites crystal

Chiastolite crystal

Green calc-silicate mineral

High quartz content

SLATE WITH PYRITES

CHIASTOLITE HORNFELS

GREEN MARBLE

HALLEFLINTA

275

Sedimentary rocks

SEDIMENTARY ROCKS ARE FORMED BY THE ACCUMULATION and consolidation of sediments (see pp. 266-267). There are three main types of sedimentary rock. Clastic sedimentary rocks, such as breccia or sandstone, are formed from other rocks that have been broken down into fragments by weathering (see pp. 282-283), which have then been transported and deposited elsewhere. Organic sedimentary rocks – for example, coal (see pp. 280-281) – are derived from plant and animal remains. Chemical sedimentary rocks are formed by

THE GRAND CANYON, USA

chemical processes. For example, rock salt is formed when salt dissolved in water is deposited as the water evaporates. Sedimentary rocks are laid down in layers, called beds or strata. Each new layer is laid down horizontally over older ones. There are usually some gaps in the sequence, called unconformities. These represent periods in which no new sediments were being laid down, or when earlier sedimentary layers were raised above sea level and eroded away.

EXAMPLES OF UNCONFORMITIES

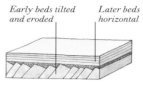

Early beds tilted and eroded　　*Later beds horizontal*

ANGULAR UNCONFORMITY

No bedding in early rocks　　*Later beds horizontal*

NONCONFORMITY

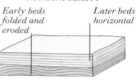

Early beds folded and eroded　　*Later beds horizontal*

DISCONFORMITY

SEDIMENTARY LAYERS OF THE GRAND CANYON REGION

Wasatch formation

Kaiparowits formation　　*Tropic formation*

Wahweap sandstone

Dakota sandstone　　*Carmel formation*　　*Pink Cliffs*　　*Bryce Canyon*　　*Zion Canyon*　　*Gray Cliffs*　　*Sevier fault*　　*White Cliffs*　　*Pipe Spring*

Temple Cap sandstone　　*Navajo sandstone*　　*Kayenta formation*　　*Moenave formation*　　*Chinle formation*　　*Shinarump member*　　*Moenkopi formation*　　*Kaibab limestone*　　*Toroweap formation*　　*Coconino sandstone*　　*Her shal*

EXAMPLES OF SEDIMENTARY ROCKS

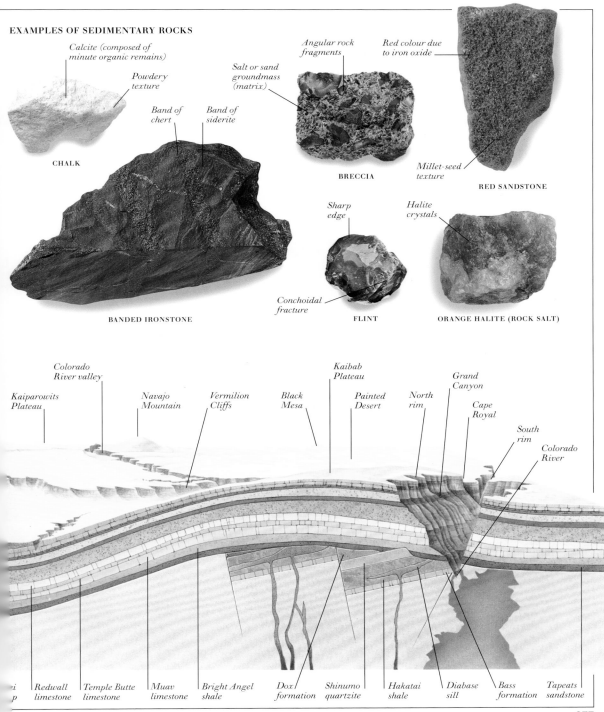

Calcite (composed of minute organic remains)

Powdery texture

CHALK

Angular rock fragments

Salt or sand groundmass (matrix)

BRECCIA

Red colour due to iron oxide

Millet-seed texture

RED SANDSTONE

Band of chert

Band of siderite

BANDED IRONSTONE

Sharp edge

Conchoidal fracture

FLINT

Halite crystals

ORANGE HALITE (ROCK SALT)

Kaiparowits Plateau

Colorado River valley

Navajo Mountain

Vermilion Cliffs

Black Mesa

Kaibab Plateau

Painted Desert

North rim

Grand Canyon

Cape Royal

South rim

Colorado River

Redwall limestone

Temple Butte limestone

Muav limestone

Bright Angel shale

Dox formation

Shinumo quartzite

Hakatai shale

Diabase sill

Bass formation

Tapeats sandstone

277

Fossils

FOSSILS ARE THE REMAINS of plants and animals that
have been preserved in rock. A fossil may be the
preserved remains of an organism itself, an impression
of it in rock, or preserved traces (known as trace fossils)
left by an organism while it was alive, such as organic
carbon outlines, fossilized footprints, or droppings. Most
dead organisms soon rot away or are eaten by scavengers.
For fossilization to occur, rapid burial by sediment is
necessary. The organism decays, but the harder parts –
bones, teeth, and shells, for example – may be preserved
and hardened by minerals from the surrounding
sediment. Fossilization may also occur even when the
hard parts of an organism are dissolved away to leave
an impression called a mould. The mould is filled by
minerals, thereby creating a cast of the organism. The study
of fossils (palaeontology) can not only show how living things
have evolved, but can also help to reveal the Earth's geological
history — for example, by aiding in the dating of rock strata.

PROCESS OF FOSSILIZATION

Sea
Ammonite
Seabed

ANIMAL DIES

Sea
Shell
Seabed

SOFT PARTS ROT

Sea
Shell
Sediment
Seabed

SHELL BURIED

Shell dissolved away and replaced by minerals
Sea
Sediment
Sediment
Seabed

SHELL FOSSILIZED

EXAMPLES OF FOSSILS

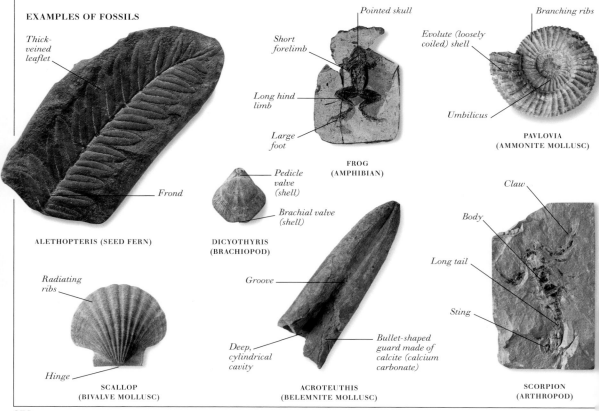

Thick-veined leaflet

Frond

ALETHOPTERIS (SEED FERN)

Short forelimb

Pointed skull

Long hind limb

Large foot

**FROG
(AMPHIBIAN)**

Pedicle valve (shell)

Brachial valve (shell)

**DICYOTHYRIS
(BRACHIOPOD)**

Branching ribs

Evolute (loosely coiled) shell

Umbilicus

**PAVLOVIA
(AMMONITE MOLLUSC)**

Radiating ribs

Hinge

**SCALLOP
(BIVALVE MOLLUSC)**

Groove

Deep, cylindrical cavity

Bullet-shaped guard made of calcite (calcium carbonate)

**ACROTEUTHIS
(BELEMNITE MOLLUSC)**

Claw

Body

Long tail

Sting

**SCORPION
(ARTHROPOD)**

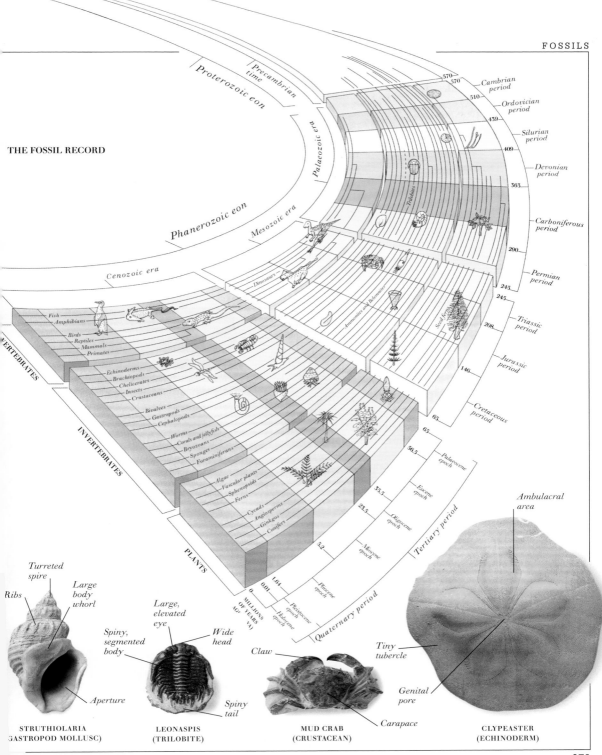

THE FOSSIL RECORD

Precambrian time

Proterozoic eon

Palaeozoic era

Phanerozoic eon

Mesozoic era

Cenozoic era

570
570
Cambrian period

510
Ordovician period

439
Silurian period

409
Devonian period

363
Carboniferous period

290
Permian period

245
245
Triassic period

208
Jurassic period

146
Cretaceous period

Dinosaurs

Ammonites and Belemnites

Seed ferns

Trilobites

65
65
Palaeocene epoch

56.5
Eocene epoch

35.5
Oligocene epoch

23.5
Miocene epoch

5.2
Pliocene epoch

1.64
Pleistocene epoch

0.01
Holocene epoch

Tertiary period

Quaternary period

MILLIONS OF YEARS AGO (MA)
0

Fish
Amphibians
Birds
Reptiles
Mammals
Primates

Echinoderms
Brachiopods
Chelicerates
Insects
Crustaceans
Bivalves
Gastropods
Cephalopods
Worms
Corals and jellyfish
Bryozoans
Sponges
Foraminiferans

Algae
Vascular plants
Sphenopsids
Ferns
Cycads
Angiosperms
Ginkgos
Conifers

VERTEBRATES

INVERTEBRATES

PLANTS

Turreted spire

Ribs

Large body whorl

Aperture

STRUTHIOLARIA
(GASTROPOD MOLLUSC)

Large, elevated eye

Spiny, segmented body

Wide head

Spiny tail

LEONASPIS
(TRILOBITE)

Claw

Carapace

MUD CRAB
(CRUSTACEAN)

Ambulacral area

Tiny tubercle

Genital pore

CLYPEASTER
(ECHINODERM)

Mineral resources

MINERAL RESOURCES CAN BE DEFINED AS naturally occurring substances that can be extracted from the Earth and are useful as fuels and raw materials. Coal, oil, and gas – collectively called fossil fuels – are commonly included in this group, but are not strictly minerals, because they are of organic origin. Coal formation begins when vegetation is buried and partly decomposed to form peat. Overlying sediments compress the peat and transform it into lignite (soft brown coal). As the overlying sediments accumulate, increasing pressure and temperature eventually transform the lignite into bituminous and hard anthracite coals. Oil and gas are usually formed from organic matter that was deposited in marine sediments. Under the effects of heat and pressure, the compressed organic matter undergoes complex chemical changes to form oil and gas. The oil and gas percolate upwards through water-saturated, permeable rocks and they may rise to the Earth's surface or accumulate below an impermeable layer of rock that has been folded or faulted to form a trap – an anticline (upfold) trap, for example. Minerals are inorganic substances that may consist of a single chemical element, such as gold, silver, or copper, or combinations of elements (see pp. 268-269). Some minerals are concentrated in mineralization zones in rock associated with crustal movements or volcanic activity. Others may be found in sediments as placer deposits – accumulations of high-density minerals that have been weathered out of rocks, transported, and deposited (on river-beds, for example).

OIL RIG, NORTH SEA

HOW COAL IS FORMED

Vegetation

Increasing layers of overlying sediment

Increasing pressure and temperature

Increasing layers of overlying sediment

Increasing pressure and temperature

Peat (about 60% carbon)

Lignite (about 70% carbon)

Bituminous coal (about 80% carbon)

PEAT

LIGNITE (BROWN COAL)

BITUMINOUS COAL

STAGES IN THE FORMATION OF COAL

Stalk

Lea[f]

PLANT MATTER

Decayed plant matter

About 60% carbon

PEAT

About 70% carbon

Crumbly texture

LIGNITE (BROWN COAL)

Powdery texture

About 80% carbon

BITUMINOUS COAL

Shiny surface

About 95% carbon

ANTHRACITE COAL

XAMPLES OF OIL AND GAS TRAPS

Impermeable
rock

Oil

Folded
impermeable
rock

ter-
urated
meable
k

Fault

FAULT TRAP

Pinch-
out

Water-saturated
permeable rock

Fault

Gas

Oil

PINCH-OUT TRAP

Anticline

Folded
impermeable
rock

Water-
saturated
permeable
rock

Gas

Oil

ANTICLINE TRAP

Folded
impermeable
rock

Water-
saturated
permeable
rock

Oil

Impermeable
salt dome

SALT-DOME TRAP

MAJOR COAL, OIL, AND GAS DEPOSITS

● Coal   ● Oil and gas

OW AN ANTICLINE TRAP IS FORMED

Layer of sediment
ontaining decayed
lant and animal
natter

Sea

ld
abed

Increasing layers
of overlying
sediment

Sea

Oil and gas formed
by chemical reactions,
heat, and pressure

**DEPOSITION OF ORGANIC
MATERIAL**

**FORMATION OF OIL
AND GAS**

Land

Sea

Anticline

Impermeable
rock layer
folded to form
oil and gas trap

Gas

Oil

Water-saturated
permeable rock

**COLLECTION OF OIL AND GAS IN
ANTICLINE TRAP**

MINERALIZATION ZONES

Volcano

Subduction zone

Oceanic crust

Mid-ocean
ridge

Continental
rust

tungsten,
uth, and copper

Copper,
zinc, gold,
and chromium

Copper,
gold, silver,
tin, lead, and
mercury

Lead,
zinc,
and
copper

Chromium

Manganese,
cobalt, and
nickel

Copper
and zinc

Weathering and erosion

WEATHERING IS THE BREAKING DOWN of rocks on the Earth's surface. There are two main types: physical (or mechanical) and chemical. Physical weathering may be caused by temperature changes, such as freezing and thawing, or by abrasion from material carried by winds, rivers, or glaciers. Rocks may also be broken down by the actions of animals and plants, such as the burrowing of animals and the growth of roots. Chemical weathering causes rocks to decompose by changing their chemical composition – for example, rainwater may dissolve certain minerals in a rock. Erosion is the wearing away and removal of land surfaces by water, wind, or ice. It is greatest in areas of little or no surface vegetation, such as deserts, where sand dunes may form.

FORMATION OF A HAMADA (ROCK PAVEMEN

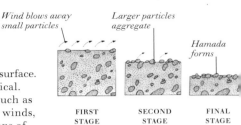

Wind blows away small particles

Larger particles aggregate

Hamada forms

FIRST STAGE   **SECOND STAGE**   **FINAL STAGE**

FEATURES OF WEATHERI AND EROSION

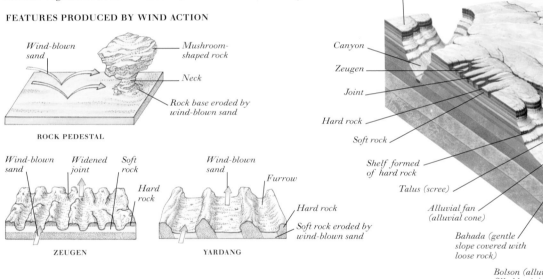

Mesa (flat-topped plateau)

Canyon

Zeugen

Joint

Hard rock

Soft rock

Shelf formed of hard rock

Talus (scree)

Alluvial fan (alluvial cone)

Bahada (gentle slope covered with loose rock)

Bolson (alluvium-filled basin)

FEATURES PRODUCED BY WIND ACTION

Wind-blown sand

Mushroom-shaped rock

Neck

Rock base eroded by wind-blown sand

ROCK PEDESTAL

Wind-blown sand

Widened joint

Soft rock

Hard rock

ZEUGEN

Wind-blown sand

Furrow

Hard rock

Soft rock eroded by wind-blown sand

YARDANG

EXAMPLES OF PHYSICAL WEATHERING PROCESSES

Heated rock surface expands

Exfoliation dome

Flaking rock

Fallen debris

EXFOLIATION (ONION-SKIN WEATHERING)

Joint expands and contracts due to temperature changes

Block of fallen rock

BLOCK DISINTEGRATION

Talus (scree)

Joint widened by frozen water

FROST WEDGING

Crack widened by tree root

Tr

TREE ROOT ACTION

SECTION THROUGH A BARKHAN DUNE

EXAMPLES OF SAND DUNES

SECTION THROUGH A BARKHAN DUNE

Strong wind

Weak wind

Direction of wind-blown sand

Windward face

Direction of sand movement

Slip face

Foreset strata

Cross-bed set

Topset strata

Bottomset strata

EXAMPLES OF SAND DUNES

Wind direction

Crescent-shaped dune

BARKHAN DUNE

Wind direction

Dune at right angle to wind

TRANSVERSE DUNE

Wind direction

Point where sand ridges meet

STAR DUNE

Wind direction

Parallel dunes

SEIF (LINEAR) DUNE

Canyon

Wadi (dry wash)

Mesa (flat-topped plateau)

Talus (scree)

Butte (flat-topped mesa remnant)

Eroded arch

Residual hill on pediment

Hamada (rock pavement)

Rock pedestal

Barkhan dune

Parabolic dune

Transverse dune

Seif (linear) dune

Inselberg (isolated, steep-sided hill)

Hard granite

lake f salt or cated clay)

Faultline

Freshwater lake

Fertile oasis

Deflation hollow created by wind erosion

Cuesta (asymmetric ridge)

Faultline

Hard sandstone

Hog's-back (steep ridge)

283

Caves

CAVES COMMONLY FORM in areas of limestone, although on coastlines they also occur in other rocks. Limestone is made of calcite (calcium carbonate), which dissolves in the carbonic acid naturally present in rainwater, and in humic acids from the decay of vegetation. The acidic water trickles down through cracks and joints in the limestone and between rock layers, breaking up the surface terrain into clints (blocks of rock), separated by grikes (deep cracks), and punctuated by sink-holes (also called swallow-holes or potholes) into which surface streams may disappear. Underground, the acidic water dissolves the rock around crevices, opening up a network of passages and caves, which can become large caverns if the roofs collapse. Various features are formed when the dissolved calcite is redeposited; for example, it may be redeposited along an underground stream to form a gour (series of calcite ridges), or in caves and passages to form stalactites and stalagmites. Stalactites develop where calcite is left behind as water drips from the roof; where the drops land, stalagmites build up.

MERGED STALACTITES

STALACTITE WITH RING MARKS

Ring mark

Doline (depression caused by collapse of cave roof)

Sink-hole

Porous limestone

Gorge where cave roof has fallen

Resurgence

Limestone terrain with clints and grikes

Impermeable rock

STALAGMITE FORMATIONS

Calcite (calcium carbonate) crystallized under water

Thin encrustations of calcite (calcium carbonate)

Scar of bare rock

Former water table

CRYSTALLINE STALAGMITIC FLOOR

CALCAREOUS TUFA

Permeable limestone

Encrustations on dead stems of small plants

Calcite (calcium carbonate)

Calcite (calcium carbonate)

Encrustations with fungoid structure

Resurgence

STALAGMITIC FLOOR

STALAGMITIC BOSS

Layer of impermeable rock

Present water table

EVELOPMENT OF A CAVE SYSTEM

Impermeable rock

Joint

edding ane

npermeable ck

STRUCTURE OF LIMESTONE STRATA

Permeable limestone

Water seeps through cracks in rock

Calcite (calcium carbonate) deposits begin to form

Stream enters permeable rock

Resurgence

Tunnel

Underground stream

INITIAL CAVE

Doline caused by collapse of cave roof

Sink-hole

Stalactite

Stalagmite

Gorge

Resurgence

Cave

Dry gallery

EXTENDED CAVE SYSTEM

NTERCONNECTED CAVE SYSTEM

Stalactite

Pillar (column)

Gorge

Stalactite

Dry gallery (former course of underground stream)

Gour (series of calcite ridges) deposited by running water

Stalagmite

Joint in rock enlarged by water

Bedding plane

Curtain of deposited calcite (calcium carbonate)

Tunnel

Cave

Passage

Cavern

Gour (series of calcite ridges)

285

Glaciers

GLACIER BAY, ALASKA

A VALLEY GLACIER IS A LARGE MASS OF ICE that forms on land and moves slowly downhill under its own weight. It is formed from snow that collects in cirques (mountain hollows also known as corries) and compresses into ice as more and more snow accumulates. The cirque is deepened by frost wedging and abrasion (see pp. 282-283), and arêtes (sharp ridges) develop between adjacent cirques. Eventually, so much ice builds up that the glacier begins to move downhill. As the glacier moves it collects moraine (debris), which may range in size from particles of dust to large boulders. The rocks at the base of the glacier erode the glacial valley, giving it a U-shaped cross-section. Under the glacier, *roches moutonnées* (eroded outcrops of hard rock) and drumlins (rounded mounds of rock and clay) are left behind on the valley floor. The glacier ends at a terminus (the snout), where the ice melts as fast as it arrives. If the temperature increases, the ice melts faster than it arrives, and the glacier retreats. The retreating glacier leaves behind its moraine and also erratics (isolated single boulders). Glacial streams from the melting glacier deposit eskers and kames (ridges and mounds of sand and gravel), but carry away the finer sediment to form a stratified outwash plain. Lumps of ice carried on to this plain melt, creating holes called kettles.

VALLEY GLACIER

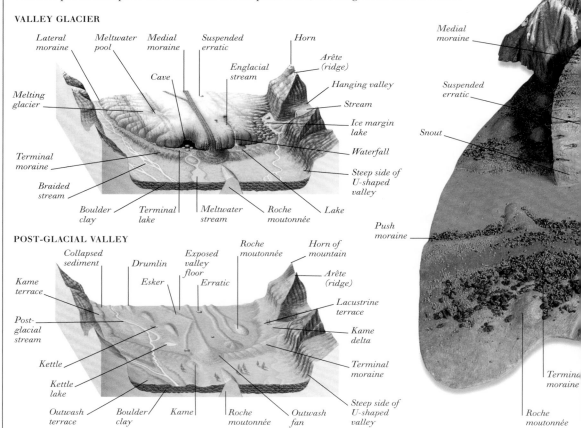

Lateral moraine
Meltwater pool
Medial moraine
Suspended erratic
Horn
Medial moraine
Arête (ridge)
Cave
Englacial stream
Hanging valley
Suspended erratic
Melting glacier
Stream
Ice margin lake
Snout
Waterfall
Terminal moraine
Steep side of U-shaped valley
Braided stream
Boulder clay
Terminal lake
Meltwater stream
Roche moutonnée
Lake
Push moraine

POST-GLACIAL VALLEY

Collapsed sediment
Drumlin
Exposed valley floor
Roche moutonnée
Horn of mountain
Kame terrace
Esker
Erratic
Arête (ridge)
Lacustrine terrace
Post-glacial stream
Kame delta
Kettle
Terminal moraine
Kettle lake
Terminal moraine
Steep side of U-shaped valley
Outwash terrace
Boulder clay
Kame
Roche moutonnée
Outwash fan
Roche moutonnée

...URES OF A GLACIER

Lateral
moraine

Firn (compressed
snow)

Tributary glacier

Moving ice

U-shaped
valley

Medial
moraine

Cirque
(corrie)

Arête
(ridge)

Tributary
moraine joins
medial moraine

Subglacial
stream

Rock being
eroded by ice

Brittle
surface ice

Viscous
flowing ice

Englacial
moraine

Crevasse

Ribbon
lake

Outwash
plain

Sediment
deposited by
meltwater

Meltwater

Stream

ICE-FALL

Slope
flattens

Rougher
surface

Ice recompresses

Ice block
tilts and twists

Steep
slope

Gentle
slope

Smooth
surface

Ice breaks
into blocks

Crevasse
deepens and
widens

CIRQUE FORMATION

Firn
(compressed
snow)

Material
loosened
by frost
wedging

Fresh
snowfall

EARLY STAGE

Moraine pulled
from ground

Steep
back wall

Glacier

Base of cirque eroded by
glacier's pivoting action

Rock lip

LATER STAGE

**U-SHAPED VALLEY
FORMATION**

Arête
(ridge)

Horn

Cirque
overspills

Glacier

DURING GLACIATION

Deepened
cirque

Deep U-shaped
valley

Hanging
valley

Tarn

AFTER GLACIATION

Rivers

RIVERS FORM PART of the water cycle – the continuous circulation of water between the land, sea, and atmosphere. The source of a river may be a mountain spring or lake, or a melting glacier. The course that the river subsequently takes depends on the slope of the terrain and on the rock types and formations over which it flows. In its early, upland stages, a river tumbles steeply over rocks and boulders and cuts a steep-sided V-shaped valley. Farther downstream, it flows smoothly over sediments and forms winding meanders, eroding sideways to create broad valleys and plains. On reaching the coast, the river may deposit sediment to form an estuary or delta (see pp. 290-291).

RIVER CAPTURE

River

Tributary erodes
headwards

River

EARLY STAGE

Dry
valley

River captu
by tribut

River flow
decreases

River flow
increases

LATER STAGE

THE WATER CYCLE

Wind

Water vapour released
into atmosphere by
trees and other plants

Wind

Water vapour
forms clouds

Water
evaporates
from sea

Water
stored in sea

River flows
into sea

Precip
falls on
ground

W
car
downstr
by r

W
evapo
from

Water seeps
underground
and flows to sea

Seabed

Sea

Sediment layers

**SATELLITE IMAGE OF GANGES
RIVER DELTA, BANGLADESH**

Ganges
River

Ganges
delta

Infertile
swampland

Distributary

Large volume
of sediment

RIVER DRAINAGE PATTERNS

RADIAL

CENTRIPETAL

PARALLEL

DENDRITIC

DERANGED

TRELLISED

ANNULAR

RECTANGULAR

STAGES IN A RIVER'S DEVELOPMENT

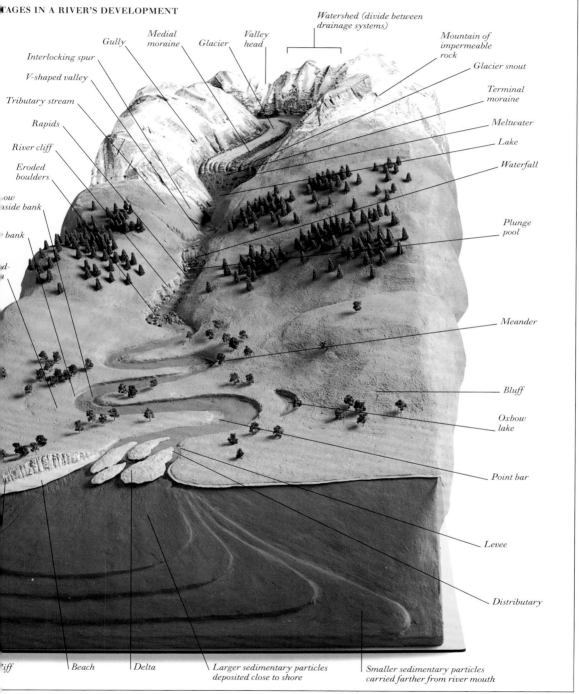

Watershed (divide between drainage systems)

Medial moraine

Gully

Glacier

Valley head

Interlocking spur

V-shaped valley

Tributary stream

Rapids

River cliff

Eroded boulders

ow side bank

bank

d-

Mountain of impermeable rock

Glacier snout

Terminal moraine

Meltwater

Lake

Waterfall

Plunge pool

Meander

Bluff

Oxbow lake

Point bar

Levee

Distributary

iff

Beach

Delta

Larger sedimentary particles deposited close to shore

Smaller sedimentary particles carried farther from river mouth

River features

RIVERS ARE ONE OF THE MAJOR FORCES that shape the landscape. Near its source, a river is steep (see pp. 288-289). It erodes downwards, carving out V-shaped valleys and deep gorges. Waterfalls and rapids are formed where the river flows from hard rock to softer, more easily eroded rock. Farther downstream, meanders may form and there is greater sideways erosion, resulting in a broad river valley. The river sometimes erodes through the neck of a meander to form an oxbow lake. Sediment deposited on the valley floor by meandering rivers and during floods helps to create a flood-plain. Floods may also deposit sediment on the banks of the river to form levees. As a river spills into the sea or a lake, it deposits large amounts of sediment, and may form a delta. A delta is an area of sand-bars, swamps, and lagoons through which the river flows in several channels called distributaries – the Mississippi delta, for example. Often, a rise in sea level may have flooded the river-mouth to form a broad estuary, a tidal section where seawater mixes with fresh water.

HOW WATERFALLS AND RAPIDS ARE FORMED

WATERFALL

RAPIDS

A RIVER VALLEY DRAINAGE SYSTEM

GORGE

BRAIDING

HEADWARD EROSION

ENTRENCHED MEANDER

NATURAL BRIDGE

WATERFALL FEATURES

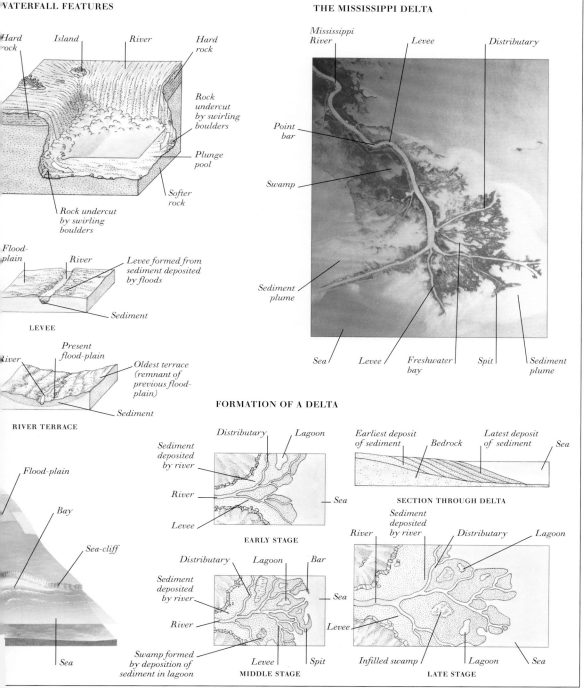

Hard rock

Island

River

Hard rock

Rock undercut by swirling boulders

Plunge pool

Softer rock

Rock undercut by swirling boulders

Flood-plain

River

Levee formed from sediment deposited by floods

Sediment

LEVEE

River

Present flood-plain

Oldest terrace (remnant of previous flood-plain)

Sediment

RIVER TERRACE

Flood-plain

Bay

Sea-cliff

Sea

THE MISSISSIPPI DELTA

Mississippi River

Levee

Distributary

Point bar

Swamp

Sediment plume

Sea

Levee

Freshwater bay

Spit

Sediment plume

FORMATION OF A DELTA

Distributary

Lagoon

Sediment deposited by river

River

Levee

Sea

EARLY STAGE

Earliest deposit of sediment

Bedrock

Latest deposit of sediment

Sea

SECTION THROUGH DELTA

Distributary

Lagoon

Bar

Sediment deposited by river

River

Sea

Swamp formed by deposition of sediment in lagoon

Levee

Spit

MIDDLE STAGE

Sediment deposited by river

River

Distributary

Lagoon

Levee

Infilled swamp

Lagoon

Sea

LATE STAGE

291

Lakes and groundwater

NATURAL LAKE OCCUR WHERE a large quantity of water collects in a hollow in impermeable rock, or is prevented from draining away by a barrier, such as moraine (glacial deposits) or solidified lava. Lakes are often relatively short-lived landscape features, as they tend to become silted up by sediment from the streams and rivers that feed them. Some of the more long-lasting lakes are found in deep rift valleys formed by vertical movements of the Earth's crust (see pp. 58-59) – for example, Lake Baikal in Russia, the world's largest freshwater lake, and the Dead Sea in the Middle East, one of the world's saltiest lakes. Where water is able to drain away, it sinks into the ground until it reaches a layer of impermeable rock, then accumulates in the permeable rock above it; this water-saturated permeable rock is called an aquifer. The saturated zone varies in depth according to seasonal and climatic changes. In wet conditions, the water stored underground builds up, while in dry periods it becomes depleted. Where the upper edge of the saturated zone – the water table – meets the ground surface, water emerges as springs. In an artesian basin, where the aquifer is below an aquiclude (layer of impermeable rock), the water table throughout the basin is determined by its height at the rim. In the centre of such a basin, the water table is above ground level. The water in the basin is thus trapped below the water table and can rise under its own pressure along faultlines or well shafts.

LAKE BAIKAL, RUSSIA

EXAMPLES OF SPRINGS

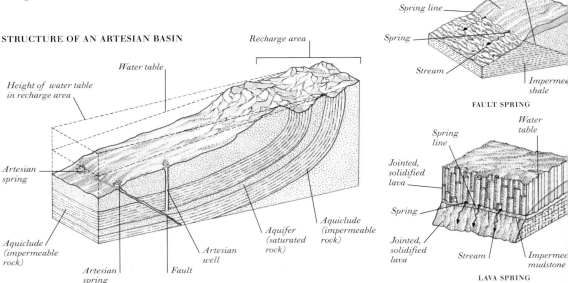

Permeable limestone
Water table
Spring line
Stream
Spring
Impermeable shale

LIMESTONE SPRING

Permeable gravel
Water table
Spring line
Stream
Spring
Impermeable clay

COASTAL (VALLEY) SPRING

Fault
Water table
Permeable sandstone
Spring line
Spring
Stream
Impermeable shale

FAULT SPRING

Water table
Spring line
Jointed, solidified lava
Spring
Jointed, solidified lava
Stream
Impermeable mudstone

LAVA SPRING

STRUCTURE OF AN ARTESIAN BASIN

Recharge area
Water table
Height of water table in recharge area
Artesian spring
Aquiclude (impermeable rock)
Artesian spring
Artesian well
Fault
Aquifer (saturated rock)
Aquiclude (impermeable rock)

FEATURES OF A GROUNDWATER SYSTEM

Zone of
aeration

Lake

Stream

Marsh

Layer
of soil
moisture

Zone of
aeration

Capillary
fringe

Water table

Saturated
zone

**CLOSE-UP OF
SURFACE LAYER**

Dry-season
water table

Present water
table (wet season)

Temporarily saturated
zone (saturated only in
wet season)

Permanently
saturated zone
(saturated in wet
and dry seasons)

EXAMPLES OF LAKES

Glacial
deposits

Lake in kettle
(former site of
ice block)

Oxbow lake
(cut-off river
meander)

River

KETTLE LAKE

OXBOW LAKE

Caldera
(collapsed
crater)

Volcanic
lake

Movement
along strike-
slip (lateral)
fault

Strike-slip
(lateral) fault

VOLCANIC LAKE

Lake in
elongated
hollow

STRIKE-SLIP (LATERAL) FAULT LAKE

Rift valley

Steep back wall
eroded by frost
and ice

Moraine
or rock lip
damming
lake

gh
ley
lls

Sinking graben
(block fault)

Tarn (circular
mountain lake)

GRABEN (BLOCK-FAULT) LAKE

TARN

THE DEAD SEA, ISRAEL/JORDAN

River
Jordan

Dead Sea

Steep rift-
valley walls

Salt left by
evaporation

Israel

Shallow
flats

Jordan

Coastlines

COASTLINES ARE AMONG THE MOST RAPIDLY changing landscape
features. Some are eroded by waves, wind, and rain, causing
cliffs to be undercut and caves to be hollowed out of solid rock.
Others are built up by waves transporting sand and small rocks in a
process known as longshore drift, and by rivers depositing sediment in
deltas. Additional influences include the activities of living organisms
such as coral, crustal movements, and sea-level variations due to
climatic changes. Rising land or a drop in sea level creates an emergent
coastline, with cliffs and beaches stranded above the new shoreline.
Sinking land or a rise in sea level produces a drowned coastline, typified
by fjords (submerged glacial valleys) or submerged river valleys.

FEATURES OF A SEA-CLIFF

Cliff-top
Cliff-face
High tide level
Low tide level
Offshore deposits
Wave-cut platform
Undercut area of cliff

FEATURES OF WAVES

Wave height
Crest
Wavelength
Trough
Shorter wavelength near beach
Circular orbit of water and suspended particles
Orbit deformed into ellipse as water gets shallower

Mature river
Headland
Bedding plane
Sea-cliff
Remnants of former headland
Estuary

LONGSHORE DRIFT

Pebble
Backwash
Movement of material along beach
Build-up of material against groyne
Beach
Groyne
Waves approaching shore at an oblique angle
Swash zone
Swash

DEPOSITIONAL FEATURES OF COASTLINES

Bay-head beach
Wave direction
Headland
Wave direction
Tombolo
Island
Wave direction
Cuspate foreland
Wave direction
Barrier beach
Lagoon

BAY HEAD BEACH   TOMBOLO   CUSPATE FORELAND   BARRIER BEACH

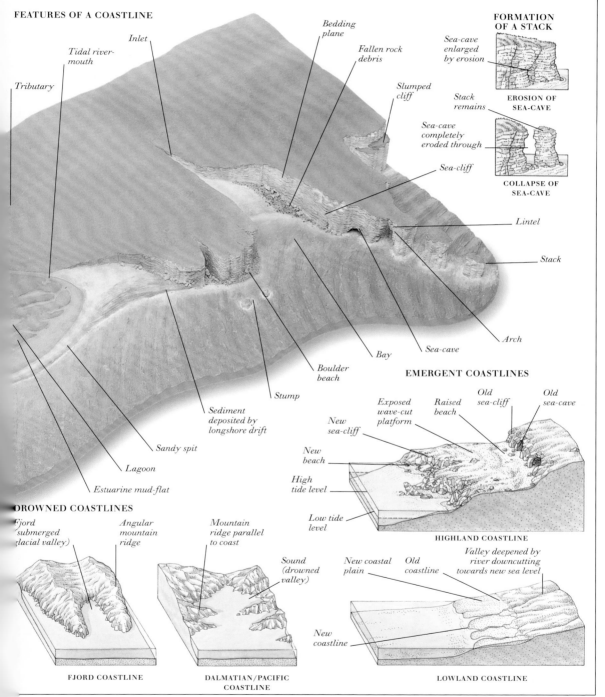

FEATURES OF A COASTLINE

Tributary

Tidal river-mouth

Inlet

Bedding plane

Fallen rock debris

Slumped cliff

Sea-cliff

Lintel

Stack

Arch

Sea-cave

Bay

Boulder beach

Stump

Sediment deposited by longshore drift

Sandy spit

Lagoon

Estuarine mud-flat

FORMATION OF A STACK

Sea-cave enlarged by erosion

EROSION OF SEA-CAVE

Stack remains

Sea-cave completely eroded through

COLLAPSE OF SEA-CAVE

EMERGENT COASTLINES

Exposed wave-cut platform

New sea-cliff

New beach

High tide level

Low tide level

Raised beach

Old sea-cliff

Old sea-cave

HIGHLAND COASTLINE

DROWNED COASTLINES

Fjord (submerged glacial valley)

Angular mountain ridge

Mountain ridge parallel to coast

Sound (drowned valley)

New coastal plain

Old coastline

Valley deepened by river downcutting towards new sea level

New coastline

FJORD COASTLINE

DALMATIAN/PACIFIC COASTLINE

LOWLAND COASTLINE

295

Oceans and seas

OCEANS AND SEAS COVER ABOUT 70 PER CENT of the Earth's surface and account for about 97 per cent of its total water. These oceans and seas play a crucial role in regulating temperature variations and determining climate. Their waters absorb heat from the Sun, especially in tropical regions, and the surface currents distribute it around the Earth, warming overlying air masses and neighbouring land in winter and cooling them in summer. The oceans are never still. Differences in temperature and salinity drive deep current systems, while surface currents are generated by winds blowing over the oceans. All currents are deflected – to the right in the Northern Hemisphere, to the left in the Southern Hemisphere – as a result of the Earth's rotation. This deflective factor is known as the Coriolis force. A current that begins on the surface is immediately deflected. This current in turn generates a current in the layer of water beneath, which is also deflected. As the movement is transmitted downwards, the deflections form an Ekman spiral. The waters of the oceans and seas are also moved by the constant ebb and flow of tides. These are caused by the gravitational pull of the Moon and Sun. The highest tides (Spring tides) occur at full and new Moon; the lowest tides (neap tides) occur at first and last quarter.

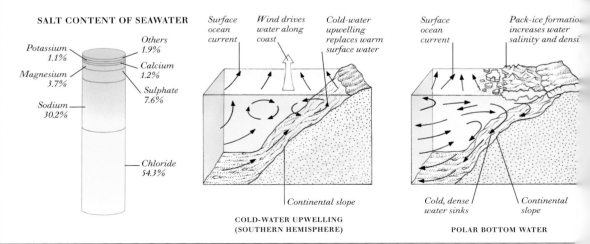

SURFACE CURRENTS

GREENWICH MERIDIAN

East Greenland Current
East Greenland Current
Alaska
North Pacific Current
Florida Current
Gulf Stream
North Atlantic Current
Canaries Current
NORTH PACIFIC GYRE
NORTH ATLANTIC GYRE
North Equatorial Current
North Equatorial Current
Equatorial Countercurrent
South Equatorial Current
South Equatorial Current
Equatorial Countercurrent
Peru Current
Brazil Current
SOUTH ATLANTIC GYRE
SOUTH PACIFIC GYRE
Humboldt Current
Falkland Current
Antarctic Circumpolar Current

OFFSHORE CURRENTS

SALT CONTENT OF SEAWATER

Potassium 1.1%
Others 1.9%
Calcium 1.2%
Magnesium 3.7%
Sulphate 7.6%
Sodium 30.2%
Chloride 54.3%

Surface ocean current
Wind drives water along coast
Cold-water upwelling replaces warm surface water
Continental slope

COLD-WATER UPWELLING (SOUTHERN HEMISPHERE)

Surface ocean current
Pack-ice formation increases water salinity and density
Cold, dense water sinks
Continental slope

POLAR BOTTOM WATER

EFFECT OF CORIOLIS FORCE

Winds and currents
deflected to right
in Northern
Hemisphere

North Pole

Coriolis
force

Equator

Original direction
of wind or current

Winds and
currents
deflected
to left in
Southern
Hemisphere

Actual direction
of wind or current

South
Pole

EKMAN SPIRAL (NORTHERN HEMISPHERE)

Wind

Surface current
caused by wind

Subsurface
current slightly
deflected by
Coriolis force

Deep current
at 180° to
surface current

Midwater current
further deflected
by Coriolis force

ARCTIC CIRCLE
(66° 32'N)

TROPIC OF
CANCER
(23° 30'N)

Kuroshio Current

North Equatorial Current

Equatorial Countercurrent

Equatorial Current

EQUATOR
(0°)

North-east Monsoon Drift

North Equatorial Current

Equatorial Countercurrent

South Equatorial Current

SOUTH
INDIAN
GYRE

West Australian Current

East Australian Current

TROPIC OF
CAPRICORN
(23° 30'S)

ANTARCTIC
CIRCLE
(66° 32'S)

80°   120°   160°   180°

80°   120°   160°   180°

HIGH
SPRING TIDE

New Moon

HOW TIDES ARE CAUSED

LOW
NEAP TIDE

Earth's orbit   Earth

Last
quarter

Moon's
gravitational
pull

HIGH
SPRING TIDE

Tidal bulge
caused by Sun's
gravitational pull

Full Moon

Tidal bulge
caused by Moon's
gravitational pull

Sun's
gravitational
pull

Equal and opposite tidal bulge
produced by centrifugal effect
due to Earth's spin

Sun's gravitational pull
reinforces centrifugal
effect, producing
large tidal
bulge

LOW
NEAP TIDE

Sun's gravitational pull
diminishes Moon's effect

First quarter

Sun

Moon's orbit

Tidal bulge where Moon's
gravitational pull is strongest

Moon

The ocean floor

THE OCEAN FLOOR COMPRISES TWO SECTIONS: the continental shelf and slope, and the deep-ocean floor. The continental shelf and slope are part of the continental crust, but may extend far into the ocean. Sloping quite gently to a depth of about 140 metres, the continental shelf is covered in sandy deposits shaped by waves and tidal currents. At the edge of the continental shelf, the seabed slopes down to the abyssal plain, which lies at an average depth of about 3,800 metres. On this deep-ocean floor is a layer of sediment made up of clays, fine oozes formed from the remains of tiny sea creatures, and occasional mineral-rich deposits. Echo-sounding and remote sensing from satellites has revealed that the abyssal plain is divided by a system of mountain ranges, far bigger than any on land – the mid-ocean ridge. Here, magma (molten rock) wells up from the Earth's interior and solidifies, widening the ocean floor (see pp. 58-59). As the ocean floor spreads, volcanoes that have formed over hot spots in the crust move away from their magma source; they become extinct and are increasingly submerged and eroded. Volcanoes eroded below sea level remain as seamounts (underwater mountains). In warm waters, a volcano that projects above the ocean surface often acquires a fringing coral reef, which may develop into an atoll as the volcano becomes submerged.

CONTINENTAL-SHELF FLOOR

Bedrock exposed by tidal scour

Shoreline

Parallel strips of coarse material left by strong tidal currents

Sand deposited in wavy pattern by weaker currents

Irregular patches of fine sand deposited by weakest currents

FEATURES OF THE OCEAN FLOOR

Sediment

Submarine canyon

Continental shelf

Course of mud river

Continental rise

Continental slope

Seamount (underwater mountain)

Guyot (flat-topped seamount)

Abyssal plain

Continental crust

Ooze (sediment consisting of remains of tiny sea creatures)

Layer of volcanic rock

Pillow lava

Volcanic crystalline rock

Oceanic crust

KEY

Calcareous ooze

Pelagic clay

Glacial sediments

Siliceous ooze

Terrigenous sediments

Continental margin sediments

Metalliferous muds

Major nodule fields

DEEP-OCEAN FLOOR SEDIMENTS

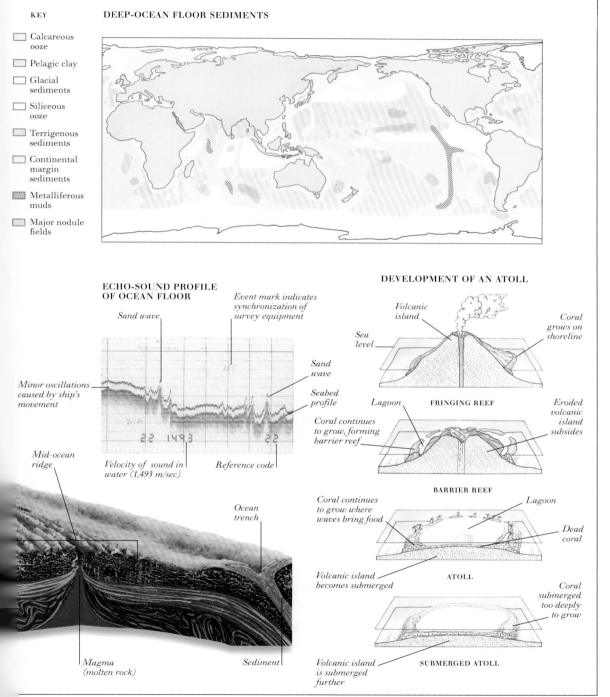

ECHO-SOUND PROFILE OF OCEAN FLOOR

Sand wave

Event mark indicates synchronization of survey equipment

Sand wave

Minor oscillations caused by ship's movement

Seabed profile

Velocity of sound in water (1,493 m/sec)

Reference code

Mid-ocean ridge

Ocean trench

Magma (molten rock)

Sediment

DEVELOPMENT OF AN ATOLL

Volcanic island

Sea level

Coral grows on shoreline

FRINGING REEF

Lagoon

Eroded volcanic island subsides

Coral continues to grow, forming barrier reef

BARRIER REEF

Coral continues to grow where waves bring food

Lagoon

Dead coral

Volcanic island becomes submerged

ATOLL

Coral submerged too deeply to grow

Volcanic island is submerged further

SUBMERGED ATOLL

299

The atmosphere

JET STREAM

THE EARTH IS SURROUNDED BY ITS ATMOSPHERE, a blanket of gases that enables life to exist on the planet. This layer has no definite outer edge, gradually becoming thinner until it merges into space, but over 80 per cent of atmospheric gases are held by gravity within about 20 kilometres of the Earth's surface. The atmosphere blocks out much harmful ultraviolet solar radiation, and insulates the Earth against extremes of temperature by limiting both incoming solar radiation and the escape of re-radiated heat into space. This natural balance may be distorted by the greenhouse effect, as gases such as carbon dioxide have built up in the atmosphere, trapping more heat. Close to the Earth's surface, differences in air temperature and pressure cause air to circulate between the equator and poles. This circulation, together with the Coriolis force, gives rise to the prevailing surface winds and the high-level jet streams.

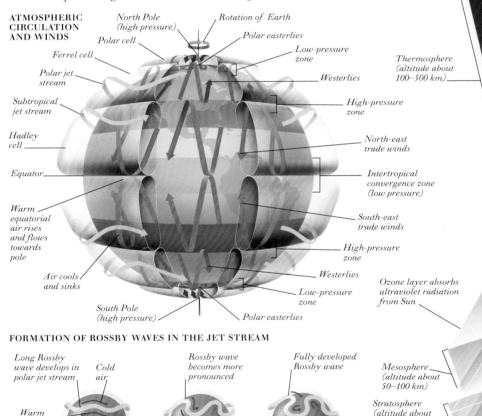

ATMOSPHERIC CIRCULATION AND WINDS

- Ferrel cell
- North Pole (high pressure)
- Polar cell
- Polar easterlies
- Rotation of Earth
- Low-pressure zone
- Polar jet stream
- Westerlies
- Subtropical jet stream
- High-pressure zone
- Hadley cell
- North-east trade winds
- Equator
- Intertropical convergence zone (low pressure)
- Warm equatorial air rises and flows towards pole
- South-east trade winds
- Air cools and sinks
- High-pressure zone
- Westerlies
- South Pole (high pressure)
- Low-pressure zone
- Polar easterlies

- Exosphere (altitude above about 500 km)
- Corona
- Thermosphere (altitude about 100–500 km)
- Ozone layer absorbs ultraviolet radiation from Sun
- Mesosphere (altitude about 50–100 km)
- Stratosphere (altitude about 10–50 km)
- Troposphere (altitude up to about 10 km)

FORMATION OF ROSSBY WAVES IN THE JET STREAM

- Long Rossby wave develops in polar jet stream
- Cold air
- Rossby wave becomes more pronounced
- Fully developed Rossby wave
- Warm air

INITIAL UNDULATION

DEEPENING WAVE

DEVELOPED WAVE

STRUCTURE OF THE ATMOSPHERE

GLOBAL WARMING

Solar radiation
re-radiated as heat

Some re-radiated
heat escapes
into space

Sun

Some re-radiated
heat reflected back
to Earth

Incoming solar
radiation

Earth

Atmosphere

**NATURALLY MODERATED
GREENHOUSE EFFECT**

Meteor (shooting star)
burns up as it passes
through atmosphere

Less re-radiated
heat escapes

Solar radiation
re-radiated as heat

More re-radiated
heat reflected
back to Earth

Aurora

Surface
temperature
rises

"Greenhouse
gases" accumulate
in atmosphere

Incoming solar
radiation

**UNBALANCED GREENHOUSE
EFFECT**

14% of incoming solar
radiation absorbed
by atmosphere

7% of incoming solar
radiation reflected
by atmosphere

COMPOSITION OF THE LOWER ATMOSPHERE

Other elements less
than 0.1%

24% of incoming
solar radiation
reflected by clouds

Argon 0.93%

Cosmic rays (high-energy
particles from space)
penetrate to stratosphere

Oxygen 21%

Some absorbed
heat re-radiated
by atmosphere

4% of incoming solar
radiation reflected by
oceans and land

Nitrogen 78%

51% of incoming solar
radiation absorbed by
Earth's surface

Some absorbed heat
re-radiated by clouds

Weather

WEATHER IS DEFINED AS THE ATMOSPHERIC CONDITIONS at a particular time and place; climate is the average weather conditions for a given region over time. Weather is assessed in terms of temperature, wind, cloud cover, and precipitation, such as rain or snow. Fine weather is associated with high-pressure areas, where air is sinking. Cloudy, wet, changeable weather is common in low-pressure zones with rising, unstable air. Such conditions occur at temperate latitudes, where warm air meets cool air along the polar fronts. Here, spiralling low-pressure cells known as depressions (mid-latitude cyclones) often form. A depression usually contains a sector of warmer air, beginning at a warm front and ending at a cold front. If the two fronts merge, forming an occluded front, the warm air is pushed upwards. An extreme form of low-pressure cell is a hurricane (also called a typhoon or tropical cyclone), which brings torrential rain and exceptionally strong winds.

TYPES OF OCCLUDED FRONT

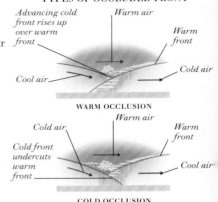

Advancing cold front rises up over warm front

Warm air

Warm front

Cool air

Cold air

WARM OCCLUSION

Cold air

Warm air

Cold front undercuts warm front

Warm front

Cool air

COLD OCCLUSION

FORMS OF PRECIPITATION

Water droplets less than 0.5 mm in diameter fall as drizzle

Water droplets coalesce to form raindrops 0.5–5.0 mm in diameter

Rising air

RAIN FROM CLOUDS NOT REACHING FREEZING LEVEL

Coalesced water droplets fall as rain

Ice crystal

Snowflake grown from ice crystal fall as snow

Rising air

Snowflake melt to fall as rain

RAIN AND SNOW FROM CLOUDS REACHING FREEZING LEVEL

Vertical air currents toss frozen water droplets up and down

Alternate freezing and melting builds up layers of

Rising air

Ice falls as hailstone

HAIL

TYPES OF CLOUD

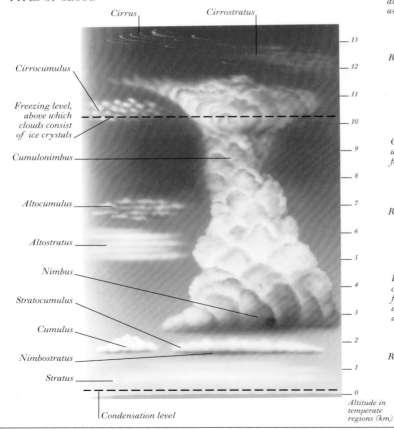

Cirrus

Cirrostratus

Cirrocumulus

Freezing level, above which clouds consist of ice crystals

Cumulonimbus

Altocumulus

Altostratus

Nimbus

Stratocumulus

Cumulus

Nimbostratus

Stratus

Condensation level

13
12
11
10
9
8
7
6
5
4
3
2
1
0

Altitude in temperate regions (km)

STRUCTURE OF A HURRICANE

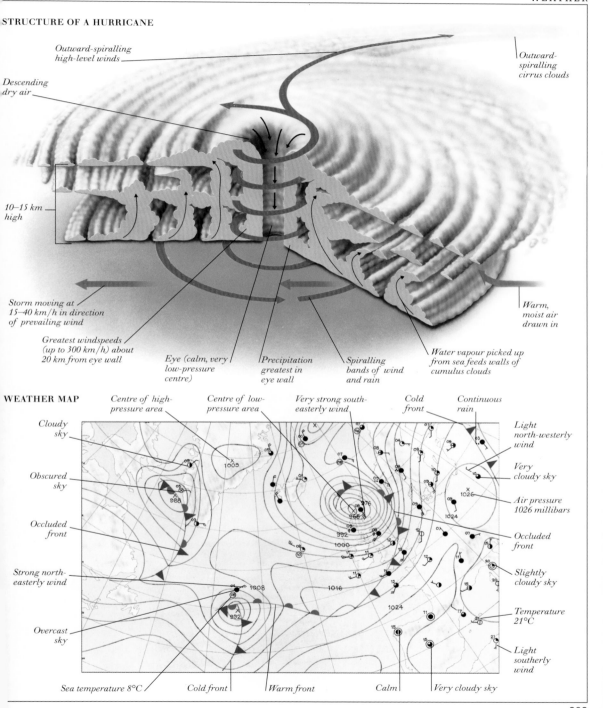

Outward-spiralling
high-level winds

Outward-
spiralling
cirrus clouds

Descending
dry air

10–15 km
high

Storm moving at
15–40 km/h in direction
of prevailing wind

Warm,
moist air
drawn in

Greatest windspeeds
(up to 300 km/h) about
20 km from eye wall

Eye (calm, very
low-pressure
centre)

Precipitation
greatest in
eye wall

Spiralling
bands of wind
and rain

Water vapour picked up
from sea feeds walls of
cumulus clouds

WEATHER MAP

Centre of high-
pressure area

Centre of low-
pressure area

Very strong south-
easterly wind

Cold
front

Continuous
rain

Cloudy
sky

Light
north-westerly
wind

Obscured
sky

Very
cloudy sky

Air pressure
1026 millibars

Occluded
front

Occluded
front

Strong north-
easterly wind

Slightly
cloudy sky

Temperature
21°C

Overcast
sky

Light
southerly
wind

Sea temperature 8°C

Cold front

Warm front

Calm

Very cloudy sky

303

PHYSICS AND CHEMISTRY

THE VARIETY OF MATTER ··························· 306

ATOMS AND MOLECULES ························· 308

THE PERIODIC TABLE ···························· 310

CHEMICAL REACTIONS ·························· 312

ENERGY ····································· 314

ELECTRICITY AND MAGNETISM ··············· 316

LIGHT ····································· 318

FORCE AND MOTION ························· 320

The variety of matter

PLANT AND INSECT
(LIVING MATTER)

MATTER IS ANYTHING THAT HAS A MASS. It includes everything from natural substances, such as minerals or living organisms, to synthetic materials. Matter can exist in three distinct states – solid, liquid, and gas. A solid is rigid and retains its shape. A liquid is fluid, has a definite volume, and will take the shape of its container. A gas (also fluid) fills a space, so its volume will be the same as the volume of its container. Most substances can exist as a solid, a liquid, or a gas: the state is determined by temperature. At very high temperatures, matter becomes plasma, often considered to be a fourth state of matter. All matter is composed of microscopic particles, such as atoms and molecules (see pp. 308-309). The arrangement and interactions of these particles give a substance its physical and chemical properties, by which matter can be identified. There is a huge variety of matter because particles can arrange themselves in countless ways, in one substance or by mixing with others. Natural glass, for example, seems to be a solid but is, in fact, a supercool liquid: the atoms are not locked into a pattern and can flow. Pure substances known as elements (see p. 310) combine to form compounds or mixtures. Mixtures called colloids are made up of larger particles of matter suspended in a solid, liquid, or gas, while a solution is one substance dissolved in another.

TYPES OF COLLOID

HAIR GEL (SOLID IN LIQUID)

SHAVING FOAM
(AIR IN LIQUID)

MIST
(LIQUID IN GAS)

EXAMPLES OF MATTER

The element silicon in pure crystalline form

Polythene is made by combining natural materials in new ways

Low pressure gases

Streaks of plasma (mixture of electrons and charged atoms)

Voltage tears electrons from atoms of low pressure gases inside

Central electrode

POLYTHENE
(SYNTHETIC POLYMER)

PURE SILICON
(SEMICONDUCTOR)

BALL CONTAINING
HIGH-TEMPERATURE GAS
(PLASMA)

Obsidian is molten volcanic rock that cools quickly, so atoms cannot form a regular pattern

Solid crystals dissolve in liquid water

Water

Potassium permanganate crystals

Azurite is found naturally with deposits of copper ore

OBSIDIAN
(NATURAL GLASS)

AZURITE
(CRYSTALLINE MINERAL)

POTASSIUM PERMANGANATE AND WATER
(SOLUTION)

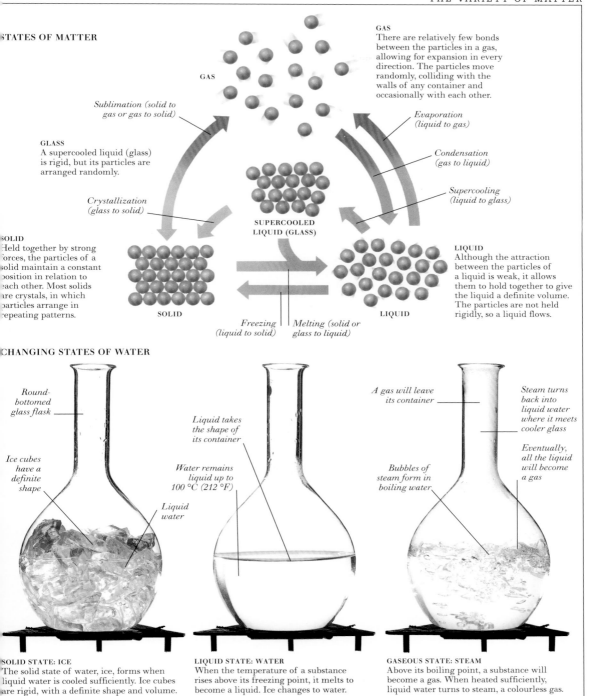

STATES OF MATTER

GAS
There are relatively few bonds between the particles in a gas, allowing for expansion in every direction. The particles move randomly, colliding with the walls of any container and occasionally with each other.

Sublimation (solid to gas or gas to solid)

GAS

Evaporation (liquid to gas)

Condensation (gas to liquid)

GLASS
A supercooled liquid (glass) is rigid, but its particles are arranged randomly.

Crystallization (glass to solid)

Supercooling (liquid to glass)

SOLID
Held together by strong forces, the particles of a solid maintain a constant position in relation to each other. Most solids are crystals, in which particles arrange in repeating patterns.

SUPERCOOLED LIQUID (GLASS)

LIQUID
Although the attraction between the particles of a liquid is weak, it allows them to hold together to give the liquid a definite volume. The particles are not held rigidly, so a liquid flows.

SOLID

LIQUID

Freezing (liquid to solid)

Melting (solid or glass to liquid)

CHANGING STATES OF WATER

Round-bottomed glass flask

Liquid takes the shape of its container

A gas will leave its container

Steam turns back into liquid water where it meets cooler glass

Ice cubes have a definite shape

Water remains liquid up to 100 °C (212 °F)

Bubbles of steam form in boiling water

Eventually, all the liquid will become a gas

Liquid water

SOLID STATE: ICE
The solid state of water, ice, forms when liquid water is cooled sufficiently. Ice cubes are rigid, with a definite shape and volume.

LIQUID STATE: WATER
When the temperature of a substance rises above its freezing point, it melts to become a liquid. Ice changes to water.

GASEOUS STATE: STEAM
Above its boiling point, a substance will become a gas. When heated sufficiently, liquid water turns to steam, a colourless gas.

Atoms and molecules

FALSE-COLOUR
IMAGE OF ACTUAL
GOLD ATOMS

ATOMS ARE THE smallest individual parts of an element (see pp. 310-311). They are tiny, with diameters in the order of one ten-thousand-millionth of a metre (10^{-10} m). Two or more atoms join together (bond) to form a molecule of a substance known as a compound. For example, when atoms of the elements hydrogen and fluorine join together, they form a molecule of the compound hydrogen fluoride. So molecules are the smallest individual parts of a compound. Atoms themselves are not indivisible – they possess an internal structure. At their centre is a dense nucleus, consisting of protons, which have a positive electric charge (see p. 316), and neutrons, which are uncharged. Around the nucleus are the negatively charged electrons. It is the electrons that give a substance most of its physical and chemical properties. They do not follow definite paths around the nucleus. Instead, electrons are said to be found within certain regions, called orbitals. These are arranged around the nucleus in "shells", each containing electrons of a particular energy. For example, the first shell (1) can hold up to two electrons, in a so-called s-orbital (1s). The second shell (2) can hold up to eight electrons, in s-orbitals (2s) and p-orbitals (2p). If an atom loses an electron, it becomes a positive ion (cation). If an electron is gained, an atom becomes a negative ion (anion). Ions of opposite charges will attract and join together, in a type of bonding known as ionic bonding. In covalent bonding, the atoms bond by sharing their electrons in what become molecular orbitals.

ATOMIC ORBITALS

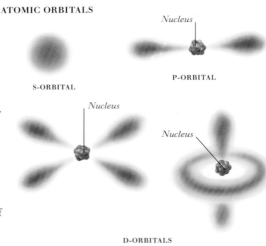

Nucleus

S-ORBITAL

P-ORBITAL

Nucleus

Nucleus

D-ORBITALS

MOLECULAR ORBITALS

Nucleus

Nucleus

Nucleus

Nucleus

π- (PI) ORBITAL

Σ- (SIGMA) ORBITAL

Nucleus

SP³-HYBRID ORBITAL

EXAMPLE OF IONIC BONDING

1s-orbital

2s-orbital

2p-orbital

2s-orbital

2p-orbital

2p-orbital

**1. NEUTRAL LITHIUM
ATOM (Li)**

1s-orbital   1s-orbital

Second shell
holds seven
electrons

**NEUTRAL FLUORINE
ATOM (F)**

Electron
transfer

Lithium atom
loses 2s electron and
becomes positively
charged (Li^+ ion)

2. ELECTRON TRANSFER

Second shell now
holds eight electrons,
and is "filled"

Fluorine atom gains
electron and becomes
negatively charged (F^- ion)

Charged atoms (ions)
held together by
electrostatic forces

Li^+ ion

F^- ion

**3. IONIC BONDING:
LITHIUM FLUORIDE MOLECULE (Li**

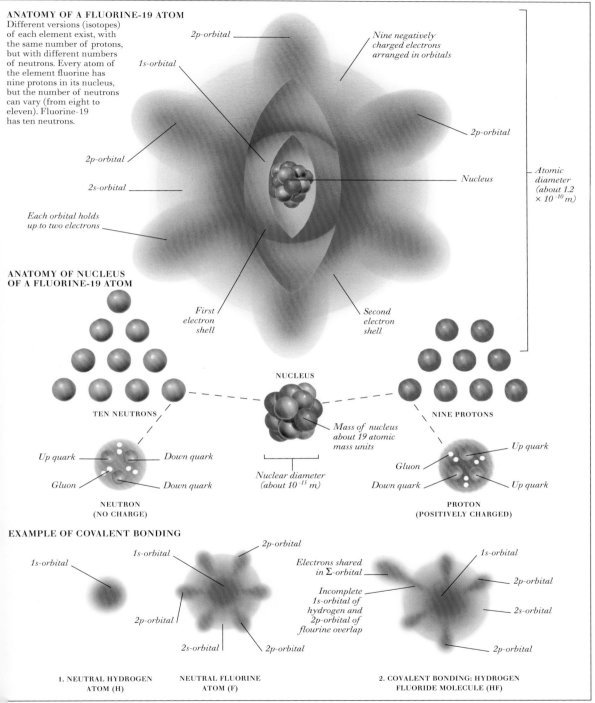

ANATOMY OF A FLUORINE-19 ATOM
Different versions (isotopes) of each element exist, with the same number of protons, but with different numbers of neutrons. Every atom of the element fluorine has nine protons in its nucleus, but the number of neutrons can vary (from eight to eleven). Fluorine-19 has ten neutrons.

2p-orbital

Nine negatively charged electrons arranged in orbitals

1s-orbital

2p-orbital

2p-orbital

2s-orbital

Nucleus

Atomic diameter (about 1.2 × 10⁻¹⁰ m)

Each orbital holds up to two electrons

ANATOMY OF NUCLEUS OF A FLUORINE-19 ATOM

First electron shell

Second electron shell

TEN NEUTRONS

NUCLEUS

NINE PROTONS

Mass of nucleus about 19 atomic mass units

Up quark

Down quark

Gluon

Down quark

Up quark

Gluon

Down quark

Up quark

Nuclear diameter (about 10⁻¹⁵ m)

NEUTRON (NO CHARGE)

PROTON (POSITIVELY CHARGED)

EXAMPLE OF COVALENT BONDING

1s-orbital

1s-orbital

2p-orbital

1s-orbital

Electrons shared in Σ-orbital

2p-orbital

Incomplete 1s-orbital of hydrogen and 2p-orbital of fluorine overlap

2s-orbital

2p-orbital

2p-orbital

2s-orbital

2p-orbital

2p-orbital

1. NEUTRAL HYDROGEN ATOM (H)

NEUTRAL FLUORINE ATOM (F)

2. COVALENT BONDING: HYDROGEN FLUORIDE MOLECULE (HF)

The periodic table

AN ELEMENT is a substance that consists of atoms of one type only. The 92 elements that occur naturally, and the 17 elements created artificially, are often arranged into a chart called the periodic table. Each element is defined by its atomic number – the number of protons in the nucleus of each of its atoms (it is also the number of electrons present). Atomic number increases along each row (period) and down each column (group). The shape of the table is determined by the way in which electrons arrange themselves around the nucleus: the positioning of elements in order of increasing atomic number brings together atoms with a similar pattern of orbiting electrons (orbitals). These appear in blocks. Electrons occupy shells of a certain energy (see pp. 308-309). Periods are ordered according to the filling of successive shells with electrons, while groups reflect the number of electrons in the outer shell (valency electrons). These outer electrons are important – they decide the chemical properties of the atom. Elements that appear in the same group have similar properties because they have the same number of electrons in their outer shell. Elements in Group 0 have "filled shells", where the outer shell holds its maximum number of electrons, and are stable. Atoms of Group I elements have just one electron in their outer shell. This makes them unstable – and ready to react with other substances.

METALS AND NON-METALS

Elements at the left-hand side of each period are metals. Metals easily lose electrons and form positive ions. Non-metals, on the right of a period, tend to become negative ions. Semi-metals, which have properties of both metals and non-metals, are between the two.

RELATIVE ATOMIC MASS

Atomic mass (formerly atomic weight) is the mass of each atom of an element. It is equal to the number of protons plus the number of neutrons (electrons have negligible mass). The figures given are the averages for all the different versions (isotopes) of each element, measured relative to the mass of carbon-12.

Atomic number
Chemical symbol
Chemical name
Relative atomic mass

1
H
Hydrogen
1.0

Atomic number is number of protons in each nucleus

Atomic number goes up by one along each period

1st transition metals

Group I	Group II						
1 **H** Hydrogen 1.0							
3 **Li** Lithium 6.9	4 **Be** Beryllium 9.0						
11 **Na** Sodium 23.0	12 **Mg** Magnesium 24.3						
19 **K** Potassium 39.1	20 **Ca** Calcium 40.1	21 **Sc** Scandium 45.0	22 **Ti** Titanium 47.9	23 **V** Vanadium 50.9	24 **Cr** Chromium 52.0	25 **Mn** Manganese 54.9	
37 **Rb** Rubidium 85.5	38 **Sr** Strontium 87.6	39 **Y** Yttrium 88.9	40 **Zr** Zirconium 91.2	41 **Nb** Niobium 92.9	42 **Mo** Molybdenum 95.9	43 **Tc** Technetium (98)	
55 **Cs** Caesium 132.9	56 **Ba** Barium 137.3	57-71	72 **Hf** Hafnium 178.5	73 **Ta** Tantalum 180.9	74 **W** Tungsten 183.8	75 **Re** Rhenium 186.2	
87 **Fr** Francium 223.0	88 **Ra** Radium 226.0	89-103	104 **Rf** Rutherfordium (267)	105 **Db** Dubnium (268)	106 **Sg** Seaborgium (271)	107 **Bh** Bohrium (270)	

s-block

d-block

Two series always separated out from the table to give it a coherent shape

Soft, silvery, and highly reactive metal

SODIUM: GROUP 1 METAL

Silvery, reactive metal

MAGNESIUM: GROUP 2 METAL

Hard, silvery metal

CHROMIUM: 1ST TRANSITION METAL

TYPES OF ELEMENT KEY:

- Alkali metals
- Alkaline earth metals
- Transition metals
- Lanthanides
- Actinides
- Poor metals
- Semi-metals
- Non-metals
- Noble gases
- Unknown chemical properties

Radioactive metal

PLUTONIUM: ACTINIDE SERIES METAL

57 **La** Lanthanum 138.9	58 **Ce** Cerium 140.1	59 **Pr** Praseodymium 140.9	60 **Nd** Neodymium 144.2
89 **Ac** Actinium (227)	90 **Th** Thorium 232.0	91 **Pa** Protactinium 231.0	92 **U** Uranium 238.0

DIAMOND

ALLOTROPES OF CARBON
Some elements exist in more than one form — these are known as allotropes. Carbon powder, graphite, and diamond are allotropes of carbon. They all consist of carbon atoms, but have very different physical properties.

Bright yellow crystal

**SULPHUR:
GROUP 6 SOLID NON-METAL**

**IODINE:
GROUP 7
SOLID NON-
METAL**

Purple-black solid turns to gas easily

GRAPHITE   **CARBON POWDER**

Boron and carbon groups   *Nitrogen and oxygen groups*   *Halogens*

Group 0

Group III	Group IV	Group V	Group VI	Group VII		
					2 **He** Helium 4.0	*Period*
5 **B** Boron 10.8	6 **C** Carbon 12.0	7 **N** Nitrogen 14.0	8 **O** Oxygen 16.0	9 **F** Fluorine 19.0	10 **Ne** Neon 20.2	*Short period*
13 **Al** Aluminium 27.0	14 **Si** Silicon 28.1	15 **P** Phosphorus 31.0	16 **S** Sulphur 32.1	17 **Cl** Chlorine 35.5	18 **Ar** Argon 40.0	

2nd transition metals   *3rd transition metals*

26 **Fe** Iron 55.8	27 **Co** Cobalt 58.9	28 **Ni** Nickel 58.7	29 **Cu** Copper 63.5	30 **Zn** Zinc 65.4	31 **Ga** Gallium 69.7	32 **Ge** Germanium 72.6	33 **As** Arsenic 74.9	34 **Se** Selenium 79.0	35 **Br** Bromine 79.9	36 **Kr** Krypton 83.8	*Long period*
44 **Ru** Ruthenium 101.1	45 **Rh** Rhodium 102.9	46 **Pd** Palladium 106.4	47 **Ag** Silver 107.9	48 **Cd** Cadmium 112.4	49 **In** Indium 114.8	50 **Sn** Tin 118.7	51 **Sb** Antimony 121.8	52 **Te** Tellurium 127.6	53 **I** Iodine 126.9	54 **Xe** Xenon 131.3	
76 **Os** Osmium 190.2	77 **Ir** Iridium 192.2	78 **Pt** Platinum 195.1	79 **Au** Gold 197.0	80 **Hg** Mercury 200.6	81 **Tl** Thallium 204.4	82 **Pb** Lead 207.2	83 **Bi** Bismuth 209.0	84 **Po** Polonium (209)	85 **At** Astatine (210)	86 **Rn** Radon (222)	
108 **Hs** Hassium (269)	109 **Mt** Meitnerium (278)	110 **Ds** Darmstadtium (281)	111 **Rg** Roentgenium (281)	112 **Cn** Copernicium (285)	113 **Uut** Ununtrium (286)	114 **Uuq** Ununquadium (289)	115 **Uup** Ununpentium (289)	116 **Uuh** Ununhexium (293)	117 **Uus** Ununseptium (294)	118 **Uuo** Ununoctium (294)	

d-block   *p-block*

Unreactive, colourless gas glows red in discharge tube

Yellow, unreactive precious metal

Soft, shiny, reactive metal

Shiny semi-metal

NOBLE GASES
Group 0 contains elements that have a filled (complete) outer shell of electrons, which means the atoms do not need to lose or gain electrons by bonding with other atoms. This makes them stable and they do not easily form ions or react with other elements. Noble gases are also called rare or inert gases.

**NEON:
GROUP 0
COLOURLESS
GAS**

**GOLD:
3RD TRANSITION METAL**   **TIN:
GROUP 4 POOR METAL**   **ANTIMONY:
GROUP 5 SEMI-METAL**

61 **Pm** Promethium (145)	62 **Sm** Samarium 150.4	65 **Eu** Europium 152.0	64 **Gd** Gadolinium 157.3	65 **Tb** Terbium 158.9	66 **Dy** Dysprosium 162.5	67 **Ho** Holmium 164.9	68 **Er** Erbium 167.3	69 **Tm** Thulium 168.9	70 **Yb** Ytterbium 173.0	71 **Lu** Lutetium 175.0
93 **Np** Neptunium (237)	94 **Pu** Plutonium (244)	95 **Am** Americium (243)	96 **Cm** Curium (247)	97 **Bk** Berkelium (247)	98 **Cf** Californium (251)	99 **Es** Einsteinium (252)	100 **Fm** Fermium (257)	101 **Md** Mendelevium (258)	102 **No** Nobelium (259)	103 **Lr** Lawrencium (262)

f-block

Chemical reactions

A CHEMICAL REACTION TAKES PLACE whenever bonds between atoms are broken or made. In each case, atoms or groups of atoms rearrange, making new substances (products) from the original ones (reactants). Reactions happen naturally, or can be made to happen; they may take years, or only an instant. Some of the main types are shown here. A reaction usually involves a change in energy (see pp. 314-315). In a burning reaction, for example, the making of new bonds between atoms releases energy as heat and light. This type of reaction, in which heat is given off, is an exothermic reaction. Many reactions, like burning, are irreversible, but some can take place in either direction, and are said to be reversible. Reactions can be used to form solids from solutions: in a double decomposition reaction, two compounds in solution break down and re-form into two new substances, often creating a precipitate (insoluble solid); in displacement, an element (eg. copper) displaces another element (eg. silver) from a solution. The rate (speed) of a reaction is determined by many different factors, such as temperature, and the size and shape of the reactants. To describe and keep track of reactions, internationally recognized chemical symbols and equations are used. Reactions are also used in the laboratory to identify matter. An experiment with candle wax, for example, demonstrates that it contains carbon and hydrogen.

SALT FORMATION (ACID ON METAL)

Glass beaker

Hydrogen gas (H_2) given off

Zinc (Zn) replaces hydrogen in acid (HCl) to form zinc chloride solution ($ZnCl_2$)

Hydrogen in acid driven off when acid meets a reactive metal

Hydrochloric acid (HCl)

Effervescence

Zinc metal chippings (Zn)

Zinc metal chippings (Zn)

THE REACTION
Hydrochloric acid added to zinc produces zinc chloride and hydrogen.
$Zn + 2HCl \rightarrow ZnCl_2 + H_2$

BURNING MATTER

Ammonium dichromate (($NH_4)_2Cr_2O_7$)

Flame

In this burning reaction, atoms form simpler substances and give off heat and light

Ammonium dichromate (($NH_4)_2Cr_2O_7$) converts to chromium oxide (Cr_2O_3)

THE REACTION
When lit, ammonium dichromate combines with oxygen from air.
($NH_4)_2Cr_2O_7 + O_2 \rightarrow Cr_2O_5 + 4H_2O + 2NO$

Nitrogen monoxide (NO) and water vapour (H_2O) given off as colourless gases

DISPLACEMENT

Copper metal (Cu)

Silver nitrate solution ($AgNO_3$)

Two metals compete for nitrate ions

Glass flask

Copper (Cu) displaces silver ions (Ag^{2+}) from silver nitrate solution ($AgNO_3$)

Blue solution of copper nitrate ($Cu(NO_3)_2$) forms

Needles of silver metal (Ag) form

THE REACTION
Copper metal added to silver nitrate solution produces copper nitrate and silver metal.
$Cu + 2AgNO_3 \rightarrow Cu(NO_3)_2 + 2Ag$

A REVERSIBLE REACTION

Flat-bottomed glass flask

Potassium Chromate solution (K_2CrO_4)

Bright yellow solution contains potassium and chromate ions

Pipette

Hydrochloric acid (HCl) added in drops

Acid causes reaction to take place

Chromate ions converted to orange dichromate ions

Potassium dichromate (KCr_2O_7) forms

Solution turns to bright orange of potassium dichromate

Sodium hydroxide (NaOH) neutralizes the acid

Pipette

Sodium hydroxide (NaOH) added in drops

Potassium dichromate (KCr_2O_7) re-forms to potassium chromate (K_2CrO_4)

Solution returns to original bright yellow colour

1. THE REACTANT
Potassium chromate dissolves in water to form potassium ions and chromate ions.
$K_2CrO_4 \rightarrow 2K^+ + CrO_4^{2-}$

2. THE REACTION
Addition of hydrochloric acid changes chromate ions into dichromate ions.
$2CrO_4^{2-} \rightarrow Cr_2O_7^{2-}$

3. REVERSING
Addition of sodium hydroxide changes dichromate ions back into chromate ions.
$Cr_2O_7^{2-} \rightarrow 2CrO_4^{2-}$

FERMENTATION

Airtight stopper

Yeast converts sugar into alcohol (C_2H_5OH) and carbon dioxide gas (CO_2)

Flat-bottomed glass flask

Yeast mixed with warm water and sugar ($C_6H_{12}O_6$)

Carbon dioxide bubbles (CO_2)

THE REACTION
Yeast converts sugar and warm water into alcohol and carbon dioxide.
$$C_6H_{12}O_6 \rightarrow 2C_2H_5OH + 2CO_2$$

DOUBLE DECOMPOSITION

Potassium iodide solution (KI)

Lead nitrate solution ($Pb(NO_3)_2$)

Two solutions swap partners

Potassium iodide solution added to lead nitrate solution

Lead iodide (PbI_2), a yellow solid, forms

Potassium nitrate solution (KNO_3) forms

1. THE REACTANTS
Potassium iodide in water (KI) and lead nitrate in water ($Pb(NO_3)_2$) each form colourless solutions.

2. THE REACTION
When the solutions are mixed, lead iodide, a precipitate, and potassium nitrate solution are formed.
$$2KI + Pb(NO_3)_2 \rightarrow PbI_2 + 2KNO_3$$

TESTING CANDLE WAX, AN ORGANIC COMPOUND

Burning produces carbon dioxide gas (CO_2) and water vapour (H_2O)

Delivery tube

Clamp stand

Delivery tube

Gases are trapped in funnel

Unburned carbon forms soot particles

Bung

Bung

Tube connection to pump that sucks gases through

U-tube

Flame

Thistle funnel

Bung

Burning candle wax

Water vapour condenses to form liquid water (H_2O)

Test tube

Water vapour trapped by solid drying agent, anhydrous copper sulphate ($CuSO_4$)

Clamp

Carbon dioxide gas (CO_2) given off

Candle wax ($C_{18}H_{38}$), a hydrocarbon, contains the elements carbon and hydrogen

Anhydrous copper sulphate ($CuSO_4$)

Calcium hydroxide ($Ca(OH)_2$) and carbon dioxide (CO_2) form insoluble calcium carbonate ($CaCO_3$): lime water becomes milky

Calcium hydroxide solution (lime water, $Ca(OH)_2$)

Anhydrous copper sulphate crystals ($CuSO_4$) combine with water vapour (H_2O) to form darker blue hydrated copper sulphate ($CuSO_4.10H_2O$)

1. THE BURNING REACTION
Burning wax produces carbon dioxide gas and water vapour.
$$2C_{18}H_{38} + 55O_2 \rightarrow 36CO_2 + 38H_2O$$

2. TESTING FOR WATER VAPOUR
A solid drying agent traps water vapour, proving the presence of hydrogen in the candle wax.
$$CuSO_4 + 10H_2O \rightarrow CuSO_4.10H_2O$$

3. TESTING FOR CARBON DIOXIDE
Calcium hydroxide in solution reacts with carbon dioxide, forming a carbonate and turning milky.
$$Ca(OH)_2 + CO_2 \rightarrow CaCO_3 + H_2O$$

Energy

ANYTHING THAT HAPPENS – from a pin-drop to an explosion – requires energy. Energy is the capacity for "doing work" (making something happen). Various forms of energy exist, including light, heat, sound, electrical, chemical, nuclear, kinetic, and potential energies. The Law of Conservation of Energy states that the total amount of energy in the Universe is fixed – energy cannot be created or destroyed. It means that energy can only change from one form to another (energy transfer). For example, potential energy is energy that is "stored", and can be used in the future. An object gains potential energy when it is lifted; as the object is released, potential energy changes into the energy of motion (kinetic energy). During transference, some of the energy converts into heat. A combined heat and power station can put some of the otherwise "waste" heat to useful effect in local schools and housing. Most of the Earth's energy is provided by the Sun, in the form of electromagnetic radiation (see pp. 316-317). Some of this energy transfers to plant and animal life, and ultimately to fossil fuels, where it is stored in chemical form. Our bodies obtain energy from the food we eat, while energy needed for other tasks, such as heating and transport, can be obtained by burning fossil fuels – or by harnessing natural forces like wind or moving water – to generate electricity. Another source is nuclear power, where energy is released by reactions in the nucleus of an atom. All energy is measured by the international unit, the joule (J). As a guide, one joule is about equal to the amount of energy needed to lift an apple one metre.

SANKEY DIAGRAM SHOWING ENERGY FLOW IN A COAL-FIRED COMBINED HEAT AND POWER STATION

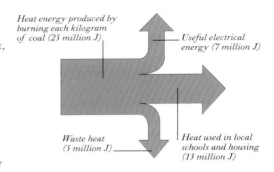

Heat energy produced by burning each kilogram of coal (25 million J)

Useful electrical energy (7 million J)

Waste heat (5 million J)

Heat used in local schools and housing (13 million J)

CROSS-SECTION OF HYDROELECTRIC POWER STATION WITH FRANCIS TURBINE

Transformer

Insulator

High voltage cable

Switch gear including circuit braker

Bushing

Rotor house

Generator unit

Gate

Generator rotor turned by turbine

Shaft

Francis turbine

Curved blade

Gate

Afterbay

Screen

Water in reservoir

Potential energy of water intake turns turbine

Penstock

Draft tube

Tailrace

Water that flows out has lost some energy

CROSS-SECTION OF NUCLEAR POWER STATION WITH PRESSURIZED WATER REACTOR

Steam generator

Concrete shielding

Water pressurizer

Steel girder framework

Control rod

Reactor core

Pump

Moderator (water)

Enriched uranium fuel

Coolant (water) takes heat from reactor core to heat exchanger

Heat exchanger

Water pumped back into steam generator

Pump

Water in heat exchanger turns to steam

Steam drives turbine

Turbine shaft turns generator

Generator produces electric current at 25,000 volts

Water cools used steam

Steam loses energy to turbine and condenses back to water

Transformer increases voltage to 300,000 volts

High voltage cable

Pylon carries high voltage electricity

Hot water to cooling tower

Cold water from cooling tower

ENERGY SYSTEMS

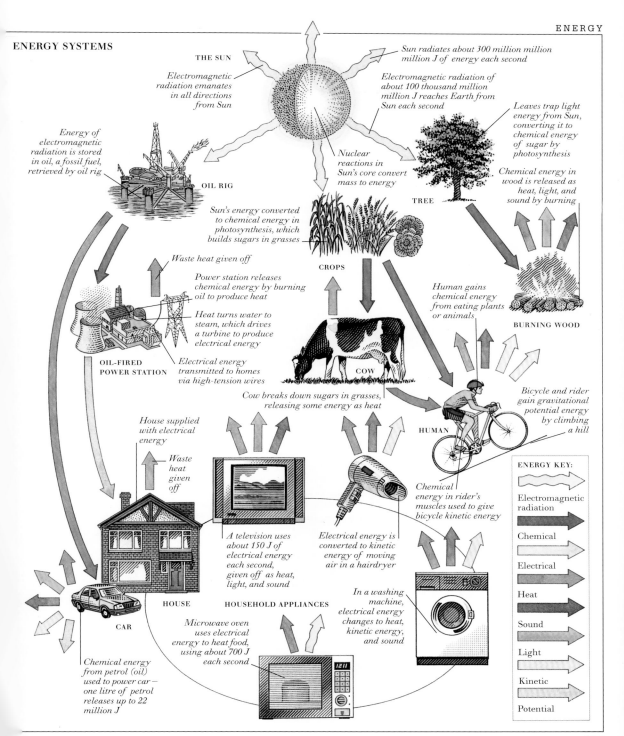

THE SUN

Electromagnetic radiation emanates in all directions from Sun

Sun radiates about 300 million million million J of energy each second

Electromagnetic radiation of about 100 thousand million million J reaches Earth from Sun each second

Energy of electromagnetic radiation is stored in oil, a fossil fuel, retrieved by oil rig

OIL RIG

Nuclear reactions in Sun's core convert mass to energy

Leaves trap light energy from Sun, converting it to chemical energy of sugar by photosynthesis

Chemical energy in wood is released as heat, light, and sound by burning

TREE

Sun's energy converted to chemical energy in photosynthesis, which builds sugars in grasses

Waste heat given off

Power station releases chemical energy by burning oil to produce heat

Heat turns water to steam, which drives a turbine to produce electrical energy

CROPS

Human gains chemical energy from eating plants or animals

BURNING WOOD

OIL-FIRED POWER STATION

Electrical energy transmitted to homes via high-tension wires

Cow breaks down sugars in grasses, releasing some energy as heat

COW

Bicycle and rider gain gravitational potential energy by climbing a hill

House supplied with electrical energy

HUMAN

Waste heat given off

A television uses about 150 J of electrical energy each second, given off as heat, light, and sound

Electrical energy is converted to kinetic energy of moving air in a hairdryer

Chemical energy in rider's muscles used to give bicycle kinetic energy

In a washing machine, electrical energy changes to heat, kinetic energy, and sound

HOUSE

HOUSEHOLD APPLIANCES

CAR

Microwave oven uses electrical energy to heat food, using about 700 J each second

Chemical energy from petrol (oil) used to power car – one litre of petrol releases up to 22 million J

ENERGY KEY:

Electromagnetic radiation

Chemical

Electrical

Heat

Sound

Light

Kinetic

Potential

Electricity and magnetism

ELECTRICAL EFFECTS result from an imbalance of electric charge. There are two types of electric charge, named positive (carried by protons) and negative (carried by electrons). If charges are opposite (unlike), they attract one another, while like charges repel. Forces of attraction and repulsion (electrostatic forces) exist between any two charged particles. Matter is normally uncharged, but if electrons are gained, an object will gain an overall negative charge; if they are removed, it becomes positive. Objects with an overall negative or positive charge are said to have an imbalance of charge, and exert the same forces as individual negative and positive charges. On this larger scale, the forces will always act to regain the balance of charge. This causes static electricity. Lightning, for example, is produced by clouds discharging a huge excess of negative electrons. If charges are "free" – in a wire or material that allows electrons to pass through it – the forces cause a flow of charge called an electric current. Some substances exhibit the strange phenomenon of magnetism – which also produces attractive and repulsive forces. Magnetic substances consist of small regions called domains. Normally unmagnetized, they can be magnetized by being placed in a magnetic field. Magnetism and electricity are inextricably linked, a fact put to use in motors and generators.

LIGHTNING

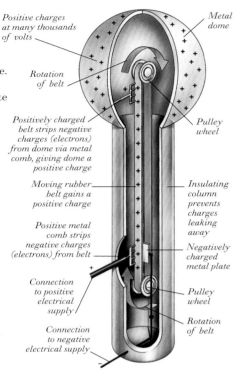

Positive charges at many thousands of volts

Metal dome

Rotation of belt

Positively charged belt strips negative charges (electrons) from dome via metal comb, giving dome a positive charge

Pulley wheel

Moving rubber belt gains a positive charge

Insulating column prevents charges leaking away

Positive metal comb strips negative charges (electrons) from belt

Negatively charged metal plate

Connection to positive electrical supply

Pulley wheel

Connection to negative electrical supply

Rotation of belt

CURRENT ELECTRICITY

Crocodile clip connector

Bulb receives 3 volts

Bulb holder

Metal wire (conductor) coated with plastic (insulator)

Bulb receives 3 volts

Bulb holder

Junction

Direction of current, opposite to electron flow by convention

Electrons flow from negative terminal to positive terminal

Switch completes or breaks circuit

Four 1.5 volt cells (total of 6 volts)

Negative terminal

Positive terminal

SERIES ELECTRICAL CIRCUIT

SIMPLE ELECTRICAL CIRCUIT

VOLTAGE
The higher the voltage, the greater the energy of electrical charges. One volt is one joule (unit of energy) per coulomb (unit of charge).

CURRENT
The greater the number of electrons moving around the circuit, the higher the current. Current is measured in amps (A). One amp equals one coulomb (unit of charge) per second.

Metal wire (conductor) coated with plastic (insulator)

Bulb holder

Bulb receives 6 volts

Bulb has high resistance

RESISTANCE
For a given voltage, the flow of current depends upon the resistance of a circuit. Resistance is the degree to which a substance resists electrical current. It is measured in ohms (Ω).

MAGNETIC FIELDS AND FORCES

Iron filings
Profile of magnetic field
Bar magnet
North-seeking pole
Like poles repel
North-seeking pole
Unlike poles attract
North-seeking pole
South-seeking pole of electromagnet
North-seeking pole
South-seeking pole
Unlike poles attract
Direction of force
South-seeking pole
South-seeking pole
Like poles repel
Electromagnet
Wire to battery

MAGNETIC DOMAINS

Domain
Direction of magnetization within domain is random
Direction of magnetization within domain has aligned
Domain aligned with magnetization has grown
Domain boundary
Domain not aligned with magnetization has shrunk
Direction of overall magnetization

UNMAGNETIZED IRON

MAGNETIZED IRON IN A MAGNETIC FIELD

GENERATING MAGNETISM FROM ELECTRICITY

Direction of magnetic field (from north pole to south pole)
Electric current produces magnetic field
Magnetic field
Coil carries electric current
Direction of current
Metal wire (conductor) coated with plastic (insulator)
Negative terminal
Positive terminal
Four 1.5 volt cells (total of 6 volts)

CIRCUIT WITH ELECTROMAGNET

GENERATING ELECTRICITY FROM MAGNETISM

Terminal box
Coil of wire
Permanent magnet
Bearing
Non-drive end
Coil of wire
Terminal
Stator
Main rotor turns in magnetic field produced by coil of wire in stator
Fan
Drive end
Coil of wire
Shaft
Secondary (exciter) rotor

ELECTRIC GENERATOR
In a generator, the rotor rotates within the magnetic field of the stator to produce an electric current.

Coil of wire rotates within magnetic field of permanent magnet
Permanent magnet
Iron core
Steel casing
Coated copper winding
Commutator
Terminal
Spindle
End of shaft
Terminal

ELECTRIC MOTOR
In a motor, magnetic forces between the winding and permanent magnet produce a rotary motion.

Light

INFRA-RED IMAGE OF A HOUSE

LIGHT IS A FORM OF ENERGY. It is a type of electromagnetic radiation, like X-rays or radio waves. All electromagnetic radiation is produced by electric charges (see pp. 316-317): it is caused by the effects of oscillating electric and magnetic fields as they travel through space. Electromagnetic radiation is considered to have both wave and particle properties. It can be thought of as a wave of electricity and magnetism. In that case, the difference between the various forms of radiation is their wavelength. Radiation can also be said to consist of particles, or packets of energy, called photons. The difference between light and X-rays, for instance, is the amount of energy that each photon carries. The complete range of radiation is referred to as the electromagnetic spectrum, extending from low energy, long wavelength radio waves to high energy, short wavelength gamma rays. Light is the only part of the electromagnetic spectrum that is visible. White light from the Sun is made up of all the visible wavelengths of radiation, which can be seen when it is separated by using a prism. Light, like all forms of electromagnetic radiation, can be reflected (bounced back) and refracted (bent). Different parts of the electromagnetic spectrum are produced in different ways. Sometimes visible light – and infra-red radiation – is generated by the vibrating particles of warm or hot objects. The emission of light in this way is called incandescence. Light can also be produced by fluorescence, a phenomenon in which electrons gain and lose energy within atoms.

MAXWELLIAN DIAGRAM OF ELECTROMAGNETIC RADIATION AS WAVES

Oscillating electric field

Wavelength

Oscillating magnetic field

Two fields at right angles

Direction of travel

ELECTROMAGNETIC RADIATION AS PARTICLES

Photon thought of as wave packet of energy

Blue light has about twice the energy of red light

Red light has long wavelength

Blue light has shorter wavelength: waves are more tightly packed

PHOTON OF RED LIGHT   **PHOTON OF BLUE LIGHT**

SPLITTING WHITE LIGHT INTO THE SPECTRUM

Prism forms spectrum by bending wavelengths at different angles

Glass prism   *White light*

Red light (wavelength: $6.2–7.7 \times 10^{-7}m$)

Orange light (wavelength: $5.9–6.2 \times 10^{-7}m$)

Yellow light (wavelength: $5.7–5.9 \times 10^{-7}m$)

Green light (wavelength: $4.9–5.7 \times 10^{-7}m$)

Blue light (wavelength: $4.5–4.9 \times 10^{-7}m$)

Violet light (wavelength: $3.9–4.5 \times 10^{-7}m$)

THE ELECTROMAGNETIC SPECTRUM

ENERGY (JOULES) 10^{-28} 10^{-27} 10^{-26} 10^{-25} 10^{-24} 10^{-23} 10^{-22} 10^{-21} 10^{-20}

WAVELENGTH (METERS) 10^4 10^3 10^2 10 1 10^{-1} 10^{-2} 10^{-3} 10^{-4}

Long-wave radio | Medium-wave radio | Short-wave radio | Very high-frequency (VHF) radio | Microwaves | Infra-radia

Radio waves

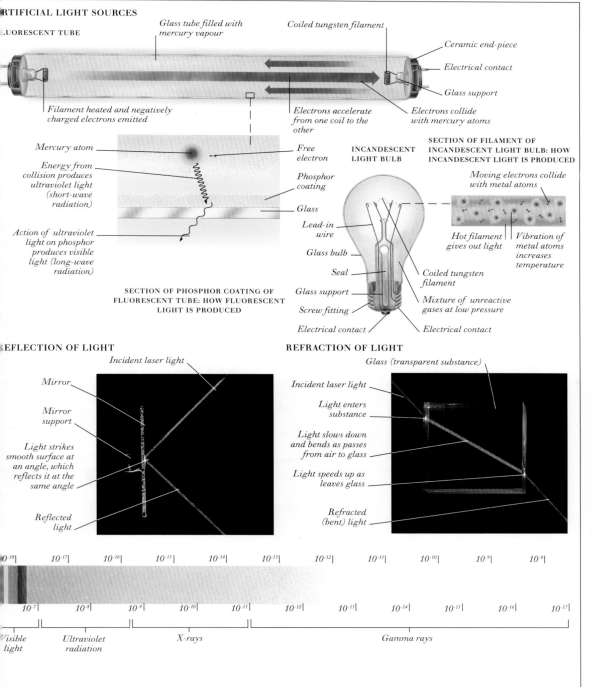

ARTIFICIAL LIGHT SOURCES

FLUORESCENT TUBE

Glass tube filled with mercury vapour

Coiled tungsten filament

Ceramic end-piece

Electrical contact

Glass support

Filament heated and negatively charged electrons emitted

Electrons accelerate from one coil to the other

Electrons collide with mercury atoms

Mercury atom

Free electron

INCANDESCENT LIGHT BULB

SECTION OF FILAMENT OF INCANDESCENT LIGHT BULB: HOW INCANDESCENT LIGHT IS PRODUCED

Energy from collision produces ultraviolet light (short-wave radiation)

Phosphor coating

Glass

Moving electrons collide with metal atoms

Action of ultraviolet light on phosphor produces visible light (long-wave radiation)

Lead-in wire

Glass bulb

Seal

Hot filament gives out light

Vibration of metal atoms increases temperature

SECTION OF PHOSPHOR COATING OF FLUORESCENT TUBE: HOW FLUORESCENT LIGHT IS PRODUCED

Glass support

Screw fitting

Electrical contact

Coiled tungsten filament

Mixture of unreactive gases at low pressure

Electrical contact

REFLECTION OF LIGHT

Incident laser light

Mirror

Mirror support

Light strikes smooth surface at an angle, which reflects it at the same angle

Reflected light

REFRACTION OF LIGHT

Glass (transparent substance)

Incident laser light

Light enters substance

Light slows down and bends as passes from air to glass

Light speeds up as leaves glass

Refracted (bent) light

10^{-18} | 10^{-17} | 10^{-16} | 10^{-15} | 10^{-14} | 10^{-13} | 10^{-12} | 10^{-11} | 10^{-10} | 10^{-9} | 10^{-8} |

10^{-7} | 10^{-8} | 10^{-9} | 10^{-10} | 10^{-11} | 10^{-12} | 10^{-13} | 10^{-14} | 10^{-15} | 10^{-16} | 10^{-17} |

Visible light

Ultraviolet radiation

X-rays

Gamma rays

Force and motion

FORCES ARE PUSHES OR PULLS that change the motion of objects. To make a stationary object move, or a moving object stop, a force is needed. A force is also required to change the speed or direction of an object. This change in speed or direction is known as acceleration. Acceleration depends on the size (magnitude) of the force, and on the mass of the object. The effects of forces were first summarized by Isaac Newton in his three laws of motion. The international unit of force, named after him, is the newton (N), which is approximately equal to the weight of one apple. Gravity – the force of attraction between any two masses – can be measured using a newton meter (spring balance). Forces are put to useful effect in machines. A simple machine, such as a wheel and axle, is a device that changes the size or direction of an applied force. It allows an applied force (the effort) to produce another force (the load). A lever uses a bar that turns on a fulcrum to exert force. In all simple machines, there is a relationship between force and distance. A small force (in a compound pulley, for instance) moves through a large distance to lift a heavy object a small distance. This is called the Law of Simple Machines.

SIMPLE MACHINES

Single-pulley system (simple pulley)

Two-pulley system (simple pulley)

Four-pulley system (compound pulley)

Pulley wheel

Pulley wheel

Two pulley wheels

Simple pulley only changes direction of a force

Effort is the same size as the load (10 N) and is pulled the same distance

Effort is half the load (5 N), but the rope must be pulled twice the distance

Effort is one quarter of the load (2.5 N), but the rope must be pulled four times the distance

One rope attached to load

Two ropes share the force and distance

Four ropes share the force and distance

Load of 10 N

Pulley wheel

Load of 10 N

SIMPLE AND COMPOUND PULLEYS

Two pulley wheels

Load of 10 N

NEWTON METERS (SPRING BALANCES)

Weight is measured using a spring

When weight pulls downwards, pointer moves along scale and measures force

Weight is 10 N

Weight is 20 N

Mass of 1 kg

Mass of 2 kg

WEIGHT AND MASS
The "mass" of an object is a measure of the quantity of matter that it possesses. Mass is usually measured in grams (g) or kilograms (kg). The "weight" of an object is the force exerted on the object's mass by gravity. Since weight is a force, its unit is the newton (N).

Wheel and axle multiplies the effort

Force is transmitted to the wheels by the chain

Pedal

Crank

Effort, provided by cyclist's muscles, is smaller than the load, but moves through a greater distance

A larger force, the load, is produced at the axle

WHEEL AND AXLE

A screw, acting like a wedge wrapped around a shaft, multiplies the effort

Effort, a turning force supplied through a screwdriver

Pitch (the angle of the screw thread)

The smaller the angle of pitch, the less force is required, but more turns are needed to move it through a greater distance

A larger force, the load, pulls the screw into wood

SCREW

Effort pushes axe into wood

A larger force, the load, moves through a smaller distance to push wood apart

Axe blade has wedge shape

Wedge multiplies effort

WEDGE

NEWTON'S THREE LAWS OF MOTION

NEWTON'S FIRST LAW
When no force acts on a body, it will
continue in a state of rest or uniform motion.

Constant speed

Newton meter shows no applied force

Mass of 1 kg

Newton meter shows no applied force

Mass of 1 kg

Mass of trolley is negligible

Trolley is not in motion, and will remain at rest until a force acts

Trolley is in motion, and will continue at a constant speed in a straight line until a force acts

NO FORCE, NO ACCELERATION: STATE OF REST

NO FORCE, NO ACCELERATION: UNIFORM MOTION

NEWTON'S SECOND LAW
When a force acts on a body, the motion of the body will change. The size of the change
will depend upon the mass of the object and the magnitude of the applied force.

Acceleration is 2 ms⁻²

Trolley and mass (1 kg) gain 2 metres per second of speed each second (2 ms⁻²)

Newton meter registers force of 2 N

Mass of 1 kg

Acceleration is 1 ms⁻²

Trolley and mass (2 kg) gain 1 metre per second of speed each second (1 ms⁻²)

Newton meter registers force of 2 N

Mass of 2 kg

With the same applied force, an object with 2 kg mass accelerates at half the rate of object with 1 kg mass

FORCE AND ACCELERATION: SMALL MASS, LARGE ACCELERATION

FORCE AND ACCELERATION: LARGE MASS, SMALL ACCELERATION

NEWTON'S THIRD LAW
If one object exerts a force on another, an equal and opposite force,
called the reaction force, is applied by the second object on the first.

Newton meters pull on each other with equal and opposite forces

Acceleration: the trolley and mass accelerate at 2 ms⁻²

Newton meter registers force of 2 N to the left

Newton meter registers force of 2 N to the right

Mass of 1 kg

Person experiences a reaction force

ACTION AND REACTION

THREE CLASSES OF LEVER

Fulcrum, between effort and load

Fulcrum

Load is applied at open end

Effort forces tongs together

Effort

Load, between effort and fulcrum

Load is smaller than effort, but moves through greater distance

is ...r than ... but moves ...h smaller ...ce

Effort is smaller than load, but moves through greater distance

Effort, between fulcrum and load

Fulcrum

CLASS 1 LEVER
Pliers consist of two class 1 levers.

CLASS 2 LEVER
Nutcrackers consist of two class 2 levers.

CLASS 3 LEVER
Tongs consist of two class 3 levers.

RAIL AND ROAD

STEAM LOCOMOTIVES ⋯⋯⋯⋯⋯⋯⋯ 324
DIESEL TRAINS ⋯⋯⋯⋯⋯⋯⋯⋯⋯ 326
ELECTRIC AND HIGH-SPEED TRAINS ⋯⋯⋯ 328
TRAIN EQUIPMENT ⋯⋯⋯⋯⋯⋯⋯ 330
TRAMS AND BUSES ⋯⋯⋯⋯⋯⋯⋯ 332
THE FIRST CARS ⋯⋯⋯⋯⋯⋯⋯⋯ 334
ELEGANCE AND UTILITY ⋯⋯⋯⋯⋯⋯ 336
MASS-PRODUCTION ⋯⋯⋯⋯⋯⋯⋯ 338
THE "PEOPLE'S CAR" ⋯⋯⋯⋯⋯⋯ 340
EARLY ENGINES ⋯⋯⋯⋯⋯⋯⋯⋯ 342
MODERN ENGINES ⋯⋯⋯⋯⋯⋯⋯ 344
ALTERNATIVE ENGINES ⋯⋯⋯⋯⋯⋯ 346
BODYWORK ⋯⋯⋯⋯⋯⋯⋯⋯⋯⋯ 348
MECHANICAL COMPONENTS ⋯⋯⋯⋯⋯ 350
CAR TRIM ⋯⋯⋯⋯⋯⋯⋯⋯⋯⋯ 352
HYBRID CAR ⋯⋯⋯⋯⋯⋯⋯⋯⋯ 354
RACING CARS ⋯⋯⋯⋯⋯⋯⋯⋯⋯ 356
BICYCLE ANATOMY ⋯⋯⋯⋯⋯⋯⋯ 358
BICYCLES ⋯⋯⋯⋯⋯⋯⋯⋯⋯⋯ 360
THE MOTORCYCLE ⋯⋯⋯⋯⋯⋯⋯ 362
THE MOTORCYCLE CHASSIS ⋯⋯⋯⋯⋯ 364
MOTORCYCLE ENGINES ⋯⋯⋯⋯⋯⋯ 366
COMPETITION MOTORCYCLES ⋯⋯⋯⋯⋯ 368

Steam locomotives

WAGONS THAT ARE PULLED along tracks have been used to transport material since the 16th century, but these trains were drawn by men or horses until the invention of the steam locomotive. Steam locomotives enabled the basic railway system to realize its true potential. In 1804, Richard Trevithick built the world's first working steam locomotive in South Wales. It was not entirely successful, but it encouraged others to develop new designs. By 1829, the British engineer Robert Stephenson had built the "Rocket", considered to be the forerunner of the modern locomotive. The "Rocket" was a self-sufficient unit, carrying coal to heat the boiler and a water supply for generating steam. Steam passed from the boiler to force the pistons back and forth, and this movement turned the driving wheels, propelling the train forwards. Used steam was then expelled in characteristic "chuffs". Later steam locomotives, like "Ellerman Lines" and the "Mallard", worked in a similar way, but on a much larger scale. The simple design and reliability of steam locomotives ensured that they changed very little in 120 years of use, before being replaced from the 1950s by more efficient diesel and electric power (see pp. 326-329).

"ROCKET" STEAM LOCOMOTIVE, 1829

Chimney

Smokebox

Leaf spring

"Rocked" nameplate

Pipe takes steam from boiler to cylinder

Regulator (throttle)

Wrought iron boiler

Remains of firebox

Valve chest

Valve setting control

Wooden buffer beam

Wooden driving wheel

Metal tyre

Axle

Ballast

Rail chair

Wrought iron rail

Wooden sleeper

Piston rod

Cylinder

Carrying wheel

Driving platform

"ELLERMAN LINES", 1949 (CUTAWAY VIEW)

Vacuum reservoir

Panel brace

Panel sheeting

Water tank

Coal space

Tender hand brake

Cab

Firebox

Brick arch

Water filler

Hand rail

Buffer

Brake vacuum pipe

Wheel guard

Axle

Axle box

Tender wheel

Brake rigging

Water float to indicate water level

Water float lever

Axle box cover

Step

Coupling

Coil spring

Footplate

Trailing wheel

Grate

Fire drawn into fire tubes

TENDER

CAB INTERIOR OF "MALLARD" EXPRESS STEAM LOCOMOTIVE, 1938

Steam sanding control
Blower isolator valve
Pressure gauge isolator valve
Vacuum brake isolator valve
Steam chest pressure gauge
Vacuum brake pressure gauge
Blower control
Regulator controls flow of steam to cylinders
Cab side-window
Vacuum brake lever
Live steam water injector control
Manual sanding lever
Reverser handle
Driver's seat
Steam-operated reversing shaft lock control
Oil can warming tray
Firebox
Firehole
Firebox door
Steam heating isolator valve
Sliding roof vent
Boiler pressure gauge
Gauge glass to show level of water in boiler
Exhaust steam water injector control
Steam heating pressure gauge
Glass deflector
Whistle lever
Cylinder drain cock lever
Control valve for hot water hose
Fireman's seat
Steam heat safety valve

Fire tube
Steam dome
Mechanical lubricator
Pipe takes steam from boiler to cylinder
Chimney
Thermal phon
Regulator valve
Superheater tube inside flue tube
Boiler
Blast-pipe
Smokebox
Smokebox door
Lubricating pipe
Piston valve
Buffer
Screw coupling
Brake shoe
Brake rigging
Driving wheel
Crank
Expansion lever
Connecting rod
Combination lever
Slide bar
Piston, linked to connecting rod
Bogie frame
Leading wheel
Cylinder
Coupling rod

STEAM LOCOMOTIVE

Diesel trains

RUDOLF DIESEL FIRST DEMONSTRATED the diesel engine
in Germany in 1898, but it was not until the 1940s that diesel
locomotives were successfully established on both passenger
and freight services, in the US. Early diesel locomotives like
the "Union Pacific" were more expensive to build than steam
locomotives, but were more efficient and cheaper to operate,
especially where oil was plentiful. One feature of diesel engines
is that the power output cannot be coupled directly to the wheels.
To convert the mechanical energy produced by diesel engines,
a transmission system is needed. Almost all diesel locomotives
have electric transmissions, and are known as "diesel-electric"
locomotives. The diesel engine works by drawing air into the
cylinders and compressing it to increase its temperature; a small
quantity of diesel fuel is then injected into it. The resulting
combustion drives the generator (more recently an alternator)
to produce electricity, which is fed to electric motors connected
to the wheels. Diesel-electric locomotives are essentially
electric locomotives that carry their own power plants,
and are used worldwide today. The "Deltic" diesel-electric
locomotive, similar to the one shown here, replaced
classic express steam locomotives, and ran
at speeds up to 160 kph (100 mph).

FRONT VIEW OF "UNION PACIFIC"
DIESEL-ELECTRIC LOCOMOTIVE, 1950s

Exhaust vent · Windscreen wiper · Horn · Cab front window · Head-lig

Cab door

Name o operatin railroad

Illumina locomot unit nur

Railro crest

Cab step · Step · Motor-driven bogie axle · Air-brake coupling hose · Centre bu eye couple

PROTOTYPE "DELTIC" DIESEL-ELECTRIC LOCOMOTIVE, 1956

Engine room vent · Inspection hatch · Engine exhaust port · Radiator fan · Engine room window · Engine room ver

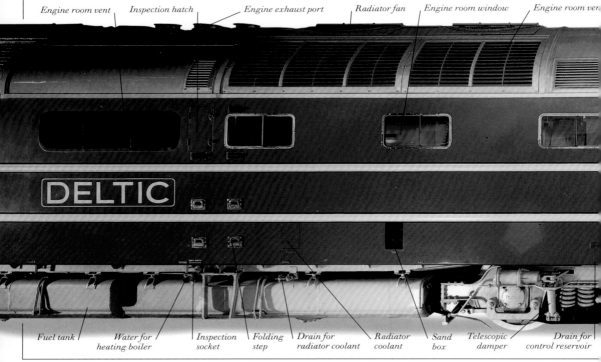

Fuel tank · Water for heating boiler · Inspection socket · Folding step · Drain for radiator coolant · Radiator coolant · Sand box · Telescopic damper · Drain for control reservoir

DIESEL ENGINE OF BRITISH RAIL CLASS 20
DIESEL-ELECTRIC LOCOMOTIVE

Exhaust vent

Cylinder head
(V-four configuration)

Turbo-charged diesel
engine drives generator

Generator
cooling fan

Generator
compartment
vent

Auxiliary
generator

Main generator
produces
electricity that
drives wheels

Main chassis
member

Innermost
wheel set on
cab-end bogie

Air brake pipe

Brake
rigging

Battery
box

Engine crankcase

Air reservoir and
isolator valves

Lubricating oil
primary pump and
fuel supply pump

Cab
Door

Driver's seat

Cab

Warning horn

Windscreen

Windscreen wiper

Cab window

Manufacturer's
logo

Cab vent

Indicator
light

Sand box

Buffer

Brake cylinder

Roller-bearing
axle box

Brake
shoe

Brake
actuating chain

Transverse leaf spring
secondary suspension

Coil spring primary
suspension

EXAMPLES OF FREIGHT CARS

BOX CAR

HOPPER CAR

REFRIGERATOR CAR

LIVESTOCK CAR

FLAT CAR WITH BULKHEADS

AUTOMOBILE CAR

Electric and high-speed trains

THE FIRST ELECTRIC LOCOMOTIVE ran in 1879 in Berlin, Germany. In Europe, electric trains developed as a more efficient alternative to the steam locomotive and diesel-electric power. Like diesels, electric trains employ electric motors to drive the wheels but, unlike diesels, the electricity is generated externally at a power station. Electric current is picked up either from a catenary (overhead cable) via a pantograph, or from a third rail. Since it does not carry its own power-generating equipment, an electric locomotive has a better power-to-weight ratio and greater acceleration than its diesel-electric equivalent. This makes electric trains suitable for urban routes with many stops. They are also faster, quieter, and less polluting. The latest electric French TGV (Train à Grande Vitesse) reaches 300 kph (186 mph); other trains, like the London to Paris and Brussels "Eurostar", can run at several voltages and operate between different countries. Simpler electric trains perform special duties – the "People Mover" at Gatwick Airport in Britain runs between terminals.

HOW ALTERNATING CURRENT (AC) ELECTRIC TRAINS WORK

Running rail for return current

Feeder station provides current

Catenary

Vacuum circuit breaker

Pantograph collects current

Thyristor converter converts current (ac) to direct current (dc)

Traction motor turns wheel

Control circuit

Transformer steps down voltage

Axle brush

FRONT VIEW OF PARIS METRO

Route number

Windscreen wiper

Unit number

Operator's initials (Régie Autonome des Transports Parisien)

Rubber running wheel

Guard for rubber wheel

Door open/shut indicator light

Driver's seat

Handle

Front light (white)

Rear light (red)

Buffing pad

Rubber guide wheel

FRONT VIEW OF ITALIAN STATE RAILWAYS CLASS 402 ELECTRIC LOCOMOTIVE

Collector strip for electric current

Double-arm pantograph

Head-light

Windscreen wiper

Italian State Railways crest

Number of electric (E) locomotive (class 402 No. 5)

Buffer

"Jumper" cable

Conventional hook-screw coupling

Front light (white)

Rear light (red)

SIDE VIEW OF SHANGHAI MAGLEV TRAIN

Automatic door

On-board levitation magnet

Driver compartment

Guide

"EUROSTAR" MULTI-VOLTAGE ELECTRIC TRAIN

Cab window

Grille over warning horn

Head-light (white)

Rear light (red)

Fibre glass reinforced plastic cover

Fibreglass reinforced plastic cover

Aerofoil wheel guard

Aerofoil wheel guard

Sanding pipe

FRONT VIEW

Cab side-window

Cab front window

Electric equipment compartment

Cab door

Side vent

3002

Leading driven axle

Horizontal telescopic damper

Third (electric) rail collector shoe

Coil spring suspension

SIDE VIEW

TGV ELECTRIC HIGH-SPEED TRAIN

Luggage rack

Reading light

Double-glazed and tinted side-window

Sliding curtain

Seat

Main overhead lighting

Automatic electric carriage end door

Antimacassar

Headrest

Armrest

Centre gangway

INTERIOR OF TGV

Cab door

Hand rail

Side vent

Roof vent

Cab side-window

Cab front window

Windscreen wiper

Emergency exit door

Access panel for servicing

Nose air deflector dam

306

SNCF

Vertical damper

Horizontal damper

SIDE VIEW OF TGV

329

Train equipment

MODERN RAILWAY TRACK consists of two parallel steel rails clipped on to a support called a sleeper. Sleepers are usually made of reinforced concrete, although wood and steel are still used. The distance between the inside edges of the rails is the track gauge. It evolved in Britain, which uses a gauge of 1,435 mm (4 ft 8½ in), known as the standard gauge. As engineering grew more sophisticated, narrower gauges were adopted because they cost less to build. The loading gauge, which is equally important, determines the size of the largest loaded vehicle that may pass through tunnels and under bridges with adequate clearance. Safe train operation relies on following a signalling system. At first, signalling was based on a simple time interval between trains, but it now depends on maintaining a safe distance between successive trains travelling in the same direction. Most modern signals are colour lights, but older mechanical semaphore signals are still used. On the latest high-speed lines, train drivers receive control instructions by electronic means. Signalling depends on reliable control of the train by effective braking. For fast, modern trains, which have considerable momentum, it is essential that each vehicle in the train can be braked by the driver or by a train control system, such as Automatic Train Protection (ATP). Braking is achieved by the brake shoe acting on the wheel rim (rim brakes), by disc brakes, or, increasingly, by electrical braking.

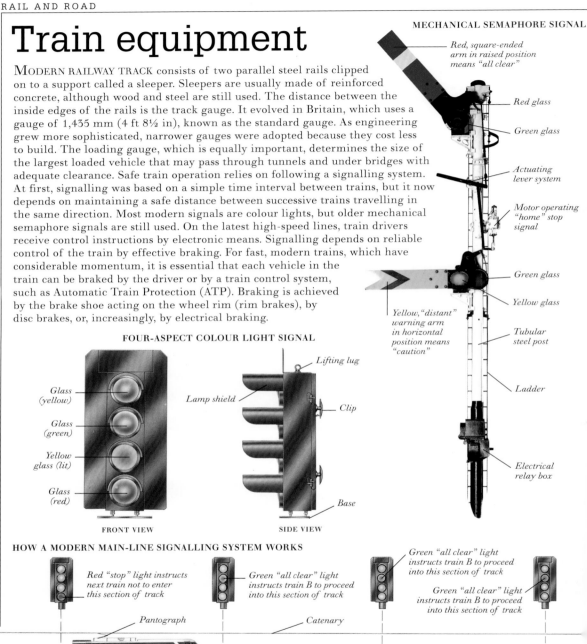

MECHANICAL SEMAPHORE SIGNAL

Red, square-ended arm in raised position means "all clear"

Red glass

Green glass

Actuating lever system

Motor operating "home" stop signal

Green glass

Yellow glass

Yellow, "distant" warning arm in horizontal position means "caution"

Tubular steel post

Ladder

Electrical relay box

FOUR-ASPECT COLOUR LIGHT SIGNAL

Glass (yellow)

Glass (green)

Yellow glass (lit)

Glass (red)

FRONT VIEW

Lifting lug

Lamp shield

Clip

Base

SIDE VIEW

HOW A MODERN MAIN-LINE SIGNALLING SYSTEM WORKS

Red "stop" light instructs next train not to enter this section of track

Green "all clear" light instructs train B to proceed into this section of track

Green "all clear" light instructs train B to proceed into this section of track

Green "all clear" light instructs train B to proceed into this section of track

Pantograph

Catenary

Train B

Track

EXAMPLES OF INTERNATIONAL TRACK GAUGES

1,000 mm
(3 ft 3 ½ in)
East Africa,
India,
Malaysia,
Chile, and
Argentina

1,067 mm
(3 ft 6 in)
Japan, Australia,
Sudan, West Africa,
South Africa, and
New Zealand

1,435 mm
(4 ft 8½ in)
US, Canada, China,
Egypt, Turkey, Iran,
Japan, Peru, Britain,
Europe, Australia,
Brazil, and Mexico

1,524 mm
(5 ft 0 in)
Russia, Spain,
Portugal, and
Finland

1,600 mm
(5 ft 3 in)
Ireland, Australia,
and Brazil

1,676 mm
(5 ft 6 in)
India, Pakistan,
and Argentina

EXAMPLES OF INTERNATIONAL LOADING GAUGES

Britain: 2.75 m (9 ft 0 in) × 3.95 m (12 ft 11 in)

Europe: 3.1 m (10 ft 2 in) × 4.5 m (14 ft 9 in)

US: 3.3 m (10 ft 10 in) × 4.9 m (16 ft 2 in)

Russia: 3.4 m (11 ft 2 in) × 5.3 m (17 ft 4 in)

1,435 mm
(4 ft 8½ in)
Standard track
gauge

1,524 mm
(5 ft 0 in)
Track gauge of Russia,
with largest loading gauge

FLAT-BOTTOMED RAIL

Flat-bottomed steel rail

Steel spring secures
rail to sleeper

Synthetic
insulating pad

Sleeper supports
track and
maintains
gauge

BULL-HEAD RAIL

Wooden "key" secures
rail in chair

Steel tapered
screw fastens
chair to
sleeper

Bull-head pattern
steel rail

Cast-iron chair

Wooden
sleeper

DISC BRAKES ON MODERN WAGON BOGIE

Base of wagon

Airbag secondary
suspension

Damper

Hand
brake
wheel

Axle

Wheel

Brake
disc

Brake calliper

Two yellow "preliminary
caution" lights instruct train
B that it must stop in two
signals time

Yellow "caution" light
instructs train B that it
must stop at next signal

Green "all clear" light
instructs train A to proceed
into this section of track

Red "stop" light instructs
train B not to enter
this section of track

Braking distance

Train A

Trams and buses

METROLINK TRAM,
MANCHESTER,
BRITAIN

As CITY POPULATIONS exploded in the 1800s, there was an urgent need for mass transportation. Trams were an early solution. The first trams, like buses, were horse-drawn, but in 1881, electric street tramways appeared in Berlin, Germany. Electric trams soon became widespread throughout Europe and North America. Trams run on rails along a fixed route, using electric motors that receive power from overhead cables. As road networks developed, motorized buses offered a flexible alternative to trams. By the 1930s, they had replaced tram systems in many cities. City buses typically have doors at both front and rear to make loading and unloading easier. Double-decker designs are popular, occupying the same amount of street space as single-decker buses but able to transport twice the number of people. Buses are also commonly used for inter-city travel and touring. Tour buses have reclining seats, large windows, luggage space, and toilets. Recently, as city traffic has become increasingly congested, many city planners have designed new tram routes to run alongside bus routes as part of an integrated transport system.

EARLY TRAM, c.1900

Trolley boom
Trolley head
Trolley base
Drop window
Upper deck
Quarter light
Brake
Stair
Lower deck
Platform
Controller
Truck
Lifeguard

MCW METROBUS, LONDON, BRITAIN

Window vent
Upper deck windscreen
Route information
Destination screen
Offside mirror
Asymmetric windscreen
Windscreen wiper
Sidelight
Head-light
Grille
Fog light
Number plate
Manufacturer's badge

Upper deck air intake
Route number
Nearside mirror
Licence holder
Turning indicator

Square roof dome
Mirror for driver to see upstairs
Operator's logo
Destination screen
Nearside mirror
Front bumper
Entrance door
Emergency door control
Turning indicator

LONDON NORTHERN
ARCHWAY STN.
41
KYV 739X

FRONT VIEW

SINGLE-DECKER BUS, NEW YORK, US

Wheelchair access

Sliding window

Sloped roof dome

Tinted glass

Air intake

Tyre

Axle

Exit door

Access panel

Sidelight

Entrance door

Bumper

SIDE VIEW

Marker light

Repeater indicator

Entrance door

Side mirror

Route number

Head-light

Turning indicator

Number plate

Bumper

FRONT VIEW

DOUBLE-DECKER TOUR BUS, PARIS, FRANCE

Tinted glass

Air intake

Access panel

Skirt

Access door

Twin rear axle

Side entrance

Single front axle

Tyre

Raked windscreen

Panoramic window

Turning indicator

Bumper

Plug-style entrance door

PaRis Vision

Sliding window vent

Upper saloon window

Advertising panel

Air intake

Lower saloon window

Fleet number

Engine access panel

Rear bumper

Emergency door control

Two-leaf style exit door

Legal lettering

London Buses logo

Axle

Tyre

Skirt

SIDE VIEW

LONDON BUSES

333

The first cars

THE EARLIEST ROAD VEHICLE powered by an engine, the Cugnot steam traction engine, was built in 1770. More practical steam carriages, such as the Bordino, were available in the early 19th century, but they were heavy and cumbersome. Restrictive laws and the introduction of railways, faster and able to carry more passengers, saw the decline of "cars" powered by steam. It was not until 1860 that the first practical power unit for road vehicles was developed, with the invention of the internal combustion engine by the Belgian Etienne Lenoir. By around 1890, Karl Benz and Gottlieb Daimler in Germany, and Albert de Dion and Armand Peugeot in France were building cars for sale to the public. These early cars, despite being primitive, expensive, and produced in limited numbers, heralded the age of the motor car.

STEAM-POWERED CUGNOT "FARDIER", 1770

Twin cylinder engine
Steam pipe
Rocking beam
Steering tiller
Wooden wheel (artillery wheel)
Chimney
Brake pedal
Seat
Wooden frame
Load space
Haystack boiler
Carrying fork
Piston rod
Ratchet wheel
Single front driving wheel
Step
Log basket
Broad, rough tyre

BORDINO STEAM CARRIAGE, 1854

Chimney
Hood iron (landau iron)
Landau body
Drop-down window
Leather hood
Fire-tube boiler
Sprung chassis
Water tank
Safety valve
Safety valve weight
Coke hopper
Chauffeur's seat (stoker's seat; spider seat; tiger seat)
Step
Tie bar
Full-elliptic leaf spring
Iron tyre
Wooden spoke
Wooden wheel (artillery wheel)
Hub
Unsprung chassis
Tie rod
Steam chest
Connecting rod
Twin-cylinder steam engine
Steam distributor valve

SIDE VIEW OF PETROL-DRIVEN BENZ MOTORWAGEN, 1886

REAR VIEW OF BENZ MOTORWAGEN, 1886

Steering tiller
Brake quadrant
Brake lever
Cooling water tank
Steering column
Full-elliptic leaf spring
Steering rack
Bevel gear
Steering link
Final drive sprocket
Steering head
Seat spring
Driven pulley
Wheel fork
Tubular chassis
Driving chain
Driving sprocket
Hub
Solid rubber tyre
Tangent-spoked wire wheel

Crown wheel
Pinion
Lubricator
Cooling tank
Fuel tank
Driving pulley
Drive belt
Big-end bearing
Groove for rope starter
Crankshaft
Flywheel

Seat squab

Candle lamp
Driver's seat
Steering tiller
Brake lever
Dashboard
Headlamp
Round pin
Splinter bar
Towing hook
Forecarriage
Steam pipe
Spoke
Frame

OVERHEAD VIEW OF BENZ MOTORWAGEN, 1886

Steering link
Footboard
Steering tiller
Brake lever
Tool and battery box
Trembler coil box
Intake pipe
Single cylinder
Fuel tank
Cooling water tank
Oil-filled lubricator
Flywheel
Crown wheel
Crankshaft
Driving pulley
Drive belt

Elegance and utility

DURING THE FIRST DECADE OF THE 20TH CENTURY, the motorist who could afford it had a choice of some of the finest cars ever made. These handbuilt cars were powerful and luxurious, using the finest woods, leathers, and cloths, and bodywork made to the customer's individual requirements; some had six-cylinder engines as big as 15 litres. The price of such cars was several times that of an average house, and their yearly running costs were also very high. As a result, basic, utilitarian cars became popular. Costing perhaps one-tenth of the price of a luxury car, these cars had very little trim and often had only single-cylinder engines.

1904 OLDSMOBILE SINGLE-CYLINDER ENGINE

Oil bottle dripfeed
Crankcase
Starting handle bracket
Exhaust pipe
Cylinder head
Cylinder
Starter cog
Carburettor
Engine timing gear
Crankshaft
Flywheel
Gear band

FRONT VIEW OF 1906 RENAULT

Canopy
Mahogany framed windscreen
Cast aluminium wheel spider
Rear window
British Automobile Association badge
Bedford cord upholstery
British Royal Automobile Club badge
Window blind
Blind pull
Window lift strap
Rear-view mirror
Broad lace trim
Lamp bracket
Oil side lamp
Windscreen support
Dashboard radiator
Mudguard (wing)
Brass bevel
Access panel
Bonnet catch
Bail handle
Lifting handle
Mirror reflector
Acetylene headlamp
Steering spindle
Chevron-tread tyre
Elliott steering knuckle
Dumb iron
Screwdown greaser
Front axle
Starting handle
Track rod

SIDE VIEW OF 1906 RENAULT

Luggage grid
Button-quilted upholstery
Mahogany-framed plate glass window
Round-corner single limousine coachwork
Rear oil lamp
Shock absorber
Hub
Hub cap
Beaded edge tyre
Tyre security bolt

1904 OLDSMOBILE TRIM AND BODYWORK

Reflector

Rear lamp

Engine cover handle

Engine cover

Mudguard

Seat back rest frame

Dashboard

Tiller

Brake pedal

Throttle pedal

Mirror

Mudguard stay

Ignition switch

Seat squab

1904 OLDSMOBILE CHASSIS

Front steering track-rod

Front spring

Brake rod

Full-elliptic steering spring

Steering wiffletree

Front axle

Rear spring

Starting handle bracket

Combined spring and chassis unit

Non-skid tyre

Brass scrollwork

Blind pull

Canopy

Openable windscreen

Brass bevel

Division

Dashboard

Oil side lamp

Bonnet

Broad lace trim

Leather upholstery

Handbrake

Steering wheel

Gear lever

Water pipe

Plug lead conduit

Acetylene headlamp

Fuel/air intake pipe

Bi-block engine

Bulb horn

Spare tyre

Dashboard radiator

Jump seat (opera seat; strapontin)

Rim clamp

Tyre carrier

Running board

Leather valance

Tyre strap

Bonnet stay

Exhaust manifold

Starting handle

Wooden artillery wheel

Mass-production

THE FIRST CARS WERE HAND-ASSEMBLED from individually built parts, a time-consuming procedure that required skilled mechanics and made cars very expensive. This problem was solved, in America, by a Detroit car manufacturer named Henry Ford; he introduced mass-production by using standardized parts, and later combined these with a moving production line. The work was brought to the workers, each of whom performed one simple task in the construction process as the chassis moved along the line. The first mass-produced car, the Ford Model T, was launched in 1908 and was available in a limited range of body styles and colours. However, when the production line was introduced in 1914, the colour range was cut back; the Model T became available, as Henry Ford said, in "any colour you like, so long as it's black". Ford cut the production time for a car from several days to about 12 hours, and eventually to minutes, making cars much cheaper than before. As a result, by 1920 half the cars in the world were Model T Fords.

FRONT VIEW OF 1913 FORD MODEL T

Throttle lever

Openable windscreen

Steering wheel

Windscreen stay

Ignition lever

Dashboard

Side lamp

Bulb horn

Spring shock absorber

Mudguard (wing)

Headlamp

Radiator

Front transverse leaf spring

Front axle

Number plate

Starting handle

Steering knuckle

Steering spindle connecting-rod

STAGES OF FORD MODEL T PRODUCTION

Left half of differential housing

Pinion

Hub bolt

Rear leaf spring (cross-member)

Steering arm

King pin

Demountable wheel

Hub brake shoe

Track rod

Steering wheel

Pinion housing

Front transverse leaf spring

Differential housing

Chassis frame

Rear axle

Front cross-member

Rear spring perch

Radius rod

Body mount

Bearing sleeve

King pin

Battery carrier

Half-shaft

Right half of differential housing

Crown wheel

Rear axle bearing

Bevel pinion

Front axle

Demountable wheel

Radius rod

Torque tube

Running-board stay

Hub brake shoe

SIDE VIEW OF 1913 FORD MODEL T

Hood

Rear seat

Hood frame

Front seat

Steering wheel

Steering column

Windscreen

Side lamp

Horn bulb

Bonnet

Radiator filler cap

Radiator filler neck

Front mudguard

Rear door

Rear mudguard (rear wing)

Spring shock absorber

Tyre valve

Drain plug

Horn

Wooden-spoked wheel

Hub cap

Running board

Valance

Spare tyre

Dummy front door

Radius rod

Radiator shell

Steering column

Drag link

Demountable wheel

Bun lamp burner

Fuel sediment bowl

Running-board bracket

Light switch

Starter switch

Headlamp rim

Headlamp

Track rod

Ruckstell axle

Bonnet clip

Steering gearbox

Handbrake

Handbrake

Starter

Rear cross-member

Brake drum

Radiator hose

Drop arm

Drag link

Crank handle

Cylinder block

Torque tube

Greaser

Transmission casing

Radiator apron

Brake rod

Tank support

Front wing stay

Carburettor

Demountable wheel

Radiator

Steering arm

Clincher wheel

Battery strap

Reflector

Bonnet clip

Fender eye bolt

Handbrake quadrant

Running-board support

Detachable rim

Headlamp shell

Running board

The "people's car"

THE MOST POPULAR CAR in the history of car manufacture is the Volkswagen Beetle, originally called the KdF Wagen. The car was developed in Germany in the 1930s by Dr. Ferdinand Porsche. At that time, Germany had only half the number of cars of Britain or France, and Adolf Hitler took a personal interest in the development of the Volkswagen ("people's car"). The intention was to provide a new industry, new jobs, and a car so cheap that anyone in work could afford it. Dr. Porsche designed a car that was cheap to build and run; its rear-mounted, air-cooled engine cut down the number of parts needed and also reduced weight. However, few civilians managed to obtain the Beetle before the outbreak of the Second World War in 1939. After the war, the Beetle proved so popular that eventually more than 20 million were sold.

CUSTOMIZED VOLKSWAGEN BEETLE

Rear lamp
Air scoop
Quarter light
Bonnet
Indicator
Tail pipe
Pressed steel wheel
Fuel filler cap

FLAT-FOUR CYLINDER ARRANGEMENT

Counterweight
Piston
Crankshaft
Big end
Connecting rod (con-rod)

Fuel tank
Steering tie-rod
Fuel tank sender unit
Fuel filler neck
Windscreen-wiper motor assembly
Steering idler
Steering box assembly
Frame head
Anti-roll bar
Suspension strut
Brake back plate
Track control arm
Pedal cluster
Dust shroud
Strut insert (shock absorber)
Front suspension top mount
Gear lever knob
Seat mount
Front road spring
Handbrake
Front suspension top mount
Floor pan (platform chassis)
Torsion bar cover
Rear brake drum
Trailing arm
Tyre
Sports wheel
Rear shock absorber
Drive shaft
Transaxle (gearbox and final drive)
Heat exchanger
Clutch and flywheel
Starter motor
Flat-four engine
Air filter
Tail pipe

BODY SHELL OF VOLKSWAGEN BEETLE

Front bumper

Bonnet release handle

Nearside headlamp unit

Chrome trim strip

Nearside front indicator lens

Bonnet

Offside headlamp unit

Offside front indicator lens

Nearside front mudguard (front wing)

Offside front mudguard (front wing)

Front wing piping

Spare-wheel well

Bonnet hinge

Front wing piping

Offside running board

Quarter light

Blade

Mirror

Arm

Nearside running board

Door catch

Windscreen wiper

Steering column

Wind deflector (baffle)

Sun roof

Quarter light

Door handle

Window winder handle

Passenger door

Window winder regulator

Body shell

Drop glass

Rear wing piping

Rear wing piping

Air intake vents

Nearside rear mudguard (rear wing)

Rear valance

Engine lid (engine cover)

Offside rear mudguard (rear wing)

Number plate light

Air intake vents

WRV 408L

Number plate

Offside rear lamp cluster (rear lamp unit)

Nearside rear lamp cluster (rear lamp unit)

Rear bumper

341

Early engines

STEAM AND ELECTRICITY were used to power cars until early this century, but neither power source was ideal. Electric cars had to stop frequently to recharge their heavy batteries, and steam cars gave smooth power delivery but were too complicated for the average motorist to use. A rival power source, the internal combustion engine, was invented in 1860 by Etienne Lenoir (see pp. 334-335). This engine converted the force of a controlled explosion into rotary motion, to turn the wheels of a vehicle. Early variations on this basic model included sleeve valves, separately cast cylinders, and the two-stroke combustion cycle. Today, many internal combustion engines, including the Wankel rotary and diesels (see pp. 346-347), use the four-stroke cycle, first demonstrated by Nikolaus Otto in 1876. The Otto cycle, often described as "suck, squeeze, bang, blow", has proved the best method of ensuring that the engine turns over smoothly and that exhaust emissions are controllable.

BERSEY ELECTRIC CAB, 1896

Port linking combustion chambers of upper and lower cylinders

Water connection

Upper paired cylinder

Spark plug

Wide piston-ring

Transfer port

Wire gauze pad

Upper piston

Flywheel

Flexible, forked connecting-rod

Counterweight

Big end

Crankcase

Mounting for tray of 40 batteries

Housing for electric motors

SECTIONED WHITE STEAM CAR, 1903

Steering wheel

Throttle wheel

Brake lever

Reverse lever

Flash steam generator

Automatic cylinder lubricator

Lamp bracket

High-pressure cylinder

Rocking lever

Exhaust pipe

Water pump

Condenser

Low-pressure cylinder

Fuel tank

Semi-elliptic spring

Brake drum

Spiral tubes

Flitch-plated wooden chassis

Drop arm

Water tank

Drag link

Dumb iron

CYCLE OF A FOUR-STROKE INTERNAL COMBUSTION ENGINE

INDUCTION STROKE ("SUCK")

Exhaust port closed
Inlet valve
Inlet port opens
Fuel and air (the "charge") sucked into cylinder
Piston moves downwards
Counterweight
Crankshaft
Crankpin

COMPRESSION STROKE ("SQUEEZE")

Exhaust port closed
Charge compressed by piston
Inlet port closed
Connecting rod (con-rod)
Piston moves upwards

POWER STROKE ("BANG")

Spark plug
Inlet port closed
Exhaust port closed
Explosion pushes piston downwards
Charge ignited by spark plug
Big end

EXHAUST STROKE ("BLOW")

Exhaust valve
Inlet port closed
Exhaust port opens
Burned gases forced out of cylinder
Piston moves upwards

16-HORSEPOWER HUMBER ENGINE, 1911

Brass housing for ignition cable
Inlet port
Water pipe
Valve cap
Spark plug
Side valve (inlet valve)
Pair-cast cylinder
Water jacket
Fan bracket
Tappet
Valve spring
Timing chain
Timing chest
Flywheel
Camshaft
Oil pump
Oil sump
Crankcase
Starting handle

DAIMLER DOUBLE-SLEEVE VALVE ENGINE, 1910

Spark plug socket
Junk ring
Cylinder head
Inlet port
Exhaust port
Inlet manifold
Outer sleeve valve
Water jacket
Cylinder wall
Inner sleeve valve
Piston
Carburettor
Engine bearer
Flywheel

OUTER SLEEVE VALVE

Oil groove

INNER SLEEVE VALVE

Sleeve port
Eye for connecting con-rods to secondary crankshaft

Modern engines

TODAY'S PETROL ENGINE WORKS on the same basic
principles as the first car engines of a century ago,
although it has been greatly refined. Modern engines,
often made from special metal alloys, are much
lighter than earlier engines. Computerized ignition
systems, fuel injectors, and multi-valve cylinder heads
achieve a more efficient combustion of the fuel/air
mixture (the charge) so that less fuel is wasted. As a result
of this greater efficiency, the power and performance of a
modern engine are increased, and the level of pollution in
the exhaust gases is reduced. Exhaust pollution levels
today are also lowered by the increasing use of special
filters called catalytic converters, which absorb many
exhaust pollutants. The need to produce ever more
efficient engines means that it can take up to seven
years to develop a new engine for a family car,
at a cost of many millions of pounds.

FRONT VIEW OF A FORD COSWORTH V6 12-VALVE

Idle control valve

Plenum chamber

Valve rocker

Oil dipstick

Power steering
pump reservoir

High-tension
ignition lead
(spark plug
lead)

Steering pump
pulley

Cogged
drive belt

Fan

Alternator

Crankshaft pulley

Viscous coupling

Oil sump

FRONT VIEW OF A FORD COSWORTH V6 24-VALVE

Idle control valve

Plenum chamber

Exhaust gas
recirculation valve

Camshaft
timing gear

Camshaft chain

Steering pump
drive pulley

Belt tensioner

Air
conditioning
pump

Alternator
cooling fan

Oil sump

Drive belt

Crankshaft pulley

SECTIONED VIEW OF A JAGUAR STRAIGHT 6

Cam follower
(bucket tappet)

Valve
spring

Cam
lobe

Cam

Combustion
chamber

Compression ring

Cam cover

Camshaft

Distributor

Cylinder head

Fan

Valve stem

Air
conditioning
refrigerant
pipe

Exhaust
valve

Suspension
self-levelling
pump

Cylinder
liner

Power
steering
pump

Water jacket

Piston

Swash plate

Connecting
rod (con-rod)

Drive belt

Main
bearing
housing

Compressor
piston

Big end

Transmission
adaptor plate

Air conditioning
compressor

Crankshaft
counterweight

Oil sump

Oil pick-
up pipe

Anti-surge
baffle

Crankcase

Oil-control ring (scraper ring)

FRONT VIEW OF A JAGUAR V12

Distributor

Air cleaner

Camshaft sprocket

Fuel injector nozzle

Inlet manifold tract

Plenum chamber

Camshaft

Cam follower

Coolant outlet

Piston ring land

Cam cover

Piston ring groove

Exhaust manifold

Piston skirt

Gudgeon pin

Viscous coupling

Cooling fan

Fan drive shaft

Alternator

Belt pulley

Alternator pulley

Piston

Crankshaft

STRAIGHT 4 CYLINDER ARRANGEMENT

Counterweight

V12 CYLINDER ARRANGEMENT

Connecting rod (con-rod)

SECTIONED VIEW OF A JAGUAR V12

Throttle butterfly

Inlet manifold

Ignition amplifier

Fuel pipe

Throttle linkage

Distributor drive shaft

Air inlet

Exhaust valve

Inlet valve

Cam cover

Timing chain

Oil feed pipe

Piston crown

Cylinder head

Piston ring land

Coolant rail (water rail)

Water pump

Exhaust heat shield

Piston

Exhaust manifold

Ancillary drive pulley

Oil pipe banjo

Timing chain drive sprocket

Drive plate

Connecting rod (con-rod)

Starter ring

Counterweight (balance weight)

Main bearing

Crankcase

Pipe to oil cooler

Sump

Oil filter

Alternative engines

THE MOST COMMON TYPE OF ALTERNATIVE ENGINE is the diesel engine, which, instead of igniting the compressed fuel/air mixture with a spark, uses compression alone, heating the mixture to the point where it explodes. A diesel engine's fuel consumption is low in comparison with similarly sized piston engines, despite its heavier, reinforced moving parts and cylinder block. Another type of engine is the rotary-combustion, first successfully developed by Felix Wankel in the 1950s. Its two trilobate (three-sided) rotors revolve in housings shaped in a fat figure-of-eight. The four sequences of the four-stroke cycle, which occur consecutively in a piston engine, occur simultaneously in a rotary engine, producing power in a continuous stream.

ROTARY-ENGINED MAZDA RX-7

Aerodynamic windscreen

Headrest

Hood bag

Front spoiler (chin spoiler)

Side marker lamp

Rubbing strake

Cast alloy wheel

WANKEL ROTARY ENGINE

OIL-PUMP HOUSING

Distributor fixing point (drive point)

FRONT SIDE HOUSING

Intake port

FRONT ROTOR CHAMBER

Trailing spark-plug hole

Dipstick tube

INTERMEDIATE HOUSING

Oil filler

Intake port

REAR ROTOR CHAMBER

Aluminium alloy backing

Oil-pump drive

Coolant passage

Leading spark-plug hole

Exhaust port

Water drain bolt

Trailing spark-plug hole

Leading spark-plug

THE WANKEL ROTARY CYCLE

Exhaust port

Intake port

Fuel/air mixture being compressed

Water passage

Burning gas expands

Trilobate rotor

Exhaust port closed

Gas continues to expand

Stationary gear (fixed gear)

Compression continues

Vacuum sucks in fuel/air mixture

Burnt gas exhausts

Rotor gear

Compressed gas ignites

Burnt gas continues to exhaust

Output shaft turns

Fuel/air mixture continues to enter

Burnt gas begins to expand

Compression begins

FORD TURBOCHARGED DIESEL ENGINE

Engine lifting eye
Rocker cover
Baffle plate
Inlet track
Turbo impeller (inlet rotor)
Turbo propeller (exhaust rotor)
Exhaust
Bell housing

Oil filler cap
Cam follower
Valve return spring
Water jacket
Water pump pulley
Compression ring
Oil-control ring
Piston
Ancillary drive belt
Water jacket
Oil cooler
Oil cooler matrix

Oil sump pan
Engine block
Oil return pipe for turbocharger
Oil filter

REAR SIDE HOUSING

Chrome plating

Exhaust port

ROTOR AND SEALS

Outer oil seal
Inner oil seal spring
Inner oil seal
Rotor bearing
Rotor gear
Side gear
Corner seal spring
Corner seal insert
Corner seal
Rotor
Balancing drilling
Apex seal

Inner oil seal groove
Outer oil seal groove
Outer oil seal spring
Hole for output shaft
Side seal spring
Side seal
Side seal groove
Apex seal groove
Apex seal spring

OUTPUT SHAFT

Front counterweight
Front eccentric rotor journal
Oil hole
Rear stationary gear (fixed gear)
V-belt pulley
Front stationary gear (fixed gear)
Main journal
Eccentric shaft
Oil jet
Rear eccentric rotor journal
Flywheel with balance weight

Bodywork

RENAULT LOGO

THE BODY OF A MODERN mass-produced car is built on the monocoque (single-shell) principle, in which the roof, side panels, and floor are welded into a single integral unit. This bodyshell protects and supports the car's internal parts. Steel and glass are used to construct the bodyshell, creating a unit that is both light and strong. Its lightness helps to conserve energy, while its strength protects the occupants. Modern bodywork is designed with the aid of computers, which are used to predict factors such as aerodynamic efficiency and impact-resistance. High-technology is also employed on the production line, where robots are used to assemble, weld, and paint the body.

Door handle

Door lock

Left-hand door glass

Left-hand quarter glass

Tail-gate support

Window washer jet

Heating element contact

Rear window glass

Tail-gate support

Tail-gate

Rear bumper

Bodyshell

Fuel cap

Right-hand quarter glass

Zinc phosphating

Degreased bare metal

Primer

Base coat colour

Cataphoresic coating

Varnish

Chrome passivation

Right-hand door glass

Door key and lock

Door handle

Left-hand door

Left-hand mirror assembly

Door hinge

Electric window motor

Rear hatch

Aerial

Side marker lamp

SIDE VIEW OF A RENAULT CLIO

Spoiler bumper

Bonnet-release cable

Bonnet

Bonnet catch

Bonnet hinge

Window winder cable

Window winder handle

Windscreen glass

Front bumper

Bonnet

Headrest

Headlamp

Door hinge

Right-hand door

Right-hand mirror assembly

Spoiler bumper

Fog-lamp

FRONT VIEW OF A RENAULT CLIO

Mechanical components

A TYPICAL MODERN CAR has several thousand individual mechanical components. These are assembled to form the car's various mechanical systems: engine and exhaust, transmission, steering, suspension, and brakes. To ensure that each system functions properly, components are manufactured to extremely fine tolerances – to within a five-hundredth of a millimetre (about one ten-thousandth of an inch) in some cases.

Alloy wheel

Hub cap

Hub nut

Hub seal

Exhaust downpipe

Silencer

Catalytic converter

Suspension spring

Rear silencer

Fuel tank

Vent pipe

Fuel tank filler neck

Electric fuel pump

Shock absorber

Brake cylinder

Brake shoe

Hub seal

Hub nut

Hub cap

Wheel trim

Torsion bar

Handbrake

Nearside rear suspension arm

Anti-roll bar

Gear lever

Steering wheel

Steering rack

Offside rear suspension arm

Steering column

Clutch pedal

Hub and brake drum

Brake pedal

Brake backplate

Throttle pedal

Clutch cable

Throttle cable

Steel wheel

**MECHANICAL COMPONENTS
OF A RENAULT CLIO, 1991**

Brake shield

Alloy wheel

Clutch release
bearing

Brake
disc

Hub

Nearside
drive shaft

Clutch pressure
plate

Track-rod
end

Upper
suspension
arm

Brake hose

Top hose

ack
d

Brake
pad

Power
steering
pump

Clutch
centre
plate

Bottom
hose

Gear-
change rod

Gearbox
(transmission)

Lower
suspension
arm

Anti-roll
bar

Starter
motor

Flywheel

Fan
motor

Electronic
ignition unit

Subframe

Power steering
belt

Exhaust
Manifold

Intake
manifold

Brake
cylinder

Water
pump

Fan motor support

Brake
servo

Alternator
belt

Alternator

Engine

Suspension
strut

Brake caliper
fixing bolt

Distributor

Brake caliper
locking plate

Brake
caliper

Air cleaner

Hub
carrier

Brake
hose

Offside
drive shaft

Lock nut and washer

Radiator

Brake disc

Front hub
bearing

Brake shield

Steel wheel

Wheel trim

351

Car trim

A MODERN CAR HAS TWO TYPES OF TRIM, according to the materials used: hard (chrome and plastics) and soft (upholstery materials). Safety and comfort are priorities in the trim's design: seats help the occupants to maintain a comfortable posture, rubber seals keep out dirt and moisture, and headlamps light the way. Older cars had interior or leather panelling cut and fitted by craftsmen; modern cars use precisely moulded plastics and seat fabrics cut by robot-controlled lasers to reduce costs and production time. Doors are now trimmed off the production line so that complex wiring can be built in.

TRIM OF A RENAULT CLIO, 1991

Rear quarter trim panel

Inner roof trim

Roof seal

Quarter trim panel

Quarter panel moulding

Rear seat belt

Rear tyre

Rear shelf

Split, folding rear seat assembly

Cen seat belt

Rea seat belt stal (cat

Tail-gate trim

Rear wiper blade

Tail-gate seal

Rear shelf radio speaker

Rear shelf radio speaker

Rear wiper arm

Ge leve sur

Number plate lamp

Rear indicator and stop lamp assembly

Rear wheel embellisher (wheel trim)

Untrimmed headrest

HALOGEN HEADLAMP BULB

Rear seat belt

Quarter panel moulding

Rear tyre

SPOTLAMP BULB

Filament

MARKER LAMP BULB

Filament

Quarter trim panel

FESTOON BULB

Rear quarter trim panel

Roof seal

Inner roof trim

Contact

Bayonet fixing

Contact

Contact

Roof moulding

Window winder handle

Door seal

Front tyre

Front wheel embellisher (wheel trim)

Door lock handle

Door pull handle

Indicator lamp

Fog-lamp

Inner sill trim

Door moulding (rubbing strip)

Inner windscreen moulding

Front seat belt

Front door radio speaker

Dash radio speaker

Front seat assembly

Sun visor

Dash panel (instrument panel)

Headlamp

Windscreen wiper bracket and spindles

Windscreen wiper blade

Interior light

Heater unit

Washer jet

Fan blade

Radio

Rear-view mirror

Centre console

Steering wheel

Fascia (dash)

Windscreen seal

Front seat frame

Sun visor

Headlamp

Windscreen wiper arm

Dash radio speaker

Front seat belt

Control stalk

Front door radio speaker

Inner windscreen moulding

Door trim panel

Inner sill trim

Door moulding (rubbing strip)

Door seal

Fog-lamp

Door pull handle

Window winder handle

Indicator lamp

Door lock handle

Front tyre

Front wheel embellisher (wheel trim)

Hybrid car

THERE HAVE BEEN SEVERAL proposed alternatives
to conventional petrol- or diesel-powered cars,
including cars that use solar or battery power. The
object is to lower harmful emissions and conserve
natural resources. One of the alternatives already
in production is the hybrid car. A hybrid vehicle uses
two or more fuels. Examples include diesel-electric
trains and mopeds. The latter combine the power
of a petrol engine with pedal power. In a hybrid car,
petrol consumption is reduced by the provision of
additional power by an electric motor during
acceleration. The motor is driven by power from
on-board batteries that are recharged by an engine-
driven generator when the car is decelerating or
cruising. Some hybrid cars transfer energy from the
wheels to a flywheel during braking. The flywheel
drives the generator, which recharges the batteries.

HONDA INSIGHT

Aerial — Aerodynamic roof

Windscreen

Wing mirror

Plastic front wings

Front air dam

Plastic bumper

Aerodynamic underside components

Cooling intake

Aluminium bonnet

SIDE VIEW OF 1-LITRE VTEC ENGINE

Motor power cables

Air-intake duct

Ignition coils

Coolant pipe

Electric motor housing

Lightweight plastic intake manifold

Lightweight magnesium alloy oil sump pan

Oil filter

Air conditioning compressor

Engine drive belt

FRONT VIEW OF 1-LITRE VTEC ENGINE

Rocker cover

Ignition coils

Dipstick

Water pump

Belt tensioner

Air conditioning compressor

Crankshaft pulley

Drive belt

HOW HYBRID POWER WORKS

Petrol engine provides power for acceleration and to generator

Electric motor

Power from generator recharges battery during deceleration

Power from battery to motor during acceleration

Inverter

Battery

Inverter controls direction of electrical current

Inverter cooling fan

REAR VIEW

Motor electronic control module (ECM)

Battery electronic control module (ECM)

Battery cooling fan

INVERTER AND BATTERY

Inverter housing

DC converter

High-voltage connector

High-voltage cables

Motor electronic control module (ECM)

Battery electronic control module (ECM)

DANGER
HIGH VOLTAGE

INVERTER ASSEMBLY

Inverter cooling fan connector

Magnesium housing for air intake

DC converter connection

Junction board

Cover mounting bracket

BATTERY ASSEMBLY

Battery cooling fan

Manifold connector

O₂ sensor

Catalyst

Rear exhaust section connector

EXHAUST WITH CATALYTIC CONVERTER

Racing cars

SINCE MOTORING BEGAN, racing cars have been a major focus of innovation in car design. Features that are now commonplace, such as disc brakes, turbochargers, and even safety belts, were used first on competition cars. Research into racing cars has contributed to a new understanding of engine performance, aerodynamics, and tyre adhesion, and has led to the development of ultra-light materials such as carbon-fibre for car bodies. A modern McLaren Formula One car has a low, streamlined body and an open cockpit but, unlike its forerunner, it also has front and rear wings that push the wheels firmly on to the track, huge tyres for extra grip, and electronic sensors that continually relay information to the pits about the car's performance.

72° V10 ENGINE

Fuel injection trumpet guard

Cam cover

Gearbox fixing stud

Water and oil pump assembly

Mercedes-Benz

Harmonically-tuned exhaust system

Cylinder head

Stressed cylinder block

BACK VIEW OF MCLAREN MERCEDES MP4-13

Upper flap

Grooved racing tyre

Warning light

Half-shaft

BRIDGESTONE

BRIDGESTONE

Diffuser

Exhaust pipe

Differential

West

Rear wing end-plate

One-piece side pod and engine cover

Side pod air outlet

SIDE VIEW OF MCLAREN MERCEDES MP4-13

Rear wing end-plate

LOCTITE

CAMOZZI

WARSTEINER

BRIDGEST

BRIDGESTONE

POTENZA

ENKEI

ENKEI

Alloy wheel

Wheel nut

Winglet

Engine cover

Head rest

On-board TV mini-camera

Engine air intake

Hakkinen

BOSS
HUGO BOSS

Mobil 1

E

Mercedes-Benz

We

Side pod

OVERHEAD VIEW OF MCLAREN MERCEDES MP4-13

Front wing
end-plate

Front wing

Nose cover

Lower
wishbone

Front
brake duct

Grooved
racing tyre

Driver's
radio
aerial

Rear-view
mirror

One-piece side pod
and engine cover

Radius arm

Rear wing
endplate

Slot

Upper
flap

Upper
wishbone

Turning
vane

Safety harness

Driver protection

Grooved
racing tyre

Rear wing
upper
mainplane

FRONT VIEW OF MCLAREN MERCEDES MP4-13

Rear wing upper
mainplane

Rear-view mirror

Radiator air intake

Upper wishbone

Lower wishbone

Engine air intake

Driver's radio aerial

Front
brake duct

Grooved racing tyre

End-plate

Rear-view
mirror

Forward rollover
structure

Steering
link

Wing supports

Front wing

Driver's radio aerial

Alloy wheel

High nose

Turning vane

Wheel nut

Front wing end-plate

Bicycle anatomy

THE BICYCLE IS A TWO-WHEELED, light-weight machine, which is propelled by human power. It is efficient, cheap, easily manufactured, and one of the world's most popular forms of transport. The first pedal-driven bicycle was built in Scotland in 1839. Since then the basic design – of a frame, wheels, brakes, handlebars, and saddle – has been gradually improved, with the addition of a chain, gear system, and pneumatic tyres (tyres inflated with air). The recent invention of the mountain bike (all-terrain bike) has been an important development. With its strong, rugged frame, wide tyres, and 21 gears, a mountain bike enables riders to reach rough and hilly areas that were previously inaccessible to cyclists.

REAR WHEEL

Tyre

Hub

Spoke

Rim

Saddle

Seat post

Seat post quick-release bolt

Cable guide

Straddle wire

Seat tube

6000

Rear cantilever brake

Seat stay

Front derailleur

Rear drop-outs

Rear hub quick-release spindle

Bottom bracket shell

Bottom bracket axle

Crank bolt

Washer

17-tooth sprocket

13-tooth sprocket

Adjustable cup

Fixed cup

Bottom bracket sleeve

Cage

Lock washer

Bottom bracket ball bearing

Freewheel locknut

Lock ring

Jockey wheel

Chain

Lock washer

Rear derailleur

23-tooth sprocket

Sprocket spacer

Derailleur cage plate

Jockey wheel

46-tooth chain ring

Toe clip

30-tooth sprocket

GEAR SYSTEM

Spoke guard

FREEWHEEL SPROCKETS

Toe strap

Pedal

Spider

Gear cable

Gearshift

Gearshift

Handlebar

Handlebar
stem

Handlebar
grip

Expander
bolt

Lock
nut

Rear brake
cable

Brake
lever

Brake lever

Top tube

Lock
washer

Top race

Cable guide

Head
tube

Top cup

Caged ball
bearings

Front brake
cable

Hub

Spoke

BICYCLE
FRAME

Bottom
cup

Down
tube

Steerer
tube

Rubber
bearing
seal

Straddle wire

Bottom
race

Toe clip

Front
cantilever
brake

Rim

Inner tube

Toe
strap

Pedal

Cantilever
brake boss

Fork blade

Left crank
arm

24-tooth
chain ring

Front hub
quick-release
spindle

36-tooth
chain ring

Handlebar

Dust cap

Saddle

Frame

Brake lever
and gearshift

Valve

Pedal

Tyre

FRONT WHEEL

Chain

Bicycles

ALTHOUGH ALL BICYCLES are made up of the same basic components, they can vary greatly in design. A racing bike, such as the Eddy Merckx model, with its light frame and steep head- and seat-angles, is built for speed. Its design forces the rider to adopt the "aerotuck", a crouched, aerodynamic position. While a touring bike resembles the racing bike in many respects, it is designed for comfort and stability on long-distance journeys. Touring bikes are characterized by more relaxed frame angles, heavy chain stays that support the rear panniers, and a long wheelbase (the distance between the wheel axles) for reliable handling. All-round bicycles, known as "hybrids", combine the light weight and speed of sports bikes with the rugged durability of mountain bikes (see pp. 358-359). Bicycles that are not designed for conventional road use include time-trial bikes, which have a short head tube, sloping top tube, "aero" handlebars, and aerodynamic tubing. Most Human Powered Vehicles (HPVs) are recumbents – the rider has a recumbent position – which maximize power output and minimize drag (resistance). Essential to the safety of all riders are helmets, and both front and rear lights; locks protect against theft.

FRONT AND REAR LIGHTS

Red rear light

White front light

HELMET

Hard outer shell

Air vent

Polystyrene padding

Quick-release strap

EDDY MERCKX RACING BICYCLE

Saddle

Saddle clamp

Seat post

Seat-post bolt

Cable guide

Rear brake cable

Brake-block bolt

Top tube (crossbar)

Steel frame

Brake block

Seat stay

Seat tube

Down tu…

Tyre

Water-bottle cage

Tyre tread

Front derailleur

Tyre wall

Wheel rim

Freewheel sprocket

STEEL LOCK

Key

Hardened steel

Chain ring

Crank

Pick-proof lock

Crank bolt

Spider

Rear derailleur

Pedal

Pulley bolt

Chain stay

Toe clip

Tension pulley

Chain

CANNONDALE SH600 HYBRID BICYCLE

Gel-filled saddle
Light-weight frame
Straight handlebar
Brake bridge
Cantilever brake
All-surface tyre

CANNONDALE ST1000 TOURING BICYCLE

Rear mudguard
Water bottle
Drop handlebar
Front mudguard
Front pannier
Large diameter aluminium tubing
Long chain stay
Rear pannier

Headset
Stem
Binder bolt
Handlebar
Front brake cable
Brake lever
Head tube
Extra
Brake pivot bolt
Brake pad
Fork
Hub quick-release lever
Spoke
Spoke nipple
Presta valve
Hub

ROSSIN ITALIAN TIME-TRIAL BICYCLE

Aero handlebar
Sloping top tube
Steep seat tube
Hollow disc wheel
Short head tube
KILLING System
FiR
Clipless pedal
Tri-spoke wheel
Narrow tyre

WINDCHEETAH SL MARK VI "SPEEDY" RACING HPV BICYCLE

Fleecy headrest
Fibreglass bucket seat
Joystick
Brake lever
53-tooth chain ring
Clipless pedal
Extended racing chain
Aluminium tubing
Drum brake
7-speed freewheel

The motorcycle

THE MOTORCYCLE HAS EVOLVED from a motorized cycle – a basic bicycle with an engine – into a sophisticated, high-performance machine. In 1901, the Werner brothers established the most viable location for the engine by positioning it low in the centre of the chassis (see pp. 364-365): the new Werner became the basis for the modern motorcycle. Motorcycles are used for many purposes – for commuting, delivering messages, touring, and racing – and different machines have been developed according to the demands of different types of riders. The Vespa scooter, for instance, which is small-wheeled, economical, and easy-to-ride, was designed to meet the needs of the commuter. Sidecars provided transport for the family until the arrival of cheap cars caused their popularity to decline. Enthusiast riders generally favour larger capacity machines that are capable of greater performance and offer more comfort. Four-cylinder machines have been common since the Honda CB750 appeared in 1969. Despite advances in motorcycle technology, many riders are attracted to the traditional looks of motorcycles like the twin-cylinder Harley-Davidson. The Harley-Davidson Glides exploit the style of the classic American V-twin engine, where the cylinders are placed in a V-formation.

1901 WERNER MOTORCYCLE

Vacuum-operated inlet valve
Bicycle-type saddle
Pulley rim rear brake
Fuel tank
Electric ignition control
Inlet-over-exhaust (IOE) engine
A2201
Alloy crankcase
Twisted rawhide drive belt
Cast iron cylinder barrel

1988 HARLEY-DAVIDSON FLHS ELECTRA GLIDE

1965 BMW R/60 WITH 1952 STEIB CHAIR

Handlebar
Head-light
Mirror
Windscreen
Adjustable link
Sidecar
Fuel tank
Sidelight
Horizontally opposed engine
Mudguard
Sidecar chassis rail
Indicator
Sidecar wheel
Sidecar lower link
Exhaust pipe
Square-section tyre
Side reflector

FRONT VIEW

Mudguard
Canvas shroud
Speedometer
Ignition lock
Tail-light
Grab handle
Tool tray
Mudguard stay
Lockable luggage boot
Silencer
Silencer bracket
Suspension linkage
Bullet-shaped sidecar body
Drum brake
Disc brake
Knock-off wheel nut
SIDE VIEW
Long leading-link fork (Earles fork)
Crash bar
Exhaust clamp

Backrest
Passenger seat
Passenger grab rail
Pannier
Luggage rack
Licence plate
Tail-light

1969 HONDA CB750

Tail-light
Seat
Mirror
Front brake lever
Seat strap
Indicator
Shock absorber
Oil tank
Telescopic fork
Mudguard stay
Disc brake
Clutch cover
Single overhead camshaft engine
Mirror
Heat shield
Passenger footrest
Brake master cylinder
Exhaust pipe
Handgrip
Front brake lever

1963 VESPA GRAND SPORT 160 MARK 1

Twist grip gear change
Monocoque chassis
Seat strap
Throttle
Front brake lever
Clutch lever
Engine cover
Seat
Head-light
Cooling grille
Horn
Tail-light
Choke
Shock absorber
Petrol tap
Kick-starter
Centre stand
Foot brake
Silencer
Rubber foot mat
Drum brake
Windscreen
Single-sided trailing-link fork
Clutch cable
Throttle cable

Padded seat
Manufacturer's logo
Light switch
Windscreen adjustor
Oil tank filler cap
Fuel tank
Head-light
Oil tank
Fog-lamp
Indicator
Telescopic fork
Side reflector
Mudguard

Gearbox
Air filter
Crash bar
Passenger footrest
45° V-twin engine
Duplex tubular cradle frame
Cast alloy wheel
Exhaust pipe
Footrest
Brake calliper
Disc brake
Brake pedal

The motorcycle chassis

THE MOTORCYCLE CHASSIS is the main "body" of the motorcycle, to which the engine is attached. Consisting of the frame, wheels, suspension, and brakes, the chassis performs various functions. The frame, which is built from steel or alloy, keeps the wheels in line to maintain the handling of the motorcycle, and serves as a structure for mounting other components. The engine and gearbox unit is bolted into place, while items such as the seat, the mudguards, and the fairing are more easily removable. Suspension cushions the rider from irregularities in the road surface. In most suspension systems, coil springs controlled by an oil damper separate the main mass of the motorcycle from the wheels. At the front, the spring and damper are usually incorporated in a telescopic fork; the rear employs a pivoted swingarm. The suspension also helps to retain maximum contact between the tyres and the road, necessary to effective braking and steering. Drum brakes were common until the 1970s, but modern motorcycles use disc brakes, which are more powerful.

1985 HONDA VF750 WITH BODYWORK

Racing number plate · Fuel tank · Frame-mounted fairing · Telescopic fork · Dual seat · Mudguard · Disc brake · Box-section swingarm · V4 engine unit · Box-section tubular cradle frame · Floating disc brake

1985 HONDA VF750 WITH BODYWORK REMOVED

Brake master cylinder · Headstock · Bracing tube · Square-section steel tubing · Rear sub-frame · Bodywork mounting point · Shock absorber top mounting · Engine mounting plate · Exhaust mounting strap · Shock absorber · Exhaust pipe · Light alloy wheel · Axle adjustor · Disc brake · Footrest hanger · Multiplate clutch · Engine cover · Radiator · Oil cooler · Disc brake calliper · Brake master cylinder · Brake pedal · Oil level window · Engine mounting bolt · Radiator pipe · Box-section swingarm · Brake torque arm · Swingarm pivot · Oil sump · V4 engine unit

DRUM BRAKE

OPERATING PARTS OF DISC BRAKE SYSTEM

Brake fluid reservoir

Master cylinder

Push-rod

Piston

Hydraulic brake fluid

Wheel disc

Calliper assembly

Piston

Brake pad

EXTERIOR OF DRUM BRAKE

Bolt hole

Torque arm

Air cooling scoop

Axle hole

Cooling fin

Speedometer drive

Cable stop

Brake plate

Operating arm

INTERIOR OF DRUM BRAKE

Torque arm

Bolt hole

Brake shoe

Pivot

Brake shoe return spring

Operating cam

Brake shoe return spring

Axle hole

High-friction material

Clutch cable

Hydraulic brake hose

Telescopic fork leg

Fork slide

Light alloy wheel

Axle

Floating disc brake

Brake calliper

SPRING/DAMPER UNIT

Rubber mounting bush

Twin rate spring

Damper rod

Damper body

Pre-load adjustor

Rubber mounting bush

HOW A SPRING/DAMPER UNIT WORKS

Rubber mounting bush

Spring

Damper rod

Non-return valve

Hydraulic fluid

Compressible gas

Hydraulic fluid chamber

Rubber mounting bush

TYPES OF TYRE

RACING SLICK TYRE

No tread pattern

TUBELESS SPORTS TYRE

Radial groove

TRIALS TYRE

Knobbly tread pattern

GENERAL-USE TYRE

Hard-wearing rubber compound

Motorcycle engines

MOTORCYCLE ENGINES must be light-weight and compact, and have a good power output. They have between one and six cylinders, can be cooled by air or water, and the capacity of the combustion chamber varies from 49cc (cubic centimetres) to 1500cc. Two types of internal combustion engine are common: the four-stroke, which is used in cars (see pp. 342-343), and the two-stroke. A basic two-stroke engine has only three moving parts – the crankshaft, the connecting rod, and the piston – but the power output is high. The engine fires every two strokes (rather than every four), giving a "power stroke" every revolution (see p. 343). Power is conveyed from the engine to the rear wheel by the transmission system. This usually consists of a clutch, a gearbox, and a final drive system. Clutches are multiplate devices, which run in oil. Gearboxes have five or six speeds and are operated by foot pedal. Shaft and belt drive systems are used in some cases, but chain drive to the rear wheel is most common.

EXTERIOR OF STANDARD TWO-STROKE ENGINE

Spark plug cap
Fuel tap
Carburettor mounting
Kick-starter
Carburettor
Cylinder head
Cooling fin
Exhaust port
Case screw
Clutch activating arm
Gear lever
Engine cover

TRANSMISSION SYSTEM

GEARBOX

1st gear
6th gear
4th gear
3rd gear
5th gear
2nd gear
Gear lever selector shaft
Input shaft
Splines for mounting gear lever
Bearing
Output shaft
Copper oil feed pipe
Splines for mounting final drive sprocket
Gear tooth
Selector fork
Aluminium outer casing

MULTIPLATE CLUTCH

Fibre plate
Key locks fibre plate to outer drum
Outer clutch drum, connected to engine
Pressure plate, connected to inner clutch drum
Springs force plates together
Straight-cut primary-drive gear
Metal plate

MODERN "O RING" DRIVE CHAIN

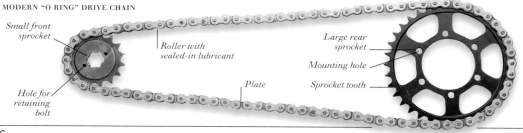

Small front sprocket
Roller with sealed-in lubricant
Large rear sprocket
Mounting hole
Sprocket tooth
Plate
Hole for retaining bolt

**VELOCETTE OVERHEAD
VALVE (OHV) ENGINE**

Screw and lock nut
tappet adjustor

Oil feed pipe

Inlet port

Spark plug lead

Cam follower

Magneto drive

Camshaft gear

Engine
mounting
bolt hole

Oil passageway

Crankcase

Oil pump

Mounting lug

Rocker arm

Rocker cover
retaining bolt

Cylinder head

Exhaust port

Cylinder head

Combustion chamber

Cooling fin

Piston

Push rod

Valve lifter

Timing gear

Engine
mounting
bolt hole

Crankshaft

Non-return valve

Oil sump

Competition motorcycles

THERE ARE MANY TYPES of motorcycle sport and in each, a specialist machine has evolved to perform to specific requirements. Races take place on roads or tracks or "off-road", in fields, dirt tracks, and even the desert. "Grand Prix" world championships in road-racing are contested by three classes: 125cc, 250cc two-strokes; the top class of 500cc two-strokes; and 900cc four-stroke machines. The latest racing sidecars have more in common with racing cars than motorcycles. The rider and passenger operate within an all-enclosing, aerodynamic fairing. The Suzuki RGV500 shown here, like other Grand Prix machines, carries advertising, which helps to cover the cost of developing motorcycle technology. In Speedway, which originated in the US in 1902, motorcycles operate without brakes or a gearbox. Off-road competition motorcycles have less emphasis on high power output. In Motocross, for example, which is held on rough terrain, they must have high ground clearance, flexible long-travel suspension, and tyres with a chunky tread pattern.

1992 HUSQVARNA MOTOCROSS TC610

Throttle cable
Handlebar brace
Long seat
Racing number
Hand protector
Radiator air vent
Flexible plastic mudguard
Light-weight exhaust system
Telescopic fork
Plastic guard
Axle
Overhead camshaft engine
Gear lever
Disc brake
Knobbly tyre
Disc brake
Brake calliper
Shock absorber
Alloy swingarm
Shock absorber linkage

1992 SUZUKI RGV500
SIDE VIEW

Exhaust pipe
Racing number
Air vent
One-piece seat and tail unit
Shock absorber
Minimal seat padding
Arched alloy swingarm

Exhaust pipe
Vent
Handlebar
Silencer
Footrest
Shock absorber mounting
Rear brake pedal
Three-spoke alloy wheel
Drive chain
Exhaust pipe
Wide, slick tyre
Axle adjustor
Disc brake

REAR VIEW

Exhaust pipe
Brake pedal
Disc brake master cylinder
Footrest
Drive chain
Light-weight alloy frame
Rear brake calliper
Slick racing tyre

1981 WESLAKE SPEEDWAY

1968 KIRBY BSA RACING SIDECAR

FRONT VIEW

SIDE VIEW

Throttle

Throttle cable

Carburettor cover

Fuel tank filler cap

Oil filler cap

Mudguard

Seat

Fuel tank

Mudguard

Wheel cover

Telescopic fork

Narrow tyre

Wide tyre

Brakeless wheel hub

Silencer

Footrest

Oil pump

Overhead valve engine

Tubular open cradle frame

Rev counter

Windscreen

All-enclosing fairing

Fuel tank

Battery

Wheel guard

Square-section tyre

Passenger windscreen

Passenger grab rail

Rev counter

Throttle cable

Exhaust pipe

All-enclosing fairing

Sidecar chassis

Fuel cap

Engine

Fibreglass wheel guard

Fairing stay

Throttle cable

Fuel tank breather

Fuel tank

Throttle

Front brake lever

Telescopic fork

Mudguard

Windscreen

Racing number

Fairing

Clutch lever

Front brake lever

Radiator

Mudguard

Hydraulic brake hose

Axle

Slick tyre

Sponsor's logo

Air vent

Braided steel hydraulic hose

Brake calliper

Carbon-fibre disc brake

Three-spoke alloy wheel

Slick tyre

Quickly detachable (QD) fairing

FRONT VIEW

Sea and Air

Ships of Greece and Rome ·············· 372

Viking Ships ·············· 374

Medieval Warships and Traders ·············· 376

The Expansion of Sail ·············· 378

A Ship of the Line ·············· 380

Rigging ·············· 382

Sails ·············· 384

Mooring and Anchoring ·············· 386

Ropes and Knots ·············· 388

Paddle wheels and Propellers ·············· 390

Anatomy of an Iron Ship ·············· 392

The Battleship ·············· 394

Frigates and Submarines ·············· 396

Pioneers of Flight ·············· 398

Early Monoplanes ·············· 400

Biplanes and Triplanes ·············· 402

World War I Aircraft ·············· 404

Early Passenger aircraft ·············· 406

World War II Aircraft ·············· 408

Modern Piston Aero-engines ·············· 410

Modern Jetliners 1 ·············· 412

Modern Jetliners 2 ·············· 414

Supersonic Jetliners ·············· 416

Jet Engines ·············· 418

Modern Military Aircraft ·············· 420

Helicopters ·············· 422

Light Aircraft ·············· 424

Gliders, Hang-gliders, and Microlights ·············· 426

Ships of Greece and Rome

ROMAN ANCHOR

Stock

Shank

Palm

Acutely
angled
arm

Ring

Crown

IN THE EXPANSIVE EMPIRES OF GREECE AND ROME, powerful fleets were needed for battle, trade, and communication. Greek galleys were powered by a sail and many oars. A new armament, the embolos (ram), was fitted on to the galley bow. As ramming duels required fast and manoeuvrable boats, extra rows of oarsmen were added, culminating in the trireme. During the fifth and fourth centuries B.C., the trireme dominated the Mediterranean. It was powered by 170 oarsmen, rowing with one oar each. The oarsmen were ranged on three levels, as the model opposite shows. The trireme also carried archers and soldiers for boarding. Galleys were pulled out of the water when not in use, and were kept in dockyard ship-sheds. The merchant ships of the Greeks and Romans were mighty vessels too. The full-bodied Roman corbita, for example, could hold up to 400 tons and carried a cargo of spices, gems, silk, and animals. The construction of these boats was based on a stout hull with planking secured by mortice and tenon. Some of these ships embarked on long voyages, sailing even as far as India. To make them easier to steer, corbitas set a fore sail called an "artemon". It flew from a forward-leaning mast that was a forerunner of the long bowsprits carried by the great clipper ships of the 19th century.

ROMAN CORBITA

Roband
(rope band)

Ceruchi
(lift)

Double halyard

Bullseye

Fore mast

Heraldic device

Antenna
(yard)

Buntline

Ring

Brace

Ruden
(brail line)

Artemon
(fore sail)

Fore stay

Oculus
(eye)

Anchor

Tabling

Sheet

Bolt rope

Prow

Windlass

Scala
(ladder)

Catena
(riding bitt)

Ancorale
(anchor rope;
anchor rode)

Hatch board

Deck beam

Zosteres (rubbing strake)

Cargo hold

ATTIC VASE SHOWING A GALLEY

Bronze mast
truck

Keraia (yard)

Kalos
(brailing
rope)

Mast

Kubernetes
(helmsman)

Embolos
(ram;
beak)

Sternpost

Pedalia
(twin rudder)

Ophthalmos
(eye)

Oar port sleeve

Kope (oar)

Masthead

Single clump block

Malus (mast)

Rope parrel

Bullet block

Antenna (yard)

Brace block

Timber fairlead

Shroud

Leather reinforcing strip

Scala (ladder)

Velum (main sail)

Sheer pole

Deadeye

Lanyard

Poop break

Poop deck

Main double halyard

Main brace

Main sheet

Hole and peg joint

Poop deck house

Clavus (tiller)

Swan neck ornament

Stern balustrade

Ring bolt

Sternpost

Gubernator (helmsman)

Wale

Planking

Shaft

Blade

Gubernacula (rudders)

Clew

Midships fence

Constratum (deck)

Bitt

Oar lanyard

ROWING POSITIONS ON A GREEK TRIREME (TRIERE)

The katastroma (deck) has been removed from this model to show the positions taken by oarsmen on a trireme.

Thranite (upper level oarsman)

Zygian (middle level oarsman)

Deck rail

Tropeter (leather grommet)

Paraxeiresia (outrigger)

Kope (oar)

Stanchion

Zugon (thwart; seat)

Thalamian (lower level oarsman)

Hyperesion (oarsman's cushion)

Pine hull

MORTICE-AND-TENON FASTENINGS FOR HULL PLANKS

Mortice

Gomphoi (dowel)

Tenon

Hull plank

Viking ships

IN THE DARK AGES and early medieval times, the longships of Scandinavia were one of the most feared sights for people of northern Europe. The Vikings launched raids from Scandinavia every summer in longships equipped with a single steering oar on the right, or "steerboard", side (hence "starboard"). A longship had one row of oars on each side and a single sail. The hull had clinker (overlapping) planks. Prowheads adorned fighting ships during campaigns of war. The sailing longship was also used for local coastal travel. The karv below was probably built as transport for an important family, while the smaller faering (top right) was a rowing boat only. The fleet of William of Normandy that invaded England in 1066 owed much to the Viking boatbuilding tradition, and has been depicted in the Bayeux Tapestry (above). Seals used by port towns and royal courts through the ages provide an excellent record of contemporary ship design. The seal opposite shows how ships changed from the Viking period to the end of the Middle Ages. The introduction of the fighting platform – the castle – and the addition of extra masts and sails changed the character of the medieval ship. Note also that the steering oar has been replaced by a centred rudder.

BOATBUILDERS TOOLS

Shave

Broad axe

Breast auger

Sheer

Master shipwright

Stempost

Hood end

Keel

T-handle auger

Axe

Strake

Tree cut for planking

Roband

Leather diagonal reinforcement

Square sail of homespun yarn

Leech (leach)

Zoomorphic head

Eye

Tooth

Braiding

Serpentine neck

Lozenge-shaped recess

Rectangular cross-band

Sternpost

Boss (rudder pivot)

DRAGON PROWHEAD

Steering oar (side rudder)

Snake-tail ornament

VIKING KARV (COASTER)

Tiller

Tye halyard

Foot

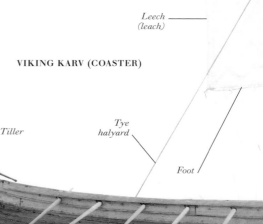

Oar

Starboard (steerboard) side

Keel

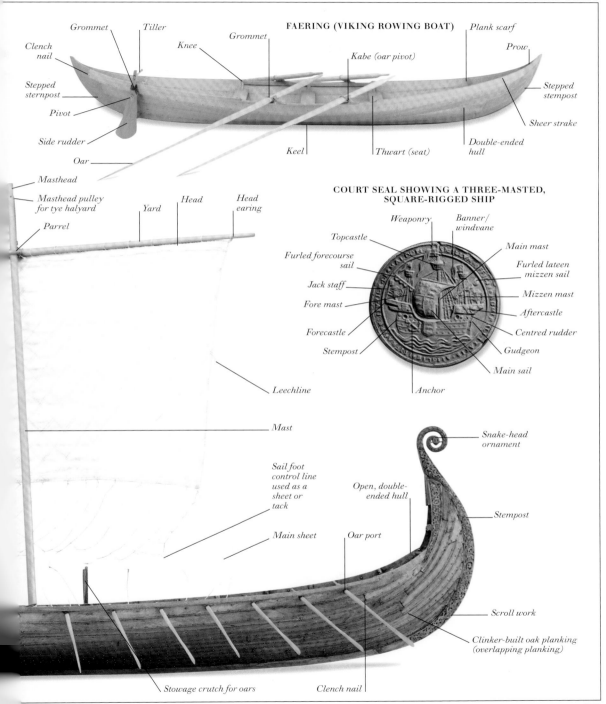

FAERING (VIKING ROWING BOAT)

Grommet

Tiller

Clench nail

Knee

Grommet

Kabe (oar pivot)

Plank scarf

Prow

Stepped sternpost

Pivot

Stepped stempost

Side rudder

Sheer strake

Oar

Keel

Thwart (seat)

Double-ended hull

Masthead

Masthead pulley for tye halyard

Yard

Head

Head earing

COURT SEAL SHOWING A THREE-MASTED, SQUARE-RIGGED SHIP

Parrel

Weaponry

Banner/ windvane

Topcastle

Main mast

Furled forecourse sail

Furled lateen mizzen sail

Jack staff

Mizzen mast

Fore mast

Aftercastle

Forecastle

Centred rudder

Stempost

Gudgeon

Leechline

Main sail

Anchor

Mast

Snake-head ornament

Sail foot control line used as a sheet or tack

Open, double-ended hull

Stempost

Main sheet

Oar port

Scroll work

Clinker-built oak planking (overlapping planking)

Stowage crutch for oars

Clench nail

Medieval warships and traders

FROM THE 16TH CENTURY, SHIPS WERE BUILT WITH A NEW FORM OF HULL, constructed from carvel (edge-to-edge) planking. Warships of the time, like King Henry VIII of England's Mary Rose, boasted awesome fire power. This ship carried both long-range cannon in bronze, and short-range, anti-personnel guns in iron. Elsewhere, ships took on a multiformity of shapes. Dhows transported slaves from East Africa to Arabia, their fore-and-aft rigged lateen sails allowing them to sail close to the wind around the lands of the Indian Ocean. The Chinese sailed to East Africa and Arabia in junks, trading goods that were carried in watertight compartments. New astronomical tools helped medieval sailors to find their way. Cross-staves and astrolabes were used to measure the altitude of the sun or stars. One of a choice of four cross-pieces was slid up or down the staff of the cross-stave – which was graduated in degrees of altitude – until its top aligned with the celestial body and its base with the horizon. The sighting rule of the astrolabe was simply lined up with a known body, and its altitude read from marks on the metal disc. With sundials, the sailor could use the shadow of the sun to show the time of day.

DHOW

Main yard
Furled lateen main sail
Mizzen yard
Parrel
Furled lateen mizzen sail
Main mast
Shroud
Parrel tackle
Mizzen mast
Tiller
Stem head
Rudder
Eye
Raking stempost

JUNK

Su-wei (fourth mast)
Topsail
Chung-ta-wei (main mast)
Wei-wei (mizzen mast)
Halyard
Erh-wei (second mast)
Sail batten
T'on-wei (port fore-mast)
Rudder head
Lug sail
Transom
Rudder
Quarterdeck house
Cargo hatch
Oar
Grapnel-type anchor

Fore topmast stay
Bowsprit
Sprit yard

SAILING WARSHIP

Fore top yard
Fore topmast
Fore topcastle
Lift
Fore yard
Fore mast
Ratline
Shroud
Fore stay
Woolding
Forecastle
Forecastle castle-deck gunport
Beakhead
Rigging rail
Chain wale (channel)
Hawse hole
Anchor cable
Stempost

Main topgallant mast

Main topgallant yard

Main top yard

Main topmast topcastle

Mizzen topmast

Main topmast stay

Mizzen top yard

Mizzen topcastle

Main topmast

Lift

Main topcastle

Lift

Main yard

Parrel

Tye

Jeer

Brace

Main stay

Mizzen mast

Mizzen yard

Main mast

Swifting tackle

Aftercastle castle-deck gunport

Upper deck gunport

Lid

Gangway

Gun carriage

Bonaventure top yard

Bonaventure topmast

Bonaventure topcastle

Bonaventure yard

Bonaventure mast

Aftercastle

Outrigger

Pivot

Chain wale (channel)

Deadeye

Transom

Rudder

Sternpost

Keel

Blindage (removable archery screen)

Wale

Main deck gunport

Carvel planking

Port bower anchor

CROSS-STAVE (CROSS-STAFF)

90 degree cross-piece (transversary)

Clamp

Boxwood staff

60 degree cross-piece

Altitude scale in degrees and minutes

30 degree cross-piece

Ocular end

10 degree cross-piece (dutch shoe)

SUNDIAL

Style of the gnomon (edge)

Needle

Gnomon

Pivot

Hour line

Dial

Swivel suspension ring

ASTROLABE

Graduated ring

Scale of degrees

Pivot

Alidade (sighting rule)

Bottom ballast

Scribed arc decoration

377

The expansion of sail

BY THE 18TH CENTURY, SAILING SHIPS had become fast and effective floating fortresses. The navies of the north European powers competed with each other by building heavily-armed fighting ships called "men-of-war". The distinctive round stern of the ship below, with its open gallery, balcony, and elaborate wood carving is typical of the period. Hulls around this time were semicircular in cross section, although many boat designers were soon to return to the V-shaped hulls used by the Vikings. Ships of the period carried more sail than ever before. A labyrinth of rigging supported the masts and yards from which the profusion of square sails were set. Ships grew higher, as extra masts were fitted above the lower mast, and the bowsprit became longer to allow the ship to carry staysails, spritsails, and jibsails. Ships went into battle in single file, so that broadsides from the multiple decks of guns would have maximum effect. Ships were classified by rates, the rating of a vessel depending on how many guns it had. A first rate ship had more than 100 guns. The guns fired solid round shot, usually made of iron.

WOODEN SAILING SHIP

Gilded truck

Main topgallant mast

Main topgallant shroud

Bolster

Trestle trees

Main topmast

Main topmast backstay

Main topmast shroud

Cap

Main top

Masthead

Mizzen topmast

Mizzen topmast stay

Mizzen top

Main top rail

Hounds

Lift

Mizzen topmast shroud

Futtock shroud

Mizzen yard

Mizzen backstay

Vang

Fiddle block

Mizzen shroud

Mizzen stay

Mizzen mast

Mizzen mast

Taffrail

Poop rail

Ma... shrou...

Ma... ma...

BOW

Brace

Lift

Foot rope

Studding sail boom

Main top rail

Studding sail yard (stuns'l yard)

Jacob's ladder

Rope preventer

Rudder chain

Rudder

Sternpost

Pintle strap

Gudgeon strap

Wash cant

Knee of the head

Hawse hole

Ship's wheel

Binnacle box

Keel

Channel

Chain

Step

Boat slide

SAIL PATTERN OF A 74-GUN SHIP

Main topgallant stay

Fore topgallant mast

Fore topgallant backstay

Gilded truck

Fore topgallant stay

Mouse and collar

Mizzen topgallant sail

Main topgallant sail

Fore mast topgallant sail

Mizzen topsail

Fore mast topsail

Fore topsail

Jibsail

Mizzen course

Main topmast stay

Fore topmast shroud

Main topmast preventer stay

Fore topmast backstay

Fore shroud

Main stay

Mainstay tackle

Fore hatch tackle

Ratline

Fore topmast

Fore top

Fore topmast stay

Fore topmast preventer stay

Main course

Fore mast course

Fore mast course

Sprit topsail

Spritsail course

Main topsail

Fore staysail

Jib boom

STERN

Truck

Jack staff

Fore mast

Cap

Bee

Rope woolding

Fore stay

Fish davit

Mainrail head

Outer spritsail yard

Spritsail yard

Foot rope

Main topgallant yard

Fore topgallant yard

Main topsail yard

Yardarm

Fore topsail yard

Main yard

Fore yard

Mizzen topmast yard

Anchor buoy

Bowsprit

Bobstay

Figurehead

Rail

Trailboard

Draught (draft) mark

Bower anchor

Tallow coating

Capstan

Clewline

Gunport

Gun

Gripe

Stern lantern

Captain's cabin (great cabin)

Upper gallery

Port

Balcony

Stern quarter gallery

379

A ship of the line

THE 74-GUN WOODEN SHIP WAS A MAINSTAY of British and French battlefleets in the late 18th and early 19th centuries. This "ship of the line" was heavy enough to fight with the most potent of rivals, yet nimble too. The length of such a ship was determined by the number of guns required for each deck, allowing enough room for crews to man them. The gun deck was about 52 m (170 ft) long. The decks had to be very strong to carry the weight of the guns. The deck planks have been removed on the vessel pictured below, to show just how close together the beams had to be to make the hull strong enough. Only timber with a perfect grain was used. The upper deck was open at the waist, but afore and abaft were officers' cabins. The forecastle and quarterdeck carried light guns and acted as platforms for working rigging and for reconnaissance. The ship's longboats (launches) were carried on booms between the gangways.

LONGBOAT

Truck · Flag halyard · Mast · Backstay · Jib halyard · Topping lift · Fore stay halyard · Peak halyard · Shroud · Main sheet · Fore sail halyard · Gaff · Boom · Parrel · Bowsprit · Traveller · Stempost · Waterline · Deadeye · Oar · Side bench

Thole pin · Windlass bar · Transom · Tiller · Planking · Rabbit line · Sheerplank · Frame · Keel · Rudder · Floor · Thwart (seat)

UPPER DECK OF A 74-GUN SHIP

Hoop · Stock · Steam grating · Cathead · Ring · Timber head · Galley stove chimney · Belfry · Waterway · Knighthead · Fore bitt · Deadeye · Gangway · Capstan · Heads (privy) · Figurehead · Head beam · Head rail · Roundhouse · Boomkin · Anchor cable · Arm · Sheave for cat tackle · Deck beam · Foremast hole · Breastwork · Forked beam · Pawl · Skid beam · Fluke · Hoop · Stock · Carling (carline) · Bulwark · Main companion way

Head · Forecastle (fo'c'sle) · Waist

BOW

Figurehead

Headboard

Main rail

Middle rail

Lower rail

Head rail

Supporter

Cat block

Ekeing

Cheek

Catted anchor

Riband

Hawse piece

Side step

Eye bolt

Main bitt

Main wale

Frame

Hawse hole

Stempost

Deadwood

STERN

Cove

Taffrail

Screen bulkhead

Balcony

Upper counter rail

Drop

Lower counter rail

Gunport lid

Filling transom

Wing transom

Timber under transom

Side counter timber

Counter timber

Tuck

Tuck rail

After fashion piece

Cant frame

Ledge

Companion ladder

Mizzen mast hole

Great cabin (captain's cabin)

Pilaster

Screen bulkhead

Hatch coaming / shot garland

Spirketting

Backstay stool

Master's sea cabin

Channel

Coaming

Ledge (batten)

Standard knee

Poop rail

Necking

Stern carving

Wardroom

Upper finishing

Taffrail

Gunport drip (eyebrow; rigol)

Rail at break of poop deck

Mizzen bitt

Clerk's cabin

Quarter gallery

Main mast hole

Mast partner

Grating

Gunport lid

Lodging knee

Quarterdeck

Poop deck

Rigging

MOST SAILING SHIPS HAVE TWO TYPES OF RIGGING. Standing rigging – kept taut by rigging screws or old-fashioned lanyards and deadeyes – refers to the ropes, wires, and chains that support the masts and yards (horizontal spars). Running rigging, which includes types of block and tackle, halyards, and sheets, is used to hoist, lower, or trim sails.

BOWSPRIT AND JIB BOOM

Outer jib stay

Inner jib stay

Inner jib tack

Bowsprit cap

Fore topmast staysail tack

Fore stay

Jib boom

Whisker boom

Butterfly plate

Upper deadeye

Lower deadeye

Chain plate

Bowsprit

Foot rope

Boom guy block

Martingale backrope

Martingale (dolphin striker)

Spear

Lizard

Chain bobstay

Handle

Eye plate lug

Parallel shaft

OTHER RIGGING FITTINGS

BELAYING PIN

MAST BAND

STANDING BLOCK

Arse (tail)

Running part

SHACKLE

Lug

Shoulder

Eye

Crown

Crown

Clear   Jaw

Swivel becket

Lug

Soft eye

Served eye splice

Standing part

Screw thread

Shank

Shoulder

Eye

Hauling part (fall)

Shell

SHACKLE PIN

Sailmaker's whipping

**BLOCK AND TACKLE
(PURCHASE; HANDY BILLY)**

RIGGING TOOLS

**RIGGER'S GAUGE FOR MEASURING THE
DIAMETER OF ROPE OR WIRE**

Cheese (cheesing)

Fore royal stay

Flying jib tack

Outer jib tack

Outer martingale stay

Middle martingale stay

nner
artingale
ay

ye

CORED BULLSEYE
AIRLEAD

Eye

Strap

SHEET LEAD

Base

RUNNING BLOCK

Shoulder   Back   Shank

HOOK

Crown

Clear

Jaw   Bill

Fixed
lug

Cheek

Penny washer
oin cover
late)

Double rope
becket

**DUTCH TRIPLE
FIDDLE BLOCK**

Flat seizing

Swallow

Strop

SPLICING FID

ROPE SERVING MALLET

**HEAVER FOR
WIRE SERVING**

PRICKERS   **HOLLOW SPIKE
FOR WIRE**   **MARLINSPIKE**

**LANYARD AND
DEADEYES**

Leather pointing

Turk's head

Hitched
hauling end

**UPPER
DEADEYE**

Swallow

Sheave
(shiver; shiv)

Standing part

LANYARD

**LOWER
DEADEYE**

Grooving

Binding

Bolt

Swallow

Face

Nut

**RIGGING SCREW
(TURNBUCKLE)**

Shroud

Spun yarn
serving

Flat wire seizing

Solid heart
thimble

Cotter pin

Fork end

Tail

Right hand
screw

Open body

Left hand
screw

Safe working
load mark

Seizing

Shoulder

Eye

Crown

383

Sails

THERE ARE TWO MAIN TYPES OF SAIL, often used in combination. Square sails are driving sa[...]
They are usually attached by parrels to yards, square to the mast to catch the following wind. On
fore-and-aft sails, such as lateen and lug sails, the luff (leading edge) usually abuts a mast or a
stay. The head of the sail may abut a gaff, and the foot a boom. Around the world, a great range of rig[...]
(sail patterns), such as the ketch, lugger, and schooner, have evolved to suit local needs. Sails are made from
strips of cloth, cut to give the sail a belly and strong enough to resist the most violent of winds. Cotton and fl[...]
are the traditional sail materials, but synthetic fabrics are now commonly used.

SECTION OF A S[...]

Seizing   **LUFF (LEADING EDGE)**   *Luff slide*   *Bolt rope*   *Head*

Round thimbl[...]

Rope strand

Grommet

Head cringle

**LEECH
(LEACH)**

*Shar[...]
point*

*Groove for
spunyarn rope*

SERVING MALLET

Flat seam

Flatboard

Handle

*Synthetic flax
(duradon)*

NEEDLES AND SEAMING TWINE

Tabling

*Seaming
twine*

Luff cloth

Needle packet

Rat's tail

Needle

SAILMAKER'S FID

Gr[...]

SAILCLOTHS

**KEVLAR
ON FLEX
FILM**

**HEAVYWEIGHT
NYLON CLOTH**

SAIL HOOK

SAILMAKER'S PALM

Crown

Strap

Thumbhole

*Cowhide
face*

MYLAR

Bill   *Shank*

**NYLON
AND
SILICON
CLOTH**

*Metal
needle pad*

BEESWAX

Handle

SAILMAKER'S MALLET

Cheek

**SYNTHETIC
FLAX
(DURADON)**

**WOVEN
DACRON**

Hide grip

Whipping

Seizing

*Groove made
by thread*

SAILMAKING TOOLS

*Copper
face*

Mizzen gaff topsail

Main sail

Main gaff topsail

Fore staysail

Jibsail

Mizzen sail

KETCH

Mizzen yard topsail

Dipping lug foresail

Standing lug mizzen

LUGGER

SAILING RIGS

Main gaff topsail

Fore topmast staysail

Fore sail

Main sail

Fore staysail

Jibsail

FISHERMAN'S SCHOONER (FORE-AND-AFT SCHOONER)

SAILS AND RUNNING RIGGING OF A DOUBLE TOPSAIL SCHOONER

Upper topsail lift

Lower topsail brace

Main topsail halyard

Flying jib halyard

Fore upper topsail

Triatic stay

Foot rope

Upper topsail brace

Outer jib halyard

Fore peak halyard

Lower topsail clewline

Fore yard lift

Fore lower topsail

Inner jib halyard

Fore throat halyard

Fore staysail halyard

Fore sail

Mast hoop

Inner jib downhaul

Outer jib downhaul

Outer jib sheet

Flying jib sheet

Inner jib sheet

Flying jib downhaul

Yard

Head

Gaff

Luff

Boom

Foot

Flying jib

Outer jib

Reef point

Fore staysail

Inner jib

Fore staysail sheet

Mooring and anchoring

FOR LARGE VESSELS IN OPEN WATER, ANCHORAGE IS ESSENTIAL. By holding a ship securely to the seabed, an anchor prevents the vessel from being at the mercy of wave, tide, and current. The earliest anchors were nothing more than stones. In later years, many anchors had a standard design, much like the Admiralty pattern anchor shown on this page. The Danforth anchor is somewhat different. It has particularly deep flukes to give it great holding power. On large sailing ships, anchors were worked by teams of sailors. They turned the drum of a capstan by pushing on bars slotted into the revolving cylinder. This, in turn, lifted or lowered the anchor chain. In calm harbours and estuaries, ships can moor (make fast) without using anchors. Berthing ropes can be attached to bollards both inboard and on the quayside. Berthing ropes are joined to each other by bends, like those opposite.

STONE ANCHOR (KILLICK)

Rope hole

TYPES OF ANCHOR

CLOSE-STOWING ANCHOR

CQR ANCHOR (SECURE ANCHOR; PLOUGH ANCHOR)

ADMIRALTY ANCHOR TYPE ACII

ADMIRALTY PATTERN ANCHOR

STOCKLESS ANCHOR

MUSHROOM ANCHOR (PERMANENT MOORING ANCHOR)

End link **ANCHOR CHAIN** *Common link* *Patent link*

DANFORTH ANCHOR

Shank

Pea (bill)

Fluke

Throat

Blade

Stock

Tripping palm *Crown*

SHACKLE, SWIVELS, AND LINK

Crown

Bolt *Lug*

GALVANIZED "D" SHACKLE

Screw thread

MOORING SWIVEL

CHAIN SWIVEL

MAILLOT (SCREW LINK)

TWIN BOLLARDS WITH RAKED PILLARS AND A HAWSER (HEAVY ROPE)

Flat

Rim

Base

ERTHING ROPES (HAWSERS)

Ship

Twin bollards

Stern
rope

Upper head
(drumhead)

Bar hole
(pigeon
hole)

Cap

Head rope

Quayside

After breast
rope

After spring
rope

Fore spring
rope

Fore breast
rope

Bollard

Strengthening
chock

MOORING ROPE BENDS

HAWSER BEND
TWO DOUBLE ROUND TURNS
AND DOUBLE HALF HITCHES)

Standing
part

Barrel

Seizing

ARRICK BEND

Seizing

Trenail
(treenail)

Strengthening
chock

Pawl slot

Lignum vitae
bearing

INGLE SHEET BEND
SWAB HITCH)

Standing
part

Bare end
(fag end)

Thin rope

Whelp

Thick rope

Three-strand hawser
belayed with
figure of eight
turns

Outboard end

Pillar

Foundry plug

Horn

WOOD
CAPSTAN
WITH A
VERTICAL
SPINDLE

Tapered
spindle

Bolt hole

Cross piece

Bitter end
(inboard end)

Spigot

Pin

387

Ropes and knots

ALL KINDS OF ROPES ARE USED AT SEA, from thin twines and yarns to thick hawsers. Synthetic fibres have been developed specifically for use at sea. Nylon ropes stretch, and so are ideal for anchoring; polypropylene has little stretch, so is ideal for halyards and sheets. Different types of knots are used for different purposes. Knots that join two ropes are called bends; hitches join a rope to another object; and bowlines produce an eye (loop) in the end of a rope. Ropes can be joined by splicing (unravelling the ends and weaving them together) or seizing (lashing the ropes together side by side).

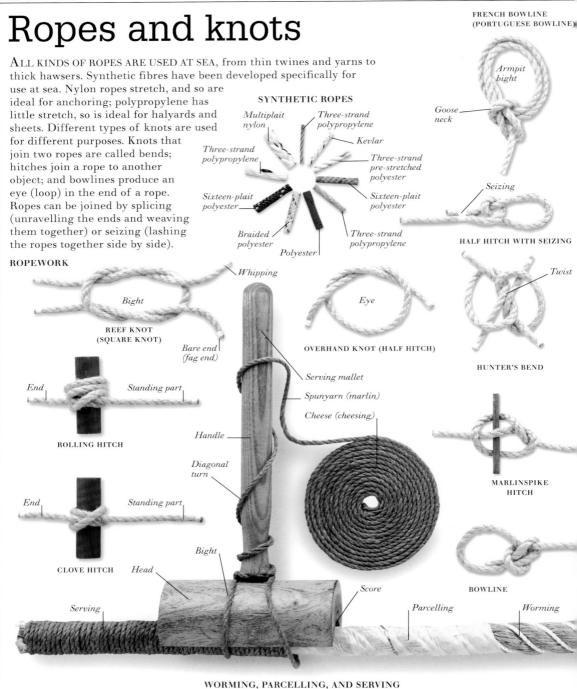

FRENCH BOWLINE (PORTUGUESE BOWLINE)

Armpit bight

Goose neck

Seizing

HALF HITCH WITH SEIZING

SYNTHETIC ROPES

Multiplait nylon

Three-strand polypropylene

Kevlar

Three-strand polypropylene

Three-strand pre-stretched polyester

Sixteen-plait polyester

Sixteen-plait polyester

Braided polyester

Polyester

Three-strand polypropylene

ROPEWORK

Bight

REEF KNOT (SQUARE KNOT)

Bare end (fag end)

Whipping

Eye

OVERHAND KNOT (HALF HITCH)

Twist

HUNTER'S BEND

End

Standing part

ROLLING HITCH

Serving mallet

Spunyarn (marlin)

Cheese (cheesing)

Handle

Diagonal turn

MARLINSPIKE HITCH

End

Standing part

CLOVE HITCH

Head

Bight

Score

BOWLINE

Serving

Parcelling

Worming

WORMING, PARCELLING, AND SERVING

THUMB KNOT

SPANISH BOWLINE

FLAT SEIZING
(ROUND SEIZING)

DOUBLE CARRICK BEND

LIGHTERMAN'S HITCH

End

*Frapped
turn*

*Heaving
line knot*

HEAVING LINE BEND

*Standing
part*

JURY MAST KNOT
(MAST HEAD BEND)

SHEET BEND (SWAB HITCH)

MANHARNESS KNOT
(BUTTERFLY KNOT;
ARTILLERY LOOP)

Cheese (cheesing)

Marlinspike

HEAVING LINE

PINNED SHEEPSHANK

Jaw

Rat tail

*Hawser laid three-strand manilla
rope with right-handed lay*

Paddle wheels and propellers

THE INVENTION OF THE STEAM ENGINE IN THE 18TH CENTURY made mechanically driven ships fitted with paddle wheels or propellers a viable alternative to sails. Paddle wheels have fixed or feathered floats, and the model shown below features both types. Feathered floats give more propulsive power than fixed floats because they are almost upright at all times in the water. Paddle wheels were superseded by the propeller on ocean-going vessels in the mid-19th century. Propellers are more efficient, work better in rough water, and are less vulnerable in collisions. The first propellers were two-bladed but later three- and four-bladed versions are more powerful; the shape and pitch of blades have also been refined over the years. At the beginning of the 18th century, tillers were superseded on many larger ships by the ship's wheel as a means of steering.

SHIP'S WHEEL

King spoke handle

Handle

Spoke

Rim plate

Felloe (rim section)

Maker's name

Nave plate

Nave

PADDLE WHEEL WITH FIXED FLOATS

Wrist pin

Limb

Fixed float

Hub

Deck beam

OSCILLATING STEAM ENGINE

Slip eccentric for slide valve

Ahead/astern controls

Slide valve

Main crank

THREE-BLADED PROPELLER

Blade

Tapered shaft hole

Hub

Keyway

Strut

Frame

Piston rod (tail rod)

Stuffing box

Oscillating cylinder

Bottom plate (bedplate)

Slide valve rod

Control platform

Pitch

Propeller blade tip trace

Blade

Propeller diameter

Hub

Propeller hub trace

PROPELLER ACTION

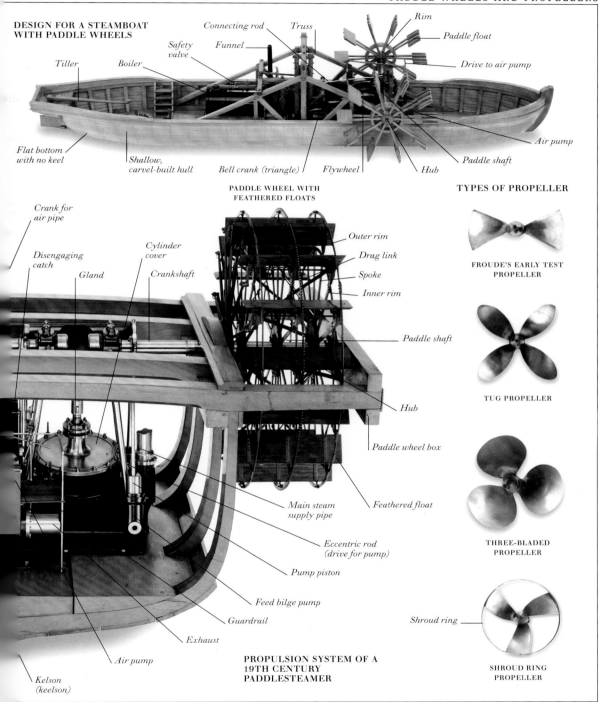

DESIGN FOR A STEAMBOAT WITH PADDLE WHEELS

Connecting rod

Truss

Rim

Paddle float

Safety valve

Funnel

Drive to air pump

Tiller

Boiler

Air pump

Flat bottom with no keel

Shallow, carvel-built hull

Bell crank (triangle)

Flywheel

Hub

Paddle shaft

PADDLE WHEEL WITH FEATHERED FLOATS

TYPES OF PROPELLER

Crank for air pipe

Disengaging catch

Cylinder cover

Gland

Crankshaft

Outer rim

Drag link

Spoke

Inner rim

Paddle shaft

Hub

Paddle wheel box

FROUDE'S EARLY TEST PROPELLER

TUG PROPELLER

Main steam supply pipe

Feathered float

Eccentric rod (drive for pump)

Pump piston

Feed bilge pump

Guardrail

THREE-BLADED PROPELLER

Exhaust

Air pump

Kelson (keelson)

PROPULSION SYSTEM OF A 19TH CENTURY PADDLESTEAMER

Shroud ring

SHROUD RING PROPELLER

Anatomy of an iron ship

IRON PARTS WERE USED IN THE HULLS OF WOODEN SHIPS AS EARLY AS 1675, often in the same form as the wooden parts that they replaced. Eventually, as on the tea clipper Cutty Sark (below), iron rigging was found to be stronger than the traditional rope. The first "ironclads" were warships whose wooden hulls were protected by iron armour plates. Later ironclads actually had iron hulls. The model opposite is based on the British warship HMS Warrior, launched in 1860, the first battleship built entirely of iron. The plan of the iron paddlesteamer (bottom), built somewhat later, shows that this vessel was a sailing ship; but it also boasted a steam propulsion plant amidships that turned two side paddlewheels. Early iron hulls were made from plates that were painstakingly rivetted together (as below), but by the 20th century vessels began to be welded together, whole sections at a time. The Second World War "liberty ship" was one of the first of these "production-line vessels".

TEA CLIPPER

Steel yard
Iron wire stay
Steel lower mast
Steel bowsprit
Wooden planking with copper sheathing
Forged iron anchor

RIVETTED PLATES

Pan head rivet
Plate
Button head rivet (snap head)
Seam

LIBERTY SHIP

Gun section
Accommodation section
Cargo derrick
Weld line
Stern section
Midships section
Cargo hold
Bow section

PLAN OF AN IRON PADDLESTEAMER

Mizzen mast
Poop deck
Lounge
Deck lantern
Main mast
Steam whistle
Crankshaft
Guardrail
Paddle wheel
Steering position
Guardrail
Binnacle
State room
After funnel
Eccentric
Connecting rod
Steering gear
Skylight
Stern
Vertical frame ladder
Mast step
Rudder
Rudder post
Heel of rudder post
Bar keel
Afterpeak
Cabin
Tank
Main mast step
Donkey boiler
Box boiler
Foundation
Reversing wheel
Bottom plate
Side lever
Cylinder
Stern framing

CUTAWAY SECTION
OF AN IRONCLAD

Bulwark cap

Waterway

Scupper

Deck planking

Upper deck stringer (tie) plate

Upper deck beam

Bulwark

Upper sheer strake

Teak backing

Topside strake

Wrought iron armour plate

Main sheer strake

Main deck tie plate

Lower deck tie plate

Upper deck pillar (stanchion)

Main deck beam

Main deck pillar (stanchion)

Lower deck beam

Lighting hole

Angle bar (I bar)

Box sister keelson

Frame

Hold pillar (stanchion)

Centre line keelson

Bilge stringer

Bilge strake

Bilge keelson

Side keelson

Bottom plating

Garboard strake

Keel

Limber hole

Floor

Forward funnel

Ventilator cowl

Capstan

Bowsprit

Fore mast

Skylight

Chimney

Hatch

Main deck

Hawse pipe

Stem

Beam

Chain locker

Bulkhead stiffener

Deep floor

Forefoot

Deck beam

Smoke box

'Tween decks ladder

Lower deck

Forepeak

Combustion chamber

Cabin

Centre girder

393

The battleship

IN THE EARLY YEARS OF THE 20TH CENTURY, sea warfare –
attacking enemy vessels or defending a ship – was
revolutionized by the introduction of Dreadnought-type
battleships like the Brazilian vessel below. These new
ships combined the latest advances in steam
propulsion, gunnery, and armour plating. The gun
turret was designed to fire shells over huge distances.
It was protected by armour 30 cm (12 in) thick. The
measurements given for the guns of this ship refer
to the bore diameter. Where "weight" is quoted, this
is the weight of the shell that the gun fires. Torpedoes –
as portrayed on the upper cigarette card (right) – were
self-propelled underwater missiles, often steered by gyro-
control. Depth charges were designed in the First World
War for use against submerged U-boats. They are
canisters filled with explosives that are detonated
by depth-sensitive pistols. The lower cigarette
card shows depth charges being fired by
a "thrower", fired from a torpedo tube,
and rolled from the stern. Ship's shields
were fitted to warships from the late
19th century onwards. The shield
shown opposite depicts a
traditional ship's cannon.

20TH CENTURY WEAPONRY

Torpedo tube

Sight

Warhead

TORPEDOES

DEPTH
CHARGES

Side-thrown
canister

Stern-rolled
canister

Torpedo-fired
canister

BRAZILIAN BATTLESHIP

Boat handling
derrick

Gunnery
spotting top

Rangefinder

Forward
funnel

Purchase wire

Light screen

Lifeboat

Searchlight

Compass

Searchlight
platform

Compass and rangefinder
platform

Leading block

Ship's wheel

Tripod mast

Navigating bridge

Boat
winch

Conning tower

Captain's shelter/
chart house

Arms of
Brazil

Weather shutter
for gun

"F" turret

Jack staff

30 cm (12 in)
gun

Skylight

Porthole

Stem
(false ram bow)

Belt
armour

Forward
accommodation
ladder

Sighting
hood

"A" turret

Turret barbette

Open gun mounting

12 cm (4.7 in) gun

Steam launch

Guest boat boom

HIP'S SHIELD

Rope moulding

Muzzle moulding

Swell of muzzle

Chase

Reinforce

gee

Astragal

Trunnion

Lion crest

adio antenna

Upper wireless and telegraphy yard (Upper W/T yard)

Topgallant mast

Wireless and telegraphy yard (W/T yard)

Lower yard

Signal gear

Ladder way

Brake slip

Davit

Clump cathead

Guardrail

Hawser fairlead

Sheet anchor

Starboard bower anchor

Lifeboat davit

Breakwater

Cable holder

Anchor chain

Bollard

Hawse pipe

Boat boom

Towing fairlead

Port bower anchor

Exhaust pipe

Searchlight

Vedette boat

Gig

After funnel

Funnel stay

Searchlight platform

After compass platform

After bridge

1.3 kg (3 pound) gun ("three pounder")

"X" turret

"Y" turret

Officer's accommodation ladder

Whaler

Davit for whaler

Flagmast

Stern walk

Scarph

Aft anchor

"P" turret

Ash chute

Hen coop

Bilge keel

Gun battery

Torpedo net boom

Turret roof rail

Propeller shaft boss

Torpedo net

Propeller shaft

Propeller

Rudder

Life buoy

395

Frigates and submarines

FROM THE MID-19TH CENTURY, ARMOURED SHIPS provided a new challenge to enemy craft. In response, huge revolving gun turrets were developed. These could fire in any direction, could be loaded from the breech very rapidly, and, instead of cannonballs, they discharged exploding shells. Modern fighting ships, like the frigate, combine heavy ship-borne armament with light helicopter weaponry. Submarines function below the surface of the sea. Their speed and ability to fire missiles from under water are their major assets. The nuclear submarine can stay under water for several years without refuelling.

Stabilizer fin

Aft hydroplane

Propeller

Rangefinder

Look out periscope

Local control cabinet

Breech wheel Loading arm

Breech block

Slide locking lever

Slide

Sighting hood

Recoil cylinder

Lower rudde

Elevating wheel

Guide for gun loading cage

Rammer lever

Gun loading cage

Training rack gearing

Blast bag (breeches)

Floor of gun house

Turret roller

Roller path

Working chamber

Training gear

Rammer

Waiting position

Roller path support

Floor

"Walking pipe" (water supply)

GUN TURRET

In this turret for two 37 cm (15 in) guns, shells are carried in a hoisting cage. The shell is rammed into the gun, followed by the propellant (charge). Once the breech is closed, the gun is ready for firing. The whole operation requires around 70 sailors.

Barbette (armour)

Main hoisting cage

Cordite handling room

Cordite supply shuttle

Cordite case

Turret trunk

Ensign staff

SONAR torpedo decoy

FRIGATE

Lynx helicopter

Rudder

Variable pitch propeller

Practice projectile

High-explosive projectile

Shell bogie

Shell room

Shell-handling gear

Hydraulic grab

Ladder wa

Steam pipework

Machinery raft

Main turbine

Machinery control room

Switchboard room

Snort mast

Conning tower

Periscope

Electronic warfare mast

NUCLEAR "HUNTER-KILLER" SUBMARINE

Control room

Sonar room

Galley

Officers' mess

Main engine steam condenser

Distiller

Diesel motor compartment

Reactor space

Wireless office

Junior ratings' mess

Carbon dioxide scrubber compartment

Torpedo compartment

SONAR transducer array

Torpedo tube

Forward hydroplane

Junior ratings' bunk space

Senior ratings' mess

Muzzle

Barrel

15 cm (6 in) SHELL
This shell is designed to burst in the air above its target.

Bursting charge (explosive)

Flash tube

Body

Wooden packing

Driving band

SHELL CASE

Expelling plate

CROSS-SECTION OF THE SHELL

Transit plug

Bullet

Surveillance RADAR

Navigation/helicopter control RADAR antenna

Mast

RADAR for gunnery and missile control

Signalling lamp

Jack staff

Seacat missile launcher

Motor whaler

Vent

Aerial rig

Oerlikon gun position

Stern gallery

Funnel

Enclosed bridge

Aerial

Exocet missile launcher

Gun turret

11 cm (4.5 in) gun

F174

RADAR for gunnery and missile control

Stabilizer

Liferaft cylinder

Signal flag compartment

Reel

Fairlead

Anchor

SONAR bulge

Breakwater

Draught (draft) mark

Anti-submarine torpedo tube

Triple "chaff" rocket launcher

Bilge keel

Pennant number

Porthole

Bollard

Pioneers of flight

FLIGHT HAS FASCINATED MANKIND for centuries, and countless unsuccessful flying machines have been designed. The first successful flight was made by the French Montgolfier brothers in 1783, when they flew a balloon over Paris. The next major advance was the development of gliders, notably by the Englishman Sir George Cayley, who in 1845 designed the first glider to make a sustained flight, and by the German Otto Lilienthal, who became known as the world's first pilot because he managed to achieve controlled flights. However, powered flight did not become a practical possibility until the invention of lightweight, petrol-driven internal combustion engines at the end of the 19th century. Then, in 1903, the American brothers Orville and Wilbur Wright made the first powered flight in their Wright Flyer biplane, which used a four-cylinder, petrol-driven engine. Aircraft design advanced rapidly, and in 1909 the Frenchman Louis Blériot made his pioneering flight across the English Channel (see pp. 400-401). The American Glenn Curtiss also achieved several "firsts" in his Model-D Pusher and its variants, most notably winning the world's first competition for airspeed at Reims in 1909.

FRONT VIEW OF WRIGHT FLYER, 1903

Biplane elevator

Pusher propeller (rear-mounted propeller)

Chain drive to starboard propeller

Fuel tank

Propeller-shaft bracing strut

Offset pilot's cradle

Take-off and landing skid

Side-mounted engine to balance pilot's weight

SIDE VIEW OF CURTISS MODEL-D PUSHER, 1911

Nine-cylinder Salmson radial engine

Pusher propeller (rear-mounted propeller)

Aileron operating arm

Wing strut

Fuel filler cap

Oil filler cap

Body cradle that pivots to control ailerons

Fuel and oil tank

Rudder control wheel

Elevator wire for diving

Lap strap

Control column

Throttle

Nose-wheel brake

Footrest

Aileron

Turnbuckle

Fuel pipe

Pneumatic tyre

Seat support strut

Elevator wire for climbing

Thin, cambered lower wing

Rubber-tyred nose-wheel

Pilot's seat

Wing-protecting skid

Engine and propeller thrust frame

Starboard main landing gear

SIDE VIEW OF WRIGHT FLYER, 1903

Plain cotton fabric

Water-filled radiator

Wing warping wire

Pusher propeller (rear-mounted propeller)

Front diagonal strut

Chain drive

Elevator drive wheel

Rigid leading edge

Steel hub

Steel propeller shaft

Interplane strut

Water pipe

Rudder

Front-mounted biplane elevator

Bracing wire

Braced rudder strut

Landing skid

Elevator control cable

Pilot's cradle

Magneto

Rudder control cable

Rudder control cable

Warping connection strut

Four-cylinder 12-HP engine

Propeller-shaft bracing strut

Softwood strut

Tailplane

Elevator control wire

Rudder

Laminated wooden boom

Rudder bracing wire

Curtiss

Elevator operating arm

Elevator

FRONT VIEW OF CURTISS MODEL-D PUSHER, 1911

Rudder control wheel

Fuel and oil tank

Nine-cylinder Salmson radial engine

Elevator operating arm

Anti-lift wire

Aileron operating arm

Starboard aileron

Port aileron

Carved interplane strut

Wing-protecting skid

Wing-protecting skid

Lift wire

Control column

Seat beam

Tubular steel leg

Interplane strut pin-jointed to front spar

Footrest

Axle

Main landing gear lateral brace

Early monoplanes

RUMPLER MONOPLANE, 1908

MONOPLANES HAVE ONE WING on each side of the fuselage. The principal disadvantage of this arrangement in early, wooden-framed aircraft was that single wings were weak and required strong wires to brace them to king-posts above and below the fuselage. However, single wings also had advantages: they experienced less drag than multiple wings, allowing greater speed; they also made aircraft more manoeuvrable because single wings were easier to warp (twist) than double wings, and warping the wings was how pilots controlled the roll of early aircraft. By 1912, the French pilot Louis Blériot had used a monoplane to make the first flight across the English Channel, and the Briton Robert Blackburn and the Frenchman Armand Deperdussin had proved the greater speed of monoplanes. However, a spate of crashes caused by broken wings discouraged monoplane production, except in Germany, where all-metal monoplanes were developed in 1917. The wings of all-metal monoplanes did not need strengthening by struts or bracing wires, but despite this, such planes were not widely adopted until the 1930s.

FRONT VIEW OF BLACKBURN MONOPLANE, 1912

Taut fabric

Carved wooden propeller

King-post

Hub bolted to propeller

Nose-ring

Pilot's viewing aperture

Exhaust valve push-rod

Gnome seven-cylinder rotary engine

Elevator hinge

Elevator

Landing gear rear cross-member

Wheel fairing

Rubber-sprung wheel

Landing gear front strut

Tailskid

Axle

Landing skid

Landing gear rear strut

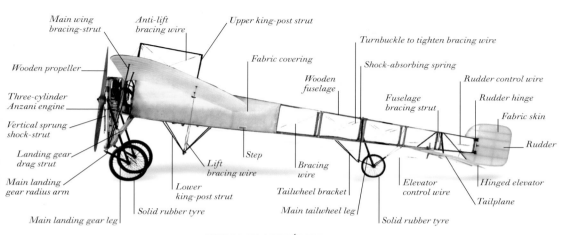

Main wing
bracing-strut

Anti-lift
bracing wire

Upper king-post strut

Fabric covering

Turnbuckle to tighten bracing wire

Shock-absorbing spring

Wooden
fuselage

Rudder control wire

Rudder hinge

Fabric skin

Wooden propeller

Three-cylinder
Anzani engine

Fuselage
bracing strut

Rudder

Vertical sprung
shock-strut

Landing gear
drag strut

Main landing
gear radius arm

Step

Lift
bracing wire

Lower
king-post strut

Bracing
wire

Tailwheel bracket

Main tailwheel leg

Elevator
control wire

Solid rubber tyre

Hinged elevator

Tailplane

Main landing gear leg

Solid rubber tyre

SIDE VIEW OF BLÉRIOT XI, 1909

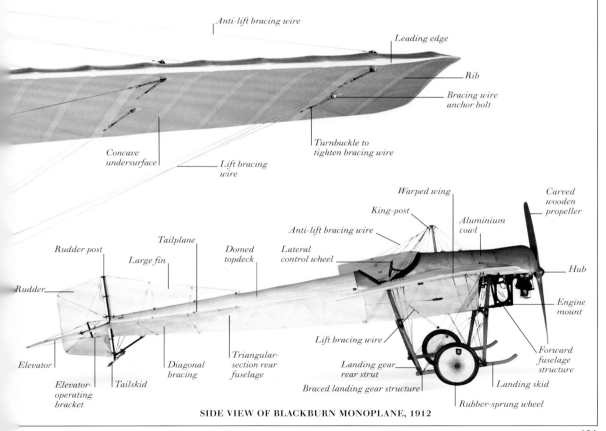

Anti-lift bracing wire

Leading edge

Rib

Bracing wire
anchor bolt

Concave
undersurface

Lift bracing
wire

Turnbuckle to
tighten bracing wire

Warped wing

Carved
wooden
propeller

King-post

Aluminium
cowl

Tailplane

Anti-lift bracing wire

Lateral
control wheel

Rudder post

Large fin

Domed
topdeck

Hub

Rudder

Engine
mount

Elevator

Lift bracing wire

Forward
fuselage
structure

Elevator-
operating
bracket

Tailskid

Diagonal
bracing

Triangular-
section rear
fuselage

Landing gear
rear strut

Braced landing gear structure

Landing skid

Rubber-sprung wheel

SIDE VIEW OF BLACKBURN MONOPLANE, 1912

Biplanes and triplanes

BIPLANES DOMINATED AIRCRAFT DESIGN until the 1930s, largely because some early monoplanes (see pp. 400-401) were too fragile to withstand the stresses of flight. The struts between biplanes' wings made the wings strong compared with those of early monoplanes, although the greater surface area of biplanes' wings increased drag and reduced speed. Many aircraft designers also developed triplanes, which had a particular advantage over biplanes: more wings meant a shorter wingspan to achieve the same lifting power, and a shorter wingspan gave greater manoeuvrability. Triplanes were most successful as fighters during World War I, the German Fokker triplane being a notable example. However, the greater manoeuvrability of triplanes was no advantage for normal flying and so most manufacturers continued to make biplanes. Many other aircraft designs were attempted. Some were quadruplanes, with four pairs of wings. Some had tandem wings (two pairs of monoplane wings, one behind the other). One of the most bizarre designs was by the Englishman Horatio Phillips: it had 20 sets of narrow wings and looked rather like a Venetian blind.

LAMINATED PROPELLER

SIDE VIEW OF AVRO TRIPLANE IV, 1910

Rudder hinge

RAF Central Flying School badge

Rudder

Fin

Navigation light

K 3215

Elevator

Rudder cable

Tailplane

Tailwheel

Bracing strut

Valve rocker

Air cooling baffle

Magneto

Wing strut

Fuel tank

Throttle

Harness

Pilot's seat

Crankcase breather pipe

Directly driven propeller

Main front strut to engine mount

Skid upper bracing strut

Limit of fuselage skin

Ash skid

Rubber cord suspension

Turnbuckle

Axle

Skid rear strut

Lateral bracing strut

Rubber tyre

Wheel rim

Wire wheel

**AVRO TUTOR
BIPLANE, 1931**

Pin joint

Aileron hinge strut

Aileron
control wire

Instructor's cockpit

Padded coaming

Pupil's cockpit

Wooden-domed
deck

RAF
roundel

Navigation light

Slat-arm fairing

Lift bracing
wire

Engine cowling

Nose-ring

Propeller hub

Laminated-wood,
fixed-pitch propeller

Metal leading edge

Exhaust
pipe

Exhaust
collector ring

Main landing gear leg

Inflation
valve

Radius
rod

Manufacturer's
logo

Recessed nose
of aileron

Aircraft
registration
code

Inspection
cover

Fabric-covered
steel-tube fuselage

Fabric-covered
aluminium and
steel wing

FRONT VIEW OF AVRO TRIPLANE IV, 1910

Unpainted, varnished fabric

Top wing

Wing strut

Middle wing

Bottom wing

Leading
edge

Fuel filler
and vent

Fixed-pitch wooden
propeller

Anti-lift
bracing wire

Rib

Landing skid

Axle

Elevator

Tailplane

Triangular-section fuselage

Lift
bracing
wire

Triangular-
section fuselage

Fuselage
bracing wire

Rudder
control cable

Lateral bracing strut

Tailplane

Rudder

Metal plate
anchorage

Elevator control cable

Longeron

Rubber cord suspension

Tailskid

Tailskid pivot

Elevator

World War I aircraft

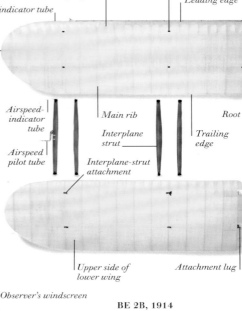

FLYING HELMET

WHEN WORLD WAR I STARTED in 1914, the main purpose of military aircraft was reconnaissance. The British-built BE 2, of which the BE 2B was a variant, was well-suited to this duty; it was very stable in flight, allowing the occupants to study the terrain, take photographs, and make notes. The BE 2 was also one of the first aircraft to drop bombs. One of the biggest problems for aircraft designers during the war was mounting machine-guns. On aircraft that had front-mounted propellers, the field of fire was restricted by the propeller and other parts of the aircraft. The problem was solved in 1915 by the Dutchman Anthony Fokker, who designed an interrupter gear that prevented a machine-gun from firing when a propeller blade passed in front of the barrel. The German LVG CVI had a forward-firing gun to the right of the engine, as well as a rear-cockpit gun, and a bombing capability. It was one of the most versatile aircraft of the war.

PORT WINGS FROM A BE 2B

- Interplane-strut attachment
- Intermediate leading-edge rib
- Airspeed-indicator tube
- Leading edge
- Wingtip
- Airspeed-indicator tube
- Main rib
- Root
- Airspeed pilot tube
- Interplane strut
- Trailing edge
- Interplane-strut attachment
- Upper side of lower wing
- Attachment lug

BE 2B, 1914

- Observer's windscreen
- Cabane strut fairing
- Engine air intake (ram scoop)
- Top-wing centre section
- Cabane strut
- Wooden propeller
- Lift bracing wire
- Pilot's windscreen
- Air-cooled V8 engine
- Plywood skin
- Control column
- Crankcase
- Padded coaming
- Buffed metal cowling
- Silencing heat exchanger
- Exhaust pipe
- Landing gear front strut
- Elevator rocking arm
- Ash skid
- Step
- Step
- Lateral control wire
- Reconnaissance camera bracket
- Pneumatic rubber tyre
- Bomb rack
- Lower-wing attachment
- 112 lb (51 kg) bomb
- Wheel cover
- V-strut

SIDE VIEW OF LVG CVI, 1917

Pilot's cockpit

Observer's cockpit

Cold-water pipe

Exhaust pipe

Starboard aileron

230-HP Benz six-cylinder water-cooled engine

7.92-mm Parabellum machine-gun

Rudder

Fin

Rudder control wire

Laminated wooden propeller

Elevator

Air ventilator inlet

Steel drive bracket

Pitot head

Pivoted, sprung tailskid

Pneumatic rubber tyre

Aircraft registration code

Interplane strut

Axle

Elevator control wire

Aircraft type

Aileron control cable

Bracing wire

Tyre inflation aperture

FRONT VIEW OF LVG CVI, 1917

Lozenge-patterned fabric

Forward-firing machine-gun

230-HP Benz six-cylinder water-cooled engine

Exhaust stack

Wooden propeller

Pitot head

Interplane strut

Anti-lift bracing wire

Lift bracing wire

Main fuel tank

Turnbuckle

Gravity-feed fuel tank

Pneumatic rubber tyre

Axle

Tailskid

Landing gear strut

Multiple rubber-cord suspension

Fixed tailplane

Rib

Rudder

Fabric covering

Elevator

Fabric lacing

Elevator hinge

Tailplane attachment

Rudder post

Steel lug

687

Aircraft registration code

Spar

Shock-absorbing spring

Steel V-strut

Trailing edge

Pivoted tailskid

National marking

Leading edge

Rib

HORIZONTAL TAIL OF A BE 2B

Early passenger aircraft

UNTIL THE 1930s, most passenger aircraft were biplanes, with two pairs of wings and a wooden or metal framework covered with fabric or, sometimes, plywood. Such aircraft were restricted to low speeds and low altitudes because of the drag on their wings. Many had an open cockpit, situated behind or in front of an enclosed – but unpressurized – cabin that carried a maximum of ten people. The passengers usually sat in wicker chairs that were not bolted to the floor, and the journey could be bumpy when flying through turbulence. Warm clothing, and ear plugs to reduce the effects of prolonged noise, were often required. During the 1930s, powerful, streamlined, all-metal monoplanes, such as the Lockheed Electra shown here, became widespread. By 1939, the advent of pressurized cabins allowed fast flights at high altitudes, where there is less turbulence. Flying boats were still necessary on many routes until 1945 because of inadequate runways and the frequency of emergency sea-landings. World War II, however, resulted in enough good runways being built for land-planes to become standard on all major airline routes.

Green starboard navigation light

Flush-riveted metal-skinned wing

Leading edge

Fuel-jettison valve

Static discharge wick

Split flap in landing position

PASSENGER CABIN TRIM

Roof trim panel

Passenger service-panel aperture

Forward bulkhead upper panel

Ash-tray

Starboard wall forward panel

Cockpit door panel

Forward bulkhead lower panel

Starboard wall mid-forward panel

SIDE VIEW OF LOCKHEED ELECTRA, 1934

Cockpit windscreen

Sliding window

Emergency escape hatch

Steel firewall

Air intake

Oil tank

Passenger window

Ventilator exit

Nose

Propeller pitch-change cylinder

Blade counterweight

Spinner mounting disc

Variable-pitch propeller

Exhaust collector ring

Landing gear door

Electrically driven split flap

Pratt & Whitney nine-cylinder radial engine

Red port navigation light

Exhaust pipe

Passenger door

Main landing gear

Brake pipe

Static discharge wick

Aileron

Aluminium wheel

Mudguard

Metal-skinned wing

Cylinder-cooling gills

Variable-pitch propeller

Cockpit windscreen

High-visibility tip

Pratt & Whitney nine-cylinder radial engine

Valve push-rod tube

Streamlined spinner

Inner wing containing fuel tank

Fixed landing light

Red filter signal light

Exhaust pipe

Single-leg main landing gear

Pilot mast

Tank drain tap

Single-leg main landing gear

Landing gear door

Landing gear fork

Battery compartment

Electrical service compartment

Brake pipe

Axle

Brake pipe

Disc brake

Landing gear fork

Pneumatic rubber tyre

Axle

Inspection cover

Tailwheel

Pneumatic rubber tyre

Roof trim

PASSENGER SEAT

Starboard wall aft panel

Bulkhead starboard trim

Backrest

Document panel

Seat button

Lap strap

Armrest

Bulkhead port trim

Starboard wall mid-aft panel

Seat anchor bolthole

Wall anchor

Floor anchor

Interior cabin trim for aft bulkhead between cabin and luggage hold

Seat cushion

PORT ENGINE COWLINGS

Rotating beacon

Starboard rudder

Inspection door

Starboard trimtab

Fixed tailplane

Tailplane

Port fin

120° nose-ring segment

Aluminium flush-riveted skin

Propeller-hub spinner

Port trimtab

NC517IN

Ventilator exit

Tailplane tip

120° cowling panel

Joining latch

Swivelling rubber-tyred tailwheel

Aircraft registration code

407

World War II aircraft

WHEN WORLD WAR II began in 1939, air forces had already replaced most of their fabric-skinned biplanes with all-metal, stressed-skin monoplanes. Aircraft played a far greater role in military operations during World War II than ever before. The wide range of aircraft duties, and the introduction of radar tracking and guidance systems, put pressure on designers to improve aircraft performance. The main areas of improvement were speed, range, and engine power. Bombers became larger and more powerful – converting from two to four engines – in order to carry a heavier bomb load; the US B-17 Flying Fortress could carry up to 6.2 tonnes (6.1 tons) of bombs over a distance of about 3,200 km (2,000 miles). Some aircraft increased their range by using drop tanks (fuel tanks that were jettisoned when empty to reduce drag). Fighters needed speed and manoeuvrability: the Hawker Tempest shown here had a maximum speed of 700 kph (435 mph), and was one of the few Allied aircraft capable of catching the German jet-powered V1 "flying bomb". By 1944, Britain had introduced its first turbojet-powered aircraft, the Gloster Meteor fighter, and Germany had introduced the fastest fighter in the world, the turbojet-powered Me 262, which had a maximum speed of 868 kph (540 mph).

PROPELLER

High-visibility yellow tip

Light-alloy propeller spinner

Variable-pitch aluminium-alloy blade

COMPONENTS OF A HAWKER TEMPEST MARK V, c.1943

STARBOARD ENGINE COWLINGS

Radiator-access cowling

Lower side-cowling

Upper side-cowling

Cowling fastener

2,400-HP Napier Sabre 24-cylinder engine

Propeller governor

Radiator header tank

Propeller drive shaft

Distributor

Ejector exhaust

Magneto

Starter motor

Cartridge starter

Engine top cowling

Upper side-cowling

Lower side-cowling

Radiator-access cowling

Cowling fastener

PORT ENGINE COWLINGS

SECTIONED B-17G FLYING FORTRESS BOMBER, c.1943

Astronavigation dome

First pilot's seat

Oxygen bottle

Upper gun turret

1,000 lb (454 kg) bomb

Radio operator's seat

Ammunition belt

Ammunition box

Waist gun

Dorsal fin

Fin

VHF aerial

Rudder

"Cheyenne type" tail-gun turret

Hand-held gun

Plastic nose

Bomb aimer's viewing panel

Chin gun turret

HF radio aerial

Bomb door

Direction-finding-aerial fairing

Navigator's seat

Sperry ball gun turret

Ammunition feed

Entrance door

Oxygen bottle

Retracted tailwheel

Tail gunner's compartment

Ammunition feed

PORT WING UNDERSIDE

Flap

Cockpit starboard access panel

Starboard tailplane

Elevator hinge

Landing gear door

Starboard elevator

Wing front fillet panel

Wing rear fillet panel

Elevator control rod

Wing fillet panel

Leading edge

Canopy rail

Seat pan

Harness strap

FUSELAGE

Canopy rail

VHF radio whip aerial

Fin

Tail fairing

Trimtab operating rod

Dorsal fin

Tailplane root

Rudder

Flat, bulletproof windscreen

Armoured seat back

Cockpit front belly panel

Cockpit centre belly panel

Tail band

Tailplane front attachment bracket

Tailplane rear attachment bracket

RAF C1-type roundel

Port elevator trimtab

Gyroscopic gunsight

Plastic cockpit canopy

Trailing edge

Rear spar trunnion

Cockpit rear belly panel

Camouflage

Wing fillet panel

Port tailplane

Wing front fillet panel

Wing rear fillet panel

TAIL

Outboard ammunition-feed blister

Cockpit port access panel

Trailing edge

Wing upper surface

HAWKER TEMPEST MARK V FIGHTER, C.1943

Aileron

Hispano Mark V 20-mm cannon

Armour-plated seat back

Rudder

Exhaust pipe

Headrest

Squadron code

Dorsal fin

Gyroscopic gunsight

Propeller spinner

RAF C1-type roundel

RAF B-type roundel

Engine air intake

Radiator

NV7

SA

Yellow-painted leading edge

PORT WING

Radiator outlet

Pitot head

Instant-identification "invasion" stripes

Retracted tailwheel

Rudder trimtab

Wingtip

409

Modern piston aero-engines

MID WEST TWO-STROKE,
THREE-CYLNDER ENGINE

PISTON ENGINES today are used mainly to power the vast numbers of light aircraft and microlights, as well as crop-sprayers and crop-dusters, small helicopters, and fire-bombers (which dump water on large fires). Virtually all heavier aircraft are now powered by jet engines. Modern piston aero-engines work on the same basic principles as the engine used by the Wright brothers in the first powered flight in 1903. However, today's engines are more sophisticated than earlier engines. For example, modern aero-engines may use a two-stroke or a four-stroke combustion cycle; they may have from one to nine air- or water-cooled cylinders, which may be arranged horizontally, in-line, in V formation, or radially; and they may drive the aircraft's propeller either directly or through a reduction gearbox. One of the more unconventional types of modern aero-engine is the rotary engine shown here, which has a trilobate (three-sided) rotor spinning in a chamber shaped like a fat figure-of-eight.

MID WEST 75-HP TWO-STROKE, THREE-CYLINDER ENGINE

Spark plug

Coolant outlet

Cylinder head

Exhaust manifold

Piston

Cylinder barrel

Exhaust port

Cylinder liner

Upper crankcase

Coolant pump

Pump drive belt

Reduction gearbox

Driven gear

Propeller drive flange

Torsional vibration damper

Sprag clutch

Gearbox drive splines

Small end

Connecting rod (con-rod)

Generator roto

Big end

Counterweight

Crankshaft

Gearbox mounting plate

Lower crankcase

Ignition trigger housing

Stato

Engine mounting plate

ROTOR AND HOUSINGS OF A MID WEST SINGLE-ROTOR ENGINE

Propeller bolt hole

Propeller drive flange

Dowel

Stud

Roller

Eccentric-shaft bearing

Propeller shaft rear bearing

Coolant jacket

Dowel

Coolant jacket

Stud hole

Stud hole

Dowel hole

Rotor chamber

Inle tract

Exhaust tract

GEARBOX CASE

FRONT HOUSING (FRONT END-PLATE)

TROCHOID HOUSING

MID WEST 90-HP TWIN-ROTOR ENGINE

Propeller-bolt collar

Propeller drive flange

Reduction gearbox

Lubricating oil feed

Engine front mounting plate

Blanking plate over air inlet

Carburettor

Upper rubber anti-vibration engine mount

Rotor-cooling air duct

Pipe clamp joint

Rotor-cooling air pump

Upper rotor-cooling air duct

Generator housing

Electric cable

Front bearing mount

Oil pump drive shaft cover

Torsional vibration damper

Fuel pipe inlet connection

Blanking plate over exhaust port

Fuel drip tray

Exhaust pipe flange

Lower rubber anti-vibration engine mount

Starter motor

Flywheel

Engine rear mounting plate

OUTPUT SHAFT OF A MID WEST ROTARY ENGINE

Balance weight

Drive gear

Front bearing

Drive gear spline

Flywheel retaining thread

Eccentric shaft

Rotor bearing

Rear bearing

Flywheel

Starterring teeth

Oil seal spacer ring

Corner bolt

Rotor tip seal

Tip seal groove

Rotor gear teeth

Rotor bearing

Cooling fins

Rotor tip spring

Balancing drilling

Rotor side seal

Side seal spring

Side seal groove

ROTOR AND SEALS

Fixed gear (stationary gear)

Engine mounting

Outlet manifold

Pump drive shaft

Fixing stud

Bolt hole

Stud hole

Dowel hole

Coolant jacket

Inlet manifold

REAR HOUSING (REAR END-PLATE)

Water pump cover and oil pump housing

Thermostat

Oil pump

WATER PUMP HOUSING

Modern jetliners 1

BAE-146 JETLINER

MODERN JETLINERS HAVE ENABLED ordinary people to travel to places where once only the wealthy could afford to go. Compared with the first jetliners (which were introduced in the 1940s), modern ones are much quieter, burn fuel more efficiently, and produce less air pollution. These advances are largely due to the replacement of turbojet engines with turbofan engines (see pp. 418-419). The greater power of turbofan engines at low speeds enables modern jetliners to carry more fuel and passengers than turbojet aircraft; a modern Boeing 747-400 (popularly known as a "jumbo jet") can fly 400 people for 13,700 km (8,500 miles) without needing to refuel. Jetliners fly at high altitudes, typically cruising at 8,000-11,000 m (26,000-36,000 ft), where they can use fuel efficiently and usually avoid bad weather. The pilot always controls the aircraft during take-off and landing, but at other times the aircraft is usually controlled by an autopilot. Autopilots are complex on-board mechanisms that detect deviations from an aircraft's route and make appropriate adjustments to the flight controls. Flight decks are also equipped with radars that warn pilots of approaching hazards, such as mountain ranges, bad weather, and other aircraft.

Shoulder cowling

Engine pylon

Hinged cowling panel

Nose cowling

Fan duct nozzle

Core-engine jet pipe

Fire-extinguisher discharge indicator

Oil-filler door

Push-in door for hand-held fire-extinguisher

Drain mast

TURBOFAN ENGINE COWLING

STRUCTURAL COMPONENTS OF A BAE-146 JETLINER

Oil-filler door for integrated-drive generator

FUSELAGE NOSE-SECTION

FUSELAGE MID-SECTION

Electrically heated, birdproof windscreen

Side window

Anchor for open door

Rain gutter

Hinge

Peephole

Finger recess

Static air-pressure plate

Forward main door aperture

Passenger window aperture

VHF omni-range and instrument-landing-system aerials

Light-alloy door frame

Main external operating handle

Multiple-pinned lock

Floor level

Radome

Toilet service connector

FORWARD MAIN DOOR

Anchor for open door

Air temperature probe

Stall warning vane

Pitot head for dynamic air pressure

Overwing fuel-filler cap

Systems connector

Overwing fuel-filler cap

Fuel contents indicator

STARBOARD WING ASSEMBLY

Centre-line (spine) of aircraft

Single-piece skin over inboard wing

Rubber sealing strip

Rubber sealing strip

Trailing edge

Trailing edge of fixed wing

Spoiler anchorage

Hydraulic actuator attachment

Pivot point

Flap-track fairing

Screw joint

Aft section

MOVABLE FLAP TRACK AND FAIRING

Hinge

INBOARD LIFT SPOILERS

Stainless-steel flap seal

Track roller

Upper carriage attached to flap

Tab-hinge line

FOWLER FLAP

Leading edge

Anchor bearing

Track

Root

Gearbox mount

Bellcrank lever

Gearbox unit

Carriage drive nut

Flap drive screw

Lower carriage

Skin lap-joint

Leading edge

Main spar bridge

Root rib

Wing-root mount containing central fuel tank

Inboard tab

Attachment structure for wing-to-fuselage fairing

Cabin air-pressure discharge valve

Floor level

Fairing of landing gear bay

Fairing of landing gear pivot

Yellow anti-corrosion paint

413

Modern jetliners 2

Landing and taxiing light

Heated de-icing leading edge

Roll-spoiler hinge

Roll-spoiler hydraulic actuator attachment

STARBOARD WING

Fixed trailing edge

Aileron hinge

Starboard navigation light

Hinge

Hydraulic actuator attachment

Spoiler arm

Aerodynamic balance

Horn balance

Hinge bracket

Recessed hinge

INTERMEDIATE LIFT SPOILER

Flap seal

OUTBOARD ROLL SPOILER

AILERON

Trimtab

Servo-tab

MAIN FOWLER FLAP

Leading edge

Flap tip

Static discharge wick attachment

Outboard tab

Tab-hinge line

FUSELAGE SPINE FAIRING

Landing gear door

Hydraulic brake pipe

Main pivot

Finger recess

Peephole

Hot-air de-icing duct

Skin lap-joint

Electrical harness

Oleo lock-jack

Passenger window aperture

Light-alloy beam

Direction bar

Brake pipe

Main external operating handle

Hinge

Shock-strut bearing

Side brace and retraction jack trunnions

Hinge

Pneumatic tyre

Outer wheel axle

Lower pivot

Pivoted trailing-link arm

Hydraulic brake pipe

Anchor for open door

Wheel hub

Cabin air-discharge aperture

STARBOARD TWIN-WHEEL MAIN LANDING GEAR

AFT MAIN DOOR

BAE-146 MODERN JETLINER

Tailplane

Logo

Rudder

Fin

Landing light

Starboard inboard engine

VHF radio aerial

Forward door for crew and service

Radome

Starboard aft service door

Flap-track fairing

Core-engine jet pipe

Main landing gear fairing

VHF aerial

Water-drain mast

STARBOARD ELEVATOR

Horn balance

Intermediate fairing (fin tip)

Aft fairing

Tab hinge

TAILPLANE FAIRINGS

Fin trailing edge

Aerodynamic balance

Forward fairing

Side fairing

Elevator chassis box

Tailplane attachment bracket

Recessed hinge

Heated de-icing leading edge

Root

FIN

Centre-line (spine)

Trimtab

Forward spar

Servo-tab

Fairing panel

Aft spar

Fin-attachment skin

Access to yaw dampers and rudder trim jack

TAILPLANE

Rain gutter

Fin leading-edge attachment

Auxiliary power unit (APU) inlet

Heated de-icing leading edge

Operating arm

Elevator hinge

Auxiliary power unit (APU) vent

Oil-cooler duct

Hinge

Skin lap-joint

Trailing edge

STARBOARD AIR-BRAKE

Tailplane tip

Aft main door aperture

Heated drain mast

FUSELAGE TAIL-SECTION

415

Supersonic jetliners

SUPERSONIC AIRCRAFT FLY FASTER than the speed of sound (Mach 1). There are many supersonic military aircraft, but only two supersonic passenger-carrying aircraft (also called SSTs, or supersonic transports) have been produced: the Russian Tu-144, and Concorde, produced jointly by Britain and France. The Tu-144 was withdrawn in 1978, after only seven months in service. The concorde remained in service from 1976 until 2003, with a break for modifications from July 2000 until October 2001. Its features included a droop nose, which lowered during take-off and landing to aid visibility from the cockpit; the pumping of fuel between forward and aft trim tanks helped stabilize the aircraft. The concorde had a narrow fuselage and shortspan wings to reduce drag during supersonic flight. Its noisy turbojet engines with afterburners enabled it to carry 100 passengers at a cruising speed of Mach 2 at 15,000-18,000 m (50,000-60,000 ft). Once an aircraft is flying faster than Mach 1, it produces a continuous air-pressure wave, which is heard as a "sonic boom".

COMPUTER-
DESIGNED SST

FRONT VIEW OF CONCORDE

Strake Fin Standby pitot he Nose-gear leg Inboard elevon-jack fairing Starboard outboard engine air-intake

OVERHEAD VIEW OF THE CONCORDE

Variable nozzle Leading edge

Toilet

Electrothermal de-icing panel Starboard forward trim tank Overhead hand-baggage bin Passenger accommodation Underfloor air-conditioning duct Seat attachment rail Life-raft VHF aerial Wardrobe Forward galley Additional crew's seat Aluminium-alloy layers and insulation Third pilot's seat Erosion-resistant radome Cockpit windscreen Retractable visor "A" frame Weather radar Visor jack Pivoted retractable frame Droop-nose hinge Cockpit air-conditioning duct Captain's seat Standby flight-control hydraulic jack Plug-type passenger door Nose-gear leg Nose-gear door Steering actuator Lateral bracing strut Telescopic strut Port forward trim tank Multi-ply high-pressure tyre Machine skin pane Upper rudder Fin Dorsal fin Emergency exit Tail cone Aft door Elevon (combined elevator and aileron) Hot-section steel and titanium skin Engine cowling Landing gear door Bogie main landing gear

SECTIONED VIEW OF THE CONCORDE

Fire-suppression bottle access panel
Cold-air unit
Static discharge wick
Elevon (combined elevator and aileron)
HF radio aerials fairing
Auxiliary power unit
Upper rudder
Tail cone
Pressurized keel box
Fuel tank
Cabin air duct
Lower-rudder power control unit
Main air duct
Emergency oxygen cylinders
Servo control-unit fairing
Emergency exit
Inspection panel
Flight-control mixing unit
Fuel-jettison pipe
Air-conditioning duct
Rear bulkhead
Aft galley unit
Rear emergency door
Tank inspection access
Inboard elevon (combined elevator and aileron)
Landing gear hydraulics
Port main landing-gear leg well
Variable nozzle
Nozzle actuator
Heat-exchanger exhaust
Elevon power control unit
Spar
Fuel pipe
Rib
VHF aerial
Four-wheel bogie
Forward ramp drive
Main landing gear cross-beam
Leading edge
Middle passenger door
Port engine fuel pumps
Port main landing gear leg
Upper lip of port engine air intakes
Retraction jack
Heat exchanger
Engine front support link
Fuel tank
Honeycomb elevon structure
Rolls-Royce Olympus Mark 610 turbojet

SIDE VIEW OF THE CONCORDE

VHF aerial
Emergency exit
Passenger window
Flight deck windscreen
Retracted visor
Nose in drooped position
Standby pitot head
Nose-leg telescopic strut
Nose-gear leg
Aerodynamic strake
Starboard forward door
Radome
Steerable twin-wheel nose-gear

Jet engines

JET ENGINES ARE USED BY MOST MILITARY and heavy aircraft, and by many helicopters. The simplest type of jet engine, or gas turbine, is the turbojet. It works by continuously burning a mixture of fuel and air in a combustion chamber to produce a jet of hot exhaust gas that is expelled through a nozzle to produce thrust. The hot gas also spins turbine blades, which, in turn, spin the blades of an air compressor; the compressor forces air into the combustion chamber. Many of the fastest aircraft use turbojets, with additional booster units called afterburners, but their use is restricted by their high noise emission. Most jetliners use turbofan jet engines, which are quieter. An enormous fan, driven by a low-pressure turbine, feeds some air into the compressor but feeds most of it through bypass ducts to join the exhaust jetstream in the tail cone. The bypass stream produces most of the thrust. Many smaller, propeller-driven aircraft use turboprop jet engines, in which the engine powers a propeller.

NPT 301 MODERN TURBOJET

Fuel sprayer
Turbine rotor
Reverse-flow combustion chamber
Radial diffuser
Centrifugal compressor
Exhaust diffuser
Inducer
Air intake
Tail cone
Jet pipe
Exhaust nozzle
Nose cone
Igniter
Alternator
Nozzle guide vane
Air impingement starter
Combustion chamber casing

Temperature and pressure sensor
Low-pressure fan
Inlet cone (rotating spinner)
Pressure line
Fan case with special structure to contain broken fan
Electronic engine control and airframe interface connector
Electronic engine control (EEC) unit
Compressor front bearing
Engine front mount
Electrical wiring harness
Fuel and oil heat exchanger
Oil filter
Compressor air bleed connection

Plenum ring for hot anti-icing air
Flow splitter
Gearbox bevel drive
Integral oil tank
High-pressure compressor
Combustion chamber
High pressure turbine
Fuel manifold
Fuel nozzle
Centrifugal compressor
Fan duct

PRATT & WHITNEY CANADA PW120 SERIES MODERN TURBOPROP

Alternator mount pad

Propeller speed probe

Reduction gearbox

Propeller hub flange

Propeller brake pad

Engine front mount

Torquemeter mount

Gearbox oil scavenge line

Autofeather unit

Air intake

Electronic engine control (EEC) unit

Oil filter

Oil tank

Oil-pressure regulating valve

Accessory drive pad

Throttle lever

Fuel-cooled oil cooler

Fuel filter

Fuel heater

Intercompressor bleed valve

Fuel manifold

Fuel

High-pressure bleed venturi connector

Turbine support case

Jet pipe connection

Oil pipe

Thermocouple bus-bar

Fuel nozzle

Igniter plug

Engine rear mount

Intercompressor diffuser pipe

Low-pressure turbine

Heat shield

Blade tip sealing shroud

Exhaust cone

Core jet pipe (exhaust fairing)

Scavenge oil line

Inter-module bolted joint

Fuel shut-off valve cable

SECTIONED PRATT & WHITNEY CANADA PW305 MODERN TURBOFAN

HOW JET ENGINES WORK

TURBOFAN

Fan sucks air in

Outer drive shaft

Exhaust gases provide extra thrust

Fan blade

Bypass air provides main thrust

Rotating blades compress air

Fuel inlet

High-pressure turbine spins outer drive shaft to drive compressor

Inner drive shaft

Fuel/air mixture ignites

TURBOPROP

Combustion chamber

Fuel inlet

Three-stage turbine driven by hot gas

Compressor sucks air in

Propeller spins to provide main thrust

Exhaust gases add a little thrust

Reduction gearbox

Rotating blades compress air

Turbine shaft drives propeller and compressor

TURBOJET

Combustion chamber

Fuel inlet

Turbine blades driven by hot gas

Compressor sucks air in

Exhaust gases provide all the thrust

Rotating blades compress air

Fuel/air mixture ignites

Turbine drives compressor via drive shaft

Modern military aircraft

MODERN MILITARY AIRCRAFT ARE AMONG THE MOST SOPHISTICATED and expensive products of the 21st century. Fighters need computer-operated controls for manoeuvrability, powerful engines, and effective air-to-air weapons. Most modern fighters also have guided missiles, radar, and passive, infra-red sensors. These developments enable today's fighters to engage in combat with adversaries that are outside visual range. Bombers carry a large weapon load and enough fuel for long-range flights. A few military aircraft, such as the Tornado and the F-14 Tomcat, have variable-sweep ("swing") wings. During take-off and landing their wings are fully extended, but for high-speed flight and low-level attacks the wings are pivoted fully back. A recent development is the "stealth" bomber, which is designed to absorb or deflect enemy radar in order to remain undetected. Earlier bombers, such as the Tornado, use terrain-following radars to fly so close to the ground that they avoid enemy radar detection.

FRONT VIEW OF A
PANAVIA TORNADO

Instrument
landing system
aerial

Birdproof
windscreen

Port variable-
incidence
air intake

Air data
probe

Wing-root
glove fairing

Starboard
inboard
stores pylon

Taileron

Starboard main
landing gear door

Main landing gear leg

Laser ranger and
marked-target seeker

Starboard nose-gear door

Steerable twin-wheel nose-gear

Radome
containing
ground-mapping
attack, and terrain-
following radar

Taxiing light

Wing extended
for take-off and
landing

Wing pivoted
back for high-
speed flight

SWING-WING F-14 TOMCAT FIGHTER

SIDE VIEW OF A PANAVIA TORNADO GR1A
(RECONNAISSANCE VERSION), 1986

Pilot's
cockpit

Navigator's
instrument console

Navigator's
cockpit

Single canopy over both
cockpits

Engine air intake

Navigation light

Flat, birdproof
windscreen

High-velocity air
duct to disperse rain

Upper "request
identification" aerial

Air data
probe

Radome containing
ground-mapping,
attack, and terrain-
following radars

UHF aerial

Angle-of-attack probe

Tacan (tactical air navigation) aerial

Emergency canopy release handle

Nose-gear
door

Steerable
nose-gear leg

Pitot
head

Twin
nose-
wheel

Hinged auxiliary
air intake

Cold air intake (ram scoop)

Heat exchanger exhaust duct

Window covering
infra-red reconnaissance camera

NORTHROP B-2 ("STEALTH" BOMBER), 1989

Starboard split rudder

Inboard elevons (combined elevators and ailerons)

Refractory (heat-resistant) skin behind exhaust outlet

Variable-incidence gust-alleviator

Wing leading edge coated with radar-absorbent material

Port wingtip rudder

Outboard elevon (combined elevator and aileron)

Leading-edge aerial

Engine aft bulkhead

Weapon-bay rear bulkhead

Wing containing fuel tank

Flight refuelling receptacle

Auxiliary air intake

Weapon-bay front bulkhead

Air intake coated with radar-absorbent material

Space for extra crew member

Ejector-seat roof hatches

Port navigation light

Two-seater cockpit

Port outboard stores pylon

Fin-tip aerial fairing

Radar warning receiver looking forwards

Instrument landing system aerial

Radar warning receiver looking rearwards

Heat exchanger air intake (ram scoop)

Extended port air-brake

Fin

Rudder

Wing-root glove fairing

Wing-root pneumatic seal

Heat exchanger hot-air exhaust

Fin-root aerial fairing

Air-brake jack

Spine end fairing

Thrust-reverser (closed)

Port fully-variable afterburner nozzle

Port flap

Port taileron (combined tailplane and aileron)

Port inboard stores pylon

Wingtip aerial fairing

Hydraulic hand-pump

Port navigation light

Lower "request identification" aerial

Powered leading-edge slat

Main-gear door

Port main landing gear

Port outboard stores pylon

Helicopters

HELICOPTERS USE ROTATING BLADES for lift, propulsion, and steering. The first machine to achieve sustained, controlled flight using rotating blades was the autogiro built in the 1920s by the Spaniard Juan de la Cierva. His machine had unpowered blades above the fuselage that relied on the flow of air to rotate them and provide lift as the autogiro was driven forwards by a conventional propeller. Then, in 1939, the Russian-born American Igor Sikorsky produced his VS-300, the forerunner of modern helicopters. Its engine-driven blades provided lift, propulsion, and steering. It could take off vertically, hover, and fly in any direction, and had a tail rotor to prevent the helicopter body from spinning. The introduction of gas turbine jet engines to helicopters in 1955 produced quieter, safer, and more powerful machines. Because of their versatility in flight, helicopters are today used for many purposes, including crop-spraying, traffic surveillance, and transporting crews to deep-sea oil rigs, as well as acting as gunships, air ambulances, and air taxis.

BELL 47G-3B1

BELL 47G-3B1

Droop stop
Main rotor hub
Blade counterweight
Blade-root attachment
Main rotor mast
Stabilizer-bar weight
Direct-vision panel
Fuel vent pipe
Protective gaiter
Frameless plastic canopy
Fuel tank
Fuel tank cradle
Tail-rotor drive shaft
Radio
Exhaust pipe
Air intake pipe
Instrument panel
Electric fuel pump
Cyclic-pitch lever
Battery
Battery overspill
Electrical inverter
Breather pipe
Pitot head
Oil tank
Anti-collision beacon
Carburettor hot-air intake pipe
Landing light
Air filter
Landing skid
Navigation light
Ground handling wheel
Valve-rocker cover
VHF omni-range aerial
Ventilator
Electric power socket
Lycoming six-cylinder engine
Collective-pitch lever
Riveted light-alloy forward fuselage section

SCHWEIZER 300C

Blade-root attachment

Three-blade main rotor

Outside air-temperature gauge

Ventilator

Flight-control rod

Anti-collision beacon

Anti-torque tail rotor

Magnetic compass

Main rotor mast

Automatic direction-finding aerial

Plastic canopy

Navigation aerial

Cyclic-pitch lever

Fuel tank

G-SAND

Tail boom

Engine air intake

Tubular bracing strut

Vertical tail

Tail rotor guard

Pitot head

Tail-rotor drive shaft

Anti-collision beacon

Tail-boom support strut

Exhaust silencer

Landing skid

Landing gear damper

Transmission drive-pulley cover

Landing light

Transponder aerial

Lycoming four-cylinder engine

High-visibility tip

Twin-blade main rotor

Anti-torque tail rotor

Anti-collision beacon

Triangular-section, unskinned rear fuselage

Elevator upper control wire

Synchronized elevator

Tail rotor hub

Tail rotor gearbox

Elevator lower control wire

Tubular tail rotor guard

Tail-rotor pitch control wire

Small fixed fin

G-BGID

Main rotor blade

Droop stop

Main rotor hub

Allison 250-C20J turboshaft engine

Anti-collision beacon

Blade-root attachment

Jet pipe

Main rotor mast

Horizontal stabilizer

Upper fin

VHF aerial

Anti-torque tail rotor

Air temperature probe

G-HUMT

Lower fin

Forward-hinged door

Flush-riveted aluminium fuselage

Tail boom

Transponder aerial

Boarding step

Baggage compartment door

Landing skid

Rear cross-tube

BELL 206 JETRANGER

423

Light aircraft

LIGHT AIRCRAFT, SUCH AS THE ARV SUPER 2 shown here, are small, lightweight, and of simple construction. More than a million have been built since World War I, mainly for recreational use by private owners. Virtually all light aircraft have piston engines, most of which are air-cooled, although some are liquid-cooled. Open cockpits, almost universal in the 1920s, have today been replaced by enclosed cabins. The cabins of high-wing aircraft have one or two doors, whereas those of low-wing aircraft usually have a sliding or hinged canopy. Most modern light aircraft are made of aluminium alloy, although some are made of wood or of fibre-reinforced materials. Light aircraft today also usually have navigational instruments, an electrical system, cabin heating, wheel brakes, and a two-way radio.

Port wingtip

Aileron mass balance

Aileron torque tube

Port aileron

PORT MAIN LANDING GEAR

Inner tube

Hub

Tyre

Brake disc

Stub axle

Landing gear leg

Brake mount

Brake pipe

Hydraulic brake calliper

Dorsal fin

Rear attachment-bracket for wing

Rear fuselage top skin

REAR FUSELAGE

Longeron

Diaphragm

Frame

Battery box

Side skin

"Skin-grip" pin

Elevator

TAILPLANE AND RUDDER

Rudder tip fairing

Rudder mass balance

Fin tip fairing

Rudder

Fin

Elevator trimtab

Drive pillar

Attachment plate

Coolant outlet

Rear fuselage bottom skin

Aluminium radiator

Air scoop

Elevator push-rod

Elevator push-rod

CONTROL RODS AND CABLES

Flap torque tube

Aileron rod

Rocking elevator arm

Aileron torque tube

Flap drive-rod

Rudder cable

Flap drive-rod

Tailplane

Coolant inlet

SIDE VIEW OF ARV SUPER 2

Spinner

Canopy

Wing

Communications aerial

Navigational aerial

Fin

Dorsal fin

Rudder

Elevator

Engine cowling

Tailplane

STARBOARD MAIN LANDING GEAR

Brake calliper

Brake pipe

Landing gear leg

Radiator

Tailskid

G-BNHB

Nose-gear

Step

Wing strut

Main landing gear

Tailskid

Aircraft registration code

Brake disc

Inner tube

Stub axle

Hub

Venturi for instruments

Tyre

PORT WING

Port top-wing fairing

Port underwing fairing

Headrest

Wing strut

Port flap

Airspeed-indicator tube

Pitot head

Port flap

SEAT ASSEMBLY

Seat cushion

Backrest

Lap strap

Quick-release mechanism

Lap-strap length adjuster

Bolted anchor

CANOPY

Direct-vision panel

Pressurized strut

Hinge

Leading-edge fairing

Moulded plastic

Canopy latch

Outside air-temperature gauge

COCKPIT

Fibreglass canopy frame

Fuel tank top skin

Rudder pedal

Cockpit coaming

Forward attachment bracket for wing

Control-column aperture

Semi-bulkhead

Engine mount

Nose-leg upper mount

Firewall

Fibreglass fuel tank

Bulkhead

Lap-strap attachment bracket

"Skin-grip" pin

THREE-CYLINDER ENGINE

Port engine cowling

Air intake box

Water outlet

Carburettor

Backplate

Fuel hose

Cylinder head

Gearbox

Propeller drive flange

Exhaust manifold

PROPELLER

Spinner

Flanged plate

Starboard engine cowling

CONTROL COLUMN AND FLAP LEVER

Elevator arm

Torque tube assembly

Control column

Throttle lever

Brake lever

Elevator push-rod

Flap lever

Flap lever detent box

Release button

Elevator trimtab lever

Carburettor hot air lever

Bearing assembly

Pilot's handgrip

INSTRUMENT PANEL

Flight instruments

Engine instruments

Glove box

Radio plugs

NOSE-GEAR

Nose-leg down tube

Steering stop

Rubber bungee (elasticated cord) shock absorber

Damper unit

Hoop

Pivoted fork

Axle bolt

Nose-wheel

STARBOARD WING

Wing strut

Starboard underwing fairing

Starboard top-wing fairing

Gliders, hang-gliders, and microlights

MODERN GLIDERS ARE AMONG the most graceful and aerodynamically efficient of all aircraft. Unpowered but with a large wingspan (up to about 25 m, or 82 ft), gliders use currents of hot, rising air (thermals) to stay aloft, and a rudder, elevators, and ailerons for control. Modern gliders have achieved flights of more than 1,450 km (900 miles) and altitudes above 15,000 m (49,000 ft). Hang-gliders consist of a simple frame across which rigid or flexible material is stretched to form the wings. The pilot is suspended below the wings in a harness or body-bag and, gripping a triangular A-frame, steers by shifting weight from side to side. Like gliders, hang-gliders rely on thermals for lift. Microlights are basically powered hang-gliders. A small engine and an open fibreglass car (trike), which can hold a crew of two, are suspended beneath a stronger version of a hang-glider frame; the frame may have rigid or flexible wings. Microlight pilots, like hang-glider pilots, steer by shifting their weight against an A-frame. Microlights can reach speeds of up to 160 kph (100 mph).

HANG-GLIDER

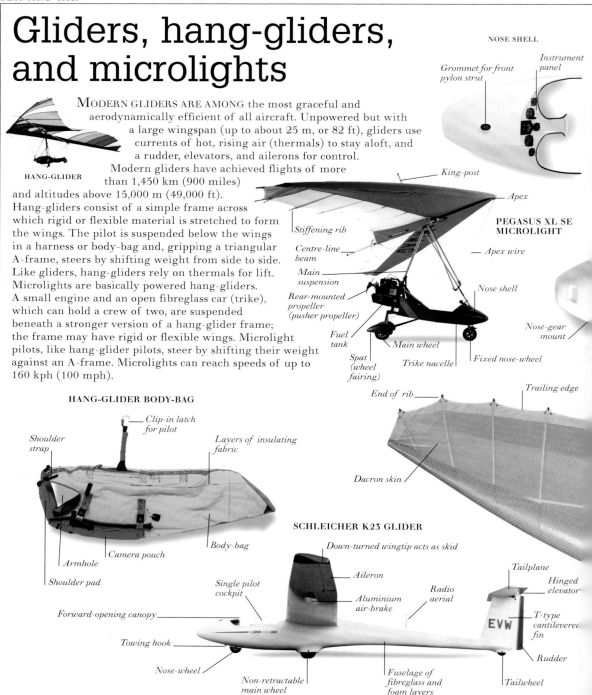

NOSE SHELL

Grommet for front pylon strut

Instrument panel

King-post

Apex

PEGASUS XL SE MICROLIGHT

Stiffening rib

Centre-line beam

Main suspension

Rear-mounted propeller (pusher propeller)

Fuel tank

Spat (wheel fairing)

Main wheel

Trike nacelle

Apex wire

Nose shell

Nose-gear mount

Fixed nose-wheel

End of rib

Trailing edge

Dacron skin

HANG-GLIDER BODY-BAG

Clip-in latch for pilot

Shoulder strap

Layers of insulating fabric

Armhole

Shoulder pad

Camera pouch

Body-bag

Forward-opening canopy

SCHLEICHER K23 GLIDER

Down-turned wingtip acts as skid

Aileron

Aluminium air-brake

Radio aerial

Tailplane

Hinged elevator

T-type cantilevered fin

Rudder

EVW

Single pilot cockpit

Towing hook

Nose-wheel

Non-retractable main wheel

Fuselage of fibreglass and foam layers

Tailwheel

SOLAR WINGS PEGASUS QUASAR MICROLIGHT

Foot throttle

Pilot's steering bar

Passenger's steering bar and footrest

Lap strap

Fuel tank filler nozzle

Spat (wheel fairing)

Engine mount

Pylon fairing

Aircraft name

Air outlet

Rear engine cowling

Pylon strut

Footbrake

Pilot's seat

Hand throttle

Pylon-strut strap

Passenger's seat

Main wing-strut

TRIKE UNIT

Trailing edge

Leading edge

Propeller drive gearbox

TWIN-CYLINDER ENGINE

Twin carburettors

Air filter

Dual ignition plug

Air cooling fan

Exhaust connection

Engine rear mount

Metal hub

Sealed lid

EXHAUST PIPE

PROPELLER

Waterproof stowage box

TRIKE NACELLE

WINGFRAME

Eyelet tensioning trailing edge to rib

Bracing cable

Rib

Centre-line beam

After silencer

Main exhaust silencer

Single spar

King-post

Leading edge

Semi-rigid fibreglass skin

Lift bracing wire

THE VISUAL ARTS

DRAWING 430

TEMPERA 432

FRESCO 434

OILS 436

WATERCOLOUR 438

PASTELS 440

ACRYLICS 442

CALLIGRAPHY 444

PRINTMAKING 1 446

PRINTMAKING 2 448

MOSAIC 450

SCULPTURE 1 452

SCULPTURE 2 454

Drawing

DRAWINGS CAN BE FINISHED WORKS OF ART, or preparatory studies for paintings and other visual arts. They can be made using a wide variety of drawing instruments such as pencils, graphite sticks, chalks, charcoal, pens and inks, and silver wires. The most common drawing instrument is the graphite pencil. A graphite pencil consists of a thin rod of graphite mixed with clay, encased in wood. Charcoal is one of the oldest drawing instruments. It is produced by firing twigs of willow, vine, or other woods at high temperatures in airtight containers. Erasers can be used to rub out marks made by drawing materials such as graphite pencils or charcoal, or to achieve a particular effect – such as smudging. Fixative is often applied – using a mouth diffuser or aerosol spray fixative – to prevent smudging once a drawing is finished. Silver lines can be produced by drawing silver wire across specially prepared paper – a technique known as silverpoint. The lines are permanent and cannot be erased. In time the silver lines oxidize and turn brown.

FIXATIVE AND MOUTH DIFFUSER

Hinge

Liquid fixative consisting of dissolved resin

Fixative is sucked into tube and sprayed on to drawing

ERASERS

Medium-soft, light line

Hard texture

PLASTIC ERASER

Soft texture

Very soft, dark line

PUTTY ERASER

CHALK, CRAYON, AND CHARCOAL

Calcite (calcium carbonate) mixed with pigment

BLUE CHALK

Iron oxide mixed with chalk

SANGUINE CRAYON

Carbonized wood

WILLOW CHARCOAL

DRAWING INSTRUMENTS

2B GRAPHITE PENCIL

8B GRAPHITE PENCIL

SILVER WIRE IN A METAL HOLDER

DRAWING BOARD

Drawing board

Paper

Drawing clip

DRAWING MATERIALS

Coloured pencil

Graphite stick

Bulldog clip

Dip pen

Pencil sharpener

Sketch book

Ink bottle

Silver lines oxidize to a light brown colour

Figures drawn in ink on top of lines

Line drawn in silverpoint using a rule

Complex perspective drawing done as a preparatory study for a painting

Vanishing point located on head of man riding rearing horse

Lines of squared pavement slabs recede toward a single vanishing point

EXAMPLE OF A SILVERPOINT DRAWING
The Adoration of the Magi, Leonardo da Vinci, 1481
Pen and ink over silverpoint on paper
16.5 × 29.2 cm (6½ × 11½ in)

Paper prepared with size (glue) and pigment

Handmade, tinted paper

Charcoal lines softened by rubbing and smudging

Blending creates depth and shadow

Broad charcoal mark

Charcoal gives strong, expressive lines

EXAMPLE OF A CHARCOAL DRAWING
Charcoal on paper

431

Tempera

THE TERM TEMPERA is applied to any paint in which pigment is tempered (mixed) with a water-based binding medium – usually egg yolk. Egg tempera is applied to a smooth surface such as vellum (for illuminated manuscripts) or more commonly to hardwood panels prepared with gesso – a mixture of chalk and size (glue). Hog hair brushes are used to apply the gesso. A layer of gesso grosso (coarse gesso) is followed by successive layers of gesso sotile (fine gesso) that are sanded between coats to provide a smooth, yet absorbent ground. The paint is applied with fine sable brushes in thin layers, using light brushstrokes. Tempera dries quickly to form a tough skin with a satin sheen. The luminous white surface of the gesso combined with the overlaid paint produces the brilliant crispness and rich colours particular to this medium. Egg tempera paintings are frequently gilded with gold. Leaves of finely beaten gold are applied to a bole (reddish-brown clay) base and polished by burnishing.

MATERIALS FOR GILDING

Parchment for protecting gold leaf from draughts

Brush

Bowl containing diluted bole

Gold leaf

Gilder's knife

Gilder's tip for picking up gold leaf

Gilder's cushion

Gold leaf smoothed and polished with a burnisher

Surface prepared with gesso

Gold leaf applied in overlapping layers

Bole brushed on to gesso

Burnisher

Agate tip

MATERIALS FOR TEMPERA PANEL PAINTING

Yolk

EGG

White

SIZE (GLUE)

GESSO

Mortar

MORTAR AND PESTLE

Pestle for crushing and grinding pigments

Lip

EGG YOLK BINDING MEDIUM

EXAMPLES OF BRUSHES

FLAT HOG HAIR BRUSH

SABLE BRUSH SIZE 6

SABLE BRUSH SIZE 1

EXAMPLE OF A TEMPERA PAINTING
Presentation in the Temple, Ambrogio Lorenzetti, 1342
Tempera on wood, 257 × 168 cm (8 ft 5⅛ in × 5 ft 6 ⅛in)

*Altarpiece
commissioned for
Siena Cathedral, Italy*

*Textured gold ornament made
by punching motifs into the
gilded surface*

*The red tinge of
the bole is just
visible beneath
the gold*

*Edge of a sheet
of gold leaf*

*Crisp edge
characteristic of
tempera painting*

*Vine black used
to create the
dim cathedral
interior*

*Highlights on
the beard made
by applying thin
layers of white
over dried paint*

*Red drapery
painted in
vermilion*

*Raised right hand
and pointing finger
is the gesture of
prophecy*

*Receding floor
tiles create the
impression of
depth*

*Patch of discoloured
varnish, left from
last cleaning*

VERDACCIO

**VERMILION AND
LEAD WHITE**

VERMILION

**RED EARTH
(IRON OXIDE)**

EXAMPLES OF PIGMENTS

MALACHITE

**ULTRAMARINE
LAPIS LAZULI**

VINE BLACK

LEAD TIN YELLOW

*Warm flesh
tones achieved
by layering
vermilion and
white over an
undercoat of
verdaccio*

*Patterned gold
halo glitters in
candlelight*

*Ultramarine
lapis lazuli, as
costly as gold,
was reserved for
significant
figures such as
the Virgin Mary*

*Craquelure
(pattern of
cracks in
the paint)*

**DETAIL FROM "PRESENTATION
IN THE TEMPLE"**

Fresco

FRESCO IS A METHOD OF WALL PAINTING. In buon fresco (true fresco), pigments are mixed with water and applied to an intonaco (layer of fresh, damp lime-plaster). The intonaco absorbs and binds the pigments as it dries making the picture a permanent part of the wall surface. The intonaco is applied in sections called giornate (daily sections). The size of each giornata depends on the artist's estimate of how much can be painted before the plaster sets. The junctions between giornate are sometimes visible on a finished fresco. The range of colours used in buon fresco are limited to lime-resistant pigments such as earth colours (below). Slaked lime (burnt lime mixed with water), bianco di San Giovanni (slaked lime that has been partly exposed to air), and chalk can be used to produce fresco whites. In fresco secco (dry fresco), pigments are mixed with a binding medium and applied to dry plaster. The pigments are not completely absorbed into the plaster and may flake off over time.

CROSS-SECTION SHOWING FRESCO LAYERS

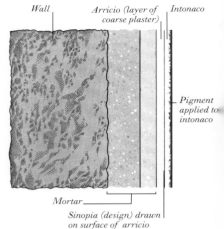

Wall

Arricio (layer of coarse plaster)

Intonaco

Pigment applied to intonaco

Mortar

Sinopia (design) drawn on surface of arricio

EXAMPLES OF EARTH COLOUR PIGMENTS

RAW UMBER

RED EARTH (IRON OXIDE)

GREEN EARTH

RAW SIENNA

INGREDIENTS FOR FRESCO WHITES

Marble slab for mixing ingredients

Bianco di San Giovanni

Slaked lime

Chalk

EXAMPLES OF FRESCO BRUSHES

Round hog hair brush

Rust-resistant twine binding

Dome-shaped hog hair brush

Pointed hog hair brush

TONDO

MUCCINI

RIGA

EXAMPLE OF A FRESCO
The Expulsion of the Merchants from the Temple, Giotto, c.1306
Fresco, 200 × 185 cm (78 × 72 in)

Temple acts as a backdrop for the action

Bianco di San Giovanni often used for fresco whites

Gold leaf applied to apostle's halo

Green earth pigment applied to robe

Child painted on top of apostle's robe

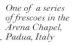

One of a series of frescoes in the Arena Chapel, Padua, Italy

Patches of azurite blue have turned green due to reaction with carbon dioxide

Hairline junction between giornate is visible

Red earth pigment applied in buon fresco has retained rich hue

Azurite blue applied in fresco secco has flaked off to reveal the plaster beneath

Dry, matt surface characteristic of buon fresco

Paint applied in buon fresco to child's face

White dove represents the Holy Ghost

Paint applied in fresco secco to child's body has flaked off

A fresco was generally worked in zones from the top down

Sinopia (design) sketched in red earth

Artist has to finish giornata before plaster dries

Junction between giornate

Area with little detail can be painted quickly, allowing a larger giornata to be completed

Highly detailed area takes a longer time to paint, restricting the size of the giornata

DETAIL FROM "THE EXPULSION"

GIORNATE (DAILY SECTIONS) IN "THE EXPULSION"

Oils

DAMMAR RESIN VARNISH

Crystals are dissolved and applied to painting to protect its surface

OIL PAINTS ARE MADE BY MIXING and grinding pigment with a drying vegetable oil such as linseed oil. The paint can be applied to many different surfaces and textures – the most common being canvas. Before painting, the canvas is stretched on a wooden frame and its surface is prepared with layers of size (glue) and primer. The two main types of brushes used in oil painting are stiff hog hair bristle brushes – generally used for covering large areas; and soft hair brushes made from sable or synthetic material – generally used for fine detail. Other tools, including painting knives, can also be used to achieve different effects. Oil paint can be applied thickly (a technique known as impasto), or can be thinned down using a solvent – such as turpentine or white spirit. Varnishes are sometimes applied to finished paintings to protect their surface and to give them a matt or gloss finish.

KIDNEY-SHAPED PALETTE

COMMERCIAL OIL PAINTS

CADMIUM RED

Lightfast opaque colour

ULTRAMARINE

Transparent colour

LINSEED OIL

Oil derived from seeds of flax plant

EQUIPMENT FOR MAKING OIL PAINT

EXAMPLES OF PIGMENTS

CADMIUM RED

CERULEAN BLUE

DOUBLE DIPPER (PALETTE ATTACHMENT)

Screw-top lid

Container for storing solvent or drying oil

EXAMPLES OF BRUSHES

HOG HAIR BRISTLE BRUSHES

Flat hog hair brush

Filbert hog hair brush

Flat hog hair brush

Filbert hog hair brush

SYNTHETIC BRUSH

Round hog hair brush

SABLE BRUSH

Long, wooden handle

Protective plastic case

Airtight jar for storing paint

Palette knife for mixing drying oil and pigment

PAINTING KNIVES

TROWEL-SHAPED PAINTING KNIFE

DIAMOND-SHAPED PAINTING KNIFE

Blade

Blade

Glass muller for grinding drying oil and pigment

Glass slab with abrasive surface

Cranked, steel shank

Cranked, steel shank

EXAMPLE OF AN OIL PAINTING
Fritillarias, Vincent van Gogh, 1886
Oil on canvas, 73.5 × 60.5 cm (29 × 24 in)

Artist's signature scratched in wet paint with the end of the brush

Background enlivened by dabs of white and green

Each leaf painted in a single, rapid stroke

Orange and blue (complementary colours) placed together to give maximum contrast and enhance one another to appear brighter

Impasto (deep ridges of paint applied in thick strokes)

Strong directional brushstrokes on table draw attention to the vase

Features of vase highlighted by generous touches of yellow

RADIAL STUDIO EASEL

Top sliding-block adjusts to canvas height

Canvas support

Height adjustment key

Angle adjustment key

Tripod

CANVAS STRETCHED ON WOODEN FRAME (VIEWED FROM THE BACK)

Staple

Canvas prepared with glue (size) and primer

Wooden frame

Unprimed canvas

EXAMPLES OF CANVASES

COTTON DUCK

FINE LINEN

COARSE LINEN

Watercolour

WATERCOLOUR PAINT IS MADE OF GROUND PIGMENT mixed with a water-soluble binding medium, usually gum arabic. It is usually applied to paper using soft hair brushes such as sable, goat hair, squirrel, and synthetic brushes. Watercolours are often diluted and applied as overlaying washes (thin, transparent layers) to build up depth of colour. Washes can be laid in a variety of ways to create a range of different effects. For example, a wet-in-wet wash can be achieved by laying a wash on top of another wet wash. The two washes blend together to give a fused effect. Sponges are used to modify washes by soaking up paint so that areas of pigment are lightened or removed from the paper. Watercolours can also be applied undiluted – a technique known as dry brush – to create a broken-colour effect. Watercolours are generally transparent and allow light to reflect from the surface of the paper through the layers of paint to give a luminous effect. They can be thickened and made opaque by adding body colour (Chinese white).

GUM ARABIC

*Natural sap fro[m]
acacia tree*

NATURAL SPONG[E]

ANATOMY OF A SABLE BRUSH

*Soft red
sable hair*

Toe (tip)

Wooden handle

SOFT HAIR BRUSHES

*Hair trimmed
and cemented
into ferrule*

ROUND SABLE BRUSH (SIZE 6)

*Round
ferrule*

*Hair tied with
clove hitch knot*

ROUND SABLE BRUSH (SIZE 1)

**TUBES OF
WATERCOLOUR PAINT**

SYNTHETIC WASH BRUSH

WINSOR GREE[N]

**SQUIRREL MOP
WASH BRUSH**

CADMIUM YELLO[W]

**PORTABLE BOX OF
WATERCOLOUR PAINTS**

Painted colour swatch

Chinese white

*Pan of
watercolour paint*

*Lid can be used for
mixing colours*

**LARGE GOAT HAKE
WASH BRUSH**

EXAMPLE OF A WATERCOLOUR
Burning of the Houses of Parliament, Turner, 1834
Watercolour on paper, 29.2 × 44.5 cm (11½ × 17½ in)

Transparent washes laid on top of each other to create tonal depth

Transparent washes allow light to reflect off the surface of the paper to give a luminous effect

Highlight scratched out with a scalpel

Paper shows through thin wash to give flames added highlight

Crowd painted with thin strokes laid over a pale wash

Undiluted paint applied, then partly washed out, to create the impression of water

EXAMPLES OF WASHES

WASH OVER DRY BRUSH
Wash laid over paint applied with dry brush gives two-tone effect

GRADED WASH
Strong wash applied to tilted paper gives graded effect

DRY BRUSH
Undiluted paint dragged across surface of paper gives broken effect

WET-IN-WET
Two diluted washes left to run together to give fused effect

EXAMPLES OF WATERCOLOUR PAPERS

SMOOTH-TEXTURED PAPER

MEDIUM-TEXTURED PAPER

ROUGH-TEXTURED PAPER

COLOUR WHEEL OF WATERCOLOUR PAINTS

Yellow (primary colour)

Secondary colours made by mixing yellow and blue

Secondary colours made by mixing red and yellow

Blue (primary colour)

Red (primary colour)

Secondary colours made by mixing blue and red

Pastels

PASTELS ARE STICKS OF PIGMENT made by mixing ground pigment with chalk and a binding medium, such as gum arabic. They vary in hardness depending on the proportion of the binding medium to the chalk. Soft pastel – the most common form of pastel – contains just enough binding medium to hold the pigment in stick form. Pastels can be applied directly to any support (surface) with sufficient tooth (texture). When a pastel is drawn over a textured surface, the pigment crumbles and lodges in the fibres of the support. Pastel marks have a particular soft, matt quality and are suitable for techniques such as blending, scumbling, and feathering. Blending is a technique of rubbing and fusing two or more colours on the support using fingers or various tools such as tortillons (paper stumps), soft hair brushes, putty erasers, and soft bread. Scumbling is a technique of building up layers of pastel colours. The side or blunted tip of a soft pastel is lightly drawn over an underpainted area so that patches of the colour beneath show through. Feathering is a technique of applying parallel strokes of colour with the point of a pastel, usually over an existing layer of pastel colour. A thin spray of fixative can be applied – using a mouth diffuser (see pp. 430-431) or aerosol spray fixative – to a finished pastel painting, or in between layers of colour, to prevent smudging.

EQUIPMENT FOR MAKING PASTELS

Glass muller

Chalk

Glass slab with abrasive surface

Gum arabic

Ivory-black pigment

Cobalt-blue pigment

EXAMPLES OF SOFT PASTELS

COBALT-BLUE HALF PASTEL

VERMILION HALF PASTEL

OLIVE-GREEN FULL PASTEL

MAUVE FULL PASTEL

BOXED PASTEL SET

Boxed set containing a mixture of portrait and landscape colours

Foam compartments protect the pastels

Soft pastel

Wooden tray

EQUIPMENT USED WITH PASTELS

PUTTY ERASER

BREAD

Soft bread suitable for erasing and blending

AEROSOL SPRAY FIXATIVE

SOFT HAIR BRUSH

TORTILLONS (PAPER STUMPS)

Soft point used for blending

Tight roll of paper

EXAMPLE OF A PASTEL PAINTING
Woman Drying her Neck, Edgar Degas, c.1898
Pastel on cardboard, 62.5 x 65.5 cm (24½ x 25½in)

Pastels applied directly to support

Rich colour of fabric created by overlaying yellows and oranges

Broken colours, characteristic of scumbling technique

Colours are blended together using fingers or tools such as tortillons

Built up layers of pastel

Toned colour of paper visible beneath thinly applied pastels

Pure bright colours laid side by side produce strong contrasts

DETAIL FROM "WOMAN DRYING HER NECK"

Feathering technique used to produce skin tones

EXAMPLES OF TEXTURED PAPERS AND PASTEL BOARDS

WATERCOLOUR PAPER(ROUGH TEXTURE)

GLASS PAPER

WATERCOLOUR PAPER (MEDIUM TEXTURE)

INGRES PAPER

FLOCKED PASTEL BOARD

CANSON PAPER

EXAMPLES OF COLOURED AND TINTED PAPERS

Acrylics

ACRYLIC PAINT IS MADE BY MIXING PIGMENT with a synthetic resin. It can be thinned with water but dries to become water insoluble. Acrylics are applied to many surfaces, such as paper and acrylic-primed board and canvas. A variety of brushes, painting knives, rollers, air-brushes, plastic scrapers, and other tools are used in acrylic painting. The versatility of acrylics makes them suitable for a wide range of techniques. They can be used opaquely or — by adding water — in a transparent, watercolour style. Acrylic mediums can be added to the paint to adjust its consistency for special effects such as glazing and impasto (ridges of paint applied in thick strokes) or to make it more matt or glossy. Acrylics are quick-drying, which allows layers of paint to be applied on top of each other almost immediately.

EXAMPLES OF BRUSHES

Sable brush

Hog hair sash brush

Synthetic hog hair brush

Synthetic sable brush

Hog hair brush

Goat hair brush

Synthetic wash brush

Ox hair brush

EXAMPLES OF PAINTS USED IN ACRYLICS

Azo yellow

Phthalo green

Cerulean blue

Phthalo blue

Quinacridone red

Titanium white

Yellow ochre

Burnt umber

Burnt sienna

Pad of disposable paper palettes

PAINTING TOOLS

Flexible, plastic blade

PLASTIC PAINTING KNIFE

Stippled effect achieved using thick paint

Plastic handle

SPONGE ROLLER

Blended tones

Striated effect

Glue spreader

Credit card

Paint spread evenly

PLASTIC SCRAPERS

Paint cup

Main lever

Nozzle

AIR-BRUSH

Uniform tone

Air hose

EXAMPLE OF AN ACRYLIC PAINTING
Acrylic on canvas, 20.5 x 26.6 cm (8 x 10½ in)

Paint applied evenly using a roller

Cotton duck canvas support (surface)

Masking tape stuck on to canvas to define main shapes, and paint applied within these areas using a roller

Flatness of rollered areas enhanced by adding gel medium to the paint

Imprecise edge around shadow where paint has seeped under masking tape

EXAMPLES OF ACRYLIC PAINTS AND TECHNIQUES

Opaque effect

Extruded (squeezed) effect

Paint applied using painting knife

PURPLE ACRYLIC PAINT

YELLOW ACRYLIC PAINT

ORANGE ACRYLIC PAINT

Transparent, watercolour effect

Translucent, impasto glaze

Thick impasto with coarse texture

BLUE ACRYLIC PAINT DILUTED WITH WATER

GREEN ACRYLIC PAINT MIXED WITH GEL MEDIUM

RED ACRYLIC PAINT MIXED WITH TEXTURE PASTE

Calligraphy

CALLIGRAPHY IS BEAUTIFULLY FORMED LETTERING. The term applies to written text and illumination (the decoration of manuscripts using gold leaf and colour). The essential materials needed to practise calligraphy are a writing tool, ink, and a writing surface. Quills are among the oldest writing tools. They are usually made from goose or turkey feathers, and are noted for their flexibility and ability to produce fine lines. A quill point, however, is not very durable and constant recutting and trimming is required. The most commonly used writing instrument in western calligraphy is a detachable, metal nib held in a penholder. The metal nib is very durable, and there are a wide range of different types. Particular types of nibs – such as copperplate, speedball, and roundhand nibs – are used for specific styles of lettering. Some nibs have integral ink reservoirs and others have reservoirs that are detachable. Brushes are also used for writing, and for filling in outlined letters and painting decoration. Other writing tools used in calligraphy are fountain pens, felt-tip pens, rotring pens, and reed pens. Calligraphy inks may come in liquid form, or as a solid ink stick. Ink sticks are ground down in distilled water to form a liquid ink. The most common writing surfaces for calligraphy are good quality, smooth -surfaced papers. To achieve the best writing position, the calligrapher places the paper on a drawing board set at an angle.

EQUIPMENT USED IN BRUSH LETTERING

Brush rest

Wolf hair brush

Goat hair brush

BRUSHES AND BRUSH REST

Liquid ink made by grinding down ink stick in distilled water

Solid carbon ink stick

Ink stone

INK STICK AND STONE

PENS, NIBS, AND BRUSHES USED IN CALLIGRAPHY

PENHOLDER

COPPERPLATE NIB

SPEEDBALL NIB

ROUNDHAND NIB AND DETACHABLE INK RESERVOIR

Feather

FELT-TIP PEN

AUTOMATIC PEN

Feather stripped for better handling

REED PEN

Barrel

SQUARE SABLE BRUSH

POINTED SABLE BRUSH

Hand-cut point

GOOSE-FEATHER QUILL

GOAT HAIR BRUSH

WOLF HAIR BRUSH

FOUNTAIN PEN AND INK

Bottle of permanent black ink

Barrel

Clip

Nib

Outer cap

EXAMPLES OF LETTERING STYLES

Apex
Bowl
Curved stroke
Stem
Inner counter
Stem
Stem
Arm
Counter
Crossbar
Inner counter
Counter
Inner counter

ROMAN CAPITALS

Cap line
X line
Ascender
Curved stroke
Ear
Arch
Base line
Descender line
Crossbar
Serif
Neck
Descender
Height of letter determined by order of nib widths

ITALIC ROMAN

Slightly pinched (curved) vertical stroke
Letter filled in using brush
Inner counter
Tail
Spine
Pointed apex

VERSAL

AN ILLUMINATED MANUSCRIPT

Style of lettering called Gothic book script
Large decorative letter used to mark the opening of a chapter
Words written carefully by hand
Gold leaf
Grid lines provide guide to position of words and pictures

CHINESE LETTERING

Rice paper
Broad brush stroke
Chinese character meaning long life
Artist's stamped signature

ARTIST'S STAMP

Stamp
Stamped signature of the artist
Ink pad

DRAWING BOARD

Adjustable set square
Blade with parallel motion

EXAMPLES OF CALLIGRAPHY PAPERS

Standard European paper
Indian handmade paper
Flecked, tinted paper
Imitation parchment paper

Printmaking 1

PRINTS ARE MADE BY FOUR BASIC printing processes – intaglio, lithographic, relief, and screen. In intaglio printing, lines are engraved or etched into the surface of a metal plate. Lines are engraved by hand using sharp metal tools. They are etched by corroding the metal plate with acid, using acid-resistant ground to protect the areas not to be etched. The plate is then inked and wiped, leaving the grooves filled with ink and the surface clean. Dampened paper is laid over the plate, and both paper and plate are passed through the rollers of an etching press. The pressure of the rollers forces the paper into the grooves, so that it takes up the ink, leaving an impression on the paper. Lithographic printing is based on the antipathy between grease and water. An image is drawn on a surface – usually a stone or metal plate – with a greasy medium, such as tusche (lihographic ink). The greasy drawing is fixed on to the plate by applying an acidic solution, such as gum arabic. The surface is then dampened and rolled with ink. The ink adheres only to the greasy areas and is repelled by the water. Paper is laid on the plate and pressure is applied by means of a press. In relief printing, the non-printing areas of a wood or linoleum block are cut away using gouges, knives, and other tools. The printing areas are left raised in relief and are rolled with ink. Paper is laid on the inked block and pressure is applied by means of a press or by burnishing (rubbing) the back of the paper. The most common forms of relief printing are woodcut, wood engraving, and linocut. In screen printing, the printing surface is a mesh stretched across a wooden frame. A stencil is applied to the mesh to seal the nonprinting areas and ink is scraped through the mesh to produce an image.

THE FOUR MAIN PRINTING PROCESSES

Paper — — Printed image

— Engraved or etched image

Metal plate — — Inked area

INTAGLIO

Printed image — — Paper

Damp surface rejects ink

Ink adheres to greasy image — — Image drawn on stone with greasy medium

LITHOGRAPHIC

Paper — — Printed image

Raised figure — — Inked surface

Wood block

RELIEF

— Wooden frame

— Stencil

Ink forced through mesh

Paper — — Printed image

SCREEN

LEATHER
INK DABBER

EQUIPMENT USED IN INTAGLIO PRINTING

ROCKER   SCRIBER   ROULETTE   SCRAPER   BURNISHER   CLAMP

**ETCHING PRESS USED FOR
INTAGLIO PRINTMAKING**

Flywheel

Paper

*Felt blanket cushions and
distributes pressure
exerted by rollers*

Spoke

*Screw
pressure
adjustor*

Handle

*Top
roller*

*Position
guide*

Printed image

*Sliding bed (plank)
is wound between
steel rollers*

*Inked-up
copper plate*

GROUND

*Acid-resistant
ground rolled
on to metal
plate before
etching*

GROUND ROLLER

*Gelatine
roller*

*Wooden
handle*

**EXAMPLES OF
PRINTING
PAPERS**

EXAMPLE OF AN INTAGLIO PRINT
Annie with a Sun Hat, Jock McFadyen, 1993
Etched copper plate, 41 × 40 cm (16 × 15¾ in)

Printmaking 2

EXAMPLE OF A LITHOGRAPHIC STONE AND PRINT
Untitled, Frederic M. Pannebaker, 1972

IMAGE DRAWN ON STONE

LITHOGRAPIC PRINT

EXAMPLE OF A SCREEN PRINT
Patrons In An Art Deco Club, Unknown, 1931

SCREEN AND SQUEEGEE

Squeegee

Rubber blade

Mesh

Wooden frame

CRAYON AND HOLDER

LITHOGRAPHIC PENCIL

TUSCHE (LITHOGRAPHIC INK) PEN

ERASING STICK

EXPANDABLE SPONGE

TUSCHE (LITHOGRAPHIC
INK) STICK

RUBBING INK

INK ROLLER

MILD ACIDIC
SOLUTION

GUM ARABIC
SOLUTION

WATER-BASED SCREEN PRINTING INKS

BLUE
ACRYLIC INK

RED
ACRYLIC INK

BROWN
TEXTILE INK

EQUIPMENT USED IN RELIEF PRINTING

V-SHAPED GOUGE

INK ROLLER

Rubber roller

LINOLEUM AND WOODCUT BLOCK

U-SHAPED GOUGE

GRAVER

Linoleum

KNIFE

Side-grain wood block

SCORPER

WOOD ENGRAVING

END-GRAIN WOOD BLOCK

INKED-UP ENGRAVED BLOCK

WOOD ENGRAVING PRINT

RELIEF-PRINTING PRESS

Spiral spring

Crown

Tympan lowered on to printing block

Piston

Printed image

Staple (frame)

Printing block

Bed is rolled under platen

Bar (pressure handle)

Platen

Drum handle

Rail

Counterweight

Drum (rounce)

Leg

Pillar (post)

Foot

Mosaic

MOSAIC IS THE ART OF MAKING patterns and pictures from tesserae (small, coloured pieces of glass, marble, and other materials). Different materials are cut into tesserae using different tools. Smalti (glass enamel) and marble are cut into pieces using a hammer and a hardy (a pointed blade) embedded in a log. Vitreous glass is cut into pieces using a pair of nippers. Mosaics can be made using a direct or indirect method. In the direct method, the tesserae are laid directly into a bed of cement—based adhesive. In the indirect method, the design is drawn in reverse on paper or cloth. The tesserae are then stuck face-down on the paper or cloth using water-soluble glue. Adhesive is spread with a trowel on to a solid surface — such as a wall — and the back of the mosaic is laid into the adhesive. Finally, the paper or cloth is soaked off to reveal the mosaic. Gaps between tesserae can be filled with grout. Grout is forced into gaps by dragging a grouting squeegee across the face of the mosaic. Mosaics are usually used to decorate walls and floors, but they can also be applied to smaller objects.

EQUIPMENT FOR BREAKING MARBLE

Sawn strip of marble, ready for breaking into cubes

Mosaic hammer

Alicante (red marble) pieces

Hardy (pointed blade) embedd[ed] in a log

NIPPERS

Hardwearing, tungsten carbide tip

Handle with rubber grip

MOSAIC TOOLS

CEMENT-BASED ADHESIVE

GROUT

EXAMPLE OF A MOSAIC (DIRECT METHOD)
Seascape, Tessa Hunkin, 1993
Smalti mosaic on board
80 cm (31½ in) diameter

SMALTI (GLASS ENAMEL)

RED SMALTI

YELLOW SMALTI

BLUE SMALTI

Gold-leaf smalti

TROWEL

Notch

Steel blade

Wooden handle

GROUTING SQUEEGEE

Wooden handle

Nicobond

Ru[bber] bla[de]

STAGES IN THE CREATION OF A MOSAIC (INDIRECT METHOD)

COLOUR SKETCH
A colour sketch is drawn
in oil pastel to give a clear
impression of how the finished
mosaic will look.

REVERSE IMAGE
Tesserae are glued face-down
on reverse image on paper.
Mosaic is then attached to solid
surface and paper is removed.

MOSAIC POT

Geometric design

Grout

MOSAIC MOSQUE DESIGN

Floral design

Geometric border

*Andamenti
(line along
which tesserae
are laid)*

*Grout fills
the gaps
between the
tesserae*

*Mosaic
mounted
on board*

*Vitreous
glass cut into
triangular
shape with
nippers*

*Gold tessera
with ripple
finish*

*Gold tessera
placed upside-
down*

FINISHED MOSAIC
Goldfish, Tessa Hunkin, 1993
Vitreous glass mosaic on board
35.5 × 25.5 cm (14 × 10 in)

*Border of square
vitreous glass*

VITREOUS GLASS

**GREEN VITREOUS
GLASS WITH GOLD LEAF**

*Plain
finish*

*Ripple
finish*

**RED VITREOUS
GLASS**

SHEETS OF VITREOUS GLASS

**BLUE VITREOUS
GLASS**

Sculpture 1

THE TWO TRADITIONAL METHODS OF MAKING SCULPTURE are carving and modelling. A carved sculpture is made by cutting away the surplus from a block of hard material such as stone, marble, or wood. The tools used for carving vary according to the material being carved. Heavy steel points, claws, and chisels that are struck with a lump hammer are generally used for stone and marble. Sharp gouges and chisels that are struck with a wooden mallet are used for wood. Sculptures formed from hard materials are generally finished by filing with rasps, rifflers, and other abrasive implements. Modelling is a process by which shapes are built up, using malleable materials such as clay, plaster, and wax. The material is cut with wire-ended tools and modelled with the fingers or a variety of hardwood and metal implements. For large or intricate modelled sculptures an armature (frame), made from metal or wood, is used to provide internal support. Sculptures formed in soft materials may harden naturally or can be made more durable by firing in a kiln. Modelled sculptures are often first designed in wax or another material to be cast later in a metal (see pp. 454-455) such as bronze. The development of many new materials in the 20th century has enabled sculptors to experiment with new techniques such as construction (joining preformed pieces of material such as machine components, mirrors, and furniture) and kinetic (mobile) sculpture.

EXAMPLES OF MARBLE CARVING TOOLS

1.1 kg (2½ lb) iron head

Ash handle

LUMP HAMMER

EXAMPLES OF WOODCARVING TOOLS

CABINET RASP

STRAIGHT GOUGE

SALMON BEND GOUGE

CHISEL

Stone for sharpening woodcarving tools

Cedar box

ARKANSAS HONE-STONE

CARVING MALLET

CALLIPERS

Curved leg

Gap measures distance between two points on a sculpture

Wing nut

WIDE MARBLE CLAW

NARROW MARBLE CLAW

POINT

FLAT CHISEL

BULLNOSE CHISEL

EXAMPLES OF RIFFLERS
(FOR STONE, MARBLE, AND WOOD)

30 CM (12 IN) RIFFLER

15 CM (6 IN) RIFFLER

Surface for sharpening stonecarving tools

DIAMOND WHETSTONE

Tiny holes along the hairline made with a point

Soft skin texture tooled with a fine-toothed marble claw

DETAIL OF SLAVE'S HEAD

EXAMPLE OF A CARVED MARBLE SCULPTURE
The Rebel Slave, Michelangelo, 1513-1516
Marble, height 213 cm (7 ft)

Hair worked with a narrow claw

Translucent white marble, quarried at Carrara, Italy

Surface rubbed smooth with rifflers and pumice

Base scored with jagged parallel cuts made with point and lump hammer

The dimensions of the marble block determine the size of the sculpture

EXAMPLE OF A CARVED WOOD SCULPTURE
Mary Magdalene, Donatello, 1454-1455
Poplar wood, height 188 cm (6 ft 2 in)

Delicately modelled hand carved with a chisel

Hair highlighted with gold leaf

Figure cut from single length of poplar

Deep ridges of hair cut with a gouge

Strut gives added support to long slender limb

Wood prepared with gesso (chalk and glue) and painted

Series of tiny punch holes, made with a fine point, outline the form

Foot carved in deep relief

Rough surface made by driving a point into the marble at an oblique angle

DETAIL OF SLAVE'S FOOT

453

Sculpture 2

EXAMPLES OF MODELLING TOOLS

WIRE-ENDED CUTTING TOOL

CURVED MOULDING TOOL

SPATULA-ENDED WAX MODELLING TOOL

ROUNDED WAX MODELLING TOOL

EXAMPLES OF BRONZE FINISHING TOOLS

HOOKED RIFFLER   **POINTED RIFFLER**

SPIRIT LAMP (FOR HEATING WAX MODELLING TOOLS)

Wick

Brass holder

Glass bowl

Methylated spirit

STAGES IN THE LOST-WAX METHOD OF CASTING
Based on Mars, Giambologna, c.1546

Wax-covered wire armature

ORIGINAL MODEL
An original, solid wax model is made and preserved so that numerous replicas can be cast.

Wax riser (vertical, hollow rod)

Chaplet (iron nail)

Wax runner (horizontal, hollow rod)

HOLLOW WAX FIGURE IS CAST
A new, hollow wax model is cast from the original model. It is filled with a plaster core that is held in place with nails. Wax runners and risers are attached.

Fire-resistant clay

FIGURE IS BAKED IN CASTING MOULD
The model is encased in clay and baked. The wax melts away (through the channels made by the wax rods) and is replaced by molten bronze.

MODELLING STAND AND ARMATURE

Aluminium wire figure

Fixed iron armature support

Marine ply modelling board

Rotating table top

Tripod

Screw-hole for fastening the iron to modelling board

Aluminium table stand

Height adjustor

EXAMPLE OF A CLAY MODEL
Madonna and Child, Henry Moore, 1943
Terracotta, height 18.4 cm (7¼ in)

Clay smoothed to create the effect of soft skin

Maquette (small sketch) modelled from a solid lump of clay

Terracotta clay, fires at 1,000°C to 1,050°C (1,832°F to 1,922°F)

Incision made with serrated tool

Model for a much larger bronze sculpture

Strips of clay, added to the model, give the effect of folded drapery

Roughly worked clay

Metal riser

Metal runner

Stump left by rod will be filed down

Golden brown colour of untreated bronze

Dark brown patina

Hole left by nail will be plugged with bronze

STATUE IS STRIPPED OF CLAY
When the bronze has cooled, the clay mould is broken open to reveal the bronze statue with solid metal runners and risers.

STATUE IS FINISHED
The nails are pulled out and a large hole is made to remove the plaster core. When the metal rods have been sawn off, the sculpture is filed to refine the surface.

STATUE IS CLEANED
Finally the work is cleaned and polished. An artificial patina (colouring) is achieved by treating the surface with chemicals.

ARCHITECTURE

ANCIENT EGYPT············458
ANCIENT GREECE············460
ANCIENT ROME 1············462
ANCIENT ROME 2············464
MEDIEVAL CASTLES AND HOUSES············466
MEDIEVAL CHURCHES············468
GOTHIC 1············470
GOTHIC 2············472
RENAISSANCE 1············474
RENAISSANCE 2············476
BAROQUE AND NEOCLASSICAL 1············478
BAROQUE AND NEOCLASSICAL 2············480
BAROQUE AND NEOCLASSICAL 3············482
ARCHES AND VAULTS············484
DOMES············486
ISLAMIC BUILDINGS············488
SOUTH AND EAST ASIA············490
THE 19TH CENTURY············492
THE EARLY 20TH CENTURY············494
MODERN BUILDINGS 1············496
MODERN BUILDINGS 2············498

Ancient Egypt

FRONT VIEW OF HYPOSTYLE HALL, TEMPLE OF AMON-RE

Cornice decorated with cavetto moulding

Campaniform (open papyrus) capital

Architrave

Papyrus-bud capital

Socle

Side aisle

Central nave

Side aisle

THE CIVILIZATION OF THE ANCIENT EGYPTIANS (which lasted from about 3100 BC until it was finally absorbed into the Roman empire in 30 BC) is famous for its temples and tombs. Egyptian temples were often huge and geometric, like the Temple of Amon-Re (below and right). They were usually decorated with hieroglyphs (sacred characters used for picture-writing) and painted reliefs depicting gods, Pharaohs (kings), and queens. Tombs were particularly important to the Egyptians, who believed that the dead were resurrected in the after-life. The tombs were often decorated – as, for example, the surround of the false door opposite – in order to give comfort to the dead. The best-known ancient Egyptian tombs are the pyramids, which were designed to symbolize the rays of the sun. Many of the architectural forms used by the ancient Egyptians were later adopted by other civilizations; for example, columns and capitals were later used by the ancient Greeks (see pp. 460-461) and ancient Romans (see pp. 462-465).

Horus, the sun-god

Architrave

Stone slab forming flat roof of side aisle

SIDE VIEW OF HYPOSTYLE HALL, TEMPLE OF AMON-RE, KARNAK, EGYPT, c.1290 BC

Kepresh crown with disc

Chons, the moon-god

Amon-Re, king of the gods

Hathor, the sky-goddess

Papyrus motif

Cartouche (oval border) containing the titles of the Pharaoh (king)

Socle

Aisle running north-south

**LIMESTONE FALSE DOOR WITH HIEROGLYPHS,
TOMB OF KING TJETJI, GIZA, EGYPT, c.2400 BC**

Hieroglyph representing a house

Lintel

Disc
representing
sun or light

Eroded
image of
Tjetji

Limestone
stela
(slab)

Hoe-shaped
hieroglyph
representing
"mr" sound

Head
of false
door

Image of
Tjetji's wife

Image of
Tjetji's
daughter

**PLANT CAPITAL OF THE
PTOLEMAIC-ROMAN PERIOD,
EGYPT, 332-30 BC**

Palm
leaf

Papyrus
flower

Papyrus
leaf

Papyrus
stem

Lotus bud

Lotus stem

Cornice decorated with
cavetto moulding

Bead
moulding

Trellis
window

Rectangular pier decorated
with hieroglyphs

Elevated roof
of central nave

Clerestory

Disc representing
sun or light

Architrave

Square
abacus

Papyrus-
bud
capital

Papyriform
column

Shaft

Scene depicting a Pharaoh (king)
paying homage to the god Amon-Re

Central nave

**ANCIENT EGYPTIAN
BUILDING DECORATION**

**DECORATED WINDOW,
MEDINET HABU, EGYPT,
C.1198BC**

**ROPE AND PATERAE
DECORATION**

**CAPITAL WITH THE HEAD OF THE
SKY-GODDESS HATHOR, TEMPLE
OF ISIS, PHILAE, EGYPT, 283-47 BC**

**LOTUS AND PAPYRUS
FRIEZE DECORATION**

Ancient Greece

THE CLASSICAL TEMPLES OF ANCIENT GREECE were built according to the belief that certain forms and proportions were pleasing to the gods. There were three main ancient Greek architectural orders (styles), which can be distinguished by the decoration and proportions of their columns, capitals (column tops), and entablatures (structures resting on the capitals). The oldest is the Doric order, which dates from the seventh century BC and was used mainly on the Greek mainland and in the western colonies, such as Sicily and southern Italy. The Temple of Neptune, shown here, is a classic example of this order. It is hypaethral (roofless) and peripteral (surrounded by a single row of columns). About a century later, the more decorative Ionic order developed on the Aegean Islands. Features of this order include volutes (spiral scrolls) on capitals and acroteria (pediment ornaments). The Corinthian order was invented in Athens in the fifth century BC and is typically identified by an acanthus leaf on the capitals. This order was later widely used in ancient Roman architecture.

CAPITALS OF THE THREE ORDERS OF ANCIENT GREEK ARCHITECTURE

Abacus
Echinus
Annulet
Trachelion (neck)

DORIC CAPITAL, THE PROPYLAEUM (GATEWAY), THE ACROPOLIS, ATHENS, GREECE, 449 BC

Abacus *Lesbian leaf pattern*
Coussinet (cushion)
Cyma reversa profile
Volute
Echinus with egg and dart decoration
Eye *Palmette*

IONIC CAPITAL, THE PROPYLAEUM (GATEWAY), TEMPLE OF ATHENA POLIAS, PRIENE, GREECE, c.334 BC

Abacus
Mask
Volute
Cauliculus
Acanthus leaf
Bell-shaped core

CORINTHIAN CAPITAL FROM A STOA (PORTICO), PROBABLY FROM ASIA MINOR

TEMPLE OF NEPTUNE, PAESTUM, ITALY, c.460 BC

Raking cornice
Pediment
Trachelion (neck) *Taenia* *Triglyph* *Metope* *Glyph (channel)*
Doric entablature
Pteron (external colonnade)
Euthynteria *Drum* *Stylobate* *Column of the Doric order*

PLAN OF THE TEMPLE OF NEPTUNE, PAESTUM

Pronaos (vestibule)

Naos wall

Anta (pilaster terminating naos wall)

Naos (cella)

Peristyle

Opisthodomos (rear portico)

Pteron (external colonnade)

Hexastyle pteron (colonnade of six columns)

ANCIENT GREEK BUILDING DECORATION

Volute

FACADE, TREASURY OF ATREUS, MYCENAE, GREECE, 1350-1250 BC

Meander

FRETWORK, PARTHENON, ATHENS, GREECE, 447-436 BC

ACROTERION, TEMPLE OF APHAIA, AEGINA, GREECE, 490 BC

Griffon (gryphon)

Raking cornice

ANTEFIXA, TEMPLE OF APHAIA, AEGINA, GREECE, 490 BC

Palmette

Volute

Regula (short fillet beneath taenia)

Eaves

Cornice

Frieze

Architrave

Capital

Shaft

Crepidoma (stepped base)

Entasis (slight curve of a column)

Intercolumniation

Fluting

461

Ancient Rome 1

IN THE EARLY PERIOD OF THE ROMAN EMPIRE extensive use was made of ancient Greek architectural ideas, particularly those of the Corinthian order (see pp. 460-461). As a result, many early Roman buildings – such as the Temple of Vesta (opposite) – closely resemble ancient Greek buildings. A distinctive Roman style began to evolve in the first century AD. This style developed the interiors of buildings (the Greeks had concentrated on the exterior) by using arches, vaults, and domes inside the buildings, and by ornamenting internal walls. Many of these features can be seen in the Pantheon. Exterior columns were often used for decorative, rather than structural, purposes, as in the Colosseum and the Porta Nigra (see pp. 464-465). Smaller buildings had timber frames with wattle-and-daub walls, as in the mill (see pp. 464-465). Roman architecture remained influential for many centuries, with some of its principles being used in the 11th century in Romanesque buildings (see pp. 468-469) and also in the 15th and 16th centuries in Renaissance buildings (see pp. 474-477).

ANCIENT ROMAN BUILDING DECORATION

FESTOON, TEMPLE OF VESTA, TIVOLI, ITALY, C.80 BC

RICHLY DECORATED ROMAN OVUM

INTERIOR OF THE PANTHEON, ROME, ITALY, 118-c.128

Inner dome, following the curve of a depressed arch

Outer saucer dome

Entablature

Curved cornice

Lesene

Cornice

Triangular pediment

Concave niche

Marble veneer

Segmental pediment

Pedestal

Series of concentric, step-like rings

Oculus

Outer saucer dome

Intermediate block

Dentil ornament

Engaged pediment

Raking cornice

Pediment

Rotunda

Octastyle portico (eight-column portico)

Entablature with inscription

FRONT VIEW OF THE PANTHEON

SIDE VIEW OF THE PANTHEON

Entablature

Pitched roof

Eaves

Intermediate block

Upper cornice

Relieving arch

Opening for ventilation

Cornice

Colonnade

Ornamental band decorated with festoons

Attached fluted pilaster

FRIEZE, FORUM OF TRAJAN, ROME, ITALY, 98-113

KEYSTONE, ARCH OF TITUS, ROME, ITALY, 81

TEMPLE OF VESTA, TIVOLI, ITALY, c.80 BC

Circular naos (cella)

Architrave

Ceiling

Fascia

Corinthian entablature

Corinthian capital

Pteron (colonnade)

Naos (cella) window

Opus incertum (concrete wall faced with irregularly shaped stones)

Egg and dart decoration

Upper torus

Scotia

Lower torus

Frieze decorated with arabesques, urns, and winged horses

Jamb with corrugated surface

Naos (cella) door

Cornice

Threshold

Podium

Oculus illuminating interior of rotunda

Coffer

Stepped side of coffer

Step-like ring

Barrel vault

Passageway

Coffer

Engaged pediment

Monolithic shaft (shaft made from a single stone)

Barrel vault

Raking cornice

Pediment

Entablature

Corinthian column

Entablature

Aedicule (tabernacle)

Festoon

Fluting

Corinthian pilaster

Base

Corinthian capital

Rotunda

Portico

463

Ancient Rome 2

FRONT VIEW OF A ROMAN MILL, 1ST CENTURY BC

SIDE VIEW OF A ROMAN MILL

Lath
Pantile
Principal rafter
Verge
Wall-plate
Eaves
Wall-post
Plain fascia
Top-plate
Floorboard
Plaster coating
Intermediate floor-joist
Sill
Stud
Foundation
Grille
Joist
Boarding

Half-round ridge tile
King-strut
Lath
Pitched roof
Principal rafter
Ashlar post
Tie-beam
Plain fascia
Wall-plate
Flat soffit
Intermediate floor-joist
Top-plate
Mill wheel
Wall-post
Sill
Binder
Wattle-and-daub wall with plaster coating
Supporting post
Floor-joist
Foundation post

THE COLOSSEUM (FLAVIAN AMPHITHEATRE), ROME, ITALY, 70-82

Bracket for velarium (awning)
Crowning cornice
Barrel vault
Horizontal gangway
Arcad
Third floor
Corinthian pilaster
Round arch
Second floor
Corinthian half-column
Entablature
Ionic half-column
First floor
Doric half-column
Ground floor
External travertine shell
Intermediate shell
Inner shell

PORTA NIGRA, TRIER, GERMANY, c.240-260

Crowning cornice

Impost

Semicircular tower

Parapet

Keystone

Round-arched window

Arcaded passageway

Voussoir

Lesene

Semicircular tower

Entablature

Cornice

Frieze

Relieving arch

Arcading

Architrave

Apse (added in Middle Ages)

Attached column

Courtyard

Round arch

Entrance to town

Capital

Shaft

Base

Facade

ROMAN WATTLE-AND-DAUB WALL, 1ST CENTURY BC

Opening to staircase

Maenianum summum (gallery)

Rectangular window

String course

Cuneus (wedge of seating)

Opus quadratum (square masonry)

Arched opening to staircase

Radiating, wedge-shaped chamber

Hazel twig framework

Clay mixture

Plaster

Paintwork

Radial wall

Opus incertum (concrete wall faced with irregularly shaped stones)

Cornice

Ambulatory corridor

Attached rectangular pier

Keystone

Impost

Tuscan capital

Voussoir

Tuscan pilaster

465

Medieval castles and houses

WARFARE WAS COMMON IN EUROPE in the Middle Ages, and many monarchs and nobles built castles as a form of defence. Typical medieval castles have outer walls surrounding a moat. Inside the moat is a bailey (courtyard), protected by a chemise (jacket-wall). The innermost and strongest part of a medieval castle is the keep. There are two main types of keep: towers called donjons, such as the Tour de César and Coucy-le-Château, and rectangular keeps ("hall-keeps"), such as the Tower of London. Castles were often guarded by salients (projecting fortifications), like those of the Bastille. Medieval houses typically had timber cruck (tent-like) frames, wattle-and-daub walls, and pitched roofs, like those on medieval London Bridge (opposite).

DONJON, TOUR DE CESAR, PROVINS, FRANCE, 12TH CENTURY

Oculus — Battlements (crenellations) — Loophole — Hemispherical cupola — Conical spire — Gallery — Flying buttress — Squinch — Hexahedral hall — Vaulted room — Semicircular turret — Main entrance — Fireplace — Bailey — Staircase to chemise (jacket-wall) — Embrasure — Chemise (jacket-wall) — Plain impost — Depressed cupola — Vaulted staircase — Motte

Loophole

SALIENT, CAERNARVON CASTLE, BRITAIN, 1283-1323

Timber cruck frame

CRUCK-FRAMED HOUSE, BRITAIN, c.1200

Blind, rounded relieving arch — Merlon — Battlements (crenellations) — Tetrahedral spire — Crenel — Loophole — Rectangular turret — Wooden staircase leading to entrance above ground level — Quoin — Timber-framed house — Cornice — Buttress — Round-arched window with twin openings — Cruck frame — Paling

TOWER OF LONDON, BRITAIN, FROM 1070

Curtain wall — Pointed relieving arch — Semicircular relieving arch — Plain string course — Bracket decorated with scroll moulding — Rectangular window — Sunken rectangular panel — Round-arched window — Semicircular salient — Loophole — Lateral circular salient

THE BASTILLE, PARIS, FRANCE, 14TH CENTURY

MEDIEVAL LONDON BRIDGE, BRITAIN, 1176 (WITH 14TH-CENTURY BATTLEMENTED BUILDING, NONESUCH HOUSE, AND TWO-TOWERED GATE)

Gate-house

Battlemented building

Chapel pier

Railing

Onion-shaped dome

Pitched roof

Shaped gable

Timber framing with ornamental woodwork

Nonesuch House

Crypt of Becket Chapel

Starling

Pier

Two-towered gate

Pointed Gothic stone arch

Oriel window

Timber framing

DONJON, COUCY-LE-CHATEAU, AISNE, FRANCE, 1225-1245

Cornice

Pointed arch

Loophole

Round arch

Parapet

Gallery

Pointed arch

Inner hall

Tribune (elevated platform)

Springing point of rib vault

Projecting rectangular pier

Window opening

Chimney-shaft

Rectangular opening

Fireplace

Archivolt decorated with torus and fascia

Bridge to castle entrance

Steps

Mezzanine (entresol) housing drawbridge windlass

Entrance

Moat

Passageway

Dodecahedral second floor

Engaged colonette

Dodecahedral first floor

Embrasure

Dodecahedral ground floor

Passageway inside structure of outer wall

Four-centred relieving arch

Niche

Corbel with sculptural decoration

Capital

String course

Ruin of segmental ramp leading to chemise (jacket-wall)

Medieval churches

DURING THE MIDDLE AGES, large numbers of churches were built in Europe. European churches of this period typically have high vaults supported by massive piers and columns. In the 10th century, the Romanesque style developed. Romanesque architects adopted many Roman or early Christian architectural ideas, such as cross-shaped ground-plans – like that of Angoulême Cathedral (opposite) – and the basilican system of a nave with a central vessel and side aisles. In the mid-12th century, flying buttresses and pointed vaults appeared. These features later became widely used in Gothic architecture (see pp. 470-471). Bagneux Church (opposite) has both styles: a Romanesque tower, and a Gothic nave and choir.

ABBEY OF ST. FOI, CONQUES, FRANCE, c.1050-c.1130

Finial

Octahedral spire

Incline

Circular staircase-turret

Loophole

Octahedral crossing tower

Round-arched window

Series of archivolts decorated with tori

Series of jambs decorated with colonettes

Pitched roof

Barrel vault

CHURCH-ROOF BOSS, BRITAIN

ROMANESQUE CAPITALS

"THE FLIGHT INTO EGYPT" CAPITAL, CATHEDRAL OF ST. LAZARE, AUTUN, FRANCE, 1120-1130

"CHRIST IN MAJESTY" CAPITAL, BASILICA OF ST. MADELEINE, VEZELAY, FRANCE, 1120-1140

Tribune (elevated platform)

Semicircular transverse arch

Vaulting shaft

Attached half-column

Round arcade arch

Romanesque capital

Twin opening of gallery bays

Arcade

Square central shaft

Compound pier

Lean-to roof

Transept

Quadrant arch

Colonette

Round stilted arch

Attached half-column

Side aisle

Main vessel

Side aisle

GROUND-PLAN OF ANGOULEME CATHEDRAL, FRANCE, FROM c.1105

Heavily moulded transverse arch

Crossing

Transept chapel

Chevet (choir with round apse and chapels)

Transept

Formeret

Engaged column

Dome

Buttress

Transverse arch with plain fascia

Nave

Nave bay

Clustered column

Vestibule

CHOIR, CHURCH OF ST. SERGE, ANGERS, FRANCE, c.1215-1220

Historiated boss

Longitudinal ridge-rib

Loophole

Diagonal rib with torus moulding

Cell

Gable

Domed rib-vault

Transverse arch

Lierne

Historiated keystone

Round-arched window

Tas-de-charge

Polyhedral abacus

Cubic abacus

Foliated capital

Attached colonette

Embrasure

Cornice

Rectangular apse

Vaulting shaft

Impost with foliated frieze

Arcade column

Bay of main vessel

Octahedral socle

Rectangular side-chapel

BAGNEUX CHURCH, FRANCE, 1170-1190

Moulded rib with an arris between two tori

Flying buttress

Roof space

Cell

Polyhedral abacus

Transverse arch

Tower vault

Square-roofed pinnacle

Lean-to roof

Oculus

Exterior wall

Triforium

Tower

Foliated capital

Pointed arch

Triple vaulting-shaft

Torus moulding

Quadripartite vault

Colonette

Formeret

Tower-vault oculus

Attached compound pier

Recessed panel

Corbel

Round arch

Pier buttress

Impost

Embrasure

Pier supporting tower

Weathering

Side aisle

Attached half-column

Base

Square socle

Intrados of arch with flat band between two tori

Nave column

Compound pier

Arcade

Nave

Choir

Octahedral socle

Bay

Attached colonette

469

Gothic 1

GOTHIC STAINED GLASS WITH FOLIATED SCROLL MOTIF, ON WOODEN FORM

GOTHIC BUILDINGS are characterized by rib vaults, pointed or lancet arches, flying buttresses, decorative tracery and gables, and stained-glass windows. Typical Gothic buildings include the Cathedrals of Salisbury and old St. Paul's in England, and Notre Dame de Paris in France (see pp. 472-473). The Gothic style developed out of Romanesque architecture in France (see pp. 468-469) in the mid-12th century, and then spread throughout Europe. The decorative elements of Gothic architecture became highly developed in buildings of the English Decorated style (late 13th-14th century) and the French Flamboyant style (15th-16th century). These styles are exemplified by the tower of Salisbury Cathedral and the staircase in the Church of St. Maclou (see pp. 472-473), respectively. In both of these styles, embellishments such as ballflowers and curvilinear (flowing) tracery were used liberally. The English Perpendicular style (late 14th-15th century), which followed the Decorated style, emphasized the vertical and horizontal elements of a building. A notable feature of this style is the hammer-beam roof.

GROUND-PLAN OF SALISBURY CATHEDRAL

Altar
Square east end
Trinity Chapel (Lady Chapel)
Monument
High altar
Reredos (choir-screen)
Processional path
Side chapel
South choir-aisle
Choir
Sacristy
East transept
Choir-stall
Crossing
Organ
Transept aisle
West transept
Staircase
Crossing pier
Arcade pier (nave pier)
Pier buttress
Arcade
North porch
Main vessel
South aisle
Nave
North aisle
Facade wall
Turret

GOTHIC TORUS WITH BALLFLOWERS

Limestone block
Block members carved into rolls
Block members cut polygonally
Pencil guideline

Early stage of ballflower carving

BLOCK AFTER INITIAL CUTTING

BLOCK WITH MEMBERS CUT INTO ROLLS

Torus
Ballflower
Fillet
Mason's mark

FINISHED BLOCK

Trinity Chapel (Lady Chapel)
Choir
Finial
Octahedral pinnacle with small spire
Blind semi-arch
Staggered triple lancet windows
Turret-like pinnacle
Parapet decorated with blind arches filled with trefoils
Mullion
Stained glass
Base
Cornice
Buttress
Lean-to roof
East transept facade

NORTH SIDE, SALISBURY
CATHEDRAL, BRITAIN, 1220-1280
(STEEPLE AND SPIRE ADDED
DURING 14TH CENTURY)

WEST FACADE,
SALISBURY CATHEDRAL

Weather-vane

Orb

Spire

Band with
lozenge
decoration

Semi-attached
gable with
small pilasters

Turret-like
pinnacle

Ballflower
decoration

Spire-like
pinnacle

Blind
gabled
arch

Traceried parapet
with lozenge
decoration

Octahedral
turret

Gable

Row of blind
arches filled
with trefoils

Battlemented
cornice

Octafoil

Cinquefoil moulding

Angle
buttress

West transept
facade

Pier buttress

Weathering

Trefoil
decoration

North
porch

Archivolt

Trefoil in a
spandrel

Blind rhombus tracery
filled with a quatrefoil

Pitched roof

Finial

Staggered
triple lancet
window

Parapet

Small
gable
crowning
buttress

Angle
buttress

North porch

Blind semi-arch

Lateral
porch

Main porch

Crocket

Aureole

Gable

Staggered triple
lancet window

Spire

Parapet

Row of blind
trefoil arches

Blind pointed
arches filled
with twin
lancets and
quatrefoils

Projecting
turret

Row of gabled
niches under
trefoil arches

Niche under small
gabled roof

Nave

Blind lancet

Flying buttress

Spire

Moulded side
of gable

Spire-like
pinnacle

Pitched roof

Flying buttress

Lateral turret

Small gable
crowning
buttress

Crocket

Buttress

Twin lancet window under pointed
arch, crowned by a quatrefoil

471

Gothic 2

CURVILINEAR (FLOWING) TRACERY FROM A
BALUSTRADE, 14TH OR 15TH CENTURY

Cyma reversa
(reversed ogee curve)

Cavetto
moulding

Plain fascia

Moulded
cornice

Cavetto
moulding with
elongated
lower part

Ogee
curve

Mouchette
(curved
dagger)

Cusp

Drop
shape

Cavetto moulding

Trefoil

Mouchette
(curved dagger)

Foliated
scrollwork

Pointed arch

Winding
cornice

Rectangular
buttress

Attached gable

Gabled
canopy

Statue

Base

Basket arch

Flamboyant
tracery

Cherub

Crocket

Figure

Niche

Attached
gable

Square
pillar

Dagger

Round
arch

Socle

Cross
motif

Base decorated
with ovolo
mouldings

Octahedral
spire

Parapet

Turret-like
pinnacle

Angle
buttress

Lancet window
with twin lancets
and crowned
with a quatrefoil

Niche

TOWER AND PART OF THE NAVE
AND CHOIR, OLD ST. PAUL'S
CATHEDRAL, LONDON,
BRITAIN, 1087-1666

Tower

Pointed arch
filled with
geometrical tracery

Turret-like
pinnacle

Flying
buttress

Mullion

Pitched roof

Lancet window

Blind lancet arch

Window filled
with early English
Perpendicular-
style tracery

Buttress

Octahedral
chapter-house

Oculus

Cloister

Gable

Couronnement

Parapet decorated
with quatrefoils

Pointed arch filled
with tracery and
three lancet windows

Clerestory
wall

Lean-to
roof

Outer wall
of side aisl

Weathering

Oculus filled
with multifoil

Early English-style window

Nave

Transept facade

Choir

Ridge

Common rafter

Architrave of window zone, also acting as collar-beam

Principal

Attached baluster

Attached column

Strut

Raised surface

Hammer-post

Bevelled edge

Arched brace

Wooden panel

Hammer-beam

Gothic window tracery

Collar-beam decorated with pearl motif

Gothic window

Arched brace

Brace

Bracket

Impost

SPIRE AND TRANSEPT ROOF, CATHEDRAL OF NOTRE DAME DE PARIS, FRANCE, c.1163-1250

Rafter

Straight brace

Beam

Gable

Round arch

Pinnacle

Oculus

Blind trefoil

Lancet arch

Trefoil arch

Cusp

Quatrefoil

Colonette

Pointed arch

Lesene

Lancet arch

Balustrade

Mullion

Triangular cornice

Cornice with chamfered edge

Geometrical tracery

Trefoil arch

Stud

Balustrade

Scissor brace

Upper collar

Principal rafter

Ridge-board

Common rafter

Octahedral spire

Roof truss of nave and transept

TRUSS OF HAMMER-BEAM ROOF, THE UPPER FRATER (LATER BLACKFRIARS' PLAYHOUSE), LONDON, BRITAIN, PROBABLY 14TH CENTURY

TYPICAL GOTHIC FEATURES

FLYING BUTTRESS OVER SIDE AISLES, MILAN CATHEDRAL, ITALY, C.1385-1485

GARGOYLE, HORSLEY CHURCH, DERBYSHIRE, BRITAIN, C.1450

Vertical strut

Intermediate collar

Raised valley-rafter

Beam

Jack-rafter

Clasped purlin

Lower collar

Scissor-beam

King-post

Queen-post

Tie-beam

Passing brace

HAMMER-BEAM ROOF, CHURCH OF ST. BOTOLPH, TRUNCH, NORFOLK, BRITAIN, 1360-1380

Renaissance 1

THE RENAISSANCE was a European movement – lasting roughly from the 14th century to the mid-17th century – in which the arts and sciences underwent great changes. In architecture, these changes were marked by a return to the classical forms and proportions of ancient Roman buildings. The Renaissance originated in Italy, and the buildings most characteristic of its style can be found there, such as the Palazzo Strozzi shown here. Mannerism is a branch of the Renaissance style that distorts the classical forms; an example is the Laurentian Library staircase. As the Renaissance style spread to other European countries, many of its features were incorporated into the local architecture; for example, the Château de Montal in France (see pp. 476-477) incorporates aedicules (tabernacles).

Crowning cornice

Arche window

Round arch

Light

Rustication

Arched doorway

Rectangular window

SIDE VIEW OF PALAZZO STROZZI, FLORENCE, ITALY, 1489 (BY G. DA SANGALLO, B. DA MAIANO, AND CRONACA)

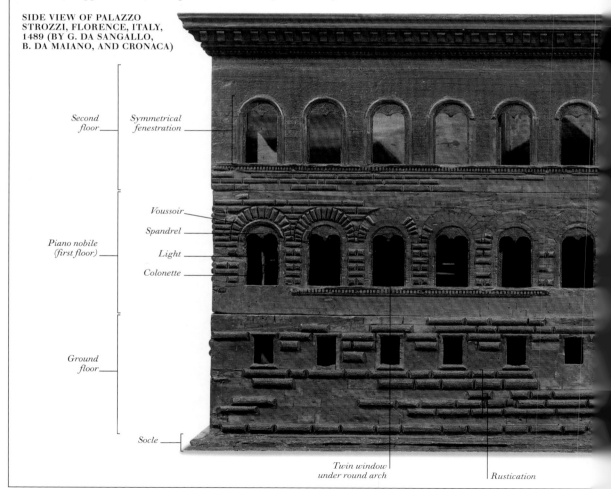

Second floor

Symmetrical fenestration

Voussoir

Spandrel

Piano nobile (first floor)

Light

Colonette

Ground floor

Socle

Twin window under round arch

Rustication

DETAILS FROM ITALIAN RENAISSANCE BUILDINGS

PANEL FROM DRUM OF DOME,
FLORENCE CATHEDRAL, 1420-1436

COFFERING IN DOME,
PAZZI CHAPEL,
FLORENCE, 1429-1461

STAIRCASE,
LAURENTIAN LIBRARY,
FLORENCE, 1559

PORTICO, VILLA ROTUNDA,
VICENZA, 1567-1569

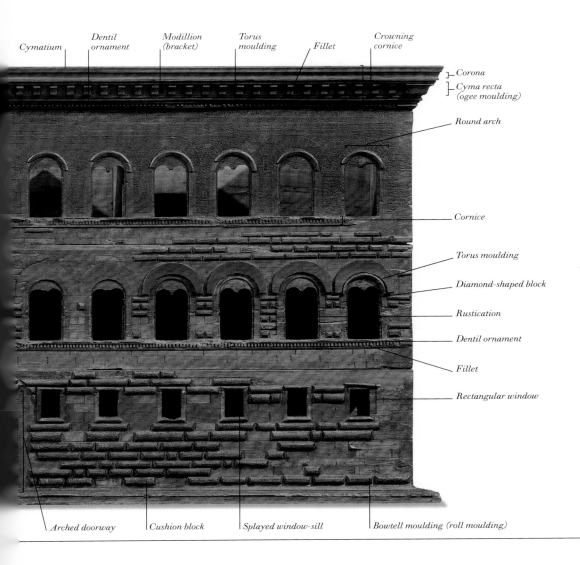

Cymatium

Dentil ornament

Modillion (bracket)

Torus moulding

Fillet

Crowning cornice

Corona

Cyma recta (ogee moulding)

Round arch

Cornice

Torus moulding

Diamond-shaped block

Rustication

Dentil ornament

Fillet

Rectangular window

Arched doorway

Cushion block

Splayed window-sill

Bowtell moulding (roll moulding)

Renaissance 2

**DETAILS FROM
EUROPEAN
RENAISSANCE
BUILDINGS**

STONE WALL, QUOINS,
AND SHELL DECORATION,
CASA DE LAS CONCHAS,
SALAMANCA, SPAIN, 1475-1483

SPIRAL-STAIRCASE
TOWER, CHATEAU DE
BLOIS, FRANCE, 1514-1530

CONICAL DOME, CHATEAU
DE CHAMBORD, FRANCE,
1519-1547

PAIR OF CHIMNEY-STACKS, PALAIS
DE FONTAINEBLEAU, FRANCE, FROM 1528

Chimney-stack

Ridge of
half-round tiles

Pitched roof

Finial

Medallion

Pinnacle

Foliated volute with
dolphin head

Gable

Head-shaped
keystone

Dormer window

Frieze with
shell-pattern
decoration

Finial

Ionic capital with
head-shaped
decoration

Putto holding
candelabrum

Blind pediment

Grotesque
figure

Medallion with
bust of Robert
de Montal

Lesene decorated
with paterae

Frieze decorated
with sculptural
wreaths, tendrils, and
grotesque figures

Lesene

Pedestal

Dado

Hipped roof

Conical spire
of turret

Fish-scale tile

Belvedere

Keystone
decorated
with scroll
ornament

Cornice
decorated with
fascias and an
ogee moulding

Rectangular
window

Transom

Aedicule
(tabernacle)

Double pilaster

Mullion

Shell

Concave,
arched niche

Small pier
decorated
with
statuette in
concave
niche

Cornice

Frieze with
scroll motif

Pseudo-Corinthian
capital

Plinth | Cornice | Architrave | Portal | Pilaster

476

**NORTH-WING STAIRCASE,
CHATEAU DE MONTAL**

Hipped roof

Eaves with
oversailing fascias
and fillets

Cornice with
fascias and ogee
mouldings

Rib vault

Column

Second-floor
landing

First-floor
landing

Pier supporting
flight of stairs

Conical spire

Turret

Loophole

Conical
corbel

Flight of
stairs

Lesene

Handrail

Pier supporting
first-floor landing

Riser   Tread

**CAMPANILE, CHURCH OF ST. EUSTACHE, PARIS,
FRANCE, 1532-1640**

Weather-vane

Orb

Fish-scale tile

Hemispherical
dome

Semicircular
torus moulding

Weathering

Ogee moulding

Fillet

Plain fascia

Small
architrave

Volute

Emphasized
keystone

Cincture

Zinc
plating

Archivolt

Plain fascia

Cavetto
moulding

Capital

Fillet

Square pillar

**GLOBE THEATRE, LONDON,
BRITAIN, 1599**

Balustrade

Thatched roof

Loft used as
storage room

Window stage

Outer wall

Railing

Post supporting
bay window

Upper-gallery
support

Stage-door

Standing
room

Bench

Round pillar
(stage-post)

Square,
carved base

Ornamental
panelling

Balcony
stage

Stage
cover

Hipped roof

Turret

Pitched
roof

Timber-
framed hut,
housing
windlass

Music gallery

Light curtain

Ornamental panelling
with concave brace
decoration

Door to
dressing-rooms

Box (gentlemen's
room)

Upper gallery
(twopenny
gallery)

Middle
gallery

Lower
gallery

Study (inner stage)
with traverse (crossing)

Platform
stage

Low
balustrade

Paling

Door to
tiring-house

Partition
separating galleries
from boxes

Baroque and neoclassical 1

THE BAROQUE STYLE EVOLVED IN THE EARLY 17TH CENTURY in Rome. It is characterized by curved outlines and ostentatious decoration, as can be seen in the Italian church details (right). The baroque style was particularly widely favoured in Italy, Spain, and Germany. It was also adopted in Britain and France, but with adaptations. The British architects Sir Christopher Wren and Nicholas Hawksmoor, for example, used baroque features – such as the concave walls of St. Paul's Cathedral and the curved buttresses of the Church of St. George in the East (see pp. 480-481) – but they did so with restraint. Similarly, the curved buttresses and volutes of the Parisian Church of St. Paul-St. Louis are relatively plain. In the second half of the 17th century, a distinct classical style (known as neoclassicism) developed in northern Europe as a reaction to the excesses of baroque. Typical of this new style were churches such as the Madeleine (a proposed facade is shown below), as well as secular buildings such as the Cirque Napoleon (opposite) and the buildings of the British architect Sir John Soane (see pp. 482-483). In early 18th-century France, an extremely lavish form of baroque developed, known as rococo. The balcony from Nantes (see pp. 482-483) with its twisted ironwork and head-shaped corbels is typical of this style.

DETAILS FROM ITALIAN BAROQUE CHURCHES

SCROLLED BUTTRESS, CHURCH OF ST. MARIA DELLA SALUTE, VENICE, 1631-1682

STATUE OF THE ECSTASY OF ST. THERESA, CHURCH OF ST. MARIA DELLA VITTORIA, ROME, 1645-1652

Attic storey — Round-arched window — Twin pilaster — Coved dome — Triple keystone — Triangular pediment — Balustrade — Re-entrant entablature — Composite capital — Attached triangular pediment — Blind window — Composite column — Composite pilaster — Socle

Raking cornice — Frieze — Panel — Door jamb — Architrave

Attached segmental pediment — Lantern — Parapet — Cornice — Finial

Dentil ornament — Urn — Modillion (bracket) — Cornice — Entablature — Raised panel — Festoon — Intermediate cornice — Volute — Fluted shaft — Base — Blind door

PROPOSED FACADE, THE MADELEINE (NEOCLASSICAL), PARIS, FRANCE, 1764 (BY P. CONTANT D'IVRY)

CIRQUE NAPOLEON (NEOCLASSICAL), PARIS, FRANCE, 1852 (BY J.I. HITTORFF)

EXTERIOR

Rectangular panel

Small polyhedral roof

Attached colonette

Polyhedral iron roof

Projecting entablature

Palmette

Sculpted frieze

Cornice

Pedestal

Smooth, vertical rustication

Smooth rustication

Statue of Amazon on horseback

Hanging wreath

Dado (die)

Plinth

Projecting pedestal

Eagle carrying festoons

INTERIOR

King-post

Statue of Minerva

Tie-beam

Orb

Painted inner roof

Brace

Polyhedral lantern

Roll moulding

Strut

Straight brace

Projecting entablature

Crest

Projecting socle

Outer wall

Attached Corinthian column

Frieze painted with scenes from classical mythology

Circle (auditorium)

Finial with cavetto moulding

Foliated panel

Transverse arch

Window hood-mould

Crowning cornice

Fascia

Volute

Dentil

Barrel vault

Raised window jamb

Clerestory level

Rectangular door leading to roofed space

Groin vault

Curved buttress

Short pilaster

Gallery level

Semi-parabolic curve

Modillion (bracket)

Semicircular arched window

Cornice

Pier-shaped pinnacle

Corinthian capital

Architrave decorated with oversailing fascias

Gallery

Cornice

Depressed arch

Foliated frieze

Small cupola

Pendentive

Balustrade

Oeil-de-boeuf ("ox-eye") window

Keystone decorated with scroll ornament

Archivolt

Formeret (wall rib)

Cornice

Archivolt decorated with plain fascias

Window jamb

Arcade

Round arch

Window-sill

Round arch

Buttress

Re-entrant corner

cade el

Base

Outer wall

Doorway connecting chapels

Socle

Side chapels

Main vessel

Side chapels

NAVE, CHURCH OF ST. PAUL-ST. LOUIS (FRENCH BAROQUE), PARIS, FRANCE, FROM 1627 (BY E. MARTELLANGE)

Baroque and neoclassical 2

ARABESQUE

Volute
Palmette
Tendril
Cornucopia

BAY-LEAF GARLAND

Bayberry
Bay leaf

PATERA

Petal
Fillet
Rosette
Ovolo (quarter-round) moulding

DECORATIVE MOULDINGS FROM ENGLISH NEOCLASSICAL BUILDINGS

Raking cornice
Representation in bas-relief of conversion of St. Paul

TRIANGULAR PEDIMENT, WEST FACADE, ST. PAUL'S CATHEDRAL

Plain pilaster
Attic storey
Entablature
Architrave
Cornice
Small pilaster
Pedestal
Semicircular cornice
Plinth
Concave, arched niche
Attached Corinthian column
Raking cornice
Pediment
Free-standing Corinthian column
Projecting side portal

MODEL BUILT IN 1674 OF PROPOSED EXTERIOR OF ST. PAUL'S CATHEDRAL (ENGLISH BAROQUE), LONDON, BRITAIN (BY C. WREN)

Cross
Orb
Small dome
Entablature
Pedestal
Gallery with balustrade
Arcade
Convex moulding
Lantern
Circular lucarne window
Dome
Plat lesene
Curved buttress
Round arch
Corinthian pilaster
Rectangular pier
Sunken lunette
Sunken panel

480

CHURCH OF ST. GEORGE IN THE EAST (ENGLISH BAROQUE), LONDON, BRITAIN, 1714-1734 (BY N. HAWKSMOOR)

SOUTH SIDE **WEST FACADE**

Fluted, circular pinnacle

Fluted capital — Pierced parapet

Plain buttress — Semicircular window

Urn — Platband

Sunken panel — Octahedral dome

Round-arched window — Triple keystone

Oeil-de-boeuf ("ox-eye") window — Cornice

Lateral pilaster-strip

Semicircular crypt-window

Octahedral turret

Plain frieze

East pediment

Semicircular apse

Emphasized keystone

Emphasized quoin

Plain pedestal — Square post — Label mould — Side entrance

Cornice — Steeple

Octahedral lantern — Stepped archivolt

Square stone block — Parapet

Three-tier belfry — Set-back buttress

Pepper-pot lantern — Cornice decorated with ogee moulding and fascias

Broken pediment — Finial

Ionic capital — Volute

Raking cornice

Continuous hood-mould

Triple band

Platband

Dog-leg staircase set in oval stone walls — Curved buttress

Ionic twin columns

Attic of drum

Drum

Arcade

Pedestal

Stepped tetrahedral roof — Statuette

Urn

Entablature — Twin columns

Rectangular window — Cruciform pedestal

Stepped cornice — Circular lucarne window

Triangular lesene

Lantern

Dome

Cornice

Raking cornice of facade pediment

Dentil ornament

Frieze

Corinthian capital

Corinthian twin pilasters

Dado

Round-arched window

Concave wall

Re-entrant — Doorway — Architrave

Emphasized keystone — Crepidoma (stepped base)

Corinthian capital

Rectangular vestibule

Baroque and neoclassical 3

DETAILS FROM BAROQUE, NEOCLASSICAL, AND ROCOCO BUILDINGS

CORNER OF THE NEW STATE PAPER OFFICE (NEOCLASSICAL), LONDON, BRITAIN, 1830-1831 (BY J. SOANE)

PORTICO, THE VYNE, HAMPSHIRE, BRITAIN, 1654 (NEOCLASSICAL)

GILT IRONWORK FROM SCREEN, PALAIS DE VERSAILLES, FRANCE, 1669-1674 (FRENCH BAROQUE)

WINDOW, PALAZZO STANGA, CREMONA, ITALY, EARLY 18TH CENTURY (ROCOCO)

ATLAS (MALE CARYATID), UPPER BELVEDERE, VIENNA, AUSTRIA, 1721 (GERMAN-STYLE BAROQUE)

BALCONY, NANTES, FRANCE, 1730-1740 (ROCOCO)

Classical-style entablature

Pantile (S-shaped roofing tile)

Fascia

Curved corbel

Smooth rustication

Cornice

Window jamb

Cornice

Frieze

Architrave

Eaves

Scroll-shaped corbel

Second-floor window

Drip-cap

Cornice

Frieze

Window architrave

First-floor window

Window-sill in the form of a frieze

Ground-floor window

Splayed window-si[ll]

MASONRY OF A NICHE IN THE ROTUNDA (NEOCLASSICAL), BANK OF ENGLAND, LONDON, BRITAIN, 1794 (BY J. SOANE)

Scoop-pattern concave moulding

Keystone

Frieze

Spandrel

Semi-dome

Voussoir

Rotunda wall

Flat, rectangular niche

Rounded niche

Flat, square niche

Vermiculated rustication

TYRINGHAM HOUSE (NEOCLASSICAL), BUCKINGHAMSHIRE, BRITAIN, 1793-1797 (BY J. SOANE)

**ROOF LEVEL
(ATTIC LEVEL)**

*Space for illumination
above unroofed central hall*

Chimney-stack

*Space above
unroofed main
staircase*

Flat roof

*Oculus illuminating
secondary staircase*

Parapet rail

Balustrade

Baluster   *Cornice*

Attic storey of convex portico

Cornice

**FIRST-FLOOR LEVEL
(CHAMER FLOOR)**

*Upper level of
central hall, open
to floor below*

Main staircase

Secondary staircase

Abacus

*Triangular
pilaster*

Pilaster capital

*Attached Tuscan
twin pilasters*

*First-floor storey
of convex portico*

Window-sill

Bow front

**GROUND-FLOOR LEVEL
(PRINCIPAL FLOOR)**

Withdrawing-room

Central hall

*Library and
breakfast-room*

Main staircase

Water-closet (toilet)

Eating-room

Secondary staircase

*Segmented
lintel course*

*Band incised with
Greek-style fret
ornament*

Window-sill

Window architrave

Window jamb

Base

Basement

Plinth

Horizontal rustication

*Vestibule
(entrance hall)*

*Ground-floor storey
of convex portico*

**FACADE OF
TYRINGHAM HOUSE**

*Chimney-
stack*

Voussoir

Basement window

Entrance door

*Circular
entrance steps*

Rail

Baluster

Parapet

Balustrade

Cornice

Entablature

Capital

Shaft

Ionic column

Base

PROSTYLE COLONNADE

Arches and vaults

ARCHES ARE CURVED STRUCTURES used to bridge spans and to support the weight of upper parts of buildings, such as domes, as in St. Paul's Cathedral (below) and the antique temple (opposite). The voussoirs (wedge-shaped blocks) that form an arch (right) support each other and convert the downward force of the weight of the building into an outward force. This outward force is in turn transferred to buttresses, piers, or abutments. A vault is an arched roof or ceiling. There are four main types of vault (opposite). A barrel vault is a single vault, semicircular in cross-section; a groin vault consists of two barrel vaults intersecting at right-angles; a rib vault is a groin vault reinforced by ribs; and a fan vault is a rib vault in which the ribs radiate from the springing point (where the arch begins) like a fan.

PARTS OF AN ARCH

Voussoir · Keystone · Crown · Abutment · Keystone · Extrados · Haunch · Intrados (soffit) · Abutment · Abutment · Impost · Intrados (soffit) · Springing point · Abutment · Span

FRONT

SIDE

ARCHES AND BASE OF DOME, ST. PAUL'S CATHEDRAL, LONDON, BRITAIN, 1675-1710 (BY C. WREN)

Inner dome · Colonnade · Pilaster · Passageway · Base · Cornice · Pendentive · Opening to passageway · Pedestal of outer dome · "Whispering Gallery" · Triangular buttress · Moulded bracket · Semi-dome · Upper barrel-vaulted passage opening on to side aisle · Abutment · Strut built into masonry to strengthen pier (added in the 20th century)

Upper arch (concealing difference in heights between main arch and minor arches) · Extrados · Intrados (soffit) · Springing point · Impost · Round arch · Barrel vault · Passage leading to side aisle · Minor arch leading to side aisle · Main arch leading to nave · Pier · Minor arch

TYPES OF ARCH

HORSESHOE ARCH (MOORISH ARCH), GREAT MOSQUE, CORDORA, SPAIN, 785

BASKET ARCH (SEMI-ELLIPTICAL ARCH), PALATINE CHAPEL, AIX-LA-CHAPELLE, FRANCE, 790-798

TUDOR ARCH, TOWER OF LONDON, BRITAIN, C.1086-1097

LANCET ARCH, WESTMINSTER ABBEY, LONDON, BRITAIN, 1503-1519

TREFOIL ARCH, BEVE MINSTER, YORKSHI BRITAIN, C.1300

TYPES OF VAULT

Transverse rib

Temporary brace

Temporary structure used to centre vault

Horizontal abutment

BARREL VAULT (TUNNEL VAULT; WAGON VAULT)

Barrel vault

Voussoir

Right-angled intersection

Groin

GROIN VAULT

Transverse ridge-rib

Longitudinal ridge-rib

Transverse arch

Diagonal rib

RIB VAULT

Tierceron (secondary rib)

Ridge-rib

Springing point

Concave-sided lozenge

Panel

FAN VAULT

ENGLISH BOND BRICKWORK OF GROIN VAULT AND RIB VAULT

Right-angled intersection

Groin

Header

Stretcher

Springing point

Cell of barrel vault

EXTRADOS OF GROIN VAULT

Stretcher

Header

Cell

Extrados of diagonal rib

Springing point

EXTRADOS OF RIB VAULT

INTERIOR DECORATION OF COFFERED VAULT

Compass

Square

Hammer

Coffer (square sunken panel)

Chamfered edge

Arris moulding

Mason's tools

COMPOSITE MODEL OF ANTIQUE FRENCH TEMPLE

Coved dome

Lesene

Series of plain fascias

Re-entrant angle

Cavetto moulding

Fillet

Cornice

Plain frieze

Architrave

Ionic capital

Chamfered corner

Keystone decorated with scroll

Plain Ionic column

Shaft

Scotia

Plinth

Dado

Base

Pedestal of lantern

Archivolt decorated with plain fascias

Abutment

Dentil

Lantern

Coved dome

Pedestal of dome

Entablature

Extrados of diagonal rib

Fluted Ionic column

Round arch

Cornice

Horizontal band

Twisted vertical band

Naos (celia)

Pedestal of column

Intercolumniation

Ionic column with twisted vertical bands (wreaths) and horizontal bands

Domes

A DOME IS A CONVEX ROOF. Domes are categorized according to the shapes of both the base and the section through the centre of the dome. The base may be circular, square, or polygonal (many-sided), depending on the plan of the drum (the walls on which the dome rests). The section of a dome may be the same shape as any arch (see pp. 484-485). Various types of dome are illustrated here: a hemispherical dome, which has a circular base and a semicircular section; a saucer dome, which has a circular base and a segmental (less than a semicircle) section; a polyhedral dome, which is a dome on a polygonal base whose sides meet at the top of the dome; and an onion dome, which has a circular or polygonal base and an ogee-shaped section. Many domes have a lantern (a turret with windows) to provide light inside.

LANTERN AND UPPER DOME TIMBERING, ST. PAUL'S CATHEDRAL

DOME TIMBERING, CHURCH OF THE SORBONNE, PARIS, FRANCE, 1635-1642 (BY J. LEMERCIER)

- Ogee-curved dome
- Window zone
- Pedestal
- Floorboard
- Ashlar piece
- Pin
- Short strut
- Mortise-and-tenon joint
- Principal rafter
- Straight brace
- Vertical post
- Tie-beam
- Circular baseplate
- Common rafter
- Straight brace
- Deeply projecting pier buttress
- Cornice
- Depressedhood-mould
- Circular lucarne window
- Floor-joist
- Hood-mould
- Waisted-oval lucarne window
- Ogee-curved window-frame
- Shaft connecting lantern and church interior

ROOF WITH LANTERN AND ONION DOME

- Weathercock
- Ellipsoid orb
- Keeled lesene
- Fish-scaletile
- Octahedral base
- Sloping roof
- Round arch
- Attached pillar
- Vertical band
- Oversailing fascia
- Octahedral base of lantern
- Onion dome
- Oversailing fascia
- Tetrahedral capital
- Return
- Window
- Torus
- Fillet
- Lantern
- Tetrahedral roof

REPRESENTATION OF DOME METALLING, CHURCH OF THE SORBONNE

- Cross
- Square rib
- Astragal
- Volute
- Roll moulding
- Buttress
- Volute
- Cornice
- Projecting pier buttress
- Inverted demi-heart torus moulding
- Waisted-oval lucarne window
- Small volute
- Gutter
- Semicircular torus moulding
- Orb
- Inverted ovolo (quarter-round)
- Fillet
- Plain fascia
- Round-arched window
- Ovolo (quarter-round)
- Fillet
- Lantern
- Dome on a circular base
- Fish-scale tile
- Hood-mould
- Parapet
- Small roll
- Fillet
- Plain fascia
- Triple lesene

486

TYPES OF DOME

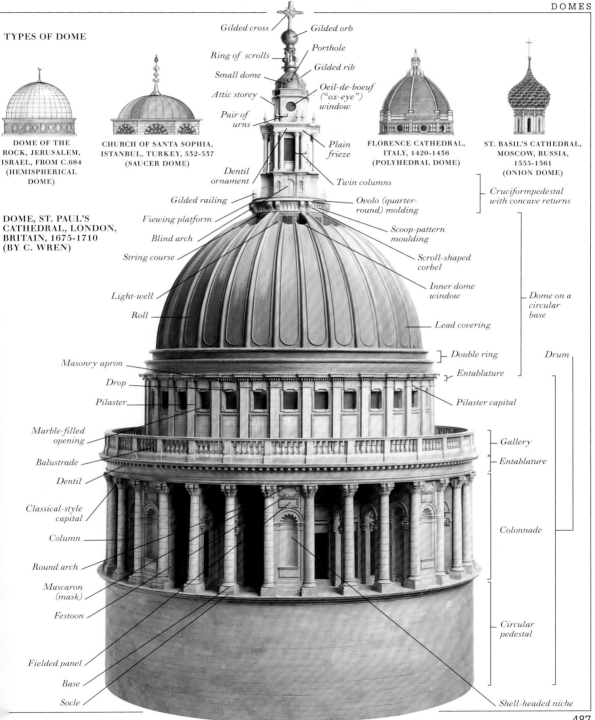

DOME OF THE ROCK, JERUSALEM, ISRAEL, FROM C.684 (HEMISPHERICAL DOME)

CHURCH OF SANTA SOPHIA, ISTANBUL, TURKEY, 532-537 (SAUCER DOME)

FLORENCE CATHEDRAL, ITALY, 1420-1436 (POLYHEDRAL DOME)

ST. BASIL'S CATHEDRAL, MOSCOW, RUSSIA, 1555-1561 (ONION DOME)

DOME, ST. PAUL'S CATHEDRAL, LONDON, BRITAIN, 1675-1710 (BY C. WREN)

Gilded cross

Gilded orb

Porthole

Ring of scrolls

Gilded rib

Small dome

Attic storey

Oeil-de-boeuf ("ox-eye") window

Pair of urns

Plain frieze

Dentil ornament

Twin columns

Gilded railing

Ovolo (quarter-round) molding

Viewing platform

Blind arch

Scoop-pattern moulding

String course

Scroll-shaped corbel

Light-well

Inner dome window

Roll

Lead covering

Double ring

Masonry apron

Entablature

Drop

Pilaster

Pilaster capital

Marble-filled opening

Gallery

Balustrade

Entablature

Dentil

Classical-style capital

Column

Colonnade

Round arch

Mascaron (mask)

Festoon

Circular pedestal

Fielded panel

Base

Socle

Shell-headed niche

Cruciform pedestal with concave returns

Dome on a circular base

Drum

487

Islamic buildings

OPUS SECTILE MOSAIC DESIGN

THE ISLAMIC RELIGION was founded by the prophet Mohammed, who was born in Mecca (in present-day Saudi Arabia) about 570 AD. In the following three centuries, Islam spread from Arabia to North Africa and Spain, as well as to India and much of the rest of Asia. The worldwide influence of Islam remains strong today. Common characteristics of Islamic buildings include ogee arches and roofs, onion domes, and walls decorated with carved stone, paintings, inlays, or mosaics. The most important type of Islamic building is the mosque – the place of worship – which generally has a minaret (tower) from which the muezzin (official crier) calls Muslims to prayer. Most mosques have a mihrab (decorative niche) that indicates the direction of Mecca. As figurative art is not allowed in Islam, buildings are ornamented with geometric and arabesque motifs, and inscriptions (frequently Koranic verses).

Bud-like onion dome

Depressed arch surrounding mihrab

Painted roof pavilion

Turkish-crescent finial

Lotus-flower pendentive

Crest

Arabic inscription

Painted minaret with censer (incense burner)

Spandrel

Series of recessed arches

Semi-dome

Arched niche within a niche

Mural resembling tomb

Polyhedral niche

Recessed colonettes

MIHRAB, JAMI MASJID (PRINCIPAL OR CONGREGATIONAL MOSQUE), BIJAPUR, INDIA, c.1636

Shield

Herring-bone pattern

Tablet flower

Spandrel with floral design

Ogee arch

Carved stone

Undulating band

Cusp

Volute

Impost

Capital with stylized floral design

Panel with fret pattern

Band with Arabic inscriptions praising Allah (God)

Attached colonette

Jali (latticed screen) with geometrical patterns

ARCH, THE ALHAMBRA, GRANADA, SPAIN, 1333-1354

Enamelled turquoise earthenware tile

Trigon

Cube with chamfered corners

Polygonal capital

Niche

Enamelled white earthenware tile

Column shaft

Arabesques of stylized plants

Enamelled lapis blue earthenware tile

MIHRAB WITH COLUMN, EL-AINYI MOSQUE, CAIRO, EGYPT, 15TH CENTURY

EXAMPLES OF ISLAMIC MOSAICS, EGYPT AND SYRIA

Star-shaped motif
Triangle of yellow marble
Greek cross of red marble
Rhombus of black marble
Stone band

STAR AND GREEK-CROSS MOSAIC

Mosaic tessellation
Stone
Black marble
Turquoise glass
Tessera (small mosaic piece)

FRET-PATTERN MOSAIC

Greek cross of black and yellow marble
Star-shaped motif
Stone band
Rhombus of red marble

STAR AND GREEK-CROSS MOSAIC

Parallelogram of black marble
Triangle of yellow marble
Rhombus of red marble
Symmetrical quadrilateral of stone
Star-shaped motif

MOSAIC OF HEXAGONS, TRIANGLES, AND SYMMETRICAL QUADRILATERALS

Hexagonal design
Band of black marble
Band of stone

HEXAGON AND BAND MOSAIC

Triangle of turquoise glass
Parallelogram of mother-of-pearl

DANCETTE-PATTERN MOSAIC

Hexagon of red marble
Symmetrical quadrilateral of black marble
Triangle of stone

MOSAIC OF HEXAGONS, TRIANGLES, AND SYMMETRICAL QUADRILATERALS

MARBLE TOMB OF ITIMAD-UD-DAULA, AGRA, INDIA, c.1622-1628

Kalasa finial (finial with orbs)
Padmakosa (lotus petal)
Parapet decorated with lattice-work
Ogee-curved roof
Chajya (deep eaves)
Domed roof
Balcony
Roof pavilion
Cusped arch
Circular top of minaret
Pietra dura inlay (slices of semi-precious stone laid in sockets)
Cornice
Bracket
Octahedral base of minaret
Spandrel decorated with arabesque
Star-pattern inlay
Sandstone plinth
Sandstone parapet decorated with lattice-work
Jali (latticed screen) with geometrical patterns
Depressed entrance arch
Sandstone stairway
Opus sectile mosaic (geometric mosaic) of stone, tile, glass, and enamel

489

South and east Asia

THE TRADITIONAL ARCHITECTURE of south and east Asia has been profoundly influenced by the spread from India of Buddhism and Hinduism. This influence is shown both by the abundance and by the architectural styles of temples and shrines in the region. Many early Hindu temples consist of rooms carved from solid rock-faces. However, free-standing structures began to be built in southern India from about the eighth century AD. Many were built in the Dravidian style, like the Temple of Virupaksha (opposite) with its characteristic antarala (terraced tower), perforated windows, and numerous arches, pilasters, and carvings. The earliest Buddhist religious monuments were Indian stupas, which consisted of a single hemispherical dome surmounted by a chattravali (shaft) and surrounded by railings with ornate gates. Later Indian stupas and those built elsewhere were sometimes modified; for example, in Sri Lanka, the dome became bell-shaped, and was called a dagoba. Buddhist pagodas, such as the Burmese example (right), are multistoreyed temples, each storey having a projecting roof. The form of these buildings probably derived from the yasti (pointed spire) of the stupa. Another feature of many traditional Asian buildings is their imaginative roof-forms, such as gambrel (mansard) roofs, and roofs with angle-rafters (below).

SEVEN-STOREYED PAGODA IN BURMESE STYLE, c.9TH-10TH CENTURY

- Gilded band
- Gilded iron hti (crown)
- Dubika (mast)
- Arrow motif
- Torus moulding with spiral carving
- Decorative eaves board
- Ogee-arched motif with decorative carvings
- Ogee-arched motif forming horn
- Hip-rafter
- Pentroof
- Undulating moulding
- Engaged pillar
- Baluster finial
- Arched entrance
- Balustrade
- Rectangular window
- Pillar
- Baluster
- Straight brace

DETAILS FROM EAST ASIAN BUILDINGS

KASUGA-STYLE ROOF WITH SUMIGI (ANGLE-RAFTERS), KASUGADO SHRINE OF ENJOJI, NARA, JAPAN, 12TH-14TH CENTURY

TERRACES, TEMPLE OF HEAVEN, BEIJING, CHINA, 15TH CENTURY

GAMBREL (MANSARD) ROOF WITH UPSWEPT EAVES AND UNDULATING GABLES, HIMEJI CASTLE, HIMEJI, JAPAN, 1608-1609

CORNER CAPITAL WITH ROOF BEAMS, POPCHU-SA TEMPLE, POPCHU-SA, SOUTH KOREA, 17TH CENTURY

PERFORATED STONE WINDOWS, TEMPLES OF VIRUPAKSHA AND MALLIKARJUNA, PATTADAKAL, INDIA, 8TH CENTURY

Tablet flower

Chain motif

Fret motif

Floral pattern

Leaf

Scroll motif

Sickle motif

Semicircle

DAGOBA STUPA, KANDY, SRI LANKA, c.2ND CENTURY BC- 7TH CENTURY AD

Chattra (umbrella)

Hanging ornament

Chattravali (shaft)

Ring with indentations symbolizing chattras

Ornamental metalwork

Yasti (tee; pointed spire)

Harmika (stylized square railing)

Auda (bell-shaped dome)

Trimala (series of three circular courses)

Circular base

SIDE VIEW AND PLAN VIEW, TEMPLE OF VIRUPAKSHA, PATTADAKAL, INDIA, c.746

Stupica (small stupa) of the Dravidian order

Dravidian finial

Blind chataya arch

Antarala (terraced tower)

Perforated window

Gopuram finial (wagon-like finial)

Bracketed capital

Small gopuram (gate-head)

Parapet

Roll cornice

Niche with statue

Gate

Plan view

Panel with bas-relief carving

Twin pilasters

Pillar

Shrine

Pradakshina (circumambulatory passage around shrine)

Mandapa (pillared hall)

Shrine chamber

Niche

Gate

The 19th century

BUILDINGS OF THE 19TH CENTURY are characterized by the use of new materials and by a great diversity of architectural styles. From the end of the 18th century, iron and steel became widely used as alternatives to wood for the framework of buildings, as in the flax-spinning mill shown here. Built in Britain in 1796, this mill exemplifies an architectural style that became common throughout the industrialized world for more than a century. The Industrial Revolution also brought mass-production of building parts – a development that enabled the British architect Sir Joseph Paxton to erect London's Crystal Palace (a building made entirely of iron and glass) in only nine months, ready for the Great Exhibition of 1851. The 19th century saw a widespread revival of older architectural styles. For example, in the USA and Germany, Neo-Greek architecture was fashionable; in Britain and France, Neo-Baroque, Neo-Byzantine, and Neo-Gothic styles (as seen in the Palace of Westminster and Tower Bridge) were dominant.

FLAX-SPINNING MILL, SHREWSBURY, BRITAIN, 1796 (BY C. BAGE)

Cast-iron wall-plate

Pitched roof

Ridge

Verge

Gutter

Machinery space

Cast-iron mortise-and-tenon joint

Anchor-joint

Inverted T-section cast-iron beam

Drain-pipe

End flange

Segmentally arched brick vault

Concrete floor

Tapering part of column

Paved ground floor

Strengthened central column

Multi-gabled roof (ridge and furrow roof)

Ridge

Furrow

Verge

Cast-iron wall-plate

Timber rafter

Gable

Gutter

Tapering part of column

Drain-pipe

Three courses of stretchers

Segmentally arched brick vault

Course of headers

Cast-iron mortise-and-tenon joint

Course of decorative headers

Tie-rod

Cast-iron lattice window

Cast-iron cruciform column

Cast-iron tenon

Inverted T-section cast-iron beam

Anchor-joint

Strengthened central column

Bonded brick wall

Stone foundation

Quoin

Jamb

Gauged arch (segmental arch of tapered bricks)

CLOCK TOWER ("BIG BEN"), PALACE OF WESTMINSTER, LONDON, BRITAIN, 1836-1868 (BY C. BARRY AND A.W.N. PUGIN)

Finial
Spire
Skylight
Cornice decorated with shields
Iron railing
Small orb
Orb

Iron tracery
Dormer window
Round arch filled with open tracery
Tetrahedral spire
Bell chamber
Balustrade
Ogee tracery arch filled with trefoil
Flying buttress
Pinnacle
Spandrel
Octahedral shaft with billet decoration
Dial
Cornice
Moulded corbel
Star-shaped corner buttress
Panelled field filled with tracery
Slender diagonal buttress
Narrow window
String course
Carved panel
Stepped storeys

DETAILS FROM BUILDINGS IN REVIVALIST STYLES

CUPOLA, MERCHANTS' EXCHANGE, PHILADELPHIA, USA, 1832-1834 (NEO-GREEK)

SCULPTURE AND PEDIMENT, OPERA HOUSE, PARIS, FRANCE, 1861-1874 (NEO-BAROQUE)

DOMED TURRET, WESTMINSTER CATHEDRAL, LONDON, BRITAIN, 1894-1903 (NEO-BYZANTINE)

Tetrahedral spire
Spire
Cornice
Archway

Finial
Finial
High-level footbridge
Lattice-work
Cast-iron tracery

Dormer head (gable) filled with blind tracery
Parapet
Heraldic shield
Cast-iron panelling
Drawbridge (bascule)
Circular turret/buttress

Moulded corbel
Steel brace
Archway

Parapet of balcony
Octahedral upper turret
Wedge-shaped corbel
String course
Stone panel
Pier

TOWER BRIDGE, LONDON, BRITAIN, 1886-1894 (BY H. JONES)

CRYSTAL PALACE EXHIBITION HALL, LONDON, BRITAIN, 1851 (BY J. PAXTON)

Longitudinal girder
Ridge and furrow glass roof-windows
Window
Crest
Cast-iron ornamental arch-plate
Semicircular barrel vault
Cast-iron trapezium
Arched facade

Octahedral column
Side exit
Sheet-iron louvre
Strengthened support
Entrance

The early 20th century

EMPIRE STATE
BUILDING, NEW
YORK, USA, 1929-1931
(BY R. H. SHREVE,
T. LAMB, AND
A. L. HARMON)

ARCHITECTURE OF THE EARLY 20TH CENTURY is notable for radical new types of steel-and-glass buildings – particularly skyscrapers – and the widespread use of steel-reinforced concrete. The steel-framed skyscraper was pioneered in Chicago in the 1880s, but did not become widespread until the first decades of the 20th century. As construction techniques were refined, skyscrapers became higher and higher; for example, the Empire State Building (right) of 1929-1931 has 102 storeys. Many buildings of this period were constructed from lightweight concrete slabs, which could be supported by cantilever beams or by pilotis (stilts), as in the Villa Savoye (below). The early 20th century also produced a great variety of architectural styles, some of which are illustrated opposite. Despite their diversity, the styles of this period generally had one thing in common: they were completely new, with few links to past architectural styles. This originality is in marked contrast to 19th-century architecture (see pp. 492-493), much of which was revivalist.

Radio mast

Circular lantern

Art deco splayed
seashell form

Stepped
plinth

Chamfered corner

Colonnaded
storey

Ziggurat-
style
step-back

Ornamentation

Set-back

Steel
mullion

Flush
window

Vertical pier

Regular
fenestration

Solid-panel
infill

Fan-like
art deco
decoration

Decorated
stone lintel

Stone
structure-line

Limestone and
granite cladding

Flat roof

Stepped
cornice

Parapet

Plinth

Ground-floor
entrance

Base

Square
bay

The Empire State Building's top 30 floors were first illuminated in colour in 1976 to honour the United States Bicentennial. This marked the beginning of the Lighting Partners Program that today sees the building lit up in specific colors for many occasions. Above, the blue, white, and red lights celebrate Independence Day.

MIDWAY GARDENS, CHICAGO, USA, 1914 (BY F. L. WRIGHT)

Flagpole

Plain coping-stone

Main floor

Orchestra shell

Tiled, shallow pitched roof

Decorated cement frieze

Terrace

Steps

Stage

Ridge

Projecting balustrade

Hip

Ornamental light

Main pavilion

Arcade

Terrace

Octagonal window

Ornamental sculpture

Flat roof

Stone plinth

Cantilevered, latticed shade

EAST SIDE

Tiled frieze

NORTH SIDE

Planting bed

Deep-set window

Slit window

Brick pier

Terrace

Stepped flat-roofs

Ornamented coping-stone

EARLY 20TH-CENTURY ARCHITECTURAL STYLES

DORMER WINDOW, STUDIO ELVIRA, MUNICH, GERMANY, 1902 (ART NOUVEAU)

AEG TURBINE HALL, BERLIN, GERMANY, 1909 (DEUTSCHER WERKBUND)

ROBIE HOUSE, CHICAGO, USA, 1909-1910 (PRAIRIE STYLE)

GRUNDTVIG CHURCH, COPENHAGEN, DENMARK, 1920 (EXPRESSIONIST)

VERTEX, CHRYSLER BUILDING, NEW YORK, USA, 1928-1930 (ART DECO)

TOWER, TOWN HALL, HILVERSUM, NETHERLANDS, 1930 (DUTCH CUBIST)

CASA DEL FASCIO, COMO, ITALY, 1932-1936 (GRUPPO SEVEN CUBIST)

MOTIF ABOVE DOORWAY, HOOVER FACTORY, LONDON, BRITAIN, 1933 (ART DECO)

Modern buildings 1

KAWANA HOUSE, JAPAN,
FROM 1987 (BY N. FOSTER)

ARCHITECTURE SINCE ABOUT THE 1950s is generally known as modern architecture. One of its main influences has been functionalism – a belief that a building's function should be apparent in its design. Both the Centre Georges Pompidou (below and opposite) and the Hong Kong and Shanghai Bank (see pp. 498-499) are functionalist buildings: on each, elements of engineering and the building's services are clearly visible on the outside. In the 1980s, some architects rejected functionalism in favour of post-modernism, in which historical styles – particularly neoclassicism – were revived, using modern building materials and techniques. In many modern buildings, walls are made of glass or concrete hung from a frame, as in the Kawana House (right); this type of wall construction is known as curtain walling. Other modern construction techniques include the intricate interlocking of concrete vaults – as in the Sydney Opera House (see pp. 498-499) – and the use of high-tension beams to create complex roof shapes, such as the paraboloid roof of the Church of St. Pierre de Libreville (see pp. 498-499).

Solar panel
Concrete frame
Pile foundation
Raft   Composite cladding-panel
SIDE VIEW

Rocker-beam
Curtain walling
Lattice-beam
Floor-beam connection   Floor
FRONT VIEW

**SERVICES FACADE, CENTRE GEORGES POMPIDOU,
PARIS, FRANCE, 1977 (BY R. PIANO AND R. ROGERS)**

Metal-faced, fire-resistant panel
Air-conditioning duct
Cooling tower
Water-pipe

Grand gallery level
Main gallery levels
Library level
Administrative level
Mezzanine gallery level
Reception level

Staircase to grand hall
Electrical plant
Water-cooled, fire-resistant column
Continuous glazing
Tinted glass
Services entrance

PRINCIPAL FACADE, CENTRE GEORGES POMPIDOU

Gallery space
External walkway
Electronically operated roller-blind
Cooling tower
Continuous glazing
Steel lattice-beam
Main truss
Terrace
Gerberette (cast-steel rocker-beam)
Cradle support for escalator
Cross-bracing
Suspended fire-resistant glass curtain
Double fire-escape staircase

Reinforced-concrete and steel floor-plate
Double floor-height
Main entrance
Glazed escalator tube
Node
Water-cooled, fire-resistant steel column

Exposed "plug-in" services

Steel lattice-beam
Dual air-conditioning unit for roof
Elevator
Elevator-motor room
Vertical-duct distribution zone

Metal sandwich-panel (insulating panel)
Gerberette (cast-steel rocker-beam)
Rose connection
Outer tension-column
External steel-lattice mullion
Water-cooled, fire-resistant cross-beam
Double fire-escape staircase

Water storage tank
Cross-bracing
Open gallery floor
Water-pipe
Steel-framed services column
Double cross-bracing

Modern buildings 2

HONG KONG AND SHANGHAI BANK, HONG KONG, 1981-1985 (BY N. FOSTER)

Inverted top-truss

Mast

Illuminated fascia

Curved glazing

External maintenance crane

Soffit

Cockpit

Counterweight

Boom

Circular access platform

Soffit

Helicopter landing-pad

Navigation light

Stepped elevation

Sun-shade louvre

Steel column

Face panel

Face panel

Horizontal window

Mullion

Hanger

Vertical window

Handrail

Composite cladding-panel

Top beam

External maintenance crane

Outer diagonal beam

Escalator

Outer bottom boom

Cross-bracing

Inner diagonal beam

Service shaft

Fire-escape staircase

Inner bottom boom

External staircase

Pin joint

Double floor-height

Refuge terrace

Double floor-height

Hanger

Full-height glazing

Sun scoop

Sun scoop

Glazed curtain wall

Two-storey stability truss (coathanger truss)

Flange

10-floor-high atrium

Vertical, glazed typhoon screen

Lightweight, column-free, steel and concrete floor

Entrance lobby

Glazed soffit

Plaza

Internal bridge

SOUTH FACADE

EAST SIDE

CHURCH OF ST. PIERRE, LIBREVILLE, GABON, 1990

Lattice-truss

Cross-bracing

Mullion

Plate connector

Paraboloid roof

Concave curve

Convex curve

Tension member

Rafter

Full-height glazing

Eaves

Bolt

Rendered, splayed outer wall

Entrance

Reinforced plinth

Concrete shoe

Inner diagonal beam

Beam housing

Pin joint

Glulam wall-plate (glued and laminated wall-plate)

Tinted glass

Circular steps

Secondary hall

Main hall

OPERA HOUSE, SYDNEY, AUSTRALIA, 1959-1973 (BY J. UTZON)

Precast concrete rib

Vaults with curved ribs

Glass wall

Mullion

Main hall

Bronze glazing bar

Precast concrete rib-segment

Continuous glazing

Solid podium

Ribbon window

Ridge

HARBOUR FACADE

Vault roof constructed of chevron-shaped, precast tiles

Vault over restaurant

Staircase

Pink cladding

Pink granite-aggregate paving slab

Main line of support

Awning

Staircase

Terrace

Solid podium

WEST SIDE

499

Music

Musical Notation ································· 502

Orchestras ···································· 504

Brass Instruments ···························· 506

Woodwind Instruments ······················· 508

Stringed Instruments ························· 510

Guitars ······································ 512

Keyboard Instruments ························ 514

Percussion Instruments ······················ 516

Drums ·· 518

Electronic Instruments ······················· 520

Musical notation

MUSICAL NOTATION IS ANY METHOD by which sounds are written down so that they can be read and performed by others. The present-day conventional system of notation uses a five-line stave (staff) – divided by vertical lines into sections known as bars – on which notes, rests, clefs, key signatures, time signatures, accidentals, and other symbols are written. A note indicates the duration of a sound and, according to its position on the stave, its pitch. Notes can be arranged on the stave in order of pitch to form a scale. A silence in the music is indicated by a rest. The clef, which is placed at the begininng of a stave, fixes the pitch. The key signature, which is placed after the clef, indicates the key. The time signature, placed after the key signature, shows the number of beats in a bar. Accidentals are used to indicate the raising or lowering of the pitch of a note.

502

Accidental sharp

Tie (bind)

Accidental natural

Unison (both clarinets play the same note)

Semibreve

Crotchet

FLUTES

OBOES

CLARINETS IN A

BASSOONS

HORNS IN D

TRUMPETS IN D

TIMPANI IN D AND A

FIRST AND SECOND VIOLINS

VIOLAS

VOICES

CELLOS

ORGAN

DOUBLE BASSES

Semibreve rest

Accidental sharp

Slur

Piano (play softly)

Pianissimo (play very softly)

Crotchet rest

Orchestras

AN ORCHESTRA IS A GROUP of musicians that plays music written for a specific combination of instruments. The number and type of instruments included in the orchestra depends on the style of music being played. The modern orchestra (also known as a symphony orchestra) is made up of four sections of instruments – stringed, woodwind, brass, and percussion. The stringed section consists of violins, violas, cellos (violoncellos), double basses, and sometimes a harp (see pp. 510-511). The main instruments of the woodwind section are flutes, oboes, clarinets, and bassoons – the piccolo, cor anglais, bass clarinet, saxophone, and double bassoon (contrabassoon) can also be included if the music requires them (see pp. 508-509). The brass section usually consists of horns, trumpets, trombones, and the tuba (see pp. 506-507). The main instruments of the percussion section are the timpani (see pp. 518-519). The side drum, bass drum, cymbals, tambourine, triangle, tubular bells, xylophone, vibraphone, tam-tam (gong), castanets, and maracas can also be included in the percussion section (see pp. 516-517). The musicians are usually arranged in a semi-circle – strings spread along the front, woodwind and brass in the centre, and percussion at the back. A conductor stands in front of the musicians and controls the tempo (speed) of the music and the overall balance of the sound, ensuring that no instruments are too loud or too soft in relation to the others.

TUBULAR BELLS

TAM-TAM (GONG)

VIBRAPHONE

XYLOPHONE

CASTANETS

TAMBOURINE

MARACAS

TRIANGLE

TRUMPETS

HORNS

CLARINETS

BASS CLARINET

HARP

SAXOPHONE

PICCOLO

SECOND VIOLINS

FIRST VIOLINS

CYMBALS

SIDE DRUM

BASS DRUM

TIMPANI

**EXAMPLE OF A LAYOUT OF THE
INSTRUMENTS FOR A MODERN
(SYMPHONY) ORCHESTRA**

TROMBONES

TUBA

BASSOONS

DOUBLE BASSOON

DOUBLE BASSES

FLUTES

OBOES

COR ANGLAIS

VIOLAS

Score

CONDUCTOR'S
STAND

CELLOS

505

Brass instruments

BRASS INSTRUMENTS ARE WIND INSTRUMENTS that are made of metal, usually brass. Although they appear in many different shapes and sizes, all brass instruments have a mouthpiece, a length of hollow tube, and a flared bell. The mouthpiece of a brass instrument may be cup-shaped, as in the cornet, or cone-shaped, as in the horn. The tube may be wide or narrow, mainly conical, as in the horn and tuba, or mainly cylindrical, as in the trumpet and trombone. The sound of a brass instrument is made by the player's lips vibrating against the mouthpiece, so that the air vibrates in the tube. By changing lip tension, the player can vary the vibrations and produce notes of different pitches. The range of notes produced by a brass instrument can be extended by means of a valve system. Most brass instruments, such as the trumpet, have piston valves that divert the air in the instrument along an extra piece of tubing (known as a valve slide) when pressed down. The total length of the tube is increased and the pitch of the note produced is lowered. Instead of valves, the trombone has a movable slide that can be pushed away from or drawn toward the player. The sound of a brass instrument can also be changed by inserting a mute into the bell of the instrument.

BUGLE

Brace

Tuning slide

Counterbalancing weight

SIMPLIFIED DIAGRAM SHOWING HOW A PISTON VALVE SYSTEM WORKS

Piston valves at rest

Air bypasses piston valves

PISTON VALVES AT REST

First piston valve pressed down

Second and third piston valves at rest

Air diverted through first valve slide

PISTON VALVE PRESSED DOWN

TRUMPET

Finger button

First piston valve

Spring returns piston valve to rest position

Second piston valve

Third piston valve

Holes divert air into valve slides

Little finger support

Music stand holder

Narrow, cylindrical tube

Flared bell

Cup-shaped mouthpiece

Mouthpiece receiver

First valve slide

First valve slide thumb hook

Second valve slide

Third valve slide finger ring

Third valve slide

Tuning slide

Tuning slide water key

Third valve slide water key

SECTIONS OF A TROMBONE

EXAMPLES OF MUTES

Flared bell

CUP MUTE

TENOR MUTE

ALTO MUTE

Inner tube

Outer tube of slide

Cup-shaped
mouthpiece

Mouthpiece
brace held
by the left
hand

Slide brace
held by the
right hand

Narrow, cylindrical tube

Water key

TROMBONE

Flared bell

Outer tube of slide

Cup-shaped
mouthpiece

TUBA

Large, flared bell

FLUGELHORN

Little
finger
support

Piston valves

Flared bell

Cup-shaped
mouthpiece

Piston valves

Cup-
shaped
mouthpiece

Valve slide

Conical
tube

HORN

Cone-shaped
mouthpiece

Finger key

Rotary valves

CORNET

Piston valves

Little finger
support

Flared
bell

Cup-
shaped
mouthpiece

Bore widens
after valves

Valve slide

Narrow,
conical bore

Valve slide

Large,
flared bell

Wide, conical tube

507

Woodwind instruments

WOODWIND INSTRUMENTS ARE wind instruments that are generally made of wood, although some are made of metal or plastic. The sound of a woodwind instrument is produced by the vibration of air in a hollow tube. The air is made to vibrate by blowing across a blow hole – as in the flute and piccolo – or by blowing through a single reed – as in the clarinet and saxophone – or a double reed – as in the bassoon, cor anglais, and oboe. The pitch of a woodwind instrument can be changed by opening or closing holes cut into the tube of the instrument.

Bell

Double reed

Bell joint

Curved crook

Conical, wooden tube

Tenor joint

Cylindrical, metal tube

Double reed

Key

Body joint

Crook

Blow hole

Head joint

Conical, wooden tube

Upper joint

Lip plate

PICCOLO

Bass joint

Double reed

Cork

Finger hole

Foot joint

Key

Right-hand rest

Key

Upper joint

Mouthpiece with single reed

Ligature

Key

Body joint

Barrel joint

Butt

Key

Middle joint

Key

Cylindrical, metal tube

Cylindrical, wooden tube

Upper joint

BASSOON

Middle joint

Finger hole

Body joint

Key

Bell joint

Conical, wooden tube

Lip plate

Head joint

Bulb-shaped bell

COR ANGLAIS

Blow hole

Key

FLUTE

Bell joint

Middle joint

Flared bell

OBOE

Bell joint

Flared bell

CLARINET

TENOR SAXOPHONE

Mouthpiece with single reed

Conical, metal tube

Upturned, flared bell

Mouthpiece with single reed

Ligature

SECTIONS OF A TENOR SAXOPHONE

Neck

Upper octave key

KEYS FOR THE LEFT THUMB

Lower octave key

Key rod

Key

Key

Key rod

KEYS FOR THE LEFT HAND

Key rod

Key

Mother-of-pearl touchpiece (button)

KEYS FOR THE RIGHT HAND

Key

Key rod

MAIN BODY OF SAXOPHONE

Conical, metal tube

KEYS FOR THE RIGHT PALM

KEYS FOR THE LEFT PALM

Tonehole

Upturned, flared bell

Mother-of-pearl touchpiece (button)

Tonehole

Pad made up of layers of felt and cork

Roller

Cup

Key rod

Key guard

Key

Metal centre of pad reflects sound

KEYS FOR THE RIGHT LITTLE FINGER

Padded key

Key guard

KEYS FOR THE LEFT LITTLE FINGER

Key guard

Stringed instruments

STRINGED INSTRUMENTS PRODUCE SOUND by the vibration of stretched strings. This may be done by drawing a bow across the strings, as in the violin; or by plucking the strings, as in the harp and guitar (see pp. 512-513). The four modern members of the bowed string family are the violin, viola, cello (violoncello), and double bass. Each consists of a hollow, wooden body, a long neck, and four strings. The bow is a wooden stick with horsehair stretched across its length. The vibrations made by drawing the bow across the strings are transmitted to the hollow body, and this itself vibrates, amplifying and enriching the sound produced. The harp consists of a set of strings of different lengths stretched across a wooden frame. The strings are plucked by the player's thumbs and fingers – except the little finger of each hand – which produces vibrations that are amplified by the harp's soundboard. The pitch of the note produced by any stringed instrument depends on the length, weight, and tension of the string. A shorter, lighter, or tighter string gives a higher note.

Scroll eye

Scroll

Peg-hole

Ebony tuning-pegs

Neck made of maple wood

Strings

Fingerboard

Rounded shoulder

Belly (soundboard)

Waist

Sound-hole

Rib

Purfling

Bridge

Tailpiece

Chin rest

Tailpiece loop fits around end-pin

End-pin (tail-pin)

SECTIONS OF A VIOLIN

Head

Point

Stick

Scroll

Scroll eye

Peg-box

Tuning-peg

Horsehair

Nut

String

Fingerboard

Rounded shoulder

Belly (soundboard)

Purfling

Waist

Sound-hole

Bridge

Tuning adjustor

Frog

Tailpiece

Screw

Chin rest

VIOLIN BOW

VIOLIN

HARP

Crown
Tuning-peg
Neck (string arm)
Shoulder
String
Soundboard
Pillar
Scroll
Scroll eye
Peg-box
Tuning-peg
Nut
Fingerboard
String
Rounded shoulder
Belly (soundboard)
Pedestal
Foot
Pedal

DOUBLE BASS BOW

Head
Point
Scroll
Scroll eye
Tuning-pegs at back of peg-box
Nut
Inward-curving stick
Horsehair
Frog
Screw
Fingerboard
String
Sloping shoulder
Belly (soundboard)
Purfling
Waist
Sound-hole
Sound-hole
Bridge
Rib
Tailpiece
Spike

VIOLA

Scroll
Tuning-peg
Scroll eye
Peg-box
Nut
ngerboard
String
ly undboard)
Rounded shoulder
Purfling
aist
nd-
Bridge
Tuning adjustor
Chin rest
Tailpiece

CELLO (VIOLONCELLO)

Waist
Bridge
Tuning adjustor
Tailpiece
Spike

DOUBLE BASS

Bridge

Guitars

THE GUITAR IS A PLUCKED stringed instrument
(see pp. 510-511). There are two types of guitar –
acoustic and electric. Acoustic guitars have hollow
bodies and six or twelve strings. Plucking the strings
produces vibrations that are amplified by their hollow
bodies. Electric guitars usually have solid bodies and
six strings. Pick-ups placed under the strings convert
their vibrations into electronic signals that are magnified
by an amplifier, and sent to a loudspeaker where they are
converted into sounds (see pp. 520-521). Electric bass
guitars are very similar in structure to electric guitars,
and produce sound in the same way, but have four
strings and play bass notes.

String
Fret
Machine head
Hollow body
Neck
Headstock
Sound-hole
B string
Bridge
G string
D string
A string
Low E string
Maker's label
Lining glued along top and bottom edge of rib
Rib
End block
Strap peg
Joint
Transverse (crosswise) strut strengthens back
Back made of two pieces of cherry wood joined together
Saddle
Bridge pin
Bridge
Binding

COMPONENTS OF AN ACOUSTIC GUITAR

Top E string

Nut

Truss rod cover

Screws

Machine heads

Headstock

Machine head

Truss rod slot

Truss rod

Fingerboard

Fretwire slot

Fretwire

Position dots

Sound-hole

Bracing

Soundboard made of two pieces of spruce joined together

EXAMPLES OF ACOUSTIC GUITARS

Rose

Sound-hole

Hollow body

String

Machine head

Bridge

Neck

Headstock

Scratchplate

WASHBURN TWELVE-STRING

Hollow, metal body

Sound-hole

Tailpiece

String

Machine head

Neck

Headstock

Resonator

DOBRO RESONATOR

EXAMPLES OF ELECTRIC GUITARS

Pick-up

Scratchplate

Solid body

String

Machine head

Bridge

Neck

Headstock

Output socket

Vibrato arm

FENDER STRATOCASTER

Pick-up

Toggle switch

Solid body

String

Machine head

Bridge

Neck

Headstock

Scratchplate

GIBSON LES PAUL

Pick-up

Solid body

String

Machine head

Bridge

Neck

Headstock

Output socket

Scratchplate

FENDER JAZZ BASS

513

Keyboard instruments

KEYBOARD INSTRUMENTS are instruments that are sounded by means of a keyboard. The organ and piano are two of the principal members of the keyboard family. The organ consists of pipes which are operated by one or more manuals (keyboards) and a pedal board. The pipes are lined up in rows (known as ranks or registers) on top of a wind chest. The sound of the organ is made when air is admitted into a pipe by pressing a key or pedal. The piano consists of wire strings stretched over a metal frame, and a keyboard and pedals that operate hammers and dampers. The piano frame is either vertical – as in the upright piano – or horizontal – as in the grand piano. When a key is at rest, a damper lies against the string to stop it vibrating. When a key is pressed down, the damper moves away from the string as the hammer strikes it, causing the string to vibrate and sound a note.

ORGAN PIPE

UPRIGHT PIANO

Muffler felt Pressure bar Tuning pin Pin block

Hammer

88–note keyboard

Keybed

Soundboard

String

Treble bridge

Har rail

Woo case

Met fran

Hite pin

Bas bria

Una corda (soft) pedal   Sostenuto pedal   Damper (sustaining) pedal

UPRIGHT PIANO ACTION

KEY AT REST

String

Damper lies against string, and stops it vibrating

Damper lever

Jack

Hammer

Hammer rest

Back check

Action lever

Capstan screw

Key released

KEY PRESSED DO

String

Damper moves away from string, allowing it to vibrate

Damper lever

Jack

Hammer strikes string

Hammer rest

Back check

Action lever

Capstan screw

Key pressed down

ORGAN CONSOLE

Pipe

Pedal stop

Swell stop

Swell manual (keyboard)

Great manual (keyboard)

Choir manual (keyboard)

Toe piston

Music stand

Choir stop

Great stop

Thumb piston

Pedal board   Foot pedal

Swell pedal

CONCERT GRAND PIANO (VIEWED FROM ABOVE)

CONCERT GRAND PIANO (FRONT VIEW)

Soundboard

Bass bridge

Hitch pin

Lid

String

Wooden case

Metal frame

Keyboard

Single bass note string

Una corda (soft) pedal

Damper (sustaining) pedal

Sostenuto pedal

Long bridge

Tenor note strings (two strings for each note)

Treble note strings (three strings for each note)

Wooden case

STEINWAY & SONS
NEW YORK HAMBURG

Hammer

Tuning pin

Wrest plank

STEINWAY

B

S18422

Keyboard lid

88-note keyboard

Percussion instruments

TEMPLE BLOCKS

PERCUSSION INSTRUMENTS are a large group of instruments that produce sound by being struck, shaken, scraped, or clashed together. Most percussion instruments – such as the tam-tam (gong), cymbals, and maracas – do not have a definite pitch and are used for rhythm and impact, and the distinctive timbre (colour) of their sound. Other percussion instruments – such as the xylophone, vibraphone, and tubular bells – are tuned to a definite pitch and can play melody, harmony, and rhythms. The xylophone and vibraphone each have two rows of bars that are arranged in a similar way to the black and white keys of a piano. Metal tubes are suspended below the bars to amplify the sound. The vibraphone has electrically operated fans that rotate in the tubes and produce a vibrato (wavering pitch) effect.

TUBULAR BELLS

Tube struck with mallet

Hollow, metal tube

Damper bar

Metal frame

Mechanism linking pedal and damper bar

Row of tubes graduated in length and pitch

Damper pedal

EXAMPLES OF BEATERS

SOFT-HEADED BEATER
Fell-covered head

HARD-HEADED BEATER
Rosewood head

MALLET
Leather-covered head

XYLOPHONE

Row of bars graduated in length and pitch

Wooden bar struck with hard-headed beater

Hollow, metal tube

Metal stand

TAM-TAM (GONG)

Tam-tam struck in centre with soft-headed beater

Cord

Metal frame

PAISTE

Rim

Large, metal disc

CYMBALS

Leather strap
fits around
player's hand

Pad protects
hands from
vibrations

Thin, convex
disc of copper
and tin alloy

SECTIONS OF A MARACA

Wooden
handle

Lead
shot

Hollow,
wooden
head

CLAVES

Hardwood sticks
clashed together to
give a sharp crack

TRIANGLE

Steel rod bent into
triangular shape

Steel beater

CASTANETS

Cord

Hollowed
wood

VIBRAPHONE

Row of bars graduated
in length and pitch

Metal bar struck
with soft-headed
beater

Metal
frame

Damper pedal

Metal tube containing
electrically operated fan
that produces vibrato
(wavering pitch) effect

Electric cable

Drums

A DRUM IS A percussion instrument that consists of a drumhead, made of skin or plastic, stretched over one or both ends of a hollow vessel (the body-shell). Drums are played in most parts of the world and are made in a number of different shapes and sizes. They can be divided into three groups according to the shape of the body-shell: frame drums (e.g., tambourines), bowl-shaped drums (e.g., timpani), and tubular drums (e.g., congas). Drums are usually sounded by striking the drumhead with the hands or with beaters, such as a hard-headed stick. The drumhead vibrates, and its vibrations are amplified by the hollow body-shell. The snare drum has wires – known as snares – stretched across the lower drumhead; the snares vibrate against the lower drumhead when the drum is played. Most drums, such as congas, do not have a definite pitch and can play only rhythms (see pp. 516-517). Other drums, such as timpani, have a definite pitch and can play melody, harmony, and rhythms. They can be tuned by adjusting the tension of the drumhead. Different types of drum can be combined together with other percussion instruments to form a drum kit. The basic components of the drum kit are bass drum, tom-toms, floor tom (tenor drum), snare drum, and cymbals.

TAMBOURINE

DRUM KIT

Crash cymbal

Tension key

Tension rod

Tom-tom

Lug

Hi-hat cymbal

Snare drum

Tripod stand

Chain

Tension screw

Felt-covered beater

Pedal

Pedal

SNARE DRUM (VIEWED FROM BELOW)

Snare mounting

Adjustable damper

Lug

Transparent lower drumhead

Upper drumhead

Snare

Snare release lever

Stick

EXAMPLES OF BEATERS

Acorn

HARD-HEADED STICK

Taper

SOFT-HEADED STICK

Felt-covered head

WIRE BRUSH

Wire bristles

Ride cymbal

Tension key

om-tom

Height adjustment key

Tension rod

Lug

Floor tom (tenor drum)

Tension rod

Lug

Wooden body-shell

Height adjustment key

Leg

Bass drum

Rubber foot

CONGAS

Metal hoop

Drumhead

Tension rod

Wooden body-shell

Tripod stand

Leg

TIMPANUM (KETTLE DRUM)

Drumhead

Tension rod

Metal hoop

Tuning gauge

Copper body-shell

Strut

Crown

Tension rod

Tuning pedal

Castor

Electronic instruments

ELECTRONIC INSTRUMENTS generate electronic signals that are magnified by an amplifier, and sent to a loudspeaker where they are converted into sounds. Synthesizers, and other electronic instruments, simulate the characteristic sounds of conventional instruments, and also create entirely new sounds. Most electronic instruments are keyboard instruments, but electronic wind and percussion instruments are also popular. A digital sampler records and stores sounds from musical instruments or other sources. When the sound is played back, the pitch of the original sound can be altered. A keyboard can be connected to the sampler so that a tune can be played using the sampled sounds. With a MIDI (Musical Instrument Digital Interface) system, a computer can be linked with other electronic instruments, such as keyboards and electronic drums, to make sounds together or in sequence. It is also possible, using music software, to compose and play music on a home computer.

ELECTRONIC DRUMS

Drum pad

Height adjustment key

Tripod

HOME KEYBOARD

Power button

Volume control

Function display

Memory record button

Tone editor control

Demonstration tune button

Pitch modulator

Multi-accompaniment system control

Tone and rhythm pattern selector

Key

SYNTHESIZER

Memory card slot

Joystick

Function display

Edit control

Data entry key pad

Sound structure guide

Volume control

Pitch modulator

Sound selection control

Key

DIGITAL SAMPLER

Internal mic

External input

Volume knob

Display illumination

D beam

SP-555

Sample

Bank buttons

Effect knobs

Effect buttons

Loop capture

Pads 1–16

WIND SYNTHESIZER

Mouthpiece

Keys for right hand

WIND CONTROLLER

Keys for left hand

POWER PACK

MIDI (Musical Instrument Digital Interface) cable

SOUND MODULE

Connecting cable

Store button

Data entry key pad

Input connector socket

Volume control

Edit control

Play button

Function display

Effect balance control

Second optical drive

Optical drive

Audio clock settings

Surround sound special effect plug-in

COMPUTER DISPLAY

Start and stop controls

Software effect plug-in

MOTU

Recorded information

Power button

Headset jack

USB ports (2)

Status light

Virtual mixing board

FireWire 800 ports (2)

SYSTEM UNIT

KEYBOARD

MOUSE

COMPUTER WITH MIDI AND AUDIO SOFTWARE SEQUENCER

521

SPORTS

SOCCER ·················· 524

AMERICAN FOOTBALL ·················· 526

AUSTRALIAN RULES AND GAELIC FOOTBALL ······ 528

RUGBY ·················· 530

BASKETBALL ·················· 532

VOLLEYBALL, NETBALL, AND HANDBALL ·········· 534

BASEBALL ·················· 536

CRICKET ·················· 538

HOCKEY, LACROSSE, AND HURLING ·········· 540

ATHLETICS ·················· 542

RACKET SPORTS ·················· 544

GOLF ·················· 546

ARCHERY AND SHOOTING ·················· 548

ICE HOCKEY ·················· 550

ALPINE SKIING ·················· 552

EQUESTRIAN SPORTS ·················· 554

JUDO AND FENCING ·················· 556

SWIMMING AND DIVING ·················· 558

CANOEING, ROWING, AND SAILING ·········· 560

ANGLING ·················· 562

Soccer

GAMES INVOLVING KICKING A BALL have a long history and were recorded in China as early as 300 BC; in medieval Europe, street football was banned as a menace to the public; only in 1863 were the rules established, specifically banning carrying the ball for all players except the goalkeeper, and separating rugby from soccer. Soccer, officially termed association football, is a team sport in which players attempt to score goals by passing and dribbling the ball down the field past opposing defenders, and kicking or heading the ball into the goal net, outwitting the defending goalkeeper. Each team consists of ten outfield players (defenders, midfielders, and strikers) and a goalkeeper. Players from the opposing team may challenge the player in possession of the ball, but an illegal or foul tackle results in a penalty if a foul occurs inside the penalty area or a free kick if outside the penalty area. The round ball used in soccer is more easily controlled than the oval balls used in American, Canadian, and Australian rules football and in rugby. The result is a more "open" or flowing game which is played and watched by millions of people worldwide.

ASSISTANT REFEREE'S FLAG

Lightweight, brightly coloured fabric

Handle with rubber grip

REFEREE'S EQUIPMENT

Red card

Yellow card

Referee's whistle

Stop-watch

SOCCER PITCH

Corner flag

Corner arc

Penalty area

Penalty mark

Referee

Halfway-line flag

Striker

Striker

Left midfielder

Central midfielder

Left back

Touch-line

Central defender

Goal

Goalkeeper

46–91 m (150–300 ft)

Goal-line

Penalty arc

Assistant referee

Centre circle

Centre spot

Halfway line

Striker

Right midfielder

Right back

Central defender

Goal area

Goal-line

PITCH MARKINGS

Halfway line

1.5 m (5 ft)

HALFWAY-LINE FLAG

Corner arc

CORNER FLAG

7.3 m (24 ft)

Goal-line

GOAL

GOALKEEPER

Goalkeeper's shirt

Glove

Shorts

Shin guard

Sock

Soccer boot

SOCCER STRIP

Open-neck collar

Lightweight, man-made fabric team shirt

Team logo

Manufacturer's logo

Ribbed welt

Sponsor's logo

Manufacturer's name

Edge cut to fit perfectly

lotto

Motta

MAKING A SOCCER BALL

Hole punched in panel for stitching

Ball size number

Mitre

F.I.F.A. APPROVED

MULTIPLEX

Mitre

MULTIPLEX

5

22–23 cm (8½–9 in)

Waxed thread

Needle

Bladder valve

Bladder made from latex rubber

Laminated panel

Panels sewn together with ball inside out

Long cotton sock

Club crest

Team shorts

Synthetic bootlace

Interchangeable nylon stud

SOCCER BOOT

525

American football

IN AMERICAN AND CANADIAN FOOTBALL, the object of the game is to get the ball across the opponent's goal line, either by passing or carrying it across (a touch-down), or by kicking it between their goalposts (a field goal). An American football team has 11 players on the field at a time, although up to 40 players can appear for each side in a single game. The agile "offence" tries to score points, and the heavy hitting "defence" holds back the opposition. When in possession of the ball, a team has four chances ("downs"), to move it at least ten yards (nine metres) up the field to make a "first down". The opposition gains possession if they fail, or by tackling and intercepting the ball. Canadian football is played on a larger field, with 12 men on each side. A team has only three chances to achieve a first down. Otherwise, the game is very similar to American football. Helmets, face masks, and layers of body padding are worn by the players for protection.

AMERICAN FOOTBALL PLAYING FORMATION

Right safety · Middle linebacker · Left safety
Right defensive tackle
Left defensive tackle
Right cornerback
Inside linebacker
Left cornerback
Outside linebacker
Right defensive end
Centre
Left defensive end
Tight end
Split end
Left tackle
Right tackle
Right guard
Left guard
Quarter back
Left half-back
Right half-back
Full back

CANADIAN FOOTBALL PLAYING FORMATION

Right defensive back · Middle linebacker · Safety · Left defensive back
Left defensive tackle
Right cornerback
Left cornerback
Left outside linebacker
Right outside linebacker
Left defensive end
Right defensive end
Wide receiver
Right guard
Wide receiver
Right defensive tackle
Right tackle
Flanker
Left guard
Running back
Centre
Left tackle
Quarter back
Full back
Half back

AMERICAN FOOTBALL FIELD

Goalpost · End-line
Goal-line
Inbound line
Side-line
Line judge
Players' bench
Referee
Umpire
Back judge
End zone

9.2 m (30 ft)

GOALPOST

49 m (160 ft 6 in)

CANADIAN FOOTBALL FIELD

Goalpost
Goal-line
Players' bench
Referee
Umpire
Yardsman
Field judge
Head linesman
Yardsman
Side-line
End zone

9.2 m (30 ft)

GOALPOST

59.5 m (195 ft)

PLAYER

Team logo
Helmet
Wrist pad
Player's number
Thigh pad
Tie to shoulder pads
Pants
Studded shoe

PROTECTIVE EQUIPMENT

28 cm (11 in)

Painted white ring
Lace
Brown pebbled leather

FOOTBALL

HELMET

Non-breakable plastic
Rubber-coated plastic
Shock absorber

SHOULDER PAD

Chest protector weight up to 2.5 kg (5 lb 8 oz)

AIR·LITE
BLUE LASER 40-42
BIKE

UPPER ARM PAD

BIKE

RIB PADS

Strap ties on to shoulder pad

ELBOW PAD

Foam-sponge filling
Tail bone pad

HIP PAD

FINGERLESS GLOVE

Screw-in stud

Rigid plastic covering

THIGH PAD

BOOT

Fold-over leather tongue

PANTS

KNEE PAD

REFEREE'S SIGNALS

TIME OUT

TOUCH-DOWN OR FIELD GOAL

PERSONAL FOUL

OFFSIDE OR ENCROACHMENT

HOLDING

ILLEGAL MOTION

FIRST DOWN

PASS INTERFERENCE

527

Australian rules and Gaelic football

VARIETIES OF FOOTBALL have developed all over the world and Australian rules football is considered to be one of the roughest versions, allowing full body tackles although participants wear no protective padding. The game is played on a large, oval pitch by two sides, each of 18 players. Players can kick or punch the ball, which is shaped like a rugby ball, but cannot throw it. Running with the ball is permitted, as long as the ball touches the ground at least once every ten metres. The full backs defend two sets of posts. Teams try to score "goals" (six points) between the inner posts or "behinds" (one point) inside the outer posts. Each game has four quarters of 25 minutes, and the team with the most points at the end of the allotted time is the winner. In Gaelic football, an Irish version of soccer (see pp. 524–525), a size 5 soccer ball is used. Each team can have 15 players on the field at a time. Players are allowed to catch, fist, and kick the ball, or dribble it using their hands or feet, but cannot throw it. Teams are awarded three points for getting the ball into the net, and one point for getting it through the posts above the crossbar. Gaelic football is rarely played outside of Ireland.

START OF PLAY

Field umpire

Centre circle

SCORING

GOAL (6 POINTS)

BEHIND (1 POINT)

AUSTRALIAN RULES FOOTBALL FIELD

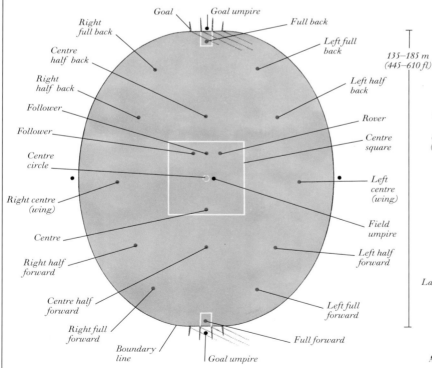

Goal

Goal umpire

Right full back

Full back

Left full back

Centre half back

Right half back

Left half back

Follower

Rover

Follower

Centre square

Centre circle

Left centre (wing)

Right centre (wing)

Field umpire

Centre

Left half forward

Right half forward

Centre half forward

Left full forward

Right full forward

Boundary line

Goal umpire

Full forward

135–185 m (445–610 ft)

6.4 m (21 ft)

Goalpost

6.4 m (21 ft)

Behind post

Behind-line

Goal-line

Goal square

GOALPOSTS

27.5 cm (10 ⅞ in)

Lace

SHERRIN
KANGAROO BRAND

Leather covering

AUSTRALIAN RULES FOOTBALL

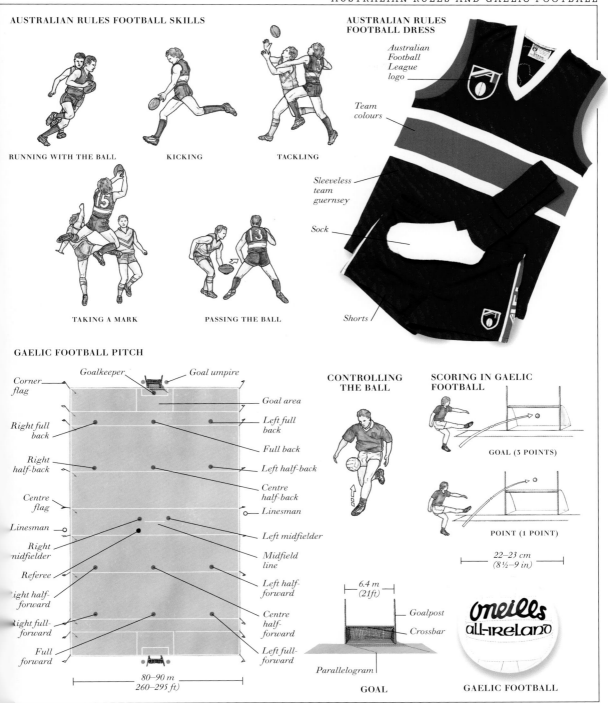

AUSTRALIAN RULES FOOTBALL SKILLS

RUNNING WITH THE BALL

KICKING

TACKLING

TAKING A MARK

PASSING THE BALL

AUSTRALIAN RULES FOOTBALL DRESS

Australian Football League logo

Team colours

Sleeveless team guernsey

Sock

Shorts

GAELIC FOOTBALL PITCH

Corner flag

Goalkeeper

Goal umpire

Goal area

Right full back

Left full back

Full back

Right half-back

Left half-back

Centre half-back

Centre flag

Linesman

Linesman

Right midfielder

Left midfielder

Referee

Midfield line

Right half-forward

Left half-forward

Right full-forward

Centre half-forward

Full forward

Left full-forward

80–90 m
(260–295 ft)

CONTROLLING THE BALL

SCORING IN GAELIC FOOTBALL

GOAL (3 POINTS)

POINT (1 POINT)

22–23 cm
(8½–9 in)

6.4 m
(21 ft)

Goalpost

Crossbar

Parallelogram

GOAL

O'neills
all-ireland

GAELIC FOOTBALL

529

Rugby

RUGBY IS PLAYED WITH AN OVAL BALL, which may be carried, thrown, or kicked. There are two codes of rugby, both played at amateur and professional levels. Rugby Union is played by two teams of 15 players. They can score points in two ways: by placing the ball by hand over the opponents' goal-line (a try, scoring four points) or by kicking it over the crossbar of the opponent's goal (a conversion of a try, scoring two points; a penalty kick, scoring three points; or a drop-kick, scoring three points). Rugby League developed from the Union game but is played by 13 players. In League games, a try scores four points; a conversion scores two points; a drop goal scores one point, and a penalty kick scores two points. Scrummages occur in both codes when play stops following an infringement.

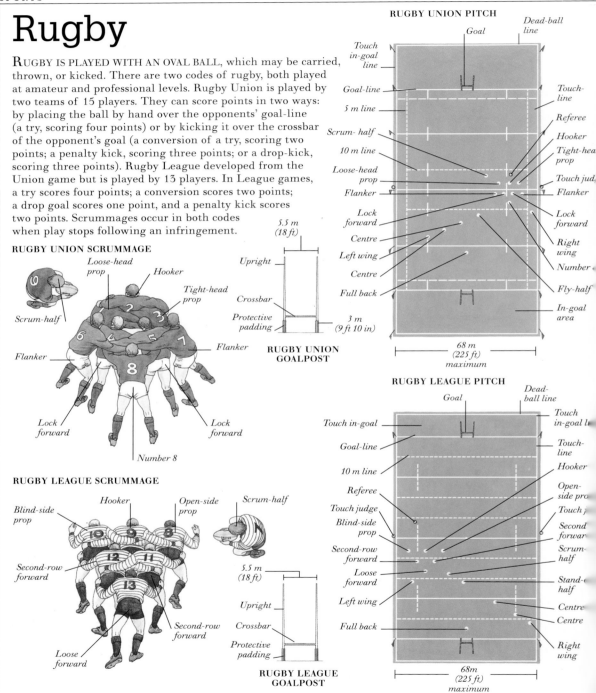

RUGBY UNION SCRUMMAGE

Loose-head prop · Hooker · Tight-head prop · Scrum-half · Flanker · Flanker · Lock forward · Lock forward · Number 8

RUGBY UNION GOALPOST

5.5 m (18 ft) · Upright · Crossbar · Protective padding · 3 m (9 ft 10 in)

RUGBY LEAGUE SCRUMMAGE

Blind-side prop · Hooker · Open-side prop · Scrum-half · Second-row forward · Second-row forward · Loose forward

RUGBY LEAGUE GOALPOST

5.5 m (18 ft) · Upright · Crossbar · Protective padding

RUGBY UNION PITCH

Goal · Dead-ball line · Touch in-goal line · Goal-line · 5 m line · Scrum-half · 10 m line · Loose-head prop · Flanker · Lock forward · Centre · Left wing · Centre · Full back · Touch-line · Referee · Hooker · Tight-head prop · Touch jud · Flanker · Lock forward · Right wing · Number · Fly-half · In-goal area · 68 m (225 ft) maximum

RUGBY LEAGUE PITCH

Goal · Dead-ball line · Touch in-goal · Goal-line · 10 m line · Referee · Touch judge · Blind-side prop · Second-row forward · Loose forward · Left wing · Full back · Touch in-goal l · Touch-line · Hooker · Open-side pro · Touch j · Second forwar · Scrum-half · Stand-half · Centre · Centre · Right wing · 68m (225 ft) maximum

RUGBY SCORING AND SKILLS

GOAL

Goal-line

TRY

PASS

PLACE KICK

FLYING TACKLE

RUGBY UNION PLAYER

Shirt in team colour

Laminated leather panel covered with textured plastic

Four-panel construction

Team shorts

Knee-high sock

Studded boot

RUGBY UNION BALL

GILBERT
REPLICA

official ENGLAND *replica ball*

28–30 cm (11–12 in)

RUGBY LEAGUE BALL

Eight-panel construction

TETLEY'S
GILBERT

Laminated leather panel covered with textured plastic

28 cm (11 in)

Button-up collar

RUGBY LEAGUE SHIRT

Short sleeve

Team crest

GILBERT

BEDFORD BLUES

CITY

RUGBY UNION SHIRT

Ankle support

Team crest

Circular stud

RUGBY BOOT

Team colour

RUGBY SHIRTS

Basketball

BASKETBALL IS A BALL GAME for two teams of five players, originally devised in 1890 by James Naismath for the Y.M.C.A. in Springfield, Massachusetts, U.S.A. The object of the game is to take possession of the ball and score points by throwing the ball into the opposing team's basket. A player moves the ball up and down the court by bouncing it along the ground or "dribbling"; the ball may be passed between players by throwing, bouncing, or rolling. Players may not run with or kick the ball, although pivoting on one foot is allowed. The game begins with the referee throwing the ball into the air and a player from each team jumping up to try and "tip" the ball to a team-mate. The length of the game and the number of periods played varies at different levels. There are amateur, professional, and international rules. No game ends in a draw. An extra period of five minutes is played, plus as many extra periods as are necessary to break the tie. In addition to the five players on court, each team has up to seven substitutes, but players may only leave the court with the permission of the referee. Basketball is a non-contact sport and fouls on other players are penalized by a throw-in awarded against the offending team; a free throw at the basket is awarded when a player is fouled in the act of shooting. Basketball is a fast-moving game, requiring both physical and mental coordination. Skilful tactical play matters more than simple physical strength and the agility of the players makes the game an excellent spectator sport.

BASKETBALL SKILLS

CHEST PASS

DRIBBLE

OVERHEAD PASS

INTERNATIONAL BASKETBALL COUBT

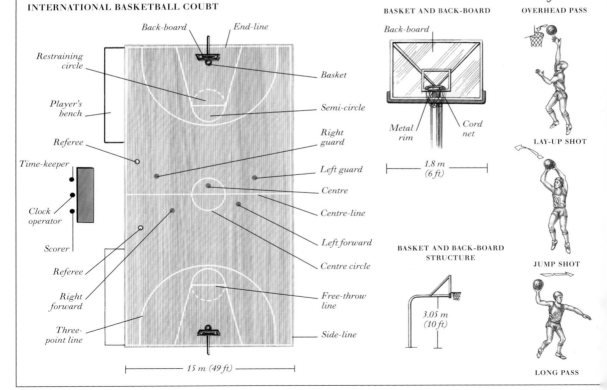

LAY-UP SHOT

JUMP SHOT

LONG PASS

Back-board
End-line
Restraining circle
Player's bench
Referee
Time-keeper
Clock operator
Scorer
Referee
Right forward
Three-point line

Basket
Semi-circle
Right guard
Left guard
Centre
Centre-line
Left forward
Centre circle
Free-throw line
Side-line

15 m (49 ft)

BASKET AND BACK-BOARD

Back-board
Metal rim
Cord net

1.8 m
(6 ft)

BASKET AND BACK-BOARD STRUCTURE

3.05 m
(10 ft)

ZONE DEFENCES

Cool,
lightweight
fabric

AMERICAN BASKETBALL VEST

Team name

Free-throw
line

Player's
number

Point man

1 – 2 – 2 ZONE

1 – 3 – 1 ZONE

24–5 cm
(9½–9¼ in)

Textured
surface for
good grip

Low heel
profile

Cushioned
sole

2 – 3 ZONE

BASKETBALL

BASKETBALL SHOE

INTERNATIONAL
REFEREE'S
SIGNALS

TECHNICAL
FOUL

INTENTIONAL
FOUL

JUMP BALL

STOP CLOCK
FOR FOUL

SUBSTITUTION

PERSONAL FOUL:
TO FREE THROWS

TRAVELLING

ILLEGAL
DRIBBLE

CHARGING WITH
THE BALL

ONE FREE
THROW

STOP CLOCK

Volleyball, netball, and handball

VOLLEYBALL, NETBALL, AND HANDBALL are fast-moving team sports played with balls on courts with a hard surface. In volleyball, the object of the game is to hit the ball over a net strung across the centre of the court so that it touches the ground on the opponent's side. The team of six players can take three hits to direct the ball over the net, although the same player cannot hit the ball twice in a row. Players can hit the ball with their arms, hands or any other part of their upper body. Teams score points only while serving. The first team to score 15 points, with a two-point margin over their opponent, wins the game. Netball is one of the few sports played exclusively by women. Similar to basketball (see pp.532–533), it is played on a slightly larger court with seven players instead of five. A team moves the ball towards the goal by throwing, passing, and catching it with the aim of throwing the ball through the opponents' goal net. Players are confined by their playing position to specific areas of the court. Team handball is one of the world's fastest games. Each side has seven players. A team moves the ball by dribbling, passing, or bouncing it as they run. Players may stop, catch, throw, bounce, or strike the ball with any part of the body above the knees. Each team tries to score goals by directing the ball past the opposition's goalkeeper into the net, which is similar to a soccer net.

VOLLEYBALL SHOTS

OVERHAND SERVE

SPIKE (SMASH)

UNDERHAND SERVE

FOREARM PASS (DIG)

VOLLEYBALL KIT

Team colours

Ribbed cuff

Cotton-knit jersey

Elasticated waist

Mizuno

Shorts

Elasticated knit fabric

Mizuno

Injected moulded padding

KNEE PADS

VOLLEYBALL COURT

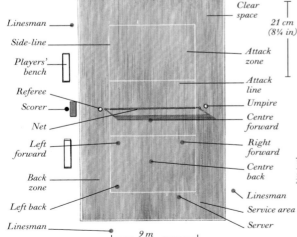

End-line

Linesman

Clear space

Linesman

Side-line

Players' bench

Referee

Scorer

Net

Left forward

Back zone

Left back

Linesman

Attack zone

Attack line

Umpire

Centre forward

Right forward

Centre back

Linesman

Service area

Server

9 m (29 ft 6 in)

Leather covering

21 cm (8¼ in)

VOLLEYBALL

Tape

Net

Antenna

Men's: 2.4 m (8 ft) Women's: 2.2 m (7 ft 4 in)

Post

VOLLEYBALL NET

NETBALL COURT

Mineral surface with non-slip tarmacadam coating

Goalkeeper

Goal circle

Defence third

Goal defence

Umpire

Scorer

Timekeeper

Scorer

Central circle

Wing attack

Goal third

Goal shooter

Goalpost

Back-line

Wing defence

Centre

Central third

Goal attack

Transverse line

Goalpost

Side-line

15.2 m (50 ft)

NETBALL

Rubber or leather covering

22.4 cm (8¼ in)

NETBALL GOALPOST AND NET

Ring

Net

3.05 m (10 ft)

NETBALL PASSES

CHEST PASS

UNDERARM PASS

SHOULDER PASS

BOUNCE PASS

HANDBALL COURT

Goal area

Guide mark

Penalty line

Players' bench

Secretary

Line-keeper

Left wing

Centre back

Left back

Goalkeeper

Goal-line referee

Goal

Net

Goal area line

Goal-line

Free-throw line

Side-line

Centre line

Court referee

Right wing

Centre forward

Right back

20m (65 ft 6in)

HANDBALL
MEN'S: 18.8 CM (7½ IN)
WOMEN'S: 17.5 CM (7 IN)

Leather covering

HANDBALL SHOE

HANDBALL NET

Crossbar

Post

Goal-line

2 m (6 ft 6 in)

HANDBALL SKILLS

OVERARM PASS

DRIBBLE

BOUNCE PASS

JUMP SHOT

Baseball

BASEBALL IS A BALL GAME for two teams of nine players.
The batter hits the ball thrown by the opposing team's pitcher,
into the area between the foul lines. He then runs round all four
fixed bases in order to score a run, touching or "tagging" each base
in turn. The pitcher must throw the ball at a height between the
batter's armpits and knees, a height which is called the "strike
zone". A ball pitched in this area that crosses over the "home plate"
is called a "strike" and the batter has three strikes in which to try
and hit the ball (otherwise he is "struck out"). The fielding team
tries to get the batting team out by catching the ball before it
bounces, tagging a player of the batting team with the ball who
is running between bases, or by tagging a base before the player
has reached it. Members of the batting team may stop safely at a
base as long as it is not occupied by another member of their team.
When the batter runs to first base, his team-mate at first base must
run on to second – this is called "force play". A game consists of
nine innings and each team will bat once during an inning. When
three members of the batting team are out, the teams swap roles.
The team with the greatest number of runs wins the game.

BATTER'S HELMET

Plastic shell

Peak

Foam padding

Wire coated in strong nylon

Plastic-coated foam padding

CATCHER'S MASK

BASEBALL PITCH

Centre field

Centre fielder

Warning track

Right fielder

Left fielder

Second baseman

Left field

Right field

Foul line

Outfield

Shortstop

First baseman

Umpire

First base

Third baseman

Infield

Third base

Home run

Coach's box

100 m (325 ft) minimum

Second base

Dugout

On-deck circle

Pitcher's mound

Pitcher

Pitcher's rubber

PITCHER'S MOUND

Batter

Home plate

Catcher

Home-plate umpire

HOME PLATE

MAKING A BASEBALL

Woollen yarn

Rubber inner casing

Horsehide strip

Cork centre

Cotton thread outer casing

Woollen strand

Red outer stitching

THE PITCHING SEQUENCE

THE WIND-UP 1

THE WIND-UP 2

THE WIND-UP 3

THE WIND-UP 4

THE RELEASE

THE FOLLOW-THROUGH

UMPIRING SIGNALS

BALL

INFIELD

STRIKE

FAIR BALL

RUNNER IS SAFE

FOUL TIP

BASEBALL EQUIPMENT

Webbed pocket

Fingers laced together

Strap

Thumb

Palm

Leather stitching

Heel

STEERHIDE LEATHER

FIELDER'S GLOVE AND BALL

PONY

Metal heel plate

AMERICAN BASEBALL BOOT

Metal toe plate

Batter's helmet

Bat

Batting glove

Team shirt

Undershirt

Pants

Spiked shoe

BATTER

Hitting area

Official Baseball

Crest

1.1 m (3 ft 6 in) maximum

Handle

Knob

BAT

537

Cricket

CRICKET IS A BALL GAME PLAYED by two teams of eleven players on a pitch with two sets of three stumps (wickets). The bowler bowls the ball down the pitch to the batsman of the opposing team, who must defend the wicket in front of which he stands. The object of the game is to score as many runs as possible. Runs can be scored individually by running the length of the playing strip, or by hitting a ball which lands outside the boundary ("six"), or which lands inside the boundary but bounces or rolls outside ("four"); the opposing team will bowl and field, attempting to dismiss the batsmen. A batsman can be dismissed in one of several ways: by the bowler hitting the wicket with the ball ("bowled"); by a fielder catching the ball hit by the batsman before it touches the ground ("caught"); by the wicket-keeper or another fielder breaking the wicket while the batsman is attempting a run and is therefore out of his ground ("stumped" or "run out"); by the batsman breaking the wicket with his own bat or body ("hit wicket"); by a part of the batsman's body being hit by a ball that would otherwise have hit the wicket ("leg before wicket" ["lbw"]). A match consists of one or two innings and each innings ends when the tenth batsman of the batting team is out, when a certain number of overs (a series of six balls bowled) have been played, or when the captain of the batting team "declares" ending the innings voluntarily.

CRICKET STROKES

FORWARD DEFENSIVE STROKE

BACKWARD DEFENSIVE STROKE

ON-DRIVE

OFF-DRIVE

PULL

HOOK

SQUARE CUT

LEG GLANCE

POSSIBLE FIELD POSITIONS FOR AN AWAY SWING BOWLER TO A RIGHT-HANDED BATSMAN (IN RED) AND OTHER FIELD POSITIONS

Long on
Long off
Umpire
Bowler
Boundary line
Non-striking batsman
Deep mid-wicket
Extra cover
Mid-on
Mid-off
Silly mid-on
Silly mid-off
Forward short leg
Cover
Square leg
Point
Deep square leg
Gulley
Square-leg umpire
Third man
Batsman
Second slip
Long leg
Leg slip
First slip
Wicket-keeper
Fine leg
Sight screen

CRICKET PITCH

Wicket-keeper
Batsman
Wicket
Bowling crease
20 m (66 ft)
Bowler
Return crease
Umpire
Non-striking batsman

CRICKET BALL AND WICKET

Leather skin
Seam
BALL
Bail
WICKET
Stump

MAKING A BAT HANDLE

Sarawak cane

Twine wrapped around handle

Rubber strip

LAMINATING THE WOOD

BINDING THE HANDLE

MAKING A BAT BLADE

Kiln-dried willow

SEASONING THE TIMBER

V-shaped splice

Blade planed by hand

CUTTING THE SPLICE

PROTECTIVE CLOTHING

Slit in leather for greater flexibility

Padding protects knuckles from injury

Mesh covering for ventilation

BATTING GLOVE

Dimpled rubber improves grip

Wrist strap

WICKET-KEEPER'S GLOVES

Polycarbonate shell with cloth covering

Peak

Foam cheek-piece for comfort and good fit

Protective plastic ear piece

HELMET

ADDING THE HANDLE TO THE BAT

Rubber grip

Shoulder of bat

Handle glued into splice

Scoop

Toe of the bat shaped

FITTING THE HANDLE

Grip rolled onto handle

Sanded and polished bat

FINISHING TOUCHES

Bat

BATSMAN

Padded glove

Cap

Wristband

White shirt

White sweater

Stripes in team colours

Thigh pad under white trousers

Knee roll

Cricket shoe

Leg pad

Dimpled rubber sole

Hockey, lacrosse, and hurling

ALL OVER THE WORLD, TEAM GAMES have evolved which require that a ball be struck or carried, and tossed at the end of a stick. Early forms of these games include hurling, shinty, bandy, and pelota. Hockey is played by men and women: two teams of eleven players try to gain and keep possession of the ball and score goals by using the hockey stick to propel the ball into their opponents' goal net. Skills such as passing, pushing, or hitting the ball by slapping or lifting it in a flicking movement, and shooting at goal are crucial. Hockey is played indoors and outdoors on grass or synthetic pitches. Lacrosse is played internationally as a 12-a-side game for women and as 10-a-side game for men. The women's pitch has no absolute boundaries but the men's pitch has clearly defined side-lines and end-lines. The ball is kept in play by being carried, thrown or batted with the crosse, and rolled or kicked in any direction. In men's and women's lacrosse, play can continue behind the marked goal areas. Similar skills are required in hurling – a Gaelic field game played on the same pitch as Gaelic football (see pp. 528–529), using the same goalposts and net. In hurling, the ball may be struck with or carried on the hurley and, when off the ground, may be struck with the hand or kicked. Goals (three points) are scored when the ball passes between the posts and under the crossbar; one point is scored when it passes between the posts and over the crossbar.

GOALKEEPER'S EQUIPMENT

Air vent

Hard shell

Face mask

Cooper XD

HELMET

Stra

Rigid palm

Padded wrist

PRO spec

GAUNTLET

HOCKEY STICK AND BALL

STICK

Handle

Tape

Steam-bent ash head

Blade

Slazenger FLEX

91 cm (3 ft)

Stitched seam

7–7.5 cm (2¼–3 in)

BALL

HOCKEY FIELD

Centre forward

Inside right

Right wing

Right half

Right back

Side-line

Corner flag

Shooting circle

Goal

Penalty spot

Five yard mark

Goal-line

Inside left

Left wing

Umpire

Centre half

Left half

Left back

Goalkeeper

55 m (180 ft)

Protective overshoe

Padding protect toes against th hard ba

Strap

GOALKEEPER'S KICKER

2.1 m (7 ft)

HOCKEY GOAL

MEN'S LACROSSE FIELD

Defender
Goalkeeper
Defender
Midfielder
Midfielder
Referee
Attacker
Attacker
Corner flag
Goal
al circle
efender
Midfielder
Chief bench official
Scorer
Penalty timekeeper
Attacker
Time-keeper

55 m (180 ft)

WOMEN'S LACROSSE FIELD

Centre
Left wing defence
Left wing attack
Third home
Second home
First home
hird man
15 m fan
ish mark
oalkeeper
oal circle
Point
ver point
Right wing defence
Time-keeper
Scorer
Penalty time-keeper
Right wing attack
Umpire

60 m (200 ft) approx

CROSSE AND BALL

Butt
Handle

HURLER

Helmet
Team shirt
Hurley
Shorts
Sock
Boot

LACROSSE SKILLS

CRADLING
THROWING
SIDE-SHOOTING

LACROSSE GOALKEEPER

Goalkeeper's stick
Helmet
Face mask
Team shirt
Leather glove
Sweat trousers
Player's number
13
Solid rubber lacrosse ball

1.8 m (6 ft)
Crossbar
Post
Peg

LACROSSE NET

Net made from gut, rawhide, or cord
Throat
Lacing
Guardstop
Pocket
Wall
Head

Leather cover around a cork centre

HURLING BALL

SCORING AT HURLING

7 m (23 ft)

GOAL (3 POINTS)
POINT (1 POINT)

Boss

HURLEY AND HURLING BALL

Grip
HURLEY
91 cm (3 ft)

Athletics

THE SPORTS that make up athletics are divided into two main groups: track events – which include sprinting, middle, and long distance running, relay running, hurdling, and walking – and field events which require jumping and throwing skills. Contests designed to test the speed, strength, agility, and stamina of athletes were held by the ancient Greeks over 4,000 years ago. However, the abolition of the Olympic Games in 393 AD meant that athletics were neglected until the revival of large-scale competitions in the mid-nineteenth century. Modern stadia offer areas reserved for the long jump, triple jump, and pole vault usually situated outside the running track. The javelin, shot, hammer, and discus are thrown within the track area. Most athletes specialize in one or two events but, in the heptathlon, women compete in seven events, held over two days: 200 m and 800 m races, 100 m hurdles, javelin, shot put, high jump, and long jump. In the decathlon, men compete in ten events over two days: 100 m, 400 m, and 1,500 m races, 110 m hurdles, javelin, discus, shot put, pole vault, high jump, and long jump.

FIELD EVENT EQUIPMENT

Steel wire

Metal rim

Head

Body

Centre weigh

Swivel

DISCUS
MEN: 2 KG (4 LB 7 OZ)
WOMEN: 1 KG (2 LB 3 OZ)

Hammer handle

HAMMER
7 KG (16 LB)

Rubber coating

Shot-pellet filling

12.7 cm (5 in)

10 cm (4 in)

MEN'S SHOT
7 KG (16 LB)

WOMEN'S SHOT
4 KG (8 LB 12 OZ)

JAVELIN   Cord grip   Shaft   Tip

Men: 2.6 m (8 ft 6 in)
Women: 2.3 m (7 ft 6 in)

ATHLETICS TRACK AND FIELD

Finishing post   Pole-vault mat   Pole-vault runway   100 m starting line

Finishing line

Hammer circle

Javelin fan

Discus circle

Steeplechase water jump

Javel runw

Lane

One l is 400

Shot-put fan

High-jump fa

Shot-put circle

High-jump mat

Discus fan

Hammer fan

Triple-jump take-off board   Triple-jump take-off line   Indicator board   Triple-jump runway   Long-jump take-off board   Landing area

TYPES OF SHOE

Lightweight construction

Reflective side strip

Wedge heel

Spiked sole

Air-cushioned sole

TRACK SHOE

RUNNING SHOE

Hollow plastic tube

RELAY BATONS

DISCUS THROW

Swing

Shift

Twist

Release

SHOT PUT

Crouch

Shift

Thrust

Release

HAMMER THROW

Swing

Entry

Lift

Release

JAVELIN THROW

Withdrawal

Half turn

Step

Drive forward

Release

HIGH JUMP

Drive

Arch

Take-off

Approach

Landing

POLE VAULT

Handstand

Push-pull

Release

Rock-back

Hang

Take-off

Plant

Landing

LONG JUMP

Take-off

Flight

Hitch-kick

Stretch

Landing

Take-off board

TRIPLE JUMP

Take-off

Hop

Skip

Jump

Take-off board

Land on foot used for take-off

Land on opposite foot

Racket sports

PROTECTIVE EYEWEAR

THE OBJECT OF ALL RACKET SPORTS is to make shots the opponent cannot return. Games are played by two players (singles) or four players (doubles). Racket shape and size is tailored to each sport, but all rackets are constructed of wood, plastic, aluminium, or high-performance materials such as fibreglass and carbon graphite. Racket strings are usually synthetic, although natural gut is still used. Tennis is played on a court divided by a low net. Opposing players serve alternate games. At least six games must be won to gain a set, and two or sometimes three sets are needed to win a match. Tennis courts may be concrete, grass, clay, or synthetic, each surface requiring a different style of play. Badminton is an indoor sport that is played with light, flexible rackets and a feather shuttlecock on a court with a high net. Players can score points only on their serve. The first to reach 15 points (11 points for women's singles) wins the game. Two games are needed to win a match. Squash and racketball are both played in enclosed courts. One player hits the ball against the front wall, and the other tries to return it before it bounces on the floor more than once. Squash rackets have smaller, rounder heads and stiffer frames than badminton rackets. In America, the game is played on a narrower court than an international court using a much harder ball. Squash games are played to nine points (international) or 15 points (American). In racketball, players use a ball that is larger and bouncier than a squash ball. The racket is thick and sturdy, with a large head, short handle, and a thong that loops around the wrist. Points can be won only when serving, and the first player to reach 21 points wins.

TENNIS RACKET

Synthetic string

Frame

Head

Logo

Throat

Grip

Butt

TENNIS COURT

Linesman

Base line

Receiver

Singles side-line

Centre mark

Service judge

Centre service line

Service line

Umpire

Net judge

Net

Doubles side-line

Right service court

Left service court

Alley

Server

Foot-fault judge

11 m (36 ft)

Headband

Racket

Tennis shirt

Tennis ball

Wristband

Tennis skirt

Tennis shoe

Sock

TENNIS PLAYER

White tape

Centre strap

Supporting post

1.1 m (3 ft 6 in)

Net

TENNIS NET

MAKING A TENNIS BALL

Vulcanized rubber

Two halves bonded together

THE CENTRE

Mixed wool and man-made fibre covering

Wilson 2

THE COVERING

Stitchless seam

Wilson 2

Bright colours visibility

THE FINISHED BALL

BADMINTON RACKET AND SHUTTLECOCK

Synthetic string

Flexible frame

Shaft

SHUTTLECOCK

Feather crown

Cork tip

RACKET

Handle

SQUASH RACKET AND SQUASH BALLS

Protective strip

Frame

Synthetic strings

Logo

SQUASH BALLS

YELLOW DOT (VERY SLOW)

WHITE DOT (SLOW)

RED DOT (FAST)

BLUE DOT (VERY FAST)

Open-throat head

Shaft

Handle

RACKET

AMERICAN SQUASH COURT

Outer boundary line

Front wall

Service line

Side-wall line

Floor

Telltale

Half-court line

Side wall

Short line

Service box

Receiver

Server

Left service court

Right service court

5.6 m (18 ft 6 in)

INTERNATIONAL SQUASH COURT

Outer boundary line

Front wall

Service line

Tin

Side-wall line

Floor

Side wall

Short line

Service box

Half-court line

Server

Left service court

Right service court

Receiver

6.4 m (21ft)

BADMINTON COURT

Receiver

Service judge

Singles side-line

Doubles side-line

Linesman

Umpire

Net

Short service line

Server

Back boundary line

Alley

Long service line (doubles)

6 m (20 ft)

White tape

Post

Net

1.5 m (5 ft)

BADMINTON NET

RACKETBALL RACKET, BALL, AND GLOVE

RACKET

Synthetic string

Frame

Logo

Throat

Leather treated to make it sticky

Short handle

Wrist thong

RACKETBALL

GLOVE

RACKETBALL COURT

Front wall

Side wall

Service line

Server

Service zone

Receiving line

Service box line

Service line

Centre court

Floor

Receiver

6 m (20 ft)

545

Golf

GOLF BALL AND TEE

THE GAME OF GOLF was first played in Scotland some 400 years ago. Players are required to hit a ball, using a wooden or iron club, from a smooth level point or "teeing ground", down the "fairway", and on to a putting green where the target hole is located. The fairway is a strip of clear land along which there are natural hazards – such as ponds and streams, man-made hazards – such as bunkers (sand-pits), and rough (areas of uncut grass). Championship golf courses have 18 holes. The object of the game is to hit the ball into each hole in turn, and to complete the "round" using as few strokes as possible. Players compete individually or in teams, playing the course together in groups of two, three, or four. The two basic forms of competition are match play and stroke play. In match play, the side winning the majority of holes over a certain number of rounds wins the match. In stroke play, the winner is the player who finishes a certain number of rounds having made the fewest strokes.

GOLF BALL WITH BALATA SURFACE

Wound yarn

Dimpled surface

Liqui

Balata cover

Membrane to contain liquid

Water obstacle

Putting green

Dog-leg hole

Elevated green

Bridge

Putting green

Pond

Clubhouse

Bunker

Hole

Practice area

Teein ground

Rough

Pathw

Fairway

AUGUSTA NATIONAL GOLF COURSE, AUGUSTA, GEORGIA, U.S.A.

Screen of trees

A TYPICAL HOLE

Teeing ground

Water obstacle　　*Bridge*　　*Fairway*　　*Wood*　　*Rough*

MAKING A WOODEN CLUB

Close grain of wood

Streamlined back

Plastic insert on face

Sand, stain, and varnish finish

Persimmon wood

Slot cut for plate

Metal sole plate protects the wood

Outline of head

RAW MATERIAL

CREATING THE BASIC SHAPE

ADDING THE LEAD WEIGHT

THE FINISHED CLUB HEAD

RANGE OF WOODEN CLUBS

10 degree loft — DRIVER

15 degree loft — 3-WOOD

21 degree loft — 5-WOOD

RANGE OF IRON CLUBS

22 degree loft — 3-IRON
26 degree loft — 4-IRON

34 degree loft — 5-IRON
38 degree loft — 6-IRON
42 degree loft — 7-IRON
46 degree loft — 8-IRON
50 degree loft — 9-IRON
56 degree loft — PITCHING WEDGE / SAND WEDGE

GOLF ACCESSORIES

GOLF SCORE RECORD

BALL MARKERS

SCORECARD AND PENCIL

TEE PEGS

PITCHMARK REPAIRER

PRACTICE BALL

Spiked sole

LIGHTWEIGHT SHOE

Flag pole or pin

Green

Bunker (sand-pit)

PUTTER, WOOD, AND IRON

WOOD

Textured vulcanized rubber grip

IRON

PUTTER

Shaped pistol grip

Stainless steel shaft

Steel shaft

Steel shaft

84 cm (33 in)

94 cm (37 in)

109 cm (43 in)

Neck

Angled neck

Heel

Toe

Blade

Heel

Toe

Groove

Neck

Face

Toe

Sole

Heel

547

Archery and shooting

TARGET SHOOTING AND ARCHERY EVOLVED as practice for hunting and battle skills. Modern bows, although designed according to the principles of early hunting bows, use laminates, fibreglass, dacron, and carbon, and are equipped with sights and stabilizers. Competitors in target archery shoot over distances of 30 m (100 ft), 50 m (165 ft), 70 m (230 ft), and 90 m (300 ft) for men, and 30 m (100 ft), 50 m (165 ft), 60 m (200 ft), and 70 m (230 ft) for women. The closer the shot is to the centre of the target, the higher the score. The individual scores are added up, and the archer with the highest total wins the competition. Crossbows are used in match competitions over 10 m (33 ft), and 30. m (100 ft). Rifle shooting is divided into three categories: smallbore, bigbore, and air rifle. Contests take place over a variety of distances and further subdivisions are based on the type of shooting position used: prone, kneeling, or standing. The Olympic biathlon combines cross-country skiing and rifle shooting over a course of approximately 20 km (12½ miles). Additional magazines of ammunition are carried in the butt of the rifles. Bigbore rifles fitted with a telescopic sight can be used for hunting and running game target shooting. Pistol shooting events, using rapid-fire pistols, target pistols, and air pistols, take place over 10 m (33 ft), 25 m (82 ft), and 50 m (165 ft) distances. In rapid-fire pistol shooting, a total of 60 shots are fired from a distance of 25 m (83 ft).

CROSSBOW AND BOLT

Laminated fibreglass bow

Bolt

Bolt rest

45 mm (1¼ in)

CROSSBOW TARGET

Stirrup held between feet whi drawing bow

Sight

Hardwood laminate limb

Dacron string

Sig

MODERN BOW

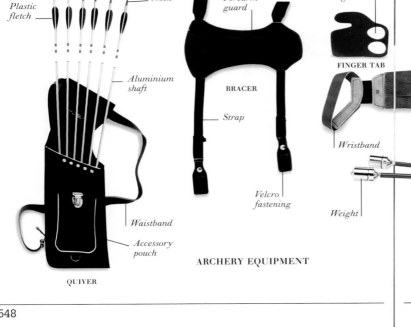

Nock

Plastic fletch

Forearm guard

Finger hole

Aluminium shaft

BRACER

Strap

FINGER TAB

Wristband

Pressure button

ARCHER'S GLOVE

Grip

Velcro fastening

Weight

V-bar stabilizers

Waistband

Accessory pouch

ARCHERY EQUIPMENT

Magnesium riser

QUIVER

SMALLBORE BIATHLON RIFLE

Rifle sight without magnifying lens

Fore sight

Barrel

Trigger

Trigger guard

5.6 mm (0.22 in) calibre bullet

Magazine

Extra magazine stored in rifle butt

155 mm (6 in)

SMALLBORE FREE RIFLE TARGET FOR 50 M (165 FT) RANGE

BIGBORE HUNTING RIFLE

Bolt handle

Bolt

Telescopic sight

Open sight

Open sight

Sling fixing point

7.62 mm (0.3 in) calibre bullet

1 m (39 in)

BIGBORE RIFLE TARGET FOR 300 M (100° FT) RANGE

TARGET PISTOL

Back sight

Fore sight

Hammer

Firing pin

Sight pin

Sight ring attachment

Magazine

9 mm (0.35 in) calibre bullet

197 mm (7¼ in)

PISTOL TARGET FOR 18 M (60 FT) RANGE

AIR PISTOL

Wooden grip shaped to fit the hand

Cocking lever and barrel

Piston

Trigger

Air-pistol pellet

155 mm (6 in)

AIR-PISTOL TARGET FOR 10 M (33 FT) RANGE

Nock

FIELD ARROW

Metal tip

Feathering

Wooden shaft

Straw butt

White inner 2 points

Aluminium longrod stabilizer

Blue outer 5 points

Yellow inner 10 points (bull's-eye)

ARCHERY TARGET

Ice hockey

ICE HOCKEY IS PLAYED by two teams of six players on an ice rink, with a goal net at each end. The object of this fast, and often dangerous, game is to hit a frozen rubber puck into the opposing team's net with a ice hockey stick. The game begins when the referee drops the puck between the sticks of two players from opposing teams, who "face off". The rink is divided into three areas: defending, neutral, and attacking zones. Players may move with the puck and pass the puck to one another along the ice, but may not pass it more than two zones across the rink markings. A goal is scored when the puck entirely crosses the goal-line between the posts and under the crossbar of the goal. A team may field up to 20 players although only six players are allowed on the ice at one time; substitutions occur frequently. Each game consists of three periods of 20 minutes, divided by breaks of 15 minutes.

GOALKEEPER

Helmet
Face mask
Throat protector
Team shirt
Butt end
Catch glove
Pants
Blocking pad
Goalkeeper's pad
Blade
Skate
Blade
Goalkeeper's stick
Heel

ICE HOCKEY RINK

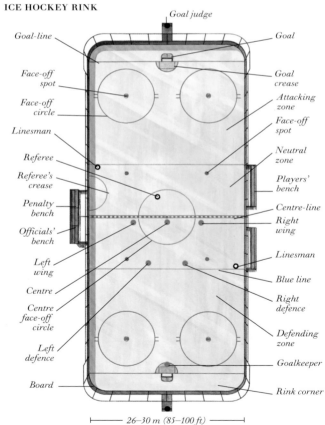

Goal judge
Goal-line
Goal
Face-off spot
Goal crease
Face-off circle
Attacking zone
Linesman
Face-off spot
Referee
Neutral zone
Referee's crease
Players' bench
Penalty bench
Centre-line
Officials' bench
Right wing
Left wing
Linesman
Centre
Blue line
Centre face-off circle
Right defence
Left defence
Defending zone
Board
Goalkeeper
Rink corner

26–30 m (85–100 ft)

THE FACE-OFF

Linesman
Facing player
Referee
Face-off circle
Facing player
Face-off spot
Puck

9.2 m (30 ft)

Goal frame
1.2 m (4 ft)
Netting
1.8 m (6 ft)
Goal crease

ICE HOCKEY GOAL

GOALKEEPER'S HELMET

Customized paintwork

Face guard

Chin protection

PLAYER'S BODY ARMOUR

Air vents

Rigid plastic shell

Manufacturer's logo

Chin strap

Foam padding

PLAYER'S HELMET

ICE HOCKEY STICKS

GOALKEEPER'S STICK

SHOULDER AND CHEST PADDING

MADE IN FINLAND

TORSPO

Pro 5000

TORSPO

Pro 500

OUTFIELD PLAYER'S STICK

147 cm (4 ft 9 in)

Shoulder padding

ELBOW PADS

Strap

Chest padding

Wrist protection

Heavy padding

TORSPO
20

Flexible gusset

Rigid finger cap

GLOVE

LEG PROTECTOR

Knee protection

Rigid plastic casing

D°R
Daignault · Rolland

CENTURION-J

16.5"
43cm

Wide lower shaft

Vulcanized rubber

7.6 cm (3 in)

FROZEN PUCK

Thin shaft

TORSPO

TORSPO

Thick foam backing

Leg pad

Ankle support

501

501

Safety heel tip

Blade   **SKATE**

Puck stopper

39 cm (15 in)

Thick blade

32 cm (12½ in)

Heel

Alpine skiing

COMPETITIVE ALPINE SKIING is divided into four disciplines: downhill, slalom, giant slalom, and super-giant slalom (Super-G). Each one tests different skills. In downhill skiing, competitors race down a slope marked out by control flags, known as "gates", and are timed on a single run only. Competitors wear crash helmets, one-piece Lycra suits, and long skis with flattened tips to minimize air resistance. Slalom and giant slalom skiiers negotiate a twisting course requiring balance, agility, and quick reactions. Courses are defined by pairs of gates. Racers must pass through each pair of gates to complete the course successfully. Competitors are timed on two runs over different courses, and the skier who completes the courses in the shortest time wins. The equipment and protective guards used by slalom skiiers are shown opposite. In Super-G races, competitors ski a single run that combines the technical challenge of slalom with the speed of downhill. The course requires skiers to complete medium-to-long radius turns at high speed, and contain up to two jumps. Clothing is the same as for downhill, but slightly shorter skis are used.

DOWNHILL SKIER

Ski goggles

Helmet

One-piece lycra ski suit

Wrist strap

Ski pole

Basket

Safety binding

Ski boot

Ski glove

Tail

ALPINE SKI SLOPE COURSES

Downhill start

Downhill racing control flag

Super-G start

Pine forest

Giant slalom start

Giant slalom gate

Slalom start

Slalom gate

Safety barrier

Finish line

Polyamide inner boot

Tongue

Upper cuff

Upper strap

Buckle

Energy-distributing bonnet

Power bar

Adjusting catch

Tension control

Sole

Lower shell of boot

Heel grip

SKI BOOT

Toe-piece

Heel-piece

Blind release lever

Wing

Anti-friction pad

Housing

Release adjustment screw

Base plate

Brake arm

SAFETY BINDING

552

SLALOM CLOTHING AND EQUIPMENT

Anti-glare lens

Elasticated strap

GOGGLES

Hard nylon shell

Padding

Strap

Chin guard

SLALOM HELMET

Extended cuff

Wrist strap

Rigid pad for hand protection

SKI GLOVE

Adjustable shoulder strap

High collar

Double-knit wool and polyester fabric

Ribbed cuff

Zip pocket

Front zip fastening

Waterproof fabric

Cuff fits over ski boot

PADDED SKI TROUSERS

PADDED SWEATER

Moulded polypropylene

HAND GUARD

Wrist strap

Grip

Shock-absorbing platform under boot

Edge

Tough polypropylene shell deflects the shaft of the slalom gate

Velcro strap

LEG GUARD

188–203 cm (74–80 in)

Shaft

Basket

SLALOM SKI POLE

Tail

Tip

SLALOM SKI

553

Equestrian sports

EQUESTRIAN SPORTS HAVE TAKEN place throughout the world for centuries: events involving mounted horses were recorded in the Olympic Games of 642 BC. Showjumping, however, is a much more recent innovation, and the first competitions were held at the beginning of the 1900s. In this sport, horse and rider must negotiate a course of variable, unfixed obstacles, making as few mistakes as possible. Showjumping fences consist of wooden stands, known as standards or wings, that support planks or poles. Parts of the fence are designed to collapse on impact, preventing injury to the horse and rider. Judges penalise competitors for errors, such as knocking down obstacles, refusing jumps, or deviating from the course. Depending on the type of competition, the rider with the fewest faults, most points, or fastest time wins. There are two basic forms of horse racing – flat races and races with jumps, such as steeplechase or hurdle-races. Thoroughbred horses are used in this sport, as they have great strength and stamina and can achieve speeds of up to 65 kph (40 mph). Jockeys wear "silks" – caps and jackets designed in distinctive colours and patterns which help identify the horses. In harness racing, the horse is driven from a light, twowheeled carriage called a sulky. Horses are trained to trot and to pace, and different races are held for each of these types of gait. In pacing races, the horses wear hobbles to prevent them from breaking into a trot or gallop. Breeds such as the Standardbred and the French Trotter have been developed especially for this sport.

SHOWJUMPING SADDLE

High cantle

Deep seat

Pommel

Forward-cut flap

Knee roll

SHOWJUMPING FENCES

Standard

Foot

Plank

UPRIGHT PLANKS

Standard

Foot

Pole

UPRIGHT POLES

Back pole

Standard

Foot

Pole

TRIPLE BAR (STAIRCASE)

Standard

Pole

Foot

HOG'S-BACK

Pillar

Wood block pair to resem a b

WALL

Hard hat

Riding jacket

Browband

Throat-latch

Rein

Jodhpurs

Cheek-piece

Showjumping saddle

Running martingale

Hindquarters

Dock

Noseband

Brushing boot

Sheepskin numnah

Girth

Stirrup iron

Riding boot

Hock joint

Gaskin

Hoof

SHOWJUMPING HORSE WITH RIDER

Fetlock joint

Pastern

Coronet

RACING SADDLE

Cut-back head

Cantle

Surcingle loop

Lightweight steel stirrup-iron

Forward-cut flap

Rawhide stirrup-leather

RACING SILKS

Plain cap

Spotted cap

Quartered cap

Plain sleeve

Plain sleeve

Striped jacket

Plain jacket

Spotted sleeve

Jacket with sash

Paddock

Clubhouse

Finishing line

Grandstand

Dirt track

Home stretch

Far turn

Clubhouse turn

Grass track

Tote board

Start of straight

Barrier

Browband

Rosette

Cheek-piece

Bridle

Noseband

Back stretch

SARATOGA RACE COURSE, SARATOGA, NEW YORK, U.S.A.

Skullcap covered with racing silk

Goggles

Driving saddle

Rein terret

Shaft

Crupper

Quartered racing silk jacket

Whip

Rubber bit-guard

Driving rein

Lightweight harness

Thimble

Girth

Seat

Stirrup

Racing sulky

Belly-band

Pacing hobble

Over-reach boot

Wheel

Pneumatic tyre

Disc covering spokes

HARNESS RACING WITH A STANDARDBRED HORSE

Judo and fencing

COMBAT SPORTS ARE BASED ON THE SKILLS used in fighting. In these sports, the competitors may be unarmed – as in judo and boxing – or armed – as in fencing and kendo. Judo is a system of unarmed combat developed in the East. Translated from the Japanese the name means "the gentle way". Students learn how to turn an opponent's force to their own advantage. The usual costume is loose white trousers and a jacket, fastened with a cloth belt. The colour of belt indicates the student's level of expertise, from white-belted novices to the expert "black belts". Competitions take place on a mat or "shiaijo", 9 or 10 m (30 or 33 ft) square in size, bounded by "danger" and "safety" areas to prevent injury. Competitors try to throw, pin, or master their opponent by applying pressure to the arm joints or neck. Judo bouts are strictly monitored, and competitors receive points for superior technique, not for injuring their opponent. Fencing is a combat sport using swords, which takes place on a narrow "piste" 14 m (46 ft) long. Competitors try to touch specific target areas on their opponent with their sword or "foil" while avoiding being touched themselves. The winner is the one who scores the greatest number of hits. Fencers wear clothing made from strong white material, which affords maximum protection while allowing freedom of movement, steel mesh masks with padded bibs to protect the fencer's neck, and a long white glove on their sword hand. Fencing foils do not have sharpened blades, and their tips end in a blunt button to prevent injuries. Three types of swords are used – foils, épées, and sabres. Official foil and épée competitions always use an electric scoring system. The sword tips are connected to lights by a long wire that passes underneath each fencer's jacket. A bulb flashes when a hit is made.

JUDO HOLDS AND THROWS

SIDE FOUR QUARTER HOLD

SINGLE WING

BODY DROP

ONE ARM SHOULDER THROW

SHOULDER WHEEL

SWEEPING LOW THROW

STOMACH THROW

KNEE WHEEL

JUDO MAT

16 m (52 ft 6 in)

Judge

Scorer

Holding time-keeper

Time-keeper

Danger area

Contestant

JUDO KIT

Draw-string

Contestant

Referee

Contest area

Safety area

Cotton trousers

Black belt

Heavy-duty cotton jacket

FENCING PISTE

Rear limit line

14 m
(46 ft)

Sabre
and épéé
warning
line

Scorer

Electrical
scoring
apparatus

Centre
line

President

Time-
keeper

On-guard
line

Body
wire

Reel

FENCING TARGET AREAS

SABREUR

FOILIST

EPEEIST

FENCING EQUIPMENT

Steel
wire
mesh

Padded
bib

MESH MASK

Woven
metal
thread

THE SABRE

THE FOIL

Martingale

THE EPEE

Cuff

METAL JACKET

GAUNTLET

Glove

**TARGET AREAS ON
THE UPPER BODY**

Mask

Wire
mesh

Bib

Under
plastron

Tierce

Sixte

Quinte

Gauntlet

Quarte

Seconde

Prime

Octave

Septime

Metal
over-jacket

Breeches

Stocking

Fencing
shoe

Button

Blade

**PARTS
OF THE
SWORD**

Guard

Tang

Leather
pad

Alternative
pistol-grip
handle

Brass
screw

Steel foil pommel

557

Swimming and diving

SWIMMING WAS INCLUDED in the first modern Olympic Games in 1896 and diving events were added in 1904. Swimming is both an individual and a team sport and races take place over a predetermined distance in one of the four major categories of stroke – freestyle (usually front crawl), butterfly, breaststroke, and backstroke. Competition pools are clearly marked for racing and anti-turbulence lane lines are used to separate the swimmers and help keep the water calm. The first team or individual to finish the race is the winner. Competitive diving is divided into men's and women's springboard and platform (highboard) events. There are six official groups of dives: forward dives, backward dives, armstand dives, twist dives, reverse dives, and inward dives. Competitors perform a set number of dives and after each one a panel of judges awards marks according to the quality of execution and the degree of difficulty.

STYLES OF DIVES

Starting position
Hands above head
Legs fully stretched
Flight
Arched back
Toes pointed
Entry
Feet together
Hands close together

FORWARD DIVE

BACKWARD DIVE

SWIMWEAR

Latex rubber moulds to shape of head

CAPS

Rubber-covered wire

NOSE CLIP

Moulded rubber

EARPLUG

SPEEDO

High neckline

Man-made stretch fabric

Drawstring

High-cut leg

Strong seam

SWIMSUIT

TRUNKS

SWIMMING POOL

Swimmer
Lane number
Starting block
Lane time-keeper
Chief time-keeper
End wall
Placing judge
Starter
Recorder
Side wall
Backstroke marker 15 m (49 ft) from end of pool
Anti-turbulence lane line
Referee
Stroke judge
Backstroke turn indicator 5 m (16 ft) from end of pool
Bottom line
Turning judge
Turning wall
Lane

23 m
(75 ft 6 in)

Perfectly steady armstand

Arms and legs align throughout flight and entry

ARMSTAND DIVE

Arms spread wide apart

Body and legs straighten for flight and entry

TWIST DIVE

Pike position

Height of dive

Shoulders fall backwards for vertical entry

REVERSE DIVE PIKED

Pike position

Hands touch toes

Feet lift up for straight entry

INWARD DIVE PIKED

FRONT CRAWL

Flutter kick

Arm pulls like a paddle

Arrow-like position

Body rolls on a central axis

| FULL BODY STRETCH | LOWER ARM PULL | STREAMLINED ARM ENTRY | SIDE-TO-SIDE BODY ROLL |

BREASTSTROKE

Straight leg

Knees together

Elbows tucked in

Arm fully extended

| BODY GLIDE | DOUBLE ARM PULL | SQUEEZING THE WATER | FROG KICK |

BACKSTROKE

Little finger enters first

Arm comes up straight

Recovering hand

Shoulder exits water first

| BODY ROLL | PULLING THROUGH | STRAIGHTENING OUT | SHOULDER LIFT |

BUTTERFLY

Palm turned outwards

Legs ready to kick down

Head clears the water

Shoulders power the stroke

| CATCHING THE WATER | DOUBLE ARM PULL | KICKING DOWN | WHOLE BODY UNDULATION |

Canoeing, rowing, and sailing

WATERBORNE SPORTS are as varied as the crafts used. There are two disciplines in rowing; sweep rowing, in which each rower has one oar and sculling, in which rowers use two oars. There are a number of different Olympic and competitive rowing events for both men and women. The number of rowers and weight classes vary. Some rowing events use a coxswain; a steersman who does not row but directs the crew. Kayaks and canoes are used in straight sprint and slalom races. Slalom races take place over a course consisting of 20 to 25 gates, including at least six upstream gates. In yacht racing, competitors must complete prescribed courses, organized by the race committees, in the shortest possible time, using sail power only. Olympic events include classes for keel boats, dinghies, and catamarans.

SAILING GEAR

Sleeveless long johns

Buoya aid

Long-sleeved jacket

Neoprene material

Belt

GLOVE

Ribbed top

Non-slip sole

High density polythene

Bootle

BOOT

Toggle

ONE-PERSON KAYAK AND PADDLE

Blade

Rim

Shaft

Nose cone

Cockpit

Back strap

Stern

Right rail

Bow

Left rail

Seat

Cockpit rim

Adjusting screw

Gate clamp

Gate

SINGLE SCULL AND OARS (WITH CLOTH DECKING REMOVED)

Neck

Shaft

Stroke-side oar

Spoon

Blade

Colours

Rigger

Grip

Bow-side oar

Button

Loom

Stretcher

Water shoot

Bung

Aft shoulder

Shoe

Keel

Sycamore beam

Sternpost

Spruce beam

Diagonal frame

Aluminium beam

Kelson (keelson)

LIFEJACKET

Backstrap rescue strap

Reinforced seam

Neck opening

Whistle

Topping-up valve

Lanyard

Waistband

Standing rigging

Spreader

Bow

SAILING DINGHY

Elastic control line

Boom

Rudder

Mast

Mainsheet

Stern

Tiller

Toestrap

Centre-board

Cockpit

Shroud

Jib fairlead

Non-slip deck surface

Slide track

Wheel

Sliding seat

Main deck

Saxboard

Wheel spacer

Forward deck

Hatch

Breakwater

In-board

Bowball

Bowpost

SCULLS

DOUBLE SCULL

SINGLE SCULL

SWEEP-ROWING BOATS

COXLESS FOUR

COXED PAIR

COXLESS PAIR

EIGHT

COXED FOUR

561

Angling

ANGLING MEANS FISHING WITH A ROD, reel, line, and lure. There are several different types of angling: freshwater coarse angling, for members of the carp family and pike; freshwater game angling, for salmon and trout; and sea angling, for sea fish such as flatfish, bass, and mackerel. Anglers use a variety of methods of catching fish. These include bait fishing, in which bait (food to allure the fish) is placed on a hook and cast into the water; fly fishing, in which a natural or artificial fly is used to lure the fish; and spinning, in which a lure that looks like a small fish revolves as it is pulled through the water. The angler uses the rod, reel, and line to cast the lure over the water. The reel controls the line as it spills off the spool and as it is wound back. Weights may be fixed to the line so that it will sink. Swivels are attached to prevent the line from twisting. When a fish bites, the hook must become embedded in its mouth and remain there while the catch is reeled in.

Keeper ring

Handgrip

Drag spindle

Disk drag

Drag washer

Disk spring

Gear retainer

Dual click gear

Retaining screw

Check slide

Check pawl cover

Check pawl

Check spring

REELS

Spool-release button

Reel foot (reel scoop)

Plate-nut

Click mechanism

Mechanical brake

Side plate

Centrifugal brake

Spool

Handle

Star drag

Level-wind system

MULTIPLIER REEL

Reel foot (reel scoop)

Unskirted spool

Handle

Line

Tension nut (drag adjustment)

Ratchet (anti-reverse device)

Handgrip

Reel

Bail arm

FIXED-SPOOL REEL

HOOKS, SWIVELS, AND WEIGHTS

Eye

Shank

Bend

Gape

ANATOMY OF A HOOK

Throat

Point

Barb

TREBLE HOOK

ABERDEEN HOOK

REVERSED BEND HOOK

EXAMPLES OF BARREL SWIVELS

HILLMAN ANTI-KINK WEIGHT

FLY ROD AND REEL

Intermediate ring

TIP SECTION

Reel seat

Screw locking nut

Tip ring

Butt cap

Disk drag housing

Reel foot (reel scoop)

Line

Drag knob screw

Butt extension

Release lever

Spool screw

Clicker plate

Drag knob

DragonFly 100

Disc Drag

Spool cover

Spool-release button

Release spring

Handle

ARTIFICIAL FLIES

Line guide

DUNKELD WET FLY

Tail   Body   Cheek

Head

Line guide cover

Hackle

Retaining screw

Ribbing

ARTIFICIAL LURES

DEVON MINNOW   Fin

Eye

Swivel

Treble hook

Tulip mount

DEER HOPPER DRY FLY

Front hackle

Eye

Tail

Hook

Wing

Head

JOINTED PLUG

Adjustable vane

Joint

Treble hook

THE MODERN WORLD

PERSONAL COMPUTER···································· 566

TABLET COMPUTER ··································· 568

FLATBED SCANNER ··································· 570

AIRBUS 380 ··································· 572

INKJET PRINTER ··································· 574

THE INTERNET ··································· 576

ELECTRONIC GAMES ··································· 578

DIGITAL CAMERA ··································· 580

DIGITAL CAMCORDER ··································· 582

HOME CINEMA ··································· 584

PERSONAL MUSIC AND VIDEO ··································· 586

MOBILE PHONES ··································· 588

GLOBAL POSITIONING SYSTEM··································· 590

VACUUM CLEANER ··································· 592

IRON AND WASHER-DRYER··································· 594

MICROWAVE COMBINATION OVEN ··································· 596

TOASTER ··································· 598

DRILL ··································· 600

HOUSE OF THE FUTURE··································· 602

RENEWABLE ENERGY ··································· 604

CLONING TECHNOLOGY ··································· 606

ROBOTS ··································· 608

HIGH-PERFORMANCE MICROSCOPES··································· 610

SPACE TELESCOPE ··································· 612

PROBING THE SOLAR SYSTEM 614

Personal computer

PERSONAL COMPUTERS (PCs) fall into two main types: IBM-compatible PCs, known simply as PCs, and Apple Macintosh PCs, known as "Macs". They differ in the way files and programs, and the user's access to them, are organized, and programs must be tailored for each type. However, in most other respects PCs and Macs have much in common. Both contain microchips, or integrated circuits, that store and process data. The "brain" of any PC is a chip known as the central processing unit (CPU), which performs mathematical operations in order to run program instructions and receive, store, and output data. The most powerful personal computer CPUs today can perform more than a billion calculations a second. Data can be input via CDs, USB memory sticks, and other storage media. Highly portable laptop and network PCs are also in widespread use. Most PCs are able to communicate with many other devices, including digital cameras (see pp. 580-81) and smartphones (see pp. 588-89).

LE*
bac*
glos
wid
scre

Keyboard

Mo

iMAC

USB ports (4)

Audio in jack

Webcam

Headphone
jack

Firewire
800 port

Powercord
connector

Ethernet
port

Mini display port

**REAR OF
iMAC**

LCD
display

Optical drive

Power connector

USB ports (2)

Keyboard

Touchpad

Fingerprint
reader

Expansion port

Remote control

Display

Digital media slot

Security
cable slot

RG-45
(network) port

HDMI
port

eSATA/
USB port

Left
touchpad
button

Right
touchpad
button

Headphone
jacks (2)

External
monitor port

HP PAVILION DV4 LAPTOP

Audio in jack

SIDE VIEW OF HP PAVILION DV4 LAPTOP

COMPONENTS OF A SYSTEM UNIT

CD drive

DVD drive

RAM chips

COOLING FAN

RAM BOARD

Floppy drive

Power button

Reset button

Chassis

CD DRIVE

SYSTEM UNIT OF A PC

SIDE CABLE

Circuit board

Video out connectors

Cooling fan

Graphics processor

Edge connector

GRAPHICS CARD

Expansion slot

Back-up battery

Microprocessor socket

Cable connector

MICROPROCESSOR

HARD DISC DRIVE

BIOS chip

Graphics card slot

RAM board sockets

MOTHERBOARD

POWER SUPPLY

DATA CABLE

Tablet computer

By THE EARLY 1990s electronic circuitry had been miniaturized to such an extent that it was possible to make small handheld computing devices. The first of these was the Personal Digital Assistant (PDA), which offered features including an address book, calendar, and notepad. In recent years, PDAs have been overtaken by smartphones with Internet and email access (see pp. 588–589). A related product is the e-book reader, which stores books in digital form and uses "electronic paper" to mimic the appearance of ink on real paper. An e-book reader no bigger than a thin paperback can store several thousand digital books in its memory. The most recent handheld computing device is the tablet computer. This looks like a thin flat display, but it is actually a complete computer. Tablet computers are typically controlled by a touch-sensitive screen and have a wireless link to other computers and the Internet. They run software applications, or apps, downloaded from the Internet. The most popular tablet computer currently is the Apple iPad. It has a multi-touch interface that enables its screen to detect the movements of fingertips. As well as selecting options and apps by touching the screen, images can be enlarged or shrunk by moving fingertips apart or together on the screen.

Sleep/wake button

APPLE IPAD   *Home button*   *App icon*

Touch data is sent as a list of finger positions to the controller where the information is used to zoom in and out of a web page

LCD with buttons displayed

Fingers alter the electric field around nearby sections of the grid

User touches clear protective screen

Controller

Touchscreeen electronics interpret the outputs from the grid to work out exactly where the fingers are

MULTI-TOUCH INTERFACE

15-cm (6-in) screen

Next page button

Previous page button

Joyst contr

ACER LUMIREAD E-READER

ELECTROMAGNETIC
INTERFERENCE SHIELDS

Cable connector

Back panel

Wi-Fi card

Battery casing

OUTER CASE

Digitizer

A4 processor

SPEAKER ASSEMBLY

Cable connector

DOCK CONNECTOR CABLE

LOGIC BOARD

POWER, VOLUME, AND
SCREEN ROTATION
LOCK CONTROLS

Antenna cable

WI-FI ANTENNA 1

HEADPHONE JACK

WI-FI ANTENNA 2

LIQUID CRYSTAL DISPLAY

LITHIUM-POLYMER BATTERY

DISPLAY DATA CABLE

COMPONENTS OF AN APPLE IPAD

Headset jack

Camera lens

Touch sensitive screen

Back button

Home button

Menu button

Touch sensitive screen

Five-way controller

Control buttons

AMAZON KINDLE E-READER

BROADCOM PERSONA TABLET

OTHER TABLET COMPUTERS

SAMSUNG GALAXY TAB

569

Flatbed scanner

SCANNERS CONVERT physical images into electronic form, allowing them to be sent over the Internet, displayed on a website, stored on a computer, and manipulated using specialized software. Scanners work by detecting and analysing light reflected from an opaque image, such as a photographic print. Some can also scan photographic transparencies by analysing light that has passed through the image. Flatbed scanners contain a unit, called the scan head, that contains a lamp, mirrors, a lens, and an array of CCDs (Charge-Coupled Devices). The carriage passes beneath the image; the lamp shines light on to or through the original; the mirrors reflect the light on to the lens, which focuses it on to the CCD array. Each CCD detects the brightness of light from a particular pixel (picture element) along a· horizontal strip and converts this data into an electric signal. For colour images, the light is usually passed through red, green, and blue filters and then directed to the CCD array so that it can be broken down into its component colours. This information is then converted to digital form. The quality of the image depends on its resolution, measured in dpi (Dots Per Inch).

SCANNER

- Power supply cable
- Integrated transparency unit (TPU)
- Glass plate
- Reflective document mat
- Start button and indicator light
- Photo print button
- Scan to email button
- Scan to Web button
- Direct current (DC) inlet
- Lock
- Inverter board
- Lamp power supply connector
- TPU connector port

FILM AND SLIDE HOLDER

- 35mm-slide holder
- 35 mm film strip holder
- Shield plate
- Panel board connector

HOW A FLATBED SCANNER WORKS

- Lens focuses light on to CCD array
- Glass plate
- Original image (photograph or artwork)
- The electronic image is converted to digital form and transmitted to a computer
- Lamp
- CCD array builds up electric charges that vary according to the brightness of the light beam
- Light beam is reflected from the original to a series of mirrors
- Carriage is moved beneath the original by a stepper motor in a rapid series of tiny steps
- Cover support

UNDERSIDE OF SCAN HEAD COVER

**COMPONENTS OF
A SCANNER**

FLATBED SCANNER

TPU connector

LID ASSEMBLY

Hinge

Underside of
lamp housing

Glass plate

Universal serial
bus (USB) port

mbly

Ferrite core

Integrated
transparency
unit (TPU)

Scan
head

Reflective
document
mat

Mirror

FCC cable

Carriage
shaft

FCC cable
slot

UNDERSIDE OF COVER

Finger recess

Underside
of control
panel

OVERHEAD VIEW

Pixel

Idler
pulley

Control panel
circuit board

**THE EFFECT OF SCANNING AT
DIFFERENT RESOLUTIONS**

15 DPI
Lowest resolution at
which you may scan.

72 DPI
Used for websites
and screen images.

300 DPI
Used for printing
books and magazines.

571

Airbus 380

CROSS-SECTION OF FUSELAGE

THE AIRBUS A380 WAS CONCEIVED in the early 1990s to compete with, and if possible replace, the Boeing 747. Work began in earnest on what was then called the A3XX in 1994. Its maiden flight was in April 2005. The A380's shape is subtly moulded to minimize drag from its ovoid fuselage. The structure makes extensive use of composite materials, such as thermoplastics and GLARE (aluminium and glass fibre). Its engines are very powerful, but also very efficient. It is claimed that when carrying 550 passengers, the A380 uses only 2.9 litres (¾ gallon) of fuel per passenger per 100km (60 miles).

INTERIOR VIEW OF BUSINESS CLASS CABIN

Galley area

Personal lighting

Concealed lighting

Storage locker

Window blind

Reclining seat

Seat control panel

Aisle

Folding foot rest

Vertical tailplane

GLARE upper fuselage

Horizontal tailplane

Obstruction light

Swept titanium fan blades

Wing landing gear

FRONT VIEW

Company logo

Split rudder

Jupp-Reese winglet

Upper deck windows

Overwi[ng] emergen[cy] exit

A380

F-WWOW

Auxiliary Power Unit (APU) exhaust

Horizontal tailplane

Tailcone fairing

SIDE VIEW

Aft door

Belly fairing

Flap track fairings

Body landing gear

INTERIOR VIEW OF GALLEY

Counter

Bar area

Storage unit

Non-slip flooring

COCKPIT

Engine warning display

Windshield

Primary flight display

Navigation display

Rudder pedal

Headrest

Overhead control panel

Sun blind

Folding table with integral keyboard

Onboard information terminal

Fly-by-wire side stick

Pilot's seat

Seatbelt attachment point

Cursor control device (CCD)

Multifunction display

Power levers

System display

Pylon forward fairing

Wing leading edge

Flap track fairings

Air intake duct

Navigation light

Antenna

Fuselage

Upper deck passenger door

Main deck passenger door

Flightdeck door

Flightdeck windscreen

A380 AIRBUS

Wing landing gear

Engine cowling

Sculpted wing-root fairing

Main deck windows

Nose landing gear

Inkjet printer

INKJET PRINTERS EXPEL ink droplets from hundreds of tiny jets, or nozzles, on to a medium, such as paper, to print an image. Each droplet corresponds to a single pixel (picture element). Black-and-white printers use only black ink, while colour printers overprint combinations of the printing colours (cyan, yellow, magenta, and black) to create a full colour range. The printhead containing the nozzles moves sideways across the paper, creating a line of pixels, before the paper moves slightly forward so the next line can be printed. Two basic methods are used to eject ink: thermal, in which ink is heated to form an expanding bubble that expels a droplet from the nozzle, and piezoelectric, in which an electric current expands a crystal causing it to push out the ink droplet. The printer shown here can print digital photographs directly from a memory card.

EPSON STYLUS PHOTO 895 COLOUR INKJET PRINTER

OVERHEAD VIEW WITH OUTER CASING REMOVED

INK CARTRIDGES

PC CARD ADAPTER

PAPER FEED COMPONENTS

Attachment clip

ROLL PAPER HOLDER ADAPTER

ROLL PAPER HOLDER

Attachment clip

PAPER SUPPORT

OVERHEAD VIEW OF CASING

Sheet feeder

Left edge guide

Right edge guide

Printer cover

Preview monitor slot

Settings display

Photo select button

Cancel button

Start print button

EPSON

Processing light

Setting select buttons

HOW A PIEZOELECTRIC INKJET PRINTHEAD WORKS

Uncharged piezoelectric crystal

Ink reservoir

Firing chamber

INKJET NOZZLE

Charged crystal expands, increasing pressure in reservoir

Ink droplet forced out of firing chamber by increased pressure in reservoir

DROPLET EJECTED

Ink sucked into reservoir by lowered pressure

Uncharged crystal contracts, lowering pressure in reservoir

CHAMBER REFILLED

The Internet

THE INTERNET CONSISTS OF TENS of thousands of computer networks linked together to form one huge global network, allowing any computer on one network to communicate with any computer on another. The two main services used on the Internet are email and the World Wide Web. Email allows text messages to be sent – along with attached computer files, images, or video clips, for example – to other computers on the Internet. The Web consists of billions of pages made up of digital files that are stored on computers across the world and can be viewed using a Web browser. The Web also provides interactive access to various services, for example banking and shopping.

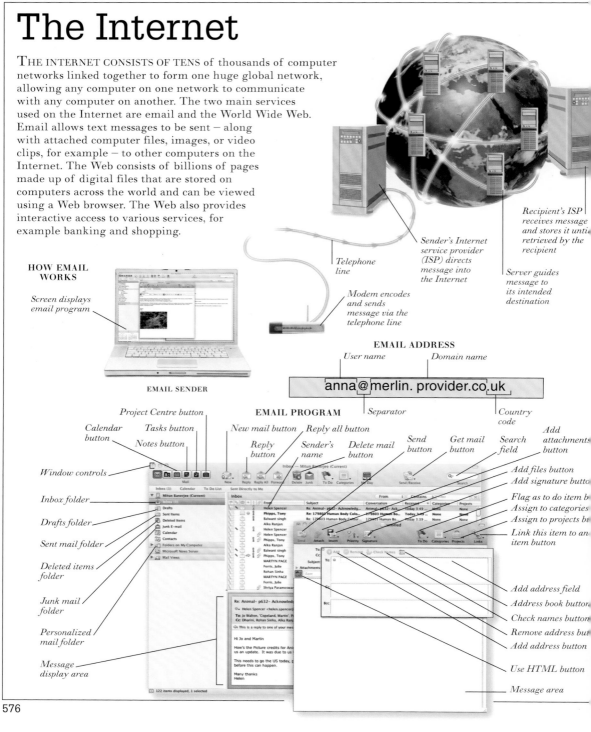

Telephone line

Modem encodes and sends message via the telephone line

Sender's Internet service provider (ISP) directs message into the Internet

Recipient's ISP receives message and stores it until retrieved by the recipient

Server guides message to its intended destination

HOW EMAIL WORKS

Screen displays email program

EMAIL SENDER

EMAIL ADDRESS

User name *Domain name*

anna@merlin. provider.co.uk

Separator *Country code*

EMAIL PROGRAM

Project Centre button

Calendar button *Tasks button*

Notes button

New mail button *Reply all button*

Reply button *Sender's name* *Delete mail button*

Send button *Get mail button* *Search field*

Add attachments button

Window controls

Inbox folder

Drafts folder

Sent mail folder

Deleted items folder

Junk mail folder

Personalized mail folder

Message display area

Add files button

Add signature button

Flag as to do item button

Assign to categories button

Assign to projects button

Link this item to an item button

Add address field

Address book button

Check names button

Remove address button

Add address button

Use HTML button

Message area

EMAIL RECIPIENT

Modem

Email program
on screen displays
received message

Computer with
email program
installed

Mouse

STREAMED INTERNET VIDEO ON-SCREEN DISPLAY

Program
name

Window
controls

Born To Be Wild

Screen

Volume slider

Rewind
button

Fast
forward
button

Full
screen
button

Play/pause
button

Seek
bar

Web browser
displaying item link

RSS (REALLY SIMPLE
SYNDICATION) FEEDS

Site
icon

Feed
name

Feed
list

Pull-down
edit menu
button

News reader
window

News item
summary

Search
field

Feed add
button

STREAMED INTERNET RADIO ON-SCREEN DISPLAY

Programme display

Window
controls

BBC World Service

real

Status
indicator

Stopped   0:00/0:00

Pause/play
control

Elapsed time
display

Volume
control

WEB PAGES

Browser menu
with navigation
buttons

Dorling Kindersley – Illustrated Reference Publisher

Search
field

Universal Resource
Locator (URL), or
web page address

DK www.dk.com

Click on a flag to visit a chosen country

Navigation area
contains links to other
parts of the site

Home page

United Kingdom   United States   Canada   Australia   Germany

Rollover button
provides links to
subsidiary page

India   South Africa   China   Spanish Language

United States

Subsidiary
page

dk.com – DK Publishing – Discover more

dk.com

Discover more at dk.com

STAR WARS DK

Hyperlink
text allows
direct
access to
another
web page
or website

UNIVERSAL RESOURCE
LOCATOR (URL) ADDRESS

Prefix

Page locator

http://www/dk.com/store_select.asp

Main website address

DK In The News

VINO

577

Electronic games

MARIO SPORTS MIX WII

VIDEO GAMES HAVE BEEN around since the early 1970s. They are played on PCs, arcade machines, on a TV using a home console, and on portable hand-held consoles. Players use devices such as joysticks and control pads with buttons to control movement and action on screen. The latest generation of consoles uses motion sensor technology to allow players to manipulate objects on screen by simply moving the controller. The most advanced game systems respond to gestures and commands spoken by a player, without any need to use a hand controller. The game itself is stored in the form of digital information on CD, DVD, or microchip – which may be integral or stored in a removable cartridge – or on an internal hard disk. A central processing unit (CPU) (see pp. 566–567) is needed to process commands from the players, while specialized graphics chips are used to process the complex mapping and texturing functions that make modern games appear so realistic.

MICROSOFT KINECT AND XBOX

X-box 36(

Eject butto

Disc tray

Ring indicator

Cooling vent

Power On/Off button

Infra-red projector

Colour camera

Kinect

Infra-red camera

Status LED indicator

KINECT (FRO PANEL REMO

NINTENDO 3DS

COMPONENTS OF NINTENDO 3DS

Inner camera

3D screen

Speaker

3D depth slider

Touch screen

Control buttons

Select key

Home key

Start key

Power On/Off button

Circle pad

Control pad

NINTENDO 3DS (OPENED UP)

Ribbon cable

SD card slot

Circuit board

SD CARD READER

Motherboard cable

Stylus holder

Motherboard cable

LOWER CASE BASE

Power connector

Game card slot

MEMS gyroscope

Headphone jack

NINTENDO 3DS MOTHERBOARD

NINTENDO Wii FIT PLUS

Wii FIT PLUS BALANCE GAME

Hand controller

ACTIVITIES ON A BALANCE BOARD

Foot/hand area

Bumper

Power LED

Wii BALANCE BOARD

Power On/Off button

D-pad

Power On/Off button

Home button

Preset –

Preset +

Effects buttons

Player LEDs

Wrist strap

Wii HAND CONTROLLER

Control pad

Wi-fi antenna

Power On/Off button

Control button pad

Touch-sensitive screen

WI-FI BOARD

LOWER CASE TOP

LOWER LCD ASSEMBLY

INFRA-RED BOARD

cle pad

Fixing screw

Positive terminal

Negative terminal

3.7 volt Lithium-ion battery

VOLUME CONTROL

BATTERY COVER

RECHARGEABLE BATTERY

CIRCLE PAD

Digital camera

FOR MORE THAN 200 YEARS, CAMERAS recorded
pictures as chemical changes in silver-containing
substances, on a strip of flexible, celluloid film.
The digital camera records pictures in electronic
form. At its heart is a specialized integrated
circuit known as a charge-coupled device (CCD).
This has millions of micro-units known as pixels.
It works in the opposite way to a miniature
computer or TV screen. Instead of electric signals
making pixels shine, when light hits a pixel it
generates a tiny electrical signal, according to
the light's colour and brightness. The signals
from the CCD's millions of pixels are analogue:
they vary continuously in a wave-like fashion.
They are converted by a microchip to digital
codes of numbers, represented as on-off electronic
pulses. The digital signals are processed and fed
to the camera's internal memory or a removable
memory device such as a data card or memory
stick. Photographs can be downloaded from a
digital camera to a computer via a cable or in
some cases a wireless link. Some digital cameras
automatically reduce blurring caused by camera
shake or fast movement, some can record video
clips as well as still pictures.

6.8cm (2.6in) liquid
crystal display

Flexible
ribbon cable

MONITOR

Protective
steel panel

CHASSIS   Keypad

Infra
recei
(rear

HOW A DIGITAL CAMERA WORKS

CCD
turns
light into
electronic
signals

Lens focuses
light

Light
from
scene

Analogue
signals

Analogue to
digital converter
microchip

Microprocessor

Digital
signals

LCD
screen

Memory
stick

In-camera
memory chip

Connector
cover

Eyelet for
camera strap

**CHROMED PLASTIC
SIDE COVER**

Flash lamp

Spea

Shoo
mode
butto

Playb
butto

Delete
button

REAR CASE

Menu
button

OK (Select)
button

Speaker mounting
bracket

Speaker

SPEAKER ASSEMBLY

COMPONENTS OF NIKON COOLPIX S1000PJ

TYPES OF DIGITAL CAMERA

Shutter release button

TOP PANEL

Projector button

Projector LED

Focusing lens

Filters

Ribbon cable

PROJECTOR ASSEMBLY

Projector assembly cover

CODEC with speaker driver and video buffet

Display controller chip

LOGIC BOARD

Projector window

Flash window

Lens

Infra-red receiver (front)

Self-timer lamp

Camera module connector

FRONT CASE

CCD image sensor

CAMERA MODULE

Lithium-ion battery

EN-EL12 RECHARGEABLE BATTERY

Lens cover motor

LENS COVER

Mode selector

Shutter button

Lens release button

DIGITAL SLR

18–55mm zoom lens

On/off button

Shutter button

Lens release button

16mm interchangeable lens

DIGITAL CAMERA WITH INTERCHANGEABLE LENS

Water-resistant case

Shutter button

Electronic flash

Strap mount

Lamp

Microphone

Lens

UNDERWATER DIGITAL CAMERA

Shutter button

Microphone

Left lens

Right lens

Flash

Lens cover

3D DIGITAL CAMERA

581

Digital camcorder

A CAMCORDER records a scene as a sequence of 25 or 30 still images per second, along with sound. It comprises a video camera to capture light from the scene, a viewfinder through which the scene may be viewed, a screen on which the recorded scene may be viewed, a charge-coupled device (CCD) to convert the visual data into an electric signal, and a means of storing the signal. Digital video cameras convert the signal into digital form – a series of separate measurements of the initial analogue (continuously varying) signal. They record the digital signal, usually on a chip or hard disk. Camcorders often have a slot where a memory card can be inserted to expand the memory and store longer recordings or more still pictures.

COMPONENTS OF A JVC EVERIO CAMCORDER

MONITOR SHELL

MONITOR MOUNT

MONITOR FRAME

MONITOR SCREEN

Screen connector

6.8-cm (2.7-in) LCD screen

OK button

Grip belt

Battery

Power/ Charge lamp

Access lamp

Zoom select lever

LCD monitor

TOP VIEW

Speaker

Play button

Auto/Manu recording bu

Info button

Menu buttor

AV terminal

LEFT SIDE

Power/charge lamp

Access lamp

LEFT OUTER SHELL

Lens cover

Microphone

LENS COVER ASSEMBLY

Speaker

SPEAKER CIRCUIT BOARD

Monitor frame

USB terminal

DC terminal

Start/Stop button

LCD monitor

Battery

REAR VIEW

Grip belt

MOTHERBOARD

Lens cover switch

CHASSIS

RIGHT OUTER SHELL

Grip belt release lever

CCD mounting peg

Lens

CCD chip

SDHC CARD

Start/Stop button

3.6-volt lithium-ion battery

Zoom select lever

LENS UNIT

SENSOR BOARD

LENS UNIT MOUNT

GRIP BELT FASTENER

OK button

GRIP BELT

REAR PANEL

CONTROL UNIT

RECHARGEABLE BATTERY

Home cinema

HOME CINEMA REPLICATES a real "movie theatre" using pictures displayed on a high-quality widescreen television set, such as a plasma TV, and surround sound from strategically sited loudspeakers. The source for sound and vision is a DVD (Digital Versatile Disc). Its player uses standard CD (Compact Disc) digital technology, but with a higher density of laser-read microscopic pits – more than 20 billion such pits in multi-level spiral tracks that, stretched out, would extend nearly 40km (25 miles). Blu-ray is a high-quality DVD system that fits much more data on its disc than standard DVDs, allowing High Definition video files to be stored. It is hard for the human ear to discern the direction of low-pitched sounds, so these emanate from a central bass speaker, often built into or below the screen unit. High-pitched sounds, the direction of which is easier to detect, emanate from mid- and high-frequency speakers positioned around the viewer. Plasma screens use fluorescent tube ("strip-light") technology. Tiny three-cell pixels, each about one millimetre across, contain red, green, and blue phosphor chemicals and a gas mix. Where electric pulses coincide for a split second in the criss-cross matrix of wire electrodes, the gas energizes and emits ultraviolet light, which in turn makes the phosphor glow.

BLU-RAY PLAYER

Ventilated case

Display panel

Open/ button

On/standby button

Disc tray

Play button

Stop button

HOW SURROUND SOUND WORKS

DVD player under screen

Centre sou channel

Subwoofer (bass unit)

Plasma screen

Front left sound channel

Front rig sound channel

Rear left sound channel

Region of most realistic sound reception

Rear righ sound channel

WIDE-SCREEN PLASMA DISPLAY

Mid-grey bezel

Damped anti-shock swivel base

16:9 (width:height) screen proportions fit human field of vision

HOW A PLASMA SCREEN WORKS

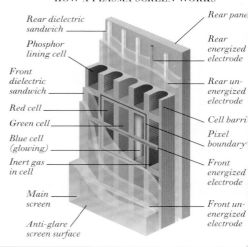

Rear dielectric sandwich

Rear pane

Phosphor lining cell

Rear energized electrode

Front dielectric sandwich

Rear un-energized electrode

Red cell

Green cell

Cell barri

Blue cell (glowing)

Pixel boundary

Inert gas in cell

Front energized electrode

Main screen

Anti-glare screen surface

Front un-energized electrode

INTERNAL VIEW OF SONY DAV-S300

Mains electricity supply lead

Internal fuse overload protection

Voltage reduction and regulation circuits

Power transistors

Power transistor heat sink (dissipator)

DVD/CD drive turntable

DVD/CD laser-reader (within compartment)

Tweeter speaker connectors

Woofer speaker connector

VCR (video cassette recorder) connections

Radio tuner aerial socket (FM)

Internal radio tuner aerial (AM)

Video input/output circuit board

Tuner settings memory microchip

Tuner/amplifier link cables

DVD/CD processor microchip

Display screen and control circuits

Power button

Sleep button

TV power button

Function button

Display button

Previous/next track buttons

Play button

Enter button

DVD display button

Enclosed DVD/CD compartment

DVD/CD sliding tray

Display screen

Ribbon connectors transfer DVD/CD signals

Control buttons

Enter button activates menu choices

Volume control

Access slot in tray for reading underside of DVD/CD

FRONT VIEW

Mains power on/off switch

DVD/CD sliding tray

Vibration-reducing damper foot

Remote control sensor

Display screen

Radio tuner FM/AM selector

Muting button

DVD/CD control buttons

Headphones socket

Volume control

REMOTE CONTROL

SONY AV SYSTEM

RM-SS300

Personal music and video

THE FIRST BATTERY-DRIVEN PORTABLE source of sound and music was the transistor radio of the 1950s. In the 1970s, the magnetic audio cassette tape allowed recordings to be played on portable tape players. Also, new metal alloys permitted the tiny but high-power magnets needed for lightweight earphones. In the 1980s, compact discs brought music into the digital era. Sony's MD, or minidisc, introduced re-recordable CDs that used magnetic and optical technology. From the mid 1990s, music could be stored in all-electronic digital form in a microchip, usually in the MP3 file format. These files can be transferred between devices and via the Internet. Today, a variety of portable media gadgets can record, play, and store video, photographs, and music in electronic form.

MP3 PLAYERS

Headphone jack

Mode switch

Volume control

Power/Play/ Pause button

ZEN

Next/Previous track control

USB port

LED

CREATIVE ZEN STONE

Headphone jack

Back/Home button

Record/Stop button

Volume control

Display

Zap button

Bass/Play mode

Earphone

On/Off/ Pause button

Shuttle switch

SONY B-SERIES MP3 PLAYER

Neck band

SONY

USB jack

Volume controls

Shuffle button

Jog lever

SONY W-SERIES WALKMAN

Subwoofer

Volume controls

Satellite speaker

JBL SPYRO SPEAKERS

Satellite cable

Speaker enclosure

Standby button

iPod

ZEPPELIN IPOD SPEAKER DOCK

Remote control

COMPONENTS OF MICROSOFT ZUNE HD

Power button

Digitizer

Home button

Front panel

Base plate

FRONT PANEL

Power button cover

CHASSIS

3.7-volt battery

Media button bezel

Audio codec chip

EEPROM memory chip

Headphone jack

Sync port

LOGIC BOARD

MICROSOFT ZUNE HD

8.4 cm (3.3 in) OLED display

Ribbon cable

DISPLAY

Back panel

Tri-wing screw

Back panel

Media button

REAR VIEW

Bottom backplate

SIDE VIEW

Power button

Touchscreen

Media button

music
videos
pictures
radio
marketplace
social
more

Headphone jack

Sync port

Home button

Mobile phones

IN THE EARLY 1990s, THE MOBILE PHONE (or cellphone) was a rare luxury, but in recent years it has outsold almost every other electrical gadget – as a professional tool, domestic convenience, and even a fashion accessory. Mobile phones have also generally shrunk in size, due to improvements in rechargeable batteries, which now store more electricity for longer in a smaller package, and to smaller, more efficient electronics that use less electricity. A "mobile" is basically a low-power radio receiver-transmitter, plus a tiny microphone to convert sounds into electrical signals, and a small speaker that does the reverse. When the mobile phone is activated, it sends out a radio signal that is answered by nearby mast transmitter-receivers. The phone locks onto the clearest signal and uses this while within range (the range of each transmitter is known as a cell). The phone continuously monitors signal strength and switches to an alternative transmitter when necessary. The phone's liquid crystal display (LCD) shows numbers, letters, symbols, and colour pictures. Newer models have a larger screen for more complex colour images, and commonly incorporate a camera, radio, and MP3 functionality. Smartphones, which are increasingly widespread, contain additional software and more may be downloaded. Smartphones typically offer Internet and email access, PDA-like functions (see pp. 568–569), and may even contain GPS navigation software.

Top microphone

Front camera

Receiver

Status bar

Earpiece

Bottom microphone | Home button | Speaker

I-PHONE 4

Menu key / Home key / Back key / Search key

LG OPTIMUS 2X

HOW A MOBILE PHONE WORKS

Phone locks onto signals from local mast within home cell

Caller sends call signal to nearest cell tower

Recipient's land-line phone (fixed at wall socket or cordless with base-set) emits ring tone

Cells are small in areas where many calls occur simultaneously (cities, suburbs)

Phone out of signal range – no reception

Activated phone auto-switches to signals from next cell as it moves across cell boundary

Landlines (or tower-to-tower links) carry phone signals to local exchange

Local mobile phone network exchange

Main telephone network exchange

Signals forwarded to non-mobile phone

Recipient's mobile phone emits ring to

Signals forwarded to relevant cell for transmission

COMPONENTS OF BLACKBERRY CURVE 8520

LCD screen

Ribbon connector

Front housing

DISPLAY

Locating tabs

Bezel

FASCIA

Keypad keys

KEYPAD

Screen connector

Camera

Trackpad

Keypad circuit board

LOGIC BOARD (FRONT)

Trackpad module

SIM card slot

LOGIC BOARD (REAR)

SCREEN LENS

BATTERY COVER

Headphone jack

Volume control keys

REAR HOUSING

BLACKBERRY CURVE 8520

Headphone jack

Screen lens

Micro USB port

Left convenience key

Trackpad

Send/call key

Menu key

Left shift key

Volume control keys

Right convenience key

End/power key

Escape/back key

Delete key

Speakerphone key

Right shift key

Lithium-ion battery

Negative terminal

Positive terminal

RECHARGEABLE BATTERY

Global positioning system

THE GLOBAL POSITIONING SYSTEM (GPS) is a network of 24 navigation satellites orbiting the Earth that people can use to pinpoint their position. The satellites orbit at a height of 20,000 kilometres (12,500 miles). A GPS receiver picks up signals from any of these satellites that are above the horizon. It uses information in each signal to work out how far away it is from the satellite. It can calculate its position on the Earth's surface when it has information from at least three satellites. A basic GPS receiver shows the latitude and longitude of its position on its screen. More advanced receivers, especially those designed for use in vehicles, show their position on a digital map. These receivers often show extra information, such as the vehicle's speed and the length of the journey. Some receivers warn drivers if they exceed the speed limit for a road and even tell drivers which traffic lane to use at the next junction. Directions are shown on the screen and also spoken by a synthesized voice.

Ante

IN-CAR GPS

Page key

On/off and screen control button

Enter key

Quit key

Rocker pad

Menu key

Speak key

Liquid crystal display (LCD) screen

Find key

Zoom keys

Route key

HOW GPS WORKS

Satellite 2

Satellite 1

The receiver takes a reading of its distance from two satellites. The receiver is located along the plane where the two resultant spheres meet

Earth

Satellite 3

A signal from a third satellite defines two positions on that plane. The position on the earth's surface is read as the correct location

Locking lever

IN-CAR MOUNTING BRACKET ASSEMBLY

MOUNTING BRACKET

QUICK-RELEASE BASE

Release catch

Ratcheted base

Speaker plug

Power plug

Data plug

COMPONENTS OF AN IN-CAR GPS

Waterproof case

Sling

High-contrast liquid crystal display (LCD) screen

GARMIN ETREX HAND-HELD GPS

Antenna

Memory battery

Data plug socket

Main printed circuit board (PCB)

Rear case

USB PROGRAMMER ASSEMBLY

Shielded receiver

Data cartridge

Universal serial bus (USB) programmer

SPARE FUSES

Front case

Liquid crystal display (LCD) assembly

Underside of control pad

Vacuum cleaner

IN A CONVENTIONAL VACUUM CLEANER, an electric motor spins a fan that sucks in air carrying dust and debris. The air is forced through tiny pores in a dust bag, trapping most particles. In the 1990s, James Dyson's dual cyclone "bag-less" design did away with the dust bag – and the reduced airflow caused by clogging of its pores. An electrically driven fan creates a partial vacuum within the machine. This sucks air into the machine past a rotating brush that loosens dirt. The air flows into a cylinder-shaped bin. As the air whirls around the bin like a miniature storm, or cyclone, larger particle are flung outwards and fall to the bottom of the bin. The air then passes through perforations into a cone-shaped inner bin and then into a series of smaller cones, spinning faster all the time and flinging smaller and smaller particle out. The nearly clean air exits the machine through micro-filters that trap the tiniest particles. Some Dyson vacuum cleaners run on a large ball instead of wheels. The ball makes it easier to steer the cleaner.

Wand handle and brushbar controls

Upper wand

Lower wand

Motorized brushbar floor tool

DYSON DC05 MOTORHEAD

CYCLONE ASSEMBLY

Air intake from hose

Air exit to bin/cyclone cover

Hose electricity connector

Inner cyclone cone

Hose slider

WASHABLE PRE-MOTOR FILTER

Microporous filter

Bin upper seal seating

Perforated shroud

Bin handle clip

Central retaining screw

DUST COLLECTION BIN

Inner bin fin

Bin upper seal

Hose slider seating

Bin base

Bin lower seal

Inner bin dust collection area

Polycarbonate plastic bin body

Bin handle

Bin cover retaining clip

Hose electricity supply

Post-motor micropore filter

Filter rim casing

**OVERHEAD VIEW OF
DYSON DC05 MOTORHEAD**

Suction
reduction
control

On/off and brushbar
motor control

Hose cuff
electrical
link

Flexible
hose
shrouding

Tool or
wand cuff

Accessory
holder

Electricity connector
to brushbar motor

Hose base

Main motor
casing

Hinged
bin/cyclone
cover

Air intake to
bin/cyclone cover

Bin cover
retaining
clip

dyson

Bin
cover
handle

Motor
air
intake

Wheel guard
and flex rewind

Main
wheel

ACCESSORIES

Nozzle

CREVICE TOOL

Textured
scraper

STAIR TOOL

Brush tool
articulation

UPHOLSTERY BRUSH

Flexible
hose
shrouding

Tool/
brushbar
connector

Wand
telescopic
link

WAND

**MOTORIZED
BRUSHBAR
FLOOR TOOL**

Wand/handle
connector

Handle
connector

Brushbar
drive
motor
cover

Roller

Sole plate
roller

Brushbar drive
belt cover

Rotating
brushbar

Sole plate

Iron and washer-dryer

IN THE DAYS BEFORE WASHING MACHINES, laundry was done by hand – washed in a barrel, squeezed in a roller-mangle, hung on a line, and smoothed with an iron heated on the hob or stove. In the 1880s electrically heated irons were one of the first home electrical appliances. Today's iron still applies heat, sometimes moistened with steam, to dampen and flatten garment fibres. Machines with electric heaters and motors took the strain out of washing from the 1910s. Up to the 1960s, three machines were needed to wash, spin, and dry. Now clothes are swirled in a rotating ribbed tub of hot water, then spun fast to throw off most of the water, before slowly tumbling in electrically heated air to dry – all in one appliance.

FRONT VIEW OF A MIELE WASHER-DRYER

Detergent tray

Control panels

Door

Filter access flap

COMPONENTS OF A STEAM IRON

Steam control knob

Spray barrel

Nose

Steam barrel

Spray nozzle aperture

Spray pump

Spray nozzle

Steam release activator

Nose

Heating elements

Water tank

Soleplate surround

Pilot light

Handle

Temperature and steam control dial

Mains spade contacts

Pilot light supply wire

SIDE VIEW OF STEAM IRON

Flex kink guard

Steam control knob

Spray and steam knobs

Temperature and steam control dial

Water tank

Soleplate

Earth wire

Securing screw mounting

Heel moulding

Mains flex clamp

Mains supply lead

Mains flex

COMPONENTS OF A MIELE WASHER-DRYER

Waste water anti-siphon pipe hook

Drum suspension springs

Water inlet hose

Water inlet connector

Detergent tray holder

Water inlet valves

Waste water pipe

Control panel

Detergent tray recess

Control panel wiring

Water inlet pipe

Stainless steel rotating drum

Drum and door seal

Drum inlet elbow

Door catch with safety cut-out

Door metal cap

Filter seal

Fluff filter impeller

Door porthole

Drain tap

Door wiring loom

Hinged front panel

Detergent tray

Fabric softener section

Water-softener dial

Filter screw cover

Filter

Tray fascia

Miele

Water hardness adjustment and filter flap lever

Microwave combination oven

CONVENTIONAL OVENS use electrically
warmed elements or a flame to heat food.
In a microwave oven heat energy is created
by electromagnetic waves produced by a
magnetron and led by waveguides into the
oven compartment. These microwaves
cannot pass through the compartment's
metal casing, being reflected within and
spread evenly by a fan. But they do pass
through most types of plastic, ceramics, and
glass. Therefore platters or containers made
from these materials are suitable for use in
microwave ovens. A combination oven also
has conventional heating elements, to grill
and "brown" in the traditional fashion, either
alone or in conjunction with microwaves.

MICROWAVE COMBINATION OVEN

Turntable rotator

Door lock

Display screen

Metal cook/grill tray (non-microwave)

Control panel

Rollers

Glass cooking turntable

Metal turntable cover (non-microwave)

Metal grill/griddle (non-microwave)

Under-turntable roller ring (non-microwave)

HOW MICROWAVES HEAT FOOD

Hydrogen atom

Oxygen atom

Each water molecule in food has two hydrogen atoms and one oxygen atom

Water molecules spin with energy from microwaves

Microwaves make water molecules vibrate

Making the molecules move generates heat

SIDE VIEW OF MICROWAVE COMBINATION OVEN

Magnetron assembly

Waveguide

Voltage regulators

Wiring loom

Mains earthing wire to case and chassis

Door

Fan electricity supply

Control panel circuitry

Main fan

Rigid metal chassis

Magnetron cooling fan

Voltage transformers

Door safety cut-out mechanism

Thermal/electrical insulation

Low-voltage supply for control circuits

Mains electrical lead

Circuit board plug

Electricity supply to magnetron

High-voltage magnetron supply

TOP VIEW OF MICROWAVE COMBINATION OVEN

Waveguide backing

Heating element cover

Heating element terminal cover

Electric heating elements

Oven compartment casing

Outer casing fitment

Microwave-proof door seals

Thermal/electrical insulation

Overheat cut-out sensor supply

Chassis earth terminal

Voltage stabilizer

Magnetron assembly

Voltage circuitry

Door

Control panel fascia

BACK VIEW OF MICROWAVE COMBINATION OVEN

Main fan electrical supply

Magnetron cooling fan

Magnetron cooling fan mounting

Magnetron perforated heat sink (dissipates warmth)

Mains electrical lead

Thermal/electrical insulation

Fan transformer

Vibration-reducing fan mounting

Cooling perforations for heating elements

Back of oven compartment

Fan dust shield

Main fan (scatters microwaves and circulates hot air)

Rear chassis plate

597

Toaster

MOST ELECTRIC TOASTERS not only grill slices of bread, they also pop them up when ready. While the slices rest on a spring-loaded rack, electric heating elements toast the bread. At the same time, a bimetallic strip heats and expands. One of the two metals in this strip expands more quickly than the other, causing the strip to curve. As it bends, it completes an electrical circuit and activates an electromagnet. The magnet attracts a catch, releasing the spring that holds the rack down in the toaster. The elements switch off, and the toasted slices pop up.

Connecting wire

Ejector bracket

Time switch

Variable time control knob

Selector switch

Screw

Screw

Switch end casting

Crumb tray

End baffle plate

Screw

Screw

Earth connection point

Cable entry point

End element connecting link

End element

Foot

Baseplate

Screw

Washer

End element wire guard

Mains input lead

Cable retaining gland

Ejector knob

Screw

Nut

Spring

Ejector bracket

Ejector assembly

Plain end casting

Switch end casting

Stainless steel cover

Selector switch

Ejector knob

Variable time control knob

Foot

Crumb tray

Fixing screw

Screw

Foot

Inner cage assembly

Centre element wire cage

End baffle plate

Stainless steel cover

Plain end casting

Foot

Screw

Screw

Element retaining stop

Nut

Washer

Screw

Nut

Washer

Screw

Centre element

Element connecting link

End element

End element wire guard

Drills

THE ELECTRICALLY POWERED MOTOR OF A POWER DRILL, cooled by a fan, turns a shaft at high speed. The shaft connects, in turn, to a system of gears that rotates a chuck even faster. Clamped by the chuck, a sharp bit cuts out the hole, and at the same time the bit's screw-shaped grooves channel the waste out of the hole. For drilling hard materials, many power drills have a hammer mechanism: when this is operated a ratchet in the gearcase causes the chuck and bit to pound in and out as they drill. A hand drill, although slower and less forceful than a power drill, is easier to control. For cutting wide holes, carpenters often prefer a brace-and-bit. This acts like a lever: the bowed handle of the brace moves a larger distance than the bit, turning the bit with extra force.

MOTOR ASSEMBLY

Commutator
Armature
Armature spindle
Fan
Motor case

Motor case
Field coils

Spring
Brush
Screw
Washer
Lead wire
Brush holder
Electromagnetic induction capacitor
Top insert blank
Hammer mechanism actuator
Screw h

Chuck key holder
Triac device
Screw

INTERNAL VIEW OF CLAMSHELL

Hammer actuator position
Gearcase position
Motor position

Trigger position

Lock button
On/off trigger

TRIGGER MECHANISM

Washer
Spring

Cable

GEAR MECHANISM

Thrust plate

Ratchet mechanism

Spindle

Gearcase cover

Chuck key

Jaw

Bit

Gearcase

Washer

Spring washer

Gearcase cover screw

Chuck keyhole

POWER DRILL

Hammer mechanism actuator

Chuck

On/off trigger

Chuck key holder

Cable

Gearcase screw

HAND DRILL

Main handle

Turning handle

Side handle

Pinion

Drive wheel

Chuck

Jaw

Bit

EXTERNAL VIEW OF CLAMSHELL

Screw hole

Exhaust vent

Air inlet

Clamshell screw

BRACE-AND-BIT

Quill

Head

Crank

Handle

Ratchet

Chuck

Jaw

Bit

House of the future

HOUSES IN THE FUTURE are likely to be more environmentally friendly and energy-efficient than older dwellings, by making better use of materials and intelligent control systems. The Integer house was designed by Cole Thompson Associates, Bree Day Partnership, and Paul Hodgkins Associates, and built in conjunction with the Building Research Establishment in the UK. One of its key features is a large conservatory that warms one side of the house. Extensive use is made of recycled, natural, and renewable materials and energy. The walls are made from timber and insulated with fibre from recycled newspaper; waste water from the bathrooms is saved and used to flush the toilets; and a wind turbine and solar panels contribute some of the electricity requirements. Many elements were prefabricated off site for ease of construction. The Integer house uses only half the energy and a third less water than a traditionally built house.

WALL CONSTRUCTION

Cellulose fibre insulation

Vertical batten

Plasterboard

Vertical batten

Red cedar boarding

Noggin

Skirting board

Breather paper

Floating floor

Cables and ducting

Wooden boarding

SIDE AND REAR VIEW OF THE INTEGER HOUSE

Single-glazed conservatory

Gutter collects rain water for use in the garden

Composter for recycling kitchen waste

FRONT VIEW OF THE INTEGER HOUSE

Turfed roof helps to regulate temperature

Passive stack vents from bathroom and toilet

Automatic louvres cool conservatory

Small windows reduce heat loss

Red cedar walls that do not require painting or staining

Intelligent electronic door-lock

Hatch for home deliveries

ROOF CONSTRUCTION

Sedum turf

Mineral wool

Timber trellis

Root-proof membrane

Polyurethane insulation

Vapour barrier

Plywood roof deck

FM and TV aerial feeds into an integrated multimedia network

Photovoltaic panel generates electricity

Solar collector heats water

Security light

Automatic louvres to cool conservatory

Window to upper floor home office

Timber bay window to living and dining area

Earth bank insulates lower floor

Blinds that open and close automatically in response to sunshine

CONSERVATORY INTERIOR

603

Renewable energy

RENEWABLE ENERGY COMES from sources that
do not become depleted as we use the energy.
When a fossil fuel such as coal is burned, it is
gone forever, but a renewable source remains
available no matter how much is used. The
tides, waves, flowing water, sunlight, and the
wind are all renewable sources of energy.
Wind and water energy are captured by a
device called a turbine. The turbine spins and
drives an electricity generator. Energy from
sunlight, or solar energy, is changed into
electricity in two main ways. One uses
mirrors to concentrate solar energy and
magnify its heating effect which is used to
change water into steam to drive turbines.
Photovoltaic cells change sunlight directly
into electricity. A cell is made from two layers
of silicon. One gives out electrons (negative
particles) and the other receives them.
Sunlight knocks electrons out of atoms where
the two layers meet, separating them from
the positive particles. The electrons are
attracted to one layer of the cell, the positive
particles to the other layer. Electrons are
naturally attracted to the positive particles,
but to come together again, the electrons
must flow out of the cell, through an external
electric circuit, or load, and back to the other
side of the cell, creating a charge. The cell
supplies electric current for as long as light
keeps falling on it.

VESTAS V47 WIND TURBINE

Blade pitch
control

Blade

Hub controller

Aerodynamic
hub cover

Blade bearing

Blade hub

Rotor lock

TIDAL POWER

Road bridge across
an estuary

Open sea

Winch
operates
turbine
floodgate

Rising tide
passes through
main floodgate
into estuary

Turbine
floodgate
closed, trapping
water behind it

RISING TIDE

Turbine floodgate
opened by winch
allows trapped
water to flow out
to the open sea

Main
floodgate
closed as
tide falls

Escaping water
drives turbine

FALLING TIDE

Gearbox

Oil cooler

Generator

Wind vane

Anemometer

Service crane

Hydraulic unit

Yaw ring

Electronic controller

Yaw control

WIND TURBINES IN A WIND FARM

HOW A GENERATOR WORKS

Slip ring collects current from coil

Carbon brush collects current from slip ring

North magnetic pole

Wire coil rotates inside magnet

Wind or water flow through turbine rotates shaft

South magnetic pole

Moving the wire past a magnet makes a current flow through it

FIRST HALF TURN

North magnetic pole

Coil makes half a turn

South magnetic pole

Direction of current reverses every half turn

SECOND HALF TURN

SOLAR POWER

Anti-reflective coating

Glass

Sunlight

Contact grid

N-type silicon

Junction

P-type silicon

Back contact grid

Electrons flow out of cell

Electric current powers external load

Light knocks electrons out of atoms

Electrons flow back to cell

HOW A PHOTOVOLTAIC CELL WORKS

Solar panel containing photovoltaic cells

Power lead-out wires

Waterproof cable connector

SOLAR PANEL

605

Cloning technology

IN A LIVING CELL THE GENETIC MATERIAL DNA (deoxyribonucleic acid) contains thousands of units called genes that carry instructions for development, growth, and repair of the living creature. During normal reproduction, half the mother's genetic material contained in an egg cell joins with half the genetic material from the father carried in a sperm cell, to form a unique new genome (set of genes) for a new life. During the early stages of embryo development, the fertilized egg divides into stem cells, which have the potential to become specialized into the hundreds of cell types in a body. Through therapeutic cloning, stem cells can be produced in a laboratory. It is hoped that in the future this technology can be used to grow new tissue that can be transplanted back into the donor to treat illness, without fear of rejection — when the body recognizes a transplanted part as "foreign" because it has different genes, and tries to destroy it. In another form of cloning, performed experimentally using animals, genetic material from a donor animal has been inserted into an egg from another animal that has been emptied of its own genetic material, to produce an animal genetically identical to the donor.

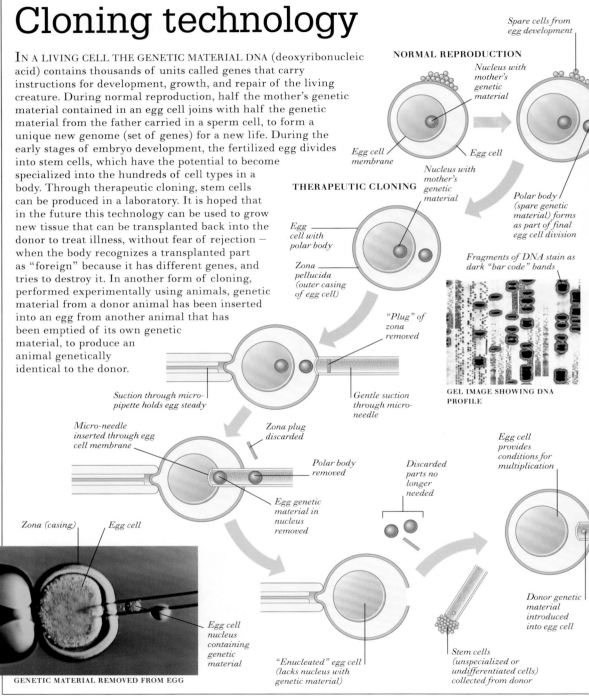

Spare cells from egg development

NORMAL REPRODUCTION

Nucleus with mother's genetic material

Egg cell membrane

Egg cell

Nucleus with mother's genetic material

Polar body (spare genetic material) forms as part of final egg cell division

THERAPEUTIC CLONING

Egg cell with polar body

Zona pellucida (outer casing of egg cell)

Fragments of DNA stain as dark "bar code" bands

"Plug" of zona removed

GEL IMAGE SHOWING DNA PROFILE

Suction through micro-pipette holds egg steady

Gentle suction through micro-needle

Micro-needle inserted through egg cell membrane

Zona plug discarded

Polar body removed

Egg genetic material in nucleus removed

Discarded parts no longer needed

Egg cell provides conditions for multiplication

Zona (casing)

Egg cell

Egg cell nucleus containing genetic material

GENETIC MATERIAL REMOVED FROM EGG

"Enucleated" egg cell (lacks nucleus with genetic material)

Donor genetic material introduced into egg cell

Stem cells (unspecialized or undifferentiated cells) collected from donor

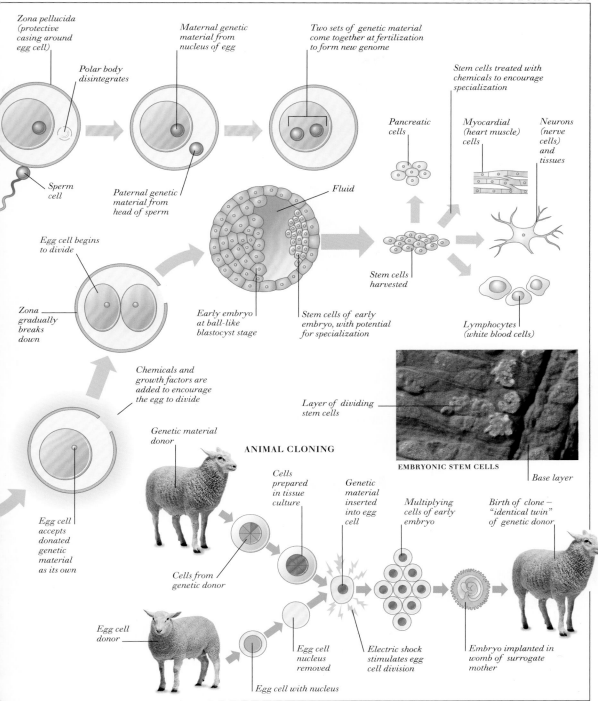

Zona pellucida (protective casing around egg cell)

Polar body disintegrates

Maternal genetic material from nucleus of egg

Two sets of genetic material come together at fertilization to form new genome

Stem cells treated with chemicals to encourage specialization

Pancreatic cells

Myocardial (heart muscle) cells

Neurons (nerve cells) and tissues

Sperm cell

Paternal genetic material from head of sperm

Fluid

Stem cells harvested

Egg cell begins to divide

Zona gradually breaks down

Early embryo at ball-like blastocyst stage

Stem cells of early embryo, with potential for specialization

Lymphocytes (white blood cells)

Chemicals and growth factors are added to encourage the egg to divide

Layer of dividing stem cells

Genetic material donor

ANIMAL CLONING

Cells prepared in tissue culture

Genetic material inserted into egg cell

Multiplying cells of early embryo

Birth of clone – "identical twin" of genetic donor

EMBRYONIC STEM CELLS

Base layer

Egg cell accepts donated genetic material as its own

Cells from genetic donor

Egg cell donor

Egg cell nucleus removed

Egg cell with nucleus

Electric shock stimulates egg cell division

Embryo implanted in womb of surrogate mother

607

Robots

ROBOTS ARE
MACHINES THAT CAN
carry out a variety of
tasks on their own,
with little or no human
control. Most robots are
mechanical arms used to build
things in factories. The end of the
robot's arm can be fitted with
different tools for gripping, drilling,
cutting, welding, and painting. Robot
toys have become popular, too. They
incorporate sensors that respond to
sounds and sometimes touch. Some of them
can even understand spoken words. Scientists are
also trying to create more advanced, human-like
robots that can see, hear, learn, and make their own
decisions. ASIMO, a robot developed by the Japanese
car manufacturer Honda, is one of these advanced
humanoid robots. ASIMO stands for Advanced Step
in Innovative MObility. It looks like a small astronaut
wearing a backpack. ASIMO can walk, talk, carry things,
recognize familiar faces, and respond to its name. It was
the first robot that could walk independently and climb
stairs. There are robot toys too, in the shape of animals
with simple artificial intelligence.

Motorized fingers

Neck joint

Shoulder joint

Battery charge
indicator

Batter
backp

ASIMO

Rigid torso

HONDA

Hip joint

Knee joint

Ankle joint

Padded foot

ASIMO HUMANOID

ELEMENTS OF ROBOT ACTION

*Information
from sensors*

**CENTRAL
PROCESSING
UNIT (CPU)**

*Pre-programmed
instructions*

*Information
from sensors
interpreted by
CPU to modify
actions*

**MECHANICAL
ACTIONS**

SENSORS

| LIGHT |
| SOUND |
| TOUCH |
| PROXIMITY |
| SMELL |
| TASTE |

Motorized fingers

Wrist joint

Elbow joint

Floor mounting

CAR-BUILDING ROBOTS

Vehicle body

Welding tool

ŠTÄUBLI

Arm up-down joint

Wrist joints

ZX165U

End effector

Arm out-in joint

Kawasaki

rm ation nt

WASAKI INDUSRIAL ROBOT

Floor-mounted base

Head touch sensor

Eye LED

Nose touch sensor

Back touch sensor

Tail LED

Camera

ROBOT DOGS

Battery

Flexible neck

Touch sensor

Infrared sensor

Whipping tail

Sonic sensor

Leg joint

ROBOREPTILE

High-performance microscopes

OPTICAL MICROSCOPES FORM A MAGNIFIED image by using lenses to bend light. Some special-purpose optical microscopes used in industry and research are designed for observing particular materials, such as living cells. They produce magnifications of up to about 2,000. Electron microscopes produce magnifications of as much as 50 million, although 2 million is more typical. Their images are formed by means of electrons focused by magnetic lenses. There are two main types: scanning electron microscopes (SEMs) scan electrons back and forth across the surface of a specimen; transmission electron microscopes (TEMs) transmit electrons through a thin slice of the specimen.

FEI TECNAI G² TRANSMISSION ELECTRON MICROSCOPE

TEM IMAGE OF A VIRUS

OPTICAL MICROSCOPE IMAGE OF DYING NERVE CELLS

Video camera

Right eyepiece

Filter turret

Objective lens

Left eyepiece

Manipulator

Manipulator

Manipulator

Specimen

Specimen stage

OLYMPUS BX51W1 OPTICAL MICROSCOPE

Electron gun housing

Evacuated column

Condenser aperture

Condenser housing

Objective lens and specimen stage

Objective aperture

Imaging system housing

Vacuum valve

Detector

Binocular eyepieces

Viewing screen

HOW A TEM WORKS

Electron gun

Electron stream

Aperture plate

Aperture creates electron beam

Condenser focuses electron beam

Specimen stage

Specimen

Objective lens refocuses image formed by electron beam

Specimen airlock

Projector lens enlarges and projects the image

Phosphor imaging screen glows when hit by electrons to create the image

Binocular eyepieces

Cooling device

Camera

Screen

TECNAI

Image controls

Mouse

Keyboard

HITACHI S-3500H SCANNING ELECTRON MICROSCOPE

Evacuated column

Image controls

Screen

Vacuum pump cabinet

S-3500H

Keyboard

HOW A SEM WORKS

Electron stream

Electron gun

Aperture plate

Aperture creates electron beam

Scanning coils direct electron beam across the specimen

Condenser lens focuses primary electron beam

Screen

Objective lens refocuses electron beam

Specimen stage

Specimen surface hit by primary electrons

Electron detector assembly

Secondary electrons from the specimen surface

Underside of caterpillar body

Caterpillar foot

SEM IMAGE OF A CATERPILLAR

611

Space telescope

SPACE TELESCOPES ORBIT THE EARTH hundreds of kilometres above the ground, their instruments collecting light from stars and galaxies. Telescopes in space have a clearer view than those on Earth, because they are unaffected by the Earth's atmosphere, which absorbs or distorts much of this radiation. There are a variety of types of space telescopes designed to observe different types of light. The Hubble Space Telescope observes infra-red, ultraviolet, and visible light. It can detect objects that are 100 times fainter than those any telescopes on Earth can see. When this 11,000-kilogram (12-ton), 13-metre (43-foot) long telescope was launched by the Space Shuttle in 1990, it was found that its primary mirror was faulty and its images were blurred. Astronauts fitted extra optics to correct the problem in 1993.

IMAGES TAKEN BY HUBBLE

Pillar of gas

CONE NEBULA

VIEW FROM COLUMBIA SPACE SHUTTLE

Space shuttle remote manipulator system (robot arm)

Solar array

Axial instrument unit

Central deflector

High-gain radio antenna

Rotating joint

Crew handrail

Aft shroud

Guidance control sensor

2.4-metre primary mirror

Aperture door mounting

Secondary baffle

33-centimetre secondary mirror

Light shield

Aperture

Aperture door

Door hinge

Epoxy resin frame

Crew handrail

Light shield

Aluminium shield

EXPLODED VIEW OF HUBBLE SPACE TELESCOPE

Hydrogen gas emissions

Young star

"WHIRLPOOL" GALAXY

"Tadpole" galaxy

DRACO CONSTELLATION

Newly formed stars

OMEGA NEBULA

"Spirograph" nebula

LEPUS CONSTELLATION

Interstellar cloud remains

PLEIADES STAR CLUSTER

Young star – LL Ori

GREAT NEBULA, ORION

Instrument bay

Batteries

Space shuttle remote manipulator system (robot arm)

Space shuttle astronaut

Instrument module

Space shuttle astronaut

Solar array supporting arm

Solar array collects solar energy for operating instruments

Crew handrail for astronauts to hold during maintenance operations

Solar array

Aft shroud

Crew handrail

HUBBLE SPACE TELESCOPE

High-gain radio antenna for communication with satellites

Aperture door acts like a camera lens cap

Aperture allows light into the mirror housing

Primary mirror housing

Light shield blocks out peripheral light

Thermal insulation to protect against extremes of temperature

High-gain radio antenna

613

Probing the Solar System

SPACE PROBES HAVE VISITED every planet in the Solar System. They take photographs and gather data that cannot be collected using Earth-based equipment. Some probes fly past or orbit around planets or moons, while others land. Two Voyager space probes flew past the outer planets in the 1970s and 1980s. Two Viking spacecraft landed on Mars in 1976. The Magellan spacecraft orbited Venus from 1989 and mapped its surface. The Pathfinder spacecraft landed on Mars in 1997 and released a rover vehicle to explore the surface. The Mars Exploration Rover (MER) Mission landed two rovers in 2003. The Cassini space probe reached Saturn in 2004, and in 2005 its mini-probe, Huygens, landed on one of its moons, Titan, and became the first probe to land on a moon of another planet.

A MAP OF JUPITER'S VAST MAGNETIC FIELD PRODUCED BY CASSINI'S INSTRUMENTS

DIONE, ONE OF SATURN'S MOONS, ORBITING ABOVE THE "A" RING

PANORAMIC VIEW OF TITAN
TAKEN AS HUYGENS DESCENDED

High-gain antenna

Sun sensor

Helium tank

Visible and infrared spectrometers

Remote sensing pallet

Wide-angle camera

Radio-isotope thermoelectric generator

Magnetometer

Fields and particles intruments

Attitude control thruster

Huygens mini probe

Main engines

Propulsion module

Heat shield

Reaction wheel

Lower equipment module

CASSINI SPACE PROBE
AND HUYGENS MINI-PROBE

THE ROCK-STREWN SURFACE OF TITAN,
PHOTOGRAPHED BY HUYGENS

Panoramic camera (Pancam)

Navigation camera (Navcam)

COBBLESTONES LYING IN TROUGHS BETWEEN DUST RIPPLES ON THE MARTIAN SURFACE, PHOTOGRAPHED BY ROVER "OPPORTUNITY"

Thruster cluster

Heat shield

Star scanner

Propellant tank

Cruise stage

Cruise electronics module

Backshell contains lander craft and rover

Low dain antenna

Pancam mast assembly

MARS EXPLORATION ROVER SPACECRAFT

Ultra-high frequency (UHF) antenna

Third stage motor

High gain antenna

Delta II launch vehicle second stage

Rover equipment deck

Magnet array

Solar array

Aft bogie

Bogie wheel strut

Front hazard avoidance camera

Aft rocker

Warm electronics box

Forward rocker

Instrument deployment device

Rocker deployment actuator

MARS EXPLORATION ROVER (MER)

Aluminium wheel

Physical map of the world

This map depicts the physical features of the Earth's surface. The continental and oceanic tectonic plates, which make up the Earth's crust, move only a few centimetres in a year. However, over the course of Earth's history, the plates have moved thousands of kilometres to create new continents, oceans, and mountain chains. Continental drift determines the distribution of the continents, propelled by currents rising from the intense heat at the Earth's centre. Tectonic forces, weathering and erosion means that the Earth's surface is constantly transforming. This map shows the surface of the Earth today, both above and below sea level.

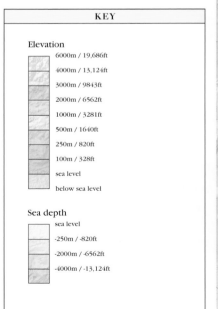

KEY

Elevation

	6000m / 19,686ft
	4000m / 13,124ft
	3000m / 9843ft
	2000m / 6562ft
	1000m / 3281ft
	500m / 1640ft
	250m / 820ft
	100m / 328ft
	sea level
	below sea level

Sea depth

	sea level
	-250m / -820ft
	-2000m / -6562ft
	-4000m / -13,124ft

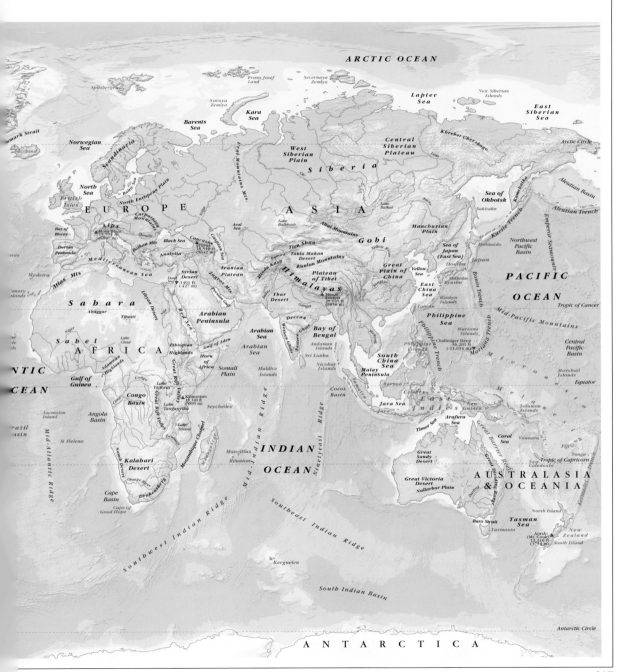

ARCTIC OCEAN

Franz Josef Land

Severnaya Zemlya

New Siberian Islands

Spitsbergen

Laptev Sea

East Siberian Sea

Novaya Zemlya

Kara Sea

Barents Sea

Arctic Circle

Khrebet Cher-skogo

Denmark Strait

Iceland

Norwegian Sea

Scandinavia

West Siberian Plain

Central Siberian Plateau

Aleutian Basin

North Sea

Baltic Sea

Siberia

Sea of Okhotsk

Kamchatka

Aleutian Trench

British Isles

EUROPE

North European Plain

Great Mountains Mts.

ASIA

Sakhalin

Amur

Emperor Seamounts

Bay of Biscay

Alps
Mont Blanc
15,771 ft
(4807 m)

Carpathian Mountains

Danube

Aral Sea

Lake Balkhash

Altai Mountains

Manchurian Plain

Sea of Japan (East Sea)

Hokkaido

Northwest Pacific Basin

Kurile Trench

Iberian Peninsula

Azores

Madeira

Black Sea

Balkan Mts

Caucasus
Mt Elbrus
18,510 ft
(5642 m)

Caspian Sea

Tien Shan

Pamirs

Gobi

Yellow River

Honshu

Japan

Bonin Trench

PACIFIC OCEAN

Anatolia

Mediterranean Sea

Iranian Plateau

Hindu Kush

Takla Makan Desert

Kunlun Mountains

Great Plain of China

Yellow Sea

Shikoku
Kyushu

Mid-Pacific Mountains

Atlas Mts

Zagros Mts

Syrian Desert

Dead Sea
▼ 1401 ft
(-427 m)

Plateau of Tibet

Yangtze

East China Sea

Ryukyu Islands

Tropic of Cancer

Canary Islands

Sahara

Libyan Desert

Nile

Red Sea

Persian Gulf

Indus

Tbar Desert

Himalayas

Mount Everest
29,035 ft
(8850 m)

Ganges

Taiwan

Philippine Sea

Mariana Islands

Central Pacific Basin

Ahaggar

Tibesti

Arabian Peninsula

Deccan

Western Ghats

Bay of Bengal

Mekong

Philippine Islands

Mariana Trench

Sahel

Lake Chad

AFRICA

Ethiopian Highlands

Gulf of Aden

Arabian Sea

Arabian Sea

Eastern Ghats

Andaman Islands

Sri Lanka

Philippine Trench

Challenger Deep
-36,201 ft
(-11,034 m)

Micronesia

Marshall Islands

Gulf of Guinea

Niger

Adamawa Highlands

Horn of Africa

Somali Plain

Maldive Islands

Nicobar Islands

South China Sea

Malay Peninsula

Equator

ATLANTIC OCEAN

Ascension Island

Congo

Lake Victoria

Great Rift Valley

Kilimanjaro
19,340 ft
(5895 m)

Seychelles

Cocos Basin

Sumatra

Borneo

Celebes

New Guinea

Solomon Islands

Melanesia

Brazil Basin

St Helena

Congo Basin

Angola Basin

Lake Tanganyika

Lake Nyasa

Java Sea

Java

East Indies

Timor Sea

Arafura Sea

Coral Sea

Vanuatu

Fiji

Tropic of Capricorn

Tonga

New Caledonia

Mid-Atlantic Ridge

Kalahari Desert

Namib Desert

Orange River

Zambezi

Mozambique Channel

Mauritius

Réunion

Mid-Indian Ridge

Ninetyeast Ridge

INDIAN OCEAN

Great Sandy Desert

Great Victoria Desert

Nullarbor Plain

Great Barrier Reef

Great Dividing Range

AUSTRALASIA & OCEANIA

Cape Basin

Cape of Good Hope

Drakensberg

Southwest Indian Ridge

Southeast Indian Ridge

Darling

North Island

Bass Strait

Tasmania

Tasman Sea

Kermadec Trench

New Zealand

Aoraki
(Mt Cook)
12,316 ft
(3754 m)

South Island

Kerguelen

South Indian Basin

Antarctic Circle

ANTARCTICA

Time zones

The world is divided into 24 time zones, measured in relation to 12 noon Coordinated Universal Time (UTC), on the Greenwich Meridian (0°). Time advances by one hour for every 15° longitude east of Greenwich (and goes back one hour for every 15° west), but the system is adjusted in line with administrative boundaries. Numbers on the map indicate the number of hours that must be added to, or subtracted from UTC to calculate the time in each zone. Thus, eastern USA (−5) is 5 hours behind UTC.

TYPES OF CALENDAR

GREGORIAN
The 365-day Gregorian calendar was introduced by Pope Gregory XIII in 1582 and is now in use throughout most of the Western world. Every four years (leap year) an extra day is added. Below are the names of the months (and number of days).

January (31)	July (31)
February (28, 29 in leap years)	August (31)
	September (30)
March (31)	October (31)
April (30)	November (30)
May (31)	December (31)
June (30)	

JEWISH
The Jewish calendar is a lunar calendar adapted to the solar year. It normally has 12 months but in leap years,which occur seven times in every cycle of 19 years, there are 13 months. The years are reckoned from the Creation (which is placed at 3761 BC); the months are Nisan, Iyyar, Sivan, Thammuz, Ab, Elul, Tishri, Hesvan, Kislev, Tebet, Sebat, and Adar, with an intercalary month (First Adar) being added in leap years.

MUSLIM
The Muslim calendar is based on a year of 12 months, each month beginning roughly at the time of the New Moon. The months are Muharram, Safar, Rabi'I, Rabi'II, Jumada I, Jumada II, Rajab, Sha'ban, Ramadan, Shawwal, Dhu l-Qa'dah, and Dhu l-Hijja.

CHINESE
The Chinese calendar is a lunar calendar, with a year consisting of 12 months. Intercalary months are added to keep the calendar in step with the solar year of 365 days. Months are referred to by a number within a year, but also by animal names that, from ancient times, have been attached to years and hours of the day.

Disclaimer:—The external boundaries of India as shown on this map are neither correct nor authentic.

Useful data

UNITS OF MEASUREMENT

METRIC UNIT	EQUIVALENT
Length	
1 centimetre (cm)	10 millimetres (mm)
1 metre (m)	100 centimetres
1 kilometre (km)	1,000 metres
Mass	
1 kilogram (kg)	1,000 grams (g)
1 tonne (t)	1,000 kilograms
Area	
1 square centimetre (cm²)	100 square millimetres (mm²)
1 square metre (m²)	10,000 square centimetres
1 hectare	10,000 square metres
1 square kilometre (km²)	1,000,000 square metres
Volume	
1 cubic centimetre (cc)	1 millilitre (ml)
1 litre (l)	1,000 millilitres
1 cubic metre (m³)	1,000 litres
Capacity (liquid and dry measures)	
1 centilitre (cl)	10 millilitres (ml)
1 decilitre (dl)	10 centilitres
1 litre (l)	10 decilitres
1 decalitre (dal)	10 litres
1 hectolitre (hi)	10 decalitres
1 kilolitre (kl)	10 hectolitres

IMPERIAL UNIT	EQUIVALENT
Length	
1 foot (ft)	12 inches (in)
1 yard (yd)	3 feet
1 rod (rd)	5.5 yards
1 mile (mi)	1,760 yards
Mass	
1 dram (dr)	27.344 grains (gr)
1 ounce (oz)	16 drams
1 pound (lb)	16 ounces
1 hundredweight (cwt) (long)	112 pounds
1 hundredweight (cwt) (short)	100 pounds
1 ton (long)	2,240 pounds
1 ton (short)	2,000 pounds
Area	
1 square foot (ft²) (in²)	144 square inches
9 square feet	1 square yard (yd²)
1 acre	4,840 square yards
1 square mile	640 acres
Volume	
1 cubic foot	1,728 cubic inches
1 cubic yard	27 cubic feet
Capacity (liquid and dry measures)	
1 fluidram (fl dr)	60 minims (min)
1 fluid ounce (fl oz)	8 fluidrams
1 gill (gi)	5 fluid ounces
1 pint (pt)	4 gills
1 quart (qt)	2 pints
1 gallon (gal)	4 quarts
1 peck (pk)	2 gallons
1 bushel (bu)	4 pecks

NUMBER SYSTEMS

ROMAN	ARABIC
I	1
II	2
III	3
IV	4
V	5
VI	6
VII	7
VIII	8
IX	9
X	10
XI	11
XII	12
XIII	13
XIV	14
XV	15
XX	20
XXI	21
XXX	30
XL	40
L	50
LX	60
LXX	70
LXXX	80
XC	90
C	100
CI	101
CC	200
CCC	300
CD	400
D	500
DC	600
DCC	700
DCCC	800
CM	900
M	1,000
MM	2,000

METRIC - IMPERIAL CONVERSIONS

TO CONVERT	INTO	MULTIPLY BY
Length		
Centimetres	inches	0.3937
Metres	feet	3.2810
Kilometres	miles	0.6214
Metres	yards	1.0940
Mass		
Grams	ounces	0.0352
Kilograms	pounds	2.2050
Tonnes	long tons	0.9843
Tonnes	short tons	1.1025
Area		
Square centimetres	square inches	0.1550
Square metres	square feet	10.7600
Hectares	acres	2.4710
Square kilometres	square miles	0.3861
Square metres	square yards	1.1960
Volume		
Cubic centimetres	cubic inches	0.0610
Cubic metres	cubic feet	35.3100
Capacity		
Litres	pints	1.7600
Litres	gallons	0.2200

IMPERIAL - METRIC CONVERSIONS

TO CONVERT	INTO	MULTIPLY BY
Length		
Inches	centimetres	2.5400
Feet	metres	0.3048
Miles	kilometres	1.6090
Yards	metres	0.9144
Mass		
Ounces	grams	28.3500
Pounds	kilograms	0.4536
Long tons	tonnes	1.0160
Short tons	tonnes	0.9070
Area		
Square inches	square centimetres	6.4520
Square feet	square metres	0.0929
Acres	hectares	0.4047
Square miles	square kilometres	2.5900
Square yards	square metres	0.8361
Volume		
Cubic inches	cubic centimetres	16.3900
Cubic feet	cubic metres	0.0283
Capacity		
Pints	litres	0.5683
Gallons	litres	4.5460

RULES OF ALGEBRA

EXPRESSION	COMMENTS	EXPRESSION BECOMES
$a + a$	Simple addition	$2a$
$a + b = c + d$	Subtract b from either side	$a = c + d - b$
$ab = cd$	Divide both sides by b	$a = cd \div b$
$(a + b)(c + d)$	Multiplication of bracketed terms	$ac + ad + be + bd$
$a^2 + ab$	Use parentheses	$a(a + b)$
$(a + b)^2$	Expand brackets	$a^2 + 2ab + b^2$
$a^2 - b^2$	Difference of two squares	$(a + b)(a-b)$
$1/a + 1/b$	Find common denominator	$(a + b)/ab$
$a/b \div c/d$	Dividing by a fraction is the same as multiplying by its reciprocal	$a/b \times d/c$

POWERS OF TEN USED WITH SCIENTIFIC UNITS

FACTOR	NAME	PREFIX	SYMBOL
10^{18}	quintillion	exa-	E
10^{15}	quadrillion	peta-	P
10^{12}	trillion	tera-	T
10^{9}	billion	giga-	G
10^{6}	million	mega-	M
10^{3}	thousand	kilo-	k
10^{2}	hundred	hecto-	h
10^{1}	ten	deca-	da
10^{-1}	one tenth	deci-	d
10^{-2}	one hundredth	centi-	c
10^{-3}	one thousandth	milli-	m
10^{-6}	one millionth	micro-	u
10^{-9}	one billionth	nano-	n
10^{-12}	one trillionth	pico-	p
10^{-15}	one quadrillionth	femto-	f
10^{-18}	one quintillionth	atto-	a

Note: The American system of numeration for denominations above one million is used in this book. In this system, each of the denominations above one billion (1,000 millions) is 1,000 times the preceding one.

BIOLOGY SYMBOLS

SYMBOL	MEANING
O	female individual (used in inheritance charts)
□	male individual (used in inheritance charts)
♀	female
♂	male
×	crossed with; hybrid
+	wild type
F_1	offspring of the first generation
F_2	offspring of the second generation

TEMPERATURE SCALES

To convert from Celsius (C) to Fahrenheit (F): $F = (C \times 9 \div 5) + 32$
To convert from Fahrenheit to Celsius: $C = (F - 32) \times 5 \div 9$
To convert from Celsius to Kelvin (K): $K = C + 273$
To convert from Kelvin to Celsius: $C = K - 273$

Celsius	-20	-10	0	10	20	30	40	50	60	70	80	90	100
Fahrenheit	-4	14	32	50	68	86	104	122	140	158	176	194	212
Kelvin	253	263	273	283	293	305	313	325	333	343	353	363	373

MATHEMATICAL SYMBOLS

SYMBOL	EXPLANATION
+	addition
-	subtraction
×	multiplication
÷	division
=	equals
≠	does not equal
>	greater than
<	less than
≥	greater than or equal to
≤	less than or equal to
∞	infinity
%	per cent
π	pi (3.1416)
°	degree
≈	is approximately equal to
∠	angle
∏	parallel to
Σ	summation
u, u	vectors
f(x)	function
!	factorial
√	square root
ξ	universal set
A ∩ B	intersection
A ∪ B	unison
A ⊂ B	subset
Ø	null set

PHYSICS SYMBOLS

SYMBOL	MEANING
α	alpha particle
β	beta ray
γ	gamma ray; photon
ε	electromotive force
η	efficiency; viscosity
λ	wavelength
μ	micro-; permeability
ν	frequency; neutrino
ρ	density; resistivity
σ	conductivity
c	velocity of light
e	electronic charge

CHEMISTRY SYMBOLS

SYMBOL	MEANING
+	plus; together with
−	single bond
•	single bond; single unpaired electron; two separate parts or compounds regarded as loosely joined
=	double bond
≡	triple bond
R	group
X	halogen atom
Z	atomic number

SCIENTIFIC NOTATION

NUMBER	NUMBER BETWEEN 1 AND 10	POWER OF TEN	SCIENTIFIC NOTATION
10	1	10^1	1×10^1
150	1.5	$10^2 (= 100)$	1.5×10^2
274,000,000	2.74	$10^8 (= 100,000,000)$	2.74×10^8
0.0023	2.3	$10^{-3} (= 0.001)$	2.3×10^{-3}

TRIGONOMETRY

Angle A (degrees)	sin A	cos A	tan A
0	0	1	0
30	1/2	$\sqrt{3}/2$	$1/\sqrt{3}$
45	$1/\sqrt{2}$	$1/\sqrt{2}$	1
60	$\sqrt{3}/2$	1/2	$\sqrt{3}$
90	1	0	∞

Shapes: Plane

Two-dimensional shapes are termed plane (or flat) shapes. Plane shapes constructed with straight sides, as illustrated here, are called polygons. They are categorized according to the number of sides they have – for example, three-sided polygons are known as triangles. A polygon that has sides of equal length and internal angles of equal size, such as a square, is said to be regular.

SCALENE TRIANGLE
A triangle (three-sided polygon) with no equal sides or angles.

ISOSCELES TRIANGLE
A triangle with only two sides and two angles equal.

RIGHT-ANGLED TRIANGLE
A triangle with one angle as a right angle (90°).

EQUILATERAL TRIANGLE
A regular triangle. All angles are 60°.

SQUARE
A regular quadrilateral. All angles are 90°.

RHOMBUS
A quadrilateral with all sides equal and two pairs of equal angles.

RECTANGLE
A quadrilateral with four right angles and opposite sides of equal length.

PARALLELOGRAM
A quadrilateral with two pairs of parallel sides.

TRAPEZIUM
A quadrilateral with one pair of parallel sides.

PENTAGON
A five-sided polygon. A regular pentagon is shown above.

HEXAGON
A six-sided polygon. A regular hexagon is shown above.

OCTAGON
An eight-sided polygon. A regular octagon is shown above.

AREAS AND PERIMETERS

The formulae for calculating the areas and perimeters of simple plane shapes were devised by Classical Greek mathematicians.

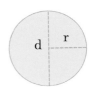

CIRCLE
r = radius
d = diameter = $2 \times r$

Circumference = $2 \times \pi \times r$
Area = $\pi \times r^2$
($\pi = 3.1416$)

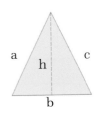

TRIANGLE
Height = h
Sides = a, b, c

Perimeter = $a + b + c$
Area = $\frac{1}{2} \times b \times h$

RECTANGLE
Sides = a, b

Perimeter = $2 \times (a + b)$
Area = $a \times b$

Shapes: Solid

Three-dimensional shapes are known as solid shapes, and include spheres, cubes, and pyramids. A solid shape with a polygon at each face is called a polyhedron.

TETRAHEDRON
A four-sided polyhedron. A regular tetrahedron is shown.

CUBE
A regular hexahedron. All sides are equal and all angles are 90°.

OCTAHEDRON
A polyhedron with eight sides.

PRISM
A polyhedron of constant cross-sections in planes perpendicular to its longitudinal axis.

PYRAMID
A polygonal base and triangular sides that meet at a point.

TORUS
A doughnut-like, ring shape.

SPHERE
A round shape, as in a ball or an orange.

HEMISPHERE
Formed when a sphere is cut exactly in half.

SPHEROID
An egg-shaped solid object whose cross-section is a circle or an ellipse.

CONE
An elliptical or circular base with sides tapering to a single point.

RIGHT CYLINDER
A tube-shaped, solid figure. A right cylinder has parallel faces.

HELIX
A twisted curve. The distance moved in one revolution is its pitch.

SURFACE AREAS AND VOLUMES

Volume refers to the amount of space that a solid object occupies. Its surface area is the sum of the area of each of its faces.

CYLINDER
Surface area =
$2 \times \pi \times r \times h + 2\pi r^2$
Volume = $\pi \times r^2 \times h$

Height = h
Radius = r

CONE
Surface area =
$\pi \times r \times l + \pi r^2$
Volume = $\frac{1}{3} \times \pi \times r^2 \times l$

Height = h
Radius = r
Side = l

RECTANGULAR BLOCK
Surface area =
$2 (a \times b + b \times c + a \times c)$
Volume = $a \times b \times c$

Sides = a, b, c

Index

A

Aa lava 273
Abacus
  Ancient Egyptian
    temple 459
  Ancient Greek building
    460
  Medieval church 469
  Neoclassical building 483
Abalone 176
Abaxial epidermis 139
Abaxial surface
  Butterwort leaf 161
  Fern pinnule 121
  Mulberry leaf 130
  Water hyacinth leaf 158
  Water lily leaf 159
  Welwitschia leaf 123
Abbey of St. Foi 468
Abdomen
  Crab 172
  Crayfish 172
  Human 211
  Insect 168-169
  Rattlesnake 185
  Scorpion 170
  Shrimp 172
  Spider 171
Abdominal aorta 215, 255
Abdominal artery 173
Abdominal cavity 215
Abdominal segment
  Butterfly 169
  Crayfish 172
  Eurypterid fossil 79
  Extinct shrimp 79
Abductor digiti minimus
  muscle 231, 233
Abductor pollicis brevis
  muscle 231
Aberdeen hook 562
Abies Concolor 66
Abomasum 198
Aboral surface
  Sea urchin 175
  Starfish 174
Abortive ovule 151
Abortive seed 146
Abrasion
  Glacier 286
  Weathering and erosion
    282
Absolute magnitude
  Hertzsprung-Russell
    diagram 23
  Stars 22
Absorption lines 22-23
Absorptive hyphae 114
Abutment 484-485
Abyssal plain 298
Acacia tree sap 438
Acadagnostus 64
Acamar 19
Acanthostachys strobilacea
  112-113
Acanthostega 80
Acanthus leaf 460
Accelerated electron 319
Acceleration 320-321
  Electric train 328
  Motorcycle 364
Access door 333
Accessory drive pad 419
Accessory pouch 548
Access panel 329, 333
Access slot 585
Accidentals 502-503
Accretion disc 27-29
AC electric train 328
Acer Lumiread e-reader
  568

Acer pseudoplatanus 131,
  151
Acer sp. 127
Acetabularia sp. 116
Acetabular labrum 225
Acetabulum
  Eryops 81
  Ornithischian 82
  Saurischian 82
Acetylene headlamp
  356-357
Achenes 150
Achernar 20
Achilles tendon 232-233
Acid
  Intaglio printing 446
  Reversible reaction 312
  Salt formation 312
Acidalia Planitia 43
Acidic solution 446, 448
Acid-resistant ground
  446-447
Acid-secreting stomach
  cell 217
Acipenser sturio 180
Acorn 151
Acoustic guitar 512-513
Acropolis 460
Acrosomal cap 259
Acroterion 460-461
Acroteuthis 278
Acrux
  Centaurus and Crux 21
  Southern stars 21
Acrylic ink 448
Acrylic paint techniques
  443
Acrylic-primed board 442
Acrylics 442-443
Actinia equina 166
Actinides 310
Actinium 310
Actinothoe sphyrodeta 166
Action 521
Action lever 514
Active galaxy 12
Active volcano 272
  Igneous and
    metamorphic rocks 275
  Mountain building 62
Actuating lever system
  330
Acuminate leaf apex
  136-137
Acute leaf apex 137
Adam's apple 212, 244-245
Adam's ring
  Neptune's rings 50
  Structure of Neptune 51
Adaptation 112
  Dryland plants 156-157
  Wetland plants 158-159
Adaxial epidermis 139
Adaxial surface
  Butterwort leaf 161
  Mulberry leaf 130
  Tree mallow leaf 131
  Water hyacinth leaf 158
  Water lily leaf 159
  Welwitschia leaf 123
Add address button 576
Add attachments button
  576
Address options button
  576
Adductor longus muscle
  225, 226
Adductor magnus muscle
  227
Adductor muscle 173
Adductor pollicis muscle
  231

Adductor tubercle 225
Adenine 216
Adhara 18, 21
Adipose tissue 215, 235
Adjustable antenna 591
Adjustable damper 518
Adjustable link 362
Adjustable vane 563
Adjusting screw 560
Admiralty anchor Type
  ACII 386
Admiralty pattern anchor
  386
Adrenal gland 215, 257
Adventitious buds 154
Adventitious roots
  Aechmea miniata 162
  Canadian pond weed
    158
  Couch grass 113
  Fern 121
  Horsetail 120
  Ivy 131
  Monocotyledon 126
  Potato 128
  Rock stonecrop 128
  Tree fern 112
  Vegetative reproduction
    154-155
  Water fern 158
  Water hyacinth 158
  Water lily 159
Advertising 368
Advertising panel 333
Aechmea miniata 162
Aedicule
  Ancient Roman
    building 463
  Renaissance building
    474, 476
AEG Turbine Hall 495
Aegyptopithecus 75
Aeration zone 293
Aerial
  Frigate 397
  Honda Insight 354
  Renault Clio 349
Aerial mammals 104
Aerial rig 397
Aerial root 162
Aerial shoot 155
Aerial stem 119, 155
Aerodynamic balance
  414-415
Aerodynamic hub cover
  604
Aerodynamic roof 354
Aerodynamic tubing 360
Aerodynamic underside
  components 354
Aerodynamic windscreen
  546
Aerofoil guard 329
"Aero" handlebars
  360-361
Aerosol spray fixative 430,
  440
"Aerotuck" position 360
Aesculus hippocastanum
  130
Aesculus parviflora 137
Afferent arteriole 257
A-frame
  Concorde 416
  Gliders, hang-gliders,
    and microlights 426
Africa
  Cretaceous period 72-73
  Earth's physical
    features 264-265
  Great Rift Valley 60
  Jurassic period 70
  Late Carboniferous
    period 66
  Middle Ordovician
    period 64
  Quaternary period 76-77
  Tertiary period 74-75
  Triassic period 68

African elephant 200-201
African plate 59
Aft anchor 395
Aft bogie 615
Aft door 416, 572
Afterbay 314
After breast rope 387
After bridge 395
Afterburner
  Jet engine 418
  Supersonic jetliner 416
Afterburner nozzle 421
Aftercastle
  Sailing warship 377
  Square-rigged ship 375
Aftercastle castle-deck
  gunport 377
After compass platform
  395
After fashion piece 381
After funnel
  Battleship 395
  Iron paddlesteamer 392
Afterpeak 392
After silencer 427
After spring rope 387
Aft fairing 415
Aft galley unit 417
Aft hydroplane 396
Aft main door 414-415
Aft rocker 615
Aft shoulder 560
Aft shroud 612, 613
Aft spar 415
Agate burnisher tip 432
Aggregate fruits 148-149
  Bramble 130
  Development 146-147
Aghulas current 297
Agnatha 178
Agropyron repens 113
Ahead/astern controls 390
Aileron
  ARV light aircraft 424
  BAe-146 components
    414
  Curtiss biplane 398-399
  Hawker Tempest
    components 409
  Lockheed Electra
    airliner 406
  LVG CVI fighter 405
  Schleicher glider 426
Aileron control wire 403
Aileron hinge strut 403
Aileron mass balance 424
Aileron operating arm 398

Air
  Atmosphere 300
  Oceans and seas 296
  Weather 302-303
Air ambulance 422
Airbag suspension 331
Air bladder 117
Air-brake
  BAe-146 components
    415
  Schleicher glider 426
  Tornado 421
Air-brake coupling hose
  326
Air-brake jack 421
Air brushes 442
Airbus 380 572-573
Air chamber 118
Air cleaner
  Jaguar V12 engine 345
  Renault Clio 351
Air compression 526
Air-conditioning 496-497
Air conditioning
  compressor 344, 354
Air-conditioning duct 417
Air conditioning pump
  344
Air conditioning
  refrigerant pipe 344
Air-cooled engine

Motorcycle engine 366
  V8 engine 404
Air cooling baffle 402
Air cooling fan 427
Air cooling scoop 365
Air-cushioned sole 543
Air data probe 420
Air exit 615
Air filter
  Bell-47 helicopter 422
  Harley Davidson FLHS
    Electra Glide 363
  Pegasus Quasar
    microlight 427
  Volkswagen Beetle 340
Air hose 442
Air impingement starter
  418
Air inlet
  Jaguar V12 engine 345
  Power drill 601
Air intake
  Concorde 416
  Double-decker tour bus
    333
  Formula One racing car
    356, 357
  Lockheed Electra
    airliner 406
  MCW Metrobus 332-333
  Modern military
    aircraft 420-421
  Single-decker bus 333
  Turbojet engine 418
  Turboprop engine 419
  Vacuum cleaner 592,
    593
Air intake box 425
Air-intake duct 354, 573
Air intake vent 341
Air mass 296
Air outlet 356, 427
Air passage
  Lambeosaurus 99
  Parasaurolophus 99
Air pistol 548-549
Air plants 162
Air pressure 303
Air pump
  Oscillating steam
    engine 391
  Steamboat 391
Air reservoir valve 327
Air resistance 552
Air rifle shooting 548
Air sac
  Chicken's egg 192
  Scots pine 122
Air scoop
  ARV Super 2 424
  Volkswagen Beetle 340
Air spaces
  Clubmoss stem 120
  Mare's tail stem 135
  Moss 119
  Root 132
  Stem 135
  Wetland plants 158-159
Airspeed-indicator tube
  ARV light aircraft 425
  BE 2B wings 404
Airspeed pitot tube 404
Air taxi 422
Air temperature 300
Air temperature probe
  BAe-146 components
    412
  Bell Jetranger
    helicopter 423
Air vent
  Bicycle helmet 360
  Hockey helmet 540
  Suzuki RGV500 368-369
Air ventilator inlet 405
Aisle
  Airbus 380 572
  Ancient Egyptian
    temple 458
  Cathedral dome 484

Gothic church 470,
  472-473
  Medieval church
    468-469
Akna Montes 37
Ala 213, 223
Alar groove 213
Alarm vibrator motor 558
Alba Fossae 43
Alba Patera 43
Albategnius 40
Albertosaurus 84
Albireo 20
Albumen 192
Albumen gland 177
Alcohol fermentation 313
Alcor 19
Alcyone 20
Aldebaran 18, 21
Alderamin 19
Alethopteris 67, 278
Algae 56, 112, 116-117
  Desmid 112
  Earth's evolution 56
  Fossil record 279
  Lichen symbiote 114
Algal cell 114
Algal layer 114
Algebra 621
Algedi 20
Algenib 19, 20
Algieba 18
Algol 19, 20
Alhambra 488
Alhena 18, 21
Alicante 450
Alidade 377
Alimentary canal 248-249
Alioth 18
  The Plough 19
Alkaid 18
  The Plough 19
Alkali metals 310
Allantoic fluid 192
Allantois 192-193
"All clear" position 530
All-enclosing fairing 369
Alley 544-545
Alligator 186
Allison 250-C20J
  turboshaft engine 423
Allium sp. 143
Allosaurus 71, 85
Allotropes 311
Alloy disc 517
Alloy frame 368
Alloy wheel
  Formula One racing car
    356, 357
  Honda VF750 364-365
  Renault Clio 350-351
  Suzuki RGV500 368-369
All-round bicycle 360
All-terrain bicycle 358
Alluvial cone 282
Alluvial fan 282
Alluvium-filled basin 282
Almach 19, 20
  Pegasus and
    Andromeda 19
Al Nair 19, 20
Alnilam 18
Alnitak
  Horsehead Nebula 16
  Orion 18
Alouatta seniculus 203
Alpha Centauri 21
Alpha Hydri 20
Alpha Mensae 20
Alphard 18, 21
Alpha Regio 36-37
Alpha ring 48
Alphecca 18, 21
Alpheratz 19, 20
  Pegasus and
    Andromeda 19
Alphonsus 40
Alpine skiing 552-553
Alps 60, 265

Alrami 21
Alsatian dog 195
Alstroemeria aurea 129
Altair 19, 20
Altar 470
Alternating current 328
Alternative engines
346-347
Alternator
  Diesel train 326
  Ford V6 12-valve
  engine 344
  Jaguar V12 engine 345
  NPT 301 turbojet 418
  Renault Clio 351
Alternator belt 351
Altitude scale 377
Alto clef 502
Altocumulus cloud 302
Alto mute 507
Altostratus cloud 302
Alto voice 502
Aludra 21
Alula 21
Aluminium 311
  Earth's composition 39
  Earth's crust 58
Aluminium alloy backing
346
Aluminium arrow shaft
548
Aluminium beam 560
Aluminium bonnet 354
Aluminium cowl 401
Aluminium flush-riveted
skin 407
Aluminium gearbox
casing 366
Aluminium racket 544
Aluminium shield 612
Aluminium wheel 406,
615
Aluminium wire figure
455
Alveolar artery and vein
247
Alveolar bone 247
Alveoli 254-255
Amaryllis 155
Amateur rules 532
Amazon Basin 39
Amazon Kindle e-reader
569
Amazon River 264
Amazonis Planitia 43
Ambiens muscle
  Albertosaurus 84
  Iguanodon 97
Ambulacral groove 79,
175
Ambulatory corridor 465
Amelodentinal junction
247
American alligator 186
American beaver 197
American black bear 195
American football 524,
526-527
American squash court
545
American squash game
544
Americium 311
Ammonia
  Jupiter's atmosphere 45
  Saturn's atmosphere 47
  Structure of Neptune 51
  Structure of Uranus 49
Ammonite 278-279
Ammonite shell 267
Ammonium dichromate
312
Ammonium
  hydrosulphide
  Jupiter's atmosphere 45
  Saturn's atmosphere 47
Ammophila arenaria 113
Ammunition 548-549
Ammunition box 408

Amnion 192-193, 260
Amniotic egg 192
Amniotic fluid 192, 260
Amniotic sac 260
Amoebocyte 166
Amphibia 182
Amphibian 80-81, 182-183
  Earth's evolution 56
  Fossil 278-279
  Primitive 68-69, 78
Amphibole 275
Amphitheatre 464-465
Amplification
  Drums 518
  Electronic instruments
  520
  Guitar 512
  Stringed instruments 510
  Vibraphone 516
  Xylophone 516
Amplifier 520
Amps 316
Ampulla
  Ear 242-243
  Fallopian tube 258-259
  Sea urchin 175
  Starfish 174
Ampullar nerve 242
Anal canal 249
Anal clasper 169
Anal fin
  Bony fish 180-181
  Lamprey 178
Anal fin ray 180
Anal flap 200
Analogue signals 580
Anal sphincter muscle
249
Anchisaurus 88-89
Anchor
  74-gun ship 380
  BAe-146 components
  412, 414
  Battleship 394-395
  Frigate 397
  Junk 376
  Roman corbita 372
  Square-rigged ship 375
  Tea clipper 392
  Types 386
  Wooden sailing ship
  379
Anchor bearing 413
Anchor buoy 379
Anchor cable
  74-gun ship 380
  Sailing warship 376
Anchor chain 386, 395
Anchoring 386-387
Anchor-joint 492
Anchor rode 372
Anchor rope 372-373
Ancient Egyptian building
458-459
Ancient Greek building
460-461, 462
Ancient Greeks 542
Ancient Roman building
462-465, 474
Ancillary drive belt 347
Ancillary drive pulley 345
Ancorale 372
Andamenti 451
Andes
  Cretaceous period 73
  Earth's external
  features 39
  Jurassic period 71
  Quaternary period 77
  Satellite map 264
  Tertiary period 75
  Triassic period 69
Androecium 140-141, 143
Andromeda 19, 20
Andromeda Galaxy 14, 19
Anemometer 605
Anemonia viridis 166
Anemophilous pollination
144

Angiogram 214
Angiospermophyta 112,
126
Angiosperms 279
Angle bar 393
Angle buttress 471, 472
Angle-of-attack probe 420
Anglerfish 180
Angling 562-563
Angoulême Cathedral
468-469
Angular mountain ridge
295
Angular notch 249
Angular process 194
Angular unconformity 276
Anhydrous copper
sulphate 313
Animal cloning 607
Animal life
  Electromagnetic
  radiation 314
  Primitive 78
Animal remains
  Fossils 278
  Sedimentary rocks 276
Animal stances 82
Animals 56, 67, 78
Anions 308
Ankle
  Anchisaurus 89
  Corythosaurus 98
  Edmontonia 95
  Herrerasaurus 86
  Human 211
  Iguanodon 96
  Pachycephalosaurus
  100
  Psittacosaurus 103
  Stegoceras 101
  Stegosaurus 93
  Triceratops 102
  Tyrannosaurus 84
Ankle joint
  Brachiosaurus 90
  Diplodocus 90
  Euoplocephalus 94
  Human 219
  Parasaurolophus 98
  Plateosaurus 88
  Stegoceras 101
  Struthiomimus 87
  Triceratops 102
  Tyrannosaurus 84
Ankylosaurs 83, 92, 94-95
Anne's Spot 47
Annual growth ring 125
Annuals 128
Annular river drainage
288
Annular tendon 241
Annulet 460
Annulus
  Fern 121
  Mushroom 115
Annulus of trunk 201
Ant 168
Anta 461
Antarala 490-491
Antarctica
  Cretaceous period
  72-73
  Earth's physical
  features 264-265
  Jurassic period 70
  Late Carboniferous
  period 66
  Quaternary period
  76-77
  Tertiary period 74-75
  Triassic period 68
Antarctic Circle
  Satellite map 265
  Surface currents 297
Antarctic circumpolar
current 296
Antares 18, 21
Antefixa 461
Antelope 198

Antenna
  Airbus 380 573
  Battleship 395
  Crab 172
  Crayfish 173
  Frigate 397
  Global positioning
  system 590, 591
  Insects 168-169
  Malacostraca 172
  Roman corbita 372-373
  Shrimp 172
  Volleyball net 534
Antennule 173
Anterior antebrachial
muscle 86
Anterior aorta 170
Anterior arch 222
Anterior brachial muscle
  Brachiosaurus 91
  Gallimimus 86
Anterior branch of spinal
nerve 223
Anterior chamber 241
Anterior chamber of
cloaca 185
Anterior crural muscle
  Brachiosaurus 90
  Gallimimus 86
Anterior dorsal fin
  Bony fish 181
  Dogfish 179
  Lamprey 178
Anterior fontanelle 220
Anterior horn 223
Anterior median fissure
223, 238
Anterior median vein 253
Anterior nasal spine
220-221
Anterior petal 141
Anterior root 258
Anterior semicircular
canal 243
Anterior sepal 141
Anterior tentacle 177
Anterior tibial artery 253
Anterior tibial muscle
  Albertosaurus 84
  Iguanodon 97
Anterior tubercle 222
Anterior wing of shell 176
Antheridium 117
  Fern 121
  Moss 119
Antherozoids 116-117
  Fern 121
  Moss 119
Anthers 140-143, 145
  Dicotyledons 126-127
  Fertilization 146-147
  Pollination process
  144-145
Anthozoa 166
Anthracite coal 280
Anthriscus sp. 135
Anthropoids 202
Anthurium andreanum
143
Antibodies 253
Anticlinal fold 60
Anticline 60-61, 62
Anticline trap 280-281
Anticlinorium 61
Anti-collision beacon
422-423
Anti-corrosion paint 413
Anticyclonic storm system
  Cloud features of
  Neptune 50
  Jupiter 44-45
  Structure of Saturn 47
Anti-friction pad 552
Anti-glare lens 553
Anti-glare screen surface
584
Antihelix 242
Anti-lift bracing wire
  Avro triplane 403

Blackburn monoplane
401
Blériot XI monoplane
401
LVG CVI fighter 405
Anti-lift wire 399
Antimacassar 329
Antimony 311
Antipodal cell 147
Anti-reflective coating 605
Anti-reverse drive 562
Anti-roll bar
  Renault Clio 350-351
  Volkswagen Beetle 340
Anti-submarine torpedo
tube 397
Anti-surge baffle 344
Anti-torque tail rotor 423
Antitragus 242
Anti-vibration engine
mount 411
Antler hammer 109
Antler harpoon 109
Antlia 18, 21
Antoniadi 41
Antorbital fenestra
  Baryonyx 83
  Camarasaurus 91
  Diplodocus 90
  Plateosaurus 88
Anura 182
Anus
  Barnacle 173
  Bony fish 181
  Butterfly 169
  Cow 198
  Crayfish 173
  Dolphin 205
  Domestic cat 195
  Elephant 200
  Human 249, 258, 261
  Octopus 176
  Rabbit 196
  Sea urchin 175
  Snail 177
  Spider 170
  Starfish 174
  Tortoise 187
Anvil 242
Aorta
  Anterior 170
  Bony fish 181
  Dogfish 179
  Dolphin 205
  Dorsal 179, 181, 182
  Human 215, 250-251,
  252, 255, 256-257
  Posterior 170
  Spider 170
  Ventral 179
Apatite 271
Ape 108, 202-203
Aperture 610, 612, 613
Aperture door 612, 613
Aperture door mounting
612
Aperture plate 611
Apex
  Beetle wing 168
  Butterfly wing 169
  Calligraphy characters
  445
  Clubmoss shoot 120
  Fern frond 121
  Fern pinnule 121
  Horsetail shoot 120
  Leaf 136-137, 154-155
  Lung 255
  Moss 119
  Pegasus XL SE
  microlight 426
  Pine shoot 125
  Snail shell 177
  Tongue 244-245
Apex wire 426
Aphelion 30-31
Aphrodite Terra 36-37
Apical bud
  Bulb 155

Pine shoot 125
Apical foramen 247
Apical meristem 134
Apical notch
  Seaweed 116
  Thalloid liverwort 118
Apollo 41
Apomixis 146
Apophysis 119
Apothecium 114
Appalachian mountains
  Late Cretaceous period
  67
  Mountain building 62
  Quaternary period 77
  Satellite map 264
  Tertiary period 75
  Triassic period 69
Apparent magnitude 22
Appendix
  Chimpanzee 202
  Human 249
  Rabbit 196
Appendix orifice 249
Apple 148-149
Apple iMac 567
Apple iPad 568-569
Apple Macintosh PCs 566
Approach 543
Apse 465, 469, 481
Aquarius 19, 20
Aquatic mammals 104
Aqueduct 256
Aqueous humour 241
Aquiclude 292
Aquifer 292
Aquiferous system 166
Aquila 19, 20
Ara 20
Ara ararauna 190
Arabesque
  Islamic building
  488-489
  Neoclassical moulding
  480
Arabia
  Cretaceous period 72
  Jurassic period 70
Arabian Desert 265
Arabic number system
591
Arachnids 170-171
Arachnoid granulation
237
Arachnoid mater 237, 240
Aral Sea 265
Araneae 170
Araucaria araucana 68
Arcade
  Ancient Roman
  building 464-465
  Baroque church 479-481
  Gothic building 470-471
  Medieval church
  468-469
  Twentieth-century
  building 495
Arcadia Planitia 43
Arch 484-485
  Ancient Roman
  building 462, 464-465
  Asian building 491
  Baroque church 479,
  480
  Calligraphy characters
  445
  Cathedral dome 487
  Features of a coastline
  295
  French temple 484-485
  Gothic church 470-473
  High jump 543
  Islamic building 488-489
  Medieval building
  466-469
  Nineteenth-century
  building 492-493
  Renaissance building
  474-475

Archaeopteryx 57, 84, 85
Arched brace 473
Arched doorway 474, 475
Arched facade 493
Archegoniophore 118
Archegonium
  Fern 121
  Liverwort 118
  Moss 119
  Scots pine 122
Archery 548-549
Archery screen 377
Archimedes 40
Architrave
  Ancient Egyptian
   temple 458-459
  Ancient Greek temple
   461
  Ancient Roman
   building 463, 465
  Baroque church
   479-481
  French temple 485
  Gothic building 473
  Neoclassical building
   478, 482-483
  Renaissance building
   476-477
Archivolt
  Baroque church 479,
   481
  French temple 485
  Gothic church 471
  Medieval building
   467-468
  Renaissance building
   477
Arch of aorta 253
Arch of Titus 463
Arch-plate 493
Archway 493
  Medieval church 469
  Moulding 485
Arctic Circle
  Satellite map 265
  Surface currents 297
Arctic Ocean 265
Arcturus 18, 21
  Hertzsprung-Russell
   diagram 23
Area measurements 590
Areas 622, 623
Areola 160
Areole 156
Arête 286-287
Argentina 331
Argon
  Atmospheric
   composition 301
  Mars' atmosphere 43
  Mercury's atmosphere 35
  Periodic table 311
  Venus' atmosphere 37
Argyre Planitia 43
Ariel 48
Aries 19, 20
Aril
  Lychee fruit 148
  Yew seed 123
A ring 46-47
Aristarchus 40
Aristillus 40
Aristoteles 40
Arkab Prior 21
Arkansas hone-stone 452
Arm
  74-gun ship 380
  Calligraphy characters
   445
  Gorilla 203
  Human 210
  Lion 194
  Roman anchor 372
  Starfish 174
  Volkswagen Beetle 341
Armature
  Power drill motor 600
  Sculpture 452, 454-455
Armature spindle 600

Arm bud 260
Armed sports 556-557
Armour
  Battleship 394
  Gun turret 396
  Ironclad 393
Armoured dinosaurs 92
Armoured seat back 409
Arm out-in joint 608
Armpit 211, 234
Armpit bight 388
Armrest 329, 407
Arm rotation joint 608
Arms of Brazil 394
Armstand dive 558-559
Arm up-down joint 608
Arrector pili muscle 235
Arriccio 434
Arrow head 109
Arse 382
Arsenic 311
Arsia Mons 43
Arsinoitherium 57, 75,
  104-105
Art deco style 495
  Twentieth-century
   building 494, 495
Artemon 372
Arterial system
  Brain 252
  Kidney 256
Arteriole 252
Artery
  Abdominal 173
  Alveolar 247
  Anterior tibial 253
  Axillary 253
  Basilar 252
  Brachial 253
  Central retinal 240
  Common carotid 215,
   251, 253
  Common iliac 215, 253,
   257
  Coronary 250-251, 253
  Digital 231, 253
  Dorsal metatarsal 253
  Epibranchial 179
  External iliac 215, 225,
   253
  Femoral 225, 253
  Gastric 253
  Hepatic 248, 252-253
  Interlobular 256
  Internal carotid 243,
   252
  Internal iliac 215, 253
  Lateral plantar 253
  Orbital 179
  Peroneal 253
  Popliteal 253
  Posterior cerebral 252
  Posterior tibial 253
  Pulmonary 182, 251,
   253, 254-255
  Pulp 247
  Radial 231, 253
  Renal 256-257
  Splenic 253
  Sternal 173
  Subclavian 215, 251,
   253
  Superior mesenteric
   253, 256
  Superior thyroid 244
  Testicular 257
  Ulnar 231, 253
  Umbilical 260
  Vertebral 223, 252
Artesian water 292
Arthropoda 168, 170, 172,
  278
Articular capsule 232
Articular cavity
  Hip joint 225
  Metatarsophalangeal
   joint 252
Artificial elements 310
Artificial fly 562-563

Artificial light 319
Artificial lure 563
Artillery loop 389
Artillery wheel 334
Artiodactyla 104,
  198-199
Artist's easel 437
Artist's signature 437,
  445
Artist's stamp 445
Art nouveau style 495
Arundinaria nitida 131
ARV Super 2 light aircraft
  424-425
Arzachel 40
Ascender 445
Ascending aorta 251
Ascending colon 249
Ascraeus Mons 43
Asexual reproduction 154
Ash
  Mountain building 62
  Rock cycle 266
  Volcano 272-273
Ash chute 395
Ash-cinder volcano 272
Ash eruptions 272
Ash head 540
Ashlar 464, 486
ASIMO humanoid
  608-609
Asia
  Cretaceous period
   72-73
  Earth's physical
   features 264-265
  Himalaya formation
   62-63
  Hominids 108
  Jurassic period 70
  Middle Ordovician
   period 64
  Quaternary period
   76-77
  Tertiary period 74-75
  Triassic period 68
Asian buildings 490-491
Asian elephant 200-201
Asparagus setaceous 64
Ass 198
Association football
  524-525
Astatine 311
Asterias rubens 175
Asterina gibbosa 175
Asteroids 52-53
  Solar System 30
Asteroxylon 78-79
Asthenosphere 58-59
Astragal
  Church of the Sorbonne
   486
  Ship's shield 395
Astragalus 183
Astrolabe 376, 377
Astronavigation dome 408
Asymmetric ridge 283
Atacama Desert 264
Atalanta Planitia 36
Athletics 542-543
Atlantic Ocean 264-265
  Quaternary period 77
  Tertiary period 75
Atlas
  Baroque building 482
  Horse 199
  Human 222
  Moon 40
Atlas mountains
  Earth's external
   features 39
  Quaternary period 77
  Satellite map 265
Atmosphere
  Earth 38-39, 64,
   300-301
  Jupiter 45
  Mars 43
  Mercury 34-35

Neptune 51
Pluto 51
Saturn 47
Uranus 49
Venus 37
Water cycle 288
Atoll 298-299
Atoll development 299
Atomic mass 309, 310
Atomic number 310
Atomic weight 310
Atoms 306, 308-309, 596
  Chemical properties 310
  Chemical reactions 312
  Periodic table 310
Atrial diastole 250
Atrial systole 251
Atrium
  Hong Kong and
   Shanghai Bank 498
  Human 215, 250-251
  Sponge 166
Attached column
  Ancient Roman
   building 465
  Baroque church 480
  Gothic building 473
  Medieval building 468-
   469
  Neoclassical building
   479
Attachment-bracket 424
Attachment clip 575
Attachment lug 404
Attachment plate 424
Attack line 534
Attack radar 420
Attic
  Baroque church
   480-481
  Cathedral dome 487
  Neoclassical building
   478, 483
Attic vase 372
Attitude control thruster
  614
Attraction 316-317
"A" turret 394
Auda 491
Audio clock settings 521
Audio codec chip 587
Audio software sequencer
  521
Auditorium 479
Auditory canal 242
Auditory meatus
  Chimpanzee 202
  Seal 204
Auger 374
Augusta National Golf
  course 546
Aureole 471
Auricle 242
Auricular surface 223
Auriga 18, 21
Aurora 38, 301
Australasia 264-265
Australia
  Cretaceous period
   72-73
  Jurassic period 70
  Late Carboniferous
   period 66
  Middle Ordovician
   period 64
  Quaternary period
   76-77
  Railway track gauge
   331
  Satellite map 265
  Tertiary period 74-75
  Triassic period 68
Australian Desert 265
Australian rules football
  524, 528-529
Australopithecus 77, 108
  Lower jaw 107
  Tertiary period 74
Autofeather unit 419

Autogiro 422
Automatic cylinder
  lubricator 342
Automatic direction-
  finding aerial 423
Automatic door 328-329
Automatic louvres 602,
  603
Automatic pen 444
Automatic Train
  Protection (ATP) 330
Automobile freight car
  327
Autopilot 412
Auxiliary air intake 420-
  421
Auxiliary generator 327
Auxiliary power unit 417
Auxiliary Power Unit
  (APU) exhaust 572
Auxiliary power unit inlet
  415
Aves 188
Avimimus 87
Avogadro 41
Avro triplane IV 402-403
Avro Tutor biplane
  402-403
Away swing bowler 538
Awning 499
Axe 109, 374
Axial gland 175
Axial instrument unit
  612
Axial tilt
  Earth 38
  Jupiter 44
  Mars 42
  Mercury 34
  Moon 40
  Neptune 50
  Pluto 51
  Saturn 46
  Uranus 48
  Venus 36
Axilla 211
Axillary artery 253
Axillary bud 134
  Dicotyledon stem 127
  Durmast oak 131
  Leaf scars 154
Axillary vein 253
Axinite 270
Axis
  Azolla sp. 158
  Horse 199
  Human 222
  Seed 152-153
  Pine cone 122
Axis of rotation
  Jupiter 44
  Mars 42
  Mercury 34
  Moon 40
  Neptune 50
  Pluto 51
  Pulsar 28
  Saturn 46
  Uranus 48
  Venus 36
Axle
  Avro triplane 402-403
  Blackburn monoplane
   400
  Bus 333
  Curtiss biplane 399
  Honda VF750 365
  Lockheed Electra
   airliner 407
  LVG CVI fighter 405
  Steam locomotive 324
Axle bolt 425
Axon 239
Aythya fuligula 188
Azimuthal map projection
  265
Azo yellow 442
Azurite 306

B
B-17G Flying Fortress
  bomber 408
Baboon 202
Bach 35
Back
  Block and tackle 383
  Elephant 200
  Horse 198
  Human 210
  Lion 195
Back-board 532
Back bone 222
Back check 514
Back contact grid 605
Background radiation 10
Back/Home button 586
Back judge 526
Back line 535
Back pocket 528
Backrest
  ARV light aircraft 425
  Lockheed Electra
   passenger seat 407
Backs
  Handball 535
  Hockey 540
  Soccer 524
  Volleyball 534
Backshell 615
Back sight 549
Backstay 378, 379, 380
Backstay stool 381
Backstroke 558-559
Back strap 560, 561
Back-up battery 567
Backward defensive
  stroke 538
Backward dive 558
Backwash 294
Back zones 534
Bacteria 56
Bactrian camel 199
Baculum 199
Badger 194
Badminton 544-545
BAe-146 jetliner
  components 412-415
Baffin Island 264
Baffle 541
Baffle plate 347
Bage, C. 492
Baggage compartment
  door 423
Bagneux Church 468-469
Bahada 282
Bail 538
Bail arm 562
Bailey 466
Bail handle 336
Bailly 40
Baird's beaked whale 205
Balaenoptera musculus 205
Balance 232
Balance and muscle
  coordination 237
Balance weight
  Jaguar V12 engine 345
  Mid West rotary engine
   411
Balancing drilling
  Mid West rotary engine
   411
  Wankel rotary engine
   347
Balanophyllia regia 167
Balata surface 546
Balcony 493
  Islamic tomb 489
  Nineteenth-century
   building 493
  Renaissance theatre
   477
  Rococo style 478, 482
  Sailing ship 378, 379,
   381
Baleen whale 204

Ball
American football 526
Australian rules football 528
Baseball 537
Basketball 533
Cricket 538
Gaelic football 528-529
Golf 546
Handball 555
Hockey 540
Hurling 541
Lacrosse 541
Netball 535
Racketball 545
Rugby 524, 530-531
Soccer 524
Squash 545
Tennis 544
Volleyball 534
Ballast 524
Ball bearings 358-359
Ballflowers 470-471
Ball marker 547
Ball size number 525
Baltica 65
Baltimore oriole 193
Baluster
Asian building 490
Gothic building 473
Neoclassical building 483
Balustrade
Asian building 490
Baroque church 479-480
Cathedral dome 487
Gothic church 472-473
Neoclassical building 478, 483
Nineteenth-century building 493
Renaissance theatre 477
Twentieth-century building 495
Balzac 55
Bamboo 131
Banana 146
Banded ironstone 277
Banded milk snake 184
Bandy 541
Bank of England 482
Banner 375
Bar
Musical notation 502
Relief-printing press 449
Bar area 573
Barb
Angling 562
Cnidocyte 167
Barberry 130-131
Barbette
Battleship 394
Gun turret 396
Bar code 606
Bare end
Reef knot 388
Single sheet bend 387
Barium 310
Bark
Bishop pine stem 125
Epiphyte 162
Lichen 114
Perennials 130-131
Stem 134
Woody plants 130-131
Bar keel 392
Barkhan dune 283
Bar line 502
Barnacle 172-173
Barnard's Star 25
Baroque style 478-483
Barosaurus 92
Barred spiral galaxy
Galaxies 12-15
Milky Way 14-15
Objects in Universe 11
Origin and expansion of

Universe 10-11
Barrel
Gun turret 397
Wood capstan 387
Barrel joint 508
Barrel vault 484-485
Ancient Roman building 465-464
Baroque church 479
Medieval church 468
Nineteenth-century building 493
Barrier beach 294
Barrier reef 299
Barry, C. 493
Bars 516-517
Bar swivel 562
Baryonyx 83, 84-85
Baryte 270
Basal disc 167
Basal scale 114
Basalt 274-275
Basaltic lava 272
Bascule 493
Base
Ancient Greek temple 461
Ancient Roman building 463, 465
Asian building 491
Baroque church 479, 481
Dome 484, 486, 487
French temple 485
Gothic church 470, 472
Medieval church 469
Neoclassical building 478, 483
Renaissance theatre 477
Sheet lead 383
Twentieth-century building 494
Twin bollards 386
Baseball 536-537
Base line
Calligraphy lettering 445
Tennis 544
Basement 483
Basement membrane of Bowman's capsule 257
Base of phalanx 230
Base plate 552
Bases 536
Basic movements 237
Basic shield volcano 272
Basidium 115
Basilar artery 252
Basilar membrane 243
Basilican system 468
Basilica of St. Madeleine 468
Basilic vein 253
Basket
Basketball 532
Ski pole 552-553
Basket arch 472, 484
Basketball 532-533
Basket star 174
Basking shark 179
Bas-relief carving 491
Bass angling 562
Bass bridge
Concert grand piano 515
Upright piano 514
Bass clarinet 504
Bass clef 502
Bass drum 504-505, 518-519
Bass formation 277
Bass joint 508
Bass notes 512
Bassoon 503, 504-505, 508
Bass/Play mode 586
Bass voice 502
Bastille 466
Bat

Baseball 537
Cricket 539
Bat (animal) 105
Batholiths 274-275
Batsman 558-559
Batten
74-gun ship 381
Junk 376
Wall construction 602
Batter 536-537
Battery
Bell-47 helicopter 422
Bersey electric cab 342
Digital video camera 582
Hubble Space Telescope 613
Inverter 355
Kirby BSA racing sidecar 369
Battery assembly 355
Battery box 327, 424
Battery carrier 338
Battery compartment 407
Battery cover 579
Battery electronic control module (ECM) 355
Battery overspill 422
Battery strap 359
Batting gloves
Baseball 537
Cricket 539
Battlemented cornice 471
Battlements 466-467
Battleship 394-395
Bauxite 268
Bay
Building 468, 469, 494
Coastline features 295
River features 291
Bay-head beach 294
Bay-leaf garland 480
Bayonet fixing 352
Bay window 477
BE 2B bomber 404-405
Beach
Coastline 294-295
River development 289
Beacon 407, 422-423
Beaded edge tyre 336
Beadlet anemone 166
Bead moulding 459
Beak
Ankylosaurus 94
Attic vase 372
Bird 188-190
Ceratopsian 100
Chelonian 186
Dolphin 204
Euoplocephalus 94
Hatching chick 192-193
Iguanodon 97
Moss 119
Octopus 176
Ornithopod 96
Panoplosaurus 94
Protoceratops 102
Psittacosaurus 103
Stegosaurus 92
Beaked whale 204
Beaker 312
Beam
BAe-146 jetliner 414
Gothic church 473
High-tension 496
Iron paddlesteamer 393
Modern building 497-499
Nineteenth-century building 492
Single skull 560
Bean
Black 153
Broad 152
Bear 104, 106, 194-195
Bearing
Electric generator 317
Jaguar V12 engine 345

Motorcycle gearbox 366
Rotary engine output shaft 411
Bearing assembly 425
Bearing housing 344
Bearing mount 411
Bearing seal 359
Bearing sleeve 338
"Beast feet" 84
Beaten gold 452
Beaters 516, 518-519
Beats 502
Beaver 196-197
Becket 383
Becket Chapel 467
Bed
Relief printing press 449
Sedimentary rocks 276
Bedding plane
Cave system 285
Coastline 294-295
Bedford cord upholstery 336
Bedplate 390
Bedrock 298
Delta formation 291
Bee 168, 379
Bee hummingbird 193
Bee pollination 144-145
Beeswax 384
Beethoven 35
Beetle 168
Begonia 129, 155
Begonia x tuberhybrida 129, 155
Behaviour 108, 237
Belaying pin 382
Belemnites 71, 278-279
Belfry
74-gun ship 380
Church of St. George in the East 481
Bell 508
Bell 206 Jetranger 423
Bell 47G-3B1 422-423
Bellatrix 18
Bell chamber 493
Bell crank 391
Bell housing 347
Bell joint 508
Bello 35
Bell Regio
Radar map of Venus 36
Structure of Venus 37
Belly
Bird 188
Caiman 186
Dolphin 204
Elephant 201
Horse 198
Lion 195
Lizard 184
Sail 384
Viola 511
Violin 510
Belly-band 555
Belly fairing 572
Belt
Jupiter 44-45
Structure of Saturn 47
Belt armour 394
Belt colour 556
Belt drive 366
Belt pulley 345
Belt tensioner 344, 364
Belvedere 476
Bench officials
Ice hockey 550
Lacrosse 541
Bending 318
Bends 587
Benguela current 297
Satellite map 264
Benz, Karl 334
Benz Motorwagen 335
Benz six-cylinder engine 405
Berardius bairdi 205

Berberis sp. 130-131
Berkelium 311
Berries 148-149
Bersey electric cab 342
Berthing ropes 387
Beryl 270
Beryllium 310
Beta Hydri 20
Beta Mensae 20
Beta Pictoris 21
Beta ring 48
Betelgeuse 18, 21
Hertzsprung-Russell diagram 23
Orion 18
Universe 10-11
Betula grossa 74
Betula lenta 76
Betulites 74
Bevel gear 335
Bevel pinion 338
Beverley Minster 484
Bezel 584
Bhagirathi Parbat 62
Bianco di San Giovanni 434-435
Biathlon rifle 549
Bib 557
Bi-block engine 337
Biceps brachii muscle 226
Biceps femoris muscle 227
Bicycle 360-361
Bicycle anatomy 358-359
Bicycle riding 315
Biennials 128
Biflagellate cell 116
Bifurcate ligament 232
"Big Ben" 493
Bigbore rifle shooting 548-549
Big end
Flat-four cylinder arrangement 340
Four-stroke cycle 343
Jaguar straight six engine 344
Mid West engine 410
Trojan engine 342
Big-end bearing 335
Bight 588
Big toe 232-233
Bile duct 189, 249
Bilge keel 395, 397
Bilge keelson 393
Bill
Danforth anchor 386
Running block 383
Sail hook 384
Bilobed leaves 123
Bin base 592
Bin cover handle 593
Bin cover retaining clip 592, 593
Binder 464
Binder bolt 361
Binding 383
Acoustic guitar 512
Iron paddlesteamer 392
Binding medium 440
Bin handle 592
Bin handle clip 592
Bin lower seal 592
Binnacle box 378
Binocular eyepieces 610, 611
Bin upper seal 592
Bin upper seal seating 592
Biology symbols 591, 621
Bipedal dinosaur 84, 96, 100
Bipinnate leaf 137
Biplane elevator 398-399
Biplanes 402-403, 408
Bipolar neuron 239
Birch 74, 76
Bird 84, 188-191
Beak 190

Earth's evolution 57
Feathers 191
Feet 190
Fossil record 279
Wing 191
"Bird feet" 96
Bird-hipped dinosaur 82, 92, 96
Bird of prey 188
Bird pollination 144
Bishop pine 124-125
Bismuth 281, 311
Bit 601
Biternate leaves 137
Bit-guard 555
Bitt
74-gun ship 380-381
Roman corbita 373
Bitter end, Hawser 387
Bituminous coal 280
Bivalves 79, 176, 278-279
Blackbacked gull 193
Black bean 153
Black belt 556
Blackberry 130, 146-147
Blackberry Curve 8520 589
Blackburn monoplane 400-401
Blackburn, Robert 400
Black dwarf 24-25
Blackheaded gull 189
Black ink cartridge 574
Black ink-cartridge clamp 574
Black holes 28-29
Galaxies 12
Massive stars 26-27
Black Mesa 277
Black rhinoceros 199
Black Sea 265
Blackstonia perfoliata 144
Black walnut 137
Black widow spider 171
Bladder
Bony fish 181
Chimpanzee 202
Dolphin 205
Domestic cat 195
Elephant 200
Human 215, 257, 258-259, 261
Lizard 185
Rabbit 196
Soccer ball 525
Swim 178, 180-181
Tortoise 187
Urinary 181
Bladder wrack 117
Blade
Butterwort 161
Calligraphy drawing board 445
Danforth anchor 386
Dicotyledon leaf 127
Fencing foil 557
Golf clubs 547
Hockey stick 540
Kayak paddle 560
Leaf surfaces 136, 138
Monocotyledon leaf 127
Propeller 390
Roman rudder 373
Sculling oar 560
Seaweed 116-117
Vegetative reproduction 154
Venus fly trap 160
Volkswagen Beetle 341
Wetland plants 158-159
Wind turbine 604
Blade bearing 604
Blade counterweight 406, 422
Blade hub 604
Blade pitch control 604
Blade-root attachment 422-423
Blade tip sealing shroud 419

Blanking plate 411
Blast bag 396
Blaslocyst 607
Blast-pipe 325
Blending 440
Blériot XI monoplane 401
Blériot, Louis
    Early monoplane 400
    Pioneers of flight 398
Blindage 377
Blind arch
    Asian building 491
    Cathedral dome 487
    Gothic church 470
Blind door 478
Blind pull 336-337
Blind release bar 552
Blinds 603
Blind-side prop 530
Blind spot 241
Blind tracery 493
Blind trefoil 473
Blind window 478
Block and tackle 382-383
Block carving 470
Block cube 478
Block disintegration 282
Block-fault lake 293
Block-fault mountain 62
Blocking pad 550
Blocks 310
Blood cells 253
Blood clotting 253
Blower control 325
Blower isolator valve 325
Blow hole 508
Blowhole 205
Blubber 204
Blue-and-yellow macaw 190
Blue cell 584
Blue-green alga 56, 78
Blue light 318
Blue line 550
Blue supergiant star
    Hertzsprung-Russell
        diagram 23
    Stellar black hole 29
Blue whale 204-205
Bluff 289
Blunt button 556-557
Blu-ray player 584
Board
    Ice hockey rink 550
    Modelling 3
    Pastels 441
Boarding 464
Board mounting 450-451
Boat boom 395
Boatbuilder's tools 374
Boat handling derrick 395
Boat slide 378
Boat winch 394
Bobstay 379
Body
    Anchisaurus 89
    Discus 542
    Dunkeld wet fly 563
    Motorcycle 364-365
    Sauropodomorpha 88
    Stringed instruments 510
Body-bag 604
Body cells 216-217
Body cradle 398
Body drop 556
Body joint
    Flute 508
    Piccolo 508
Body landing gear 572
Body mount 338
Body organs 214-215
Body padding 526
Body sections
    Insect 168
    Scorpion 170
    Spider 170-171
Body-shell 518-519
Bodyshell
    Renault Clio 348-349

Volkswagen Beetle 341
Body tackles 528
Body clip 339
Body temperature
    regulation
    Dinosaurs 92
    Mammals 104
Body wire 557
Bodywork 348-349
    Racing cars 356
    Volkswagen Beetle 341
Bodywork mounting point
    364
Boeing 747-400 412
Bogie axle 326
Bogie frame 325
Bogie main landing gear
    416
Bogie wheel strut 615
Boiler
    Box boiler 392
    Donkey boiler 392
    Steamboat with paddle
        wheels 391
    Steam locomotives
        324-325
Boiler pressure gauge 325
Boiler water level 525
Bole base 432-433
Bollard
    Battleship 395
    Frigate 397
    Mooring and anchoring
        386-387
Bolson 282
Bolster 378
Bolt
    Church of St. Pierre
        499
    Lower deadeye 383
    Shackle 386
    Toaster 598
Bolted anchor 425
Bolt hole
    Drum brake 365
    Mid West rotary engine
        411
    Twin bollards 387
Bolt rest 548
Bolt rope 372, 384
Bolts 548-549
Bomb 404, 408
Bomb aimer's viewing
    panel 408
Bomb door 408
Bomber
    Modern military
        aircraft 420
    World War I aircraft
        404-405
    World War II aircraft
        408-409
Bomb rack 404
Bonaventure mast 377
Bonaventure topcastle 377
Bonaventure topmast 377
Bonaventure top yard 377
Bonaventure yard 377
Bonded brick wall 492
Bonding
    Chemical reactions 312
    Covalent 309
    English bond 485
    Gases 307
    Ionic 308
    Liquids 307
Bone cell 217, 225
Bone marrow smear 225
Bones
    Fossil 278
    Human 224-225, 230,
        232
Bone structure 108
Bone surface 80
Bonnet
    1906 Renault 337
    Ford Model T 339
    Renault Clio 349
    Volkswagen Beetle
        340-341

Bonnet catch 336, 349
Bonnet clip 339
Bonnet-release cable 349
Bonnet-release handle
    541
Bonnet stay 337
Bony crest
    Baryonyx 83
    Corythosaurus 98
    Lambeosaurus 99
    Parasaurolophus 99
Bony dorsal shield 78
Bony fish 180-181
Bony frill 100
Bony nodule
    Pachycephalosaurus
        100
    Prenocephale 100
Bony ridge 100
Bony shelf 100, 101
Bony spike 100
Bony strut 83
Bony studs 92
Bony tendons 96
Boom
    Battleship 394-395
    Curtiss Model-D pusher
        399
    Double topsail
        schooner 385
    Guest boat boom 394
    Hong Kong and
        Shanghai Bank 498
    Longboat 380
    Rigging 382
    Sailing dinghy 561
Boomkin 380
Bootes 18, 21
Boots
    American football 527
    Baseball 537
    Hurling 541
    Riding 554
    Rugby 531
    Ski 552
    Soccer 525
Bordino Steam Carriage
    334-335
Borealis Planitia 35
Borneo 265
Boron 311
Boss
    Church roof 468-469
    Hurley 541
    Viking karv 374
Bothriolepididae 65
Botryoidal habit 270-271
Bottom ballast 377
Bottom bracket 358
Bottom hose 351
Bottom plate 390, 392-393
Bottom race 359
Bottomset strata 283
Boudin 60-61
Boulder beach 295
Boulder clay 286
Bounce pass 535
Boundary
    Cricket 538
    Mantle-crust 39
    Outer core-mantle 39
Boundary line
    Australian rules football
        528
    Badminton 545
    Cricket 538
    Squash 545
Bow
    74-gun ship 381
    Kayak 560
    Sailing dinghy 561
    Stringed instruments
        510
    Wooden sailing ship
        578
Bowball 561
Bow drill 109

Bower anchor
    Battleship 395
    Sailing warship 377
    Wooden sailing ship
        379
Bow front 483
Bowl 445
Bowler 538
Bowline 388, 389
Bowling crease 538
Bowman's capsule 256
Bowman's space 257
Bow ornament 375
Bowpost 561
Bows 548
Bow section 392
Bow-side oar 560
Bowsprit
    Iron paddlesteamer 393
    Longboat 380
    Rigging 382
    Sailing warship 376
    Tea clipper 392
    Wooden sailing ship
        378-379
Bowsprit cap 382
Bowtell moulding 475
Box 477
Box boiler 392
Box fold 61
Box freight car 327
Boxing 556
Box-leaved milkwort 144
Box-section tubular
    cradle frame 364
Box sister keelson 393
Boxwood staff 377
Brace
    Asian building 490
    Barrel vault 485
    Dome 486
    Double topsail
        schooner 385
    "Ellerman Lines" steam
        locomotive 324
    Gothic building 473
    Neoclassical building
        479
    Nineteenth-century
        building 493
    Roman corbita 372
    Sailing warship 377
    Trombone 506
    Wooden sailing ship 578
Brace-and-bit 600-601
Brace block 573
Bracer 548
Brachial artery 253
Brachialis muscle 226
Brachial plexus 238
Brachial valve 278
Brachiocephalic trunk 251
Brachiocephalic vein 253
Brachiopods 278-279
Brachioradialis muscle 226
Brachiosaurus 88, 90-91
Brachytophosaurus 98
Bracing 513
Bracing cable 427
Bracing strut 401-402, 423
Bracing tube 364
Bracing wire
    Blériot XI monoplane
        401
    LVG CVI fighter 405
    Wright Flyer 399
Bracken 121
Bracket
    Baroque church 479
    Cathedral dome 484
    Gothic building 473
    Islamic tomb 489
    Medieval building 466
    Neoclassical building
        478
    Renaissance building
        475
Bracket shell 58
Bracteoles

Dehiscent fruit 151
Ice-plant 129
Live-for-ever 129
Bracts 141-143
    Bromeliad 113
    Dicotyledon flower 127
    Durmast oak 131
    Florists'
        chrysanthemum 129
    Guzmania lingulata 163
    Ice-plant 129
    Indehiscent fruit 150
    Live-for-ever 129
    Peruvian lily 129
    Rose 131
    Slender thistle 129
    Wind-pollinated plant
        144
Bract scales 122
Braided polyester 388
Braided stream 286
Braiding
    Dragon prowhead 374
    River features 290
Brailing rope 372
Brail line 372
Brain
    Bird 189
    Bony fish 181
    Butterfly 169
    Chimpanzee 202
    Crayfish 173
    Dogfish 179
    Dolphin 205
    Domestic cat 195
    Elephant 200
    Hominid 108
    Human 236-237
    Lizard 185
    Octopus 176
    Rabbit 196
    Spider 170
Braincase 108
Brain cavity 100
Brainstem 236
Brake 332, 350
Brake actuating chain 327
Brake arm 552
Brake back plate 340, 350
Brake block 360
Brake bridge 361
Brake cable 365
Brake calliper
    ARV light aircraft 424
    Disc brake 365
    Harley-Davidson FLHS
    Honda VF750 364-365
    Husqvarna Motocross
        TC610 368
    Renault Clio 351
    Suzuki RGV500 368-369
    Wagon bogie 331
Brake cylinder 327,
    350-351
Brake disc
    ARV light aircraft 424
    Renault Clio 351
    Wagon bogie 331
Brake drum 339-340, 342
Brake duct 357
Brake fluid 565
Brake hose 351
Brakeless wheel hub 274
Brake lever
    ARV light aircraft 425
    Benz Motorwagen 335
    Bicycle 359
    Eddy Merckx racing
        bicycle 361
    Harley-Davidson FLHS
    Kirby BSA 369
    Suzuki RGV500 369
    White Steam Car 342
    "Windcheetah" racing
        HPV bicycle 361
Brake master cylinder
    Harley-Davidson FLHS

Electra Glide 363
Honda VF750 364
Suzuki RGV500 368
Brake mount 424
Brake pad
    Disc brake 365
    Eddy Merckx racing
        bicycle 361
    Renault Clio 351
    Wagon bogie 331
Brake pedal
    Harley-Davidson FLHS
    Electra Glide 363
    Honda VF750 364
    Oldsmobile bodywork
        337
    Renault Clio 350
    Steam-powered
        Cugnot 334
    Suzuki RGV500 368
Brake pipe
    ARV light aircraft 424
    BAe-146 components
        414
    Lockheed Electra
        airliner 406-407
Brake pivot bolt 361
Brake plate 365
Brake quadrant 335
Brake rigging
    British Rail Class 20
        diesel engine 327
    "Ellerman Lines" steam
        locomotive 324-325
Brake rod 337, 339
Brake servo 351
Brake shield 351
Brake shoe 350
    "Deltic" diesel-electric
        locomotive 327
    Drum brake 365
    "Ellerman Lines" steam
        locomotive 325
    Renault Clio 350
Brake slip 395
Brake torque arm 364
Brake vacuum pump 324
Braking
    Motorcycle 364
    Train 330
Braking control system
    330
Braking distance 331
Bramante 35
Bramble 130, 146-147
Branched leaf venation 127
Branches
    Bishop pine 124
    Clubmoss 120
    Crab cactus 129
    Dicotyledons 127
    Horsetail 120
    Perennials 130-131
    Seaweed 117
    Sporophore 114
    Woody plants 130-131
Branchial heart 176
Branching bracteole 151
Branchiostegal ray 181
Branchlet 114
Branch trace 125
Brassavola nodosa 162
Brass bevel 336-337
Brass housing for ignition
    cable 343
Brassica sp. 132
Brass instruments 504-505,
    506-507
Brazil 331
Brazilian battleship
    394-395
Brazilian current 296
Brazilian Highlands 264
Bread 598
Breakfast-room 483
Breakwater
    Battleship 395
    Frigate 397
    Single scull 561

Breast
  Bird 188
  Horse 199
  Human 211
Breast auger 374
Breast bone 218
Breast stroke 558-559
Breastwork 380
Breather paper 602
Breather pipe 422
Breccia 276-277
Breech 596
Breech block 396
Breeches 557
Breech wheel 396
Breve rest 502
Brick arch 324
Brick pier 495
Brick vault 492
Brick wall 492
Bridge
  Acoustic guitar 512-513
  Battleship 394-395
  Cello 511
  Double bass 511
  Electric guitar 513
  Frigate 397
  Golf course 546
  London Bridge 466-467
  Medieval castle 467
  Modern building 498
  Viola 511
  Violin 510
Bridge pin 512
Bridges 330
Bridle 555
Bright Angel shale 277
B ring 46-47
Britain 331
Brittle stars 174-175
Broad axe 374
Broad bean 133, 152
Broadcom Persona tablet
  569
Broad disc 79
Broad lace trim 336-337
Broadside 378
Broken pediment 481
Bromeliads 112-113
  Epiphytic 162-163
Bromine 311
Bronchi 254
Bronchial nerve 254
Bronchial tree 254
Bronchial vein 254
Bronchiole and alveoli 254
Bronchus
  Frog 182
  Human 215, 255
Bronze casting 452
Bronze finishing tools 454
Bronze mast truck 572
Bronze statue 455
Broomrape 163
Browband 554-555
Brow horn 102
Brow horn core 103
Brown alga 116
Brown scales 121
Brown seaweed 116-117
Brow ridge
  Australopithecus 108
  Gorilla 203
  Homo sapiens 108
Browser menu 577
Brush 452, 444, 600
Brushbar 592, 593
Brushbar drive belt cover
  593
Brushbar motor control
  593
Brush holder 600
Brushing boot 554
Brush lettering equipment
  444
Brush rest 444
Brush tool articulation
  593
Bryce Canyon 276

Bryophyta 118
Bryophytes 112, 118-119
Bryozoans 279
Bryum sp. 112
Buccal cavity
  Bird 189
  Chimpanzee 202
  Dolphin 205
  Domestic cat 195
  Elephant 200
  Pachycephalosaurus
    100
  Rabbit 196
  Tortoise 187
Buccal mass 176
Buccinator muscle 229
Bucket seat 361
Bucket tappet 344
Bud
  Adventitious 154
  Aechmea miniata 162
  Apical meristem 134
  Begonia 129
  Bishop pine 124
  Broomrape 163
  Clematis flower 131
  Dicotyledons 127
  Durmast oak 131
  Florists'
    chrysanthemum 129
  Horse chestnut 130
  Larkspur 141
  Lily 140
  Lime 143
  London plane 134
  Moss 119
  Oxalis sp.121
  Pine needle 125
  Rhizome 155
  Root tuber 154-155
  Rose 131
  Rowan twig 131
  Stolon 154
  Water lily 159
Buddhist style 490
Budh Planitia 35
Bud scale
  Bishop pine 124
  Dicotyledon stem 127
  London plane 134
  Pine shoot apex 125
Buffer
  "Deltic" diesel-electric
    locomotive 327
  "Ellerman Lines" steam
    locomotive 324-325
  Italian State Railways
    Class 402 328
  "Rocket" steam
    locomotive 324
Buffing pad 328
Bugle 506
Bulb
  Renault Clio 352
  Vegetative reproduction
    154-155
Bulb horn
  1906 Renault 337
  Ford Model T 338
Bulbil 154-155
Bulbourethral gland 259
Bulkhead
  ARV Super 2 425
  Flat freight car 327
Bulkhead stiffener 393
Bulkhead trim 407
Bulldog clip 430
Bullet 397, 549
Bullet block 373
Bullet-shaped guard 278
Bull-head rail 331
Bullnose chisel 452
Bull's-eye 549
Bulwark
  74-gun ship 380
  Ironclad 393
Bumblebee 168
Bumper
  Bus 332-333

Honda Insight 354
Renault Clio 348-349
Volkswagen Beetle 341
Bung 313, 560
Bunkers 546-547
Bunk space 397
Buntline 372
Buon fresco 434-435
Buoy 379
Buoyant wetland plants 158
Burmese pagoda 490
Burning reaction 312, 313,
  315
Burnisher 432, 446
Bursting charge 397
Buses 332-333
Business class cabin 572
Bush 605
Bushes 130-131
Bushing 314
Butt
  Bassoon 508
  Lacrosse crosse 541
  Tennis racket 544
Butt cap 563
Butte
  Igneous rock structures
    274
  Weathering and erosion
    283
Buttercup 127, 132-133
Butterfly 168
Butterfly knot 389
Butterfly plate 382
Butterfly swimming
  stroke 558-559
Butterwort 160-161
Butt extension 563
Buttock
  Horse 198
  Human 210
Button head rivet 392
Button-quilted upholstery
  336
Buttress 484
  Baroque church 478-481
  Dome 486
  Gothic church 470-473
  Medieval building 466,
    468-469
  Nineteenth-century
    building 493
Butt section 562

C

3C275 (quasar) 11
Caarduus tenuiflorus 129
Cab 324, 327
Cabane strut 404
Cabbage 132
Cab-end bogie 327
Cabin
  74-gun ship 380-381
  Iron paddlesteamer
    392-393
  Wooden sailing ship 379
Cabin air-discharge
  aperture 414
Cabin air duct 417
Cabin air-pressure
  discharge valve 413
Cabinet rasp 452
Cabin trim 406-407
Cable 600-601
Cable entry point 598
Cable guide 558-559, 360
Cable holder 395
Cable retaining gland 598
Cables and ducting 602
Cable stop 365
Cacti
  Desert survivors 112
  Dryland adaptation 156
  Herbaceous flowering
    plants 129
Cadmium 311

Cadmium red 456
Cadmium yellow 438
Caecum
  Bird 189
  Brachiosaurus 90
  Chimpanzee 202
  Cow 198
  Digestive 176, 173
  Gut 170
  Human 249
  Octopus 176
  Pyloric 181-174
  Rabbit 196
  Rectal 174
Caelum 18
Caernarvon Castle 466
Caesium 310
Caiman 186-187
Calamus 191
Calcanean tendon
  232-233
Calcaneum 183, 199
Calcareous ooze 299
Calcareous plates 172
Calcareous tufa 284
Calcite (calcium
  carbonate)
  Blue chalk 430
  Carbonates 269
  Cave 284-285
  Fossils 278
  Mohs scale 271
  Sedimentary rocks 277
  Testing candle wax 313
Calcite curtain 285
Calcite ossicle 174
Calcite ridge 284-285
Calcium 310
  Earth's composition 39
  Earth's crust 58
  Seawater salt content
    296
Calcium line 23
Caldera
  Igneous rock structures
    275
  Lake formation 293
  Volcano 272
Caledonian mountains
  Late Carboniferous
    period 67
  Triassic period 69
Calendars 618
Calf 210
Californian purple sea
  urchin 175
Californium 311
Calliactis parasitica 166
Calligraphy 444-445
Calliper assembly 365
Callipers 452
Callisto 44
Caloris Basin 34-35
Caloris Montes 35
Calypte helenae 193
Calyptra 119
Calyx 140
  Allium sp. 143
  Century 144
  Human 256
  Simple succulent berry
    149
Cam 344
Camarasaurus 91
Cambium 126
Cambrian period
  Fossil record 279
  Geological timescale 56
Camcorder 582
Cam cover
  Jaguar straight six
    engine 344
  Jaguar V12 engine 345
  72° VTO engine 356
Camera module 581
Camellia 137
Camels 198-199
Camera 608, 611
  Digital 580-581

Digital video 582-583
Camera pouch 426
Cam follower
  Ford diesel engine 347
  Jaguar straight six
    engine 344
  Jaguar V12 engine 345
  Velocette OHV engine
    367
Cam lobe 344
Camouflage 409
Camouflage coloration
  192
Campaniform capital 458
Campanile 477
Camptosaurus 70, 97
Camshaft 343-345
Camshaft gear 367
Camshaft sprocket 345
Camshaft timing gear 344
Canada 331
Canadian football 524,
  526-527
Canadian pond weed
  158-159
Canal
  Sea urchin 175
  Starfish 174
Canals 42
Canaries current 296
Cancel button 575
Cancellous bone 224
Cancer 18, 21
Candelabrum 476
Candle lamp 335
Candle wax 312-313
Canes Venatici 18, 21
Canine tooth
  Bear 106, 194
  Chimpanzee 202
  Human 246
  Hyaenodon 107
  Lion 194
  Opossum 106
  Smilodon 107
  Toxodon 106
Canis familiaris 195
Canis Major 18, 21
Canis Minor 18, 21
Canister 394
Cannon 376, 394
Cannon bone 198-199
Cannonball bicycle 361
Canoeing 560-561
Canopus 15
Canopy
  1906 Renault 336-337
  ARV light aircraft
    424-425
  Bell-47 helicopter 422
  Daimler engine 343
  Ford Model T 339
  Hawker Tempest
    components 409
  Oldsmobile engine 336
  Schleicher glider 426
  Schweizer helicopter
    423
Canopy latch 425
Canopy rail 409
Canson paper 441
Cant frame 381
Cantilever beam 494
Cantilever brake 358, 361
Cantilever brake boss 359
Cantilevered shade 495
Cantle
  Racing saddle 555
  Showjumping saddle
    554
Canvas
  Acrylic paint 442
  Oil paint 436
  Preparation 437
Canvas shroud 362
Canvas support 437
Canyon
  Sedimentary rocks
    276-277

Weathering and erosion
  282-283
Cap
  Alga 116
  Fungus 114-115
  Radicle tip 153
  Wood capstan 387
  Wooden sailing ship
    378-379
Capacity measurements
  590
Cape gooseberry 149
Capella 18, 21
Cape Royal 277
Capillary fringe 293
Capillary network 254
Capital
  Ancient Egyptian
    building 458-459
  Ancient Greek building
    458, 460-461
  Ancient Roman
    building 458, 463, 465
  Asian building 490, 491
  Baroque church 479,
    481
  Cathedral dome 487
  Domed roof 486
  French temple 485
  Islamic mosque 488
  Medieval building
    467-469
  Neoclassical building
    478, 483
  Ptolemaic-Roman
    period 459
  Renaissance building
    476-477
  Romanesque style 468
Capitate bone 230
Capitulum 129, 142
Cap line 445
Capricornus 19, 20
Capstan 387
  74-gun ship 380
  Iron paddlesteamer 393
  Wooden sailing ship
    379
Capstan screw 514
Capsule
  Dry fruit 150-151
  Moss 112, 119
Captain's cabin 379, 381
Captain's seat 416
Captain's shelter 394
Capybara 196-197
Carapace 172-173, 187
Carbon
  Atomic mass 510
  Bows 548
  Candle wax 312-313
  Coal formation 280
  Minerals 268
  Periodic table 311
  Small stars 24-25
  Structure of red
    supergiant 26
Carbonates 269
Carbon atom 138
Carbon bush 605
Carbon dioxide
  Earth's atmosphere
    300
  Gas 312-313
  Mars' atmosphere 43
  Photosynthesis 138
  Respiratory system 255
  Scrubber compartment
    597
  Structure of comet 53
  Venus' atmosphere 37
Carbon graphite racket
  544
Carbonic acid 284
Carboniferous period
  56-57, 66-67
  Reptiles 80
Carbon ink stick 444
Carbonized wood 430

Carbon monoxide
  Mars' atmosphere 43
  Venus' atmosphere 37
Carbon powder 311
Carbon-rich earth layers 66
Car-building robots 609
Carburettor
  ARV light aircraft 425
  Mid West twin-rotor engine 411
  Pegasus Quasar microlight 427
  Two-stroke engine 366
Carburettor cover 369
Carburettor hot-air intake pipe 422
Carburettor hot air lever 425
Cardiac notch 248
Cardiac region of stomach 179
Cardiac stomach 174
Cardiac vein 250
Carduus tenuiflorus 129
Cargo-carrying boat
  Dhow 376
  Junk 376
  Liberty ship 392
  Roman corbita 372-373
  Tea clipper 392
Cargo derrick 392
Cargo hatch 376
Cargo hold 372, 392
Car, hybrid 354
Caribbean plate 59
Caribbean Sea 264
Carina 21
Carinal canal 120
Carina plate 173
Carling 380
Carmel formation 276
Carnallite 271
Carnassial teeth 194
Carnivores 104, 194-195
  Jurassic period 70
  Theropod 84
  Triassic period 68
Carnivorous plants 160-161
  Pitcher plant 113
Carotid canal 220
Carp 180
Carpals
  Bird 189
  Bird's wing 191
  Domestic cat 195
  Elephant 201
  Frog 183
  Hare 197
  Horse 199
  Kangaroo 206
  Lizard 184
  Platypus 206
  Rhesus monkey 202
  Seal 204
Carp angling 562
Carpathian mountains 77, 265
Carpels 140-141
  Dehiscent fruit 151
  Fertilization 146-147
  Fruit development 148-149
  Insect-pollinated plant 144
  Lemon fruit 148
  Ovary 140
  Stigma 140
  Style 140
Carpel wall 148, 151
Carpophore 151
Carpus
  Crab 172
  Crayfish 173
  Human 218
Carrara white marble 453
Carriage 413, 570
Carriage drivebelt 574

Carriage shaft 571
Carrick bend 387, 589
Carrion crow 193
Carrot 128, 132
Carrying fork 334
Carrying wheel 524
Cartilage
  Auricle 242
  Bony fish 180
  Meatus 242
  Wrist 230
Cartilaginous fish 178-179, 180
Cartouche 458
Caruncle 213
Carved sculpture 452, 453
Carved stone 488
Carvel-built hull 376, 591
Carvel planking 376, 377
Carving
  Asian building 490-491
  Gothic building 470
  Sculpture 452
Carving mallet 452
Caryopses 113, 150
Casa de las Conchas 476
Casa del Fascio 495
Caspian Sea 265
Cassette compartment lid 582
Cassini Division 46, 47
Cassini space probe 614
Cassiopeia 19
Cassowaries 188
Cast alloy wheel 546
Cast aluminium wheel spider 336
Castanea sativa 136, 150
Castanets 504, 517
Casting 452, 454
Cast-iron 492-493
Cast-iron chair 331
Cast iron cylinder barrel 363
Castle-deck gunport 376-377
Castles, 374, 466-467
Castor 18, 21
Castor canadensis 197
Cat 104, 194-195
Catalyst 355
Catalytic converter 344, 350, 556
Catamaran 560
Cataphoresic coating 348
Cataphyll 152
Cat block 381
Catcher's mask 536
Catch glove 550
Catena 372
Catenary 328, 330
Caterpillar 168, 169, 611
  Eggs 192
Catharine 40
Cathead
  74-gun ship 380
  Battleship 395
Cathedral of St. Lazare 468
Cations 308
Catkin 144
Catted anchor 381
Cattle 104, 198
Caucasus 265
Caudal fin 178, 179, 180-181
Caudal musculature 90, 95
Caudal plate 92-93
Caudal spike 92-93
Caudal vertebrae
  Ankylosaurus 95
  Archaeopteryx 85
  Crocodile 186
  Diplodocus 90
  Domestic cat 195
  Elephant 201
  Eryops 81
  Euoplocephalus 95

Gallimimus 86
Hare 197
Horse 199
Iguanodon 96, 97
Kangaroo 206
Kentrosaurus 93
Lizard 184-185
Parasaurolophus 98
Plateosaurus 89
Platypus 206
Rhesus monkey 202
Seal 204
Stegoceras 101
Stegosaurus 93
Struthiomimus 87
Triceratops 102
Tuojiangosaurus 93
Tyrannosaurus 84-85
Westlothiana 81
Caudate nucleus 237
Caudex 113
Caudo-femoral muscle 97
Cauliculus 460
Caulophryne jordani 180
Cave bear skull 77
Caves 284-285
  Coastline 294-295
  Glacier 286
Cavetto moulding
  Ancient Egyptian building 458-459
  Baroque church 479
  French temple 485
  Gothic building 472
  Renaissance building 477
Cavies 196
Cayley, Sir George 398
CCD (Charge-Coupled Devices) 570
C clef 502
CD/DVD drive 567
Cedar-tree laccolith 274
Ceilings 463, 484
Celestial equator
  Stars of northern skies 18-19
  Stars of southern skies 20-21
Celestial poles 18
Celestial sphere 18
Cell
  Alga 116-117
  Body 217
  Building 469, 485
  Chusan palm leaf 130
  Clubmoss stem 120
  Collar 166
  Dicotyledon 126-127
  Epidermal 166
  Epiphytic orchid 162
  Fern rachis 121
  Horsetail stem 120
  Leaf 126, 139
  Marram grass 113
  Monocotyledon 126-127
  Moss 119
  Mushroom 115
  Photosynthesis 138-139
  Pine 124-125
  Pore 166
  Root 132-133
  Root tip 152
  Sinus 112
  Spirogyra sp. 117
  Stem 134-135
  Wetland plants 158-159
Cella 461, 463, 485
Cell body 239
Cell membrane 217
Cell nuclear membrane 216
Cell nucleus 217
Cell nucleus residue 234
Cello 503-505, 510
Cells 607
Cellulose fibre insulation 602
Cell wall

Alga 112, 116
Leaf 159
Palisade mesophyll 139
Root 132
Spirogyra sp. 117
Stem surface 156
Celsius temperature scale 590
Cement-based adhesive 450
Cement gland 173
Cement-rendered wall 494
Cenozoic era 57, 74, 76
  Fossil record 279
Censer 488
Centaurium erythraea 144
Centaurus 18, 21
Centaurus A (radio galaxy) 13
Centaurus and Crux 21
Central Asia 64
Central bulge 12, 14
Central canal 238
Central computer control 328
Central deflector 612
Central electrode 306
Central nervous system 238
Central peak
  Degas and Brönte 34
  Venus' craters 36
Central retinal artery 240
Central retinal vein 240
Central shield 187
Central sulcus 236-237
Centre
  American football 526
  Australian football 528
  Basketball 532
  Canadian football 526
  Lacrosse 541
  Netball 535
  Rugby 530
Centre-board 561
Centre buck-eye coupler 326
Centre circle
  Australian rules football 528
  Basketball 532
  Ice hockey 550
  Netball 535
  Soccer 524
Centre console 553
Centre court 545
Centred rudder 375
Centre element 599
Centre field 536
Centre flag 529
Centre forward 540
Centre gangway 329
Centre Georges Pompidou 496-497
Centre girder 393
Centre half 540
Centre half-back 528, 529
Centre half-forward 528, 529
Centre line 413, 415
  Fencing piste 557
  Ice hockey 550
  Soccer 524
Centre-line beam 426-427
Centre line keelson 393
Centrifugal brake 562
Centrifugal compressor 418
Centrifugal effect 297
Centriole 217
Centripetal river drainage 288
Centrum 187
Cephalapsis 65
Cephalic groove 173
Cephalic vein
  Human 253
  Octopus 176

Cephalopods 176, 279
Cephalothorax
  Crayfish 173
  Malacostraca 172
  Scorpion 170
  Shrimp 172
  Spider 170-171
Cepheus 19
Ceramic end-piece 319
Ceratopsia 83, 103
Ceratosauria 83
Ceraunius Tholus 43
Cercidyphyllum sp. 72
Cerebellum 212, 236-237, 238
Cerebral areas 237
Cerebral ganglion 169, 177
Cerebral vessel 257
Cerebrum 212, 236-237, 238
Cereoid cactus 129
Cerium 310
Ceropegia woodii 157
Ceruchi 372
Cerussite 269
Cervical musculature
  Euoplocephalus 94
  Gallimimus 86
Cervical nerves 258
Cervical plate 92-93
Cervical rib 84, 96, 100-101, 103
Cervical vertebrae
  Archaeopteryx 85
  Arsinoitherium 104
  Bird 189
  Brachiosaurus 91
  Crocodile 186
  Domestic cat 195
  Elephant 201
  Eryops 80
  Hare 197
  Horse 199
  Human 212, 222, 245
  Iguanodon 96
  Kangaroo 206
  Kentrosaurus 93
  Lizard 184
  Parasaurolophus 99
  Plateosaurus 88
  Platypus 206
  Rhesus monkey 202
  Seal 204
  Stegoceras 101
  Stegosaurus 93
  Struthiomimus 87
  Toxodon 106
  Tuojiangosaurus 93
  Tyrannosaurus 84
Cervix 258-259
Cervus elephas 199
Cetaceans 204-205
Cetiosaurus 91
Cetorhinus maximus 179
Cetus 19, 20
Chaffinch 193
Chain
  Bicycle 358-359, 360-361
  Drum kit 518
  Wheel and axle 320
  Wooden sailing ship 378
Chain bobstay 382
Chain drive
  Motorcycle clutch 362
  Werner motorcycle 366
  Wright Flyer 398-399
Chain locker 393
Chain motif 491
Chain plate 382
Chain swivel 386
Chain wale 376-377
Chaja 489
Chalcedony 271
Chalk 431
  Tempera 432
  Gesso 434

Pastel making 440
Fresco 434
Sedimentary rocks 277
Chamber
  Building 465, 491
  Gun turret 396
Chambers
  Seaweed 116
  Stomach 198
  Substomatal 139
Chamfered corner 485, 488, 494
Championship golf courses 546
Change 321
Chang Jiang 265
Channel
  74-gun ship 381
  Sailing warship 376-377
  Temple of Neptune 460
  Wooden sailing ship 378
Channelled wrack 116
Chapel
  Baroque church 479
  Gothic church 470
  Medieval church 469
Chapel pier 467
Chaplet 454
Chapter-house 472
Charcoal drawing 430-431
Charentais melon 149
Charge
  Four-stroke cycle 343
  Modern engines 344
Charged atom 306, 308
Charged particle 316
Charging with ball 533
Charon 50
Chart house 394
Chase 395
Chassis
  Digital camera 580
  First cars 334-335
  Ford Model T 338 .
  Kirby BSA sidecar 369
  Microwave combination oven 596
  Monocoque 363
  Motorcycle 362, 364-365
  Microsoft Zune HD 587
  Oldsmobile chassis 337
  Panhard-system
  Volkswagen Beetle 340
  White Steam Car 342
Chassis earth terminal 597
Chassis electrical plug 357
Chassis frame 338
Chassis number 327
Chataya arch 491
Châteaux 474, 476-477
Chat selector button 576
Chattra 491
Chattravali 490-491
Chauffeur's seat 334
Checkerbloom 156
Check pawl 562
Cheek
  74-gun ship 381
  Dunkeld wet fly 563
  Horse 199
  Human 212
  Running block 383
  Sailmaker's mallet 384
  Stegosaurus 92
Cheek horn 103
Cheek-piece
  Harness racer 555
  Showjumper 554
Cheek pouch 98, 196
Cheek teeth
  Ankylosaurs 92
  Carnivores 194
  Ornithopods 96
  Tetralophodon 104

Theropods 84
Cheese 382, 588-589
Cheiracanthus 65
Cheirolepis 65
Chekhov 35
Chela 170, 172, 173
Chelicera 79
Chelicerae 170-171
Chelicerates 279
Cheliped
  Crab 172
  Crayfish 173
Chelonia 186.
Chemical bond 307
Chemical change 280-281
Chemical energy 314-315
Chemical equations 312
Chemical properties
  Electrons 308, 310
  Substances 306
Chemical reactions
  312-313
Chemical sedimentary
  rocks 276
Chemical symbols 312,
  591
  Periodic table 310-311
Chemical weathering 282
Chemise 466-467
Chemistry symbols 621
Cherry 148
Cherry wood 512
Chert 277
Cherub 472
Chervil 135
Chest
  Gorilla 203
  Human 211, 214
  Lion 194
Chestnut 198
Chest padding 551
Chest manual 514
Chest pass 532, 535
Chest protector 527
Chevet 469
Chevron 81, 85, 87, 89, 93,
  95-96, 98, 101-102
Chevron fold 61
Chevron-tread tyre 336
Chi1 Orionis 18
Chi2 Orionis 18
Chiastolite hornfels 275
Chihuahuan Desert 264
Chile 331
Chimney
  Bordino Steam Carriage
  334
  "Ellerman Lines" steam
  locomotive 325
  Iron paddlesteamer 393
  "Rocket" steam
  locomotive 324
Chimney-shaft 467
Chimney-stack 476, 483
Chimpanzee 202-203
Chin
  Bird 188
  Human 211, 212
China
  Ball games 524
  Late Carboniferous
  period 66-67
  Middle Ordovician
  period 64-65
  Ornithopod 96
  Railway track gauge 331
  Thyreophorans 92
Chinese calendar 618
Chinese characters 445
Chinese junk 376
Chinese white 438
Chin groove 199
Chin guard 553
Chin gun turret 408
Chinle formation 276
Chin rest 510-511
Chin spoiler 346
Chipmunk 196
Chirostenotes 87
Chisel 452-453

Chlamydomonas sp. 116
Chlorenchyma 120
Chloride 296
Chlorine 311
Chlorophyll 138
  Chloroplast 139
  Photosynthesis pigment
  116, 138, 162
Chlorophyta 116
Chloroplast 138-139
  Alga 112
  Chlamydomonas sp.
  116
  Envelope 139
  Epiphytic orchid 162
  Internal view 139
  Spirogyra sp. 117
Choanocyte 166
Choir 468-469, 470, 472
Choir manual 514
Choir-screen 470
Choir-stall 470
Choir stop 514
Chondrichthyes 178
Chondrostean fish 69
Chong Ch'ol 35
Chordae tendineae 251
Chorioallantoic
  membrane 192
Chorion 260
Choroid 240
Christian architecture 468
Christmas rose 139
Chromate ion 312
Chrome passivation 348
Chrome plating 347
Chrome trim strip 341
Chromium
  Mineralization zones
  281
  Oxide 312
  Periodic table 310
Chromosphere 32-33
Chrysalis 168
*Chrysanthemum
  morifolium* 129
Chryse Planitia 43
Chrysler Building 495
Chrysocyon brachyurus
  195
Chuck 601
Chuck key 601
Chung-ta-wei 376
Church
  Santa Sophia 487
  Sorbonne 486
  St. Botolph 473
  St. Eustache 477
  St. George in the East
  478, 481
  St. Maclou 470, 472
  St. Maria della Salute
  478
  St. Maria della Vittoria
  478
  St. Paul-St. Louis
  478-479
  St. Pierre de Libreville
  496, 499
  St. Serge 469
Church-roof boss 468
Chusan palm 127, 130
Ciconia ciconia 188
Cigarette lighter adapter
  and speaker cable 590
Ciliary body 241
Cincture 477
Cinder 272
Cinder cone
  Igneous rock structures
  274
  Volcanic structure 273
Cinema, home 584-585
Cinnabar 271
Cinquefoil moulding 471
Circle 479, 622
Circle area measurement
  590
Circle pad 579

Circuit 316
Circuit board 579, 582,
  585, 589
Circuit board plug 596
Circuit breaker 314
Circular mountain lake
  293
Circulatory system
  252-255
Circumference 622
Cirque 286-287
Cirque formation 287
Cirque Napoleon 478-479
Cirri 172
Cirrus cloud
  Neptune 50
  Structure of Mars 43
  Weather 302-303
Citrus limon 148
City bus 332
Civet 194
Cladding 494, 496,
  498-499
Cladode 129
Cladonia floerkeana 114
Cladonia portentosa 114
Clam 176
Clamp
  Cross-stave 377
  Intaglio printing 313
  U-tube 446
Clarinet 503-504, 508
Classical-style
  architecture 474, 478,
  482
Clastic sedimentary rocks
  276
Claves 517
Clavicle
  Bird 189
  Bony fish 181
  Eryops 80
  Human 211, 218
  Kangaroo 206
  Rhesus monkey 202
Clavius 40
Clavus 373
Claw
  Albertosaurus 84
  Anchisaurus 89
  Archaeopteryx 85
  Beetle 168
  Bird 188
  Bumblebee 168
  Caiman 187
  Chick 193
  Crab 172
  Crayfish 173
  Dinosaur 83
  Herrerasaurus 86
  Kangaroo 207
  Lizard 184
  Marble sculpture 452
  Pachycephalosaurus
  100
  Psittacosaurus 103
  Scorpion 170
  Spider 171
  Stegoceras 101
  Terrapin 187
  Tyrannosaurus 84
Clawed feet 190, 206
Clay 298
Clay daub 465
Clay modelling 452, 455
Clay mounds 286
Clear space 534
Cleavage 270
Clef 502
Cleithrolepis granulatus
  69
Cleithrum 80
Clematis 130-131, 137
Clench nail 375
Cleomedes 40
Cleopatra Patera 37

Clerestory 459, 472, 479
Clew 373
Clewline 379, 385
Cliffs
  Coastlines 294-295
  River's stages 289
  Sedimentary rocks
  276-277
Climate
  Carboniferous period
  66
  Geological time 56
  Oceans and seas 296
  Weather 302
Climatic change
  Coastline 294
  Geological time 56
Clincher wheel 339
Clinker-built hull 375
Clinker-built oak planking
  375
Clints 284-285
Clitoris 258
Cloaca
  Bird 189
  Brachiosaurus 90
  Dogfish 179
  Euoplocephalus 95
  Frog 182
  87
  Lizard 185
  Spider 170
  Tortoise 187
Cloacal opening 185
Clock operator 532
Clock tower 493
Cloister 472
Cloning technology
  606-607
Close-stowing anchor 386
Cloud deck 50-51
Cloud features
  Neptune 50
  Saturn 46
  Venus 36
Clouds
  Earth's atmosphere 301
  Jupiter 44-45
  Mars 42-43
  Neptune 50-51
  Saturn 46-47
  Uranus 48-49
  Venus 36-37
  Water cycle 288
  Weather 302-303
Cloud shadow 50
Clouds of dust and gas
  Life of massive star 24
  Milky Way 14-15
  Nebulae and star
  clusters 16-17
  Origin and expansion of
  Universe 11
  Small stars 24
Cloud-top temperature
  Structure of Jupiter 45
  Structure of Neptune 51
  Structure of Saturn 47
  Structure of Uranus 49
Clove hitch 388
Cloven hoof 198
Clubmosses 64, 66,
  120-121
Clump cathead 395
Clustered column 469
Clutch 364, 566
Clutch and flywheel 340
Clutch cable 350, 363, 365
Clutch centre plate 351
Clutch cover 563
Clutch lever 363, 369
Clutch pedal 350
Clutch pressure plate 351
Clutch release bearing
  351

Earth's evolution 57
  Mineral resources
  280-281
  Power stations 314
  Sedimentary rocks 276
  Steam locomotive 324
Coal-forming forests 57
Coal measures 61
Coaming 381
Coastal spring 292
Coaster 374-375
Coastlines 294-295
  Cave 284
Cobalt
  Mineralization zones
  281
  Periodic table 311
Cobra lily 160-161
Coccosteus 65
Coccygeal cornu 223
Coccygeal vertebrae 222
Coccyx 218, 222
Cochlea 242-243
Cocking lever 549
Cockpit
  Airbus 380 573
  Avro biplane 403
  Kayak 560
  LVG CVI fighter 405
  Modern military
  aircraft 420-421
  Sailing dinghy 561
  Schleicher glider 426
Cockpit canopy 409
Cockpit coaming 425
Cocoa 148
Coconino sandstone 276
Cocos nucifera 155
Cocos plate 59
Cod 180
Codiaeum variegatum 136
Coelenterata 166
Coeliac trunk 256-257
Coelodonta 76-77, 104
Coelophysidae 69
Coelurus 87
Coenobium 116
Coffer 463, 485
Coffered vault 485
Coffering 475
Cogged drive belt 344
Coil spring
  "Ellerman Lines" steam
  locomotive 324
  Motorcycle 364
Coil suspension spring
  "Deltic" diesel-electric
  locomotive 327
  "Eurostar" multi-
  voltage electric train
  329
  Wagon bogie 331
Coke hopper 334
Cold air intake 420
Cold-air unit 417
Cold front 302-303
Cold occlusion 302
Cold-water pipe 405
Cold-water upwelling 296
Coleoptera 168
Coleus sp. 134
Collagen and elastic fibres
  252
Collapsed crater 293
Collar
  Cathedral of Notre
  Dame de Paris 473
  Sea anemone 167
  Snail 177
Collar-beam 473
Collar bone 211, 218
Collar cell 166
Collar of horsetail 120
Collecting duct 256
Collecting tubule 256
Collective lever 422
Collenchyma 126, 134-135
Colliding plates 272
Colloids 306

Colon
  Butterfly 169
  Cow 198
  Human 215, 249, 259
  Rabbit 196
Colonette
  Gothic church 473
  Islamic building 488
  Medieval building
  467-469
  Neoclassical building
  479
  Renaissance building
  474
Colonnade
  Ancient Greek building
  460-461
  Ancient Roman
  building 462-463
  Cathedral dome 484,
  487
  Neoclassical building
  483
Colonnaded storey 494
Colorado River
  Earth's evolution 57
  Grand Canyon 277
  Valley 277
Colosseum 462, 464-465
Colour 270
Colour changes 312-313
Colour ink cartridge 574
Colour ink-cartridge
  clamp 574
Colour light signals 330
Colour wheel 439
Colpus 144
Columba 18, 21
Columella 119, 145
Column
  Ancient Egyptian
  building 458-459
  Ancient Greek building
  458, 460
  Ancient Roman
  building 458, 462-463,
  465
  Baroque church
  480-481
  Cathedral dome 487
  Cave system 285
  French temple 485
  Gothic church 473
  Islamic mosque 488
  Medieval church
  468-469
  Modern building
  496-498
  Monocotyledonous
  flower 126
  Neoclassical building
  478-479, 483
  Nineteenth-century
  building 492-493
  Renaissance building
  477
Coma 52-53
Coma Berenices 18, 21
Combat sports 556-557
Combination lever 325
Combustion 326
Combustion chamber
  Capacity 366-567
  Iron paddlesteamer
  393
  Jaguar straight six
  engine 344
  Jet engines 418-419
Combustion cycle 410
Comets 30, 52-53
Common bile duct 252
Common blackheaded
  gull 189
Common brittle star 175
Common carotid artery
  215, 251, 253
Common centaury 144
Common crus 243
Common digital extensor

muscle 84, 97
Common elder 143
Common English ivy 131
Common horse chestnut 130
Common horsetail 120
Common Iguana 82
Common iliac artery 215, 253, 257
Common iliac vein 215, 253, 257
Common ivy 137
Common lime 143
Common link 586
Common mulberry 130
Common peroneal nerve 238
Common rafter 473, 486
Common starfish 175
Common tern 193
Common time 502
Communication 108
Communications aerial 424
Commutator 600
Commuters 363
Compact bone 224-225
Compact disc 584, 586
Companion cells 152-154
Companion ladder 381
Companion way 380
Company logo 572
Compass
Battleship 394
Vault decoration 485
Compass and rangefinder platform 394
Competent bed rock 61
Competition motorcycles 568-569
Competitions
Archery 548
Diving 558
Judo 556
Rowing 560
Skiing 552-553
Complete mesentery 167
Composite capital 478
Composite column 478
Composite pilaster 478
Composite volcano 272
Composter 602
Compound eye
Beetle 168
Bumblebee 168
Butterfly 169
Crab 172
Crayfish 172
Damselfly 168
Malacostraca 172
Shrimp 172
Compound inflorescence 131, 142
Compound leaf 130-131, 136
Compound pier 468-469
Compound pulleys 320
Compounds 268, 306, 308
Compound succulent fruit 148-149
Compound umbel 143
Compressible gas 365
Compression
Faults and folds 60
Glacier 286
Igneous and metamorphic rocks 274
Mineral resources 280
Mountain building 62
Rock cycle 266
Compression ring
Ford diesel engine 347
Jaguar straight six engine 344
Compression stroke 343
Compressor 418
Compressor piston 344
Compsognathus 70
Computer
and E-mail program 677

Electronic instruments 520
Laptop 567
Modern bodywork 348
Tablet 568-569
Computerized ignition system 344
Concave brace 477
Concave moulding 482
Concave wall 478, 481
Concealed lighting 572
Conceptacles 116-117
Concert grand piano 515
Concha
Ear 242
Nasal 221, 241
Conchoidal fracture
Extrusive igneous rocks 275
Fracture 270
Sedimentary rocks 277
Concorde 416-417
Concrete 492, 494, 496-499
Concrete shielding 314
Concrete shoe 499
Concrete track 328
Concrete wall 463, 465, 496
Condensation 307
Nuclear power station 314
Testing candle wax 313
Condensation level 302
Condenser 342
Condenser aperture 610
Condenser housing 611
Condenser lens 611
Conducting tissue 119
Conductor
Electrical circuit 316
Generating magnetism 317
Orchestra 504
Conductor's stand 505
Condylactis sp. 166
Condyle
Carnivore 194
Human 220
Cone 623
Cones
Bishop pine 124
Gymnosperms 122
Igneous and metamorphic rocks 274
Pine 122
Scots pine 122
Smooth cypress 123
Volcanoes 272-273
Welwitschia 123
Yew 123
Cone sheet 274
Cone stalk 124
Cone surface area measurement 590
Cone volume measurement 590
Congas 519
Congo Basin 59
Conical bore 507
Conical dome 476
Conical map projection 265
Conical spire 466, 476
Conical volcano 272
Conifer
Cretaceous period 72
Earth's evolution 57
Fossil record 279
Gymnosperm 122-125
Jurassic period 70
Triassic period 68
Coniferophyta 122
Conjugation 117
Conjunctiva 241
Connecting rod
Bordino Steam Carriage 334
Flat-four cylinder arrangement 340

Four-stroke cycle 343
Iron paddlesteamer 392
Jaguar straight six engine 344
Jaguar V12 engine 345
Mid West two-stroke engine 410
Steamboat with paddle wheels 391
Connecting wire 598
Connective tissue cells
Connectors 569
Conning tower 394, 397
Conocephalum conicum 118
Con-rod 340, 343-345
Conservation of Energy Law 314
Conservatory 602, 603
Console 579
Constellations 18-21, 613
Constratum 373
Constrictor snakes 184
Construction sculpture 452
Contact 352
Contact grid 605
Contact metamorphism 274
Contant d'Ivry 478
Contest area 556
Contests
Head-butting 100
Shooting 548
Continental crust 58-59
Mineralization zones 281
Mountain building 62-63
Ocean floor 298
Continental drift 58
Continental margin sediments 299
Continental rise 298
Continental Sea 75, 75
Continental shelf
Ocean floor 298
Prehistoric Earth 69, 71
Rock cycle 267
Continental slope
Ocean floor 298
Offshore currents 296
Rock cycle stages 267
Continents
Formation of the Earth 38, 56
Earth's physical features 264-265
Geological time 56
Contrabassoon 504-505
Contractile vacuole 116
Control cabinet 396
Control circuit 328
Control buttons 585
Control column
ARV light aircraft 425
BE 2B bomber 404
Curtiss biplane 398-399
Control-column aperture 425
Control flag 552
Controller 352
Control line 561
Control panel 571, 595, 596
Control panel and disc tray cover 584
Control panel boards 597
Control panel fascia 597
Control panel microchips 596
Control panels 595
Control panel wiring 595
Control platform 590
Control reservoir drain 326
Control rod 314, 424
Control room 397
Control stalk 353

Convection cell 33
Convection current 38
Convective zone 24, 33
Converging plates 63
Conversion 530
Convex portico 483
Cook/grill tray 596
Cooking 108
Coolant 314
Coolant inlet 424
Coolant jacket 410-411
Coolant outlet
ARV light aircraft 424
Jaguar V12 engine 345
Mid West two-stroke engine 410
Coolant passage 346
Coolant pipe 354
Coolant pump 410
Coolant rail 345
Cooling device 611
Cooling fan 345, 567
Cooling fin
Drum brake 365
Mid West rotary engine 411
Two-stroke engine 366
Velocette OHV engine 367
Cooling intake 534
Cooling perforations 597
Cooling tank 355
Cooling tower
Centre Georges Pompidou 496-497
Nuclear power station 314
Cooling water tank 335
Co-orbital moons 46
Coping-stone 495
Copper
Mineral resources 280-281
Minerals 268
Periodic table 311-312
Copper body-shell 519
Copper face 384
Copper nitrate solution 312
Copper ore 306
Copper plate nib 444
Copper sheathing 392
Copper sulphate 313
Coprates Chasma 43
Copulatory bursa
Butterfly 169
Snail 177
Coracoid
Bird 189
Diplodocus 90
Euoplocephalus 94
Gallimimus 86
Triceratops 102
Turtle 187
Tyrannosaurus 84
Coral 78, 166-167
Atoll development 299
Fossil record 279
Corallina officinalis 117
Coral reef
Earth's evolution 56
Ocean floor 298
Cor Anglais 504-505, 508
Corbel
Cathedral dome 487
Medieval building 467, 469
Neoclassical building 482
Nineteenth-century building 493
Renaissance building 477
Rococo style 478
Corbita 372-373
Cor Caroli 18, 21

Cordaites 67
Cordate leaf bases 136-137
Cordite case 396
Cordite handling room 396
Cordite supply shuttle 396
Core
Earth 38-39
Helix Nebula 17
Massive stars 26-27
Moon 40
Neutron stars and black holes 28-29
Small stars 24-25
Structure of comet 53
Structure of Earth 39
Structure of Jupiter 45
Structure of Mars 43
Structure of Mercury 35
Structure of Neptune 51
Structure of Pluto 51
Structure of Saturn 47
Structure of Uranus 49
Structure of Venus 37
Core-engine jet pipe 412, 415
Core jet pipe 419
Core temperature
Structure of Earth 39
Structure of Jupiter 45
Structure of main sequence star 24
Structure of red giant 25
Structure of red supergiant 26
Structure of Saturn 47
Structure of Sun 33
Structure of Uranus 49
Corinthian capital 460, 463, 479, 481
Corinthian column 463-464, 479-480
Corinthian entablature 463
Corinthian order 460, 462
Corinthian pilaster 463-464, 480-481
Coriolis force 296-297, 300
Cork
Oboe 508
Stems 154-155
Woody dicotyledons 127
Corms 154-155
Corn 112
Cornea 241
Corner arc 524
Corner seal 347
Cornet 506
Cornice
Ancient Egyptian temple 458-459
Ancient Greek building 460-461
Ancient Roman building 462-465
Asian building 491
Baroque church 479-481
Dome 484, 486
French temple 485
Gothic church 470-473
Islamic tomb 489
Medieval building 466-467, 469
Neoclassical building 478-479, 482-483
Nineteenth-century building 493
Renaissance building 474-477
Twentieth-century building 494
Cornucopia 480
Corolla 140, 142-143
Corona
Earth's atmosphere 300
Palazzo Strozzi 475

Sun's atmosphere 32-33
Corona Australis 19
Corona Borealis 18, 21
Coronal section through brain 236-237
Coronal suture 220
Coronary artery 250-251, 253
Coronary sinus 250
Corona temperature 33
Coronet 198, 554
Coronoid process 194, 220
Corpus albicans 258
Corpus callosum 236-237
Corpus cavernosum 259
Corpus luteum 258
Corpus spongiosum 259
Corridor 465
Corries 286-287
Corrugator supercilii muscle 228-229
Cortex
Apical meristem 134
Canadian pond weed 158-159
Clubmoss stem 120
Dicotyledon 127
Epiphytic orchid 162
Hair 234
Horsetail stem 120
Kidney 256
Lichen 114
Monocotyledon 127
Moss 119
Pine 125
Radicle 152
Rhizome 155
Root 152-153
Stems 154-155
Water hyacinth 158
Water lily 159
Corundum 271
Corvus 18, 21
Corvus corone 193
Corynactis viridis 166
Corythosaurus 96, 98
Cosmic background radiation 10
Cosmic ray 301
Costal cartilage 218
Costal facet 223
Costal margin 168, 169
Costal shield 187
Cotter pin 383
Cotton duck canvas 437, 443
Cotyledon 126, 152-153
Development 132
Dicotyledon 126
Dry fruit seed 150-151
Embryo development 147
Epigeal germination 153
Hypogeal germination 152
Monocotyledon 126
Pine 122
Root development 132
Seed 152-153
Succulent fruit seed 148-149
Couch grass 113
Coucy-le-Chateau 466-467
Coulomb 316
Counter
Calligraphy lettering 445
Counterbalancing weight 506
Counter, galley 573
Counter rail 381
Counter timber 381
Counterweight
Flat-four cylinder arrangement 340
Four-stroke cycle 343
Hong Kong and Shanghai Bank 498

Jaguar V12 engine 345
Output shaft 347
Relief printing press 449
Rotary engine output shaft 410
Trojan engine 342
V12 cylinder arrangement 345
Country code 576
Coupling
Conventional hookscrew 328
"Ellerman Lines" steam locomotive 324
Coupling rod 325
Couronnement 472
Course
Asian building 491
Medieval building 466-467
Neoclassical building 483
Nineteenth-century building 492-493
Court referee 535
Court
Basketball 532
Handball 535
Netball 535
Volleyball 534
Court seal 375
Courtship display 188
Courtyard 465, 466
Coussinet 460
Covalent bonding 308-309
Cove 581
Coved dome 478, 485
Cover point 541
Cover support 570
Coverts 188, 191
Cow 198
Cowhide face 384
Cowling fastener 408
Cowling panel 407, 412
Coxa
Beetle 168
Crayfish 173
Scorpion 170
Coxswain 560
CQR anchor 386
Crab 172
Crab apple 126
Crab cactus 129
Crab Nebula 28
Cracks 284-285
Cradle frame
Honda VF750 364
Weslake Speedway motorcycle 369
Cradling 541
Crane 498
Cranial nerves 238
Cranium
Ankylosaurus 94
Archaeopteryx 85
Australopithecus 108
Bat 105
Camarasaurus 91
Diplodocus 90
Elephant 201
Eryops 80
Euoplocephalus 94
Homo sapiens 108
Hyaenodon 107
Iguanodon 96
Kentrosaurus 93
Lambeosaurus 99
Moeritherium 105
Opossum 106
Pachycephalosaurus 100
Panoplosaurus 94
Parasaurolophus 99
Plateosaurus 88
Prenocephale 100
Protoceratops 102
Stegoceras 100
Stegosaurus 93

Struthiomimus 87
Styracosaurus 102
Toxodon 106
Triceratops 103
Tuojiangosaurus 93
Tyrannosaurus 84
Crank 320
Brace-and-bit 601
Eddy Merckx racing bicycle 360
"Ellerman Lines" steam locomotive 325
Crank bolt 358, 360
Crankcase
BE 2B bomber 404
British Rail Class 20 diesel engine 327
Humber engine 343
Jaguar straight six engine 344
Jaguar V12 engine 345
Mid West two-stroke engine 410
Oldsmobile engine 336
Trojan engine 342
Velocette OHV engine 367
Werner motorcycle 362
Crankcase breather pipe 402
Crank handle 339
Crankpin 345
Crankshaft
Benz Motorwagen 335
Flat-four cylinder arrangement 340
Four-stroke cycle 343
Iron paddlesteamer 392
Mid West two-stroke engine 410
Oklsmobile engine 336
Oscillating steam engine 391
Straight four cylinder arrangement 345
Two-stroke engine 366
Velocette OHV engine 367
Crankshaft counterweight 344
Crankshaft pulley 344, 355
Crash bar 362-363
Crash cymbal 518
Crash helmet 552
Crater
Mercury's North Pole 35
Northern stars 18
Oceanus Procellarum 40
Southern stars 21
Surface features of Mars 42
Crayfish 172-173
Crayon 448
Creative Zen Stone 586
Creeping stems 154
Clubmoss 120
Strawberry 128
Cremasteric fascia 259
Cremocarp 150-151
Crenellation 466
Crepidoma 461, 481
Crescent-shaped dune 283
Crest
Building 479, 488, 493
Fold formation 60
Horse 199
Lizard 184
Ship's shield 395
Crested porcupine 197
Cretaceous period 72-73
Fossil record 279
Geological time 56-57
Crevasse 287
Crevice 284
Crevice tool 593
Crew handrail 612, 613

Crew's seat 416
Cricket (animal) 168
Cricket (game) 558-559
Cricoid cartilage 255
Cricothyroid ligament 244
Cricothyroid muscle 229, 244-245
C ring 46-47
Cringle 384
Crista 242
Crocket 471-472
Crocodile clip connector 316
Crocodiles 68, 73, 186-187
Crocodylus niloticus 186
Crocoite 271
Cronaca 474
Crook 508
Crop
Bird 189
Butterfly 169
Octopus 176
Snail 177
Crop-duster 410
Crops 315
Crop-sprayer 410, 422
Cross
Baroque church 480
Dome 486-487
Motif 472
Crossandra nilotica 145
Crossbar
Calligraphy characters 445
Eddy Merckx racing bicycle 360
Gaelic football 529
Handball 535
Hurling 541
Rugby 550
Cross-bed set 283
Crossbow 548
Cross-bracing 497-499
Cross-country skiing 548
Crosse 540-541
Crossing 469-470, 477
Crossing tower 468
Cross-member 538-539
Cross-piece 376-377, 387
Cross-pollination 144
Cross-staff 377
Cross-stave 376-377
Cross tube 423
Crosswise strut 512
Crotchet rest 502-503
Croton 156
Crouch 198
Croup 198
Crow 193
Crown
Bird 188
Building 484, 490
Danforth anchor 386
Harp 511
Head 212
Relief-printing press 449
Rigging 382-383
Roman anchor 372
Sail hook 384
Shackle 386
Teeth 247
Timpanum 519
Crowning cornice
Ancient Roman building 464, 465
Baroque church 479
Renaissance building 474-475
Crown wheel
Benz Motorwagen 335
Ford Model T 338
Cruciform column 492
Cruciform pedestal 481, 487
Cruck frame 466
Cruise electronics module 615

Cruise stage 615
Crumb tray 598-599
Crupper 555
Crusafontia 56
Crus cerebri of midbrain 257
Crus of diaphragm 255
Crust
Moon 41
Ocean floor 298
Pulsar 28
Regional metamorphism 274
Structure of comet 53
Structure of Earth 38-39
Structure of Mars 43
Structure of Mercury 35
Structure of Venus 37
Crustaceans 172-173
Arthropoda 170
Cretaceous period 72-73
Fossil 279
Crustal movement
Coastline 294
Faults and folds 60
Mineralization zones 280
Mountain building 62
Rock cycle 266
Volcano 272
Crustal plate boundary 39
Crustal plates 58-59, 60
Crustose lichen 114
Crutch
Viking karv 375
Crux-Centaurus Arm 14
Crypt 467
Crypt-window 481
Crystalline external crust 28
Crystalline stalagmitic floor 284
Crystallization 307
Crystal Palace Exhibition Hall 492-493
Crystals
Faults 60
Intrusive igneous rocks 275
Mineral features 270-271
Minerals 268-269
Solids 307
Crystal systems 270
Ctenidium 176
CT scan 214
Cube 623
Cubic crystal 270
Cubic system 270
Cubital fossa 211
Cuboid bone 232
Cucumis melo 149
Cud 198
Cuesta 283
Culm 131
Cumulonimbus cloud 302
Cumulus cloud 302
Cuneate leaf base 136-137
Cuneus 465
Cup 509
Cup mute 507
Cupola 466, 479, 493
Cupressus glabra 123
Cup-shaped mouthpiece 506-507
Cup surrounding stomata 157
Cupula 242
Cupule 150
Curium 311
Current 296-297
Current electricity 316
Cursor control device (CCD) 573
Curtain 477, 497
Curtain wall 466, 496, 498
Curtiss, Glenn 398

Curtiss Model-D Pusher 398-399
Curved buttress 478-481
Curved cornice 462
Curvilinear tracery 470, 472
Cuscuta europaea 163
Cushion
Doric capital 460
Rowing positions 373
Cushion star 175
Cusp
Asian building 488
Gothic building 472-473
Structure of a tooth 247
Cuspate fold 61
Cuspate foreland 294
Cusped arch 489
Cuspidate leaf apex 137
Cutaneous nerve 238
Cuticle
Bishop pine needle 125
Dryland plants 156
Golden barrel cactus 156
Hair 234
Haworthia truncata 157
Leaf 139
Lithops brom fieldii 157
Marram grass 113
Monocotyledon leaf 126
Nail 251
Rose stem 135
Rush stem 135
Wetland plants 158
Cuttlefish 176
Cutty Sark 392
Cyanotrichite 269
Cycadophyta 122
Cycads 68, 122-123, 279
Cycas revoluta 68, 123
Cycas sp. 68
Cyclic-pitch lever 422-423
Cyclone assembly 592
Cyclonic storm
Structure of Earth 39
Structure of Mars 43
Structure of Neptune 50
Cyclostomata 178
Cygnus 19, 20
Cylinder
Diesel train 326
Early engines 342-343
"Ellerman Lines" steam locomotive 325
Iron paddlesteamer 392
Modern piston aero-engines 410
Motorcycle 362, 566
Oldsmobile engine 336
"Rocket" steam locomotive 324
Cylinder barrel
Mid West two-stroke engine 410
Werner motorcycle 362
Cylinder block 339
Cylinder-cooling gills 407
Cylinder drain cock lever 325
Cylinder head
72° V10 engine 356
ARV light aircraft 425
British Rail Class 20 diesel engine 327
Daimler engine 343
Jaguar straight six engine 344
Jaguar V12 engine 345
Mid West two-stroke engine 410
Oldsmobile engine 336
Two-stroke engine 366
Velocette OHV engine 367
Cylinder liner
Jaguar Straight six engine 344
Mid West two-stroke

engine 410
cylinder shape 623
Cylinder surface area measurement 590
Cylinder volume measurement 590
Cylinder wall 343
Cylindrical fault 61
Cylindrical map projection 264
Cyma recta 475
Cyma reversa 460, 472
Cymatium 475
Cymbals 504-505, 516-517
Drum kit 518
Cyme 129, 145
Cypress 123
Cypselas 150
Cyrillus 40
Cystic duct 248
Cytoplasm
Chlamydomonas sp. 116
Diatom 116
Human 217
Palisade mesophyll 139
Root cell 132
Thalassiosira sp. 116
Cytosine 216

D

Dacron 548
Dacron sailcloth 384
Dacron skin 426
Dactylus 172-173
Dado
Baroque church 481
French temple 485
Neoclassical building 479
Renaissance building 476
Dagger 472
Dagoba stupa 490-491
Daimler double-sleeve valve engine 343
Daimler, Gottlieb 334
Daisy gypsum 269
Dakota sandstone 276
D'Alembert 41
Dalmatian coastline 295
Da Maiano, B. 474
Damped anti-shock swivel base 584
Damper
Piano 514
TGV electric high-speed train 329
Wagon bogie 331
Damper bar 514
Damper body 365
Damper pedal
Concert grand piano 515
Tubular bells 516
Upright piano 514
Vibraphone 517
Damper unit 425
Damp lime-plaster 434
Damselfly 168
Dancette-pattern mosaic 489
Dandelion 150
Danforth anchor 386
Danger area 556
Danilova 36
Dark mica 274
Dark nebulae 16
Darlingtonia californica 160-161
Dart sac 177
Darwin 43
Da Sangallo, G. 474
Dash 353
Dashboard
1906 Renault 337
Bordino Steam Carriage 335

Ford Model T 338
Dashboard radiator 336-337
Dash panel 353
Dash radio speaker 353
Data cartridge 591
Data plug 591
Data plug socket 591
Daucus curola 128, 132
Daughter bulbs 154
Daughter plants 154
Davit 595
D-block 310-311
DC converter 355
DC converter connection 355
DC current 328
DC socket 586
Dead-ball line 530
Deadeye
    74-gun ship 380
    Longboat 380
    Rigging 382-383
    Roman corbita 373
    Sailing warship 377
Deadnettle 155
Dead organisms 278
Dead plant encrustations 284
Dead Sea 292-293
Deadwood 381
Debris
    Glacier 286-287
    Mountain building 62
    Ray crater 34
Decathlon 542
Decidual plate 260
Deciduous plants 150-151
Deciduous teeth 246
Deciduous trees 72
Deck
    Greek trireme 373
    Roman corbita 373
Deck beam
    74-gun ship 380
    Ironclad 392
    Paddle steamer 390, 393
    Roman corbita 372
Deck house 375, 376
Deck lantern 392
Deck planking 393
Deck rail 373
Decorative letter 445
Deep cracks 284-285
Deep current systems 296-297
Deepened valley 295
Deep floor 393
Deep mid wicket 538
Deep-ocean floor 298
Deep-ocean floor sediments 299
Deep peroneal nerve 238
Deep relief carving 453
Deep square leg 538
Deer 104, 198-199
Deer hopper dry fly 563
Defence 526, 535
Defenders
    Ice hockey 550
    Lacrosse 541
    Soccer 524
Defending zones 550
Defensive back 526
Defensive end 526
Defensive tackle 526
Deflation hollow 283
Degreased bare metal 348
Dehiscence 150-151
    Fern spore 121
    Pollen sac 144
Dehiscent fruits 150-151
Dehydration 152
De-icing leading edge 414, 415
Deimos 42
Deinonychus 73
Deinotherium 77

Dekla Tessera 37
de la Cierva, Juan 422
Deleted items folder 576
Delete mail button 576
Delphinium 150
Delphinium orientalis 141
Delphinium sp. 151
Delphinus 19, 20
Delta
    Coastline 294
    River features 290
    River 288-289
    Rock cycle 266-267
Delta Andromedae 19
Delta Crucis 21
Delta formation 291
Delta Hydri 20
Delta II launch vehicle second stage 615
Delta ring 48
Deltavjalia vjatkensis 81
"Deltic" diesel-electric locomotive 326-327
Deltoid leaf 137
Deltoid ligament 232
Deltoid muscle 226-227
Demountable wheel 538-539
Dendrite 239
Dendritic copper 268
Dendritic gold 268
Dendritic river drainage 288
Deneb 19, 20
    Hertzsprung-Russell diagram 23
Deneb Algedi 19, 20
Deneb Kaitos 19, 20
Denebola 18, 21
Dens 222
Density
    Formation of black hole 29
    Massive stars 26-27
    Small stars 24-25
    Stellar black hole 29
Dentary 181
Dentary bone 96, 102, 107
Dentate leaf margin
    Hogweed 129
    Ice-plant 129
    Live-for-ever 129
    Mulberry 130
    Rock stonecrop 128
Dentil
    Ancient Roman building 462
    Baroque church 479, 481
    Cathedral dome 487
    French temple 485
    Neoclassical building 478
    Renaissance building 475
Dentine 247
Deoxyribonucleic acid strand 139
Deperdussin, Armand 400
Depressed arch
    Ancient Roman building 462
    Islamic building 488-489
Depressions 302
Depressor anguli oris muscle 228-229
Depressor labii inferioris muscle 229
Depth charge 394
Derailleur cage plate 358
Deranged river drainage 288
Dermal armour 95
Dermal papilla 235
Dermis 234-235
Derrick 392, 395
Descender 445
Descending colon 249

Desert 39, 57
    Carboniferous to Permian period 66
    Earth's physical features 264-265
    Rock cycle 266
    Weathering and erosion 282-283
Desertification 57, 76
Desiccated clay 283
Design
    Fresco 434-435
    Modelled sculpture 452
    Mosaic 449
Deslandres 40
Desmid 112
Destination screen 332
Detachable bud 154
Detachable ink reservoir 444
Detachable rim 339
Detector 610
Detergent tray 594, 595
Detergent tray holder 595
Detergent tray recess 595
Deuterium nucleus 22
Deutscher Werkbund style 495
Devonian fish 65
Devonian period 64-65, 80
    Fossil record 279
    Geological time 56
    Primitive life 78
Devon minnow 563
Dewlap 184
Dextral strike-slip fault 61
Dhow 376
Diabase sill 277
Diagonal bracing 401
Diagonal reinforcement 374
Diagonal strut 599
Diagonal turn 388
Dial
    Clocktower 493
    Sundial 377
Diameter 622
    Atoms 308
    Earth 30
    Fluorine-19 atom 309
    Fluorine-19 nucleus 309
    Jupiter 26, 44
    Jupiter's moons 44
    Life of massive star 26-27
    Life of small star 21-26
    Mars 30
    Mars' moons 42
    Mercury 30
    Moon 40
    Neptune 51
    Neptune's moons 50
    Planets 30-31
    Pluto 31
    Saturn 27, 46
    Saturn's moons 46
    Stars 22
    Sun 32
    Uranus 27, 48
    Uranus' moons 48
    Venus 30
Diamond 311
    Mineral features 270-271
    Native elements 268
Diamond-shaped painting knife 442
Diamond whetstone 452
Diaphragm
    ARV Super 2 424
    Chimpanzee 202
    Domestic cat 195
    Elephant 200
    Human 215, 254-255
    Rabbit 196
Diastema 106
Diatom 116
Diceros bicornis 199

Dichasial cyme 143
Dicksonia antarctica 70, 112-113
Dicloelosia bilobata 65
Dicotyledon 126-127, 141-143
Dicyothyris 278
Didelphis 106
Didelphis virginiana 207
Dielectric sandwich 584
Diesel-electric train 326
Diesel fuel injection 326
Diesel motor compartment 397
Diesel, Rudolph 326
Diesel train 324, 326-327
Differential 356
Differential housing 338
Diffuser 356
Digestive caecum 173, 176
Digestive enzymes 160
Digestive gland
    Snail 177
    Spider 170
Digestive glands/zones
    Butterwort 161
    Monkey cup 161
    Venus fly trap 160
Digestive system
    Cow 198
    Human 248-249
Digit 105
Digital artery 231, 253
Digital camcorder 582-583
Digital camera 581
    5D digital camera 581
    Digital camera with interchangeable lens 581
    Digital SLR 581
    Underwater digital camera 581
Digital extensor muscle 94
Digital flexor muscle 84
Digital media slot 567
Digital nerve 231
Digital sampler 520-521
Digital vein 253
Digital video camera 582-583
Digitate leaf 137
Digits
    Bird 189
    Bird's wing 191
    Frog 182
    Kangaroo 207
    Rabbit 196-197
    Rat 196
    Salamander 182
    Seal 204
Dilator muscle 241
Dilsea carnosa 117
Dimetrodon loomisi 67
Dinghy 560
Dinosaur cladogram 83
Dinosaur 56-57, 80, 82-83
    Fossil record 279
Dionaea muscipula 160
Dione 46, 614
Dip 60
Diplodocus 70, 88, 90-91
Dip pen 430
Dipping bed rock 60-61
Dipping lug foresail 585
Diprotodon 76
Dip-slip fault 61
Dipstick 554
Dipstick tube 346, 356
Dipterus valenciennesi 81
Direct current 328
Direct current (DC) inlet 571
Direction bar 414
Direction-finding-aerial fairing 408
Direct method mosaic creation 450

Direct-vision panel
    ARV light aircraft 425
    Bell-47 helicopter 422
Dirt track motorcycle racing 368
Disc
    Basal 167
    Crab 166-167
    Liverwort 118
    Pedal 167
    Sea anemone 166-167
    Starfish 174
    Starfish fossil 79
Disc brake
    Harley-Davidson FLHS Electra Glide 362-363
    Honda CB750 363
    Honda VF750 364
    Husqvarna Motocross TC610 368
    Lockheed Electra airliner 407
    Motorcycle 364-365
    Suzuki RGV500 368-369
Disc brake calliper 364, 368-369
Disc florets 129, 142, 145
Disconformity 276
Discovery Rupes 35
Discus 542-543
Disk drag 562-563
Displacement reactions 312
Display button 585
Display controller chip 581
Display panel
    Blu-ray recorder 584
    Display screen 585, 596
    Display screen and control circuits 585
Distal convoluted tubule 256-257
Distal interphalangeal joint 251
Distal phalanx 219, 230, 252
Distal tarsal 183
Distance lines
    Gaelic football 529
    Rugby 550
Distance running 542
Distance signalling 330
Distilled water 444
Distiller 597
Distributary
    River features 290-291
    Rivers 288-289
Distributor
    Hawker Tempest Mark V 408
    Jaguar straight six engine 344
    Jaguar V12 engine 345
    Renault Clio 351
Distributor drive shaft 345
Distributor fixing point 346
Diving 558-559
DNA 139, 216, 606
Dobro resonator 513
Dock 554
Document panel 407
Document table 571
Dodder 163
Dog 104, 194-195
Dogfish 178-179, 192
Dog-leg hole 546
Dog-leg staircase 481
Doline 284-285
Dolomedes fimbriatus 171
Dolphins 204-205
Dolphin striker 382
Domain name 576
Dome 484, 486-487
    Ancient Roman building 462
    Asian building 490-491

Baroque church 480-481
French temple 485
Islamic building 488
Medieval building 467, 469
Neoclassical building 478
Renaissance building 475-477
Domed receptacle 142
Domed roof 489
Domed topdeck 401
Domed turret 493
Dome metalling 486
Dome of the Rock 487
Dome timbering 486
Dome volcano 62, 272
Donjon 466-467
Donkey boiler 392
Donor genetic material 606, 607
Door
    Ancient Egyptian tomb 458-459
    Ancient Roman building 463
    Baroque church 479
    Bell 206 jetliner 425
    Double-decker touring bus 333
    Gatwick Express "People Mover" 528
    MCW Metrobus 332-333
    Microwave combination oven 596
    Neoclassical building 478
    Renaissance theatre 477
    Renault Clio 349
    Single-decker bus 333
    TGV electric high-speed train 329
    Washer-dryer 594
Door catch 341
Door catch with safety cut-out 595
Door frame 412
Door glass 348
Door handle 341, 348
Door hinge 612
Door jamb 478
Door key and lock 348
Door lock 596, 602
Door metal cap 595
Door moulding 353
Door porthole 595
Door safety cut-out mechanism 596
Door trim panel 353
Doorway 474-475, 479, 481, 495
Door wiring loom 595
Doppler 41
Dorado 21
Doric capital 460
Doric column 460, 464
Doric half-column 464
Doric order 460
Dormancy
    Horse chestnut bud 130
    Seed 152
Dormant volcano 272
Dormer head 493
Dormer window 476, 493, 495
Dorsal abdominal artery 173
Dorsal aorta
    Bony fish 181
    Dogfish 179
    Frog 182
Dorsal blood vessel 169
Dorsal fin
    ARV light aircraft 424
    Bony fish 181
    Concorde 416
    Dogfish 179
    Dolphin 205
    Lamprey 178

World War II aircraft 408-409
Dorsal fin ray 181
Dorsal interosseous muscle 233
Dorsal lobe 158
Dorsal mantle cavity 176
Dorsal margin of shell 176
Dorsal metatarsal artery 253
Dorsal plate 78, 92-93
Dorsal scale 184, 186
Dorsal scute 95
Dorsal spine base 78
Dorsal venous arch 253
Dorsal vertebrae
  Archaeopteryx 85
  Brachiosaurus 90
  Diplodocus 90
  Eryops 80
  Euoplocephalus 94
  Gallimimus 86
  Iguanodon 96
  kentrosaurus 93
  Parasaurolophus 99
  Pareiasaur 81
  Plateosaurus 88
  Stegoceras 101
  Stegosaurus 93
  Struthiomimus 87
  Tuojiangosaurus 93
  Tyrannosaurus 84
Dorsum 213
Double-arm pantograph 328
Double bass 503-505, 510, 511
Double bassoon 504-505
Double-decker bus 332-333
Double decomposition reaction 312-313
Double-dipper palette attachment 436
Double-ended hull 375
Double flat 502
Double halyard 373
Double helix 216
Double-planet system
  Earth 38
  Pluto 50
Double-pyramid crystal 270
Double reed 508
Double rope becket 383
Doubles 544
Double samaras
  Dry fruit 150-151
  Sycamore 131
Double scull 561
Double sharp 502
Double topsail schooner 385
Dowel
  Mid West single rotor engine 410
  Mortiee-and-tenon fastening 373
Dowel hole 410-411
Downfolds 60
Downhaul 385
Downhill skiing 552
"Downs" 526
Downthrow 60
Down tube 360
Dox formation 277
dpi (Dots Per Inch) 570
Draco 19, 20
Draft mark
  Frigate 397
  Wooden sailing ship 379
Drafts folder 576
Draft tube 314
Drag
  Biplanes and triplanes 402
  Cycling 360
  Early monoplane 400

Early passenger aircraft 406
Drag knob 563
Drag link
  19th century paddlesteamer 391
  Ford Model T 339
  White Steam Car 342
Dragon prowhead 374
Drag spindle 562
Drag washer 562
Drainage systems divide 289
Drain mast 412, 415
Drain-pipe 492
Drain plug 339
Drakensberg 265
Draught mark 379, 397
Dravidian finial 491
Dravidian style 490
Drawbridge 493
Drawbridge windlass 467
Drawing 430-431
Drawing board 430, 444-445
Drawing instruments 430
Drawing materials 430
Dreadnought-type battleship 394
Dressing-room 477
Dribbling
  Basketball 532
  Gaelic football 528
  Handball 534-535
  Soccer 524
Drill 600-601
D ring 46-47
Drip-cap 482
Drive 547
Drive belt 354, 335, 344, 362
Drive bracket 405
Drive chain 366, 368
Drive end 317
Drive gear 411
Driven gear 410
Driven pulley 335
Drive pillar 424
Drive plate 345
Drive point 346
Driver 547
Driver protection 357
Driverless train 328
Driver's platform 324
Driver's radio aerial 357
Driver's seat
  Bordino Steam Carriage 335
  "Deltic" diesel-electric locomotive 327
  "Mallard" express steam locomotive 325
  Paris Metro 328
Drive shaft
  Jet engine 419
  Renault Clio 351
  Volkswagen Beetle 340
Drive sprocket mounting spline 366
Drive-wheel 601
Driving band 397
Driving chain 335
Driving pulley 335
Driving rein 555
Driving saddle 555
Driving sprocket 335
Driving wheel 324-325
Drizzle 502
Dromiceiomimus 86
Droop nose 416
Droop stop 422-423
Drop 381
Drop arm
  Ford Model T 339
  White Steam Car 342
Drop-down window 334
Drop glass 341
Drop goal 530
Drop handlebar 361

Drop-kick 530
Drop tank 408
Drop window 332
Drowned coastline 294-295
Drowned valley 295
Drum 486
  Ancient Greek building 460
  Baroque church 481
  Cathedral dome 487
  Relief printing press 449
  Washer-dryer 595
Drum and door seal 595
Drum brake
  BMW R/60 362
  Motorcycle 364-365
  Vespa Grand Sport 160
  Mark 1 363
  "Windcheetah" racing HPV bicycle 361
Drumhead 387
Drum inlet elbow 595
Drumlins 286
Drum pad 520
Drums 518-519, 520
Drum suspension springs 595
Drupelets 146-149
Drupes 131, 148-149
Dry air 303
Dry brush 438-439
Dry capacity measurements 590
Dry fresco 434-435
Dry fruits 150-151
  Couch grass 113
  Durmast oak 131
  Sycamore 131
Dry gallery 284-285
Drying agent 313
Dry lake bed 283
Dryland plants 156-157
Dryopteris filix-mas 120-121
Dryosaurus 70
Dry pericarps 130
Dry season 293
Dry wash 283
Dual click gear 562
Dual ignition plug 427
Dual seat 364
Dubhe 18
  The Plough 19
Dubika 490
Duck 188
Duck-billed platypus 206-207
"Duckbills" 96
Duct 496, 497
Duct of Bellini 256
Ductus deferens 259
Dugout 536
Dumb iron 336, 342
Dummy front door 339
Dunkeld wet fly 563
Duodenum
  Bird 189
  Cow 198
  Elephant 200
  Frog 182
  Human 215, 248-249
  Rabbit 196
  Tortoise 187
Duplex tubular cradle frame 363
Duradon 384
Dura mater 223, 237, 240
Durmast oak 131
Dust
  Asteroids, comets, and meteoroids 52-53
  Mars 42-43
  Moon 41
  Nebulae and star clusters 16-17
  NGC 2997 (spiral galaxy) 12

Overhead view of our galaxy 14
  Solar system 30
  Venus' atmosphere 37
Dust cap 359
Dust cloud
  Geological time 56
  Large Magellanic Cloud 12
  Mars 42-43
  Milky Way 14-15
  Nebulae and star clusters 16-17
  Origin and expansion of Universe 11
  Volcano 272
Dust collection bin 592
Dust lane
  Centaurus A 13
  Horsehead Nebula 16
  NGC 2997 (spiral galaxy) 12
  Optical image of Rings and dust lanes 48
  Trifid Nebula 16
Dust particles 53
Dust shroud 340
Dust storm 43
Dust tail 52-53
Dutch cubist style 495
Dutch shoe 377
Dutch triple fiddle block 383
DVD/CD control buttons 585
DVD/CD drive turntable 585
DVD/CD laser-reader 585
DVD/CD on-screen menu display button 585
DVD/CD processor microchip 585
DVD/CD sliding tray 585
DVD/CD stop button 585
DVD display button 585
DVD player 584-585
Dwarf crocodile 82
Dwarf shoot 124-125
Dyke 274
Dyke swarm 274
Dynastes hercules 12
Dyson DC05 vacuum cleaner 592-593
Dysprosium 311

E
Ear
  Calligraphy characters 445
  Elephant 200
  Gorilla 203
  Hare 196
  Horse 198
  Human 210, 212, 242-243
  Kangaroo 207
  Rabbit 196
  Rat 196
Eardrum
  Chick 193
  Frog 182
  Human 243
  Lizard 184
Earles fork 562
Early desertification 57
Early engines 342-343
Early English
  Perpendicular-style tracery 472
Early English-style window 472
Early monoplanes 400-401
Early passenger aircraft 406-407
Early tram 332
Early voyagers 374-375

Earphone 586
Earpiece 588
Earplug 558
Earth 38-39
  Cretaceous period 73
  Energy emission from Sun 22
  Jurassic period 71
  Objects in Universe 11
  Phases of the Moon 41
  Primitive life 78-79
  Quaternary period 77
  Solar eclipse 52
  Solar System 30
  Tertiary period 75
  Tides 297
  Triassic period 69
Earth-ball fungus 115
Earth bank 603
Earth connection 598
Earth formation 56-57
Earth pigments 434
Earthquake anatomy 63
Earthquake region 39
Earthquakes
  Crustal movement 58
  Faults and folds 60
  Mountain building 62-63
Earth's atmosphere 38-39, 78, 300-301
Earth's composition 39
Earth's core 58-59
Earth's crust 38-39, 58-59
  Igneous and metamorphic rocks 274
  Lake formation 292
  Volcano 272
Earth's crustal plates 62, 64
Earth's energy 314
Earth's evolution 56-57
Earth's external features 39
Earth's formation 38, 56, 64
Earth's interior
  Ocean floor 298
  Rock cycle 266
  Structure 39
Earth's layers 38
Earth's magnetic field 38
Earth's mantle 38-39, 58-59
Earth's orbit 297
Earth's physical features 264-265
Earth's rotation 38
  Atmospheric circulation and winds 300
  Oceans and seas 296
  Satellite mapping 264
Earth's satellite 38
Earth's surface
  Atmosphere 300-301
  Earth's physical features 264
  Formation of the Earth 38-39
  Geological time 56
  Mineral resources 280
  Mountain building 62
  Oceans and seas 296
  Precambrian to Devonian period 64
  Rock cycle 266
Earth's tilt 38
Earth wire 594
Earwig 168
East Africa 331
East Asian buildings 490-491
East Australian current 297
East Greenland current 296
Eaves
  Ancient Greek building 461
  Ancient Roman

building 462, 464
  Islamic tomb 489
  Modern building 499
  Neoclassical building 482
  Renaissance building 477
Eaves board 490
Eccentric 592
Eccentric rod 391
Eccentric rotor journal 347
Eccentric shaft 347, 411
Eccentric-shaft bearing 410
Echidna nebulosa 180
Echidnas 206
Echinocactus grusonii 156
Echinoderms 174, 279
Echinus 460
Echinus esculentus 175
Echo-sounding 298
Ecliptic
  Inclination of planetary orbits 31
  Stars of northern skies 18-19
  Stars of southern skies 20-21
ECM 355
Ecphora 75
Ectoderm 167
Eddy Merckx racing bicycle 360-361
Edible sea urchin 175
Edmontonia 95
Eel 180
EEPROM memory chip 587
Efferent arteriole 256-257
Effervescence 312
Effort 320-321
Egg cells 606-607
Eggs 192-193
  Amphibian 78, 80
  Baltimore oriole 193
  Bee hummingbird 193
  Bird 188
  Butterfly 168
  Capsule 192
  Carrion crow 193
  Case 192
  Chaffinch 193
  Chicken 192
  Common tern 193
  Dinosaur 82
  Dogfish 192
  Frog 182-183, 192
  Giant stick insect 192
  Greater backblacked gull 193
  Hatching 192
  Human 258, 260
  Indian stick insect 192
  Leaf insect 192
  Maiasaura 98
  Membrane 193
  Ostrich 193
  Quail 192-193
  Reptile 66, 184
  Titanosaurid 91
  Willow grouse 193
Egg tempera 432
Egg-tooth 192-193
Egg white 192
Egg yolk binding medium 432
Egypt 331
Egyptian building 458-459
Eichhornia crassipes 158
Eighteenth-century building 481
  Baroque 481
  Neoclassical 478, 482-483
Eighth-century building 490-491
Einsteinium 311
Eisila Regio 36-37

Ejaculatory duct 259
Ejecta
  Degas and Bronte 34
  Features of supernova 27
  Ray crater 34
  Venusian craters 32
Ejector assembly 599
Ejector exhaust 408
Ejector-seat roof hatches 421
Ekeing 381
Ekman spiral 296-297
El-Ainyi Mosque 488
Elapsed time display 577
Elasmobranchs 178
Elastic fibre 252, 254
Elastic rocks 60
Elbow
  Anchisaurus 89
  Corythosaurus 98
  Edmontonia 95
  Gorilla 203
  Horse 199
  Human 210
  Iguanodon 97
  Lion 194
  Psittacosaurus 103
  Stegoceras 101
  Stegosaurus 92
  Triceratops 102
Elbow guard 553
Elbow joint
  Brachiosaurus 91
  Diplodocus 90
  Eryops 80
  Euoplocephalus 94
  Human 218
  Parasaurolophus 99
  Plateosaurus 88
  Stegoceras 101
  Triceratops 102
  Tyrannosaurus 84
Elbow pad 527, 551
Elder 150-151, 140 143
Electrical braking 330
Electrical cells 316-317
Electrical charge imbalance 316
Electrical circuit 316
Toaster 598
Electrical contact 319
Electrical effects 316
Electrical energy 314-315
Electrical harness 414
Electrical inverter 422
Electrical plant 496
Electrical relay 596
Electrical relay box 330
Electrical service compartment 407
Electrical supply 316
Electrical wiring harness 418
Electric bass guitars 512
Electric cable 517
Electric car 342
Electric charge 308
Electric coil 517
Electric current 316-317, 328. 603
Electric equipment compartment 329
Electric fuel pump 422
Electric generator 317
Electric guitar 512-513
Electric heating elements 597
Electric ignition control 362
Electricity 316-317
Electricity connector to brushbar motor 595
Electricity generation
  Diesel train 326
Electric train 326
  Magnetism 317
Electricity supply 590
Electric locomotive 324, 328-329

Electric motor
  Diesel train 326
  Electric train 328
  Tram 332
Electric motor/generator 357
Electric motor housing 354
Electric power line 328, 402
Electric power socket 422
Electric scoring system 556-557
Electric street tramway 332
Electric toaster 598
Electric train 328-329
Electric tram 332
Electric transmission 326
Electric window motor 349
Electrode 306
Electromagnet 317, 598
Electromagnetic induction capacitor 600
Electromagnetic radiation 314-315, 318
Electromagnetic spectrum 318-319
Electron 308, 316
  Atomic number 310
  Fluorine-19 309
Electron beam 611
Electron detector assembly 611
Electron gun 611
Electron gun housing 610
Electron microscope 610
Electronic controller 605
Electronic control signals 330
Electronic control-unit connector 356
Electronic drums 520
Electronic engine control (EEC) unit 418-419
Electronic games 578-579
Electronic ignition unit 351
Electronic impulses 584
Electronic instruments 520-521
Electronic signals 512
Electronic warfare mast 597
Electrons 605
Electron shell 308-309, 310
Electron stream 611
Electron transfer 308
Electrostatic forces 308, 316
Electrostatic generator 316
Electrothermal de-icing panel 416
Element retaining stop 599
Elements 306, 308
  Atomic mass 310
  Minerals 268
  Periodic table 310-311
Elephant 90, 104, 200-201
  Elephas maximus 200
Elevated green 546
Elevating wheel 396
Elevation 498
Elevator
  ARV light aircraft 424
  BAe-146 components 415
  Bell-47 helicopter 423
  Biplanes and triplanes 402-403
  Curtiss biplane 399
  Early monoplanes 400-401
  Hawker Tempest

components 409
  Schleicher glider 426
  World War 1 aircraft 405
  Wright Flyer 399
Elevator arm 425
Elevator chassis box 415
Elevator control cable 399, 403
Elevator control rod 409
Elevator control wire
  Bell-47 helicopter 47
  Bleriot XI monoplane 401
  Curtiss biplane 399
  LVG CVI fighter 405
Elevator drive wheel 399
Elevator hinge
  BAe-146 components 415
  BE 2B tail 405
  Blackburn monoplane 400
  Hawker Tempest components 409
Elevator operating arm 599
Elevator-operating bracket 401
Elevator push-rod 424-425
Elevator rocking arm 404
Elevator trimtab 424, 409
Elevator wire 398
Eleventh-century building 466, 468
Elevon 416-417, 421
Elevon-jack fairing 416
Elevon power control unit 417
"Ellerman Lines" steam locomotive 324-325
Elliott steering knuckle 356
Ellipsoid orb 486
Elliptical galaxy 11-12
Elliptical orbit 30
Elliptic leaf 137
Elm 144, 150
El Nath 18, 21
Elodea canadensis 158-159
Elodea sp. 159
Elongating root 133, 153
Elrathia 64
Eltanin 19
Elytron 168
Email 576, 577
Email address 576
Email program 576, 577
Email sender 576
Emarginate apex 136
Embellisher 353
Embolos 372
Embryo 607
  Cotyledon 152-153
  Dry fruit seed 150-151
  Fertilization 146-147
  Germination 152-153
  Human 260
  Reptile 80
  Seed leaf 152
  Succulent fruit seed 148-149
Embryonic root 150, 152-153
Embryonic shoot 147
  Epigeal germination 153
  Hypogeal germination 152
  Pea seed 150
  Pine 122
  Seed axis 152-153
Embryo sac 146-147
Emergency canopy release handle 420
Emergency door control 332-333

Emergency escape hatch 406
Emergency exit 416-417
Emergency oxygen cylinder 417
Emergent coastlines 294-295
Emission nebula 11-12, 14, 16-17
Empire State Building 494
Enamel
  Islamic buildings 488-489
  Teeth 247
Enceladus 46
Encke 40
Encke Division 46-47
Enclosed bridge 397
Enclosed DVD/CD compartment 585
Encroachment 527
End 388-389
End baffle plate 598-599
End block 512
End effector 608
EN-EL12 rechargeable battery 581
End element 598-599
End-grain wood block 449
End-line
  American football 526
  Basketball 532
  Men's Lacrosse 540
  Volleyball 534
End link 586
Endocardium 250
Endocarp 146-147, 148-149
Endoderm 167
Endodermis
  Bishop pine needle 124
  Canadian pond weed stem 158-159
  Dicotyledon 127
  Epiphytic orchid 162
  Fern rachis 121
  Horsetail stem 120
  Mare's tail stem 135
  Monocotyledon 127
  Pine root 125
  Root 152-153
  Water hyacinth root 158
Endomysium 228
Endoperidium 115
Endoplasmic reticulum 239
Endopod 172
Endoscopic view
  Alimentary canal 248
  Vocal cords 245
Endoskeleton 174
Endosperm 147
Endosteum 225
Endothecium 144
Endothelium 252
End-pin 510
End-plate
  Formula One racing car 356-357
  Modern piston aero-engine 410-411
End-plate aerodynamic skirt 357
End zone 526
En echelon fractures 60-61
Energized electrode 584
Energy 314-315
  Chemical reactions 312
  Electron shells 310
  Light 318
  Renewable 604-605
Energy conversion 138
Energy emission from Sun 22
Engaged column 469
Engaged pediment 462-463
Engine 342-347, 410-411, 418-419

1906 Renault 337
1-litre VTEC 354
72° V10 356
ARV light aircraft 425
BAe-146 jetliner 415
BMW R/60 362
Bordino Steam Carriage 334
Diesel 326
Early monoplane 400-401
Hawker Tempest components 408
Helicopter 422-423
Honda CB750 363
Honda VF750 364
Kirby BSA 369
Lockheed Electra airliner 406-407
Motorcycles 362, 364, 366-367
Oldsmobile engine 336
Pegasus Quasar microlight 427
Pioneers of flight 398-399
Renault Clio 350-351
Velocette overhead valve (OHV) 367
Volkswagen Beetle 340
Engine aft bulkhead 421
Engine air intake
  BE 2B bomber 404
  Concorde 416
  Formula One racing car 356, 357
  Hawker Tempest fighter 409
  Schweizer helicopter 423
  Tornado 420
Engine and propeller thrust frame 398
Engine bearer 343
Engine block 347
Engine cover
  Formula One racing car 356, 357
  Honda VF750 374
  Oldsmobile bodywork 337
  Two-stroke engine 366
  Vespa Grand Sport 160 Mark 1 363
  Volkswagen Beetle 341
Engine cowling
  Airbus 380 573
  ARV light aircraft 424-425
  Avro biplane 403
  Concorde 416
  Hawker Tempest components 408
  Lockheed Electra airliner 407
  Pegasus Quasar microlight 427
Engine crankcase 327
Engine drive shaft 354
Engineering 496
Engine front mount 418-419
Engine front support link 417
Engine fuel pump 417
Engine instruments 425
Engine lid 341
Engine lifting eye 347
Engine mounting
  ARV light aircraft 425
  Blackburn monoplane 401
  Honda VF750 364
  Modern piston aero-engine 411
  Pegasus Quasar microlight

Velocette OHV engine 367
Engine pylon 412
Engine rear mount
  Pegasus Quasar microlight 427
  Turboprop engine 419
Engine room 326
Engine timing gear 336
Engine warning display 573
Englacial moraine 287
Englacial stream 286
England 92
English baroque style 480-481
English bond brickwork 485
English Decorated style 470
English ivy 131
English Perpendicular style 470, 472
Engraving 446
Enif 19, 20
  Pegasus and Andromeda 19
Ensign staff 396
Entablature
  Ancient Greek building 460
  Ancient Roman building 462-465
  Baroque church 480-481
  Cathedral dome 487
  French temple 485
  Neoclassical building 478-479, 482-483
Entasis 461
Enter button 585
Enter key 590
Enteromorpha linza 117
Entomophilous pollination 144
Entrance
  Islamic tomb 489
  Medieval building 466-467
  Modern building 496-499
  Neoclassical building 485
  Nineteenth-century building 493
  Twentieth-century building 494
Entrenched meander 290
Entresol 467
Enucleated egg cell 606
Enzyme 160
Eocene epoch
  Fossil record 279
  Geological timescale 57
Eon
  Fossil record 279
  Geological time 56-57
Epée 556-557
Epibranchial artery 179
Epicardium 250
Epicentre 63
Epicotyl 152-153
Epicranial aponeurosis 237
Epidermal cell 166
Epidermis
  Apical meristem 134
  Canadian pond weed stem 159
  Clubmoss stem 120
  Dicotyledon 126-127
  Epiphytic orchid 162
  Fern rachis 121
  Flower 142
  Horsetail stem 120
  Human 234-235
  Leaf 139
  Marram grass 113
  Monocotyledon 126-127
  Moss 119

636

Multi-layered 162
Pine needle 124
Pine stem 125
Prickle 135
Radicle 152
Rhizome 155
Root 132-133
Stem 134-135
Water hyacinth 158
Water lily 159
Epididymis 259
Epidote 269
Epigeal germination 152-153
Epiglottis
Elephant 200
Human 212, 244-245, 248, 255
Epiphysis 230
Epiphytes 112, 162-163
Epithelial cell 217
Epithelium 254
Epoccipital bone 102
Epoch
Fossil record 279
Geological time 56-57
Epoxy resin frame 612
Epsilon Centauri 21
Epsilon Crucis 21
Epsilon Hydri 20
Epsilon ring 48-49
Epson Stylus Photo 895 colour inkjet printer 574
Equal-shock intensity lines 63
Equator
Atmosphere 300
Quaternary period 76
Saturn 47
Satellite map 265
Surface currents 297
Equatorial air 300
Equatorial current 296-297
Equatorial furrow 144
Equatorial Zone 45
Equestrian sports 554-555
Equisetites sp. 66
Equilateral triangle 622
Equisetum arvense 70, 120
Equuleus 19, 20
Era
Fossil record 279
Geological time 56-57
Eraser 430
Erasing stick 448
Erbium 311
Erect limb stance 82
Erh-wei 376
Eridanus 19, 20
E ring 46
Erosion 282-283
Coastline 294-295
Lake formation 293
Ocean floor 298
River features 290-291
Rock cycle 267
Sedimentary rocks 276
Eryops 80-81
Escalator 497-498
Escape/back button 589
Esker 286
Estonioceras perforatum 65
Estuarine mud-flat 295
Estuary 288, 290-294
Eta Centauri 21
Eta Mensae 20
Eta Orionis 18
Eta ring 48
Eta Sagittarii 21
Etching 446
Ethernet port 566
Euathlus emilia 170
Euoplocephalus 94-95
Eurasia 76
Eurasian plate 59
Europa 44

Europe
Cretaceous period 72-73
Earth's physical features 264-265
Electric train 328
Electric tram 332
Jurassic period 70
Loading gauge 331
Middle Ordovician period 64
Quaternary period 76
Railway track gauge 331
Tertiary period 74-75
Triassic period 68
European field elm 144
European hard-screw coupling 402
Europium 311
"Eurostar" multi-voltage electric train 528-529
Eurypterid fossil 79
Eustachian tube 243
Eustreptospondylus 85
Euthynteria 460
Evacuated column 610, 611
Evaporation 307
Event horizon 28-29
Evergreens 130-131
Everlasting pea 129
Evolute shell 278
Evolution
Earth 56-57
Living things 278
Excretory pore 177
Excurrent pore 166
Exfoliation 282
Exhaust
Catalytic converter 355
Ford diesel engine 347
Modern mechanics 350-351
Paddlesteamer 391
Exhaust clamp 362
Exhaust collector ring 403, 406
Exhaust cone 419
Exhaust connection 427
Exhaust diffuser 418
Exhaust downpipe 350
Exhaust fairing 419
Exhaust gas recirculation valve 344
Exhaust heat shield 345
Exhaust manifold
1906 Renault 337
ARV light aircraft 425
Jaguar V12 engine 345
Mid West two-stroke engine 410
Renault Clio 351
Exhaust nozzle 418
Exhaust pipe
Avro biplane 403
Bell-47 helicopter 422
BMW R/60 362
Brazilian battleship 395
Harley-Davidson FLHS
Electra Glide 363
Formula One racing car 356
Hawker Tempest fighter 409
Honda CB750 363
Honda VF750 364
Kirby BSA 369
Lockheed Electra airliner 406-407
Oldsmobile engine 336
Pegasus Quasar microlight 427
Suzuki RGV500 568
White Steam Car 342
World War I aircraft 404-405
Exhaust pipe flange 411
Exhaust port
"Deltic" diesel-electric

locomotive 326
Four-stroke cycle 343
Mid West 75-HP engine 410
Two-stroke engine 367
Velocette OHV engine 367
Wankel engine 347
Wankel rotary cycle 346
Exhaust silencer 423, 427
Exhaust stack 405
Exhaust steam water injector control 325
Exhaust stroke 343
Exhaust system 368
Exhaust tract 410
Exhaust valve 343-345
Exhaust valve push-rod 400
Exhaust vent
British Rail Class 20 diesel engine 327
Drill 601
"Union Pacific" locomotive 326
Exine 144-145
Exit door 333
Exocarp 146-149
Exoccipital bone 183
Exocet missile launcher 397
Exodermis 162
Exoperidium 115
Exopod 172
Exoskeleton
Insect 168
Malacostraca 172
Spider 171
Exosphere 300
Exothermic reactions 312
Expander bolt 359
Expandible sponge 448
Expansile jaw 85
Expansion lever 325
Expansion of sail 378-379
Expansion slot 567
Expelling plate 397
Expiration 255
Exploding shell 396, 397
Expressionist style 495
Extended cave system 285
Extended port air-brake 421
Extensor digitorum brevis muscle 233
Extensor digitorum longus tendon 233
Extensor digitorum tendon 251
Extensor hallucis brevis muscle 233
Extensor hallucis longus tendon 233
Extensors of hand 227
External anatomy
Body 210-211
Brain 237
Ear 242-243
Foot 233
Hand 231
Sperm 259
External auditory meatus
Homo erectus 108
Homo sapiens 108, 220, 242
External crust 28
External elastic lamina 252
External iliac artery 215, 225, 253
External iliac vein 215, 253
External monitor port 567
External nostril 184
External oblique muscle 226
External occipital crest 220
External pubo-ischio-

femoral muscle 97
External skeleton
Insect 168
Malacostraca 172
Spider 171
External spermatic fascia 259
External urinary meatus 258
Extinct geyser 275
Extinction
Dinosaur 56, 74, 82, 104
Life 66
Pleistocene mammals 76
Extinct volcano 62, 272
Igneous rock structures 275
Mountain building 62
Ocean floor 298
Extrados 484-485
Extra period 532
Extrusive rocks 274, 275
Eye
Allosaurus 85
Amphibian 182
Anchisaurus 89
Angling hook 562
Beetle 168
Bird 188
Bony fish 181
Brachiosaurus 91
Bumblebee 168
Butterfly 169
Caiman 186
Carnivore 194
Chick 192-193
Corythosaurus 98
Crab 172
Crayfish 173
Crocodilian 186
Deer hopper dry fly 563
Devon minnow 563
Dhow 376
Dogfish 178
Dolphin 204
Elephant 201
Figurehead 374
Forward-facing 194
Frog 182
Gallimimus 86
Gorilla 203
Greek and Roman ships 372
Herrerasaurus 86
Horse 198
Human 211, 212, 240-241
Iguanodon 97
Kangaroo 207
Knot 388
Lamprey 178
Lion 194
Lizard 184
Median 170
Octopus 177
Pachycephalosaurus 100
Psittacosaurus 103
Rabbit 196
Rat 196
Rattlesnake 185
Rigging 382-383
Salamander 182
Scallop 176
Scorpion 170
Seal 204
Shrimp 172
Simple 170-171
Snail 177
Snake 185
Spider 170
Stegoceras 101
Stegosaurus 92
Terrapin 187
Triceratops 102
Trilobite fossil 78
Tyrannosaurus 84
Westlothiana 87

Eyeball 241
Eye bolt 381
Eyebrow
74-gun ship 381
Human 212
Eyelash 212
Eyelid
Caiman 186
Human 213
Snake 184
Terrapin 187
Eyepieces 610, 611
Eye plate lug 582
Eyespot 116

F

F-14 Tomcat fighter 420
Fabric 384
Fabric covering
Aluminium and steel wing 403
BE 2B tail 405
Blériot XI monoplane 401
Steel-tube fuselage 403
Fabric lacing 405
Fabric skin 401
Fabric softener section 595
Fabry 41
Facade
Ancient Greek building 461
Ancient Roman building 465
Baroque church 480-481
Gothic church 470-472
Modern building 496-499
Neoclassical building 478, 483
Nineteenth-century building 493
Renaissance building 474
Facade pediment 481
Facade wall 470
Face
Deadeye 383
Human 211
Sailmaker's mallet 384
Face mask
American football 526
Fencing 557
Hockey goalkeeper 540
Ice hockey goalkeeper 550
Lacrosse goalkeeper 541
Slalom skiing 553
Facet 222-223
Faering 374-375
Fag end 387, 388
Fahrenheit temperature scale 590
Fairing 364, 369
Fairing of landing gear 413
Fairing panel 415
Fairlead
Battleship 395
Frigate 397
Rigging 383
Roman corbita 373
Fairway 546
Falciform ligament 248
Falco tinnunculus 189
Falkland current 296
Fall 382
Fallopian tube 258-259, 261
False acacia 136
False anthers 141
False door 458-459
False fruit 148-149
False ram bow 394
"False ribs" 218

False septum 151
Falx cerebri 237
Fan
Jaguar straight six engine 344
Jet engines 418-419
Microwave combination oven 596-597
Power drill 600
Fan blade
Renault Clio 353
Turbofan 419
Fancase 418
Fan drive shaft 345
Fan duct nozzle 412
Fan dust shield 597
Fan fold 61
Fang 170
Fan transformer 597
Fan motor 351
Fan vault 484-485
Farming axe 109
Fascia
Ancient Roman building 463-464
Baroque church 479, 481
Dome 486
French temple 485
Gothic building 472
Medieval building 467, 469
Mobile phones 589
Modern building 498
Neoclassical building 482
Renaissance building 476-477
Renault Clio 353
Fast forward button 577
Fat
Cells 217
Tissue 215, 235
Faultline
Lake formation 292
Mountain building 62-63
Weathering and erosion 283
Fault plane 60
Faults 60-61, 292
Mineral resources 280
Mountain building 62
Oil and gas traps 281
Showjumping competitions 554
Fault spring 292
Fault structure 60
Fault trap 281
F-block 311
FCC cable 571
F clef 502
Feather 188, 191
Feathered float 391
Feathering 440-441
Feather shuttlecock 544-545
Feather star 174
Feed bellow button 577
Feed bilge pump 591
Feeder station 328
Feed list 577
Feed name 577
Feet
Human 232-233
Theropods 84
Fei Tecnai G2 transmission electron microscope 610
Feldspar 267, 269, 275
Felloe 390
Felt blanket 447
Felt-covered beater 516
518-519
Felt-tip pen 444
Female
Body 210, 211

Pelvis 218, 258
Reproductive organs
  259
Female apex 119
Female cones
  Bishop pine 124
  Gymnosperm 122
  Pine 122, 124
  Smooth cypress 123
  Yew 123
Female flower organs
  140-143
Female flower remains
  148
Female flowers 143, 144,
  148
Female gametes
  Fertilization 146-147
  Gymnosperm 122
  Scots pine 122
  Seaweed 116-117
  Yew 123
Female receptacles 117
Female reproductive
  organs
  Fern 121
  Fruit 148
  Moss 119
  Plants 144
Femoral artery 225, 253
Femoral musculature 86
Femoral nerve 238
Femoral vein 253
Femoro-tibial muscle 84
Femur
  Albertosaurus 84
  Archaeopteryx 85
  Beetle 168
  Bird 189
  Brachiosaurus 90
  Butterfly 169
  Crocodile 186
  Dinosaur 82
  Domestic cat 195
  Elephant 201
  Eryops 81
  Euoplocephalus 94
  Frog 183
  Gallimimus 86
  Hare 197
  Horse 199
  Human 218-219,
  224-225
  Iguanodon 96-97
  Kangaroo 206
  Kentrosaurus 93
  Lizard 184
  Parasaurolophus 98
  Pareiasaur 81
  Plateosaurus 88
  Platypus 206
  Rhesus monkey 202
  Scorpion 170
  Seal 204
  Spider 171
  Stegoceras 101
  Stegosaurus 93
  Struthiomimus 87
  Toxodon 107
  Triceratops 102
  Tuojiangosaurus 93
  Turtle 187
  Tyrannosaurus 84
Fencing 556-557
Fender eye bolt 339
Fender jazz bass guitar
  513
Fender stratocaster guitar
  513
Fenestration 474, 494
Fermentation 313
Fermium 311
Fern 120-121
  Fossil 66, 279
  Life-cycle 121
  Prehistoric Earth 68, 70,
  72
  Tree fern 112-113
Ferrel cell 300

Ferrite core 571
Fertile horsetail stem
  120
Fertile oasis 283
Fertilization 146-147
  Fern 121
  Gymnosperm 122
  Scots pine 122
  Seaweed 117
Festoon
  Ancient Roman
  building 462-463
  Cathedral dome 487
  Neoclassical building
  478-479
Fetal skull 220
Fetlock 199, 554
Fetus 260-261
Fibre 134-135
Fibreglass 548
  Bow 548
  Bucket seat 361
  Canopy frame 425
  Fuel tank 425
  Racket 544
  Reinforced plastic cover
  329
  Wheel guard 369
Fibre insulation 602
Fibre plate 366
Fibrils 32
Fibrin 253
Fibrous capsule 256
Fibrous habit 271
Fibrous pericardium 250
Fibrous septum 245
Fibula
  Albertosaurus 84
  Brachiosaurus 90
  Crocodile 186
  Diplodocus 90
  Domestic cat 195
  Elephant 201
  Eryops 81
  Euoplocephalus 94
  87
  Hare 197
  Horse 199
  Human 219, 232-233
  Iguanodon 96-97
  Kangaroo 206
  Lizard 184
  Parasaurolophus 99
  Plateosaurus 88
  Platypus 206
  Rhesus monkey 202
  Seal 204
  Stegoceras 101
  Stegosaurus 93
  Struthiomimus 87
  Toxodon 107
  Triceratops 102
  Turtle 187
  Tyrannosaurus 84
Fibulare 183
Ficus carica 148
Ficus sp. 157
Fid 383, 384
Fiddle block 378, 383
Held arrow 549
Field coil 600
Fielder's glove 537
Field events 542
Fielding 538
Field goal 526-527
Field judge 526
Field positions 538
Fields and particles
  instruments 614
Field umpire 528
Fifteenth century
  Mihrab 488
  Renaissance building
  474-475
  Style 462, 470
  Terrace 490
  Tracery 472
Fig 137, 148

Fighters 404-405, 408-409,
  420
Fighting 556
Fighting platform 374
Figurehead
  74-gun ship 380-381
  Wooden sailing ship
  379
Figure of eight turns 387
Filament
  Alga 116
  Dicotyledon flower
  126-127
  Fern 121
  Fertilization 146-147
  Flowers 140-141, 143
  Fungal 114-115
  Jellyfish 167
  Light bulb 319
  Nebulae and star
  clusters 16-17
  Sun 32-33
  Moss 119
  Pollination 144
Filbert hog hair brush 436
File status indicator 577
Filicinophyta 120
Filiform papilla 244
Filing 455
Filled shell 310-311
Fillet
  Ancient Greek temple
  461
  Dome 486
  French temple 485
  Gothic building 470
  Neoclassical moulding
  480
  Renaissance building
  475, 477
  Riling transom 381
Film and transparency
  holder 570
Filter 576
Filter access flap 594
Filter rim casing 592
Filter seal 595
Filter screw cover 595
Filter turret 610
Fimbria 258-259
Fin
  Anal 178, 181
  ARV light aircraft 424
  Avro biplane 402
  BAe-146 components
  415
  Blackburn monoplane
  401
  Caudal 178-181
  Concorde 416
  Devon minnow 563
  Dorsal 178-179, 181,
  205
  Helicopter 423
  Lockheed Electra
  airliner 407
  Lungfish 81
  LVG CVI fighter 405
  Pectoral 178, 180-181
  Pelvic 179-181
  Schleicher glider 426
  Tornado 421
  Ventral 179
  World War II aircraft
  408-409
Final drive and gearbox
  340
Final-drive sprocket 335
Fin-attachment skin 415
Find key 590
Fine leg 558
Fine linen canvas 437
Fine-toothed marble claw
  453
Finger
  Anchisaurus 89
  Gorilla 203
  Human 211
  Iguanodon 97

Pachycephalosaurus 100
Psittacosaurus 103
Stegoceras 101
Theropod 84
Fingerboard 510-511, 513
Finger-claw 83, 85
Finger hole 508
Finger key 507
Fingerless glove 527
Fingernail 231
Finger recess 571
Finger tab 548
Finial
  Asian building 490-491
  Baroque church 479,
  481
  Gothic church 470-471
  Islamic building
  488-489
  Medieval building 468
  Neoclassical building
  478
  Nineteenth-century
  building 493
  Renaissance building
  476
Finishing line 542,
  554-555
Fin leading-edge
  attachment 415
Finned tail 80
Fin-root aerial fairing 421
Fin tip 415
Fin tip fairing 421, 424
Fin trailing edge 415
Fir 66
Fire 108
Fireball 10
Firebox 324-325
Fire-escape 497-498
Fire extinguisher 328
Fire-extinguisher
  discharge indicator 412
Fire-hole 325
Fire-making tools 109
Fireman's seat 325
Fire opal 270
Fireplace 466-467
Fire-resistant clay 454
Fire-resistant curtain 497
Fire-resistant panel 496
Fire-tube boiler 334
Fire tubes 324-325
Firewall 406, 425
Firewire ports 560
Firewire socket 587
Firing 452
Firing chamber 575
Firing pin 549
Firn 287
First century 462-464
"First down" 526-527
First pilot's seat 408
First quarter 41
First rate ship 378
First slip 558
First transition metals 310
First violin 503, 504-505
First wheel set 329
Fish
  Bony 180-181
  Breathing 180
  Cartilaginous 178
  Fossil 279
  Holostean 73
  Jawless 178-179
Fish davit 379
Fisherman's schooner 385
Fishing tackle 109
Fish-scale tile 476-477,
  486
Fishtail nectaries 160
Fissure 247
Fissures 157
Fissure volcano 272
Fixative 430, 440
Fixed float 390

Fixed gear 346-347, 411
Fixed lug 383
Fixed-spool reel 562
Fixing screw 599
Fjord 294-295
Flagella 166
Flagellum
  Beetle 168
  Chlamydomonas sp.
  116
  Moss 119
  Seaweed gametes 117
  Snail 177
  Sperm 259
Flag halyard 380
Flagmast 395
Flag pin 547
Flagpole 495
Flaking rock 282
Flamboyant tracery 472
Flame 312-313
Flamingo 188, 190
Flamsteed 40
Flange 492, 498
Flanged plate 425
Flank
  Bird 188
  Cow 198
Flanker
  Canadian football 526
  Rugby 530
Flank spike 95
Flap
  ARV light aircraft 425
  Formula One racing car
  356, 357
  Hawker Tempest
  components 409
  Lockheed Electra
  airliner 406
  Tornado 421
Flap drive screw 413
Flap lever 425
Flap seal 413, 414
Flap tip 414
Flap torque tube 424
Flap track 413
Flap-track fairing 413,
  415, 572, 573
Flared bell
  Brass instruments
  506-507
  Woodwind instruments
  508-509
Flash lamp 580
Flash steam generator 342
Flash tube 397
Flask 312-313
Flat
  Musical notation 502
  Twin bollards 386
Flatbed scanner 570-571
Flatboard 384
Flat bottom 591
Flat-bottomed rail 331
Flat chisel 452
Flat cone 272
Flatfish angling 562
Flat-four engine 340
Flat freight car 327
Flat horse-races 554
Flat laminae 138
Flat roof
  Ancient Egyptian
  building 458
  Neoclassical building
  483
  Twentieth-century
  building 494-495
Flat seam 584
Flat seizing 383, 389
Flat soffit 464
Flattened pericarp 151
Flattened petiole 160
Flattened stem 129
Flat-topped plateau 275,
  282
Flat-topped seamount 298
Flat wire seizing 383

Flavian amphitheatre 464
Flax-spinning mill 492
Fleet number 333
Flesh-eaters 194
Flesh-eating dinosaur 70
Flesh tones 453
Fleshy aril 148
Fleshy axis 143
Fleshy fruit 146-147
Fleshy hair 140
Fleshy infolded receptacle
  148
Fleshy scale leaf 155
Fleteh 548
Flexible hose shrouding
  593
Flexible ribbon cable 580
Flex kink guard 594
Flexor digitorum longus
  muscle 233
Flexor digitorum tendon
  231
Flexor hallucis longus
  muscle 233
Flexor pollicis brevis
  muscle 231
Flexor retinaculum
  muscle 231
Flexors of forearm 226
Flexors of hand 227
Flexor tubercle 85
Flex rewind 593
Flight 543
Flight-control hydraulic
  jack 416
Flight-control mixing unit
  417
Flight-control rod 423
Flight controls 412
Flightdeck door 573
Flightdeck windscreen 573
Flight feathers 188, 191
Flight instruments 425
Flight refuelling
  receptacle 421
Flint 277
Flint tools 108-109
Flipper
  Dolphin 204
  Seal 204
Flitch-plated wooden
  chassis 342
Float 390-391
Floating disc brake
  364-365
Floating floor 602
"Floating" rib 218
Flocked plaster board 441
Floodgate 604
Flood-plain 289-291
Floods 290
Floor
  Gun turret 396
  Ironclad 393
  Longboat 380
  Modern building
  496-498
  Nineteenth-century
  building 492
  Twentieth-century
  building 494-495
Floor anchor 407
Floorboard 464, 486
Floor-joist 464
Floor-mounted base 608
Floor pan 340
Floor torn 518-519
Florence Cathedral 475,
  487
Florets 142
Florists'
  chrysanthemum 129
  Ultraviolet light 145
Florida current 296
Florists' chrysanthemum
  129
Flower bud
  Aechmea miniata 162
  Broomrape 163

Bulb 155
Clematis 131
Florists'
chrysanthemum 129
Hibiscus 127
Ice-plant 129
Live-for-ever 129
Oxalis sp. 157
Peruvian lily 129
Rose 131
Water lily 159
Wind pollination 144
Flowering plant 57, 70, 72
Flowering shoot 155
Flowers 140-143
  Brassavola nodosa 162
  Bromeliad 113
  Broomrape 163
  Buds 140-141, 143
  Clematis 131
  Colour 140, 144-145
  Dicotyledons 126-127,
  141-143
  Dodder 163
  Epiphytes 162-163
  Everlasting pea 129
  Florists'
  chrysanthemum 129
  Guzmania lingulata
  163
  Ice-plant 129
  Involucre 129
  Monocotyledons 126,
  140-141, 143
  Peruvian lily 129
  Pollination 144-145
  Rose 131
  Russian vine 131
  Scented 144
  Stem arrangements 143
  Ultraviolet light 145
  Vegetative reproduction
  154
  Water lily 159
  Yew 123
Flower scars 154
Flower spike 143, 155
Flower stalk
  Brassavola nodosa 162
  Bulbil 154
  Clematis 131
  Dry fruit 150-151
  Fertilization 146-147
  Florists'
  chrysanthemum 129
  Fruit development
  146-147
  Monocotyledons
  140-141, 143
  Oxalis sp. 157
  Rose 131
  Rowan 131
  Russian vine 131
  Succulent fruit 148-149
  Sycamore 131
  Water lily 159
Flow splitter 418
Fluff filter impeller 595
Fluid 306
Fluke
  74-gun ship 380
  Danforth anchor 386
Fluorescent light 318-319
Fluorine 308-309, 311
Fluorite 271
  Halides 269
Flush-riveted aluminium
  fuselage 425
Flush-riveted metal-
  skinned wing 406
Flush window 494
Flute 503, 504-505, 508
Fluted pilaster 462
Fluted pinnacle 481
Fluted shaft 478
Flute tube 325
Fluting 461, 463
Flutter kick 559
Fly 168

Fly-by-wire side stick 573
Fly fishing 562
Fly-half 550
Flying boat 406
Flying buttress
  Gothic building 470-473
  Medieval building 466,
  468-469
  Nineteenth-century
  building 493
Flying Fortress bomber
  408
Flying helmet 404
Flying jib 385
Flying reptile 70
Flying tackle 551
Fly rod 562-563
Flywheel
  Benz Motorwagen 335
  Early engines 342-343
  Etching press 447
  Mid West rotary engine
  411
  Oldsmobile engine 336
  Renault Clio 351
  Steamboat 591
Flywheel retaining thread
  411
Flywheel with balance
  weight 347
FM and TV aerial 603
Focke, Anthony 404
Fo'c'sle 380
Focus 63
Focusing lens 581
Fog 42-43
Fog-lamp 349, 353
Fog light 352, 363
Foil 556-557
Foilist 557
Foil pommel 557
Folded rock 60, 266
  Impermeable rock 281
  Mineral resources 280
  Strata 60-61
Folded schist 274
Folding foot rest 572
Folding mountain range
  274
Folding step 326
Folding table with
  integral keyboard 573
Fold mountains 62
Fold of mucous
  membrane 249
Folds 60-61
Foliage leaf
  Bishop pine 124
  Bud 124
  Bulb 155
  Germination 152-153
  Monocotyledons 126
  Parasitic plant 162
  Pine 124-125
  Rhizome 155
  Seedling 152-153
  Stem bulbil 155
  Yew 123
Foliated capital 469
Foliated frieze 469, 479
Foliated panel 479
Foliated scrollwork 472
Foliated volute 476
Foliate papilla 244
Foliose lichen 114
Foliose thallus 114
Follicle
  Dehiscent dry fruit
  150-151
  Hair 255
  Ovary 258
Fomalhaut 19, 20
Fontanelle 220
Font colour button 576
Font menus button 576
Food storage
  Bulb 155
  Corm 155
  Embryo 147

Rhizome 155
Root tuber 155
Scale leaf 155
Seed 152
Succulent 156-157
Swollen stem 113, 155
Foot
  Anchisaurus 89
  Bird 190
  Caiman 186-187
  Corythosaurus 98
  Cow 198
  Diplodocus 90
  Duck 188
  Elephant 90
  Gorilla 203
  Harp 511
  Herrerasaurus 86
  Horse 198
  Human 210
  Iguanodon 96
  Kangaroo 207
  Pachycephalosaurus
  100
  Relief-printing press
  449
  Sails 374, 385
  Slug 176
  Snail 177
  Stegoceras 101
  Stegosaurus 92
  Toaster 598-599
  Tyrannosaurus 84
  Tube 174
  Webbed 188
  Westlothiana 81
Football 524-525
Footboard 335
Foot brake 363
Footbridge 493
Foot-fault judge 544
Foot mat 363
Foot pedal 366, 514
Footplate 324
Footrest
  Curtiss biplane 398-399
  Suzuki RGV500 368
  Weslake Speedway
  motorcycle 368
Footrest hanger 364
Foot rope 378-379, 382,
  385
Foot throttle 427
Foramen caecum 244
Foramen magnum 220
Foraminiferans 279
Force 320-321
  "Force play" 536
Ford Cosworth V6
  12-valve engine 344
Ford Cosworth V6
  24-valve engine 344
Ford, Henry 338
Ford Model T 338-339
Ford turbocharged diesel
  engine 347
Fore-and-aft rigged lateen
  sails 376
Fore-and-aft sails 384
Fore-and-aft schooner 385
Forearm
  Gorilla 203
  Horse 199
  Human 210
  Movement 227
Forearm guard 548
Forearm pass 534
Fore bitt 380
Fore breast rope 387
Forecarriage 335
Forecastle
  74-gun ship 380
  Sailing warship 376
  Square-rigged ship 375
Forecastle castle-deck
  gunport 376
Forefoot
  Caiman 186
  Diplodocus 90

Edmontonia 95
Elephant 90
Iron paddlesteamer 393
Stegosaurus 92
Fore hatch tackle 379
Forehead
  Bird 188
  Dolphin 204
  Elephant 200-201
  Horse 199
  Human 211, 212
Foreleg
  Caiman 186
  Elephant 201
  Lizard 184
  Terrapin 187
Forelimb
  Anchisaurus 89
  Bird 188
  Corythosaurus 98
  Edmontonia 95
  Frog 182
  Hare 196
  Herrerasaurus 86
  Iguanodon 97
  Kangaroo 207
  Pachycephalosaurus
  100
  Psittacosaurus 103
  Rabbit 196
  Rat 196
  Salamander 182
  Stegoceras 101
  Stegosaurus 92
  Thyreophorans 92
  Triceratops 102
  Tyrannosaurus 84
Forelock 199
Fore lower topsail 385
Fore mast
  Iron paddlesteamer 392
  Roman corbita 372
  Sailing warship 376
  Square-rigged ship 375
  Wooden sailing ship
  379
Fore mast course 379
Foremast hole 380
Fore mast topgallant sail
  379
Fore mast topsail 379
Forepeak 379
Fore royal stay 383
Fore sail 372, 385
Fore sail halyard 380
Foreset strata 283
Fore shroud 379
Foresight
  Rifle 549
  Target pistol 549
Foreskin 259
Fore spring rope 387
Fore stay
  Rigging 382
  Roman corbita 372
  Sailing warship 376
  Wooden sailing ship
  379
Fore staysail 379, 385
Forest-dwelling mammals
  74
Fore throat halyard 385
Fore top 379
Fore topcastle 376
Fore topgallant mast 379
Fore topmast 376, 379
Fore topmast stay 376, 379
Fore topmast staysail 385
Fore topmast staysail tack
  382
Fore topsail 379
Fore upper topsail 385
Forewing 169
Fore yard 376, 379
Fore yard lift 385
Forged iron anchor 392
Fork
  ARV Super 2 425
  Eddy Merckx racing

bicycle 361
  Harley-Davidson FLHS
  Electra Glide 363
  Honda CB750 363
  Motorcycle 364
  Vespa Grand Sport 160
  Mark 1 563
Fork blade 359
Forked beam 380
Forked connecting-rod
  342
Fork end 383
Fork slide 365
Formeret 469, 479
Fornax 19, 20
Fornix 236-237
Fortifications 466
Forum of Trajan 463
Forward bulkhead panel
  406
Forward deck 561
Forward defensive stroke
  538
Forward dive 558
Forward door 415, 417
Forward-facing eyes 194
Forward fairing 415
Forward-firing machine-
  gun 405
Forward funnel 393, 395
Forward fuselage
  structure 401
Forward galley 416
Forward hydroplane 397
Forward main door 412
Forward ramp drive 417
Forward rocker 615
Forward rollover
  structure 557
Forwards 532, 534-535
Forward short leg 558
Forward spar 415
Fossa ovalis 237
Fossil fuel 280-281,
  314-315
Fossilization 278
Fossil record 279
Fossils 278-279
  Acanthostega skull 80
  Ankylosaurus tail club
  95
  Birch leaf 74, 76
  Blue-green algae 78
  Brachiopod 65
  Clubmoss 66
  Eurypterid 79
  Fern 66
  Graptolite 65
  Horsetail 66
  Hyaenodon skull 107
  Jawless fish 78
  Land plant 64
  Lungfish 81
  Nautiloid 65
  Palm bark 74
  Shark teeth 67
  Starfish 79
  Swamp plant 64
  Sweetgum leaf 76
  Titanosaurid egg 91
  Trilobite 78
Fossil skeleton
  Archaeopteryx 85
  Bat 105
  Parasaurolophus 98
  Pareiasaur 81
  Struthiomimus 87
  Westlothiana 81
Foster, N. 496, 498
Foul lines 556
Fouls 552
Foul tackle 524
Foul tip 557
Foundation
  Ancient Roman
  building 464
  Iron paddlesteamer 392
  Modern building 496
  Nineteenth-century

building 492
Foundry plug 387
Fountain pen 444
Four-aspect colour light
  signal 330
Four-chambered heart
  104
Four-cylinder 12-HP
  engine 399
Four-cylinder motorcycle
  363
Four-footed dinosaur 88,
  92, 96, 100
Four-pulley system 320
Four-stroke combustion
  engine 366
Four-stroke cycle 343
Fourteenth century 474
  Arch 488
  Gothic building 471-473
  Medieval building
  466-467
  Roof 490
  Style 470
Fourth mast 376
Four-wheel bogie 417
Fovea 224
Fowler flap 413, 414
Foxes 194
Fracastorius 40
Fracture 270
Fractured rock 34
Fragaria x ananassa 128,
  150
Fra Mauro 40
Frame
  74-gun ship 381
  ARV light aircraft 424
  Bicycle 358-359
  Cannondale SH600
  Digital video 582
  Hybrid bicycle 361
  Concert grand piano
  515
  Concorde 416
  Harley-Davidson FLHS
  Electra Glide 363
  Honda VF750 364
  Ironclad 393
  Longboat 380
  Medieval house 466
  Modelled sculpture 452
  Modern building 496
  Motorcycle 364
  Oscillating steam
  engine 390
  Racing bicycle 360
  Relief-printing press
  449
  Single scull 560
  Steam-powered Cugnot
  335
  Steel 494
  Upright piano 514
  Weslake Speedway
  motorcycle 368
Frame angle 360
Frame drum 518
Frame head 340
Frame-mounted fairing
  364
Fram Rupes 35
Francis turbine 314
Francium 310
Frapped turn 389
Free nerve ending 235,
  239
Freestyle swimming
  stroke 558
Free-throw line 532-533,
  535
Freewheel 361
Freewheel lock nut 358
Freewheel sprocket 360
Freezing 307
Freezing level 302
Freight car 327
Freight service 326

French baroque style 479, 482
French bowline 388
French Flamboyant style 470
French trotter 554
Fresco 434-435
Freshwater bay 291
Freshwater angling 562
Freshwater lake
  Lakes and groundwater 292
  Weathering and erosion 283
Freshwater turtle 186
Fret 512-513
Fret-pattern mosaic 488-489
Fretwork 461, 491
Frieze
  Ancient Egyptian building 459
  Ancient Greek building 461
  Ancient Roman building 463, 465
  Baroque church 479, 481
  Cathedral dome 487
  French temple 485
  Medieval church 469
  Neoclassical building 478-479, 482
  Renaissance building 476
  Twentieth-century building 495
Frigate 396-397
Fring 46-47
Fringed crumble cap 115
Fringilla coelebs 193
Fringing reef 299
Frog 182-183
  Double bass bow 511
  Eggs 183, 192
  Fossil 278
  Violin bow 510
Frog kick 559
Frond
  Fern 120-121
  Seaweed 116-117
  Tree fern 112-113
Front air dam 354
Frontal bone
  Bony fish 181
  Chimpanzee 202
  Human 212-213, 220-221
Frontalis muscle 226, 228-229
Frontal lobe 236-237
Frontal notch 213
Frontal process 221
Frontal rib 161
Frontal sinus 212, 245
Front axle
  1906 Renault 336-337
  Ford Model T 338
  Honda VF750 365
  Husqvarna Motocross TC610 368
  Kirby BSA 369
Front brake cable
  Bicycle 359
  Eddy Merckx racing bicycle 361
Front brake lever 363
Front bumper 332
Front cantilever brake 359
Front crawl 558-559
Front cylinder exhaust pipe 368
Front derailleur 358-360
Front hazard avoidance camera 615
Front leg 168-169
Front light
  Bicycle 360
  Paris Metro 328
  Italian State Railways

Class 402 328
Frontoparietal bone 183
Frontozygomatic suture 220
Front spring 337
Front wheel
  Bicycle 359
Front wing 168
Frost wedging 282, 286-287
Frozen harbour puck 550-551
Fruit
  Bramble 130
  Couch grass 113
  Development 146-147
  Dry 150-151
  Durmast oak 131
  Peach 131
  Pitcher plant 113
  Rowan 131
  Succulent 148-149
  Sycamore 131
Fruit wall 148-149, 150-151
Fruticose lichen 114
Fruticose thallus 114
"F" turret 394
Fucoxanthin 116
Fucus spiralis 116
Fucus vesiculosus 116, 117
Fuel/air intake pipe 337
Fuel and oil heat exchanger 418
Fuel and oil tank 398-399
Fuel cap 348, 369
Fuel contents indicator 413
Fuel-cooled oil cooler 419
Fuel drip tray 411
Fuel filler and vent 403
Fuel filler cap
  Curtiss biplane 398
  Volkswagen Beetle 340
Fuel filler neck 340
Fuel filter 419
Fuel heater 419
Fuel hose 425
Fuel injection 344, 356
Fuel inlet 419
Fuel-jettison pipe 417
Fuel-jettison valve 406
Fuel manifold 418-419
Fuel nozzle 418-419
Fuel pipe
  Concorde 417
  Curtiss biplane 398
  Jaguar V12 345
Fuel reservoir 568
Fuel sediment bowl 339
Fuel shut-off valve cable 419
Fuel sprayer 418
Fuel supply pump 327
Fuel tank
  Avro triplane 402
  Benz Motorwagen 335
  BMW R/60 362
  Concorde 417
  "Deltic" diesel-electric locomotive 326
  Harley-Davidson FLHS Electra Glide 363
  Helicopter 422-423
  Honda VF750 364
  Lockheed Electra airliner 407
  LVG CVI fighter 405
  Pegasus XL SE microlight 426
  Renault Clio 350
  Suzuki RGV500 369
  Werner motorcycle 362
  Weslake Speedway motorcycle 368
  White Steam Car 342
  Wright Flyer 398

Fuel tank breather 369
Fuel tank cradle 422
Fuel tank filler cap 369
Fuel tank filler neck 350
Fuel tank filler nozzle 427
Fuel tank sender unit 340
Fuel tank top skin 425
Fuel tap 366
Fuel vent pipe 422
Fulcrum 320-321
Full back
  American football 526
  Australian rules football 527
  Canadian football 526
  Gaelic football 529
  Rugby 550
Full back line 529
Full-elliptic leaf spring 334-335
Full-elliptic steering spring 337
Full forward 528-529
Fumaroles 272-273
Funaria hygrometrica 119
Funaria sp. 119
Functionalism 496
Function button 585
Function display 520-521
Fundus 258
Fungal filament 114-115
Fungi 112, 114-115, 133
Fungia fungites 167
Fungiform papilla 244
Fungoid-structure encrustations 284
Funicle 150
Funnel
  Battleship 395
  Frigate 397
  Iron paddlesteamer 392-393
  Lizard 185
  Octopus 176-177
  Steamboat with paddle wheels 391
Funnel guide 126
Funnel stay 395
Furcula 189
Furled forecourse sail 375
Furled lateen main sail 376
Furled lateen mizzen sail 375, 376
Furnerius 40
Furrow 282
Furud 21
Fused carpels 140, 144, 151
Fused petals 142, 145
Fused receptacles 149
Fuselage 401, 409, 424, 572, 573
Fuselage bottom skin 424
Fuselage bracing wire 403, 426
Fuselage mid-section 412
Fuselage nose-section 412
Fuselage skin 403
Fuselage spine fairing 414
Fuselage tail-section 415
Fuselage top skin 424
Fuses 591
Fusion crust 52
Futtock shroud 378

G

Gabbro 267, 274
Gable
  Gothic building 470-473
  Medieval building 467, 469
  Nineteenth-century building 492-493
  Renaissance building 476
Gabled arch 471

Gacrux 21
Gadolium 311
Gaelic football 528-529
Gaff 380, 385
Gagarin 41
Gait 554
Galactic centre 14, 18, 20
Galactic nucleus 12-13
Galactic plane 14-15
Galaxy 10-15, 613
Galena 268
Galeocerdo cuvier 179
Galilean moons 44
Galium aparine 150
Gallbladder
  Domestic cat 195
  Human 248, 252
  Rabbit 196
  Tortoise 187
Galle ring 50-51
Gallery
  74-gun ship 381
  Ancient Roman building 465
  Baroque church 479-480
  Cathedral dome 487
  Frigate 397
  Medieval building 466-468
  Modern building 496-497
  Renaissance theatre 477
  Wooden sailing ship 378-379
Galley 372-397
Galley area, business class cabin 572, 573
Gallimimus 82, 84, 86-87
Gallium 311
Galois 41
Galvanized "D" shackle 386
Gambrel roof 490
Game target shooting 548
Gamete 154
  Brown seaweed 116-117
  Bryophyte 118-119
  Fern 120-121
  Fertilization 146-147
  Gymnosperm 122
  Moss 112
  Pine 122
  Vegetative reproduction 154
  Yew 123
Gametophyte
  Bryophyte 118-119
  Fern 120-121
  Liverwort 118
  Moss 112, 119
Gamma 18, 21
Gamma Centauri 21
Gamma Hydri 20
Gamma Mensae 20
Gamma radiation 10
Gamma ray 22, 318-319
Gamma ring 40
Ganges plain 63
Ganges River delta 288
Ganglion 173, 177
Gangway
  74-gun ship 380
  Colosseum 464
  Sailing warship 377
Ganymede 44
Gape
  Angling hook 562
  Dolphin 204
Garboard strake 393
Gargoyle 473
Garmin Etrex hand-held GPS 591
Garnet 267
Garnet-mica schist 267
Garnierite 270

Garudimimus 86
Gas 306-307
  Asteroids, comets, and meteoroids 52-53
  Chemical reactions 313
  Massive stars 26-27
  Mineral resources 280-281
  NGC 2997 (spiral galaxy) 12
  Small stars 24-25
  Stellar black hole 29
Gas blanket 300
Gas cloud
  Earth's formation 56
  Milky Way 14
  Nebulae and star clusters 16-17
  Origin and expansion of Universe 10-11
Gas current 29
Gas deposit 57, 281
Gaseous exchange in alveolus 255
Gaseous water 49
Gas exchange 134
  Leaf 138-139
  Photosynthesis process 138
  Root 132
  Sunken stoma 156-157
  Wetland plants 158
Gas formation 280-281
Gas giants
  Jupiter 44-45
  Neptune 50-51
  Saturn 46-47
  Solar System 30-31
  Uranus 48-49
Gaskin 198, 554
Gas loop 32-53
Gas molecule 53
Gassendi 40
Gas shell 16-17, 25
Gas tail 52-53
Gastralia 85, 87
Gastric artery 253
Gastrocnemius muscle
  Albertosaurus 84
  Euoplocephalus 94
  Human 226-227
  Iguanodon 97
Gastroepiploic vein 253
Gastropod mollusc 75
Gastropods 176, 279
Gastrovascular cavity 167
Gas turbine 418
Gate
  Building 467, 490-491
  Canoeing 560
  Downhill skiing 552
  Hydroelectric power station 314
Gate clamp 560
Gate-house 467
Gateway 460
Gatwick Express "People Mover" 528
Gauge 330-331
Gauge class 325
Gauged arch 492
Gauntlet 540, 557
Gavialis gangeticus 186
G clef 502
Gear band 336
Gearbox
  ARV light aircraft 425
  Ford Model T 339
  Harley-Davidson FLHS Electra Glide 363
  Motorcycle 364, 366
  Renault Clio 351
  Volkswagen Beetle 340
  Wind turbine 605
Gearbox bevel drive 418
Gearbox case 410
Gearbox drive spline 410

Gearbox fixing stud 556
Gearbox mount 413
Gearbox oil scavenge line 419
Gearbox unit 413
Gear cable 359
Gearcase 601
Gearcase position 600
Gear change 363
Gear-change rod 351
Gear lever
  1906 Renault 337
  Husqvarna Motocross TC610 368
  Renault Clio 350
  Two-stroke engine 366
Gear lever knob 340
Gear lever surround 552
Gear ratios 361
Gear retainer 562
Gear shift 359
Gear system 358, 366
Gears
  Drills 600
  Motorcycle 366
Gelatine roller 447
Gemini 18
Gemma 118
Generative nucleus 147
Generator 317
  British Rail class 20 diesel engine 327
  Diesel train 326
  Electric train 326
  Nuclear power station 314
  Van de Graaff 316
  Wind turbine 605
Generator cooling fan 327
Generator housing 411
Generator rotor
  Hydroelectric power station 314
  Mid West engine 410
Generator unit 314
Genetic material 606, 607
Genioglossus muscle 245
Geniohyoid muscle 245
Genome 607
Genital plate 175
Gentlemen's room 477
Geographic pole 58
Geological time 56-57, 279
Geranium pratense 144
Gerberette 497
Gerbil 196
German-style baroque 482
Germany 526
Germinal epithelium 258
Germination 152-153
  Cabbage seed 152
  Epigeal 152-153
  Fern spore 121
  Hypogeal 152-153
  Mushroom spore 115
  Pine 122
  Pollen grain 146-147
Gesso 432, 453
Get mail button 576
Geyser 272-273, 275
Gharial 186
Ghost anemone 166
Giant redwood 112
Giant slalom 552
Giant stars 22-23, 26
Gibbon 202
Gibson Les Paul guitar 513
Gig 395
Gilded band 490
Gilded cross 487
Gilded orb 487
Gilded rib 487
Gilded truck 578-579
Gilding materials 451, 452
Gill

Bivalves 176
Bony fish 180-181
Dogfish 178-179
Fungi 114-115
Lamprey 178
Newt 182
Salamander 182
Tadpole 183
Gill filament 180
Gill opening 178
Gill raker 180
Gill slit 178-180
Gilt ironwork 482, 490
Ginger 155
Gingiva 247
Ginkgo 68, 70, 72, 122-123, 279
Ginkgo biloba 68, 123
Ginkgophyta 122
Ginkgo pluripartita 72
Giornate 454-455
Giraffa camelopardalis 199
Giraffe 198-199
Girder 493
Girdle 116
Girdle scar 123
Girth
    Harness racer 555
    Showjumper 554
Gizzard
    Bird 189
    Brachiosaurus 91
    Euoplocephalus 94
    Gallimimus 86
Glabella
    Human skull 213, 221
    Trilobite fossil 78
Glacial deposits 286-287, 292-293
Glacial periods 56-57, 76
Glacial sediments 299
Glacial streams 286
Glacier Bay 286
Glacier features 286-287
Glaciers 286-287
    Prehistoric Earth 66, 76
    River's stages 289
    Rock cycle 266-267
    Weathering and erosion 282
Glacier snout 286, 289
Gladiolus 154-155
Gland
    19th century
        paddlesteamer 391
    Axial 171
    Butterwort 161
    Cement 173
    Green 173
    Monkey cup 161
    Mucous 177
    Pedal 177
    Poison 170, 176
    Rectal 179
    Salivary 177
    Silk 170
    Venus fly trap 160
Glans penis 259
GLARE upper fuselage 572
Glass 307
    Buildings 492, 494
    Photovoltaic cell 605
    Tesserae 450
Glass bulb 319
Glass cooking turntable 596
Glass curtain 497
Glass deflector 325
Glass enamel 450
Glass flask 312
Glass mosaic 489
Glass muller 436, 440
Glass pane 494
Glass paper 441
Glass plate 570, 571
Glass prism 318
Glass slab 436, 440

Glass tube 319
Glass wall 496, 499
Glazing
    Acrylic paints 442
    Modern building 496-499
    Twentieth-century building 494
Glazing bar 499
Gleba 114-115
Glechoma hederacea 154
Gleditsia triacanthos 137
Glenoid cavity 80
Gliders 426-427
Global positioning system (GPS) 590-591
Global warming 301
Globe 264
Globe Theatre 477
Globular cluster 12, 16, 21
Globule 24, 26
Glomerulus 256-257
Gloriosa superba 143
Glory lily 143
Gloss finish
    Acrylics 442
    Oil painting 436
Glossopteris 67
Gloster Meteor fighter 408
Glove box 425
Gloves
    American football 527
    Baseball fielder 537
    Cricket batsman 539
    Cricket wicket-keeper 539
    Fencing 556-557
    Ice hockey 551
    Lacrosse goalkeeper 541
    Racketball 545
    Sailing 560
    Skiing 552-553
    Soccer goalkeeper 525
Glucose 138
Glulam wall-plate 499
Gluon 309
Gluteal fold 210
Gluteus maximus muscle 227
Gluteus medius muscle 225
Gluteus minimus muscle 225
Glyph 460
Gnathostomata 178, 180
Gneiss 274
Gnetophytes 122
Gnome seven-cylinder rotary engine 400
Gnomon 377
Goal
    Australian rules football 528
    Gaelic football 529
    Hockey 540
    Hurling 541
    Ice hockey 550
    Lacrosse 541
    Rugby 530-531
    Soccer 524
Goal area
    Gaelic football 529
    Handball 535
    Soccer 524
Goal attack 535
Goal circle 535, 541
Goal crease 541, 550
Goal defence 535
Goal judge 550
Goalkeeper
    Australian rules football 528
    Football rules 524
    Gaelic football 529
    Handball 534-535
    Hockey 540
    Ice hockey 550
    Lacrosse 541

Netball 535
Soccer 525
Goalkeeper's equipment 540
Goalkeeper's gloves 525
Goalkeeper's helmet 550-551
Goalkeeper's kicker 540
Goalkeeper's pad 550
Goalkeeper's shirt 525, 550
Goalkeeper's stick 550
Goal line
    American football 526
    Australian rules football 528
    Handball 535
    Hockey 540
    Ice hockey 550
    Rugby 530
    Soccer 524
Goal line referee 535
Goal net 524, 534, 550
Goalposts
    American football 526
    Australian rules football 528
    Gaelic football 529
    Netball 535
    Rugby 530
Goal shooter 535
Goal square 528
Goal third 535
Goal umpire 528-529
Goat 198
Goat hair brush 438, 442
    Calligraphy 444
Goat hake wash brush 438
Gobi Desert 265
Goggles
    Harness racing 555
    Skiing 552-553
    Swimming 558
Gold 31, 268, 280-281, 438
Gold chalcopyrite 271
Golden barrel cactus 156
Golden lion tamarin 203
Gold leaf 432
    Fresco 435
    Illumination 444-445
    Smalti 450
    Vitreous glass 451
    Wood sculpture highlighting 453
Golf 546-547
Golgi complex 217
Gomphoi 373
Gomphus 373
Gonad
    Jellyfish 167
    Octopus 176
    Sea anemone 167
    Sea urchin 175
    Starfish 174
Gondwana
    Cretaceous period 72
    Jurassic period 70-71
    Late Carboniferous period 66-67
    Middle Ordovician period 64-65
Gong 504, 516
Goniastrea aspera 167
Gonopore
    Barnacle 173
    Sea urchin 175
    Snail 177
    Starfish 174
Goose-feather quill 444
Goosegrass 150
Goose neck 388
Gopher 196
Gopuram finial 491
Gorge
    Cave 284-285
    River features 290
Gorilla 202-203
Gothic architecture 468, 470-473
Gothic book script

lettering 445
Gothic stone arch 467
Gothic torus 470
Gouge
    Relief printing 446, 449
    Woodcarving 454-453
Gour 284-285
Goya 55
GPS 590-591
Grab handle 362
Graben 61
Graben lake 293
Gracilis muscle 226-227
Graded wash 439
Graffian follicle 258
Graffias 21
Gran Chaco 264
Grand Canyon 57, 226-227
Grand piano 514-515
"Grand Prix" world championships 368
Grandstand 555
Granite-aggregate slab 499
Granite cladding 494
Granular stalk 114
Granum 139
Grape hyacinth 155
Graphics card 567
Graphite 268, 311
Graphite pencil 430
Graphite stick 430
Grapnel-type anchor 376
Grasping tail 202
Grass 113
Grate 324
Grating 380-381
Graver 449
Gravitation (gravity)
    Atmosphere 300
    Force and motion 320
    Neutron stars and black holes 28
    Oceans and seas 296-297
    Universe 10
Gravitational pull 296-297
Gravity-feed fuel tank 405
Gray Cliffs 276
Grease 446
Greaser 339
Great Bear Lake 264
Great cabin 379, 381
Great Dark Spot 50-51
Greater blackbacked gull 193
Greater flamingo 190
Greater omentum 214
Greater palatine foramen 220
Greater trochanter of femur 224-225
Greater wing coverts 188
Greater wing of sphenoid bone 220-221
Great Lakes 264
Great manual 514
Great Mosque 484
Great Red Spot 44-45
Great Rift Valley 60
Great saphenous vein 253
Great stop 514
Greek ship 372-373
Greek-style fret ornament 483
Green (golf) 547
Green alga 112, 116-117
Green calc-silicate mineral 275
Green cell 584
Green chlorophyll pigment 116, 138
Green earth 434-435
Green fluorite 269
Green gland 173
Greenhouse effect 36, 300-301
"Greenhouse gas" 301
Greenland

Cretaceous period 73
Late Carboniferous period 66
Middle Ordovician period 64
Satellite map 264
Green light 318, 330-331
Green seaweed 117
Green snakelock anemone 166
Green starboard navigation light 406
Greenwich Meridian
    Satellite map 264-265
    Surface currents 296
Gregorian calendar 681
Grey matter 236-237, 238
Grey squirrel 197
Grey whale 204
Grid lines 445
Griffon 461
Grikes 284
Grille
    "Eurostar" warning horn 329
    Roman Mill 464
Grill/griddle 596
Grimaldi 40
Grip
    Sailmaker's fid 384
    Sailmaker's mallet 384
Gripe 379
Groin
    Arches and vaults 485
    Human body 211
Groin pad 527
Groin vault 479, 484-485
Grommet 373, 375, 384, 426
Groove
    Rope starter 335
    Serving mallet 384
Grooved racing tyre 356, 557
Groove for FCC cable 571
Grooving 385
Grotesque figure 476
Ground handling wheel 422
Ground ivy 154
Ground-mapping radar 420
Groundmass 268-269
Ground roller 447
Groundwater 292-293
    Volcanic structure 273
Grout 450-451
Growing point 153
Growing tip 79
Growth line
    Fossilized jawless fish 78
    Snail 177
Groyne 294
Grundtvig Church 495
Gruppo Seven Cubist 495
Grus 19, 20
Gryposaurus 96, 99
Guanine 216
Guard
    American football 526
    Basketball 532
    Fencing foil 557
Guard cell 138-139
Guardrail 391-392, 395
Guardstop 541
Gubernator 373
Gudgeon 375
Gudgeon pin 345
Gudgeon strap 378
Guest boat boom 594
Guiana Highlands 264
Guidance control sensor 612
Guide hair 126
Guide mark 535
Guide wheel 328
Guinevere Planitia 36, 37

Guitars 510, 512-513
Gula Mons 37
Gulf of Mexico 264
Gulf Stream 296
Gull 189, 193
Gulley 538
Gully 289
Gum 247
Gum arabic 438
    Lithographic printing 446, 448
    Pastel making 440
Gun
    1.3 kg gun 395
    3 pound gun 395
    4.5 in gun 397
    4.7 in gun 394
    11 cm gun 397
    12 cm gun 394
    12 in gun 394
    30 cm gun 394
    Battleship 394
    Frigate 397
    Measurements 394
    Sailing warship 376
    Wooden sailing ship 578, 579
Gun battery 395
Gun carriage 377
Gun deck 380
Gun loading cage 396
Gunnery control radar dish 397
Gunnery spotting top 394
Gunport 381
    Sailing warship 376-377
    Wooden sailing ship 579
Gun position 397
Gun section 392
Gunship 422
Gun turret 396-397
    Battleship 394
    Frigate 397
    World War II aircraft 408
Gut caecum 170
Gutenberg discontinuity 39
Gutter 486, 492, 602
Guzmania lingulata 162-163
Gymnosperm 122-125
Gynoecium 140
Gypsum 271
Gyroscopic gunsight 409

H

Habit 270-271
Habitat 112
    Dryland plants 156-157
    Wetland plants 158-159
Hackle 563
Hackly fracture 270
Hadar 21
Hadley cell 300
Hadrosaur 96, 98-99
Hadrosaurus 96, 99
Haemal spine 180
Haematite 268
Hafnium 310
Hagfish 178
Hail 302
Hair 234-235
    Cobra lily 160
    Golden barrel cactus 156
    Inflorescence 140, 142
    Insulating 104, 107
    Mammal 104
    Marram grass 113
    Monocotyledon 126
    Pitcher plant 113
    Root 132
    Venus fly trap 160
    Water fern leaf 158

Hair bulb 235
Hair cell 242-243
Hairdryer 315
Hair follicle 234-235
Hair gel 306
Hair-like sepal 142
Hair shaft 235
Hakatai shale 277
Hale-Bopp Comet 53
Half-back 526, 529
Half-back flank 528
Half-column 464, 468-469
Half-court line 545
Half-forward 529
Half-forward flank 528
Half-fruit 151
Half hitch 388
Half-shaft
    Ford Model T 338
    Formula One racing car
    356
    Half turn 543
Halide 269
Halite crystal 277
Hall
    Asian building 491
    Hypostyle 458
    Medieval building
    466-467
    Modern building 496,
    499
    Neoclassical building
    483
Halleflinta 275
Halley's Comet 52
"Hall-keeps" 466
Hallux
    Anchisaurus 89
    Archaeopteryx 85
    Herrerasaurus 86
    Human 232
    Tyrannosaurus 84
Halo 14
Halogen headlamp bulb
    352
Halogens 311
Halo ring 44
Halyard
    Double topsail
    schooner 385
    Junk 376
    Longboat 380
    Rigging 382
    Roman corbita 372, 373
    Viking karv 374
Hamada 282-283
Hamal 19, 20
Hamate bone 230
Hammer 242, 285
    Antler 109
    Athletics 542
    Concert grand piano
    515
    Mosaic 450
    Target pistol 549
    Upright piano 514
Hammer actuator 600-601
Hammer-beam roof 470,
    473
Hammerhead shark 179
Hammer throw 543
Hand
    Anchisaurus 89
    Human 210
    Iguanodon 97
    Pachycephalosaurus
    100
    Primate 203
    Stegoceras 101
    Tyrannosaurus 84
Handball 554-555
Handbrake 337, 339-340,
    550
Handbrake control shaft
    338
Handbrake quadrant 339
Hand brake wheel 331
Hand drill 600-601
Hand-held gun 408

Handle
    Belaying pin 382
    Brace-and-bit 601
    Steam iron 594
Handlebars
    Bicycle 358-359
    BMW R /60 362
    Cannondale SH600
    hybrid bicycle 361
    Cannondale ST 1000
    touring bicycle 361
    Eddy Merckx racing
    bicycle 361
    Suzuki RGV500 368
Handle connector 593
Handling
    Motorcycle 360
    Touring bicycle 364
Hand protector 368
Hand rail
    "Ellerman Lines" steam
    locomotive 324
    Modern building 498
    Renaissance building
    477
    Sailmaker's mallet 384
    Serving mallet 384, 388
    Ship's wheel 390
    TGV electric high-
    speed train 329
    Twentieth-century
    building 494
Hands 230-231
Handstand 543
Hand throttle 427
Handy Billy 382-383
"Handy man" 108
Hanger 498
Hang-gliders 426-427
Hanging valley 286-287
Hapteron 116-117
Hard disk drive 567
Hard endocarp 146-147,
    149
Hard granite 283
Hard hat 554
Hard-headed beater 516,
    518-519
Hard metals 310
Hardness 270-271
Hard palate 212, 245
Hard rock 60
    Faults and folds 60
    Glacier 286
    River features 290-291
    Weathering and erosion
    282
Hard trim 352
Hardwood implements
    452
Hardwood laminate limb
    548
Hardwood panels 452
Hardwood sticks 517
Hardy 450
Hare 196-197
Harley-Davidson FLHS
    Electra Glide 362-363
Harmika 491
Harmon, A.L. 494
Harmonically-tuned
    exhaust system 356
Harmony
    Drums 518
    Percussion instruments
    516
Harness
    Avro triplane IV 402
    Equestrian sports 555
    Harness racing 554
Harness strap 409
Harp 504, 510-511
Harpoon point 109
Hash mark 541
Hastate leaf 128
Hatch
    Cargo 376
    For home deliveries 602
    Iron paddlesteamer 393

Single scull 561
Hatch board 372
Hatch coaming 381
Hatching egg 192-193
Hatchling 98
Hathor Mons 37
Haunch 484
Haustoria 163
Haustration of colon 249
Haversian system 225
Hawker Tempest 408-409
Hawksmoor, N. 478, 481
Haworthia truncata 157
Hawse hole
    74-gun ship 381
    Sailing warship 376
    Wooden sailing ship
    378
Hawse piece 381
Hawse pipe 393, 395
Hawser 386-387
Hawser fairlead 395
Hawthorne 35
Haystack boiler 334
Haze 37, 47
Head
    74-gun ship 380
    Allosaurus 85
    Beetle 168
    Brace-and-bit 601
    Bumblebee 168
    Butterfly 169
    Caterpillar 169
    Ceratopsian 100
    Deer hopper dry fly 563
    Double bass bow 511
    Double topsail
    schooner 385
    Dunkeld wet fly 563
    Femur 224-225
    Frog 182
    Hammer 542
    Human 211, 212-213
    Insect 168
    Lacrosse crosse 541
    Lamprey 178
    Pachycephalosaurus
    100
    Phalanx 230
    Prosauropod 88
    Racing bicycle 360
    Racing saddle 554
    Rattlesnake 185
    Sail 375, 584
    Sauropodomorph 88
    Serving mallet 388
    Snail 177
    Sperm 259
    Stegoceras 101
    Stegosaurus 92
    Tennis racket 544
    Thyreophoran 92
    Ulna 231
    Violin bow 510
Headband 544
Head beam 380
Headboard 581
Head-butting contest 100
Head crest 96
Head cringle 384
Head data cable 574
Head data cable support
    574
Head earing 375
Headers
    Brickwork 485
    Nineteenth-century
    building 492
Head horn 94
Head joint 508
Headlamp
    Bordino Steam Carriage
    335
    Bulbs 352
    Ford Model T 338-339
    Renault Clio 349, 353
    Volkswagen Beetle 341
Headland 294
Head-light

BMW R/60 362
"Eurostar" multi-
    voltage electric train
    329
Harley-Davidson FLHS
    Electra Glide 363
Italian State Railways
    Class 402 528
MCW Metrobus 332
Single-decker bus 333
"Union Pacific"
    locomotive 326
Vespa Grand Sport 160
Mark 1 363
Head linesman 526
Headphone jack 578, 586,
    587
Head rail 580-581
Headrest
    Airbus 380 273
    ARV light aircraft 425
    Formula One racing car
    356
    Hawker Tempest
    fighter 409
    Mazda RX-7 346
    Renault Clio 349, 352
    TGV electric high-
    speed train 329
    "Windcheetah" racing
    HPV bicycle 361
Head rope 387
Headset 361
Headstock
    Acoustic guitar 512-513
    Electric guitar 513
    Honda VF750 364
Head tube 359-361
Headward erosion 290
Headwaters 288
Hearing 237, 242
Heart
    Bird 189
    Bony fish 181
    Branchial 176
    Butterfly 169
    Chimpanzee 202
    Crayfish 173
    Dogfish 179
    Dolphin 205
    Domestic cat 195
    Elephant 200
    Euoplocephalus 94
    Frog 182
    Gallimimus 86
    Human 214-215,
    250-251
    Lizard 185
    Mammal 104
    Octopus 176
    Rabbit 196
    Snail 177
    Spider 170
    Systemic 176
    Tortoise 187
Heartbeat sequence
    250-251
Heart bulge 260
Heartwood 125
Heat 314-315
    Chemical reactions
    312
    Global warming
    300-301
    Igneous and
    metamorphic rocks 274
Heat absorption 92
Heated filament 319
Heater element contacts
    548
Heater unit 353
Heat exchanger
    Concorde 417
    Nuclear power station
    314
Heat exchanger air intake
    421
Heat exchanger exhaust

duct 420
Heat exchanger hot-air
    exhaust 421
Heating element cover
    597
Heating elements 594
Heating element terminal
    cover 597
Heat radiation 92
Heat shield
    Jet engine 419
    Motorcycle 363
    Space probes 614
Heat trapping 300
Heaver for wire serving
    383
Heaving line 389
Heavy chemical elements
    27
Hedera colchica 137
Hedera helix 131, 137
Heel
    Horse 198
    Human 210
    Rudder post 392
Heel moulding 594
Heine 45
Heka 18
Helen Planilia 36
Helianthus annulus 142
Heliconia peruviana 143
Helicoprion bessonowi 67
Helicopter landing-pad
    498
Helicopters 396, 410,
    422-423
Helium
    Jupiter 44-45
    Massive stars 26
    Mercury's atmosphere
    35
    Neptune's atmosphere
    51
    Pluto's atmosphere 51
    Periodic table 311
    Saturn 46-47
    Small stars 24-25
    Sun 32
    Uranus' atmosphere 49
Helium-3 nucleus 22
Helium-4 nucleus 22
Helium line 23
Helium tank 614
Helix 242, 623
Helix Nebula 17
Helleborus niger 139
Hellenic plate 59
Helmet
    American football
    526-527
    Baseball batter 536
    Bicycle 360
    Cricket 539
    Hockey goal keeper 540
    Hurling 541
    Ice hockey 550-551
    Lacrosse goalkeeper
    541
    Skiing 542
Helmsman 372-373
Hemicyclaspis 56
Hemisphere 623
Hemispherical dome 477,
    486-487, 490-491
Hen coop 395
Hepaticae 118
Hepatic artery 248,
    252-253
Hepatic portal vein 253
Heptathlon 542
Heracleum sp. 151
Heracleum sphondylium
    129
Heraldic device 372
Herbaceous plants 126,
    128-129
    Structure 112-113
    Woody 130-131
Herbaceous stems 154

Herbivores
    Carnivora 194
    Jurassic period 70
    Marginocephalian 100
    Ornithopodian 96
    Prosauropods 88-89
    Sauropodomorphian 88
    Triassic period 68
Hercules 19, 20, 40
Herds 88
Hermaphrodite duct 177
Hermit shale 276
Herodotus 40
Herrerasaurids 68, 86
Herring-bone pattern 488
Hertzsprung 41
Hertzsprung-Russell
    diagram 22-23
Hesperidium 148
Hestia Rupes 37
Heterocentrotus
    mammillatus 175
Heterodontosaurus 83
Heteropoda venatoria 171
Hexagon 622
Hexagonal system 270
HF radio aerial 408
HF radio aerials fairing
    417
Hibiscus 126-127
Hide 105
Hide grip 384
Hieroglyphs 458-459
High altar 470
High-altitude cloud 45, 50
Highboard diving 558
High-density minerals 280
High-energy particle 301
High-energy radiation 22
High-explosive projectile
    396
High-gain antenna 615
High-gain radio antenna
    612, 615
High-jump 542
Highland coastline 295
High-level jet streams 300
High nose 357
High-performance
    microscopes 610-611
High-pressure areas
    302-303
High-pressure bleed
    venturi connector 419
High-pressure
    compressor 418
High-pressure cylinder
    342
High-pressure turbine 418
High-pressure zone 300
High-speed trains 328-329
High Spring tide 296-297
High temperature gas 506
High-tension beam 496
High-tension ignition lead
    344
High tension wire 315
High tide 296-297
High-velocity air duct 420
High voltage cable 314,
    355
High-voltage connector
    355
High-voltage magnetron
    supply 596
Hi-hat cymbal 518
Hilbert 41
Hillman anti-kink weight
    562
Hilum
    Dehiscent fruit seed
    151
    Epigeal germination
    153
    Hypogeal germination
    152
    Succulent fruit seed
    148-149
Himalayas

Earth's physical
features 264-265
Geological time 56-57
Formation 60, 62-62
Mountain building
62-63
Quaternary period 77
Tertiary period 74
Himeji Castle 490
Hind foot
Caiman 187
Stegosaurus 92
Hindgut 173
Hind leg
Amphibian 182
Beetle 168
Bumblebee 168
Butterfly 169
Caiman 187
Elephant 200
Frog 182
Hare 196
Iguanodon 97
Lizard 185
Rabbit 196
Terrapin 187
Hind limb
Anchisaurus 89
Corythosaurus 98
Edmontonia 95
Frog 182
Iguanodon 96
Kangaroo 207
Pachycephalosaurus
100
Prosauropod 88
Psittacosaurus 103
Rabbit 197
Rat 196
Salamander 182
Stegoceras 101
Stegosaurus 92
Theropods 84
Thyreophoran 92
Triceratops 102
Tyrannosaurus 84
Hindlimb bone 105
Hind wing 168-169
ARV light aircraft 425
BAe-146 components
412-415
Hinge 571
Hinge bracket 414
Hinge cell 113, 160
Hinged bin/cyclone cover
593
Hingeless bivalve shell 79
Hingeline 60
Hip
Anchisaurus 89
Human 211
Kangaroo 207
Lion 195
Midway Gardens 495
Stegosaurus 92
Hip girdle 80
Hip joint 218, 224-225
Brachiosaurus 90
Diplodocus 90
Gallimimus 86
Parasaurolophus 98
Plateosaurus 88
Stegoceras 101
Struthiomimus 87
Hip pad 527
Hippeastrum sp. 155
Hipped roof 476-477
Hippocampus kuda 180
Hippophae rhamnoides
136
Hippopotamus 198
Hippopotamus amphibius
77
Hippuris vulgaris 135
Hip-rafter 490
Hispano Mark V 20-mm
cannon 409
Historiated boss 469
Historiated keystone 469

Hitachi S-3500H scanning
electron microscope
611
Hitched hauling end 383
Hitch-kick 543
Hitch pin
Concert grand piano
515
Upright piano 514
Hittorff, J.I. 479
Hobbles 554
Hock 195, 198
Hockey 540-541
Hock joint 195
Hog hair brush 432, 434
Hog's-back 283
Hog's-back jump 554
Hogweed 129, 150-151
Hohenbuehelia petaloides
115
Hoisting cage 396
Holden 43
Holdfast 116-117
Holding 527
Holding timekeeper 556
Hold pillar 393
Hole and peg joint 373
Hollow disc wheel 561
Hollow pith cavity 120
Holmium 311
Holocene epoch
Fossil record 279
Geological timescale 57
Holostean fish 73
Homarus sp. 73
Home cinema 584-585
Home key 578
Homeosaurus pulchellus
71
Home page 577
Home plate 536
Home run 536
"Home" signal 330
Hominid 74-75, 108-109,
202
Homocephale 101
Homo erectus 108
Homo habilis 108
Homo sapiens 57, 76,
108-109
Honda CB750 362-363
Honda Insight 354
Honda VF750 364-365
Hone-stone 452
Honesty 150-151
Honeycomb coral 167
Honey guides 140-141,
145
Honey locust 137
Hong Kong and Shanghai
Bank 496, 498
Honshu 265
Hood
Battleship 394
Ford Model T 359
Gun turret 396
Jellyfish 167
Pitcher plant 160
Hood bag 346
Hood end 374
Hood frame 339
Hood iron 334
Hood-mould 479, 481, 486
Hoof 198, 554
Hoofbone 105, 198
Hoof-like nail 36-37
Hook
Angling 562
Cricket 538
Deer hopper dry fly 563
Devon minnow 563
Rigging 383
Sail 384
Hooked beak 190
Hooked pericarps 150
Hooked riffler 454
Hooker 550
Hoop 580, 425
Hoover Factory 495

Hop 543
Hopper freight car 327
Horizon 576
Horizontal bed rock 61
Horizontal cleavage 270
Horizontal damper 329
Horizontal fissure 255
Horizontally opposed
engine 362
Horizontal movement 60
Horizontal, stabilizer 423
Horizontal tailplane 572
Horn
Ford Model T 359
Glacier 286-287
Mooring 387
Musical instrument
503, 504
"Union Pacific"
locomotive 326
Vespa Grand Sport 160
Mark 1 563
Horn balance 414, 415
Horn bulb 339
"Horned faces" 100
Horny beak 96
Horse 104-105, 198-199
Horse chestnut 150, 157
Horse-drawn vehicle 532
Horsehair bow 510-511
Horsehead Nebula 16
Horse riding 554-555
Horseshoe arch 484
Horsetail 120-121
Horsley Church 473
Horst 61
Horu Geyser 272
Hose base 593
Hose cuff electrical link
593
Hose electricity supply
connector 592
Hose slider 592
Hose slider seating 592
Host plants 162-163
Hot-air de-icing duct 414
Hot mineral springs 272
Hot spot
Black holes 29
Earth's crust 58
Ocean floor 298
Hot water jet 273
Hound 578
Hour line 377
Household appliances 315
House of the future
602-603
Housing
Alpine skiing 552
Electric motor 342
House spider 171
Howe 36
Howea forsteriana 126
Howler monkey 202
HP Pavilion DV4 laptop
566
Hti 490
Huang He 265
Huayangosaurus 93
Hub
1906 Renault 336
ARV light aircraft 424
Benz Motorwagen 335
Bicycle wheels 558-559
Blackburn monoplane
400-401
Bordino Steam Carriage
334
Eddy Merckx racing
bicycle 361
Paddle wheel 390-391
Pegasus Quasar
microlight 427
Propellers 391
Renault Clio 351
Wright Flyer 399
Hub and brake drum 350
Hub bearing 351
Hubble Space Telescope

612-613
Hub bolt 338
Hub brake shoe 338
Hub cap
1906 Renault 336
Ford Model T 339
Renault Clio 350
Hub carrier 351
Hub controller 604
Hub nut 350
Hub quick release lever
361
Hub seal 350
Hudson Bay 264
Hull
Carvel-built 376, 391
Clinker-built 375
Cross-section 378
Double-ended 375
Greek and Roman ships
372-373
Iron and wood 392
Hull plank 373
Human body 210-211
Human classification
108
Human Powered Vehicles
(HPV) 358, 360
Humans 57, 76, 108, 202,
315
Humber engine 343
Humboldt current 296
Humerus
Archaeopteryx 85
Arsinoitherium 104
Bird 189, 191
Brachiosaurus 91
Diplodocus 90
Domestic cat 195
Elephant 201
Eryops 80
Euoplocephalus 94
Frog 183
Gallimimus 86
Hare 197
Horse 199
Human 218
Iguanodon 96
Kangaroo 206
Kentrosaurus 93
Pareiasaur 81
Plateosaurus 88
Stegoceras 100
Struthiomimus 87
Toxodon 106
Triceratops 102
Tyrannosaurus 84
Humic acid 284
Hunter-killer submarine
396-397
Hunter's bend 388
Hunting 108, 548
Huntsman spider 171
Hurdle races 554
Hurdling 542
Hurling 540-541
Hurricane 302-303
Husk 150
Husqvarna Motocross
TC610 368
Huygens mini-probe 614
Hyaenodon 74, 107
Hyaline cartilage 225
Hybrid bicycle 360-361
Hybrid car 354
Hybrid power 355
Hydra 18, 21
Hydrated copper sulphate
313
Hydraulic actuator
attachment 413, 414
Hydraulic brake calliper
424
Hydraulic brake hose 369
Hydraulic brake pipe 414
Hydraulic fluid
Disc brake 365
Spring/damper unit 365

Hydraulic grab 396
Hydraulic hand-pump 421
Hydraulic hose 369
Hydraulic unit 605
Hydrocarbon 313
Hydrochloric acid 312
Hydrochoerus
hydrochaeris 197
Hydroelectric power-
station 314
Hydrogen 308, 310
Candle wax 312-313
Covalent bonding 309
Jupiter's atmosphere 45
Massive stars 26
Mercury's atmosphere
35
Nebulae and star
clusters 16-17
Neptune's atmosphere
51
Nuclear fusion in Sun
22
Salt formation 312
Saturn's atmosphere 47
Small stars 24-25
Sun 22
Uranus' atmosphere 49
Hydrogen alpha line 23
Hydrogen atom 138, 596
Hydrogen beta line 23
Hydrogen fluoride 308
Hydrogen gamma line 25
Hydrogen gas 312
Hydrogen nucleus 22
Hydrogen requirement
138
Hydrogen sulphide 51
Hydroplane 396-397
Hydroxide 268
Hydrus 20
Hyena 194
Hymenoptera 168
Hyoglossus muscle 244
Hyoid bone 244-245, 255
Hypacrosaurus 99
Hypaethral temple
460-461
Hypersion 593
Hyperlink 577
Hyphae
Fungus 114-115
Mycorrhizal association
133
Hypocotyl 152-153
Hypodermis
Gynosperm 125
Human 235
Hypogeal germination
152-153
Hypoglossal nerve 244
Hypogymnia physodes
114
Hypostyle hall 458-459
Hypothalamus 236
Hypsilophodon 72, 82
Hypural 180
Hystrix africaeaustralis
197

I

I bar 393
IBM-compatible PCs 566
Ice 66, 307
Glacier 286-287
Weathering and erosion
282
Ice age 56
Ice-age mammals 76
Ice block
Ice-fall 287
Lake formation 293
Ice-cap 287
Ice crystal 302
Ice cube 307
Ice erosion 287
Ice-fall 287

Ice hockey 550-551
Ice margin lake 286
Ice-plant 128-129
Ice sheet 76
Ichthyosaur 70-71
Ichthyostega 56, 80
Icons 576
Icterus galbula 193
Idle control valve 344
Idocrase 270
Igneous intrusion 274
Igneous rock 266-267,
274-275
Igniter 418
Igniter plug 419
Ignition amplifier 345
Ignition coils 354
Ignition control 362
Ignition lever 338
Ignition switch 337
Ignition trigger housing
410
Iguana iguana 82
Iguanodon 73, 96-97
Ileocaecal fold 249
Ileum
Bird 189
Frog 182
Human 226, 249
Rabbit 196
Iliac crest 224-225
Iliac fossa 224
Iliac spine 224
Iliacus muscle 225
Ilio-femoral muscle 84, 97
Ilio-fibular muscle 84, 97
Ilio-ischial joint 82
Iliopsoas muscle 226
Ilio-pubic joint 82
Ilio-tibial muscle
Albertosaurus 84
Euoplocephalus 94
Iguanodon 97
Ilium
Archaeopteryx 85
Bird 189
Diplodocus 90
Eryops 81
Euoplocephalus 94
Frog 183
Gallimimus 86
Human 218
Iguanodon 96-97
Kentrosaurus 93
Ornithischian 82
Parasaurolophus 98
Plateosaurus 88
Saurischian 82
Stegoceras 100-101
Stegosaurus 93
Struthiomimus 87
Toxodon 106
Tuojiangosaurus 93
Illuminated manuscript
432
Illumination 444-445
iMac 566
Image controls 611
Imaging system housing
610
Imaging the body 214
Imago 168
Immature pitcher 161
Immature spur 141
Impasto 436-437, 442
Impeller 347
Imperial-Metric
conversions 591, 620
Imperial unit
measurements 590
Impermeable clay 292
Impermeable mudstone 292
Impermeable rock
Cave 284-285
Lake 292
Mineral resources
280-281

River's stages 289
Impermeable salt dome 281
Impermeable shale 292
Impost
  Ancient Roman building 465
  Cathedral dome 484
  Gothic building 473
  Islamic building 488
  Medieval building 466, 469
In-board 561
Inboard elevon 417, 421
Inboard elevon-jack fairing 416
Inboard end 587
Inboard engine 415
Inboard lift spoilers 413
Inboard trimtab 413
Inbound line 526
Inbox folder 576
Incandescent light 318-319
In-car GPS 590-591
In-car mounting bracket assembly 590
In-camera memory chip 580
Incident laser light 319
Incisive canal 245
Incisor teeth
  Bear 194
  Chimpanzee 202
  Elephant 201
  Human 245, 246
  Lion 194
  Rabbit 196
  Rodent 196
  Toxodon 106
Incline 468
Incompetent bed rock 61
Incomplete mesentery 167
Incurrent pore 166
Incus 242
Indehiscent fruit 150
Index finger 230-231
India
  Cretaceous period 72-73
  Jurassic period 70
  Himalaya formation 62-63
  Late Carboniferous period 66
  Middle Ordovician period 64
  Mountain building 62-63
  Quaternary period 76-77
  Railway track gauge 331
  Tertiary period 74-75
  Threophorans 92
  Triassic period 68
Indian ocean 73, 75, 77, 265
Indian stick insect 192
Indicator
  "Deltic" diesel-electric locomotive 327
  Bus 333
  Harley-Davidson FLHS Electra Glide 363
  Honda CB750 363
  MCW Metrobus 332
  Volkswagen Beetle 340
Indicator assembly 352
Indicator board 542
Indicator lamp 353
Indicator lens 541
Indirect method mosaic creation 450-451
Indium 311
Indo-Australian plate 59
Inducer 418
Induction stroke 343
Indus 20
Indusium 121

Industrial Revolution 492
Inert gas 311, 584
Inferior articular process 225
Inferior concha 212, 241
Inferior extensor retinaculum 253
Inferior meatus 245
Inferior mesenteric vein 255
Inferior nasal concha 221, 241, 245
Inferior oblique muscle 241
Inferior orbital fissure 221
Inferior rectus muscle 241
Inferior vena cava 215, 252-253, 257
Infertile swamp 288
Infield 536-537
Infilled swamp 291
Inflated petiole 158
Inflation valve 405
Inflorescences 140
  Aechmea miniata 162
  Bromeliad 113
  Catkin 144
  Compound 142-143
  Couch grass 113
  Dodder 163
  Stem arrangements 143
Inflorescence stalk 140-143
  Aechmea miniata 162
  Brassavola nodosa 162
  Everlasting pea 129
  Indehiscent fruit 150
  Peach 131
  Peruvian lily 129
  Rowan 131
  Russian vine 131
  Succulent fruit 148
  Vegetative reproduction 154-155
  Wind-pollinated plant 144
Inflorescence types
  Capitulum 129, 142
  Compound umbel 143
  Dichasial cyme 143
  Raceme 129
  Single flower 143
  Spadix 143
  Spherical umbel 143
  Spike 143, 155, 162
Infraorbital foramen 221
Infraorbital margin 213, 221
Infra-red radiation 318-319
  Energy emission from Sun 22
  Infra-red map of our galaxy 15
Infra-red board 579
Infra-red camera 578
Infra-red receiver 580
Infra-red projector 578
Infra-red sensor 609
Infraspinatus muscle 227
Infratemporal fenestra
  Baryonyx 85
  Camarasaurus 91
  Diplodocus 90
  Heterodontosaurus 83
  Lambeosaurus 99
  Panoplosaurus 94
  Parasaurolophus 99
  Plateosaurus 88
  Protoceratops 102
  Triceratops 103
Infratemporal foramen 106-107
Ingres paper 441
Initial cave 285
Ink 430, 444
Ink-cartridge replacement button 574

Ink cartridges 574
Ink dabber 446
Inkjet nozzle 575
Inkjet printer 574-575
Ink outlet hole 574
Ink pad 445
Ink reservoir 444, 575
Ink roller 448, 449
Ink sac 176
Ink stick 444
Ink stone 444
Inlay 488-489
Inlet 295
Inlet cone 418
Inlet manifold
  Daimler engine 343
  Jaguar V12 engine 345
  Mid West single-rotor engine 411
Inlet manifold tract 345
Inlet-over-exhaust (IOE) engine 362
Inlet port 345, 367
Inlet rotor 347
Inlet tract 410
Inlet valve 345, 345, 362
Inner bin fin 592
Inner bud scales 154
Inner cage assembly 599
Inner clutch drum 366
Inner core 38-39, 41
Inner counter 445
Inner cyclone cone 592
Inner dome 484
Inner floret 129, 142
Inner jib downhaul 585
Inner jib halyard 585
Inner jib stay 582
Inner jib tack 582
Inner layer of cortex
  Dicotyledon 127
  Epiphytic orchid 162
  Monocotyledon 127
  Wetland plants 158-159
Inner mantle 44-47
Inner martingale stay 383
Inner membrane 139
Inner planetary orbits 31
Inner posts 528
Inner tepal 126, 140, 143
Inner tube 359, 424, 507
Inner vane 191
Innings 536, 538
Inorganic substances 280
Inscription 487
Insectivorous plants 113, 160-161
Insects 168-169, 279
  Cretaceous 72-73
  Plant food 160-161
  Pollinators 144-145
Inselberg 283
Insoluble solids 312
Inspection cover
  Avro biplane 403
  Lockheed Electra airliner 407
Inspection door 407
Inspection panel 417
Inspiration 255
Instep 211
Instrument bay 613
Instructor's cockpit 403
Instrument console 420
Instrument deployment device 615
Instrument landing system aerial 420-421
Instrument module 613
Instrument panel
  ARV light aircraft 425
  Bell-47 helicopter 422
  Renault Clio 353
  Schweizer helicopter 426

Generating magnetism 317
Hydroelectric power station 314
Intaglio printing 446-447, 448
Intake manifold 351, 354
Intake pipe 335
Intake port 346
Integral ink reservoir 444
Integrated transparency unit (TPU) 570, 571
Integrated transport system 352
Integument
  Ovule 147
  Scots pine 122
Intelligent electronic door-lock 602
Intentional foul 533
Interalveolar septum 254
Intercellular leaf space 159
Interception 526
Inter-City travel 332
Intercolumniation 461, 485
Intercompressor bleed valve 419
Intercompressor diffuser pipe 419
Intercostal muscle 91, 255
Interdental papilla 247
Interdental septum 247
Interglacial period 76
Integer house 602, 603
Interior light 353
Interlobular artery 256
Interlobular vein 256
Interlocking spur 289
Intermediate housing 346
Intermediate lamella 225
Intermediate ring 563
Internal capsule 237
Internal carotid artery 245, 252
Internal combustion engine
  First cars 354
  Motorcycle engine 366
  Pioneers of flight 398
Internal crust 28
Internal elastic lamina 252
Internal fuse overload protection 585
Internal iliac artery 215, 253
Internal iliac vein 253
Internal jugular vein 253
Internal skeleton 174
Internal spermatic fascia 259
Internal urethral orifice 257
Internal urethral sphincter muscle 257
International referees signals 533
International rules 532
International squash 544-545
International track gauge 331
Internet 576-577
Internet service provider (ISP) 576
Internode
  Canadian pond weed 158-159
  Horsetail 120
  Ice-plant 129
  Live-for-ever 129
  London plane 134
  Rhizome 155
  Rock stonecrop 128
  Rose stem 130
  Stem 154
  Stolon 154
Interopercular bone 181
Interosseous ligament 232

Interphalangeal joint
  Baryonyx 85
  Human 231, 233
Interplane strut 599, 404-405
Interradicular septum 247
Interrupter gear 404
Interstellar cloud remains 613
Intertragic notch 242
Intertrochanteric line 225
Intertropical convergence zone 300
Interventricular septum 251
Intervertebral disc 212, 218, 223, 245, 261
Intestinal muscle 226
Intestine
  Bony fish 181
  Butterfly 169
  Chimpanzee 202
  Cow 198
  Crayfish 173
  Dogfish 179
  Dolphin 205
  Elephant 200
  Frog 182
  Gallimimus 86
  Human 214
  Large 195, 202
  Lizard 185
  Sea urchin 175
  Small 182, 185, 187, 195, 198, 200, 202
  Spider 170
  Tortoise 187
Intrados 469, 484
Introitus 258
Intrusive rocks 26, 275
Invasion stripes 409
Invertebrates
  Earth's evolution 56
  Fossil record 279
  Insects 168-169
  Marine 65
Inverted ovolo 486
Inverter 355
Inverter board 570
Inverter cooling fan 355
Inverter cooling fan connector 355
Inverter housing 355
Inward dive 558, 559
Io 44
Iodine 311
Ion 308
Ionic bonding 308
Ionic capital 460
  Baroque church 481
  French temple 485
  Renaissance building 476
Ionic column
  Baroque church 481
  French temple 485
  Neoclassical building 483
Ionic half-column 464
Ionic order 460
Iota Centauri 21
Iota Pegasi 19
Iota Sagittarii 21
iPhone 4 588
Ipomoea batatas 154
Iran 331
Ireland 331
Iridium 311
Iridocorneal angle 241
Iris
  Human 213, 226, 241
  Linear leaf 137
  Octopus 177
  Iris lazica 137
Iron 311
  Earth's composition 39
  Earth's crust 58
  Golf club 547
  Magnetic domains 317

Meteorite 52
Nineteenth-century buildings 492
Structure of Mercury 35
Structure of Venus 37
Iron armature support 455
Ironclad 392-393
Iron club 546-547
Iron filings 317
Iron hull 392-393
Iron oxide
  Earth pigments 434
  Flesh-coloured pigments 433
  Sanguine crayon 430
  Sedimentary rocks 267, 277
Iron oxide dust 42
Iron paddlesteamer 392-393
Iron pyrite 79, 270
Iron railing 493
Iron roof 479
Iron ship 392-393
Iron, steam 594
Iron tracery 493
Iron tyre 334
Ironwork 478, 482
Irregular galaxy 10-12, 15
Irreversible reactions 312
Ischial tuberosity 224
Ischium
  Archaeopteryx 85
  Bird 189
  Crayfish 173
  Diplodocus 90
  Eryops 81
  Euoplocephalus 94
  Frog 185
  Human 218, 224
  Iguanodon 96
  Ornithischian 82
  Parasaurolophus 98
  Plateosaurus 88
  Saurischian 82
  Stegoceras 100-101
  Stegosaurus 93
  Struthiomimus 87
  Triceratops 102
  Tyrannosaurus 84
Ishtar Terra 36-37
Islamic buildings 488-489, 489
Islamic mosaic 489
Islands 291, 294
Isocline 61
Isolated single boulders 286
Isolated steep-sided hill 285
Isolator valve 325, 327
Isosceles triangle 622
Isoseismal lines 63
Isotopes 310
ISP 576
Israel 293
Isthmus
  Reproductive system 258-259
  Water hyacinth 158
Italian State Railways Class 402 328
Italic Roman lettering 445
Item link 577
Itonaco 434
Ivy 130-131, 137

J

Jack 514
Jacket-wall 466
Jack-rafter 473
Jack staff
  Battleship 394
  Frigate 397
  Square-rigged ship 375
  Wooden sailing ship 379
Jacob's ladder 378
Jagged fracture 270

Jaguar straight six engine 344
Jaguar V12 engine 345
Jali 488-489
Jamb
　Ancient Roman temple 463
　Baroque church 479
　Medieval church 468
　Neoclassical building 478, 482-483
　Nineteenth-century building 492
Jami Masjid 488
Javelin 542-543
Jaw
　Brace-and-bit 601
　Hand drill 601
　Human 212, 220-221
　Power drill 601
　Rope 389
Jawbone
　Allosaurus 85
　Australopithecus 107-108
　Ceratopsian 100
　Dolphin 204
　Horse 105
　Human 220, 247
　Ornithopod 96
　Shark 178
　Snake 184
　Theropods 84
Jawless fish 78, 178-179, 180
JBL Spyro speakers 586
Jeer 377
Jejunum 249
Jelly 192
Jellyfish 78, 166-167
　Earth's evolution 56
　Fossil record 279
Jet engine 412, 418-419
Jetliners 412-415
Jet pipe 418-419, 423
Jet pipe connection 419
Jetstream 300, 418
Jewel anemone 166
Jewel Box 11
Jewish calendar 618
Jib boom 379, 382
Jib fairhead 561
Jib halyard 380
Jibsail 378, 379, 385
Jib sheet 385
Jib stay 382
Jib tack 582, 583
Jockey 554-555
Jockey wheel 358
Jodhpurs 554
Joint
　Cave 284-285
　Coastline 295
　Faults and folds 61
　Jointed plug 19
　Weathering and erosion 282
Jointed leg 79, 168
Jointed pincer 79
Jointed solidified lava 292
Jointed stem 131
Joints 224-225, 608
Joist 464, 486
Jones, H. 493
Jordan 293
Joule 314, 316
Journal 347
Joystick 361, 520
Judo 556-557
Jugal bar 201
Jugal bone 96, 102-103
Jugal plate 94
Juglans nigra 137
Jugular vein 215
Juice sac 148
"Jumbo jet" 412
Jumps 552, 554
Jump seat 337
Jump shot 532, 535

Junction
　Electrical circuit 316
　Giornata 434-435
　Photovoltaic cell 605
Junction board 355
Juncus sp. 135
Junior ratings' mess 397
Junk 376
Junk mail folder 576
Junk ring 343
Jupiter 30-31, 44-45, 614
Jupp-Reese winglet 572
Jurassic period 70-71
　Fossil record 279
　Geological time 57
Jury mast knot 389
Justicia aurea 144
Juvenile volcano 275
JVC Everio camcorder 582

K

Kabe 375
Kaibab limestone 276
Kaibab Plateau 277
Kaiparowits formation 276
Kaiparowits Plateau 277
Kalahari Desert 265
Kalanchoe daigremontiana 154
Kalasa finial 489
Kalos 572
Kame delta 286
Kame terrace 286
Kangaroo 206-207
Kappa Pegasi 19
Kara Kum 265
Karv 374
Kasugado Shrine of Enjoji 490
Kasuga-style roof 490
Katastroma 373
Kaus Australis 19, 20
　Sagittarius 21
Kaus Borealis 21
Kaus Meridionalis 21
Kawana House 496
Kawasaki industrial robot 609
Kayak 560
Kayenta formation 276
Kazakstania 65
Kedrostis africana 113
Keel
　Battleship 595
　Bird 189
　Frigate 397
　Ironclad 393
　Iron paddlesteamer 392
　Longboat 380
　Sailing warship 377
　Viking ship 374-375
　Wooden sailing ship 378
Keel boat 560
Keeled lesene 486
Keeler 41
Keelson (Kelson) 560
　19th century paddle steamer 391
　Ironclad 393
Keep 466
Keeper ring 562
Kelvin temperature scale 590
Kendo 556
Kentosaurus 92-93
Kepler 40
Keraia 372
Keratin 234
Kestrel 189
Ketch 384, 385
Kettle 286
Kettle drum 519
Kettle lake 293
　Post-glacial valley 286
Kevlar 384, 388
Key

Concert grand piano 515
　Home keyboard 520
　Motorcycle clutch 366
　Musical notation 502
　Steel lock 360
　Synthesizer 520
　Upright piano 514
　Woodwind instruments 508-509
Keyboard 521, 566, 611
Keyboard instruments 514-515, 520
Key guard 509
Keypad 589
Key rod 509
Key signature 502
Keystone 484
　Ancient Roman building 463, 465
　Baroque church 479, 481
　French temple 485
　Medieval church 469
　Neoclassical building 478, 482
　Renaissance building 476-477
Keyway 390
Kick-stand 363
Kick-starter 363, 366
Kidney
　Bird 189
　Bony fish 181
　Brachiosaurus 90
　Dogfish 179
　Dolphin 205
　Domestic cat 195
　Elephant 200
　Frog 182
　Gallimimus 86
　Human 215, 256-257
　Lizard 185
　Octopus 176
　Rabbit 196
　Snail 177
　Tortoise 187
Kidney ore haematite 268
Kidney-shaped palette 436
Killer whale 205
Killick 386
Kiln 452
Kimberlite 268, 275
Kinetic energy 314-315
Kinetic sculpture 452
King pin 338
King-post 473, 479
　Early monoplane 400-401
　Pegasus Quasar microlight 427
　Pegasus XL SE microlight 426
King-post strut 401
King spoke handle 390
Ring strut 464
King vulture 190
Kirby BSA racing sidecar 369
Kittiwake 190
Kiwis 188
Knee
　Anchisaurus 89
　Corythosaurus 98
　Faering 375
　Gorilla 203
　Horse 199
　Human 211
　Iguanodon 96
　Kangaroo 207
　Lion 195
　Pachycephalosaurus 100
　Psittacosaurus 103
　Rabbit 197
　Stegoceras 101
　Stegosaurus 92
　Tyrannosaurus 84
　Wooden ships 581

Knee joint
　Brachiosaurus 90
　Diplodocus 90
　Euoplocephalus 94
　Human 219
　Parasaurolophus 98
　Plateosaurus 88
　Stegoceras 101
　Struthiomimus 87
　Toxodon 107
　Triceratops 102
　Tyrannosaurus 84
Knee of the head 378
Knee pad 527, 534
Knee roll 539, 554
Knife
　Palette 436
　Relief printing 446, 449
Knighthead 380
Knots 388-389
Knuckle 210
Koala 207
Kochab 18
Kope 372-373
Korolev 41
Krypton 311
Kuan Han-ch'ing 35
Kubernetes 372
Kuiper belt 30, 50
Kunzite 271
Kuroshio current 297

L

Labellum 126, 145
Label mould 481
Labia 258
Labial palp 168
Labrum 168
Laburnum x watereri 137
Laccolith 273-275
Lacerta 19, 20
Lacertilia 184
Lacrimal apparatus 241
Lacrimal bone
　Bony fish 181
　Human 221
　Protoceratops 102
Lacrimal canaliculus 241
Lacrimal gland 241
Lacrimal punctum 241
Lacrimal sac 241
Lacrosse 540-541
Lacuna
　Bones and joints 225
　Clubmoss 120
　Mare's tail 135
　Wetland plants 158-159
Lacustrine terrace 286
Lada Terra 36, 37
Ladder
　74-gun ship 381
　Battleship 394
　Frigate 396
　Iron paddlesteamer 392, 393
　Roman corbita 372-373
　Train equipment 330
　Wooden sailing ship 378
Ladder way 395-396
Lady Chapel, Salisbury Cathedral 470
Lagomorpha 196
Lagoon
　Atoll development 299
　Coastline 294-295
　River features 290-291
Lagoon Nebula 21
Lagopus lagopus 193
Lagostomus maximus 197
Lake Baikal 265
Lake Erie 264
Lake Huron 264
Lake Michigan 264
Lake Nyasa 265
Lake Ontario 264

Lakes 292-293
　Glacier 286-287
　Groundwater system 293
　Igneous rock structures 275
　River features 290
　River's stages 289
　Rock cycle 266-267
　Weathering and erosion 283
Lake Superior 264
Lake Tanganyika 265
Lake Victoria 265
Lakshmi Planum 37
Lambda Andromedae 19
Lambda Pegasi 19
Lambdoid suture 220
Lambeosaurus 96, 98-99
Lamb, T. 494
Lamella 139
Lamina 156
　Butterwort 161
　Couch grass 113
　Dicotyledon leaf 127
　Human 222-223
　Leaf 138
　Monocotyledon leaf 127
　Seaweed 116-117
　Succulent 113
　Vegetative reproduction 154
　Water hyacinth leaf 158
　Water lily leaf 159
Laminaria digitata 116-117
Laminates 548
Lamium sp. 135
Lamp 570, 571
Lamp bracket 336, 342
Lamp cluster 341
Lampland 287
Lamprey 178
Lampropeltis ruthveni 184
Lampropeltis triangulum annulata 184
Lamp shield 550
Lanceolate leaf 120, 131, 136
Lancet 471
Lancet arch 473, 484
Lancet window 470-472
Land 39
　Amphibians 80
　Animals 64
　Atmosphere 301
　Plants 56, 64
　Rivers 288
　Vertebrates 82
Landau body 334
Landau iron 334
Landing 477
Landing and taxiing light 414
Landing gear 406-407, 424-425, 573
Landing-gear damper 423
Landing-gear door
　BAe-146 components 414
　Concorde 416
　Hawker Tempest components 409
　Lockheed Electra airliner 407
Landing gear drag strut 401
Landing gear fork 407
Landing gear front strut 400, 404
Landing gear hydraulics 417
Landing gear leg 424
Landing gear rear cross-member 400
Landing gear rear strut 400-401
Landing gear strut 405
Landing light
　BAe-146 jetliner components 414-415

Bell-47 helicopter 422
Lockheed Electra airliner 407
Schweizer helicopter 423
Landing skid
　Avro triplane 403
　Blackburn monoplane 400-401
　Helicopter 422-423
　Wright Flyer 399
Land movement 59
Land plants 56, 78
Landscape features 290-291, 294
Land surface removal 282
Land turtle 186
Lane
　Athletic track 542
　Swimming pool 558
Lane time-keeper 558
Langrenus 40
Language 108
Langur 202
Lantern 486
　Baroque church 480-481
　French temple 485
　Neoclassical building 478-479
　Twentieth-century building 494
　Wooden sailing ship 379
Lanthanides 310
Lanthanum 310
Lanyard
　Lifejacket 561
　Oar 373
　Rigging 382-583
　Roman corbita 373
Lap 542
Lapilli 272
Lap strap
　ARV light aircraft 425
　Curtiss biplane 398
　Lockheed Electra passenger seat 407
　Pegasus Quasar microlight 427
Laptop computer 566, 567
Laptops 567
Large intestine
　Brachiosaurus 90
　Chimpanzee 202
　Domestic cat 195
　Euoplocephalus 94
　Human 215
Large Magellanic Cloud
　Hydrus and Mensa 20
　Our galaxy and nearby galaxies 15
　Stars of southern skies 20-21
Large mammals 57
Larkspur 141, 151
Larus marinus 193
Larus ridibundus 193
Larva 168
Laryngeal prominence 212, 244-245
Larynx
　Amphibian 182
　Human 214-215, 244
Laser ranger 420
Lateen sail 375, 376, 384
Lateral angle 213
Lateral bracing strut 402-403, 416
Lateral branch
　Adventitious roots 158-159
　Horsetail 120
　Vegetative reproduction 154
Lateral bud 134
　Begonia 129
　Dicotyledon 127
　Horse chestnut 130

645

Leaf scars 154
London plane tree 134
Rhizome 155
Rowan twig 131
Stem bulbil 155
Stolon 154
Lateral canal
  Human 247
  Starfish 174
Lateral caudal
  musculature 87
Lateral column 223
Lateral control wheel 401
Lateral control wire 404
Lateral dorsal aorta 179
Lateral epicondyle 225
Lateral fault 61
Lateral fault lake 293
Lateral lacuna 257
Lateral line 181
Lateral malleolus 233
Lateral mass 222
Lateral moraine 286-287
Lateral plantar artery 253
Lateral plate 78
Lateral rectus muscle
  240-241
Lateral root 133
  Broomrape host 163
  Carrot 128
  Dicotyledon 127
  Germination 152-153
  Horse chestnut 130
  Seedling 152-153
  Strawberry 128
  Sweet pea 128
Lateral root scar 128
Lateral sepal 141
Lateral shield 187
Lateral shoot 156
Lateral strike-slip fault 61
Lateral sulcus 257
Lateral tepal 126
Lateral vein 136, 159
Lateral ventricle 237
Lath 464
Lathyrus latifolius 129
Lathyrus odoratus 128
Latissimus dorsi muscle
  227
Latrodectus mactans 171
Lattice-beam 496-497
Latticed screen 488-489
Latticed shade 495
Lattice-truss 499
Lattice window 492
Lattice-work 493
Laurasia
  Cretaceous period 62
  Jurassic period 70-71
  Late Carboniferous
  period 66-67
Laurentia 65
Laurentian Library
  474-475
Lava 62
  Igneous and
  metamorphic rocks
  274-275
  Mountain building 62
  Rock cycle 266
  Volcano 272-273
Lava eruptions 272
Lava flow 273
  Contact metamorphism
  274-275
  Mars 42
  Rock cycle 266
Lava fragments 272
Lavatera arborea 131
Lava types 273
Lavinia Planitia 36-37
Lawrencium 311
Layering
  Fresco 434-435
  Pastel colours 440
Lay-up shot 552
LCD see Liquid crystal
  display (LCD)

LCD monitor 583
Leach 374, 384
Lead
  Mineralization zones
  281
  Minerals 268
  Periodic table 311
Lead covering 487
Leading block 394
Leading edge
  Avro biplane 403
  Avro triplane 403
  BAe-146 components
  413, 414-415
  BE 2B tail 405
  BE 2B wings 404
  Blackburn monoplane
  401
  Concorde 416-417
  Hawker Tempest
  components 409
  Lockheed Electra
  airliner 406
  Northrop B-2 bomber
  421
  Pegasus Quasar
  microlight 427
  Wright Flyer 399
Leading-edge aerial 421
Leading-edge fairing 425
Lead-in wire 319
Lead iodide 313
Lead nitrate 313
Lead shot 517
Lead wire 600
Leaf axis 137
Leaf bases 128, 136-137
  Aechmea miniata 162
  Couch grass 113
  Dicotyledon 127
  Florists'
  chrysanthemum 129
  Guzmania lingulata
  162-163
  Hogweed 129
  Monocotyledon 126-127
  Sago palm 123
  Seedling leaf 152
  Water hyacinth 158
Leaf blade
  Butterwort 161
  Dicotyledon 127
  Leaf surface 136, 138
  Monocotyledon 127
  Vegetative reproduction
  154
  Venus fly trap 160
  Wetland plants 158-159
Leaf insect 192
Leafless branch 120
Leaflets 136-137
  Everlasting pea 129
  Fern 120-121
  Horse chestnut leaf 130
  Mahonia 130-131
  Monocotyledon 126
  Pinna 121, 136-137
  Rose 131
  Rowan 130
  Sago palm 123
  Tree fern 112-113
Leaflet stalk 137
Leaf-like structures
  141-143
  Dehiscent fruit 151
  Dicotyledon flower 127
  Guzmania lingulata 163
  Ice-plant 129
  Live-for-ever 129
  Peruvian lily 129
  Slender thistle 129
  Wind pollination 144
Leaf margin 129
  Aechmea miniata 162
  Slender thistle 129
  Vegetative reproduction
  154
Leaf notch 154
Leaf primordium 134

Leaf scar
  Begonia 129
  Elder 130
  Horse chestnut 130
  Ice-plant 128-129
  London plane 134
  Rock stonecrop 128
Leaf shape 136-137
Leaf sheath 129
Leaf spring 338
Leaf spring suspension
  327
Leaf stalk 128, 136-137
  Chusan palm 130
  Clematis 131
  Cobra lily 160
  Common horse
  chestnut 130
  Dicotyledon 127
  Everlasting pea 129
  Florists'
  chrysanthemum 129
  Kedrostis africana 113
  Maidenhair tree 123
  Monocotyledon 126-127
  Mulberry 130
  Oxalis sp. 157
  Passion flower 130
  Peach 131
  Seedling 153
  Strawberry 128
  String of hearts 157
  Tree fern 112
  Tree mallow 131
  Vegetative reproduction
  154-155
  Venus fly trap 160
  Water lily 159
  Wind pollination 144
Leaf succulents
  Haworthia truncata 157
  Lithops bromfieldii 157
  Lithops sp. 156
Leaf trace 127
Leaf venation 129
  Leafy liverwort 118
  Leafy thallus 114
  Lean-to roof 468-470, 472
  Leather ball making 525
Leather grommet 373
Leather hood 334
Leather ink dabber 446
Leather pad 557
Leather upholstery 337
Leather valance 337
Leathery exocarps 148
Leaves 136-137
  Abaxial surface 123, 130
  Adaxial surface 123, 130
  Aechmea miniata 162
  Apex 136-137
  Apical meristem 134
  Barberry 130-131
  Bishop pine 124
  Brassavola nodosa 162
  Bromeliad 112-113
  Broomrape 163
  Butterwort 161
  Canadian pond weed
  158-159
  Carnivorous plants
  160-161
  Cheekerbloom 136
  Chusan palm 130
  Classification 136-137
  Clematis 130-131
  Clubmoss 120
  Cobra lily 160
  Couch grass 113
  Dicotyledon 126-127
  Dryland plants 156-157
  Durmast oak 131
  Epiphyte 162-163
  Fern 120-121
  Florists'
  chrysanthemum 129
  Germination 152-153
  Guzmania lingulata
  162-163

Haworthia truncata 157
Hinge cell 113
Hogweed 129
Horsetail 120
Intercellular space 139
Ivy 131
Kedrostis africana 113
Lamina 136
Lithops bromfieldii 157
Liverwort 118
London plane tree 134
Maidenhair tree 123
Margin 136
Marram grass 113
Midrib 136
Monkey cup 161
Monocotyledon 126-127
Moss 112, 119
Mulberry 130
Orange lily 154
Oxalis sp. 157
Parasite host 163
Passion flower 130
Peach 131
Photosynthesis 134,
  138-139
Pine 122, 124-125
Pitcher development
  161
Pitcher plant 113,
  160-161
Primordia 134
Rock stonecrop 128
Rose 130-131
Rosettes 162-163
Rowan 130
Sago palm 123
Scots pine 122
Seedling 152-153
Slender thistle 129
Smooth cypress 123
Stomata 139
Strawberry 128
Tendrils 161
Toadflax 129
Tree fern 112-113
Tree mallow 131
Vegetative reproduction
  154-155
Veins 136, 138-139
Venus fly trap 160
Water fern 158
Water hyacinth 158
Water lily 159
Welwitschia 122-123
Xerophyte 156-157
Yew 123
Le Corbusier 494
LEDs 608
Leda Planitia 36, 37
Ledge 381
Leech 374, 384
Leechline 375
Left edge guide 575
Leg
  Amphibian 182
  Caiman 186-187
  Crab 172
  Crayfish 172-173
  Crocodilian 186
  Elephant 200
  Frog 182
  Gorilla 203
  Human 210
  Kangaroo 207
  Lizard 184-185
  Relief-printing press
  449
  Salamander 182
  Scorpion 170
  Shrimp 172
  Spider 170-171
  Tadpole 183
  Terrapin 187
  Tripod congas stand
  519
"Leg before wicket" 538
Leg bud 260
Leg pad 539, 551

Leg protector 551
Leg slip 558
Legumes 150
Leibnitz 41
Lemercier, J. 486
Lemming 196
Lemon 148
Lemur 202-203
Lemur catta 205
Lenoir, Etienne
  Early engines 342
  First cars 354
Lens
  Flatbed scanner 570
  Human body 241
  Microscope 610, 611
Lens cover 581
Lens cover assembly 582
Lenticels 130-131, 134
Lentiform nucleus 237
Leo 18, 21
Leo Minor 18, 21
Leonaspis 279
Leonid meteor shower 52
Leontopithecus rosalia 203
Lepidodendron 66-67
Lepidoptera 168
Lepidotes maximus 73
Leptoceratops 103
Lepus 21
Lesbian leaf pattern 460
Lesene
  Ancient Roman
  building 462, 465
  Baroque church
  480-481
  Dome 486
  French temple 485
  Gothic church 475
  Renaissance building
  476-477
Lesser trochanter of
  femur 225
Lesser wing covert 188
Lesser wing of sphenoid
  bone 221
Letronne 40
Lettering 444-445
Levator anguli oris
  muscle 229
Levator labii superioris
  muscle 229
Levator palpebrae
  superioris muscle 241
Levee 289-291
Level-wind system 562
Lever 320-321
Le Verrier ring 50-51
LG Optimus 2X 588
Liang K'ai 35
Libellulium longialatum
  73
Liberty ship 392
Libra 18, 21
Library 483, 496
Licence holder 332
Lichens 114-115
Lid
  Moss 119
  Pitchers 161
  Ships for war and trade
  377
Lid assembly 571
Lierne 469
Life 56, 78-79, 300
Lifeboat 394
Lifeboat davit 395
Life buoy 395
Life-cycle
  Brown seaweed 117
  Fern 121
  Insect 168
  Moss 119
  Mushroom 115
  Plants 112
  Scots pine 122
Lifeguard 552
Lifejacket 561
Life of massive star 26-27

Life of small star 24-25
Life-raft 416
Liferaft cylinder 397
Lift
  Athletics 543
  Centre Georges
  Pompidou 497
  Double topsail
  schooner 385
  Roman corbita 372
  Sailing warship
  376-377
  Wooden sailing ship
  378
Lift bracing wire
  Biplanes and triplanes
  403
  Early monoplane
  400-401
  Pegasus Quasar
  microlight 427
  World War I aircraft
  404-405
Lifting handle 336
Lifting lug 330
Lift spoiler 413, 414
Lift wire 399
Ligament
  Bifurcate 232
  Cricothyroid 244
  Deltoid 232
  Falciform 248
  Foot 232
  Hip joint 224
  Iliofemoral 224
  Interosseus 232
  Ovarian 258
  Periodontal 247
  Plantar
  calcaneonavicular 232
  Posterior
  cuneonavicular 232
  Posterior
  tarsometatarsal 232
  Pubofemoral 224
  Talonavicular 232
  Zonular 241
Ligature 508, 509
Light 314-315, 318-319
  Chemical reactions
  312
  Renaissance building
  474
  Seed germination 152
  Translucent "window"
  157
  Twentieth-century
  building 495
  Ultraviolet 145
Light aircraft 410, 424-425
Light Emitting Diode 583
Lighterman's hitch 389
Light hour 14
Lighting hole 393
Light level sensor 581
Lightning 45, 316
Lights
  Bicycle 360
  MCW Metrobus 332
Light screen 394
Light shield 612, 613
Light switch 339
Lightweight plastic intake
  manifold 354
Light-well 487
Light year 14
Lignite 280
Lignum vitae bearing
  387
Ligulate ray floret 129
Lilienthal, Otto 398
Lilium bulbiferum 154
Lilium sp. 153, 138,
  140-141, 155
Lily
  Bulbil 154-155
  Flower 140-141
  Leaf surface 138
Limb

Mammal 104
Paddlesteamer 390
Reptile 80
Structure of a fold 60
Limber hole 393
Lime 145
Lime-resistant pigment 434
Limestone
  Cave 284
  Contact metamorphism 274
  Faults and folds 60
  Fossilized blue-green alga 78
  Lower Carboniferous 60
Limestone block 470
Limestone cladding 494
Limestone false door 459
Limestone spring 292
Limestone strata 284
Lime water 313
Limonite groundmass 268-269
Limpet 176
Linaria sp. 129
Line 562
Linea alba 226
Linear dune 283
Linear leaf 129, 137
Linebacker 526
Line guide 563
Line judge 526
Line of sight 41
Linesman
  Badminton 545
  Gaelic football 529
  Ice hockey 550
  Soccer 524
  Tennis 544
  Volleyball 534
Lingual nerve 244
Lingual tonsil 245
Link 386
Linocut 446
Linoleum block 446, 449
Linseed oil 436
Lintel
  Building 459, 494
  Coastline 295
Lintel course 483
Lion 194-195
Lion crest 395
Lionfish 180
Lip
  Flower 126, 145
  Human 212-213
  Lamprey 178
  Pollination 145
Lip of trunk 200-201
Lip plate 508, 508
Lip tension 506
Liquidambar styraciflua 76
Liquid capacity measurements 590
Liquid crystal display (LCD)
  Apple iPad 568
  Garmin Etrex hand-held GPS 591
  HP Pavilion DV4 laptop 567
  JVC Everio camcorder 582-583
  Nikon Coolpix S1000PJ 580
Liquid helium 45
Liquid hydrogen 44-47
Liquid ink 444
Liquids 306-307
Litchi chinensis 148
Lithification 266
Lithium 308, 310
Lithium fluoride molecule 308
Lithium-ion battery 589
Lithium-ion rechargeable battery 579

Lithium-polymer battery 569
Lithographic printing 446
Lithographic printing equipment 448
Lithops bromfieldii 157
Lithops sp. 156
Lithosphere 58-59
Little finger 230-251
Little grebe 190
Little toe 252-253
Live-for-ever 128-129
Liver
  Bird 189
  Bony fish 181
  Chimpanzee 202
  Dogfish 179
  Dolphin 205
  Domestic cat 195
  Euoplocephalus 94
  Frog 182
  Gallimimus 86
  Human 214, 248, 252
  Lizard 185
  Rabbit 196
  Tortoise 187
Liverworts 112, 118-119
Livestock freight car 327
Living organisms 306
Lizard 184-185, 382
"Lizard-feet forms" 88
Lizard-hipped dinosaurs 82, 88-89
Llama 198
Load 320-321
Loading arm 396
Loading gauge 330-331
Load space 334
Lobby 498
Lobe
  Liverwort 118
  Venus fly trap 160
Lobed leaf 129, 131
Lobsters 172
Lobule 242
Local Arm 14
Local control cabinet 396
Lock button 600
Lock forward 530
Lockheed Electra airliner 406-407
Locking lever 590
Lock nut 351, 359
Locks 360
Lock washer 358-359
Locomotion 104
Locomotives 324-329
Lodging knee 381
Loft 477
Log basket 354
Logic board 581
Loin
  Horse 198
  Human 210
London Bridge 466-467
London plane tree 134
Longboat 380
Long bridge 515
Long-distance cycling 360
Long-distance running 542
Longeron 403, 424
Longitudinal channels 120
Longitudinal fissure 256-257
Long jump 542-543
Long leading-link fork 362
Long leg 538
Long off 538
Long on 538
Long pass 552
Long radius turns 552
Longrod stabilizer 549
Longship 374-375
Longshore drift 294-295
Long-travel suspension 568

Long-wave radio 318
Look out periscope 396
Loom 560
Loop 388-389
Looped prominence 32-33
Loophole
  Medieval building 466-469
  Renaissance building 477
Loop of Henlé 256
Loose forward 530
Loose-head prop 530
Lopolith 274
Lora 127, 130
Lorises 202
Lost-wax casting method 454
Lotus flower 488
Lotus petal 489
Loudspeaker 520
Lounge 392
Louvre 495, 498
Love-in-a-mist 150-151
Lowell 43
Lower Carboniferous Limestone 60
Lower crankcase 410
Lower crux of antihelix 242
Lower deadeye 382-383
Lower deck 393
Lower-energy radiation 22
Lower epidermis 139, 159
Lower eyelid 213
Lower equipment module 614
Lower fin 423
Lower haze 37
Lower LCD assembly 579
Lower lobe of lung 215, 254-255
Lower seed axis 152-153
Lower topsail 385
Lower-wing attachment 404
Lower yard 395
Low gain antenna 615
Lowland coastline 295
Low Neap tide 297
Low pressure areas 300, 302-303
Low pressure gases 306
Low tides 296-297
Low-voltage supply 596
Lozenge 471, 485
Lucarne window 480-481, 486
Lufengosaurus 89
Luff 384-385
Lug 382, 386
Lugger 384
Lug sail
  Junk 376
  Sail types 384
Lumbar nerves 258
Lumbar vertebrae
  Crocodile 186
  Domestic cat 195
  Hare 197
  Horse 199
  Human 222-223
  Kangaroo 206
  Platypus 206
  Rhesus monkey 202
  Seal 204
Lumbrical muscle 231
Lump hammer 452-453
Lunae Planum 43
Lunaria annua 151
Lunate bone 230
Lunette 480
Lung
  Amphibian 182
  Bird 189
  Brachiosaurus 91

Chimpanzee 202
Dolphin 205
Domestic cat 195
Elephant 200
Euoplocephalus 94
Frog 182
Gallimimus 86
Human 214-215, 252, 254-255
Lizard 184-185
Rabbit 196
Snail 177
Snake 184
Spider 170
Tortoise 187
Lungfish 80, 81
Lunule 251
Lures 562-563
Lutetium 311
LVG CVI fighter 405
Lychee 148
Lycoming four-cylinder engine 423
Lycoming six-cylinder engine 422
Lycopodophyta 64, 120
Lymphocytes 253
Lynx 18, 21
Lynx helicopter 396
Lyra 19, 20
Lysosome 217

M

M22 (globular cluster) 21
Macaques 202
Macaws 190
Mach 41
Machine-gun 404-405
Machine heads 512-513
Mackenzie-Peace River 264
Mackerel angling 562
Maquette 455
Macrobius 40
Macrofibril 234
Macrospicule 33
Macs 566
Macula 240-241
Madagascar 265
Madreporite 174, 175
Madrillus sphinx 203
Maenianum summum 465
Magazine 548-549
Magellanic Cloud 15, 20
Maginus 40
Maglev train 328-329
Magma
  Igneous and metamorphic rocks 26
  Mountain building 63
  Ocean floor 298-299
  Rock cycle 266
  Volcanoes 272
Magma reservoir
  Igneous rock structures 275
  Volcanic structure 273
Magnesium 310
  Earth's composition 39
  Earth's crust 58
  Seawater salt content 296
Magnesium alloy oil sump pan 554
Magnesium housing for air intake 355
Magnesium riser 548
Magnet 598, 605
Magnet array 615
Magnetic axis 28
Magnetic compass 423
Magnetic field 38
Magnetism 316-317
Magneto
  Avro triplane 402
  Hawker Tempest components 408

Wright Flyer 399
Magneto drive 367
Magnetometer 614
Magnetosphere 38
Magnetron assembly 596, 597
Magnetron cooling fan 596, 597
Magnetron cooling fan mounting 597
Magnetron perforated heat sink 597
Magnitude 22
Magnolia 57, 72
Mahonia 130-131
Maidenhair tree 122-123
Maillot 586
Main deck passenger door 573
Main deck windows 573
Main engines 614
Main fan 596, 597
Main fan electrical supply 597
Main-line signalling system 330-331
Main motor casing 593
Main printed circuit board (PCB) 579
Mainrail head 379
Main sail
  Dhow 376
  Roman corbita 373
  Sailing rigs 585
  Square-rigged ship 375
Main screen 584
Mains earthing wire 596
Mains electricity supply lead 585
Main sequence star
  Massive stars 26
  Objects in Universe 11
  Small stars 24
  Stars 22-23
Mains flex 594
Mains flex clamp 594
Main sheer strake 393
Main sheet
  Longboat 380
  Roman corbita 373
  Sailing dinghy 561
  Viking karv 375
Main shroud 378
Mains lead 597-598
Main spar bridge 413
Mains power on/off switch 585
Mains spade contacts 594
Main stay 377, 379
Mains supply lead 594
Maintenance button 574
Main topcastle 377
Main topgallant mast 377, 378
Main topgallant sail 379
Main topgallant stay 379
Main topmast 377, 379
Main topmast topcastle 377
Main topsail 379
Main topsail halyard 385
Main topsail yard 379
Main top yard 377
Main turbine 597
Main wale 381
Main wing bracing-strut 401
Main wing-strut 427
Main yard
  Dhow 376
  Sailing warship 377
  Wooden sailing ship 379
Maize 127
Major calyx 256
Major coverts 188, 191
Malachite 433

Malacostraca 172
Malaysia 331
Male
  Bladder 257
  Body 210, 211
  Pelvis 259
  Reproductive organs 259
  Urinary tract 257
Male apex 119
Male catkin 144
Male cone 122-123, 24
Male fern 120-121
Male flower organs 140-143
Male flowers
  Fertilization 146-147
  Gymnosperms 122
  Painter's palette 143
  Seaweed 116-117
  Succulent fruit 148
  Wind-pollinated plant 144
"Mallard" express steam locomotive 324-325
Mallet
  Marble carving 452
  Ships and sailing 383, 384, 388
  Tubular bells 516
Malleus 242
Malpighian tubule
  Butterfly 169
  Spider 170
Malus 373
Malus sp. 126
Malus sylvestris 149
Mammals 104-107
  Carnivora 194
  Cetacea 204
  Cretaceous period 72
  Earth's evolution 56-57
  Fossil record 279
  Jurassic period 70
  Lagomorpha 196
  Large 57
  Marsupalia 206
  Monotremata 206
  Pinnipedia 204
  Primates 202
  Proboscidea 200
  Rodentia 196
  Shrew-like 70
  Small 56
  Tertiary period 74-75
  Ungulates 198
Mammoth 107
Mammut 75
Mammuthus 76, 77, 104
Mandapa 491
Mandarinfish 180
Mandible
  Acanthostega 80
  Ankylosaurus 94
  Arsinoitherium 104
  Baryonyx 83
  Bat 105
  Bear 194
  Beetle 168
  Bird 188-189
  Bony fish 181
  Camarasaurus 91
  Chimpanzee 202
  Crayfish 173
  Crocodile 186
  Diplodocus 90
  Elephant 201
  Eryops 80
  Euoplocephalus 94
  Hare 197
  Heterodontosaurus 83
  Horse 199
  Human 220-221, 244-245
  Hyaenodon 107
  Iguanodon 96
  Kangaroo 206
  Lambeosaurus 99
  Lion 194

Moeritherium 105
Panoplosaurus 94
Parasaurolophus 99
Phiomia 105
Plateosaurus 88
Protoceratops 102
Rattlesnake 185
Rhesus monkey 202
Seal 204
Stegoceras 100-101
Styracosaurus 102
Toxodon 106
Triceratops 103
Turtle 187
Tyrannosaurus 84
Mandrills 202-203
Mane 194, 199
Manganese 281, 310
Manharness knot 589
Manifold connector 355
Manilla rope 589
Manipulator 610
Man-of-war 378
Mansard roof 490
Mantellisaurus 96-97
Mantle
 Earth 38-39, 58-59, 63
 Mars 43
 Mercury 35
 Moon 41
 Molluscs 176-177
 Neptune 51
 Pluto 51
 Regional
  metamorphism 274
 Uranus 49
 Venus 37
Maple 127
Map projections 264-265
Maracas 504, 516-517
Marble 274
Marble block 453
Marble breaking
 equipment 450
Marble mosaic 489
Marble sculpture 452
Marble tessera 450
Marble veneer 462
Marchantia polymorpha
 118
Mare Crisium 40
Mare Fecunditatis 40
Mare Frigoris 40
Mare Humorum 40
Mare Imbrium 40
Mare Ingenii 41
Mare Moscoviense 41
Mare Nubium 40
Mare Orientale 41
Mareotis Fossae 43
Mare Serenitatis 40
Mare Smithii 41
Mare's tail 135
Mare Tranquillitatis 40
Mare Vaporum 40
Margaritifer Sinus 43
Margin
 Lamina 116-117, 161
 Leaf 129, 136-137
 Needle 124
 Water lily leaf 159
Marginal shield 187
"Margined heads" 100
Marginocephalians 83,
 100-103
Maria 40
Marine invertebrates
 65
Marine plants 56
Marine reptiles 57, 70
Marine sediments 280
Marine turtles 186
Mariopteris 66
Markab 19, 20
Markeb 21
Marlin 388
Marlinspike 383, 389
Marmosets 202

Marram grass 113
Mars 30, 42-43, 615
Mars Exploration Rover
 (MER) 615
Mars Exploration Rover
 spacecraft 615
Marsh 293
Marsupials 104, 206-207
Martellange, E. 479
Martingale 382, 557
Martingale stay 583
Mary Rose 376
Mascaron 487
Mask 460, 487, 536
 Ancient Roman
  building 465
 Cathedral dome 484
 Neoclassical building
  482
Masonry apron 487
Mason's mark 470
Mason's tools 485
Mass
 Atoms and molecules
  309, 320
 Earth 30
 Jupiter 26, 44
 Mars 30
 Mercury 30
 Neptune 31
 Planets 30-31
 Pluto 31
 Saturn 31
 Stars 22
 Uranus 31
 Venus 30
Massive habit 270-271
Massive stars 26-27
Mass measurements 590
Massospondylidae 89
Mass-production 338-339,
 492
Mass transportation 332
Mast
 Battleship 394
 Frigate 397
 Greek galley 372
 Iron paddlesteamer 392
 Junk 376
 Longboat 380
 Roman corbita 373
 Sailing 561
 Sailing warship 376-377
 Submarine 397
 Tea clipper 392
 Three-masted square-
  rigged ship 375
 Viking karv 375
 Wooden sailing ship
  378-379
Mast band 382
Master cylinder
 Disc brake 365
 Harley-Davidson FLHS
  Electra Glide 363
 Honda VF750 564
Master shipwright 574
Master's sea cabin 381
Masthead
 Roman corbita 373
 Viking karv 375
 Wooden sailing ship
  378
Mast head bend 389
Masthead pulley for tye
 halyard 575
Mast hoop 385
Mastoid fontanelle 220
Mastoid process 220, 242
Mast partner 381
Mast step 592
Mast truck 372
Matar 21
Match play 546
Maternal blood pool 260
Maternal blood vessel 260
Mathematical symbols 621
Mato Grosso 264
Matter 306-307

Electrical charge 316
Identification 312
Mature ruptured follicle
 258
Mawsonites spriggi 65
Maxilla
 Ankylosaurus 94
 Baryonyx 83
 Bear 194
 Bony fish 181
 Camarasaurus 91
 Chimpanzee 202
 Diplodocus 90
 Elephant 201
 Eryops 80
 Euoplocephalus 94
 Frog 183
 Horse 105
 Human 212, 220-221,
  244-245, 246, 248
 Iguanodon 96
 Lion 194
 Pachycephalosaurus 100
 Prenocephale 100
 Stegoceras 100
 Toxodon 106
Maxillary fenestra 90
Maxilliped 173
Maxwellian diagram 318
Maxwell Montes 36, 37
Mazda RX-7 346
McLaren Mercedes MP4-
 13 356-357
MCW Metrobus 332-333
ME 262 fighter 408
Meadow cranesbill 144
Meadow rue 137
Meadow sage 145
Meander 461
Meanders 288-289, 290
Measurement units 620
Meatus 242-243
Mechanical semaphore
 signal 350
Mechanical weathering
 282
Mechanics 350-351
Mechanism of respiration
 255
Medallion 476
Media guide button 577
Medial epicondyle 225
Medial malleolus 233
Medial moraine
 Glaciers 286-287
 River's stages 289
Medial rectus muscle
 240-241
Median canal 243
Median cubital vein 253
Median eye 170
Median glossoepiglottic
 fold 244
Median nerve 238
Median sulcus 244
Median wing coverts 188
Medieval castles 466-467
Medieval churches
 468-469
Medieval houses 466-467
Medinet Habu, Egypt 459
Mediterranean Sea 74,
 265
Mediterranean sea
 anemone 166
Medium-wave radio 318
Medulla 114, 234, 256
Medulla oblongata 212,
 256-257
Medullary cavity 224
Medullary pyramid 256
Medullary ray 125
Medullosa 66
Megaspores 122
Megazostrodon 104
Megrez 19
Meiolania 77
Meissner's corpuscle
 234-235, 239

Melanin 234
Melanosaurus 68, 88-89
Melon 149, 205
Melting glacier 286, 289
Meltwater 287, 289
Meltwater pool 286
Membrane
 Chloroplasts 139
 Chorioallantoic 192
 Egg 193
 Shell 192
 Thylakoid 139
Memory stick 581
Mendel 41
Mendeleev 41
Mendelevium 311
Meninges 257
Menkalinan 21
Menkar 19, 20
Menkent 21
Mensa 20, 21
Mental foramen 213,
 220-221
Mentalis muscle 229
Mental protuberance 221
Mental symphysis 220
Mentolabial sulcus 213
Menu key 590
Merak 19
Merchants' Exchange 493
Mercury 30, 34-35
Mercury (metal) 281, 311,
 319
Mericarp 151
Meristematic cells 154
Merlin 466
Mermaid's purses 192
Mersenius 40
Merus 172, 173
Merycoidodon 75
Mesa 275, 277, 282
Mesentery 167, 182
Mesocarp 146-147, 148,
 148-149
Mesoglea 167
Mesohyal 166
Mesophyll 135
 Bishop pine needle 124
 Dicotyledon leaf 126
 Marram grass 113
 Monocotyledon leaf
  126
 Palisade layer 139
 Spongy layer 139
Mesosphere 300
Mesothorax 168
Mesozoic era
 Cretaceous period 72
 Dinosaurs 82
 Fossil record 279
 Geological timescale 57
 Jurassic period 70
 Reptiles 80
 Triassic period 68
Mess 397
Message area 576
Message display area 576
Metacarpals
 Archaeopteryx 85
 Arsinoitherium 104
 Baryonyx 85
 Bird 189, 91
 Brachiosaurus 91
 Cow 198
 Diplodocus 90
 Domestic cat 195
 Elephant 90, 201
 Eryops 80
 Euoplocephalus 94
 Frog 183
 Gallimimus 86
 Hare 197
 Horse 198-199
 Human 218-219, 230
 Kangaroo 206
 Lizard 184
 Parasaurolophus 99
 Plateosaurus 88
 Platypus 206

Rhesus monkey 202
Seal 204
Stegoceras 100
Toxodon 106
Triceratops 103
Tyrannosaurus 84
Metacarpophalangeal
 joint 85
Metal cook/grill tray 596
Metal grill/griddle 596
Metalliferous muds 299
Metalling 486
Metal modelling
 implements 452
Metal needle pad 384
Metal nib 444
Metal riser 455
Metal runner 455
Metal tyre 324
Metal wire conductor
 316-317
Metals 310
Metamorphic aureole 26
Metamorphic rocks 26,
 274-275, 266-267
Metamorphosis
 Amphibian 182
 Frog 183
 Insect 168
Metasoma 170
Metatarsals
 Albertosaurus 84
 Archaeopteryx 85
 Brachiosaurus 90
 Crocodile 186
 Domestic cat 195
 Elephant 201
 Eiyops 81
 Euoplocephalus 94
 Frog 183
 Hare 197
 Horse 199
 Human 218-219, 232
 Iguanodon 96-97
 Kangaroo 206
 Lizard 184
 Parasaurolophus 98
 Plateosaurus 88
 Platypus 206
 Rhesus monkey 202
 Scorpion 170
 Seal 204
 Spider 171
 Stegoceras 100-101
 Struthiomimus 87
 Toxodon 107
 Triceratops 102
Metathorax 168
Metaxylem 127, 132-133
Meteor 52, 301
Meteorite
 Asteroids, comets, and
  meteoroids 52
 Earth's atmosphere 38
 Moon 41
 Ray crater 34
Meteorite impact 34, 40
Meteoroids 52-53
 Solar System 30
Methane
 Jupiter 45
 Neptune and Pluto
  50-51
 Saturn 47
 Uranus 48-49
Methane cirrus clouds
 50-51
Metis Regio 36
Metope 460
Metric-Imperial
 conversions 620
Metric unit
 measurements 590
Metridium senile 166
Metrobus 332-333
Metrolink tram 332
Mexican hat plant 154
Mexican mountain king
 snake 184

Mexican true red-legged
 tarantula 170
Mexico 331
Mezzanine 467, 496
Miaplacidus 21
Mica 26, 270
Mice 104, 196
Michelangelo 35
Micrasterias sp. 112
Microfilament 217
Microlights 410, 426-427
Micro-needle 606
Micro-organisms 58, 78
Microphone 581
Micro-pipette 606
Microporous filter 592
Microprocessor
 Personal computer 567
 Digital camera 580
Microscopes 610-611
Microsoft Kinect 578
Microsoft Zune HD 587
Microsporangium 122
Microspores 122
Microsporophyll 122
Microtubule 217, 239
Micro-USB (Universal
 Serial Bus) socket 589
Microwave oven 615
Microwave radiation 10
Microwave combination
 oven 596-597
Microwaves 318, 596
Midbrain 256
Middle ear ossicles 242
Middle finger 230-231
Middle leg
 Beetle 168
 Bumblebee 168
 Butterfly 169
Middle lobe of lung 215,
 254-255
Middle meatus 241, 245
Middle nasal concha 212,
 221, 241, 245
Middle phalanx 219, 230,
 252
Middle rail 381
Midfielders
 Gaelic football 529
 Lacrosse 541
 Soccer 524
Midgut 173
Mid-latitude band 36
Mid-latitude cyclones 302
Mid-ocean ridge 281,
 298-299
Mid-off 538
Mid-on 538
Midrib
 Dicotyledon leaf
  126-127
 Durmast oak leaf 131
 Fern fronds 121
 Hogweed leaf 129
 Ice-plant leaf 129
 Live-for-ever leaf 129
 Liverwort 118
 Monkey cup 161
 Moss leaf 119
 Spiral wrack 116
 Sweet chestnut leaf 136
 Tree fern 113
 Venus fly trap 160
 Water lily leaf 159
Midships fence 373
Midships section 392
Midwater current 297
Midway Gardens 495
Mid West single-rotor
 engine 411
Mid West twin-rotor
 engine 411
Mid West two-stroke
 engine 410
Miele washer-dryer 594,
 595
Mihrab 488
Milan Cathedral 473

648

Milankovic 43
Milk snake 184
Milk teeth 246
Milky quartz 268, 271
Milky Way 14-15
  Northern stars 18
  Solar System 30
  Stars of southern skies
   20
Mill 462, 464, 492
Millstone grit 60-61
Milne 41
Milton 35
Mimas 46
Mimosa 21
Mimulopsis solmsii 145
Minaret 488-489
Mineral-filled fault 60-61
Mineral-rich deposits
  298
Minerals 268-269
  Carnivorous plants 160
  Epiphytes 162
  Fossils 278
  Mineral features 270-271
  Mineral resources
   280-281
  Photosynthesis 138-139
  Wetland plants 158
  Xylem vessel 134
Mineral spicules 166
Mineral spring 273
Mineral wool 603
Minim 502
Minmi 95
Minor calyx 256
Minor coverts 188, 191
Mint 109
Mintaka 18
Miocene epoch
  Fossil record 279
  Geological timescale 57
Mira 19, 20
Mirach 19, 20
Miranda 48
Mirfak 19, 20
Mirzam 18, 21
Missile launcher 397
Mississippi period 56
Mississippi Delta 290-291
Mississippi-Missouri River
  264
Mississippi River 291
Mist 306
Mistle thrush 190
Mistletoe 162
Mitochondrial crista 217
Mitochondrial sheath 259
Mitochondrion 217, 239
Mitral valve 251
Mixosaurus 57
Mizar 19
Mizzen backstay 378
Mizzen bitt 381
Mizzen course 379
Mizzen mast
  Dhow 376
  Iron paddlesteamer 392
  Junk 376
  Sailing warship 377
  Square-rigged ship 375
  Wooden sailing ship
   378
Mizzen sail 375, 385
Mizzen shroud 378
Mizzen stay 378
Mizzen top 378
Mizzen topcastle 377
Mizzen topgallant sail 379
Mizzen topmast 377, 378
Mizzen topsail 379
Mizzen yard 376-377, 378
Moat 466-467
Mobile phones 588-589
Mobile sculpture 452
Modelling 452
Modelling tools 454
Modem 576, 577
Moderator 314

Modern buildings 496-499
Modern engines 344-345
Modern humans 57
Modern jetliners 412-415
Modern military aircraft
  420-421
Modern piston aero-
  engines 410-411
Mode switch 586
Modified cuticle 157
Modified lateral shoots
  156
Modified leaflets 129
Modified leaves
  Barberry 130-131
  Cobra lily 160
  Dryland plants 156-157
  Everlasting pea 129
  Golden barrel cactus
   156
  Pitcher development 161
  Spines 156
  Strawberry 128
Modified shoots 156
Modified stipules 128-129
Modillion
  Baroque church 479
  Neoclassical building
   478
  Renaissance building
   475
Moenave formation 276
Moenkopi formation 276
Moeritherium 104
Mohorovic discontinuity
  59
Mohs scale 270-271
Molar tooth
  Arsinoitherium 104
  Australopithecus 107
  Bear 106, 194
  Chimpanzee 202
  Elephant 201
  Horse 105
  Human 246
  Hyaenodon 107
  Moeritherium 105
  Opossum 106
  Phiomia 105
  Toxodon 106
Molecular orbitals 308
Molecules 306, 308-309
Molluscs 176-177
  Belemnite 71
  Nautiloid 69
Molten bronze 454
Molten core 39
Molten rock
  Igneous and
   metamorphic rocks 274
  Matter 306
  Ocean floor 298
  Plate movements 58
  Rock cycle 266
  Volcanoes 272
Molybdate 269
Molybdenum 310
Mongooses 194
Monkey cup 161
Monkeys 202-203
Monitor
  Digital camera 580
Monoceros 18, 21
Monoclinal fold 60
Monocline 61
Monoclinic system 270
Monocoque chassis 363
Monocoque shell 348
Monocotyledonous petals
  140, 143
Monocotyledonous sepals
  126, 140, 143
Monocotyledons 126-127,
  140-141, 143
Monodon monoceros 205
Monograptus convolutus 65
Monolithic shaft 463
Monoplanes 400-401, 402,
  406

Monotremes 206-207
Montes Apenninus 40
Montes Cordillera 41
Montes Jura 40
Montes Rook 41
Monteverdi 35
Montgolfier brothers 398
Monument 470
Moon 40-41
  Objects in Universe 11
  Solar eclipse 32
  Tides 296-297
Moonquake region 41
Moons
  Jupiter 44
  Mars 42
  Neptune 50
  Saturn 46
  Solar System 30
  Uranus 48
Mooring 386-387
Moorish arch 484
Moraine 286-287, 292-293
Moray eel 180
Mortar 452
Mortice 373
Mortise 486, 492
Morus nigra 130
Mosaic 450-451
  Islamic building
   488-489
  Tools 450
Mosque 484, 488
Mosses 112, 114, 118-119
  Epiphytic 162
  Life-cycle 119
  Structure 119
Moth 168
Motherboard
  Digital camcorder 583
  Personal computer
   567
Motherboard cable 578
Mother's milk 104
Motion 320-321
Motion sensor 579
Motocross motorcycle
  racing 368
Motor air intake 593
Motor assembly 574
Motorcycle chassis 362,
  364-365
Motorcycle engines
  366-367
Motorcycle racing 368
Motorcycles 362-363
Motorcycle sidecar 362,
  369
Motor-driven bogie axle
  326
Motor electronic control
  module (ECM) 355
Motor end plate 228, 239
Motorhead 592, 593
Motorized buses 332
Motor neuron 228, 239
Motor operating signal
  330
Motor whaler 397
Motte 466
Mouchette 472
Mould 278
Moulded bracket 484
Moulded corbel 493
Moulding 485
  Ancient Egyptian
   temple 458-459
  Asian building 490
  Baroque church
   480-481
  Dome 486-487
  Gothic church 471-472
  Medieval building 466,
   469
  Neoclassical building
   479-480, 482
  Renaissance building
   475-477
  Ship's shield 395

Moulding tool 454
Moulds 114
Moulting 171
Mounds 286
Mountain bikes 358, 360
Mountain building 56, 58,
  62-63
Mountain hollows 286
Mountain lake 288
Mountain ranges
  Earth's physical
   features 264
  Faults and folds 60
  Geological time 56
  Igneous and
   metamorphic rocks 274
  Mountain building 62
  Ocean floor 298
  Plate movements 59
Mountain ridge 295
Mountain ring 34
Mountains 62-65, 267
Mountain spring 288
Mounting bracket 590
Mounting bush 565
Mounting splines 366
Mouse 521, 566, 611
Mouse and collar 379
Mouth
  Barnacle 173
  Bony fish 180-181
  Cobra lily 160
  Cow 198
  Crayfish 173
  Dogfish 179
  Dolphin 204
  Elephant 200
  Frog 182
  Gorilla 203
  Horse 199
  Human 211, 212,
   244-245, 248
  Jellyfish 167
  Kangaroo 204
  Lamprey 178
  Lizard 184
  Pitcher plant 161
  Rabbit 196
  Rat 196
  Sea anemone 166-167
  Seal 204
  Sea urchin 175
  Snail 177
  Spider 170
  Starfish 174-175
Mouth diffuser 430, 440
Mouthpiece
  Brass instruments 506
  Clarinet 508
  Tenor saxophone 509
  Trumpet 506
  Wind synthesizer 521
Movement
  Gas particles 307
  Objects 320
MP3 players 586
MRI scan
  Head 214
  Brain 236
Mt. Everest 264
Mu Andromedae 19
Muav limestone 277
Muccini brush 434
Mucosa 248
Mucosal gland 254
Mucous gland 177
Mucronate leaf apex 137
Mucus-secreting
  duodenal cells 217
Mud 267, 273
Mud crab 279
Mud-flat 295
Mudguard
  1906 Renault 336-337
  BMW R/60 with Steib
   chair 362
  Cannondale ST 1000
   touring bicycle 361
  Ford Model T 338-339

Harley-Davidson FLHS
  Electra Glide 363
Honda VF750 364
Husqvarna Motocross
  TC610 568
Kirby BSA 369
Lockheed Electra 406
Motorcycle 364
Suzuki RGV500 369
Volkswagen Beetle 341
Weslake Speedway
  motorcycle 369
Mudguard stay 337, 362,
  363
Mud pools 272-273
Mud river 298
Mulberry 130
Muliphen 21
Mullion
  Gothic church 470,
   472-473
  Modern building
   497-499
  Renaissance building
   476
  Small-scale rock
   formation 60-61
  Twentieth-century
   building 494
Multicellular animals 56
Multicellular organisms
  78
Multicellular soft-bodied
  animals 56
Multifoil 472
Multifunction display 573
Multi-gabled roof 492
Multiplait nylon 388
Multiple clutch 364, 366
Multiple fruits 148-149
Multiplier reel 562
Multi-ply tyre 416
Multipolar neuron 239
Multi-touch interface 568
Mu Orionis 19
Mu Pegasi 19
Musa 'lacatan' 146
Muscari sp. 155
Musci 118
Muscle 226-229
  Abductor digiti
   minimus 231, 233
  Adductor longus 225
  Adductor magnus 227
  Adductor pollicis 231
  Abductor pollicis brevis
   231
  Anal sphincter 249
  Arrector pili 235
  Cricothyroid 244-245
  Dilator 241
  Dorsal interosseous 231
  Energy system 315
  Extensor digitorum
   brevis 233
  Extensor hallucis brevis
   233
  Flexor digitorum
   longus 233
  Flexor hallucis longus
   233
  Flexor pollicis brevis
   231
  Flexor retinaculum 231
  Genioglossus 245
  Geniohyoid 245
  Gluteus medius 225
  Gluteus minimus 225
  Hyoglossus 244
  Iliacus 225
  Inferior oblique 241
  Inferior rectus 241
  Intercostal 255
  Internal urethral
   sphincter 257
  Lateral rectus 240-241
  Levator palpebrae
   superioris 241
  Lumbrical 231

  Medial rectus 240-241
  Myohyoid 245
  Opponens digiti minimi
   231
  Opponens pollicis 231
  Orbicularis oris 245
  Papillary 251
  Pectineus 225
  Peroneus brevis 233
  Peroneus longus 233
  Psoas major 225, 257
  Pyloric sphincter 249
  Soleus 233
  Sphincter 241
  Styloglossus 244
  Superior longitudinal
   245
  Superior oblique 241
  Superior rectus 241
  Tensor tympani 245
  Thyrohyoid 245
  Tibialis anterior 233
  Tibialis posterior 233
  Urethral sphincter 257
  Vastus lateralis 225
  Vastus medialis 225
Muscovite 269
Muscular septum 176
Mushroom anchor 386
Mushroom coral 167
Mushrooms 114, 115
Music 514, 586
Musical Instrument
  Digital Interface (MIDI)
   system 520-521
Musical manuscript
  502-503
Musical notation 502-503
Musical score 502-503,
  505
Music gallery 477
Musicians 504
Music software 520
Muslim calendar 618
Mussels 176
Mussosaurus 68
Mutes 506-507
Muttaburrasaurus 97
Muzzle 199, 397
Mycelium 114-115
Mycorrhizal association
  133
Myelin sheath 239
Mylar 35
Myocardium 250-251
Myofibril 228
Myohyoid muscle 245
Myometrium 260

N

Nail
  Corythosaurus 98
  Edmontonia 95
  Elephant 90
  Human 231
  Iguanodon 96-97
  Stegosaurus 92
  Triceratops 102
Nair Al Zaurak 19, 20
Naismath, James 552
Namib Desert 265
Naos 461, 463, 485
Nape 188, 210
Napier Sabre 24-cylinder
  engine 408
Naris
  Anchisaurus 89
  Ankylosaurus 94
  Arsinoitherium 104
  Australopithecus 108
  Baryonyx 83
  Brachiosaurus 91
  Camarasaurus 91
  Corythosaurus 98
  Edmontonia 95
  Eryops 80
  Euoplocephalus 94

Homo erectus 108
Homo habilis 108
Homo sapiens 108
Hyaenodon 107
Iguanodon 96
Lambeosaurus 99
Moeritherium 105
Opossum 106
Panoplosaurus 94
Parasaurolophus 99
Plateosaurus 88
Protoceratops 102
Smilodon 107
Stegoceras 100-101
Stegosaurus 92
Styracosaurus 102
Triceratops 102-103
Tyrannosaurus 84
Narrow gauge track 331
Narwhal 205
Nasal bone
  Ankylosaurus 94
  Bear 194
  Frog 183
  Human 220-221
  Lion 194
  Panoplosaurus 94
  Protoceratops 102
  Toxodon 106
Nasal cavity
  Chimpanzee 202
  Domestic cat 195
  Elephant 200
  Human 245, 248
  Rabbit 196
Nasal horn 104
Nasalis 229
Nasal passage 200
Nasal plug 205
Nasal septum 213, 221, 241
Nash 21
Nasion 221
Nasolacrimal duct 241
Nasopharynx 245
Natal cleft 210
Natal cocoon 24, 26
Native elements 268
Natural bridge 290
Natural elements 310
Natural fly 562
Natural forces 314
Natural glass 306
Natural gut strings 544
Natural lakes 292
Natural satellites 40
Natural sponge 438
Nautiloid mollusc 69
  Fossil 65
Navajo mountain 277
Navajo sandstone 276
Nave
  Ancient Egyptian temple 458-459
  Baroque church 479
  Cathedral dome 484
  Gothic church 470-473
  Medieval church 468-469
  Ship's wheel 390
Navel 211, 260
Nave plate 590
Navicular bone 232
Navigating bridge 394
Navigational aerial 423-424
Navigation area 577
Navigation buttons 577
Navigation camera (Navcam) 615
Navigation display 573
Navigation light 573
Navigator's cockpit 420
Navigator's seat 408
Navka 37
Nazea plate 59
Neanderthals 108
Neap tides 296-297
Nebulae 16-17

Cone 612
Galaxies 12-13
  Great, Orion 613
  Life of massive star 26
  Milky Way 14-15
  NGC 1566 (Seyfert galaxy) 13
  Omega 613
  Small stars 24
  Structure of nebula 24
Neck
  Acoustic guitar 512-513
  Anchisaurus 89
  Calligraphy character 445
  Corythosaurus 98
  Electric guitar 513
  Golf club 547
  Harp 511
  Horse 199
  Human 211, 224-225, 247, 258-259
  Iguanodon 97
  Pachycephalosaurus 100
  Rat 196
  Sauropodomorpha 88
  Sculling oar 560
  Stegoceras 101
  Stegosaurus 92
  Stringed instruments 510
  Tenor saxophone 509
  Theropod 84
  Violin 510
Necking 514
Nectar 142, 160-161
Nectaries 141, 144-145, 160-161
Needles
  Bishop pine 124
  Pine 124-125
  Scots pine 122
  Yew 123
Nefertiti Corona 37
Negative electric charge 316
Negative ions 308, 310
Neo-Baroque style 492-493
Neo-Byzantine style 492-493
Neoclassical style 478-483, 496
Neodymium 310
Neo-Gothic style 492-493
Neo-Greek style 492-493
Neon 35, 311
Nepenthes mirabilis 161
Nephron 256
Neptune 31, 50-51
Neptunides polychromus 12
Neptunium 311
Nerve
  Ampullar 242
  Bronchial 254
  Cervical 238
  Cochlear 243
  Common peroneal 238
  Cranial 238
  Cutaneous 238
  Deep peroneal 238
  Digital 251
  Femoral 238
  Hypoglossal 244
  Lingual 244
  Lumbar 238
  Median 238
  Optic 240
  Posterior tibial 238
  Pudendal 238
  Pulp 247
  Radial 238
  Sacral 238
  Sciatic 238
  Spinal 223, 238
  Superficial peroneal 238

Superior laryngeal 244
Thoracic 258
Ulnar 251, 258
Vestibular 243
Vestibulocochlear 243
Nerve cell 217, 257, 239
Nerve cord 173
Nerve fibre 235
Nerve ring 175
Nervous system 176, 238-239
Nervous tissue 166
Netball 534-535
Network port 566
Neural spine
  Arsinoitherium 104
  Bony fish 180
  Brachiosaurus 90
  Eryops 81
  Euoplocephalus 95, 87
  Iguanodon 96
  Parasaurolophus 98
  Plateosaurus 89
  Stegoceras 100-101
  Stegosaurus 93
  Toxodon 106
  Triceratops 102
  Tuojiangosaurns 93
  Tyrannosaurus 85
Neurofilament 239
Neuron 259
Neurotransmitter 239
Neutralization 312
Neutrino 22
Neutron 22, 28
Neutrons 308, 309, 310
Neutron stars 28-29, 26-27
New Guinea 265
New mail button 576
New Moon 41
News item summary 577
News reader window 577
New State Paper Office 482
Newton (N) 320
Newton, Isaac 320
Newton meter 320-321
Newton's Motion laws 320-321
Newts 182
New World monkeys 202-203
New Zealand 265, 272
Next/Previous track control 587
Next file button 577
Next key 568
NGC 1566 (Seyfert galaxy) 13
NGC 2997 (spiral galaxy) 12
NGC 4406 (elliptical galaxy) 11
NGC 4486 (elliptical galaxy) 12
NGC 5236 (spiral galaxy) 11
NGC 5754 (colliding galaxies) 9
NGC 6656 (globular cluster) 21
NGC 6822 (irregular galaxy) 11
Nib types 444
Niche
  Ancient Roman building 462
  Asian temple 491
  Baroque church 480
  Cathedral dome 487
  Gothic church 471-472
  Islamic building 488
  Medieval building 467
  Neoclassical building 482
  Renaissance building 476
Nigella damascena 151

Nikon Coolpix S1000PJ 580-581
Nile crocodile 186
Nimbostratus cloud 302
Nimbus cloud 302
Nineteenth-century buildings 479, 482, 492-493, 494
Ninth-century building 490
Nintendo 3DS 578
Nintendo Wii Fit Plus 579
Niobe Planitia 36, 37
Niobium 310
Nippers 450
Nipple
  Human 211
  Marsupials 206
Nissl body 259
Nitrate ions 312
Nitrates 160
Nitrogen
  Atmospheric composition 301
  Helix Nebula 17
  Mars' atmosphere 43
  Periodic table 311
  Pluto's atmosphere 51
  Venus' atmosphere 37
Nitrogen dioxide gas 312
Nobelium 311
Noble gases 310-311
Nock 548
Noctis Labyrinthus 42, 43
Nocturnal mammals 104
Node
  Bamboo 131
  Brassavola nodosa 162
  Canadian pond weed 158-159
  Couch grass 113
  Dicotyledons 127
  Horsetail 120
  Ice-plant 129
  Live-for-ever 129
  Rhizome 155
  Rock stonecrop 128
  Rose stem 130
  Stems 154
  Stolon 154
  Strawberry 128
Node of Ranvier 228, 239
Nodule fields 299
Nodules 128
Noggin 602
Nonconformity 276
Non-drive end 317
Nonesuch House 467
Non-explosive eruptions 272
Non-flowering plants 68
Non-metals 310
Non-return valve 367
Non-skid tyre 357
Non-slip flooring 573
North America
  Appalachian Mountains 62
  Cretaceous period 72-73
  Earth's physical features 264
  Jurassic period 70
  Late Carboniferous period 66
  Middle Ordovician period 64
  Quaternary period 76-77
  Tertiary period 74-75
  Triassic period 68
North American Cordillera 71
North American period 56
North American plate 59
North Atlantic current 296
North Atlantic Gyre 296
North Atlantic Ocean 39, 71, 73

North East Africa 64
North-easterly wind 303
North-east monsoon 297
North-east trade winds 300
North Equatorial Belt 45
North Equatorial current 296-297
Northern Hemisphere 296-297
North Galactic Pole 15
North magnetic polar region 28
North Pacific current 296
North Pacific Gyre 296
North polar aurora 45
North polar ice-cap 43
North Pole
  Atmospheric circulation and winds 300
  Coriolis force 297
  Jupiter 44
  Mars 42
  Mercury 34
  The Moon 40
  Neptune 50
  Pluto 51
  Pulsar 28
  Saturn 46
  Uranus 48
  Venus 36
North rim 277
North Temperate Zone 45
North Tropical Zone 45
North-westerly wind 303
Nose
  B-17 bomber 408
  Concorde 416-417
  Iron 594
  Horse 198
  Human 211-212, 244-245
  Lion 194
  Lockheed Electra airliner 406
  Rabbit 196
  Rat 196
Noseband 554, 555
Nose clip 558
Nose cone 418, 560
Nose cover 357
Nose cowling 412
Nose-end bogie 327
Nose-gear
  ARV light aircraft 424-425
  Concorde 417
  Tornado 420
Nose horn 102, 103
Nose landing gear 573
Nose-ring
  Avro biplane 403
  Blackburn monoplane 400
Nose-wheel
  ARV light aircraft 425
  Curtiss biplane 398
  Pegasus XL SE microlight 426
  Tornado 420
Nostril
  Bird 188
  Chick 193
  Crocodilians 186
  Dolphin 205
  Domestic cat 195
  Elephant 200
  Frog 182
  Gorilla 203
  Horse 198
  Human 213
  Kangaroo 207
  Lion 194
  Lizard 184
  Monkey 202
  Rat 196
  Rattlesnake 185
  Seal 204
Nostril pocket 80

Notes 502, 506
Nothosaurian reptile 69
Notre Dame de Paris 470, 473
Nozzle
  Concorde 416-417
  Jet engines 418-419
  Tornado 421
  Vacuum cleaner 593
NPT 301 turbojet 418
N-type silicon 605
Nu Andromedae 19
Nucellus 147
Nuchal plate 187
Nuchal ring 95
Nuchal shield 187
Nuclear energy 314
Nuclear fusion
  Massive stars 26
  Small stars 24
  Stars 22
  Sun 32
Nuclear "hunter-killer" submarine 396-597
Nuclear power station 314
Nuclear reactions 315
Nucleolus 216, 239
Nucleoplasm 216
Nucleus
  Asteroids, comets, and meteoroids 52-53
  Atoms and molecules 308, 309
  Chlamydomonas sp. 116
  Cnidocytes 167
  Egg cell 606, 607
  Endosperm 147
  Fungal cell 115
  Galaxies 12-13
  Generalized human cell 216
  Muscle cell 228
  Neuron 239
  Overhead view of our galaxy 14
  Palisade mesophyll cell 159
  Pollen 122
  Pollen tube 147
  Roots 132
  Scots pine pollen 122
  Side view of our galaxy 14
  Synergid 147
  Thalassiosira sp. 116
Nuctenea umbratica 171
Number systems 620
Nunki 19, 20-21
Nu Orionis 18
Nut
  Deadeye 383
  Dry fruit 150
  Durmast oak 131
  Toaster 598
Nutcrackers 321
Nutlets 150
Nutrients
  Carnivorous plants 160
  Epiphyte supply 162
  Phloem sieve tube 134
  Plant transport 159
Nylon and silicon cloth 584
Nymphaea sp. 159
Nyssa sylvatica 137

O

O_2 sensor 353
Oak 74
Oar
  Greek and Roman ships 372-373
  Junk 376
  Longboat 380
  Viking ships 374-375
Oarweed 116-117
Oasis 283

Oberon 48
Objective aperture 610
Objective lens 610, 611
Object mass 320
Oblique-slip fault 61
Oboe 504-505, 508
Obovate leaves 137
Observer's cockpit 405
Observer's windscreen 404
Obsidian 275, 506
Obstruction light
  572Obturator canal 224
Obturator membrane 224
Occipital bone 202, 220
Occipital condyle 107,
  194, 220
Occipital lobe 236-237
Occipital region 106
Occluded fronts 302-303
Ocean currents 296-297
Ocean floor 298-299,
  266-267
Oceanic crust
  Earth's crust 58-59
  Mineralization zones
  281
  Mountain building
  62-63
  Ocean floor 298
Oceanic seahorse 180
Ocean ridges 58-59
Oceans 39, 296-297, 301
Ocean trenches
  Ocean floor features
  299
  Offshore currents 296
  Plate movements 58
Oceanus Procellarum 40
Ocellus 176
Octafoil 471
Octagon 622
Octahedron 623
Octastyle portico 462
Octave 557
Octopus 176-177
Ocular end 377
Oculus
  Ancient Roman
  building 462-463
  Gothic church 472-473
  Medieval building 466,
  469
  Neoclassical building
  483
  Roman corbita 372
Odd-toed ungulates
  198-199
Odontoblast 247
Oeil-de-boeuf window
  Baroque church 479,
  481
  Cathedral dome 487
Oerlikon gun position
  397
Oesophagus
  Barnacle 173
  Bird 189
  Brachiosaurus 91
  Butterfly 169
  Chimpanzee 202
  Cow 198
  Dogfish 179
  Dolphin 205
  Domestic cat 195
  Elephant 200
  Human 212, 215, 245,
  248
  Lizard 185
  Rabbit 196
  Snail 177
  Spider 170
  Starfish 174
  Tortoise 187
Off-road motorcycle
  racing 368
Offshore deposits 294
Ogee 395
Ogee arch 488
Ogee-arched motif 490

Ogee curve 472
Ogee-curved dome 486
Ogee-curved roof 489
Ogee moulding 475-477, 481
Ogee tracery 493
Ohms 316
Oil
  Clutches 366
  Diesel trains 326
  Energy storage 315
  Mineral resources
  280-281
Oil bottle dripfeed 336
Oil cooler 347, 364, 605
Oil-cooler duct 415
Oil cooler matrix 347
Oil damper 364
Oil deposit formation 57
Oil deposits 281
Oil dipstick 544
Oil duct 151
Oil feed 411
Oil feed pipe 345, 366, 367
Oil filter
  1-litre VTEC engine
  354
  Ford diesel engine 347
  Jaguar V12 engine 345
  Turbofan engine 418
  Turboprop engine 419
Oil-fired power station
  315
Oil formation 280-281
Oil paints 436-437
Oil pipe banjo 345
Oil-pressure regulating
  valve 419
Oil pump
  Humber engine 343
  Mid West single-rotor
  engine 411
  Velocette OHV engine
  367
  Weslake speedway bike
  369
Oil rig 315
Oil side lamp 336-337
Oil sump
  Honda VF750 364
  Humber engine 343
  Modern engines 344-345
  Velocette OHV engine
  367
Oil tank
  Bell-47 helicopter
  components 422
  Harley-Davidson FLHS
  Electra Glide 363
  Lockheed Electra
  airliner 406
  Turbofan engine 418
  Turboprop engine 419
Oil traps 281
Oldsmobile 336-337
Old World monkeys
  202-203
Olecranon 85
Olenellus 64
Oleo lock-jack 414
Olfactory bulb 181
Oligocene epoch
  Fossil record 279
  Geological timescale 57
Olivine
  Igneous rock 267
  Meteorites 52
  Silicates 269
Olivine gabbro 275
Olympus BX51W1 optical
  microscope 610
Olympus Mons 42-43
Omasum 198
Omega Centauri 21
Omicron Andromedae 19
Omicron1 Canis Majoris
  21
Omicron2 Canis Majoris
  21
Omicron Orionis 18

Omicron Sagittarii 21
Omnivores 84
Omohyoid muscle 229
Onboard information
  panel 573
One-toed ungulates 198
Onion dome 467, 486-488
Onion-skin weathering
  282
On/off/pause button 586
On-screen display 577
Onyx 268
Oocyte 258
Oogonium 117
Oort Cloud 30, 52
Oospheres 116-117
  Fern 121
  Moss 119
Ooze 298
Open cluster 16
Open gun mounting 394
Opera House, Paris 493
Opera House, Sydney 496,
  499
Opercula 180
Opercular bone 181
Operculum
  Bony fish 180-181
  Cnidocyte 167
  Giant stick insect eggs
  192
  Indian stick insect eggs
  192
  Leaf insect eggs 192
  Moss 119
Ophidia 184
Ophiothrix fragilis 175
Ophiuchus 19, 20
Ophthalmos 372
Opisthodomos 461
Opisthosoma 170-171
Opossums 206, 207
Opponens digiti minimi
  muscle 231
Opponens pollicis muscle
  231
Opportunity 615
Optical drive 567
Optical map of our galaxy
  14-15
Optical microscope 610
Optic chiasma 236
Optic disc 240-241
Optic nerve 240
Option connector 571
Opus incertum 463, 465
Opus quadratum 465
Opus sectile mosaic
  488-489
Oral arm 167
Oral cavity 248
Oral disc 166-167
Oral surface 175
Orange citrine 271
Orange halite 269, 277
Orange light 318
Orangutans 202
Ora serrata 241
Orb 486
  Baroque church 480
  Cathedral dome 487
  Gothic church 471
  Neoclassical building
  479
  Nineteenth-century
  building 493
  Renaissance building
  477
Orbicularis oculi muscle
  226, 242
Orbicularis oris muscle
  228-229, 245
Orbicular lamina 158
Orbicular leaves 137
Orbit
  Acanthostega 80
  Ankylosaurus 94
  Archaeopteryx 85
  Arsinoitherium 104

Australopithecus 108
Baryonyx 83
Bear 194
Bird 189
Bony fish 181
Camarasaurus 91
Chimpanzee 202
Diplodocus 90
Elephant 201
Eryops 80
Euoplocephalus 94
Heterodontosaurus 83
Homo erectus 108
Homo habilis 108
Homo sapiens 108
Horse 199
Hyaenodon 107
Iguanodon 96
Inner planetary 30
Lambeosaurus 99
Lion 194
Lizard 184
Opossum 106
Outer planetary 31
Pachycephalosaurus
  100
Panoplosaurus 94
Parasaurolophus 99
Plateosaurus 88
Platypus 206
Prenocephale 100
Protoceratops 102
Rattlesnake 185
Rhesus monkey 202
Smilodon 107
Stars of northern skies
  18
Stars of southern skies
  20
Stegoceras 100-101
Styracosaurus 102
Toxodon 106
Triceratops 103
Tyrannosaurus 84
Orbital artery 179
Orbital cavity 220
Orbital motion 31, 52
Orbital plane
  Earth 38
  Jupiter 44
  Mars 42
  Mercury 34
  Neptune 50
  Pluto 51
  Saturn 46
  The Moon 40
  Uranus 48
  Venus 36
Orbitals 508-509, 510
Orbital speed (velocity)
  Mercury 34
  Solar System 30-31
Orb spider 171
Orchestra layout 504-505
Orchestral instruments
  504-505
  Musical notation
  502-503
Orchestras 504-505
Orchestra shell 495
Orchids 126, 133, 162
Orcinus orca 205
Ordovician period 64-65
  Fossil record 279
  Geological time 56
  Primitive life 78
Organ 514, 502-503
Organic compound 313
Organic material
  deposition 281
Organic remains 276-277,
  280
Organ of Corti 243
Oriel window 467
"O Ring" drive chain 366
Orion 18, 21, 24
Orion Arm 14
Orion Nebula 15, 17, 18
Orion's belt 15-16

Ornament
  Asian building 491
  Baroque church 479,
  481
  Cathedral dome 487
  Islamic building 488
  Neoclassical building
  483
Ornithischia 68-69, 82-83
  Marginocephalians 100
  Ornithopods 96
  Stegosaurs 92-93
  Thyreophorans 92
Ornithomimosaurs 86-87
Ornithopoda 83
Ornithopods 96-97, 98-99
Ornithorhynchus anatinus
  207
Orobanche sp. 163
Orogenesis 62-63
Oropharynx 245
Orpiment 270-271
Orthoclase 269, 271
Orthorhombic system 270
Os 258-259
Oscillating cylinder 390
Oscillating electric field
  318
Oscillating magnetic field
  318
Oscillating steam engine
  390-391
Osculum 166
Osmium 311
Ossicles 79, 174
Ossicles of middle ear
  242
Osteichthyes 180
Osteocyte 225
Osteolaemus tetraspis 82
Osteon 225
Ostiole 117
Ostium
  Crayfish 173
  Sea anemone 167
  Spider 170
  Sponge 166
Ostrich 188, 193
Otters 194
Otto cycle 342
Otto, Nikolaus 342
Ouranosaurus 97
Outboard ammunition-
  feed blister 409
Outboard elevon 421
Outer bud scale 134
Outer casing fitment 597
Outer core 38-39, 41
Outer ear
  Brachiosaurus 91
  Stegoceras 101
  Stegosaurus 92
Outer electrons 310-311
Outer envelope 25-26
Outer fertilized floret 142
Outer jib downhaul 385
Outer jib halyard 385
Outer jib sheet 385
Outer jib stay 382
Outer lamella 225
Outer mantle
  Jupiter 44-45
  Saturn 46-47
Outer tepals
  Glory lily 143
  Lily 140
  Monocotyledons 126
Outfield 536
Outlet manifold 411
Output tray 574
Outrigger 373, 377
Outwash fan 287
Outwash plain 287
Outwash terrace 286
Ovary
  Barnacle 173
  Bony fish 181
  Brachiosaurus 90
  Butterfly 169

Chimpanzee 202
Crayfish 173
Dogfish 179
Epigeal germination
  153
Fertilization 146-147
Flower 140-143
Gallimimus 86
Human 258-259
Hypogeal germination
  152
Insect pollination 144
Lizard 185
Rose 131
Spider 170
Succulent fruit 148-149
Tortoise 188
Ovate leaf
  Ice-plant 129
  Live-for-ever 129
  Strawberry 128
Ovda Regio 36, 37
Oven compartment 597
Overarm pass 535
Overhand knot 388
Overhand serve 534
Overhead camshaft
  engine 368
Overhead control panel
  573
Overhead pass 532
Overhead valve engine
  (OHV) 367, 369
Over-reach boot 555
Overs 538
Oversailing fascia 477,
  482, 486
Overthrust fold 61
Overturned fold 61
Overwing emergency exit
  572
Oviduct
  Barnacle 173
  Brachiosaurus 90
  Butterfly 169
  Crayfish 173
  Dogfish 179
  Lizard 185
  Spider 170
  Tortoise 187
Ovolo 486
Ovolo moulding
  Cathedral dome 487
  Gothic church 472
  Neoclassical building
  480
Ovotestis 177
Ovules 140-143
  Bishop pine 124
  Dehiscent fruit 151
  Fertilization 146
  Pine 122
  Scots pine 122
  Smooth cypress 123
  Yew 123
Ovuliferous scales
  Bishop pine 124
  Pine 122
  Scots pine 122
  Smooth cypress 123
  Yew 123
Ovum
  Ancient Roman
  building 462
  Fertilization 146-147
  Scots pine 122
Oxalis sp. 157
Oxbow lake 293
  River features 290
  River's stages 289
"Ox-eye" window
  Baroque church 479,
  481
  Cathedral dome 487
Oxides 268
Oxygen
  Atmospheric
  Atom 596
  Composition 301

Early micro-organisms 78
Earth's composition 39
Earth's crust 58
Earth's formation 38, 64
Helix Nebula 17
Mars' atmosphere 43
Mercury's atmosphere 35
Periodic table 311
Photosynthesis 138
Seed germination 152
Structure of red supergiant 26
Respiration 255
Oxygenated blood 255
Oxygen bottle 408
Oxygen group 311
Oyashio current 297
Oyster fungus 114
Oysters 176
Ozone 64
Ozone layer 300

P
Pachycephalosaurus 69, 85, 100
Pachypteris sp. 68
Pachyrhinosaurus 103
Pacific coastline 295
Pacific Ocean 264-265, 272
Pacific plate 59
Pacing races 554
Pacing sulky 554-555
Pacinian corpuscle 254-255
Pack-ice 296
Packing tissue
  Dicotyledon leaf 126
  Fern rachis 121
  Golden barrel cactus 156
  Haworthia truncata 157
  Horsetail stem 120
  Leaf succulents 157
  Lithops bromfieldii 157
  Monocotyledon leaf 126
  Roots 132-133
  Stem 134-135
  Stem succulents 156
  String of hearts 157
  Water lily leaf 159
Padded coaming
  Avro biplane 403
  BE 2B bomber 404
Paddle
  Eurypterid fossil 79
  Kayak 560
Paddlesteamer
  19th century 390-391
  Iron 392-393
Paddle wheels 390-391, 392
Padmakosa 489
Page key 590
Page locator 577
Pagoda 490
Pahoehoe 272
Painted Desert 277
Painting knives 436, 442
Painting tools 442
Pair-cast cylinder 343
Paired cylinder 342
Palace of Westminster 492-493
Palaeocene epoch
  Fossil record 279
  Geological timescale 57
Palaeontology 278
Palaeozoic era
  Fossil record 279
  Geological time 56
Palais de Fontainebleau 476

Palais de Versailles 482
Palatine Chapel, Aix-le-Chapelle 484
Palatine tonsil 212, 244-245
Palatoglossal arch 244
Palazzo Stanga 482
Palazzo Strozzi 474-475
Pale calcite 26
Pale feldspar 26
Palette 143, 456
Palette knife 436
Paling 466, 477
Palisade mesophyll 126, 159
Palladium 311
Palm
  Danforth anchor 386
  Hand 211
  Roman anchor 372
  Sailmaker's 384
  Tertiary plant 74
Palmar arch 253
Palmaris longus tendon 251
Palmar vein 253
Palmate leaves 130, 136
Palmate venation 129
Palmette 460-461, 479-480
Palmoxylon 74
Pamirs 265
Pampas 264
Panavia Tornado GR1A 420-421
Pancam mast assembly 615
Pancreas
  Bird 189
  Bony fish 181
  Chimpanzee 202
  Dogfish 179
  Domestic cat 195
  Frog 182
  Human 215, 249
  Rabbit 196
  Tortoise 187
Pandas 194
Panduriform leaves 136
Pane 494
Panel 485
  Asian building 491
  Baroque church 479-481
  Cathedral dome 487
  Gothic building 473
  Islamic building 488
  Medieval building 466, 469
  Modern building 496-499
  Neoclassical building 478-479
  Nineteenth-century building 493
  Renaissance building 475
  Twentieth-century building 494
Panel board connector 570
Pangaea 66, 68-69, 70
Panniers 360, 361, 362
Panoplosaurus 94
Panicle 131
Panoramic camera (Pancam) 615
Pantheon 462-463
Pantile 464, 482
Pantograph 528, 530
Pan troglodytes 202
Paper
  Acrylic paint 442
  Calligraphy 444, 445
  Pastels 440
  Printing processes 446, 447
  Watercolours 438
Paper feed components 575

Paper hopper 574
Paper output stacker 574
Paper stumps 440
Paper support 575
Papilla
  Flower 140
  Hair 235
  Renal 256
  Tongue 244
Papillary muscle 251
Pappus 142
Papyriform column 459
Parabellum machine-gun 405
Parabolic dune 283
Paraboloid roof 496, 499
Parachute seed dispersal 150
Paradise palm 126
Paragaster 166
Parallel dunes 283
Parallelogram 622
Parallel river drainage 288
Parallel shaft 582
Parallel venation 126
Parana River 264
Parapet
  Ancient Roman building 465
  Asian building 491
  Baroque church 481
  Dome 486
  Gothic church 470-472
  Islamic tomb 489
  Medieval building 467
  Neoclassical building 478, 483
  Nineteenth-century building 493
  Twentieth-century building 494
Parapet rail 483
Paraphysis 117, 119
Parasaurolophus 98-99
Parasitic anemone 166
Parasitic cone 272-273
Parasitic plants 162-163
Parasitic volcano 275
Paraxeiresia 373
Parcelling 388
Parchment
  Gilding 432
  Imitation 445
Pareiasaur 81
Parenchyma
  Dicotyledon leaf 126
  Dryland plants 156-157
  Fern rachis 121
  Golden barrel cactus 156
  Horsetail stem 120
  Monocotyledon leaf 126
  Pine stem 125
  Roots 132
  Stems 134-135
  Water lily leaf 159
Parent plant 154
Parietal bone
  Bony fish 181
  Chimpanzee 202
  Human 220-221
Parietal fenestra 102
Parietal lobe 236-237
Parieto-occipital sulcus 236-237
Parietosquamosal frill 102-103
Paripteris 66
Paris Metro 528
Paroccipital process
  Iguanodon 96
  Plateosaurus 88
Parrel
  Dhow 376
  Longboat 380
  Sailing warship 377
  Viking karv 375
Parrel beads 584

Parrel tackle 376
Parthenon 461
Partial solar eclipse 32
Partial veil 115
Particle attraction 307
Particle properties 318
Passiflora caerulea 130
Passing brace 473
Passion flower 130
Passive stack vents 602
Pastels 440-441
Pastern 198-199, 554
Pasteur 41
Patagonia 264
Patella
  Domestic cat 195
  Elephant 201
  Hare 197
  Horse 199
  Human 219
  Platypus 206
  Rhesus monkey 202
  Scorpion 170
  Spider 171
Patellar surface 225
Patera
  Neoclassical building 480
  Renaissance building 476
Pause/play control 577
Paved floor 492
Pavilion 489, 495
Paving slab 499
Pavlova 37
Pavlovia 278
Pavo 20
Pavonis Mons 43
Paw 195
Pawl 380
Pawl slot 387
Paxton, J. 492-493
Pazzi Chapel 475
PCB see printed circuit board (PCB)
PC card adapter 574
PCs 566
PDAs 568, 588
Pea
  Dry fruit 150
  Danforth anchor 386
Peach 131, 148
Peacock 20
Peak halyard 380
Peat 280
Peccaries 198
Pecopteris 66
Pectineus muscle 225-226
Pectoral fin
  Bony fish 180-181
  Lamprey 178
Pectoral fin ray 181
Pectoralis major muscle 226
Pedal board 514
Pedal cluster 340
Pedal-damper bar mechanism 516
Pedal disc 167
Pedal-driven bicycle 358
Pedal gland 177
Pedalia 372
Pedals
  Bass drum 518
  Bicycle 520, 358-359
  Eddy Merckx racing bicycle 360
  Harp 511
  Hi-hat cymbal 518
  Piano 514
  Rossin Italian time-trial bicycle 361
Pedal stop 514
Pedestal
  Ancient Roman building 462
  Baroque church 480-481
  Dome 484, 486-487

French temple 485
Harp 511
Neoclassical building 479
Renaissance building 476
Pedice 168
Pedicel
  Brassavola nodosa 162
  Clematis 131
  Dicotyledon flower 127
  Dry fruit 150-151
  Fertilization 146-147
  Florists' chrysanthemum 129
  Flowers 140-141, 145
  Fruit development 146-147
  Oxalis sp. 157
  Pitcher plant 113
  Rose 151
  Rowan 131
  Russian vine 131
  Succulent fruit 148-149
  Sycamore 131
  Vegetative reproduction 154
  Water lily 159
Pedicle of vertebra 223
Pedicle valve 278
Pediment
  Ancient Greek building 460
  Ancient Roman building 462-463
  Baroque church 480-481
  Neo-Baroque building 493
  Neoclassical building 478
  Renaissance building 476
Pedipalp 170-171
Peduncle 140, 142-143
  Aechmea miniata 162
  Brassavola nodosa 162
  Everlasting pea 129
  Florists' chrysanthemum 129
  Indehiscent fruit 150
  Peach 131
  Peruvian lily 129
  Rowan 131
  Russian vine 131
  Succulent fruit 148-149
  Toadflax 129
  Vegetative reproduction 154
  Wind-pollinated plant 144
Peephole 412, 414
Pegasus 19, 20
Pegasus Quasar microlight 426-427
Pegasus XL SE microlight 427
Peg-box 510-511
Pegmatite 26
Peg of vertebra 222
Pelagic fin 299
Pelecypoda 176
Peloneustes philarcus 71
Pelota 540
Pelvetia canaliculata 116
Pelvic fin
  Bony fish 180-181
  Dogfish 179
Pelvis
  Bird 189
  Bony fish 181
  Dinosaur 81
  Domestic cat 195
  Elephant 201
  Hare 197
  Horse 199
  Human 256, 258, 259
  Kangaroo 206
  Lizard 184
  Platypus 206

Rhesus monkey 202
Seal 204
Turtle 187
Penalty area 524
Penalty box 524
Penalty kick 530
Penalty spot 529, 540
Pencils 430
Pencil sharpener 430
Pencil slate sea urchin 175
Pendentive 479, 484, 488
Penguins 188
Penis
  Barnacle 173
  Dolphin 205
  Human 211, 259
  Snail 177
Pennant number 397
Pennsylvanian period 56
Penny washer 383
Pens 430
Penstock 314
Pentagon 622
Pentaradiate symmetry 174
Pentroof 490
Penumbra 32
Pepo 148
Pepper-pot lantern 481
Perch 180
Percolation 280
Percussion instruments 516-517
  Drums 518-519
  Electronic 520
  Orchestral arrangement 504-505
Perennials 128, 130-131
Pereopod 172-173
Perforated shroud 592
Perianth 140
Pericardial cavity 250
Pericarp 148
  Dry fruit 150-151
  Embryo development 147
  Fruit development 146-147
  Succulent fruit 148-149
  Sycamore 131
Pericranium 257
Pericycle 127, 132
Periderm 125
Peridium 115
Perihelion 30-31
Perimeters 622
Perineum 258
Periodic table 310-311
Periodontal ligament 247
Periodontium 247
Periosteum 225
Peripheral nervous system 238
Peripteral temple 460-461
Periscope 396, 397
Perissodactyla 104, 198-199
Peristome tooth 119
Peristyle 461
Peritoneum 249, 257
Permeable limestone
  Caves 284-285
  Lake formation 292
Permeable rock 292
Permeable sandstone 292
Permian period 66-67
  Fossil record 279
  Geological time 57
Peroneal artery 253
Peroneus brevis muscle 227, 253
Peroneus brevis tendon 253
Peroneus longus muscle 253
Peroxisome 217
Perseus 19, 20
Perseus Arm 14-15

Persian ivy 137
Personal computer 566-567
Personal digital assistants (PDAs) 568
Personalized mail folder 576
Personal lighting 572
Personal music and video 586-587
Perspective drawing 431
Peru current 296
Peruvian lily 129
Petal moulding 480
Petals 140-143
  Clematis 131
  Colour 140, 144-145
  Dicotyledons 126-127
  Everlasting pea 129
  Fertilization 146
  Insect pollination 145
  Monocotyledons 126
  Peruvian lily 129
  Rose 131
  Water lily 159
Petavius 40
Petiole 128, 136-137
  Chusan palm 130
  Clematis 131
  Cobra lily 160
  Dicotyledons 127
  Everlasting pea 129
  Florists' chrysanthemum 129
  Horse chestnut 130
  Kedrostis africana 113
  Maidenhair tree 123
  Monocotyledons 126-127
  Mulberry 130
  Oxalis sp. 157
  Passion flower 130
  Peach 131
  Rock slonecrop 128
  Seedling 153
  Strawberry 128
  String of hearts 157
  Tree fern 112
  Tree mallow 131
  Vegetative reproduction 154
  Venus fly trap 160
  Water Inacinth 158
  Water lily 159
  Wind-pollinated plant 144
Petiolule 137
Petrol 315
Peugeot, Armand 334
Phacops 64
Phaeophyta 16
Phaet 21
Phalaenopsis sp. 126
Phalanges
  Cow 198
  Crocodile 186
  Diplodocus 90
  Domestic cat 195
  Elephant 90
  Eryops 80-81
  Frog 183
  Hare 197
  Horse 198-199
  Kangaroo 206
  Lizard 184
  Parasaurolophus 99
  Plateosaurus 88
  Platypus 206
  Rhesus monkey 202
  Seal 204
  Stegoceras 100-101
  Triceratops 102-103
  Turtle 187
  Tyrannosaurus 84
Phalanx
  African elephant 201
  Archaeopteryx 85
  Arsinoitherium 104
  Baryonyx 85, 87

Horse 105
  Human 219, 230
  Plateosaurus 88
  Stegoceras 100
  Struthiomimus 87
  Toxodon 107
Phallus impudicus 114
Phanerozoic eon 279
Pharyngeal tubercle 220
Pharynx
  Bony fish 180-181
  Dogfish 179
  Human 212, 244
  Sea anemone 167
  Sea urchin 175
Phascolarctos cinereus 207
Phaseolus sp. 153
Phases of the Moon 41
Phekda 19
Phellem
  Pine root 125
  Stem 134-135
  Woody dicotyledon 127
Phi Andromedae 19
Phidias 35
Philippine plate 59
Phillips, Horatio 402
Philoxenus 55
Philtral ridge 213
Philtrum 213
Phiomia 104
Phloem 138
  Bishop pine 124-125
  Clubmoss stem 120
  Dicotyledons 126-127
  Dodder host 163
  Epiphytic orchid 162
  Fern rachis 121
  Horsetail stem 120
  Marram grass 113
  Monocotyledons 126-127
  Parasite host 163
  Photosynthesis 158
  Pine root/stem 125
  Radicle 152
  Root 132-133
  Sieve tube 154
  Stem 134-135
  Water hyacinth root 158
  Water lily leaf 159
Phloem fibres 134-135
Phloem sieve tube 134
Phobos 42
Phoebe Regio 36
Phoenicopterus ruber 190
Phoenix 19, 20
Phorusrhacos 74
Phosphates 269
Phosphate/sugar band 216
Phosphor imaging screen 611
Phosphor lining cell 584
Phosphorus 311
Photomicrographs of skin and hair 235
Photons 518
Photo print button 570
Photo select button 575
Photosphere 32-33
Photosynthesis 112, 116, 134, 156, 138-159
  Carnivorous plants 160-161
  Organelle 116, 139
Photosynthetic cells 139
  Bishop pine 124
  Coconut palm stem 135
  Water lily leaf 159
Photosynthetic region 157
Photosynthetic tissue
  Cacti 156
  Dicotyledon leaf 126
  Horsetail stem 120
  Marram grass 113
  Monocotyledon leaf 126
  Rush stem 135
Photovoltaic cell 603
Photovoltaic panel 603

Phyla 116
Phyllode 160
Phylum 116
Physalis peruviana 149
Physeter catodon 205
Physical map of the world 616-617
Physical weathering 282
Physics symbols 621
Pi2 Orionis 18
Pi3 Orionis 18
Pi4 Orionis 18
Pi5 Orionis 18
Pi6 Orionis 18
Pia mater 237, 240
Piano 503, 514
Piano nobile 474, 494
Piano, R. 496
Piazza 474
Pi Canis Majoris 21
Piccolo 504, 508
Pictor 21
Pier 484
  Ancient Egyptian temple 459
  Ancient Roman building 465
  Baroque church 480
  Gothic church 470
  Medieval building 467-469
  Renaissance building 476-477
  Twentieth-century building 494-495
Pier buttress 469-471, 486
Pietra dura inlay 489
Piezoelectric inkjet printhead 575
Pigments 433, 434, 436
Pigs 104, 198
Pilaster
  74-gun ship 381
  Ancient Greek building 461
  Ancient Roman building 463-465
  Asian temple 490-491
  Baroque church 479-481
  Cathedral dome 484, 487
  Gothic church 471
  Neoclassical building 478, 483
  Renaissance building 476
Pileus 114-115
Pillar
  Asian buildings 490-491
  Domed roof 486
  Gothic church 472
  Ironclad 393
  Renaissance building 477
  Twin bollards 587
Pillow lava 298
Pilotis 494
Pilot light 594
Pilot's cockpit
  LVG CVI fighter 405
  Tornado 420
Pilot's cradle 398-399
Pilot's seat
  Airbus 380 573
  Avro biplane 402
  Curtiss biplane 398
  Pegasus Quasar microlight 427
Pin
  Capstan 387
  Dome timbering 486
Pinacocyte 166
Pineal body 212, 236
Pine hull 573
Pines 122, 124-125
Pinguicula caudata 161
Pinion
  Benz Motorwagen 335
  Ford Model T 338

Hand drill 601
Pinna
  Elephant 201
  Everlasting pea 129
  Fern 121
  Gorilla 203
  Human 242-243
  Kangaroo 207
  Leaves 136-137
  Rabbit 196
  Rat 196
  Sago palm 123
  Tree fern 112-113
Pinnacle
  Baroque church 479, 481
  Gothic church 470, 472-473
  Medieval church 469
  Nineteenth-century building 493
  Renaissance building 476
Pinnate leaves 136-137
  Mahonia 130-131
  Rowan 130
  Sago palm 123
Pinned sheepshank 389
Pinnipedia 204
Pinnule 121, 137
Pinocytotic vesicle 217
Pintle strap 378
Pinus muricata 72, 124-125
Pinus sp. 122, 124-125
Pinus sylvestris 122
Pi Pegasi 19
Pipette 312
Pips 148-149
Pi Sagittarii 21
Pisanosaurus 68
Pisces Austrinus 19, 20
Piscis 19, 20
Pisiform bone 230
Piste 556, 557
Pistol shooting 548
Piston
  Disc brake 365
  Early engines 342-343
  "Ellerman Lines" steam locomotive 325
  Ford diesel engine 347
  Mid West two-stroke engine 410
  Modern engines 344-345
  Relief-printing press 449
  Steam locomotive 324
  Two-stroke engine 366
  Velocette OHV engine 367
  Volkswagen Beetle 340
Piston engines 410-411, 424
Piston rod 324, 334, 390
Piston valves
  Brass instruments 506
  Cornet 507
  "Ellerman Lines" steam locomotive 325
  Flugelhorn 507
  Stringed instruments 510
  Trumpet 506
  Tuba 507
Pisum sativum 150
Pitatus 40
Pitch
  Brass instruments 506
  Drums 518
  Musical notation 502
  Percussion instruments 516
  Propeller action 390
  Screw thread angle 320
  Woodwind instruments 508
Pitched roof

Ancient Roman building 462, 464
  Gothic church 471-472
  Medieval building 466-468
  Nineteenth-century building 492
  Renaissance building 476-477
  Twentieth-century building 495
Pitcher 536
Pitcher plants 113, 160-161
Pitches
  Australian rules football 528
  Baseball 536
  Cricket 558
  Gaelic football 529
  Lacrosse 540
Pitching wedge
  Baseball 537
  Golf 547
Pitfall traps 160
Pith
  Apical meristem 134
  Bishop pine stem 125
  Dicotyledon stem 127
  Epiphytic orchid 162
  Horsetail stem 120
  Monocotyledon root 127
  Pine stem 125
  Stems 134-135
Pith cavity 155
Pitot head
  ARV light aircraft 425
  BAe-146 jetliner components 412
  Bell-47 helicopter 422
  Concorde 416-417
  Hawker Tempest fighter 409
  LVG CVI fighter 405
  Schweizer helicopter 423
  Tornado 420
Pitot mast 407
Pituitary gland 212, 236
Pivot
  Astrolabe 377
  BAe-146 jetliner components 414
  Drum brake 365
  Sundial 377
  Viking ships 374-375
Pixel 570, 571
Place kick 530
Placenta
  Dry fruit 150-151
  Fern pinnule 121
  Human 260
  Succulent fruit 148-149
Placental mammals 74, 104
Placer deposits 280
Plagioclase feldspar 275
Plains viscacha 197
Planck 41
Plane shapes 622
Planetary nebula
  Nebulae and star clusters 17
  Small stars 24-25
Planetary rotation 30
Planets
  Jupiter 44-45
  Mars 42-43
  Mercury 34-35
  Neptune 50-51
  Pluto 50-51
  Saturn 46-47
  Solar System 30-31
  Uranus 48-49
  Venus 36-37
Planking
  Ironclad 393
  Longboat 380

Roman corbita 373
Sailing warship 377
Tea clipper 392
Plantar calcaneonavicular ligament 232
Plant bodies 116
Plant capital 459
Plant-eating dinosaurs 68, 70
Plant matter 280
Plant remains
  Fossils 278-279
  Mineral resources 280
  Sedimentary rocks 276
Plants 56, 66
  Electromagnetic radiation 314
  Flowering 57, 70, 72
  Fossil record 279
  Non-flowering 68
Plant variety 112-113
Plasma 306
Plasma display 584
Plasma screen 584
Plaster 452, 464-465
Plasterboard 602
Plastic bumper 354
Plastic fletch 548
Plastic front wings 354
Plastic insulator 316, 317
Plastic rackets 544
Plastid 116
Platanus x acerifolia 134
Platband 481
Plate
  Etching press 477
  Motorcycle clutch 366
  "O Ring" drive chain 366
Plateau
  Neptune's rings 50
  Structure of Neptune 51
Plateaus 276-277
Plate boundaries 62, 273
Plate clip 587
Platelets 253
Plate movements 58-59
  Faults and folds 60
  Mountain building 62-63
Platen 449
Plateosaurus 69, 88-89
Plate tectonics 58-59
Platform
  Cathedral dome 487
  Early tram 352
  Medieval building 467-468
  Modern building 498
Platform diving 558
Platlorm stage 477
Platinum 311
Plat lesene 480
Plato 40
Platypus 206-207
Platysma 229
Playa 283
Play button 585´
Player's bench
  American football 526
  Basketball 532
  Handball 535
  Ice hockey 550
  Volleyball 554
Play/pause control 577
Plaza 498
Pleiades 14, 16, 19, 20
Pleistocene epoch
  Fossil record 279
  Geological timescale 57
Pleistocene period 76
Plenum chamber 344-345
Plenum ring 418
Pleopod 172
Plesiochelys latiscutata 73
Plesiosaurs 70-71
Pleurotus pulmonarius 114
Plica circulare 249

Plicate lamina 127
Pliers 321
Plinth
  Baroque church 480
  French temple 485
  Islamic tomb 489
  Modern building 499
  Neoclassical building
    479, 483
  Renaissance building 476
  Twentieth-century
    building 494-495
Pliocene epoch
  Fossil record 279
  Geological timescale
    57
Plough anchor 386
Plug-ins 521
Plug lead conduit 337
Plugs 272-273
  Igneous rock structures
    274
Plumage 188
Plume 45
Plumose anemone 166
Plumule 147, 152-153
Plunge 60
Plunge pool 289, 291
Pluto 31, 50-51
Plutonium 310-311
Plywood roof deck 603
Plywood skin 404
Pneumatic tyres 358, 555
Podetium 114
Podium 463, 499
Point
  Angling hook 562
  Cricket 538
  Double bass bow 511
  Sailmaker's fid 384
  Sculpting tool 452-453
  Violin bow 510
Point bar
  Mississippi Delta 291
  River's stages 289
Pointed arch 466, 467,
  469, 472
Pointed hog hair brush
  434
Pointed riffler 454
Pointed sable brush 444
Pointing 383
Poison duct 170
Poison gland
  Octopus 176
  Spider 170
Polacanthus 95
Polar band 36
Polar body 606, 607
Polar bottom water 296
Polar easterlies 300
Polar fronts 302
Polar hood 36
Polaris 14, 18-19
Polar jet stream 300
Polar nuclei 146
Poles 297, 300
Pole star 14, 18
Pole vault 542
Polian vesicle 175
Poll 199
Pollen 140, 142, 144-145
  Dicotyledon flower 126
  Fertilization 146-147
Pollen-forming structures
  122
Pollen grains 144-145
  Fertilization 146-147
  Pine 122
  Scots pine 122
Pollen sac wall 144
Pollen tubes
  Fertilization 146-147
  Scots pine 122
Pollination 144-145, 122
Pollux 18, 21
Polonium 311
Polycarbonate plastic bin
  592

Polyester 388
Polygala chamaebuxus
  144
Polygnotus 35
Polygonum
  baldschuanicum 131
Polyhedral dome 486-487
Polypropylene rope 388
Polythene 306
Polytrichum commune 119
Polyurethane insulation
  603
Pome 131, 149
Pommel 554
Pond weeds 158
Pons 212, 236-237
Poop break 373
Poop deck
  74-gun ship 381
  Iron paddlesteamer 392
  Roman corbita 373
Poop rail
  74-gun ship 381
  Wooden sailing ship
    378
Poor metals 310-311
Popchu-Sa Temple 490
Popliteal artery 253
Popliteal fossa 210
Porch 470-471
Porcupines 196-197
Pore
  Bishop pine needle 124
  Blackberry 147
  Dryland plants 156-157
  Elder stem 130
  Epigeal germination
    153
  False fruit 148
  Gas exchange 138, 158
  Golden barrel cactus
    156
  Haworthia truncata 157
  Leaf 138-139
  Liverwort 118
  Monocotyledon leaf 126
  Nuclear membrane 217
  Perennial bark 130-131
  Pollen grain 144-145
  Seed 153
  Sponge 166
  Water absorption 150,
    153
  Wetland plants 158
  Woody plants 130-131
  Woody stems 134
Porifera 166
Porocyte 166
Porous limestone 284
Porous stipe 114
Porphyritic andesite 275
Porpoises 204
Porrima 21
Porsche, Ferdinand 340
Port
  Trojan two-stroke
    engine 342
  Wooden sailing ship
    379
Portal 476, 480
Portal vein 252
Porta Nigra 462, 465
Port bower anchor 377,
  395
Port foremast 376
Porthole
  Battleship 394
  Dome 487
  Frigate 397
Portico
  Ancient Greek building
    460-461
  Ancient Roman
    building 462-463
  Neoclassical building
    482-483
  Renaissance building
    475
Portugal 331

Portuguese bowline 388
Position guide 447
Positive electric charge
  316
Positive ions 308, 310
Positive metal comb 316
Positive terminal 316, 317
Positron 22
Post 481, 486
Postabdominal spine 169
Postacetabular process 82
Postcentral gyrus 237
Post-crural musculature
  90
Posterior antebrachial
  musculature 86, 91
Posterior aorta 170
Posterior arch 222
Posterior border of vomer
  220
Posterior brachial muscle
  86, 91
Posterior branch of spinal
  nerve 223
Posterior cerebral artery
  252
Posterior chamber 241
Posterior chamber of
  cloaca 185
Posterior column 223
Posterior crural muscle 87
Posterior cuneonavicular
  ligament 232
Posterior dorsal fin
  Bony fish 181
  Dogfish 179
  Lamprey 178
Posterior horn 223
Posterior nasal aperture
  220
Posterior nasal spine 220
Posterior part of tongue
  245
Posterior petal 141
Posterior root 223, 258
Posterior semicircular
  canal 243
Posterior sepal 141
Posterior tarsometatarsal
  ligament 232
Posterior tentacle 177
Posterior tibial artery 253
Posterior tibial nerve 258
Posterior tubercle 222
Posterior vena cava 182
Posterior wing of shell 176
Posterolateral horn 94
Post-glacial stream 286
Post-glacial valley 286
Post-modernism 296, 496
Post-motor micropore
  filter 592
Potassium 35, 58, 286, 310
Potassium chromate
  solution 312
Potassium dichromate
  ions 312
Potassium iodide 312-313
Potassium nitrate 313
Potassium permanganate
  306
Potato 128
Potential energy 314, 315
Potholes 284
Pouch 206
Power bar 552
Power drill 600-601
Power button
  Home cinema 585
  Inkjet printer 574
  Personal computer
    566-567
Power levers 573
Power output 360, 366
Power/play/pause button
  586
Power plug 591
Power stations 314, 315
Power steering belt 351

Power steering pump 344,
  351
Power stroke 343
Power-to-weight ratio
  328
Power transistor heat sink
  (dissipator) 585
Power transistors 585
Practice projectile 396
Pradakshina 491
Praesepe 18
Prairie style 495
Praseodynium 310
Pratt & Whitney Canada
  turbofan engine
  418-419
Pratt & Whitney Canada
  turboprop engine 419
Pratt & Whitney radial
  engine 406-407
Praxiteles 35
Preacetabular process 82
Precambrian period 56,
  64-65, 279
Precambrian seas 78
Precentral gyrus 237
Precious metals 311
Precipitate 312
Precipitation 288, 302-303
Predatory dinosaurs 84
Predatory theropods 88
Predentary bone
  Arsinoitherium 104
  Iguanodon 96
  Lambeosaurus 99
  Protoceratops 102
  Triceratops 103
Prefix 577
Prehensile tail 202
Prehistoric foods 109
Pre-load adjustor 365
Premaxilla
  Baryonyx 83
  Arsinoitherium 104-105
  Bony fish 181
  Chimpanzee 202
  Elephant 201
  Frog 183
  Iguanodon 96
  Lambeosaurus 99
Premolars
  Australopithecus 107
  Bear 106, 194
  Chimpanzee 202
  Horse 105
  Human 246
  Lion 194
Prenocephale 100-101
Preopercular bone 181
Preparatory drawing
  430-431
Prepubic process
  Iguanodon 96
  Parasaurolophus 98
  Stegosaurus 93
Prepubis
  Ornithischian 82
  Stegoceras 100-101
Prepuce 259
Preserved remains 278
Press
  Etching 447
  Lithographic printing
    446
  Relief-printing 449
Pressed steel wheel 340
Pressure
  Formation of black hole
    29
  Igneous and
    metamorphic rocks 274
  Mineral resources 280
  Stellar black hole 29
  Volcanic features 273
Pressure line 418
Pressure plate 366
Pressurized cabin 406
Pressurized keel box 417
Pressurized strut 425

Pressurized water reactor
  314
Presta valve 361
Presynaptic axon 239
Presynaptic membrane
  259
Preview monitor slot 575
Preview monitor socket
  574
Previous file button 577
Previous key 568
Previous/next track
  buttons 585
Previous track control 587
Prickers 383
Prickle
  Blackberry 147
  Bramble stem 150
  Rose stem 130
  Slender thistle 129
Primary bronchus 215
Primary colours 439
Primary-drive gear 366
Primary flight display 573
Primary flight feathers
  188, 191
Primary follicle 258
Primary leaf 121
Primary mirror 612
Primary mirror housing
  613
Primary mycelium 115
Primary remiges 188, 191
Primary root 152-153
  Germination 152-153
  Seedling 152-153
Primary teeth 246
Primary thallus 114
Primary xylem 125, 135
Primer 348, 436
Primitive crocodilians 68
Primitive life-forms 64
Primitive mammals 206
Principal arteries and
  veins 253
Principal rafter
  Ancient Roman mill 464
  Dome 486
  Gothic building 473
Printer 574-575
Printer cover 574, 575
Printing block 449
Printing papers 447
Print making 446-447,
  448-449
Prism 318, 623
Prismatic habit 271
Privy 380
Probactosaurus 97
Probes, space 614-615
Proboscidea 104
Proboscis 169, 201
Procambial strand 134
Procerus muscle 229
Processing cooling fan
  567
Processing light 575
Processional path 470
Procompsognathus 87
Procoptodon 76
Procyon 8, 21
Procyon lotor 195
Production line
  Mass-production 338
  Modern bodywork 348
  Modern trim 352
Programme display 577
Program name 577
Projectile 396
Projector assembly 581
Projector lens 611
Prokaryotes 78
Prolegs 169
Promethium 311
Prominence 32-33
Pronaos 461
Pronotum 168
Pro-otic bone 183

Propagative structures
  154-155
Propellant 396
Propellant tank 615
Propeller 390-391
  ARV light aircraft 425
  Battleship 395
  Biplanes and triplanes
    402-403
  Early monoplanes
    400-401
  Ford diesel engine 347
  Frigate 396
  Hawker Tempest
    components 408
  Lockheed Electra
    airliner 406-407
  Pegasus Quasar
    microlight 427
  Pioneers of flight
    398-399
  Submarine 396
  World War I aircraft
    404-405
Propeller-bolt collar 411
Propeller brake pad 419
Propeller drive flange
  ARV light aircraft 425
  Modern piston aero-
    engines 410-411
Propeller drive gearbox
  427
Propeller drive shaft 408
Propeller-hub spinner 407
Propeller shaft
  Brazilian battleship 395
  Wright Flyer 399
Propeller shaft boss 395
Propeller-shaft bracing
  strut 398-399
Propeller shaft rear
  bearing 410
Propeller speed probe 419
Propeller spinner 408, 409
Propodus 172, 173
Propylaeum 460
Prosauropoda 83
Prosauropods 88
Proscapular process 187
Prosimians 203
Prosimii 202
Prosoma 170, 171
Prostate gland 257, 259
Prostyle colonnade 483
Protactinium 310
Protective clothing
  American football 528
  Cricket 559
  Ice hockey 550-551
Protective eyewear 544
Protective gaiter 422
Protective outer layer 125
Protective root covering
  153
Protective scale 134
Protective scale leaf 155
Protein body 112
Protein fibres 166
Protein matrix 166
Protein synthesis site 139
Proterozoic eon 279
Proteus 50
Prothallus 121
Prothorax 168
Protista 112, 116
Protoceratops 102-103
Protogalaxies 10-11
Proton 508, 316
  Atomic mass 310
  Atomic number 310
  Fluorine-19 309
  Nuclear fusion 22
Protonema 119
Protostar 24, 26
Protoxylem
  Dicotyledon root 127
  Monocotyledon root 127
  Root 132-133
Proventriculus

Bird 189
Crayfish 173
Prow 372, 375
Prowhead 374
Proxima Centauri 18
Proximal convoluted
  tubule 256-257
Proximal interphalangeal
  joint 231
Proximal phalanx 230, 232
Prunus persica 131
Psathyrella candolleana
  115
Pseudocarps 148-149
Pseudo-Corinthian capital
  476
Psi Sagittarii 21
Psittacosaurus 100, 103
Psoas major muscle 225,
  257
Pterapsis 65
Pterichthyodes 65
Pteridium aquilinum 121
Pterois volitans 180
Pteron 460-461, 463
Pterosaurs 70-71
Pterygoid bone 183
Pterygoid hamulus 220
Pterygoid plate 220
Ptolemaeus 40
Ptolemaic-Roman period
  459
"P" turret 395
P-type silicon 605
Pubic bone 261
Pubic ramus 257
Pubic symphysis 258
Pubis
  Archaeopteryx 85
  Bird 189
  Diplodocus 90
  Eryops 81
  Gallimimus 86
  Human 218, 224, 259
  Iguanodon 96
  Ornithischian 82
  Plateosaurus 88
  Saurischian 82
  Stegosaurus 93
  Struthiomimus 87
  Tyrannosaurus 84
Pubofemoral ligament 224
Pudenda 211
Pudendal nerve 238
Puffballs 114
Pugin, A.W.N. 493
Pull-down edit menu
  button 577
Pulley bolt 360
Pulley rim rear brake 362
Pulley wheel
  Simple pulleys 320
  Van de Graaff generator
    316
Pulmonary artery
  Frog 182
  Human 251, 253,
    254-255
Pulmonary semilunar
  valve 251
Pulmonary trunk 251, 255
Pulmonary vein 251, 253,
  254
Pulp artery and vein 247
Pulp chamber 247
Pulp horn 247
Pulp nerve 247
Pulsar 28
Pumice 275
  Marble carving 453
Pump
  Nuclear power station
    314
  Testing candle wax 313
Pump drive belt 410
Pump drive shaft 411
Pump piston 391
Pupa 168
Pupil

Caiman 186
  Human 213, 226, 241
Pupil's cockpit 403
Puppis 18, 21
Purchase 382-383
Purchase wire 394
Pure substances 306
Purfling 510, 511
Purkinje's cells 257
Purlin 473
Pusher propeller
  Pegasus Quasar
    microlight 426
  Pioneers of flight
    398-399
Push moraine 286
Push-rod 365, 367
Putter 547
Putting green 546
Putto 476
Putty eraser 430, 440
"P" wave 63
Pygal shield 187
Pygostyle 189
Pylon 314
Pylon fairing 427
Pylon forward fairing 573
Pylon strut 427
Pyloric caecum
  Bony fish 181
  Starfish 174
Pyloric duct 174
Pyloric region of stomach
  179
Pyloric sphincter muscle
  249
Pyloric stomach 174
Pyramid 458, 623
Pyrenees 77, 265
Pyrenoid 112, 116
Pyrites 268
  Intrusive igneous rocks
    275
Pyroclasts 272
Pyromorphite 269
Pyroxene 52, 267
Pyxis 18

Q

Quadrant arch 468
Quadrate bone 181
Quadratojugal bone
  Frog 183
  Heterodontosaurus 83
Quadrilateral 489
Quadripartite vault 469
Quadrupedal dinosaurs
  88, 92, 96, 100
Quadruplanes 402
Quark 309
Quarter back 526
Quarterdeck 580-581
Quarterdeck house 376
Quarter gallery 381
Quarter glass 348
Quarter light 340-341
Quarter panel moulding
  352
Quarter trim panel 352
Quartz
  Colour 271
  Metamorphic rock 267
  Oxides/hydroxides 268
Quasar (quasi-stellar
  object)
  Galaxies 12
  Objects in Universe 11
  Origin and expansion of
    Universe 10-11
Quasar nucleus 13
Quaternary period 57,
  76-77
  Fossil record 279
Quatrefoil 471-473
Quaver 502
Quayside 387
Queen-post 473

Quercus palustris 74
Quercus petraea 131
Quick-release base 590
Quick-release mechanism
  425
Quick-release strap 360
Quill
  Drill 601
  Feather 191
  Writing tool 444
Quinacridone red 442
Quit key 590
Quiver 548
Quoin
  Baroque church 481
  Medieval building 466
  Nineteenth-century
    building 492
  Renaissance building
    476

R

Rabbit line 380
Rabbits 196-197
Raccoons 194-195
Raceme 129
Rachilla 137
Rachis 136-137
  Bipinnate leaf 137
  Couch grass 113
  Everlasting pea 129
  Feather 191
  Fern 121
  Hogweed 129
  Pinnate leaf 136-137
  Rowan leaf 130
  Tree fern 112
  Tripinnate leaf 137
Racing bicycle 560
Racing car 356-357
Racing chain 361
Racing colours 554-555
Racing saddle 554
Racing sidecar 368-369
Racing "silks" 554-555
Racing tyre 365
  Formula One racing car
    556-557
  Suzuki RGV500 368-369
Racketball 544-545
Racket sports 544-545
Radar
  Modern jetliners 412
  Modern military
    aircraft 420-421
  World War II aircraft
    408
RADAR antenna 397
RADAR for gunnery and
  missile control 397
Radial artery 231, 253
Radial canal
  Jellyfish 167
  Sea urchin 175
  Starfish 174
Radial cartilage 180
Radial diffuser 418
Radial engine
  Curtiss biplane 398-399
  Lockheed Electra
    airliner 406-407
Radial groove 365
Radial nerve
  Human 238
  Sea urchin 175
Radial river drainage 288
Radial spoke 617
Radial studio easel 437
Radial wall 465
Radiation 38
  Electromagnetic 314
  Energy emission from
    Sun 22
  Galaxies 12-13
  Nebulae and star
    clusters 16
  Ozone formation 64

Universe 10
Radiative zone
  Structure of main
    sequence star 24
  Structure of Sun 33
Radiator
  1906 Renault 336-337
  ARV light aircraft 424
  Ford Model T 338-339
  Hawker Tempest
    fighter 409
  Honda VF750 364
  Kirby BSA 369
  Renault Clio 351
  Wright Flyer 399
Radiator-access cowling
  408
Radiator air vent 368
Radiator apron 339
Radiator coolant 326
Radiator fan 326
Radiator filler neck 339
Radiator header tank 408
Radiator hose 339
Radiator outlet 409
Radiator pipe 364
Radiator shell 339
Radicle
  Dry fruit 150
  Embryo development
    147
  Epigeal germination
    153
  Hypogeal germination
    152
Radio
  Bell-47 helicopter 422
  Renault Clio 353
  Streamed Internet 577
Radio aerial 426
Radio antenna 395
Radio galaxies 12-13
Radio image 13
Radio-isotope thermo-
  electric generator 614
Radio lobe 13
Radio mast 494
Radio operator's seat 408
Radio plugs 425
Radio speaker 353
Radio tuner aerial socket
  (FM) 585
Radio tuner FM/AM
  selector 585
Radio-ulna 183
Radio wave beam 28
Radio-wave emission 15
Radio waves
  Electromagnetic
    spectrum 318
  Pulsar 28
  Radio image of
    Centaurus A 13
Radium 310
Radius
  Archaeopteryx 85
  Arsinoitherium 104
  Baryonyx 85
  Bird 189, 191
  Circle 622
  Crocodile 186
  Diplodocus 90
  Domestic cat 195
  Elephant 90, 201
  Eryops 80
  Euoplocephalus 94
  Hare 197
  Horse 199
  Human 218, 230-231
  Iguanodon 96
  Kangaroo 206
  Lizard 184
  Parasaurolophus 99
  Pareiasaur 81
  Plateosaurus 88
  Platypus 206
  Rhesus monkey 202
  Seal 204
  Stegoceras 100-101

Struthiomimus 87
Toxodon 106
Triceratops 102
Turtle 187
Radius arm 357
Radius rod
  Avro Tutor biplane 403
  Ford Model T 338-339
Radome
  BAe-146 jetliner 415
  Concorde 416-417
  Tornado 420
Radon 311
Radula 176-177
RAF Central Flying School
  badge 402
RAF roundels 403, 409
Raft 496
Rafter
  Ancient Roman mill 464
  Dome 486
  Gothic building 473
  Modern building 499
  Nineteenth-century
    building 492
Raft spider 171
Rail
  Electric tram 352
  Kayak 560
  Neoclassical building
    483
  Relief-printing press
    449
  Train 330-331
  Wooden sailing ship
    379
Rail chair 324
Railing
  Asian building 490-491
  Cathedral dome 487
  Medieval building 467
  Nineteenth-century
    building 493
  Renaissance theatre 477
Railroad crest 526
Railway system 324
Rain 302
Rain erosion 294
Rain gutter 412, 415
Rainwater
  Caves 284
  Weathering and erosion
    282
Raised beach 295
Raja clavata 179
Raked windscreen 333
Raking cornice
  Ancient Greek building
    460-461
  Ancient Roman
    building 462-463
  Baroque church
    480-481
  Neoclassical building
    478
Raking stempost 376
Ram 372
Ramaria formosa 114
Ramentum 112, 121
Rammer 396
Ramp 467, 494
Ram scoop
  BE 2B bomber 404
  Tornado 420-421
Rangefinder
  Battleship 394
  Gun turret 396
Ranks 514
Ranunculus sp. 127,
  132-133
Raphe 153
Rapid-fire pistols 548
Rapids
  River features 290
  River's stages 289
Rare earths 310
Rare gases 311
Ras Algethi 20
Ras Alhague 19, 20

Rasp 452
Raspberry 149
Rat 104, 196
Ratchet
  Brace-and-bit 601
  Fixed-spool reel 562
Ratcheted base 590
Ratchet mechanism 601
Ratchet wheel 334
Rating 578
Ratings' mess 397
Ratline 376, 379
Rat's tail 384
Rat tail 389
Rattlesnake 185
Raw sienna 434
Raw umber 434
Ray
  Branchiostegal 181
  Caudal fin 180
  Dorsal fin 181
  Jawless fish 178
  Liverwort 118
  Mercury 34
  Near side of the Moon
    40
  Parenchyma cells 134
  Pectoral fin 181
Ray crater 54
Ray florets
  Florists'
    chrysanthemum 129
  Sunflower 142, 145
Reactants 312
Reaction wheel 614
Reactive metals 310-311
Reactor core 314
Reactor space 397
Rear axle 358
Rear axle adjustor 364, 368
Rear bearing 411
Rear brake 362
Rear brake cable 359, 360
Rear brake calliper 368
Rear brake pedal 368
Rear bulkhead 417
Rear cantilever brake 358
Rear case 591
Rear chassis plate 597
Rear cylinder exhaust
  pipe 368
Rear derailleur 358, 360
Rear door 339
Rear drop-outs 358
Rear hatch 349
Rear hub quick-release
  spindle 358
Rear indicator 362
Rear lamp
  Oldsmobile trim 337
  Volkswagen Beetle
    340
Rear leaf spring 338
Rear light
  Bicycle 360
  Italian State Railways
    Class 402 328
  Paris Metro 328
Rear limit line 557
Rear-mounted propeller
  Pegasus Quasar
    microlight 426
  Pioneers of flight
    398-399
Rear oil lamp 336
Rear shelf 352
Rear shock absorber 340
Rear sub-frame 364
Rear tail light 329
Rear-view mirror
  1906 Renault 336
  Formula One racing car
    357
  Renault Clio 353
Receiver
  American squash 545
  Badminton 545
  International squash
    545

Racketball 545
Tennis 544
Receiving line 545
Receptacles
Algae 116
Dicotyledon flower 127
Dry fruit 150-151
Fertilization 147
Flower 140-56
Rose 131
Seaweeds 116-117
Succulent fruit 148-149
Recessed arch 488
Recessed hinge 414, 415
Rechargeable battery
Digital camera 581
Nintendo Wii Fit
Plus 579
Recharge area 292
Reclining seat 572
Recoil cylinder 396
Reconnaissance camera
420
Recorded information 521
Recording light 583
Record/Stop button 586
Rectal caecum 174
Rectal gland 179
Rectangle 622
Rectangular block 623
Rectangular cross-band
374
Rectangular pier 465, 467,
480
Rectangular river
drainage 288
Rectangular window
Ancient Roman
building 474
Asian building 490
Baroque church 481
Medieval building 466
Renaissance building
474, 476
Rectum
Bird 189
Butterfly 169
Chimpanzee 202
Cow 198
Dogfish 179
Dolphin 205
Elephant 200
Frog 182
Human 215, 248-249,
258-259, 261
Lizard 185
Rabbit 196
Starfish 174
Tortoise 187
Rectus abdominis muscle
226
Rectus femoris muscle
226
Recumbent fold 61
Red algae 117
Red blood cells 217, 253
Red-brown crocoite 271
Red card 524
Red cedar boarding 602
Red cell 584
Red deer 199
Red dwarf 23
Red earth 433, 434-435
Red filter signal light 407
Red giant
Small stars 24-25
Stars 22-23
Red howler monkey 203
Red light 318
Main-line signalling
system 330, 331
Red light photon 318
Red marble 450
Red port navigation light
406
Red sandstone 277
Red seaweeds 117
Red spot 44-45
Red supergiant

Massive stars 26-27
Stars 22-23
Reduction gearbox
Early piston aero-
engines 410-411
Jet engines 419
Turboprop engine 419
Redwall limestone 277
Red warning light
Italian State Railways
Class 402 328
Paris Metro 328
Redwood trees 70
Reed pen 444
Reef knot 388
Reef point 385
Reel
Angling equipment
562-563
Fencing piste 557
Frigate 397
Reel foot 562-563
Reel scoop 562-563
Reel seat 563
Re-entrant angle 485
Re-entrant corner 479
Referee
American football 526
Basketball 532
Gaelic football 529
Ice hockey 550
Judo 556
Lacrosse 541
Rugby 530
Soccer 524
Swimming 558
Volleyball 534
Referee's crease 550
Refe'ree's equipment 524
Referee's signals
American football 527
Basketball 533
Reflection 318
Reflection nebula 16
Reflector
Ford Model T 339
Oldsmobile trim 337
Refraction 318-319
Refractory (heat-resistant)
skin 421
Refrigerator freight car
327
Régie Autonome des
Transports Parisien 328
Regional metamorphism
274
Regional weather 302
Registers 514
Regolith (soil) 41
Regula 461
Regulator
"Mallard" express
steam locomotive 325
"Rocket" steam
locomotive 324
Regulator valve 525
Regulus 18, 21
Rein 554
Reinforce 395
Reinforced concrete 494,
497
Sleepers 330
Reinforced plinth 499
Rein terret 555
Relative atomic mass 310
Relay baton 543
Relay running 542
Release 517, 543
Release adjustment screw
552
Release button 425
Release catch 590
Release lever 563
Release spring 563
Relief 458
Relief printing 446
Relief printing equipment
449
Relieving arch

Ancient Roman
building 462, 465
Medieval building
466-467
Remiges 188, 191
Remote control 584, 585
Remote control sensor
585
Remote sensing palette
614
Removable archery
screen 377
Renaissance buildings
474-477
Renal artery 256-257
Renal column 256
Renal papilla 256
Renal pelvis 256
Renal sinus 256
Renal vein 256-257
Renault (1906) 336-337
Renault Clio 348-353
Renault logo 348
Renewable energy
604-605
Renoir 35
Repeater indicator 333
Repeating pattern 507
Replum 151
Reply all button 576
Reply button 576
Reproduction
Algae 116-117
Cloning 606-607
Fertilization 146-147
Flowering plants 140
Liverwort 118
Moss 118-119
Vegetative 154-155
Reproductive canal 94
Reproductive chamber
116
Reproductive organs
259
Reproductive structures
Flower 140-143
Pollination 144
Reproductive system
258-259
Reptiles 80-81, 184-187
Carboniferous period
66
Dinosaurs 82-83
Fossil record 279
Jurassic period 70
Present-day 82
Rhynchosaurian 71
Synapsid skull 67
Triassic period 68
Reptilia 184, 186
Repulsion 316-317
"Request identification"
aerial 421
Re-radiated heat 300-301
Reredos 470
Rescue strap 561
Reservoir 314
Reset button 560
Resin canal
Bishop pine needle 124
Pine root/stem 125
Resistance 316
Resonator 513
Respiration 255
Respiratory system
254-255
Rest
Musical notation 502
Newton's first motion
law 321
Resurgence 284-285
Retaining bolt hole 366
Retaining screw 562, 563
Reticulum
Digestive system of a
cow 198
Southern stars 20
Retina 240-241
Retraction jack 417

Retractor muscle 167
Retreating glacier 286
Retrices 188
Retroarticular process 83
Return 486-487
Rev counter 369
Reversed bend hook 562
Reversed dive piked 559
Reverse dip-slip fault 61
Reverse dive 558
Reverse-flow combustion
chamber 418
Reverse lever 325
Reverser handle 325
Reverse shock wave 27
Reversible reactions 312
Reversing shaft lock
control 325
Reversing wheel 392
Revivalist style 493-494
Rewind button 577
Rhamphodopsis 65
Rhamphorhynchus sp. 71
Rheas 188
Rhenium 310
Rhesus monkey 202
Rhinoceroses 198-199
Rhizine 114
Rhizoids 118-119
Alga 116
Fern 121
Liverwort 118
Moss 119
Rhizomes 154-155
Fern 121
Herbaceous flowering
plants 128
Horsetail 120
Water hyacinth 158
Water lily 159
Rhizophore 120
Rho1 Sagittarii 21
Rhodium 311
Rhodophyta 116
Rhomboideus major
muscle 227
Rhomboid leaves 137
Rhombus 622
Rhopalium 167
Rhynchosaurian reptile 71
Rhynchosaurs 68-69, 71
Rhyolite 274-275
Rhyolitic lava 272
Rhythm
Drums 518
Percussion instruments
516
Rhythm pattern selector
520
Rib
Acoustic guitar 512
Archaeopteryx 85
Avro triplane 403
Baroque church 479
BE 2B tail 405
BE 2B wings 404
Bird 189
Blackburn monoplane
401
Bony fish 181
Brachiosaurus 90
Concorde 417
Crocodile 186
Diplodocus 90
Dome 486-487
Domestic cat 195
Double bass 511
Elephant 201
Eryops 80
Euoplocephalus 94
Gallimimus 86
Hare 197
Herbaceous (lowering
plant 128
Horse 199
Kangaroo 206
Lizard 184
Medieval church 469
Modern building 499

Pareiasaur 81
Pegasus Quasar
microlight 426-427
Pegasus XL SE
microlight 426
Plateosaurus 88
Platypus 206
Rhesus monkey 202
Seal 204
Snake 185
Stegoceras 101
Struthiomimus 87
Toxodon 107
Triceratops 102
Tyrannosaurus 84
Violin 510
Westlothiana 81
Riband 381
Ribbon connectors 585
Ribbon Lake 287
Ribbon window 499
Rib cage
Carnivores 195
Human 218
Ribosome
Chloroplast 139
Human cell 217
Rib vault 469, 484-485
Gothic building 470
Medieval building 467
Renaissance building
477
Rice paper 445
Ride cymbal 519
Ridge
Epigeal germination 153
False septum 151
Gothic building 473
Modern building 499
Nineteenth-century
building 492
Seed 153
Twentieth-century
building 495
Ridge and furrow roof 492
Ridge-board 473
Ridge-rib 469, 485
Ridges 286-287
Ridge tile 464, 476
Riding bit 372
Riding jacket 554
Riffler 452, 453, 454
Rifle 548, 549
Rift valley 58
Lake formation 292-293
Rig 384-385
Riga brush 434
Rigel
Northern stars 18
Orion 18
Southern stars 21
Star magnitudes 22
Rigger 501
Rigger's gauge 382
Rigging 382-383
Iron 392
Sailing dinghy 561
Wooden sailing ship
378-379
Rigging rail 376
Rigging tools 382-383
Right-angled triangle 622
Right cylinder 623
Right edge guide 575
Right whales 204
Rigid rock 60
Rigol 381
Rim
Bicycle wheel 358-359
Kayak paddle 560
Paddle wheel 391
Tam-tam 516
Twin bollards 386
Rim brake 330
Rim clamp 337
Rim of pitcher 161
Rim plate 390
Rim section 390
Rind 149

Ring
74-gun ship 380
Mushroom 115
Roman corbita 372
Ring 1986 U1R 48
Ring 1986 U2R 48
Ring 6 48
Ring bolt 373
Ring canal
Sea urchin 175
Starfish 174
Ring dyke 26
Ring finger 230-231
"Ring of Fire" 272
Ring of trunk 201
Rings
Jupiter 44-45
Neptune 50-51
Saturn 46-47
Uranus 48-49
Rings 4 and 5 48
Ring scar 130, 131
Ring-tailed lemur 203
Rink corner 550
Riojasaurus 89
Ripple finish 451
Riser
Bronze casting 454, 455
Staircase 477
Rising air
Atmospheric circulation
and winds 300
Precipitation 302
Rising land 294
Risorius muscle 229
Rissa tridactyla 190
Ritchey 43
River Amur 265
River banks 289, 290
River-bed 289
River capture 288
River cliff 289, 290
River Congo 265
River course 288
River development 289
River drainage patterns
288
River features 290-291
River flow 290
River Ganges 288
River Jordan 293
River Lena 265
River Mekong 265
River-mouth 290
River Nile 264-265
River Ob-Irtysh 265
Rivers 288-289
Earth's physical
features 264
River features 290-291
Rock cycle 266-267
Weathering and erosion
282
River source
River features 290
Rivers 288
River's stages 288-289
River terrace 290-291
River valley 288, 289, 290
Rivetted plates 592
Road spring 340
Roband 372, 374
Robie House 495
Robinia pseudoacacia 156
Roboreptile 609
Robots 608-609
Robot dogs 609
Roche 41
Roches moutonnées 286
Rock compression 60
Rock crystal 271
Rock cycle 266-267
Rock debris 295
Rock deformations 60, 61
Rocker 41
Rocker arm 366
Rocker-beam 496-497
Rocker cover 347, 354
Rocker deployment

actuator 615
Rock erosion 282
Rocker keypad 591
Rocker pad 590
"Rocket" steam
  locomotive 324
Rocket launcher 397
Rock fracture 60
Rock ground mass 269
Rocking beam 334
Rocking elevator arm
  424
Rocking lever 342
Rock layer
  Caves 284
  Faults and folds 60
Rock lip
  Cirque formation 287
  Tarn lake 293
Rock mounds 286
Rock particles 266-267
Rock pavement 282-283
Rock pedestal 282-283
Rock prisms 61
Rocks
  Faults and folds 60-61
  Fossils 278-279
  Igneous and
    metamorphic rocks
    274-275
  Mineral resources 280
  Minerals 268
  Rock cycle 266-267
  Sedimentary rocks 276
  Weathering and erosion
    282
Rock salt
  Halides 269
  Sedimentary rocks
    276-277
Rock scar 284
Rock stonecrop 128
Rock strata 60, 61
  Fossils 278
Rock stress 60, 61
Rock tension 60, 61
Rocky Mountains 73, 75,
  77, 264
Rocky planets
  Mars 42-43
  Mercury 34-35
  Solar System 30-31
  Venus 36-37
Rococo style 478
Rod 562-563
Rodentia 104, 196
Rodents 196-197
Rod-shaped structure 144
Rogers, R. 496
Roll 400
Roller
  Mid West single-rotor
    engine 410
  Motorized brushbar
    floor tool 593
  "O Ring" drive chain
    366
  Painting tool 442
  Printing equipment 447,
    449
  Tenor saxophone 509
Roller-bearing axle box
  327
Roller-blind 497
Roller path 396
Rollers 596
Rolling hitch 388
Rollover button 577
Roll paper holder 575
Roll paper holder adapter
  575
Roll paper manipulation
  button 574
Roll spoiler 414
Roll-spoiler hydraulic
  actuator attachment
  414
Rolls-Royce Olympus
  Mark 610 turbojet 417

Roman anchor 372
Roman architecture
  462-465
Romanesque style 468,
  470
Roman corbita 372-373
Roman mill 464
Roman number system
  591
Roman ships 372-373
Roof boss 468
Roof construction 603
Roof dome 332, 333
Roofed space 479
Roofing tile 482
Roofless temple 460
Roof moulding 352
Roofs 484
  Ancient Egyptian
    temple 458-459
  Ancient Roman
    building 462
  Asian building 490
  Baroque church 481
  Dome 486
  Gothic building 470-473
  Hammer-beam 470, 473
  Islamic building
    488-489
  Medieval building 467,
    468
  Modern building
    496-499
  Neoclassical building
    479, 483
  Nineteenth-century
    building 492
  Renaissance building
    476-477
  Twentieth-century
    building 494-495
Root
  BAe-146 jetliner
    components 413, 415
  BE 2B wings 404
  Tooth 247
Root canal 247
Root cap
  Broad bean 133
  Radicle 155
Root growth 282
Root hairs 132
Root nodule 128
Root of tail 198
Root parasite 163
Root-proof membrane
  603
Root rib 413
Roots 132-133
  Adventitious 112-113
  Amaryllis 155
  Begonia 155
  Brassavola nodosa 162
  Broomrape host 163
  Carrot 128
  Cell division 133
  Clubmoss 120
  Couch grass 113
  Dehiscent fruit 150
  Dicotyledons 127
  Elongation region 133
  Embryo 147
  Epigeal germination
    153
  Epiphytes 162-163
  Fern 121
  Germination 152-153
  Ginger 155
  Gladiolus 155
  Golden barrel cactus
    156
  Grape hyacinth 155
  Horse chestnut 130
  Horsetail 120
  Hypogeal germination
    152
  Ivy 131
  Kedrostis africana 113
  Lily 155

Monocotyledons
  126-127
Mycorrhizal association
  133
Oxalis sp. 157
Pine seedling 122
Potato 128
Rock stonecrop 128
Seedling 152-153
String of hearts 157
Sweet pea 128
Sweet potato 155
Vegetative reproduction
  154-155
Water hyacinth 158
Water transport 138
Root scar 282
Root succulents 157
Root tip 152-153
  Radicle 152-153
Root tubers 154-155, 157
Rope and paterae
  decoration 459
Rope band 372
Rope hole 386
Rope moulding 395
Rope parrel 373
Rope preventer 378
Ropes 388-389
Rope serving mallet 383
Rope strand 384
Rope woolding 379
Rope work 388
Rorquals 204
Rosa sp. 130-131, 135
Rose 130-131
Rose quartz 271
Rosette
  Epiphytic plants
    162-163
  Neoclassical building
    480
Rosette Nebula 11
Rossby waves 300
Rossin Italian time-trial
  bicycle 361
Rostellum 16
Rostral bone 102, 103
Rostrum
  Crayfish 173
  Dolphin 204
Rotary engine 346-347
  Blackburn monoplane
    400
  Modern piston aero-
    engines 410-411
Rotary valves 507
Rotating beacon 407
Rotating drum 595
Rotating joint 612
Rotational period 36
Rotor
  Mid West rotary engine
    411
  Rotor and seals 347
Rotor blade 423
Rotor chamber
  Mid West single-rotor
    engine 410
  Wankel rotary engine
    346
Rotor gear 346-347
Rotor gear teeth 411
Rotor house 314
Rotor hub
  Bell-47 helicopter 422
  Schweizer helicopter
    423
Rotor journal 347
Rotor lock 604
Rotor mast 422-423
Rotunda 462-463, 482
Rough 546
Rough endoplasmic
  reticulum 217
Rough terrain motorcycle
  racing 368
Rough-textured paper
  439, 441

Roulette 446
Rounce 449
Round arch
  Ancient Roman
    building 464-465
  Baroque church
    479-480
  Dome 484, 486-487
  French temple 485
  Gothic church 473
  Medieval building
    467-469
  Nineteenth-century
    building 495
  Renaissance building
    474-475
Round-arched window
  Ancient Roman
    building 465
  Baroque church 481
  Dome 486
  Medieval building 466,
    468-469
  Neoclassical building
    478
Round ball 524
Round-corner single
  limousine coachwork
    536
Roundel
  Avro biplane 403
  Hawker Tempest
    fighter 409
Roundhead nib 444
Roundhouse 380
Round pin 335
Round shot 378
Round thimble 384
Route information 332
Route key 590
Rover 528
Rover equipment deck
  615
Rowan 130-131
Rowing 560-561
Rowing boat 375
Rowing positions on a
  Greek trireme 373
RSS (really simple
  syndication) feeds 577
Rubber bungee shock
  absorber 425
Rubber cord suspension
  402-403
Rubber guide wheel 328
Rubber mounting bush
  365
Rubber puck 550-551
Rubber roller 449
Rubber sealing strip 413
Rubber-sprung wheel
  400-401
Rubber tyre 402
Rubber-tyred running
  wheel 328
Rubber wheel-guard 328
Rubber wheels
  Paris Metro 328
  "People Mover" 328
Rubbing
  Charcoal drawing 431
  Relief printing 446
Rubbing ink 448
Rubbing strake
  Mazda RX-7 346
  Roman corbita 372
Rubbing strip 353
Rubens 35
Rubidium 510
Rubus fruticosus 150,
  146-147
Rubus idaeus 149
Ruckman 528
Rucknover 528
Ruckstell axle 339
Rudder
  ARV light aircraft 424
  Avro biplane 402
  Avro triplane 403

BAe-146 jetliner 415
Battleship 395
BE 2B bomber 405
Blackburn monoplane
  401
Blériot XI 401
Concorde 416-417
Curtiss biplane 399
Dhow 376
Frigate 396
Greek and Roman ships
  372-373
Iron paddlesteamer
  392
Junk 376
Lockheed Electra
  airliner 407
Longboat 380
LVG CVI fighter 405
Northrop B-2 bomber
  421
Sailing dinghy 561
Sailing warship 377
Schleicher glider 426
Submarine 596
Tornado 421
Viking boats 374-375
Wooden sailing ship
  378
World War II aircraft
  408-409
Wright Flyer 399
Rudder cable
  ARV light aircraft 424
  Avro biplane 402
Rudder chain 378
Rudder head 376
Rudder hinge
  Avro biplane 402
  Blériot XI monoplane
    401
Rudder mass balance 424
Rudder pedal 425, 573
Rudder post
  BE 2B bomber 405
  Blackburn monoplane
    401
  Iron paddlesteamer 392
Rudder power control unit
  417
Rudder strut 399
Rudder tip fairing 424
Rudder trimtab 409
Ruden 372
Rudimentary ear 260
Rudimentary eye 260
Rudimentary liver 260
Rudimentary mouth 260
Rudimentary vertebra 260
Ruellia grandiflora 145
Ruffini corpuscle 235, 239
Ruga 248
Rugby 524, 530-531
Rugby League 530-531
Rugby Union 530
Rules of algebra 621
Rumen 198
Ruminants 198
Rumpler monoplane 400
Run 536
Runners
  Bronze casting 454-455
  Rock stonecrop 128
  Strawberry 128
  Vegetative reproduction
    154
Running 542
Running back 526
Running block 383
Running board
  Ford Model T 339
  1906 Renault 337
  Volkswagen Beetle 341
Running martingale 554
Running part 382
Running rail 328
Running rigging 382-383,
  385
Running shoe 543

Running track 542
Running wheel 328
Runs 538
Rupes 34
Rupes Altai 40
Rush 135
Russian vine 131
Rustication
  Neoclassical building
    479, 482-483
  Renaissance building
    474-475
Rusts 114
Ruthenium 311

S
62 Sagittarii 21
Sabik 20
Sable brush
  Acrylics 442
  Calligraphy 444
  Oil paints 436
  Tempera 432
  Watercolours 438
Sabres 556-557
Sabreur 557
Sabre warning line 557
Sacajawea 37
Saccule 243
Sacral foramen 223
Sacral nerves 258
Sacral plexus 258
Sacral promontory 223
Sacral vertebra 183
Sacral vertebrae
  Diplodocus 90
  Eryops 81
  Human 223
  Iguanodon 96
  Parasaurolophus 98
  Plateosaurus 88
  Stegoceras 101
Sacristy 470
Sacrum
  Crocodile 186
  Domestic cat 195
  Elephant 201
  Hare 197
  Horse 199
  Human 218, 223, 259
  Kangaroo 206
  Lizard 184
  Rhesus monkey 202
  Seal 204
Saddle
  Acoustic guitar 512
  Bicycle 358-359
  Cannondale SH600
    hybrid bicycle 361
  Eddy Merckx racing
    bicycle 360
  Horse racing 555
  Show jumping 554
  Werner motorcycle 362
Saddle clamp 360
Safety area 556
Safety barrier 552
Safety belt 356
Safety binding 552
Safety harness 557
Safety valve
  Bordino steam carriage
    354
  Steamboat 391
Safe working load mark 383
Sagartia elegans 166
Sagitta 20
Sagittal crest 107, 194
Sagittal section through
  brain 236
Sagittarius 19-21
Sagittarius Arm 14
Sago palm 123
Sahara 39, 264-265
Sail
  Roman corbita 372-373
  Square-rigged ship 375

Types 384-385
Viking karv 374
Sail batten 376
Sailcloths 584
Sail foot control line 375
Sail hook 384
Sailing 560-561
Sailing rigs 384-385
Sailing warship 376-377
Sailmaker's whipping 382
Sailmaking tools 584
Sail patterns 379, 384
Saiph 18
Salamanders 182
Salient 466
Salisbury Cathedral
470-471
Saliva 244
Salivary gland
Butterfly 169
Snail 177
Salmon 190, 180
Salmon angling 562
Salmon bend gouge 452
Salmson radial engine
398-399
Salt
Dead Sea 293
Seawater sail content
296
Saltasaurus 72, 91
Salt-dome trap 281
Salt formation 312
Salt groundmass 277
Salt lakes 292
Samaras
Dry fruit 150
Sycamore 131, 150
Samarium 311
Sambucus nigra 130-131,
143
Samotherium 74
Samsung Galaxy Tab 569
San Andreas fault 58,
62-63
Sand-bars 290
Sand box 326, 327
Sand dunes
Rock cycle 267
Weathering and erosion
282-283
Sand groundmass 277
Sanding pipe 329
Sand-pits 546
Sandstone
Marble tomb of Itimad-
Ud-Daula 489
Sedimentary rocks 276
Sand wave 299
Sand wedge 547
Sandy deposits 298
Sandy spit 295
Sanguine crayon 430
Sankey diagram 314
Sappho Patera 37
Sapwood 125
Saratoga Race Course 553
Sarcolemma 24
Sarcomere 24
Sarcophilus harrisii 207
Sarcoplasmic reticulum
24
Sarcorhamphus papa 190
Sarracenia purpurea 113
Sartorius muscle 226
Satellite 264
Satellite cable 586
Satellite map 264-265
Satellite speaker 586
Saturated zone 292-293
Saturn 46-47, 614
Solar System 31
Saucer dome 486-487
Ancient Roman
building 465
Saurischia 82-83, 84, 88
Sauropoda 83
Sauropodomorpha 83, 88
Sauropodomorphs 88-91

Sauropods 70, 88
Savannah 74
Save as draft button 576
Saxboard 561
Saxophone 504, 508-509
Scala 372-373
Scale (musical) 502
Scale leaf scar 124, 155
Scale leaves
Bishop pine 124
Bulb 155
Corm 155
Epiphytic orchid 162
Hypogeal germination
152
Pine 122, 125
Plumule 152
Rhizome 155
Sago palm 123
Stem bulbil 155
Scalene triangle 622
Scalenus medius muscle
229
Scale of degrees 377
Scales
Asteroxylon 79
Bishop pine 124
Bony fish 180
Bract 122
Brassavola nodosa 162
Caiman 186
Cartilaginous fish 178
Crocodilians 186
Dicotyledons 127
False fruit 148
Fern fronds 121
Insects 168
Lepidoptera wings 168
Lizard 184
Mushroom 115
Ovuliferous 122-124
Pine cone 122
Pine shoot apex 125
Rattlesnake 185
Sago palm 122
Tree fern 112
Yew 123
Scallop 176
Fossil 278
Scalloped hammerhead
shark 179
Scalp 254, 236-237
Scaly lichens 114
Scaly skin
Anchisaurus 89
Corythosaurus 98
Dinosaurs 82
Edmontonia 95
Echthyostega 80
Iguanodon 97
Pachycephalosaurus
100
Psittacosaurus 103
Reptile 80
Snake 184
Stegosaurus 92
Triceratops 102
Tyrannosaurus 84
Westlothiana 81
Scandinavia 64, 69
Scandium 310
Scan head 571
Scanner 570-571
Scanning coils 611
Scanning electron
microscope (SEM) 610,
611
Scan to e-mail button 570
Scan to web button 570
Scapania undulata 118
Scape 168
Scaphoid bone 230
Scaphoid fossa 242
Scaphonyx fischeri 69
Scapula
Archaeopteryx 85
Arsinoitherium 104
Bird 189
Bony fish 181

Brachiosaurus 91
Crocodile 186
Diplodocus 90
Domestic cat 195
Elephant 201
Eiryops 80
Euoplocephalus 94
Gallimimus 86
Hare 197
Horse 199
Human 210, 218
Iguanodon 96
Kangaroo 206
Lizard 184
Parasaurolophus 99
Pareiasaur 81
Plateosaurus 88
Platypus 206
Rhesus monkey 202
Seal 204
Stegoceras 101
Struthiomimus 87
Toxodon 106
Triceratops 102
Turtle 187
Tyrannosaurus 84
Scapular muscle 91
Scarlet star 162-163
Scarph 395
Scars
Horse chestnut 130
Leaf 128-30, 134
Rowan twig 131
Scavenge oil line 419
Scelidosaurus 71
Scent 144
Scheat 19, 20
Schedar 19
Schickard 40
Schist 26
Schizoearpic dry fruits
150-151
Schleicher K23 glider 426
Schlumbergera truncata
129
Schooner 384-385
Schrodinger 41
Schubert 35
Schwann cell 228, 239
Schweizer 300c 423
Sciatic nerve 238
Scientific notation 621
Scintigram 214
Scissor brace 475
Sciuris carolinensis 197
Sclera 213, 240
Sclereid 159
Sclerenchyma
Fern rachis 121
Horsetail stem 120
Marram grass 113
Monocotyledon leaf 126
Stems 134-135
Sclerenchyma fibres 135
Scleroderma citrinum 115
Sclerotic ring 90, 99
Scooter 50-51
Score 547
Scorecard 547
Scorer
Basketball 532
Fencing contest 557
Judo contest 556
Lacrosse 541
Netball 535
Volleyball 534
Scoria 273
Scoring
Australian rules football
528
Badminton 544
Baseball 536
Basketball 532
Cricket 538
Gaelic football 529
Hockey 540
Hurling 540-541
Netball 534

Rugby 530-531
Tennis 544
Volleyball 534
Seorper 449
Scorpion 170, 278
Scorpiones 170
Scorpius 19, 20
Scotia 463, 485
Scots pine 122
Scraper 46
Scraper ring 344
Scratchplate 513
Scree 282-283
Screen
Computer 576, 577, 611
French baroque
building 482
Hydroelectric power
station 314
Islamic building
488-489
Screen printing 448
Streamed Internet
video 577
Twentieth-century
building 494
Screen bulkhead 381
Screen lens 589
Screen printing 446, 448
Screw 320
Acoustic guitar 513
Double bass bow 511
Power drill 600
Toaster 598
Violin bow 510
Screw coupling 525
Screw down greaser 556
Screw fitting 319
Screw hole 600
Screw joint 413
Screw link 386
Screw locking nut 563
Screw pressure adjustor
447
Scriber 446
Scroll
Cello 511
Double bass 511
Viola 511
Violin 510
Scrolled buttress 478
Scroll motif 470, 491
Scroll moulding 466
Scroll ornament 476, 479,
485
Scroll-shaped corbel.482,
487
Scrollwork 472
Scrotum 211, 259
Scrum-half 530
Scrummages 530
Scull 561
Sculling 560
Scull oar 560
Sculpted wing-root fairing
573
Sculptor 19, 20
Sculptural decoration 467
Sculpture 452-455, 493,
495
Sculptured testa 151
Scumbling 440-441
Scupper 595
Scute 186
Scutellum 168
Scutum 19
Scutum plate 175
Scyphozoa 166
Sea
Anticline trap 281
Fossils 278
Hurricane structure 303
River features 290-291
Sea anemone 166-167
Sea angling 562
Seabed
Fossils 278
Ocean floor 298
River features 290

Rivers 288
Seabed profile 299
Sea buckthorn 136
Seacat missile launcher
397
Sea-cave 295
Sea-cliff 294-295
River features 291
Sea creature remains 298
Sea cucumber 174
Sea daisies 174
Sea-dwelling organic
structures 78
Sea-floor spread 58
Seahorse 180
Sea level 66
Sea-level variations 294
Sea lilies 174
Sea lion 204
Seals 204-205
Seam
Rivetted plates 392
Sail 584
Seaming twine 384
Seamounts 298
Sea of Japan 265
Search field 576, 577
Searchlight 394-595
Seas 296-297
Igneous and
metamorphic rocks 275
Rivers 288
Satellite map 265
Seasons 72
Seat
1906 Renault 337
Driver's 525, 528
Faering 375
Fireman's 325
First cars 354-335
Ford Model T 339
Greek trireme 573
Harley-Davidson FLHS
Electra Glide 363
Honda CB750 565
Honda VF750 564
Husqvarna Motocross
TC610 368
Kayak 560
Longboat 380
Motorcycle 364
Racing sulky 555
Renault Clio 352-355
Showjumping saddle
554
Suzuki RGV500 368
TGV electric high-
speed train 329
Vespa Grand Sport 160
Mark 1 563
Weslake Speedway
motorcycle 369
Seat angle 360
Seat assembly 425, 553
Seat attachment rail 416
Seat back rest frame 337,
352-353
Seat beam 399
Seat belt catch 352
Seat control panel 572
Seat cushion 407, 425
Sea temperature 303
Seat frame 553
Seating 465
Seat mount 340
Seat pan 409
Seat post 558, 560
Seat post quick-release
boll 358
Seat spring 335
Seat squab 335, 337
Seat stay 358, 560
Seat support strut 398
Seat tube 358, 360, 361
Sea urchins 174-175
Seawater
River features 290

Salt content 296
Seaweeds 116-117
Seaworm 78
Sebaceous gland 234-235
Secondary baffle 612
Secondary bronchus 215
Secondary colours 439
Secondary conduit
272-273
Rock cycle 266
Secondary crater 34
Secondary flight feathers
188, 191
Secondary follicle 258
Secondary mirror 612
Secondary mycelium 115
Secondary phloem
134-135
Secondary remiges 188,
191
Secondary rotor 317
Secondary suspension 327
Secondary thallus 114
Secondary vascular tissue
134
Secondary xylem 125,
134-135
Second-century building
462
Second electron shell 509
Second mast 376
Second-row forward 530
Second slip 538
Second toe 232
Second violins 503,
504-505
Second wheel set 529
Secretory gland 161
Secretory thyroid gland
cells 217
Secretory vesicle 216
Secure anchor 386
Security light 605
Sediment
Coastlines 294-295
Fossils 278
Glaciers 286-287
Lakes 292
Mineral resources 280
Mountain building
62-65
Ocean floor 298-299
River features 290-291
Rivers 288
Rock cycle 266-267
Sedimentary rocks
276-277
Igneous and
metamorphic rocks 274
Rock cycle 266-267
Sedna Planitia 36-37
Sedum rupestre 128
Sedum spectabile 128-129
Seed
Apomixis 146
Apple 149
Cape gooseberry 149
Dehydration 152
Dispersal 148-151
Dormancy 152
Dry fruit 150-151
Embryo development
147
Fig 148
Germination 132,
152-153
Goosegrass 150
Gymnosperms 122
Hilum 148-149, 151-153
Hogweed 151
Honesty 151
Larkspur 151
Lemon 148
Love-in-a-mist 151
Lychee 148
Melon 149
Parts 152-153
Pea 150
Pine 122

Raspberry 149
Root development 132
Scots pine 122
Smooth cypress 123
Strawberry 149
Succulent fruit 148-149
Sweet chestnut 150
Sycamore 131, 151
Wind dispersal 150
Wings 150-151
Yew 123
Seed axis 152-153
Seed coat 132, 152-153
Dry fruit 150-151
Embryo development 147
Epigeal germination 153
Hypogeal germination 152
Succulent fruit 148-149
Seed fern 278
Seed leaves 126, 152-153
Dry fruit 150-151
Embryo development 147
Epigeal germination 153
Hypogeal germination 152
Pine 122
Succulent fruit 148-149
Seedlings
Epigeal germination 153
Hypogeal germination 152
Pine 122
Seed-producing organs 148-149
Seed scar 122
Seed stalks 150
Seed wings 151
Seek bar 577
Segmental arch 492
Segmental pediment 462, 478
Segnosauria 83
Seif dune 283
Seismic activity 58
Seizing 383, 384, 387, 388-389
Selaginella sp. 120
Select key 578
Selector fork 366
Selector switch 598-599
Selenite 270
Selenium 311
Self-pollination 144
SEM 601, 611
Semaphore signal 330
Semen 217
Semi-arch 470-471
Semibreve 502-503
Semi-bulkhead 425
Semi-circle 532
Semicircular canals 243
Semicircular tower 465
Semi-conductor 306
Semi-dome 484, 482, 488
Semi-elliptical arch 484
Semi-elliptic leaf spring 342
Semilunar fold 249
Semi-metals 310-311
Seminal receptacle 169
Spider 170
Seminal vesicle 259
Semiquaver 502
Semi-solid core 37
Semi-solid outer core 41
Semi-sprawling stance 82
Westlothiana 81
Semitendinosus muscle 227
Send button 576
Sender's name 576
Senior ratings' mess 397
Sensory antenna 168
Sensory hinge 160

Sensory tentacle 176
Sent mail folder 576
Sepal 140-143
Clematis 131
Dicotyledons 126-127
Dry fruit 150-151
Everlasting pea 129
Fertilization 146-147
Monocotyledons 126
Peruvian lily 129
Pitcher plant 113
Pollination 145
Rose 131
Succulent fruit 149
Sepal remains 146-147
Sepal sheath 141
Separated carpels 151
Separator 576
Septime 557
Septum 115
False 151
Interventrieular 251
Nasal 213, 241
Placenta 260
Sequencer 521
Sequoiadendron sp. 70
Series electrical circuit 316
Serif 445
Serous pericardium 250
Serpens Caput 18, 21
Serpens Cauda 19, 20
Serpentes 184
Serpentine neck 574
Serrated tooth 84, 85, 88
Serrate leaf margins 129
Serratus anterior muscle 226
Server 534, 544 , 545, 576
Server Service 544
Service area 554
Service box line 545
Service court 544, 545
Service crane 605
Service door 415
Service judge 544, 545
Service line 544, 545
Service shaft 498
Service zone 545
Serving 388
Serving mallet 383, 384, 388
Servo control-unit fairing 417
Servo-tab 414, 415
Sesamoid bone 198
Seta 112, 119
Set-back buttress 481
Set square 445
Settings control panel 574
Settings display 574, 575
Setting select buttons 575
Seven Sisters 14
Seventeenth century 474
Building 479-481, 488
Capital 490
Dome 486-487
Roof 490
Style 490
Tomb 489
Seventh century
Building 491
Sevier fault 276
Sex cells 154
Fertilization 146-147
Gametophyte plants 120
Gymnosperms 122
Liverwort 118
Moss 118-119
Sextans 21
Sexual reproduction
Algae 116-117
Bryophytes 119
Flowering plants 140-141
Mosses 118-119
Seaweed 116-117
Spirogyra sp. 117

Seyfert 41
Seyfert galaxies 12-13
Shackle 382, 386
Shackle pin 382
Shaft
Ancient Egyptian column 459
Ancient Greek temple 461
Ancient Roman building 463, 465
Arrow 548
Asian building 490-491
Badminton racket 545
Electric generator 517
Feather 191
Femur 225
French temple 485
Golf club 547
Harness racer 555
Hydroelectric power station 314
Javelin 542
Kayak paddle 560
Medieval church 468-469
Modern building 498
Neoclassical building 478, 483
Nineteenth-century building 493
Phalanx 230
Power drill 600
Roman Corbita 373
Sculling oar 560
Ski pole 553
Squash racket 545
Shaft drive 366
Shale
Contact metamorphism 274
Grand Canyon 277
Shallow carvel-built hull 391
Shallow Hats 293
Shank
Anatomy of a hook 562
Danforth anchor 386
Hook 383
Roman anchor 372
Sail hook 384
Shackle pin 382
Shannon bone 199
Shape
Chemical reactants 312
Matter 306-307
Periodic table 310
Shapes (plane; solid) 622
Sharks 178-179, 180
Sharp 502
Sharpey's fibre 225
Shaula 19, 20
Shave 374
Shaving foam 506
Shearing 61
Sheave 383
Sheave for cat tackle 380
Sheep 198
Sheepskin numnah 554
Sheer 374
Sheerplank 580
Sheer pole 373
Sheer strake 375, 393
Sheet 372, 375, 382
Sheet anchor 395
Sheet bend 389
Sheet feeder 575
Sheet-iron louvre 493
Sheet lead 383
Shelf formation 282
Shell
379 cm shell 397
6 in shell 397
Building 464, 476
Chelonians 186
Crab 172
Dorsal margin 176
Egg 192-193
Exploding 394, 396-397

Fossil 278
Massive stars 26
Mollusc 176-177
Octopus 176
Rib 176
Rudiment 176
Scallop 176
Small stars 24-25
Snail 177
Standing block 382
Terrapin 187
Ventral margin 176
Shell bogie 396
Shell case 397
Shelled invertebrates 56
Shelley 35
Shell-like fracture 270
Shell room 396
Shelly limestone 267
"Shiaijo" 556
"Shield bearers" 92
Shielded receiver 591
Shield plate 570
Shield volcano 42
Shin
Herrerasaurus 86
Human 211
Shinarump member 276
Shin guard
Slalom skiing 553
Soccer 525
Shinty 540
Sbinumo quartzite 277
Ship 387
74-gun ship 379, 380-581
Ship of the line 380-381
Ship's cannon 376, 394
Ships of Greece and Rome 372-373
Ship's shield 394-395
Ship's wheel 378, 390, 394
Shipwright 374
Shiv 383
Shiver 383
Shock absorber
1906 Renault 336
American football helmet 527
ARV light aircraft 425
Honda CB750 363
Honda VF750 564
Renault Clio 350
Suzuki RGV500 368
Vespa Grand Sport 160
Mark 1 363
Volkswagen Beetle 340
Shock-absorbing platform 553
Shock-absorbing spring 401, 405
Shock-strut 401
Shock waves 27
Path 63
Athletics 543
Basketball 533
Golf 547
Handball 535
Rowing 560
Shoot
Broomrape 163
Embryo 147
Horsetail 120
Hypogeal germination 152
Pine 125
Vegetative reproduction 155
Shoot apex 125
Shooting 548-549
Shooting circle 540
Shooting positions 548
Shoreline
Coastlines 294
Continental-shelf floor 298
Short line 545
Shorts

Australian rules football 529
Hurling 541
Soccer 525
Volleyball 534
Short saphenous vein 253
Shortstop 536
Short-wave radio 318
Shot
Field events equipment 542
Gun 378
Shot garland 381
Shot put 543
Shot-put circle 542
Shot-put fan 542
Shoulder
Anchisaurus 89
Cello 511
Corythosaurus 98
Double bass 511
Gorilla 203
Harp 511
Horse 199
Human 210
Iguanodon 97
Rabbit 196
Rigging 382-383
Stegoceras 101
Stegosaurus 92
Viola 511
Violin 510
Shoulderblade 210, 218
Shoulder cowling 412
Shoulder girdle 80
Shoulder joint
Brachiosaurus 91
Gallimimus 86
Human 218
Parasaurolophus 99
Plateosaurus 88
Triceratops 102
Tyrannosaurus 84
Shoulder pad 426
Shoulder padding 551
Shoulder pass 535
Shoulder spikes
Edmontonia 95
Euoplocephalus 94
Shoulder wheel throw 556
Showjumping 554
Shreve, R.H. 494
Shrew-like mammals 70
Shrimp 172
Fossil 79
Shrine 490-491
Shroud
Dhow 376
Longboat 380
Rigging 383
Roman corbita 373
Sailing dinghy 561
Sailing warship 376
Shrubs 130-131
Shuffle button 586
Shutter button 581
Shutter for gun 394
Shuttlecock 544-545
Shuttle switch 586
Sickle motif 491
Sidalcea malviflora 136
Side aisle
Cathedral dome 484
Gothic church 472-473
Medieval church 469
Side bench 580
Side brace and retraction jack trunnions 414
Sidecar
BMW R/60 362
Motorcycle racing 368-369
Side chapel 469-470, 479
Side counter timber 381
Side-cowling 408
Side drum 504-505
Side fairing 415
Side forequarter hold 556
Side gear 347

Side housing 346-347
Side lamp 338-339
Sidelight 332, 333, 362
Side-line
American football 526
Badminton 545
Basketball 532
Handball 535
Hockey 540
Men's lacrosse 540
Netball 535
Tennis 541
Volleyball 534
Side marker lamp 346, 349
Side-mounted engine 398
Side plate 562
Side pod 356, 357
Side reflector 562, 563
Siderite band 277
Side rudder 374-375
Side-shooting 541
Side vent 329
Side wall 545, 558
Side-wall line 545
Sideways erosion
River features 290
Rivers 288
Sierra Madre 264
Sierra Nevada 57, 75
Sieve tubes 134
Sieving beak 188
Sif Mons 37
Sight 394
Sight pin 549
Sight screen 538
Sighting hood
Battleship 394
Gun turret 396
Sighting rule 376-377
Sights 548-549
Sigma Canis Majoris 21
Sigmoid colon 249
Signal flag compartment 597
Signal gear 395
Signalling systems 330-331
Sikorsky, Igor 422
Silence 502
Silencer
Harley-Davidson FLHS Electra Glide 362
Renault Clio 350
Suzuki RGV500 368
Vespa Grand Sport 160
Mark 1 363
Weslake Speedway motorcycle 369
Silencing heat exchanger 404
Silicate core 51
Silicate dust 53
Silicate material 39
Silicate rock 39
Silicates 269
Siliceous ooze 299
Silicon 26
Earth's composition 39
Earth's crust 58
Periodic table 311
Variety of matter 306
Siliquas 150-151
Silk gland 170
Sill 26
Ancient Roman mill 464
Renaissance building 475
Twentieth-century building 494
Sill trim 353
Silly mid-off 538
Silly mid-on 538
Silurian period
Fossil record 279
Geological time 56
Silver
Mineral resources 280-281

Minerals 268
Periodic table 311-312
Streak 271
Silver lines 450-451
Silver molybdenite 271
Silver nitrate solution 312
Silverpoint 450, 431
Silver wire 450
Silvery metals 510
SIM (Subscriber Identity
   Module) card slot 589
Simple electrical circuit
   316
Simple eye 170-171
Simple leaves 136-137
   Entire 130
   Hastate 128
   Herbaceous flowering
      plants 128-129
   Lanceolate 131
   Lobed 131
Simple machines 320
Simple Machines Law
   320
Simple succulent fruits
   148-149
Single bass note siring
   515
Single-celled micro-
   organisms 78
Single clump block 375
Single cylinder 335
Single-decker bus 352, 333
Single flowers 140-141,
   143
Single front driving wheel
   354
Single-glazed
   conservatory 602
Single-leg main landing
   gear 407
Single overhead cam
   engine 363
Single-piece skin 413
Single-pulley system 320
Single reed 508, 509
Singles 5
Single scull 560, 561
Single sheet bend 387
Single-sided trailing-link
   fork 363
Single wing hold 556
Singularity
   Formation of black hole
      29
   Stellar black hole 29
Sinistral strike-slip fault
   61
Sink-holes 284-285
Sinking land 294
Sinopia 434, 435
Sinous venosus sclerae
   241
Sinuous cell wall 156
Sinus
   Frontal, 212, 245
   Green alga 112
   Renal 256
   Superior sagittal 212
Sinus Borealis 69
Sinus Irid um 40
Siphon
   Octopus 176-177
   Sea urchin 175
Siphonoglyph 167
Sirius
   Canis Major 21
   Northern stars 18
   Our galaxy and nearby
      galaxies 15
   Southern stars 21
   Spectral absrsplion
      lines 25
   Star magnitudes 22
Sirius A 25
Sirius B 25
Site icon 577
Sixteenth century
   Building 476-477

Staircase 472
Style 462, 470
Size (glue) 431, 452, 436
Skarn 26
Skate
   Chondrichthyes 178
   Ice hockey 550, 551
Skeletal muscle 228
Skeletal muscle fibre 228
Skeleton
   Archaeopteryx 85
   Arsinoitherium 104-105
   Baryonyx hand 85
   Bat 105
   Bird 189
   Bony fish 180-181
   Cow's foot 198
   Crocodile 186
   Diplodocus 90
   Domestic cal 195
   Klephant 201
   Eryops 80-81
   Frog 185
   Hare 197
   Horse 199
   Human 218-219
   Iguanodon 96
   Kangaroo 206
   Kentrosaurus 95
   Lizard 184
   Parasurolophus 98-99
   Pareiasaur 81
   Plateosaurus 88-89
   Platypus 206
   Rhesus monkey 202
   Seal 204
   Snake 185
   Spider 171
   Sponge 166
   Stegoceras 100-101
   Stegosaurus 95
   Struthiomimus 87
   Toxodon 106
   Triceralops 102-103
   Tuofiaiigosairius 95
   Turile 187
   Tyrannosaurus 84-85
   Westlothiana 81
Sketch book 450
Skid 402, 404
Skid beam 580
Ski goggles 552, 553
Skiing 552, 553
Skilled movements 257
Skin
   Amphibian 80, 182
   Drumhead 518
   Lizard 184
   Reptile 80
   Snake 184
   Succulent fruits 148-149
   Waterproof 81
Skin and hair 234-235
"Skin-grip" pin 424-425
Skin lap-joint 413, 414,
   415
Skin tones 441
Ski pole 552
Skirting board 602
Skis 552
Skull
   Acanthostega 80
   Alligator 186
   Ankylosaurus 94
   Australopithecus 108
   Baryonyx 85
   Bear 194
   Bird 189
   Camarasaurus 91
   Chimpanzee 202
   Crocodilians 186
   Diplodocus 90
   Domestic cat 195
   Elephant 201
   Euoplocephalus 94
   Fetal 220
   Gharial 186
   Hadrosaurs 96
   Hare 197

Heterodontosaurus 85
Homo erect us 108
Homo habilis 108
Horse 199
Human 108, 212, 218,
   220-221, 222, 236-257
Hyaenodon 107
Iguanodon 96
Kangaroo 206
Lambeosaurus 99
Lion 194
Lizard 184
Marginocephalian 100
Moeritherium 105
Octopus 176
Opossum 106
Pachycephalosaurs 100
Pachycephdlosaurus
   100
Phiomia 105
Plateosaurus 88
Platypus 206
Prenocephale 100
Protoceratops 102
Rattlesnake 185
Rhesus monkey 202
Seal 204
Smilodon 107
Stegoceras 100
Styracosaurus 102
Synapsid reptile 67
Tortoise 77
Turtle 187
Skull bones 81
Skullcap 555
Skunks 194
Skylight
   Battleship 394
   Building 495, 494
   Iron paddlesteamer
      392-393
Skyscraper 494
Slab
   Ancient Egyptian
      building 458-459
   Modern building 499
   Twentieth-century
      building 494
Slaked lime 434
Slalom
   Skiing 552
   Canoeing 560
Slalom clothing 553
Slalom equipment 553
Slalom gate 552
Slat 421
Slate 274, 275
Sleep button 585
Sleeper 324, 351
Sleeve port 543
Sleeve valve 543
Slender thistle 129
Slick racing tyre 365
   Kirby BSA 369
   Suzuki RCV500 369
Slide 396
Slide bar 325
Slide brace 507
Slide locking lever 396
Slide track 561
Slide valve 590
Sliding bed 447
Sliding curtain 329
Sliding seat 561
Sliding window 333
Sling fixing point 349
Slip face 285
Slip faults 61
Slipher 43
Slope structure 60
Sloping roof 486
Slug 176
Slumped cliff 295
Slur 503
Smallbore rifle shooting
   548
Smallbore rifle target 549
Small intestine
   Brachiosaurus 90

Chimpanzee 202
Cow 198
Domestic cat 195
Elephant 200
Euoplocephalus 94
Frog 182
Human 214, 249
Lizard 185
Tortoise 187
Small Magellanic Cloud
   Hydrus and Mensa 20
   Our galaxy and nearby
      galaxies 15
   Stars of southern skies
      20
Small stars 24-25
Small theropods 87
Small-scale rock
   deformities 61
Smalti 450
Smalti mosaic 450
Smartphones 588-589
Smash 554
Smell 244
Smilodon 107
Smokebox 324, 325
Smoky quartz 268
Smooth cypress 125
Smooth endoplasmic
   reticulum 216
Smudging 430, 431
Smuts 114
Snail 176-177
Snake-head ornament 375
Snakes 184-185
Snap head 592
Snare 518
Snare drum 518
Snort mast 597
Snout
   Anchisaurus 89
   Caiman 186
   Croeodilians 186
   Dogfish 178
   Edmontonia 95
   Herrerasaurus 86
   Iguanodonts 96
   Jawless fish fossil 78
   Pachycephalosaurus
      100
   Rat 196
Snow
   Glaciers 286-287
   Weather 302
Snowflake moray eel 180
Snowflakes 302
Soane, J. 478, 482-483
Sobkou Planitia 35
Soccer 524-525
Soccer kit 525
Socle
   Ancient Egyptian
      temple 458
   Baroque church 479
   Cathedral dome 487
   Gothic church 472
   Medieval church 469
   Neoclassical building
      478-479
   Renaissance building
      474
Soda lite 269
Sodium 35, 58
   Periodic table 310
   Seawater salt content
      296
Sodium hydroxide 312
Sodium lines 23
Soffit 464, 484, 498
Soft eye 382
Soft hair brush 436, 338,
   440
Soft-headed beater 516,
   517, 519
Soft metals 310
Soft palate 212, 245
Soft pastels 440
Soft pedal 514, 515
Soft rock

River features 290
Weathering and erosion
   282
Software effect plug-in
   521
Solanum tuberosum 128
Solar array 612, 613, 615
Solar array supporting
   arm 613
Solar cell 603
Solar collector 605
Solar day 34
Solar eclipse 32
Solar flare 32-33
Solar panel 496, 605
Solar power 605
Solar radiation 300-301
Solar system 38, 30-31,
   614-615
Solar wind
   Earth's magnetosphere
      58
   Structure of comet 53
   Sun 32
Solarium 494
Solar Wings Pegasus
   Quasar microlight 427
Sole of foot 254
Soleplate 593
Soleplate roller 593
Soleplate surround 594
Soleus muscle 227, 233
Solfataras 272-273
Solid body 512, 513
Solid crystals 306
Solid heart thimble 385
Solidified lava
   Lake formation 292
   Volcanoes 272-273
Solid ink stick 444
Solid rubber tyre 335
Solids 306-307
   Chemical reactions 312
Solid shapes 622
Solutions 306, 312-313
Sonic sensor 609
Sombrero 12
Somites 79
SONAR bulge 397
SONAR torpedo decoy 396
SONAR transducer array
   597
Sonic boom 416
Sony B-series MP3 player
   586
Sony DAV-S300 585
Sony W-series walkman
   586
Soot particles 313
Sophocles 35
Soralium 114
Sorbus aucuparid 130-131
Soredia 114
Sori 120-121
Sostenuto pedal 514, 515
Sound 514-515
   Coastline 295
   Musical notation 502
Soundboard
   Acoustic guitar 513
   Concert grand piano
      515
   Harp 511
   Upright piano 514
   Viola 511
   Violin 510
Sound channels 584
Sound-hole
   Acoustic guitar 512-513
   Cello 511
   Double bass 511
   Viola 511
   Violin 510
Sound module 521
South Africa 64
South America 264
   Cretaceous period
      72-75

Jurassic period 70
Late Carboniferous
   period 66
Middle Ordivician
   period 64
Quaternary period
   76-77
Tertiary period 74-75
Triassie period 68
South American plate 59
South Asian buildings
   490-491
South Atlantic Gyre 296
Satellite map 265
South Atlantic Ocean 39,
   73
South-east trade winds
   300
South-easterly wind 303
South Equatorial Belt 45
South equatorial current
   296-297
Southerly wind 303
Southern Hemisphere
   296-297
Southern polar region 64
South Galactic Pole 15
South Indian Gyre 297
South magnetic polar
   region 28
South Pacific Gyre 296
South Pacific Ocean 39
South polar ice-cap
   Structure of Mars 43
   Surface of Mars 42
South Pole
   Atmospheric circulation
      and winds 300
   Coriolis force 297
   Earth 58
   Jupiter 44
   Mars 42
   Mercury 34
   The Moon 40
   Neptune 50
   Pluto 51
   Pulsar 28
   Saturn 46
   Uranus 48-49
   Venus 56
South rim 277
South seeking pole 517
South Temperate Belt 45
South Temperate Zone
   45
South Tropical Zone 45
Space 300-301
Space probes 614-615
Space shuttle astronaut
   613
Space shuttle remote
   manipulator system
   (robot arm) 612, 613
Space telescope 612-613
Spadix 145
Span 484
Spandrel
   Gothic church 471
   Islamic building
      488-489
   Neoclassical building
      482
   Nineteenth-century
      building 495
   Renaissance building
      474
Spanish bowline 389
Spar
   BAe-146 jetliner
      components 415
   BE 2B tail 405
   Concorde 417
   Pegasus Quasar
      microlight 427
Spare tyre 337, 359
Spare wheel well 341
Spark plug 342-343, 410
Spark plug cap 366
Spark plug hole 346

660

Spark plug lead 344
Spar trunnion 409
Spat 426-427
Spathe 145
  Horsetails 120
Spawn 182-185, 192
Speaker
  Digital video 583
  Electronic music
    system 521
  Headphones 586
  System unit 567
Speaker assembly 580
Speaker plug 591
Speak key 590
Spear 382
Spear head 109
Specimen 610, 611
Specimen airlock 611
Specimen stage 610,
  611
Spectral absorption lines
  22-23
Spectral type 22-23
Specular haematite 268
Speech 237
Speed
  Forces 320
  Gearbox 366
Speedball nib 444
Speedometer 362
Speedometer drive 565
Sperm 258-259
Spermatheca
  Snail 177
  Spider 170
Sperm cell 217, 607
Sperm duct 195
Spermoviduct 177
Sperm whale 204-205
Sperry-ball gun turret
  408
Sphenethmoid bone 183
Sphenoidal fontanelle 220
Sphenoidal sinus 212,
  245
Sphenoid bone 220
Sphenopsids 279
Sphenopteris latiloba 72
Sphere 623
Spherical umbel 145
Spheroid 623
Sphincter muscle
  Anal 249
  Iris 241
  Pyloric 249
  Sea anemone 167
  Urelhral 257
Sphyrna lewini 179
Spica 18, 21
Spicule 32, 33
Spieules 166
Spider
  Arachnid 170-171
  Bicycle 338, 360
Spider seat 334
Spigot 387
Spike
  Aechnea miniata 162
  Dodder 163
  Double bass 511
  Flower 143
  Grape hyacinth 155
  Thyreophorans 92-93
  Volleyball 534
Spiky cupule 150
Spinal column 258
Spinal cord
  Bird 189
  Bony fish 181
  Chimpanzee 202
  Dogfish 179
  Dolphin 205
  Domestic cat 195
  Elephant 200
  Human 212, 217, 225,
    256, 258, 261
  Lizard 185
  Rabbit 196

Spinal ganglion 223, 238,
  243
Spinal nerve 223, 238
Spindle 601
Spine
  Aechmea miniata 162
  Barberry 130-131
  Bromeliad 113
  Calligraphy character
    445
  Cnidoeyte 167
  Diatom 116
  Dryland plants 156
  Golden barrel cactus 156
  Haemal 180
  Herbaceous flowering
    plants 128-129
  Human 218, 222-223
  Mahonia 130-131
  Modern jetliners 413,
    415
  Neural 180
  Sea urchin 174
  Starfish 174
Spine end fairing 421
Spinner
  ARV light aircraft
    424-425
  Hawker Tempest
    components 408
  Hawker Tempest
    fighter 409
  Lockheed Electra
    airliner 407
  Turbofan engine 418
Spinneret 170-171
Spinner mounting disc 406
Spinning lure 562
Spinose-dentate margin
  129
Spinous process 222-223
Spiny anteaters 206
Spiny leaflets 130-131
Spiracle
  Acanthostega 80
  Caterpillar 169
  Spider 170
Spiral arm
  Galaxies 12-15
  Milky Way 14
Spiral ganglion 243
Spiralling clouds 302
Spiralling low-pressure
  cells 302
Spiralling rain 305
Spiralling winds 302-305
Spiral scroll 460
Spiral spring 449
Spiral staircase 472, 476
Spiral tubes 342
Spiral valve 179
Spiral wrack 116
Spire
  Asian building 490-491
  Gothic church 470-471,
    475
  Medieval building 466,
    468
  Ninetee nth-century
    building 493
  Renaissance building
    476-477
Spirit lamp 454
Spirketting 381
Spirogyra sp. 117
Spit 291
Splayed window-sill 475,
  482
Spleen
  Bony fish 181
  Chimpanzee 202
  Domestic cat 195
  Elephant 200
  Frog 182
  Human 215, 249
Splenic artery 255
Splicing fid 383
Splint bone 198
Splinter bar 335

Splintery fracture 270
Split flap 406
Split line 151
Split-open pollen sac 144
Split rudder 421, 572
Spoiler 546, 349
Spoiler anchorage 413
Spoiler arm 414
Spoke
  Bicycle wheel 358-359
  Bordino Steam Carriage
    335
  Eddy Merckx racing
    bicycle 361
  Etching press 447
  Paddle wheel 391
  Ship's wheel 390
Spoked wheel
  Bievcle 358-359
  Pacing sulky 555
Spoke guard 358
Spoke nipple 361
Sponge roller 442
Sponges 166-167
  Fossils 279
Spongocoel 166
Spongy bone 224
Spongy mesophyll 126,
  139
Spongy tissues 156
Spool 562
Spoon 560
Spoon-shaped tooth 91
Sporangia 120-121
Sporangiophore 120
Sporangium 79
Spore-case 79
Spore-producing
  structures
  Fern 121
  Fungi 114-115
  Lichen 114
  Moss 112
Spores
  Clubmoss 120
  Fern 120-121
  Fungi 114-115
  Horsetail 120
  Lichen 114
  Liverworts 118
  Mosses 1 18-119
  Mushroom 115
Sporophores 114-115
Sporophyles
  Clubmoss 120
  Fern 120-121
  Horsetail 120
  Liverworts 118
  Moss 112, 118-119
Sports car 354
Sports wheel 340
Sprag clutch 410
Spray and steam knobs
  594
Spray barrel 594
Spray nozzle 594
Spray pump 594
Spreader 561
Spring
  Lakes and
    Groundwater 292
  Motorcycle 366
  Power drill 600
  Toaster 599
Spring and chassis unit
  337
Spring balance 320
Springboard diving 558
Spring/damper unit 365
Springing point 467,
  484-485
Spring line 292
Spring perch 338
Spring petiole 160
Spring shock absorber
  338-339
Spring tides 296-297
Spring-trap mechanism
  160

Spring washer 601
Spring wood xylem 134
Sprint races 560
Sprinting 542
Sprilsail 378
Sprit yard 376
Sprocket 358, 366
Spruce 513
Spruce beam 560
Sprung chassis 334
Spunyarn 388
Spun yarn serving 383
Spur 169
Spur gear 574
Spurious wing 191
Squadron code 409
Squamala 184
Squamosal bone 183
Squamous suture 220
Squainulose lichens 114
Squamulose thallus 114
Square 622
Square cut 538
Square knot 388
Square leg 538
Square-leg umpire 558
Square masonry 465
Square rib 486
Square-rigged ship 375
Square sail 374, 378, 384
Square-section steel
  tubing 364
Square-section tyre 362,
  369
Squash 544, 545
Squeegee 448
Squid 176
Squinch 466
Squirrel 196-197
Squirrel hair brush 458
Squirrel mop wash brush
  458
SST 416-417
St. John's wort 145
St. Basil's Cathedral 487
St. Paul's Cathedral
  Arch 484
  Baroque style 478,
    480-481
  Dome 480, 486-487
  Old 470, 472
Stabilizer 397, 548
Stabilizer-bar weight 422
Stabilizer fin 396
Stable elements 310, 311
Stack 295
Staff 577, 396
Stage 477, 495
Stage-door 477
Stained glass 470
Stainless steel cover 599
Staircase
  Ancient Roman
    building 465
  Baroque church 481
  Gothic church 470, 472
  Medieval building 466
  Modern building
    496-497, 499
  Neoclassical building
    483
  Renaissance building
    474-477
Staircase turret 468
Stairs 477
Stair tool 593
Stairway 489
Stalactites 284-285
Stalagmites 284-285
Stalagmitic boss 284
Stalagmitic floor 284
Stalk
  Algae 116
  Barnacle 173
  Dicotyledons 127
  Flower 140
  Fungi 114-115
  Liverwort 118
  Monocotyledons 128

Moss 112, 119
Pitcher plant 113
Seaweed 117
Stem succulent 113
Water lily 159
Stalked barnacle 173
Stalked secretory glands
  161
Stalk scar 123
Stall warning vane 412
Stamen remains 146-147,
  150
Stamens 140-143
  Anther 140-143
  Dicotyledon flower
    126-127
  Fertilization 146-147
  Filament 140-145
  Insect-pollination 144
  Monocotyledon flower
    126
  Rose 131
Stamp 445
Stance
  Dinosaurs 82
  Hominids 108
  Westlothiana 81
Stanchion 373, 393
Standard 554
Standardised horse 554,
  555
Standard European paper
  445
Standard knee 381
Standby pitot head
  416-417
Standing block 382
Standing lug mizzen 585
Standing part
  Hawser bend 387
  Rigging 382-383
  Single sheet bend 387
Standing position 348
Standing rigging 382-385
Stand-off half 530
Stapes 242
Staple 449
Starbirlh region 16
Starboard side 374
Starch grains 139
  Chlamydomonas sp.
    116
  Orchid root 133
Star clusters 16-17, 615
  Objects in Universe 11
  Our galaxy and nearby
    galaxies 14
Star coral 167
Star drag 562
Star dune 285
Starfish 174-175
  Fossil 79
Star formation in Orion 24
Starling 467
Star magnitudes 22
Stars 22-25, 613
  Massive stars 26-27
  Milky Way 14-15
  Neutron stars and black
    holes 28-29
  Small stars 24-25
  Star clusters 16, 613
  Sun 32-35
Star scanner 615
Star-shaped parenchyma
  135
Star-shaped sclereids 159
Stars of northern skies
  18-19
Stars of southern skies
  20-21
Starter 339, 558
Starter cog 336
Starter motor
  Hawker Tempest
    components 408
  Mid West twin-rotor
    engine 411
  Renault Clio 351

Volkswagen Beetle 340
Starter ring 345
Starling block 558
Starting handle 336-337,
  338, 343
Start print button 575
Stale room 392
Static air-pressure plate
  412
Static discharge wick 406
Static electricity 316
Stationary gear' 346-347,
  411
Slalor 410
Statue 472, 478
Statue creation 455
Statuette 476, 481
Status indicator 577
Staurikosaurus 69
Stay 325, 592
Staysail 378, 383
"Stealth" bomber 420-421
Steam 275, 507
  Locomotives 324, 325
  Nuclear power station
    314
  Oil-fired power station
    315
Steam barrel 594
Steamboat with paddle
  wheels 391
Steam car 334, 342
Steam chest 334
Steam chest pressure
  gauge 325
Steam condenser 397
Steam control knob 394
Steam dome 325
Steam engine 390-391
Steam generator 314
Steam grating 380
Steam iron 594
Steam launch 394
Steam locomotive 324,
  325
Steam pipe 334-335
Steam pipework 397
Steam-powered Cugnol
  "Fardier" 334
Steam release activator
  594
Steam whistle 392
Steel 492
Steel and concrete floor
  498
Steel and titanium skin
  416
Steel beater 517
Steel brace 493
Steel column 497-498
Steel floor-plate 497
Steel frame 360, 364
Steel girder framework
  314
Steel lattice-beam 497
Steel lock 560
Steel mullion 494
Steel point 452
Steel rails 330
Steel-reinforced concrete
  494
Steel sleeper 330
Steel wheel 340, 350-351
Steeple 471, 481
Steeplechase 554
Steep ridge 283
Steerboard side 374
Steerer tube 359
Steering 350, 364
Steering actuator 416
Steering arm 338-339
Steering box assembly 340
Steering column
  Benz Motorwagen 335
  Ford Model T 339
  Renault Clio 351
  Volkswagen Beetle 341
Steering gear 392

Steering gearbox 339
Steering head 335
Steering idler 340
Steering knuckle 338
Steering link 335
Steering oar 374
Steering pump pulley 344
Steering rack 335, 350
Steering spindle 336
Steering stop 425
Steering tie-rod 340
Steering tiller 334-335, 337
Steering track-rod 337
Steering wheel
  1906 Renault 337
  Ford Model T 338-339
  Renault Clio 350, 353
  White Steam Car 342
Steering wiffletree 337
Stegoceras 100-101
Stegosauria 83
Stegosaurus 71, 92
Steib chair 362
Stela 459
Stele
  Dicotyledons 127
  Monocotyledons 127
  Root 132-133
Stellar core 17
Stellar spectral absorption lines 22-23
Stellate parenchyma 135
Stem 134-135
  Aechmea miniata 162
  Asteroxylon 79
  Bamboo 131
  Barberry 130-131
  Battleship 394
  Begonia 129
  Bishop pine 124-125
  Brassavola nodosa 162
  Bromeliad 113
  Broomrape 163
  Calligraphy character 445
  Canadian pond weed 158-159
  Chusan palm 130
  Clubmoss 120
  Corallina officinalis 117
  Couch grass 113
  Crab cactus 129
  Dicotyledons 126-127
  Dodder 163
  Eddy Merckx racing bicycle 361
  Epiphytes 162-163
  Everlasting pea 129
  Florists' chrysanthemum 129
  Flower arrangements 143
  Golden barrel cactus 156
  Guzmania lingulata 162-163
  Hogweed 129
  Horsetail 120
  Ice-plant 128-129
  Iron paddlesteamer 393
  Ivy 131
  Kedrostis africana 113
  Live-for-ever 128-129
  Liverwort 118
  Maidenhair tree 123
  Maple 127
  Monocotyledons 126-127
  Moss 119
  Parasitic plants 163
  Passion flower 130
  Peach 131
  Perennials 130-131
  Sago palm 123
  Strawberry 128
  String of hearts 157
  Vegetative reproduction 154-155
  Water fern 158

Welwitschia 123
Woody plants 130-131
Woody stem 134
Yew 123
Stem bases
  Bulbil 155
  Guzmania lingulata 162-163
Stem branch 129
Stem bulbils 155
Stem cambium 126
Stem cells 606, 607
Stem head 376
Stempost
  74-gun ship 381
  Dhow 376
  Longboat 380
  Sailing warship 376
  Viking ships 374-375
Stem projections 156
Stem segments 129
Stem succulents 113, 156-157
Stem tubers 128, 154
Stencil 446
Step
  74-gun ship 381
  ARV light aircraft 424
  BE 2B bomber 404
  Blériot XI monoplane 401
  Medieval building 467
  Modern building 499
  Neoclassical building 483
  Steam-powered Cugnot 334
  Twentieth-century building 495
  Wooden sailing ship 378
Stephenson, Robert 324
Stepped roof 481
Stepped stempost 375
Stepped sternpost 375
Sterile hairs 117, 119
Sterile ray 119
Sterile ray floret 142
Sterile shoot 142
Sterile whorl 116
Stern
  74-gun ship 381
  Iron paddlesteamer 392
  Kayak 560,
  Sailing dinghy 561
  Wooden sailing ship 378-379
Sterna hirundo 193
Sternal artery 173
Sternal bone 96, 102
Stern balustrade 373
Stern carving 381
Stern framing 392
Stern gallery 397
Stern lantern 379
Sternocleidomastoid muscle 226-227, 229
Sternohyoid muscle 229
Sternpost
  Greek galley 372
  Roman corbita 373
  Sailing warship 377
  Single scull 560
  Viking ships 374-375
  Wooden sailing ship 378
Stern quarter gallery 379
Stern rope 587
Stern section 392
Sternum
  Bird 189
  Domestic cat 195
  Elephant 201
  Hare 197
  Horse 199
  Human 218
  Kangaroo 206
  Seal 204
Stern walk 395

Stibnite 268
Stick insect 192
Stiff brush 436
Stifle 198
Stigma
  Damselfly 168
  Dicotyledon flower 126-127
  Fertilization 146-147
  Flower 140-143
  Pollination 144-145
Stigma remains 146-147, 150-151
Stilt 494
Stilted arch 468
Sting 170
Stinging cells 166
Stinkhorn 114
Stipe 114-115, 116-117
Stippled effect 442
Stipule
  Begonia 129
  Everlasting pea 129
  Passion flower 130
  Rose 131
  Seedling leaf 152
  St. John's wort 145
  Strawberry 128
Stirrup
  Crossbow 548
  Ossicles of middle ear 242
  Saddle 555
Stoa 460
  Ancient Roman building 463, 465
  Islamic building 488
Stock
  74-gun ship 380
  Danforth anchor 386
  Roman anchor 372
Stockless anchor 386
Stomach
  Barnacle 173
  Bird 189
  Bony fish 181
  Chimpanzee 202
  Cow 198
  Crayfish 173
  Dogfish 179
  Dolphin 205
  Domestic cat 195
  Elephant 200
  Frog 182
  Human 214, 248
  Jellyfish 167
  Lizard 185
  Octopus 176
  Babbit 196
  Ruminants 198
  Snail 177
  Starfish 174
  Tortoise 187
Stomach throw 556
Stomata
  Dryland plants 156-157
  Golden barrel cactus 156
  Haworthia truncata 157
  Monocotyledon leaf 126
  Photosynthesis role 138-139
  Pine needle 124
  Wetland plants 158
Stone
  Succulent fruits 148
  Lithographic printing 446, 448
  Sculpture 452
Stone canal 174, 175
Stone plate 446, 448
Stony-iron meteorite 52
Stony meteorite 52
Stop lamp assembly 352
Stop signal 330
Stopwatch 524

Storage locker 572
Storage organs
  Bulb 155
  Corm 155
  Rhizome 155
  Scale leaf 155
  Seed 152
  Succulent tissue 156-157
  Swollen stem 113, 155
  Tubers 128, 155
  Underground 154-155
Storage unit 573
Store button 521
Stores pylon 420-421
Stork 188
Storm 303
Straddle wire 358, 359
Straight 555
Straight four cylinder arrangement 345
Straight gouge 452
Straight handlebar 361
Strake
  Concorde 416-417
  Ironclad 393
  Roman corbita 372
  Viking ships 374-375
Straportin 337
Strap-shaped leaf 162
Strata 276
  Faults and folds 60-61
  Sedimentary rocks 276
Stratocumulus cloud 302
Stratosphere
  Earth's atmosphere 300-301
  Jupiter's atmosphere 45
  Mars' atmosphere 43
  Saturn's atmosphere 47
Stratum basale 235
Stratum corneum 235
Stratum granulosum 235
Stratum spinosum 235
Stratus cloud 302
Strawberry 128, 150
Straw butt 549
Streak 270-271
Stream
  Glaciers 286-287
  Groundwater system 293
  Spring examples 292
Streamed Internet radio on-screen display 577
Streamed Internet video on-screen display 577
Streamlined spinner 407
Strengthening tissue
  Fern rachis 121
  Horsetail stem 120
  Marram grass 113
  Monocotyledon leaf 126
  Stems 154-155
  Water lily leaf 159
Stress 61
Stretcher
  Brickwork 485
  Nineteenth-century building 492
  Single scull 560
Stretches 555
Striated effect 442
Striation 46
Strike
  Baseball 536
  Baseball umpire signal 537
  Slope structure 60
Striker 524
Strike-slip fault 61
Strike-slip fault lake 293
Strike zone 536
Strindberg 35
String
  Acoustic guitar 512-513
  Cello 511
  Concert grand piano 515

Double bass 511
Electric guitar 513
Harp 511
Upright piano 514
Viola 511
String arm 511
String course
  Ancient Roman building 465
  Cathedral dome 487
  Medieval building 466-467
  Nineteenth-century building 493
Stringed instruments 510, 511
  Guitar 512, 513
  Orchestral arrangement 504, 505
Strings
  Guitar 512-513
  Racket 544
  Violin 510
Strix aluco 190
Strobili 120
Stroke judge 558
Stroke play 546
Strokes 546
Stroke-side oar 560
Stroma 139
Stroma thylakoid 139
Strongylocentrotus purpuratus 175
Strontium 310
Strop 383
Strut
  Dome 484, 486
  Gothic building 473
  Marble sculpture support 453
  Neoclassical building 479
  Paddlesteamer 390
  Timpanum 519
Strut insert 340
Struthio camelus 188
  Egg 193
Struthiolaria 279
Struthiomimus 84, 87
Stub axle 424
Stud
  Ancient Roman mill 464
  Gothic building 473
  Mid West single rotor engine 410
Studding sail boom 378
Studding sail yard 378
Studio Elvira 495
Study 477
Stuffing box 390
Stump
  Coastline 295
  Wicket 538
Stupa 490-491
Stupica 491
Sturgeon 180
Style 140-143
  Fertilization 146-147
  Monocotyledon flower 126
  Pitcher plant 113
  Pollination 144-145
  Rowan fruit 131
Style of the gnomon 377
Style remains
  Dry fruit 150-151
  Fruit development 146-147
  Succulent fruit 148-149
Stylet 167
Stylobate 460
Styloglossus muscle 244
Styloid process 220, 243
Styracosaurus 102, 103
Subacute leaf apex 136-137
Subarachnoid space 237
Subclavian artery 215, 251, 253
Subclavian vein 253

Subduction 58
Subduction zone 281
Subframe 351
Subgenital pit 167
Subglacial stream 287
Sublimation 307
Sublingual fold 245
Sublingual gland 244-245
Submandibular gland 244
Submarine 396-397
Submarine canyon 298
Submerged atoll 299
Submerged glacial valleys 294-295
Submerged river valleys 294
Subopercular bone 181
Substitutions 532, 550
Substomatal chamber 139
Substrate 112
Substratum 115
Subsurface current 297
Subtropical jet stream 300
Subwoofer 586
Succulent fruits 148-149, 150
  Bramble 130
  Development 146-147
  Peach 131
  Rowan 131
Succulent leaves 128, 157
Succulent plants 156-157
Succulents 112
  Leaf 157
  Stem 156-157
  Stem and root 157
  Trailing stem 157
Succulent stem 129
Sucker
  Lamprey 178
  Octopus 176
Sucking stomach 170
Suction reduction control 593
Sugar
  Fermentation 312
  Formation 138
  Photosynthesis 315
  Transport 139
Sulcus terminalis 244
Sulky 554-555
Sulphates 269, 296
Sulphides 268
Sulphur 39, 268
  Periodic table 311
Sulphur dioxide 37
Sulphuric acid 36-37
Sulphurous gases 273
Sumatra 265
Sumigi 490
Summer petiole 160
Summit caldera 42
Sump 343, 344-345
Sump pan 354
Sun 32-33, 38
  Atmosphere 301
  Comet tails 48
  Earth's energy 314
  Electromagnetic radiation 314-315
  Energy emission from Sun 22
  Light 318
  Milky Way 11
  Objects in Universe 11
  Oceans and seas 296-297
  Ozone formation 64
  Solar eclipse 32
  Solar System 30-31
  Stars 22-23
Sun blind 573
Sundew 160
Sundial 376, 377
Sunflower 140, 142, 145
Sunken stoma 157
Sunlight and photosynthesis 138
  solar power 605

Sun roof 341
Sun scoop 498
Sun sensor 614
Sunspots 32-33
Sun visor 350, 353
Supai group 277
Superclusters 10
Supercooling 307
Supercool liquid 306-307
Superficial peroneal
  nerve 258
Superficial skeletal
  muscles 226-227
Superfluid neutrons 28
Super-giant slalom
  (Super-G) skiing 552
Supergiant stars
  Massive stars 26
  Stars 22-23
  Stellar black hole 29
Supergranule 33
Superheater 325
Superior articular facet
  222
Superior articular process
  222-223
Superior concha 212
Superior laryngeal nerve
  244
Superior longitudinal
  muscle 245
Superior meatus 245
Superior mesenteric
  artery 253, 256
Superior mesenteric trunk
  257
Superior mesenteric vein
  253
Superior nasal concha
  245
Superior oblique muscle
  241
Superior orbital fissure
  221
Superior ramus of pubis
  224, 257
Superior rectus muscle
  241
Superior sagittal sinus
  212, 237
Superior thyroid artery
  244
Superior vena cava 215,
  251, 252-253, 255
Supernova
  Massive stars 26-27
  Nebulae and star
    clusters 16
  Neutron stars and black
    holes 29
Supernova remnant
  Nebulae and star
    clusters 16-17
  X-ray image of Crab
    Nebula 28
Supersonic flight 416
Supersonic jetliners
  416-417
Supersonic transport
  416-417
Supporter 381
Supporting tissue
  Bishop pine stem 125
  Dicotyledon leaf 126
  Stems 134-135
Supraoccipital bone 181
Supraoccipital crest 84
Supraoesophageal
  ganglion 173
Supraorbital fissure 221
Supraorbital foramen 221
Supraorbital margin 213,
  220, 221
Supraorbital notch 213
Supraorbital ridge
  Chimpanzee 202
  Stegaceras 100
  Styracosaurus 102
Suprarenal gland 257

Suprarenal vein 257
Suprascapula 183
Suprasternal notch 211
Surangular bone 102
Surcingle loop 555
Surface areas 623
Surface currents 296-297
Surface deposits 273
Surface layer 293
Surface ocean current 296
Surface streams 284
Surface temperature 39
  Stars 22
  Structure of main
    sequence star 24
  Structure of Mars 43
  Structure of Mercury 35
  Structure of Neptune 51
  Structure of red giant
    25
  Structure of red
    supergiant 26
  Structure of Venus 37
  Sun 33
Surface terrain 284
Surface vegetation 282
Surface winds 300
Surrogate mother 607
Surround sound 584
Surround sound special
  effect plug-in 521
Surveillance RADAR 397
Suspended erratic 286
Suspension
  "Deltic" diesel-electric
    locomotive 327
  Microlight 426
  Motocross racing 368
  Motorcycle 364
Suspension arm 350-351
Suspension linkage 362
Suspension spring 350
Suspension strut 340, 351
Suspension top mount 340
Sustaining pedal 514, 515
Suture 202
Su-wei 376
Suzuki RGV500 368, 369
Swab hitch 387, 389
Swallow 585
Swallow-hole 284
Swamp 290-291
Swan neck ornament 373
Swash plate 344
Swash zone 294
S waves 63
Sweat duct 235
Sweat gland 234-235
Sweat pore 234-235
Sweep rowing 560
Sweep-rowing boat 561
Sweeping low throw 556
Sweet chestnut 136, 144,
  150
Sweetgum 76
Sweet pea 128
Sweet potato 154
Swell manual 514
Swell of muzzle 395
Swell pedal 514
Swell stop 514
Swept titanium fan blades
  572
Swifting tackle 377
Swim bladder 178,
  180-181
Swimmeret 172
Swimming 558, 559
Swimming pool 558
Swimwear 558
Swingarm 364, 368
"Swing-wings" 420
Switch 316
Switchboard room 397
Switch end casting
  598-599
Switch gear 314
Swivel becket 382
Swivels

Mooring and anchoring
  386
  Angling 562, 563
  Swivel suspension ring
    377
Swollen leaf base 154-155
Swollen stem base
  Guzmania lingulata
    163
  Kedrostis africana 113
  Oxalis sp. 157
Swollen stem 154-155
Sword 556-557
Sycamore 131, 150-151
Sycamore beam 560
Syconium 148
Syenite 275
Symbiosis
  Lichens 114
  Mycorrhizal association
    133
Symbols
  Biology 591
  Chemistry 591
  Communication 108
  Mathematics 591
  Music 502, 503
  Physics 591
Symphony orchestra 504,
  505
Synapsid reptile skull 67
Synaptic knob 228, 239
Synaptic vesicle 239
Sync port 587
Syncarpous gynoecium
  140
Synchiropus splendidus
  180
Synchronized elevator 423
Syncline 60, 61, 62
Synclinorium 61
Synergid nucleus 147
Synsacrum 189
Synthesizer 520
Synthetic brush 436, 438
Synthetic flax 384
Synthetic hog hair brush
  442
Synthetic materials 306
Synthetic polymer 306
Synthetic resin 442
Synthetic ropes 388
Synthetic sable brush 442
Synthetic strings 544, 545
Synthetic wash brush 458,
  442
Syria Planum 42, 43
System display 573
Systems connector 413
System unit 567

T

Tabernacle 463, 474, 476
Tab hinge 415
Tablet computer 568-569
Tablet flower 488, 491
Tabling 572, 584
Tabular habit 271
Tacan aerial 420
Tachybaptus ruficollis 190
Tack 375
Tackling
  American football 526
  Australian rules football
    528, 529
  Rugby 531
  Soccer 524
Tactical air navigation
  (Tacan) aerial 420
Tadpoles 182-183, 192
Taenia 460
Taenia colica 249
Taffrail 378, 381
Tail
  Amphibian 182
  Anchisaurus 89
  BE 2B bomber 404

Caiman 187
Calligraphy character
  445
Corythosaurus 98
Crocodilians 186
Deer hopper dry fly 563
Dolphin 205
Dunkeld wet fly 563
  87
Hare 196
Hawker Tempest
  components 409
Herrerasaurus 86
Horse 198
Ichthyostega 80
Iguanodon 96
Iguanodonts 96
Kangaroo 206
Lion 195
Lizard 184-185
Lungfish 81
Monkey 202
Ornithopods 96
Pachycephalosaurus
  100
Prehensile 202
Rabbit 196-197
Rat 196
Rattlesnake 185
Rigging 382-383
Salamander 182
Sauropodomorpha 88
Schweizer helicopter
  423
Scorpion 170
Ski 552-553
Stegoceras 101
Stegosaurus 93
Triceratops 102
Tyrannosaurus 84
Westlothiana 81
Tail area 78
Tail boom 423
Tail bud 260
Tail bumper 417
Tail club 95
Tail cone 416-417, 418
Tailcone fairing 572
Tail crest 187
Taileron 420-421
Tail fairing 409
Tail feathers 188
Tail fluke 205
Tail-gate 348
Tail gunner's
  compartment 408
Tail-gun turret 408
Tail-light
  BMW R/60 362
  Harley-Davidson FLHS
    Electra Glide 362
  Honda CB750 363
  Vespa Grand Sport 160
  Mark 1 363
Tailpiece 510, 511
Tail-pin 510
Tail pipe 340
Tailplane
  Airbus 380 572
  ARV light aircraft 424
  BAe-146 jetliner 415
  BK 2B tail 405
  Biplanes and triplanes
    402-403
  Blackburn monoplane
    401
  Blériot XI monoplane
    401
  Curtiss biplane 399
  Hawker Tempest 409
  Lockheed Electra
    airliner 407
  Schleicher glider 426
Tailplane fairing 415
Tailplane root 409
Tailplane tip 407, 415
Tailrace 314
Tail rod 390

Tail rotor 422-423
Tail-rotor drive shaft 422,
  423
Tail rotor gearbox 423
Tail shield 78
Tailskid
  ARV light aircraft 424
  Avro triplane 403
  BE 2B bomber 405
  Blackburn monoplane
    400-401
  LVG CVI fighter 405
Tail spike 92
Tail spine 79
Tail unit 368
Tailwheel
  Avro biplane 402
  B-17 bomber 408
  Hawker Tempest
    fighter 409
  Lockheed Electra
    airliner 407
  Schleicher glider 426
Tailwheel leg 401
Take-off and landing skid
  398
Takla Makan Desert 265
Talc 270-271
Tallow coating 379
Talonavicular ligament
  232
Talons 188
Talus 282-283
Talus bone 232
Tamarins 202, 203
Tambourine 504, 518
Tam-tam 504, 516
Tandem wings 402
Tank 592
Tank drain tap 407
Tank inspection access
  417
Tank support 339
Tantalum 310
Tantalus Fossae 43
Tapeats sandstone 277
Tapir 198
Tappet 343
Tappet adjustor 367
Tap root 128
Tarantula Nebula 26-27
  Large Magellanic Cloud
    12
Tarantulas 170-171
Target areas 556, 557
Target hole 546
Target pistol 548, 549
Target shooting 548, 549
Tarn 293
  U-shaped valley
    formation 287
Tarsal bone
  Albertosaurus 84
    87
  Iguanodon 97
Tarsals
  Crocodile 186
  Domestic cat 195
  Elephant 201
  Frog 183
  Hare 197
  Horse 199
  Kangaroo 206
  Lizard 184
  Platypus 206
  Rhesus monkey 202
  Seal 204
Tarsiers 202
Tarsomere 13
Tarsometatarsus 189
Tarsus
  Beetle 168
  Bird 188
  Human 219
  Scorpion 170
  Spider 171
Tas-de-charge 469
Tasmanian devil 207
Taste 244

Taste bud 244
Tau Orionis 18
Taurus 19, 20
Taurus mountains 77
Tau Sagittarii 21
Tawny owl 190
Taxiing light 414, 420
Taxus baccata 70, 123
Tea clipper 392
Team crest 531
Team jersey 529
Team name 533
Tear fault 61
Technetium 310
Technosaurus 69
Tee 546
Teeing ground 546
Tee peg 547
Teeth
  Ankylosaurus 92
  Bear 106
  Caiman 186
  Canine 194, 202
  Carnassial 194
  Carnivores 194
  Ceratopsian 100
  Cheek 194
  Chimpanzee 202
  Crocodilians 186
  Extinct shark 67
  Hadrosaur 96
  Hominid 108
  Horse 105
  Human 246-247
  Iguanodont 96
  Incisor 194, 196, 201,
    202
  Lamprey 178
  Leaf-shaped 88-89
  Molar 194, 201, 202
  Ornithopod 96
  Premolar 194, 202
  Rabbit 196
  Rodents 196
  Theropod 84
  Thyreophoran 92
  Venus fly-trap 160
Teeth development 246
Tegenaria gigantea 171
Telephone line 576
Telescope, space 612-613
Telescopic damper 326,
  329
Telescopic fork
  Harley-Davidson FLHS
    Electra Glide 363
  Honda CB750 363
  Honda VF750 364
  Husqvarna Motocross
    TC610 368
  Motorcycle 364
  Suzuki RGV500 368
  Weslake Speedway
    motorcycle 369
Telescopic sight 548, 549
Telescopic strut 416
Television 315
Telltale 576
Tellurium 311
Tellus Regio 36, 37
Tellus Tessera 37
Telson 172
  Fossil 79
TEM 610, 611
Tempe Fossae 43
Tempera 432, 433
Temperate latitudes 302
Temperature
  Atmosphere 300-301
  Chemical reactions
    312-313
  Formation of black hole
    29
  Germination 152
  Matter 306-307
  Mineral resources 280
  Oceans and seas 296
  Stellar black hole 29
  Weather 302-303

Temperature and pressure sensor 418
Temperature and steam control dial 594
Temperature changes
  Atmosphere 301
  Oceans and seas 296
  Weathering and erosion 282
Temperature scales 621
Tempered pigment 432
Temple 484-485
  Ancient Egyptian 458
  Ancient Greek 460-461
  Ancient Roman 462-463
  Asian 490
Temple blocks 516
Temple Butte limestone 277
Temple Cap sandstone 276
Temple of Amon-Re 458-459
Temple of Aphaia 461
Temple of Athena Polias 460
Temple of Heaven 490
Temple of Isis 459
Temple of Mallikarjuna 491
Temple of Neptune 460-461
Temple of Vesta 462-463
Temple of Virupaksha 490-491
Tempo 504
Temporal bone
  Chimpanzee 202
  Human 220-221, 242
Temporal lobe 257
Temporalis muscle 226-227, 229
Tendon
  Achilles 232-233
  Annular 241
  Calcanean 232-233
  Extensor digitorum longus 233
  Extensor digitorum 231
  Extensor hallucis longus 233
  Flexor digitorum 231, 87
  Palmaris longus 251
  Peroneus brevis 253
Tendril
  Arabesque 480
  Clematis 130
  Dogfish egg 192
  Everlasting pea 129
  Monkey cup 161
  Passion flower 130
Tennis 544
Tennis racket 544
Tenon
  Flax spinning mill 492
  Hull plank fastening 373
Tenor drum 518-519
Tenor joint 508
Tenor mule 507
Tenor note strings 515
Tenor saxophone 509
Tenor voice 502
Tension
  Drums 518
  Faults and folds 60-61
  Mountain building 62
Tension-column 497
Tension control 552
Tension key 518, 519
Tension member 499
Tension pulley 360
Tension rod 518, 519
Tension screw 518
Tensor fasciae latae muscle 226
Tensor tympani muscle 243
Tentacle

Coelentrates 166
Jellyfish 167
Molluscs 176-177
Scallop 176
Sea anemone 166-167
Snail 177
Tenth century
  Building 490
  Style 468
Tepal scar 140
Tepal
  Flower parts 140, 143
  Monocotyledons 126
  Peruvian lily 129
Terbium 311
Teres major muscle 227
Teres minor muscle 227
Tergum plate 175
  Egg 193
Terminal box 317
Terminal bronchiole 254
Terminal bud
  Bishop pine 124
  Horse chestnut 130
  London plane 134
  Rhizome 155
  Root tuber 154-155
  Stems 134
  Stolon 154
Terminal ileum 249
Terminal lake 286
Terminal moraine
  Glaciers 286
  Rivers 289
Terminal pinna 136
Terminal ring 259
Terminus 286
Terrace
  Asian building 490-491
  Modern building 497-499
  Twentieth-century building 494-495
Terracotta clay 455
Terrain-following radar 420
Terrapin 186-187
Terrestrial animal 74
Terrestrial mammal 104
Terrigenous sediment 299
Tertiary bronchus 215
Tertiary period 57, 74, 75
  Fossil record 279
Tessellation 489
Tessera 450, 489
Test 174-175
Testa
  Dry fruit 150-151
  Embryo development 147
  Epigeal germination 153
  Hypogeal germination 152
  Succulent fruit seed 148-149
Testicle 259
Testicular artery 257
Testicular vein 257
Test is
  Barnacle 175
  Dolphin 205
  Domestic cat 195
  Human 259
  Rabbit 196
Test tube 313
Tetanurae 83
Tethus Regio 36
Tethys 46
Tethys Sea
  Cretaceous period 73
  Jurassic period 71
  Tertiary period 74, 75
  Triassic period 69
Tetragonal system 270
Tetrahedron 623
Tetralophodon 75, 104
Text 444
Textured papers 441

Textured scraper 593
TGV electric high-speed train 329
Thalamian 573
Thalamus 236-237
Thalassiosira sp. 116
Thalictrum delavayi 137
Thallium 311
Thalloid liverwort 118
Thallus
  Algae 116-117
  Lichen 114
  Liverwort 118
  Seaweed 116-117
T-handle auger 574
Thar Desert 265
Tharsis Tholus 43
Thatched roof 477
Thaumasia Fossae 43
Themis Regio 36
The Plough 19
Therapeutic cloning 606
Theobroma cacao 148
Therapsids 104
Thermal/electrical insulation 596, 597
Thermal insulation 613
Thermals 426
Thermocouple bus-bar 419
Thermogram 214
Thermosphere
  Earth's atmosphere 300
  Mars' atmosphere 43
  Venus' atmosphere 37
Thermostat 411
Theropoda 85
Theropods 84-87
Thesium alpinum 145
Theta 1 Sagittarii 21
Theta Andromedae 19
Theta Pegasi 19
Thetis Regio 36
Thick skull 46
Thigh
  Anchisaurus 89
  Bird 188
  Corythosaurus 98
  Gorilla 203
  Horse 198
  Human 211
  Iguanodon 96
  Kangaroo 207
  Lion 195
  Psittacosaurus 103
  Stegoceras 101
  Stegosaurus 92
  Triceratops 102
  Tyrannosaurus 84
Thigh musculature 90
Thigh pad 527
Thimble
  Harness racing 555
  Rigging 383, 384
Third-century building 465
Third home 541
Third man 538, 541
Third rail 328
Third stage motor 615
Thirteenth century
  Building 467, 469-471
  Style 470
Thirty-five mm file strip holder 570
Thistle funnel 313
Thole pin 380
Thoracic cavity 255
Thoracic leg 169
Thoracic nerve 258
Thoracic pleurae 78
Thoracic segment 79
Thoracic vertebrae
  Crocodile 186
  Domestic cat 195
  Hare 197
  Horse 199
  Human 222

Kangaroo 206
Platypus 206
Rhesus monkey 202
Seal 204
Thoracolumbar vertebrae
  Elephant 201
  Lizard 184
Thorax
  Cirripedia 172
  Human 211
  Insects 168-169
Thorium 310
Thornback ray 179
Thoroughbred horse 554
Thranite 373
Thread 167
Three-blade main rotor 423
Three-cylinder Anzani engine 401
Three-cylinder engine 425
Three-lobed stigma 143
Three-masted square-rigged ship 375
Three-point line 532
Three pounder 395
Three-toed ungulates 198
Threshold 463
Throat
  Angling hook 562
  Bird 188
  Danforth anchor 386
  Human 212, 244-245
  Lacrosse crosse 541
  Racketball racket 545
  Squash racket 545
  Tennis racket 544
Throatlatch 199
Throttle
  Avro triplane 402
  Curtiss biplane 398
  "Rocket" steam locomotive 324
  Suzuki RGV500 363
  Vespa Grand Sport 160
  Mark 1 363
  Weslake Speedway motorcycle 369
Throttle butterfly 345
Throttle cable 350
  Harley-Davidson FLHS Electra Glide 363
  Husqvarna Motocross TC610 368
  Kirby BSA racing sidecar 369
  Suzuki RGV500 369
  Weslake Speedway motorcycle 369
Throttle lever 419, 425
Throttle linkage
  Ford Model T 338
  Jaguar V12 engine 345
  Oldsmobile trim 337
  Renault Clio 350
Throttle wheel 342
Throw
  Judo 556
  Structure of a fault 60
Thrower 542
Throw-in 532
Thrushes 188
Thrust 543
Thruster cluster 615
Thrust fault 61
Thrust plate 601
Thrust-reverser 421
Thulium 311
Thumb 211, 230-231
Thumb-claw
  Anchisaurus 89
  Apatosaurus 83
  Baryonyx 83, 85
  Massospondylus 83, 89
  Plateosaurus 88
Thumbhole 508
Thumb knot 589
Thumb piston 514

Thumb-spike 96-97
Thwart 373, 375, 380
Thylakoid 139
Thymine 216
Thyreophora 85
Thyreophorans 92-93, 94-95
Thyristor converter 328
Thyrohyoid membrane 244
Thyrohyoid muscle 229, 244
Thyroid cartilage 245, 255
Thyroid gland 214-215, 217, 244-245, 255
Tibetan plateau 63
Tibia
  Archaeopteryx 85
  Beetle 168
  Butterfly 169
  Crocodile 186
  Diplodocus 90
  Domestic cat 195
  Elephant 201
  Eryops 81
  Gallimimus 86
  Hare 197
  Horse 199
  Human 219, 232-233
  Iguanodon 96-97
  Kangaroo 206
  Lizard 184
  Parasaurolophus 99
  Plateosaurus 88
  Platypus 206
  Rhesus monkey 202
  Scorpion 170
  Seal 204
  Spider 171
  Stegoceras 101
  Stegosaurus 93
  Struthiomimus 87
  Toxodon 107
  Triceratops 102
  Turtle 187
  Tyrannosaurus 84
Tibiale 183
Tibial flexor muscle 97
Tibialis anterior muscle 226, 233
Tibialis posterior muscle 233
Tibiofibula 183
Tibiotarsus 189
Tidal bulge 297
Tidal currents 296-297, 298
Tidal flow 296
Tidal levels 295
Tidal power 604
Tidal river-mouth 295
Tidal scour 298
Tidal waves 58
Tides 294, 297
Tie
  Basketball match 532
  Bordino Steam Carriage 334
  Musical notation 502, 505
Tie-beam
  Ancient Roman mill 464
  Dome 486
  Gothic church 473
  Neoclassical building 479
Tie plate 393
Tierceron 485
Tie rod 334, 340
Tiger seat 334
Tiger shark 178-179
Tight end 526
Tight-head prop 530
Tile
  Dome 486
  Islamic mosque 488
  Modern building 499

Neoclassical building 482
Renaissance building 476-477
Tiled roof 495
Tilia sp. 134
Tilia x europaea 143
Tiller
  Dhow 376
  First cars 334-335
  Longboat 380
  Oldsmobile trim 337
  Roman corbita 373
  Sailing dinghy 561
  Steamboat with paddle wheels 391
  Viking ships 374-375
Till and rotation
  Jupiter 44
  Mars 42
  Mercury 34
  The Moon 40
  Neptune 50
  Pluto 51
  Saturn 46
  Uranus 48
  Venus 36
Timber frame
  Ancient Roman building 462, 464-465
  Dome 486
  Medieval building 466-467
  Renaissance building 477
Timber head 380
Timber rafter 492
Timber trellis 603
Timbre 516
Time interval signal 330
Timekeeper
  Basketball 532
  Fencing contest 557
  Handball 535
  Judo contest 556
  Lacrosse 541
  Netball 535
  Swimming 558
Time signature 502
Time switch 598
Time-trial bicycle 360
Time zones 618-619
Timing chain 343, 345
Timing chest 343
Timing gear 367
Timpani 503, 504, 505, 518
Timpanum 519
Tin 311
  Mineralization zones 281
  Squash 545
Tinatin Planitia 37
Tinted paper 441
Tip of dodder stem 163
Tip ring 563
Tip section 563
Tissue culture 607
Titan 614
Titania 48
Titanium 310
Titanohyrax 74
Toad 182
Toadflax 129
Toaster 598-599
Toe
  Albertosaurus 84
  Anchisaurus 89
  Archaeopteryx 85
  Bird 188
  Caiman 186-187
  Corythosaurus 98
  Golf club 547
  Gorilla 203
  Herrerasaurus 86
  Human 211, 232-233
  Iguanodon 96-97
  Lion 194

Lizard 184
Pachycephalosaurus 100
Psittacosaurus 103
Stegoceras 101
Tyrannosaurus 84
Toe clip 360
Toenail
  Elephant 200
  Gorilla 203
  Human 253
Toe piston 514
Toe strap 358-359
Toggle switch 513
Toilet 416, 485
Tolstoj 35
Tomb 458-459, 489
Tomb of Itimad-ud-daula 489
Tomb of King Tjetji 459
Tombolo 294
Tom-toms 518-519
Tondo brush 434
Tone editor control 520
Tonehole 509
Tone pattern selector 520
Tongs 321
Tongue
  Allosaurus 85
  Caiman 186
  Chimpanzee 202
  Corythosaurus 98
  Cow 198
  Dolphin 205
  Domestic cat 195
  Elephant 200
  Human 212, 226, 244, 248
  Iguanodon 97
  Lamprey 178
  Lion 194
  Rabbit 196
  Rattlesnake 185
  Ski boot 552
T'on-wei 376
Tool and battery box 335
Tool/brush-head connector 593
Tool or wand cuff 593
Tools
  Rigging 382-383
  Sailmaking 384
  Viking boatbuilding 374
Tooth
  Acanthostega 80
  Anchisaurus 89
  Ankylosaurus 94
  Arsinoitherium 104
  Australopithecus 108
  Baryonyx 83
  Camarasaurus 91
  Diplodocus 90
  Dragon prowhead 374
  Eryops 80
  Euoplocephalus 94
  Heterodontosaurus 83
  Homo habilis 108
  Human 108, 246-247, 248
  Iguanodon 97
  Lambeosaurus 99
  Moeritherium 105
  Pastels application 440
  Phiomia 105
  Plateosaurus 88
  Protoceratops 102
  Smilodon 107
  Triceratops 103
  Tyrannosaurus 84
Toothless beak
  Ankylosaurs 92
  Corythosaurus 98
  Euoplocephalus 94
  Gallimimus 86
  Theropods 84
  Triceratops 102
Topaz 271
Topcastle 373, 377
Topgallant mast

Battleship 395
Sailing warship 377
Wooden sailing ship 378-379
Top hose 351
Topmast 377, 378
Topping lift 380
Topping-up valve 561
Top-plate 464
Top race 359
Topsail
  74-gun ship 379
  Double topsail schooner 385
  Junk 376
Topset strata 283
Topside strake 393
Top sliding block 457
Tornado GR1A 420-421
Torosaurus 100
Toroweap formation 276
Torpedo 394-397
Torque arm 364, 365
Torquemeter mount 419
Torque tube 358-359
Torque tube assembly 425
Torrential rain 302
Torsional vibration damper 410-411
Torsion bar 350
Tortillon 440, 441
Tortoise 186
Tortoise skull 77
Torus
  Ancient Roman building 463
  Asian building 490
  Dome 486
  Gothic building 470
  Medieval building 467-469
  Renaissance building 475, 477
  Shapes: solid 623
Total solar eclipse 32
Tote board 555
Touch-down zone 526
Touch-in goal line 530
Touch judge 530
Touch line
  Rugby 550
  Soccer 524
Touchpad 566
Touchpiece 509
Touchscreen 568-569, 578-579, 587
Touch sensor 609
Tour buses 332
Tour de César 466
Touring bicycle 360, 361
Tourmaline 269
Tower
  Ancient Roman building 465
  Asian building 490-491
  Clock 493
  Gothic church 472
  Islamic building 488
  Medieval building 466-467, 468-469
  Modern building 496-499
  Nineteenth-century building 492-493
  Renaissance building 476
  Twentieth-century building 495
Tower Bridge 492-493
Tower vault 469
Towing fairlead 395
Towing hook 335, 426
Town Hall 495
Toxodon 76, 106, 107
TPU connector 571
Trabecula 250-251
Trace fossils 278
Tracery

Gothic building 470-473
Nineteenth-century building 493
Trachea
  Bird 189
  Brachiosaurus 91
  Chimpanzee 202
  Dolphin 205
  Domestic cat 195
  Elephant 200
  Gallimimus 86
  Human 212, 215, 244-245, 248, 255
  Lizard 185
  Rabbit 196
  Spider 170
  Tortoise 187
Trachelion 460
Trachycarpus fortunei 127, 130
Track 413
Track control arm 340
Track events 542, 543
Track gauge 330, 331
Track rod
  Elegance and utility 336-337
  Ford Model T 338-339
  Renault Clio 351
Track shoe 543
Traction motor 328
Trade winds 300
Traffic congestion 332
Traffic surveillance 422
Tragus 242
Trailboard 379
Trailing arm 340
Trailing edge
  BAe-146 jetliner components 413, 414, 415
  BE 2B tail 405
  BE 2B wings 404
  Hawker Tempest components 409
  Pegasus Quasar microlight 426-427
Trailing-link arm 414
Trailing wheel 324
Train equipment 330-331
Training gear 559
Trains
  Diesel 326-327
  Electric 328-329
  High-speed 328-329
  Steam 324-525
Trams 332-333
Transaxle 340
Transept
  Gothic church 470, 473
  Medieval church 468-469
Transfer port 542
Transformation 168
Transformer 314, 328
Transform fault 59
Transistor 584
Transitional cell mucosa 257
Transition metals 310, 311
Transit plug 397
Translucent crystal 271
Translucent impasto glaze 443
Translucent white marble 453
Translucent "window" 157
Transmission 350-351
Transmission adaptor plate 344
Transmission electron microscope (TEM) 610, 611
Transmission system 326, 366

North wing, Chateau de Monlal 476
Sailing warship 377
Transparency holder 570
Transparent glassy crystal 271
Transparent lower drumhead 518
Transparent tissue 160
Transparent wash 439
Transpiration 136
Transponder aerial 423
Transportation lock 571
Transport system 332
Transport tissue
  Golden barrel cactus 156
  Monocotyledons 126
  Photosynthesis 138-139
Transversary 377
Transverse arch 485
  Baroque church 479
  Medieval church 468-469
Transverse colon 249
Transverse dune 283
Transverse foramen 222
Transverse leaf spring 338
Transverse line 555
Transverse process
  Human 222-223
  Plateosaurus 89
  Tyrannosaurus 85
Transverse rib 485
Transverse strut 512
Trapezium 17, 622
Trapezium bone 230
Trapezius muscle 226-227, 229
Trapezoid bone 230
Traps
  Butterwort 161
  Cobra lily 160
  Monkey cup 161
  Pitcher plant 115, 160-161
  Sundew 160
  Venus fly trap 160
Traveller 380
Travelling 553
Travertine shell 464
Tray fascia 595
Tread 477
Tread pattern 365
Treasury of Atreus 461
Treble bridge 514
Treble clef 502
Treble hook 562-563
Treble note strings 515
Treble voice 502
Tree 66-67, 130-131
  Energy storage 315
  Epiphytes 162-163
  Gymnosperms 122-125
Tree fern 112-113
Tree mallow 131
Tree root action 282
Treenail 587
Trefoil
  Gothic church 470-473
  Nineteenth-century building 493
Trefoil arch 473, 484
Trellis window 459
Trellised river drainage 288
Trembler coil box 335
Trenail 587
Trestle trees 378
Trevithiek, Richard 324
Triac device 600
Trials tyre 365
Triangle
  Shapes: plane 622
  Musical instrument 504, 517
  Steamboat with paddle wheels 391

Triangle mosaic 489
Triangular buttress 484
Triangular fossa 242
Triangular horn 85
Triangular lesene 481
Triangular pediment 462
Triangular-section fuselage
  Avro triplane 403
  Bell-47 helicopter 423
  Blackburn monoplane 401
Triangulum 19, 20
Triangulum Australe 21
Triassic period 68-69
  Fossil record 279
  Geological time 57
Triatic stay 585
Tribune 467-468
Tributary
  Coastlines 295
  Rivers 288
Tributary moraine 287
Tributary stream 289
Triceps brachii muscle 227
Triceratops 100, 102-103
Trichome 156
  Marram grass 113
Triclinic system 270
Tricolpate pollen grain 145
Tricuspid valve 251
Triere 373
Trifid Nebula 16
Trifoliate leaves 128, 130
  Laburnum 137
  Oxalis sp. 157
Triforium 469
Trigger
  Air pistol 549
  Biathlon smallbore rifle 549
  Cnidocyte structure 167
Trigger hair 160
Trigger mechanism 600
Trigger position 600
Triglyph 460
Trigon 488
Trigonal system 270
Trigone 257
Trigonometry 621
Trike nacelle 426-427
Trilete mark 145
Trilobate rotor 346
Tri-lobed tail 81
Trilobites 64, 78
  Earth's evolution 56
  Fossil record 279
Trim 352-353
  1906 Renault 356-357
  Oldsmobile trim 357
  Renault Clio 350-351
  Volkswagen Beetle 341
Trimala 491
Trimtab 407, 414, 415
Trim tank 416-417
Trinity Chapel, Salisbury Cathedral 470
Tripinnate leaves 137
Triplanes 402-403
Triple bar jump 554
Triple jump 542
Triple spine 130-131
Tripod mast 394
Tripod stand
  Congas 519
  Drum kit 518
  Electronic drums 520
  Modelling stand 455
  Radial studio easel 437
Tripping palm 386
Tripping ring 372
Triquetral bone 230
Trireme 372-373
Tri-spoke wheel 361, 368, 369
Triton 50

Tri-wring screw 587
Trochanter
  Beetle 168
  Scorpion 170
  Spider 171
Trochlea
  Baryonyx 85
  Human 241
Trochoid housing 410
Trojan two-stroke engine 342
Trolley 332
Trombone 504, 505, 506, 507
Tropeter 373
Trophoblast 260
Tropic formation 276
Tropic of Cancer
  Satellite map 265
  Surface currents 297
Tropic of Capricorn
  Satellite map 265
  Surface currents 297
Tropical cyclone 302
Tropical orchids 162
Tropical rainforest 39, 66
Troposphere
  Earth's atmosphere 300
  Jupiter's atmosphere 45
  Mars' atmosphere 43
  Saturn's atmosphere 47
  Venus' atmosphere 37
Trout 180
Trout angling 562
Truck
  Early tram 352
  Greek galley 372
  Longboat 380
  Wooden sailing ship 378-379
Truncate leaf base 137
Trunk
  Elephant 200-201
  Mammoth 107
  Phiomia 105
  Tree fern 112
  Woody flowering plant 130-131
Trunnion 395
Truss
  Gothic church 473
  Modern building 497-499
  Steam boat with paddle wheels 391
Truss rod 513
Try 530, 531
T-section beam 492
Tsiolkovsky 41
T-type cantilevered fin 426
Tu-144 416
Tuba 504, 505
Tube fret 174, 175
Tubeless sports tyre 365
Tuber
  Broomrape 145
  Dryland plants 157
  Horsetail 120
  Potato 128
  Vegetative reproduction 155
Tubercle
  Corythosaurus 98
  Golden barrel cactus 156
  Sea urchins 174
  Starfish 174
  Stem projections 156
Tubular bells 504, 516
Tubular chassis 335
Tubular drums 518
Tubular open cradle frame 369
Tubular petioles 160
Tuck 381
Tudor arch 484
Tufted duck 188

Tug propeller 391
Tulip mount 563
Tuner/amplifier link
 cables 585
Tuner sellings memory
 microchip 585
Tungsten
 Mineralization zones
  281
 Periodic table 310
Tungsten carbide lip 450
Tungsten filament 319
Tunica adventitia 252
Tunica intima 252
Tunica media 252
Tuning adjustor 510-511
Tuning pedal 519
Tuning peg 510, 511
Tuning pin 514, 515
Tuning slide 506
Tunnel
 Cave 285
 Trains 350
Tunnel vault 485
Tuojiangosaurus 92
Tupelo 137
Turbine
 Energy 314-315
 Floodgate 604
 Jet engines 418-419
 Nuclear "Hunter-Killer"
  submarine 397
Turbo-charged diesel
 engine 327
Turbocharger 356
Turbofan engine 418-419
 Landing gear 412
Turbo impeller 347
Turbojet engine 418-419
 Landing gear 412
 Supersonic jetliner 416
Turbo propeller 347
Turboprop engine 418-419
Turdus viscivorus 190
Turfed roof 602, 603
Turgai strait 71
Turkish crescent finial 488
Turk's head 383
Turnbuckle
 Avro triplane 402
 Blackburn monoplane
  401
 Curtiss biplane 398
 LVG CVI fighter 405
 Rigging screw 383
Turn indicator 558
Turning force 320
Turning indicator 332, 333
Turning judge 558
Turning vane 357
Turns 555
Turntable 596
Turntable rotator 596
Turpentine 436
Turret 486
 Baroque church 481
 Battleship 394-395
 Gothic church 470-471
 Gun turret 396
 Medieval building 466,
  468
 Nineteenth-century
  building 493
 Renaissance building
  476-477
Turtle 72-73, 186-187
Tuscan capital 465
Tuscan pilaster 465, 483
Tusche 446
Tusche pen 448
Tusche stick 448
Tusk
 Elephant 200-201
 Mammoth 107
 Phiomia 105
TV mini-camera 356
TV power button 585
Tweeter loudspeaker
 connectors 585

Twelfth century
 Building 466-467
 Church 469, 473
 Roof 490
 Style 468, 470
Twentieth-century
 buildings 494-495
Twin-blade main rotor 423
Twin carbon-fibre disc
 brake 369
Twin carburettors 427
Twin-cylinder engine
 Harley-Davidson 362
 Pegasus Quasar
  microlight 427
 Steam-powered Cugnot
  334
Twin-domed forehead 200
Twine 384
Twin-lobed leaf blade 160
Twin nose-wheel 420
Twin rate spring 365
Twin rear axle 333
Twin rudder 372
Twin-wheel main landing
 gear 414
Twin-wheel nose-gear
 417, 420
Twist 388
Twist dive 558, 559
Twisted wire habit 271
Two-lobed stigma 142
Two-pulley system 320
Two-seater cockpit 421
Two-stroke combustion
 engine 366
Two-toed ungulates 198
Two-towered gate 467
Tyagaraja 35
Tycho 40
Tye 377
Tye halyard 374
Tympan 449
Tympanic bullet 194
Tympanic canal 243
Tympanic membrane 243
Tympanum
 Frog 182
 Quail chick 193
Typhoon 502
Tyrannosaurus 73, 84-85
Tyre
 1906 Renault 336-337
 ARV light aircraft 424
 Avro triplane 402
 BAe-146 jetliner 414
 Bicycle 358-359
 Blériot XI monoplane
  401
 BMW R/60 362
 Cannondale SH600
  hybrid bicycle 361
 Curtiss biplane 398
 Double-decker tour bus
  355
 Eddy Merckx racing
  bicycle 360
 First cars 534-335
 General use 365
 Lockheed Electra
  airliner 406
 MCW Metrobus 333
 Metal 324
 Motocross racing 368
 Motorcycle 365
 Pacing sulky 555
 Pneumatic 358, 555
 Racing car 356-357
 Renault Clio 352-353
 "Rocket" steam
  locomotive 324
 Rossin Italian time-trial
  bicycle 361
 Single-decker bus 333
 Slick racing 365
 Suzuki RGV500 368-369
 Trials 365
 Tubeless sports 365
 Volkswagen Beetle 340

World War I aircraft
 404-405
Tyre carrier 357
Tyre tread 560, 565, 368
Tyre wall 360
Tyringham House 483

U

UHF aerial 420
UK loading gauges 331
Ulmus minor 144
Ulna
 Archaeopteryx 85
 Arsinoitherium 104
 Baryonyx 85
 Bird 189, 191
 Brachiosaurus 91
 Crocodile 186
 Diplodocus 90
 Domestic cat 195
 Elephant 90, 201
 Eryops 80
 Euoplocephalus 94
 Gallimimus 86
 Hare 197
 Horse 199
 Human 218, 230
 Iguanodon 96
 Kangaroo 206
 Kentrosaurus 93
 Lizard 184
 Parasaurolophus 99
 Pareiasaur 81
 Plateosaurus 88
 Platypus 206
 Rhesus monkey 202
 Seal 204
 Stegoceras 100, 101
 Stegosaurus 93
 Struthiomimus 87
 Toxodon 106
 Triceratops 102
 Tuojiangosaurus 93
 Turtle 187
 Tyrannosaurus 84
Ulnar artery 251, 253
Ulnar nerve 251, 238
Ultra-high frequency
 (UHF) antenna 615
Ultramarine lapis lazuli 433
Ultrasound scan 214
Ultraviolet light 145, 319
Ultraviolet radiation 22,
 319
Ultraviolet solar radiation
 300
Umbels 143
Umbilical artery and vein
 260
Umbilical cord 260-261
Umbilicus 211, 260
Umbo 176
Umbra 32
Umbrella 491
Umbriel 43
UMD drive ribbon cable
 379
Umpire
 American football 526
 Badminton 545
 Baseball 536
 Cricket 538
 Hockey 540
 Lacrosse 541
 Netball 535
 Tennis 544
 Volleyball 554
Umpire signals 537
Una corda pedal 514, 515
Unarmed combat 556
Underarm pass 535
Underframe 332
Underground mycelium
 115
Underground stem 154
Underground storage
 organs 154-155

Underground stream
 284-285
Underground water
 Lake formation 292
 Rivers 288
Underhand serve 534
Under plastron 557
Under-turntable roller
 ring 596
Underwater digital camera
 581
Underwater mountains
 298
Underwing fairing 425
Unenergized electrode
 584
Ungulates 198-199
Unicellular organisms 56
Unified leaf pair 157
Uniform motion 321
"Union Pacific" diesel
 train 326
Unipolar neuron 239
Unison 503
Unit number 328
Units of measurement 620
Universal resource
 locator (URL) address
 577
Universal serial bus (USB)
 ports 566, 567, 570
Universal serial bus (USB)
 programmer 591
Universal veil 114-115
Universe 10-11
Unmapped region
 Degas and Brontë 34
 Structure of Mercury 35
Unnilennium 311
Unnilhexium 310
Unniloctium 311
Unnilpentium 310
Unnilquandium 310
Unnilseptium 310
Unreactive gas mixture
 319
Unreactive metals 311
Unstable elements 310
Unukalhai 21
Upcurved edge 191
Upfold 60
Upfold trap 280
Upholstery 356-337
Upholstery brush 593
Uplifted block fault
 mountain 62
Upper arm 210
Upper Belvedere 482
Upper Carboniferous Coal
 Measures 61
Upper Carboniferous
 Millstone Grit 60-61
Upper crankcase 410
Upper crux of antihelix
 242
Upper deadeye 382-383
Upper deck 380
Upper deck passenger
 door 573
Upper deck windows 572
Upper epidermis 159
Upper eyelid 213
Upper fin 423
Upper finishing 381
Upper Frater 473
Upper gallery 379
Upper head 387
Upper jaw 212, 220-221,
 244-245, 246, 248
Upper jaw tusk 105
Upper joint
 Clarinet 508
 Cor Anglais 508
 Oboe 508
Upper lobe of lung 215,
 254-255
Upper octave key 509
Upper rudder 416-417
Upper seed axis 152-153

Upper sheer strake 393
Upper topsail 385
Upper wireless and
 telegraphy yard 395
Upright man 108
Upright piano 514
Upright planks jump 554
Upright poles jump 554
Upsilon Sagittarii 21
Upstream gates 560
Upthrow 60
Urachus 257
Ural mountains
 Cretaceous period 73
 Earth's physical
  features 265
 Jurassic period 71
 Late Carboniferous
  period 67
 Triassic period 69
Uranium 310
Uranium fuel 314
Uranius Tholus 43
Uranus 48-49
 Solar System 31
Ureter
 Bird 189
 Bony fish 181
 Domestic cat 195
 Elephant 200
 Frog 182
 Human 215, 256-259
 Lizard 185
 Rabbit 196
 Snail 177
Ureteric orifice 257
Urethra
 Chimpanzee 202
 Domestic cat 195
 Human 256-257, 259,
  261
 Rabbit 196
Urethral opening 259
Urethral sphincter muscle
 257
Urinary bladder 181
Urinary system 256-257
Urinogenital opening
 Bony fish 181
 Dolphin 205
URL 577
Urn 478, 481, 487
Urodela 182
Uropod 172
Urostyle 183
Ursa Major 18, 19
Ursa Minor 18, 21
Ursus americanus 195
Ursus spelaeus 77, 106
U-shaped gouge 449
USB see Universal serial
 bus (USB)
USB ports 566
USB port 566, 586
USB programmer
 assembly 591
User name 576
U-shaped valley 286-287
Uterine wall 260-261
Uterus
 Chimpanzee 202
 Elephant 200
 Human 258-259
Utricle 243
U-tube 313
Utzon, J. 499
Uvula 212, 245, 248

V

V1 "flying bomb" 408
V12 cylinder arrangement
 345
V4 engine unit
 British Rail Class 20
  diesel 327
 Honda VF750 364
Vacuole

Chlamydomonas sp.
 116
Diatom 116
Human cell 216
Palisade mesophyll
 139
Vacuum brake lever 325
Vacuum circuit braker
 328
Vacuum cleaner 592-593
Vacuum operated inlet
 valve 362
Vacuum pump cabinet
 611
Vacuum reservoir 324
Vacuum valve 610
Vagina
 Chimpanzee 202
 Elephant 200
 Human 258-259, 261
 Snail 177
 Spider 170
Valance
 1906 Renault 337
 Ford Model T 339
 Volkswagen Beetle 341
Valency electrons 310
Vallate papillae 244
Vallecular canal 120
Valles Marineris 43
Valley
 Coastline 294
 Glacier 286-287
 Grand Canyon 277
 Mountain 62
 River features 290
 River 288-289
 Rock cycle stages 267
Valley floor erosion 267
Valley head 289
Valley rafter 473
Valley spring 292
Vālmiki 35
Valve 359
Valve chest 324
Valve cusp 252
Valve lifter 367
Valve return spring 347
Valve rocker 344, 402
Valves
 Bivalves 176
 Dehiscent fruit 151
 Indehiscent fruit 150
 Scallop 176
Valve slide 506, 507
Valve spring 343, 344
Valve system 506
Vanadium 310
Van Allen radiation belt 38
Van de Graaff 41
Van de Graaff generator
 316
Vane 191
Van Eyck 35
Vang 378
Vanishing point 431
Vapour barrier 603
Variable incidence air
 intake 421
Variable incidence gust-
 alleviator 421
Variable nozzle 416-417
Variable pitch aluminium-
 alloy blade 408
Variable pitch propeller
 396
Variable time control
 knob 598-599
Variegated lamina 131,
 137
Varnish 348, 436
Vasa recta 256
Vascular cambium
 154-155
Vascular plants 279
Vascular plexus 255
Vascular strand 149
Vascular system 162-163
Vascular tissue 150

666

Aerial shoot 155
Apical meristem 154
Bishop pine 124
Canadian pond weed 159
Clubmoss stem 120
Corm 155
Dicotyledon 127
Dodder 163
Epiphytic orchid 162
Fern rachis 121
Higher plants 118-119
Horsetail stem 120
Marram grass 113
Monocotyledon 126-127
Parasite host 163
Perennials 130-131
Pine needle 124
Pine root/stem 125
Radicle 152
Rhizome 155
Root 132-133
Stem 134-135
Water hyacinth root 158
Water lily leaf 159
Woody plants 130-131
Vas deferens
  Domestic cat 195
  Human 259
  Rabbit 196
Vastitas Borealis 43
Vastus lateralis muscle 225-226
Vastus medialis muscle 225-226
Vault 484-485, 496
  Ancient Roman building 462-464
  Baroque church 479
  Gothic church 470
  Medieval building 467-469
  Modern building 496, 499
  Nineteenth-century building 492-493
  Renaissance building 477
Vaulting shaft 468-469
V-belt pulley 347
VCR connections 585
Vedette boat 395
Vega 19, 20
  Our galaxy and nearby galaxies 15
Vegetable oil 456
Vegetative reproduction 154-155
Veil 114-115
Vein
  Alveolar 247
  Anterior median 253
  Axillary 253
  Basilic 253
  Brachiocephalic 253
  Bronchial 254
  Cardiac 250
  Central retinal 240
  Cephalic 176, 253
  Common iliac 215, 253, 257
  Dicotyledon leaf 126-127
  Digital 253
  External iliac 215, 253
  Femoral 253
  Gastroepiploic 253
  Great saphenous 253
  Hepatic portal 253
  Hogweed leaf 129
  Inferior mesenteric 253
  Inferior vena cava 215, 252-253, 257
  Insect 168, 169
  Interlobular 256
  Internal iliac 253
  Internal jugular 253
  Jugular 215
  Leaf 136, 158-139

Median cubital 253
Monocotyledon leaf 126
Palmar 253
Portal 252
Pulmonary 251, 253, 254
Pulp 247
Renal 256-257
Short saphenous 253
Subclavian 253
Superior mesenteric 253
Superior vena cava 215, 251, 252-253, 255
Suprarenal 257
Testicular 257
Tree mallow leaf 131
Umbilical 260
Water hyacinth leaf 158
Water lily leaf 159
Vela 18, 21
Velamen 162
Velarium 464
Velar scale 115
Vela Supernova Remnant 17
Vellum 452
Velocette overhead valve (OHV) engine 367
Velum 373
Vena cava
  Frog 182
  Inferior 215, 252-253, 257
  Superior 215, 251, 252-253, 255
Vendelinus 40
Veneer 462
Venomous snake 184
Vent
  Frigate 397
  Igneous rock structures 275
  Mountain building 62
  Rock cycle 266
  Suzuki RGV500 368
  Volcano 272-273
Ventilation 462
Ventilator 422, 425
Ventilator exit 406-407
Ventral abdominal artery 173
Ventral antebrachial muscle 94
Ventral aorta 179
Ventral fin 179
Ventral margin of shell 176
Ventral nerve cord 169, 173
Ventral scale 184, 186
Ventricle
  Brain 236-237
  Heart 215, 250-251, 252
Ventricular diastole 251
Ventricular systole 251
Venturi 424
Venus 36-37
  Solar System 30
Venus fly trap 160
Verdaccio 433
Verge 464, 492
Vermiculated rustication 482
Vermilion 433
Vermilion border of lip 213
Vermilion Cliffs 277
Versal lettering 445
Vertebra 261
  Bony fish 180
  Cervical 212, 222
  Frog 183
  Lumbar 222-223
  Rattlesnake 185
  Rudimentary 260
  Thoracic 222-223
  Turtle 187
Westlothiana 81
Vertebral artery 223, 252

Vertebral body 223
Vertebral column 218, 222, 257
Vertebral foramen 222-223
Vertebral shield 187
Vertebrates 56, 64, 104
  Fossil record 279
Vertex
  Building 495
  Human body 212
Vertical air current 302
Vertical batten 602
Vertical cleavage 270
Vertical damper 329
Vertical frame ladder 392
Vertical movement
  Faults and folds 60
  Lake formation 292
Vertical pupil 186
Vertical ridge 129
Vertical spindle 387
Vertical stroke 445
Vertical tailplane 572
Very high frequency (VHF) radio 318
Vesicle 148
Vespa Grand Sport 160
  Mark 1 563
Vespa scooter 362, 363
Vessel
  Baroque church 479
  Gothic church 470
  Medieval church 468-469
Vesta Rupes 37
Vestas A47 wind turbine 604
Vestibular canal 243
Vestibular membrane 243
Vestibular nerve 243
Vestibule
  Ancient Greek temple 461
  Baroque church 481
  Human body 212, 245
  Medieval church 469
  Neoclassical building 483
Vestibulocochlear nerve 243
VHF aerial
  B-17 bomber 408-409
  BAe-146 jetliner 415
  Bell Jetranger helicopter 423
  Concorde 416-417
  VHF radio 318
VHF omni-range aerial
  Bell-47 helicopter 422
  Concorde 417
VHF omni-range and instrument-landing-system aerial 412
Vibraphone 504, 516, 517
Vibration-reducing damper foot 58
Vibration-reducing fan mounting 597
Vibrations
  Brass instruments 506
  Stringed instruments 510
Vibrato arm 513
Vibrato effect 516, 517
Vibrissa
  Lion 194
  Rabbit 196
  Rat 196
  Seal 204
Vicia faba 133, 152
Video
  Digital 582-583
  Streamed Internet 577
Video camera 610
Video input/output circuit board 585
Viewfinder 582
Viewing screen 610

Viewing window 581
Viewing window objective lens aperture 580
Viking ships 374-375
Villa Rotunda 475
Villa Savoye 494
Villi of mucosa 248
Viola 503, 504, 505, 510, 511
Violent eruptions 272
Violet light 318
Violin 503, 504, 505, 510
Violoncello 510-511
Virginia opossum 207
Virgo 18, 21
Virtual mixing board 521
Visceral cartilage 254
Visceral hump 177
Visceral pericardium 250
Viscous coupling 344-345
Visible and infrared spectrometers 614
Visible light 318-319
Vision 237
Visor 416-417
Visual recognition 237
Vitreous glass mosaic 451
Vitreous glass tessera 450, 451
Vitreous humour 240
Vitta 151
Vivaldi 35
Vocal cords 245
Voices 503
Volans 21
Volcanic activity
  Mineralization zones 280
  Rock cycle 266
Volcanic eruption 26
Volcanic gases 64
Volcanic island 58, 299
Volcanic lake 293
Volcanic lava
  Jupiter 44
  Mars 42
  The Moon 40
  Venus 36
Volcanic mountain 62
Volcanic rock 298, 306
Volcano 58, 63, 272-273
  Jupiter 44
  Locations 273
  Mars 42
  Mineralization zones 281
  Mountain building 62-63
  Ocean floor 298
  Vent 62
  Venus 36
Volkmann's canal 247
Volkmann's vessel 225
Volkswagen Beetle 340-341
Volleyball 534-535
Voltage 306, 316
Voltage circuitry 597
Voltage reduction and regulation circuits 585
Voltage regulators 596
Voltage stabilizer 597
Voltage transformers 596
Volume 306, 307
Volume control
  Electronic instruments 520, 521
  Streamed internet radio 577
  Home cinema 585
  Nintendo Wii Fit Plus 579
Volumes 623
Volume slider 577
Volute
  Ancient Greek building 460-461

Baroque church 479, 481
Dome 486
Islamic building 488
Neoclassical building 478, 480
Renaissance building 476-477
Volva 114-115
Volvox sp. 116
Vomer 221
Von Kármàn 41
Voussoir 484-485
  Ancient Roman building 465
  Neoclassical building 482
  Renaissance building 474
V-shaped gouge 449
V-shaped valley
  River features 290
  Rivers 288-289
V-strut 404-405
VTEC engine 354
V-twin engine 362, 363
Vulpecula 19
Vulture 190
Vulva 200
Vyāsa 35
Vyne 482

W
Wadi 283
Wagner 35
Wagon 324
Wagon bogie 330
Wagon vault 485
Wahweap sandstone 276
Waist
  74-gun ship 380-381
  Human 210
  Stringed instruments 510-511
Waistband 548
Waist gun 408
Wale
  74-gun ship 381
  Roman corbita 373
  Sailing warship 376-377
Walkway 497
Wall
  Ancient Greek temple 461
  Ancient Roman building 462, 465
  Baroque building 478-479, 481
  Carpel 148, 151
  Cell 112, 117, 132, 139
  Concrete 496
  Fruit 148-151
  Fungal tissue 115
  Glass 496
  Gothic church 470
  Islamic building 488
  Medieval building 466-467, 469
  Modern building 498-499
  Neoclassical building 479, 482
  Nineteenth-century mill 492
  Ovary 140, 150
  Renaissance building 476-477
  Twentieth-century building 494
Wall anchor 407
Wall construction 602
Wall panel 406-407
Wall painting 434
Walrus 204
Walter 40
Wand 592, 593
Wand handle and

brushbar controls 592
Wand/handle connector 593
Wand telescopic link 593
Wankel, Felix 346
Wankel rotary engine 346-347
Wannanosaurus 101
Wardrobe 416
Wardroom 381
Warhead 394
Warm air 300, 302-303
Warm blood
  Mammals 104
  Theropods 84
Warm electronics box 615
Warm front 302-303
Warm occlusion 302
Warm periods 56
Warning horn 327, 329
Warning light 328, 356
Warship
  74-gun ship 379, 380-381
  Battleship 394-395
  Frigate 396-397
  Ironclad 392-393
  Man-of-war 378-379, Sailing warship 376-377
  Submarine 396-397
Wasatch formation 276
Washable pre-motor filter 592
Wash cant 578
Washer-dryer 594-595
Wash over dry brush 439
Washburn twelve-string guitar 513
Washer
  Bicycle 358
  Power drill 600-601
  Toaster 598-599
Washer jet 553
Washes 438, 439
Washing machine 315
Wasp 168
Waste heat 314-315
Waste water anti-siphon pipe hook 595
Waste water pipe 595
Water 58, 66
  Absorption 150
  Amphibian 80
  Changing states 307
  "Deltic" diesel-electric locomotive 326
  Energy generation 314-315
  Epiphyte supply 162
  Fermentation 313
  Lithographic printing 446
  Mars 42
  Molecule 138
  Oceans and seas 296
  Photosynthesis 138
  Pollination 144
  Reversible reactions 312
  Seed germination 152-155
  Solutions 306
  Storage organs 156-157
  Transport 154, 159
Water and oil pump assembly 356
Waterborne sports 560-561
Water-closet 483
Watercolour 438-439
Watercolour paint pan 438
Watercolour paper 439, 441
Watercolour-style acrylic painting 442, 445
Water connection 342
Water-cooled engine 366
Water cycle 288
Water density 296

Water distribution 264
Water droplets 45
Waterfall 291
  Glacier 286
  River 289-290
  Rock cycle 267
Water fern 158
Water float 324
Water hardness
  adjustment and filter
  flap lever 595
Water hyacinth 158
Water ice
  Jupiter's atmosphere
  45
  Mercury's atmosphere
  47
  Structure of comet 53
  Structure of Mars 43
  Structure of Neptune 51
Water-ice fog 42
Water-ice permafrost 43
Water inlet connector 595
Water inlet hose 595
Water inlet pipe 595
Water inlet valves 595
Water jacket
  Daimler engine 343
  Ford diesel engine 347
  Humber engine 343
  Jaguar straight six
  engine 344
Water key 506, 507
Water lily 158-159
Waterline 380
Water obstacle 546
Water outlet 425
Water passage 346
Water pipe
  1906 Renault 337
  Humber engine 343
  Wright Flyer 399
Water pressurizer 314
Waterproof acrylic paint
  442
Waterproof cable
  connector 605
Waterproof covering
  Bishop pine needles
  124
  Golden barrel cactus
  156
  Haworthia truncata 157
  Lithops bromfieldii 157
  Monocotyledon leaf 126
  Rush stem 135
  Wetland plants 158
Waterproof shell 80
Waterproof ski clothing
  553
Waterproof skin 81
Waterproof stowage box
  427
Water pump
  Hybrid car 354
  Jaguar V12 engine 345
  Renault Clio 351
  White Steam Car 342
Water pump pulley 347
Water rail 314
Water reactor 314
Water-retaining cuticle 78
Water salinity 296
Water-saturated
  permeable rock
  Lakes and groundwater
  292
  Mineral resources
  280-281
Watershed 289
Water shoot 560
Water softener dial 599
Water-soluble glue 450
Water storage tank 497
Water-storing
  parenchyma 156-157
Water supply
  Gun turret 596
  Steam locomotive 324

Water table
  Cave system 284
  Lake formation 292
Water tank
  Bordino Steam Carriage
  334
  "Ellerman Lines" steam
  locomotive 324
  Steam iron 594
  White Steam Car 342
Water vapour
  Chemical reactions
  312-313
  Hurricane structure
  Jupiter's atmosphere 45
  Mars' atmosphere 43
  Saturn's atmosphere 47
  Venus' atmosphere 37
  Water cycle 288
Water vascular system
  174
Waterway 380, 593
Wattle-and-daub
  Ancient Roman
  building 462, 464-465
  Medieval house 466
Wave 294, 298
  Erosion 294
  Features 294
  Properties 518
Wave-cut platform 295
Waveguide 596, 597
Wavelength 518
Wavellite 269
Wavering pitch 516, 517
Wavy foliation 267
Wax riser 454
Wax runner 454
Waxy cuticle 156, 157
Waxy fruit skin 149
Waxy laminae 159
Waxy zone 161
Weapon-bay bulkhead 421
Weaponry 75
Weasel 194
Weather 302-303
Weathercock 486
Weathering 282-283
  Gothic church 471-472
  Medieval church 469
  Mineral deposits 280
  Renaissance building
  477
  Rock cycle 266
  Sedimentary rocks 276
Weather radar 416
Weather shutter for gun
  394
Weather-vane 471, 477
Web
  Frog 182
  Internet 576
Webbed feet 188, 190
Web browser 577
Web pages 577
Webcam 576
Website address 577
Weight
  Arch 484
  All-round bicycle 360
  Bolts 548
  Measurement 320, 590
  Motorcycle engine 566
  Newton meters 320
Weights 562
Wei-wei 376
Welding tool 608
Weld line 392
Welt 122-123
Welwitschia mirabilis
  122-123
Werner motorcycle 362
Weslake Speedway
  motorcycle 369
West Africa 73
West Australian current
  297
Westerlies 300

Westlothiana 67, 80-81
Westminster Abbey 484
Westminster Cathedral
  493
Wet-in-wet wash 458, 459
Wetland plants 158-159
Wet season 295
Wet wash 458
Wezen 18
  Canis Major 21
Whaler 395
Whales 204-205
Wheat 109, 150
Wheel
  1906 Renault 337
  Alloy 356, 357
  Bicycle 358-359
  Diesel motor output 326
  First cars 354-355
  Force/motion 320
  Ford Model T 338-339
  Harley-Davidson FLHS
  Electra Glide 363
  Mars exploration rover
  (MER) 615
  Mazda RX-7 346
  Motorcycle 364
  Pacing sulky 555
  Paddle 390-391
  Renault Clio 350-351
  Rossin Italian time-trial
  bicycle 361
  Ship 378, 390, 394
  Single scull 561
  Volkswagen Beetle 340
  Weslake Speedway
  motorcycle 369
Wheel axle
  BAe-146 jetliner 414
  Touring bicycle 360
Wheelbase 360
Wheelchair access 333
Wheel fairing
  Blackburn monoplane
  400
  Pegasus Quasar
  microlight 427
  Pegasus XL SE
  microlight 426
Wheel fork 355
Wheel guard 324, 369, 593
Wheel hub 414
Wheel nut 356, 357
Wheel sets 327, 329
Wheel sparer 561
Whelp 387
Whetstone 452
Whip 555
Whipping 384, 388
Whisker
  Lion 194
  Rabbit 196
  Rat 196
  Seal 204
Whisker boom 382
"Whispering Gallery" 484
Whistle
  Iron paddlesteamer 392
  Life jacket 561
  Referee 524
Whistle lever 325
White belt 556
White blood cells 217, 253
White Cliffs 276
White diamond 268
White dwarfs
  Small stars 24-25
  Stars 22-23
White feldspar 275
White-grey crystal 271
White light 318
White matter
  Cerebrum 236-237
  Spinal cord 238
White of eye 213
White oval
  Jupiter 44-45
  Saturn 46
White spirit 436

White Steam Car 542
White stork 188
White warning light 528
White whale 204
Whorls
  Flower 140
  Green alga cell 116
  Sepals 144, 149
Wicket 558
Wicket-keeper 538
Wide-angle camera 614
Widened joint 282
Wide receiver 526
Wide-screen plasma
  display 584
Wiener 41
Wi-fi antenna 569, 579
Wi-fi board 579
Wii balance board 579
Wii hand controller 579
Willow grouse 193
Wind
  Atmosphere 300
  Ekman spiral 297
  Energy generation 314
  Oceans and seas
  296-297
  Rock cycle 266-267
  Water cycle 288
  Weather 302
  Weathering and erosion
  282-283
Windspeed 503
Windcheetah SL Mark VI
  "Speedy" racing HPV
  bicycle 361
Wind chest 514
Wind controller 521
Wind deflector 341
Wind-dispersed seeds
  150-151
Wind erosion 282-283
  Coastline 294
Winding cornice 472
Wind instruments 508,
  509
  Brass 506, 507
  Electronic 520
  Woodwind 508, 509
Windlass
  Buildings 467, 477
  Roman corbita 372
Windlass bar 380
Window
  Ancient Egyptian
  building 459
  Ancient Roman
  building 463, 465
  Asian building 490-491
  Baroque church
  479-481
  Dome 486-487
  Dormer 495
  Double-decker tour bus
  333
  "Eurostar" multi-
  voltage electric train 329
  Gothic building 470-475
  MCW Metrobus 333
  Medieval building
  466-469
  Modern building 498,
  499
  Neoclassical building
  478, 482-483
  Nineteenth-century
  building 492-493
  Renaissance building
  474, 476
  Rococo style 482
  Single-decker bus 333
  TGV electric high-
  speed train 329
  Twentieth-century
  building 494-495
Window blind 336, 572
Window controls 576, 577
Window-frame 486
Window glass 348

White Steam Car 542 [duplicate column]
Window jamb 479, 482,
  483
Window-sill
  Baroque church 479
  Neoclassical building
  482-485
  Twentieth-century
  building 494
Window shade button 577
Window stage 477
Wind-pollinated plants
  144
Windscreen
  Airbus 380 573
  BAe-146 jetliner
  components 412
  BE 2B bomber 404
  BMW R/60 sidecar 362
  Concorde 416-417
  "Deltic" diesel-electric
  locomotive 327
  Double-decker tour bus
  333
  Ford Model T 339
  Harley-Davidson FLHS
  Honda Insight 354
  Electra Glide 363
  Hawker Tempest
  components 409
  Kirby BSA racing
  sidecar 362
  Lockheed Electra
  airliner 406-407
  Tornado 420
Windscreen wiper
  "Deltic" diesel-electric
  locomotive 327
  "Eurostar" multi-
  voltage electric train 329
  Italian State Railways
  Class 402 528
  MCW Metrobus 332
  Paris Metro 328
  TGV electric high-
  speed train 329
  "Union Pacific"
  locomotive 326
  Volkswagen Beetle 341
Windsor green 458
Windspeed 503
Wind synthesizer 521
Wind turbine 604, 605
Wind-up 537
Windvane 375, 605
Windward face 283
Wing
  1906 Renault 336
  Alula 191
  ARV light aircraft
  424-425
  Australian rules football
  528
  Avro biplane 403
  BAe-146 jetliner
  components 413, 414
  BE 2B wings 404
  Beetle 168
  Biplanes and triplanes
  402
  Bird 188, 191
  Blackburn monoplane
  401
  Bones 191
  Bumblebee 168
  Butterfly 169
  Cobra lily 160
  Coverts 188
  Curtiss biplane 398
  Deer hopper dry fly
  563
  Developing 192
  Dry fruit 150-151
  Early monoplanes 400
  Feather 188, 191
  Ford Model T 358
  Formula One racing car
  357
  Gliders, hang-gliders,
  and microlights 426

Handball 535
Hawker Tempest
  components 409
Hockey 540
Ice hockey 550
Lockheed Electra
  airliner 406
Pine seed 122
Pitcher plant 113
Rugby 530
Scots pine seed 122
Showjumping fence
  554
Ski boot safety binding
  552
Spurious 191
Sycamore 151
Wing assembly 413
Wing attack 535, 541
Wing case 168
Wing defence
  Lacrosse 541
  Netball 535
Winged seeds
  Scots pine 122
  Sycamore 131, 151
Winged stem 129
Wing end-plate 357
Wing-feather impression
  85
Wing fillet panel 409
Wingframe 427
Wing landing gear 572,
  573
Wing leading edge 573
Winglet 556
Wing mirror 354
Wing piping 341
Wing-protecting skid
  598-599
Wing-root glove fairing
  420-421
Wing-root mount 413
Wing scar 122
Wing stay 339
Wing strut
  ARV light aircraft
  424-425
  Avro triplane 402-403
  Curtiss biplane 398
Wing supports 357
Wingtip
  ARV light aircraft 424
  BE 2B wings 404
  Hawker Tempest
  components 409
  Schleicher glider 426
Wingtip aerial fairing 421
Wing vein 168, 169
Wing warping 400
Wire armature 454, 455
Wire bristle brush 519
Wire coil 605
Wire-ended cutting tool
  454
Wire-end tools 452
Wire gauze pad 342
Wireless and telegraphy
  yard 595
Wireless office 397
Wires 518
Wire wheel 402
Wiring loom 596
Wishbone
  Bird 189
  Formula One racing car
  357
Withdrawal stride 543
Withdrawing-room 483
Withers 199
Wolf 195
Wolffian duct 179
Wolf hair brush 444
Wollastonite 271
Womb 258-259
Women's lacrosse field
  540, 541
Women's shot 542
Wood

668

Golf club 547
Sculpture 454
Wood block 446, 449
Wood capstan 387
Woodcarving 452, 453
Woodcut 446
Wooden arrow 109
Wooden artillery wheel 337
Wooden bar 516
Wooden boarding 602
Wooden body 510
Wooden body-shell 519
Wooden buffer 324
Wooden case 514, 515
Wooden-domed deck 403
Wooden driving wheel 324
Wooden frame
  Harp 511
  Printing mesh 446, 448
  Sculpture 452
  Steam-powered Cugnot
    "Fardier" 334
Wooden golf clubs 546, 547
Wood engraving 446, 447
Wood engraving print 449
Wooden grip 549
Wooden hearth 109
Wooden "key" 351
Wooden packing 397
Wooden panel 473
Wooden sailing ship
  378-379
Wooden sleeper 324, 331
Wooden spoke 334
Wooden-spoked wheel 339
Wooden stands 554
Wooden wheel 334
Woodwind instruments
  504, 505, 508, 509
Woodwork 467
Woody flowering plants
  126, 130-131
Woody pericarps 150
Woody plants 126

Woody scales
  Bishop pine cone 124
  Smooth cypress 123
Woody stem 134-135
Woofer loudspeaker
  connector 585
Woolding 376
Work 314
Working chamber 396
World War I aircraft
  404-405
World War II aircraft
  408-409
World Wide Web 576
Worming 388
Worms
  Earth's evolution 56
  Fossil record 279
Woven dacron 384
Wrack 116-117
Wren, C. 478
  Baroque church 480
  Cathedral dome 484, 487
Wrest plank
  Concert grand piano 515
  Upright piano 514
Wright brothers
  Modern piston aero-
    engines 410
  Pioneers of flight
    398-399
Wright, F. L. 495
Wright Flyer 398-399
Wrist
  Corythosaurus 98
  Elephant 90
  Human 211, 230-231
  Iguanodon 97
  Stegosaurus 92
  Triceratops 102
Wrist joint
  Baryonyx 85
  Brachiosaurus 91
  Diplodocus 90

Euoplocephalus 94
Human 218
Parasaurolophus 99
Plateosaurus 88
Robot 608
Stegoceras 100, 101
Tyrannosaurus 84
Wrist pin 390
Wrist position 444
Writing tools 444
Wrought iron boiler 324
Wrought iron rail 324
Wuerhosaurus 93
Wulfenite 269

X

Xerophytes 156-157
Xi2 Sagittarii 21
Xi Orionis 18
Xi Pegasi 19
X line 445
X-ray 318-319
  Colon 214
  Gallbladder 214
  Hand 230
X-ray emission 28
X-ray image of Crab
  Nebula 28
"X" turret 395
Xylem
  Bishop pine 124
  Clubmoss stem 120
  Dicotyledons 126-127
  Dodder host 163
  Epiphytic orchid 162
  Fern rachis 121
  Higher plants 118-119
  Horsetail stem 120
  Marram grass 113
  Monocotyledons
    126-127
  Pine needle 124

Pine root/stem 125
Radicle 152
Root 132
Stem 134-135
Water hyacinth root 158
Water lily leaf 159
Xylem fibres 134-135

Y

Yacht racing 560
Yangchuanosaurus 85
Yangtze River 265
Yard 382
  Battleship 395
  Double topsail
    schooner 385
  Greek and Roman ships
    372, 373
  Steel 392
  Tea clipper 392
  Viking karv 375
Yardang 282
Yardarm 379
Yardsman 526
Yasti 490, 491
Yaw control 605
Yaw ring 605
Year
  Earth 30
  Jupiter 30
  Mars 30
  Mercury 26, 34
  Neptune 31
  Planets 30-31
  Pluto 31
  Saturn 31
  Uranus 31
  Venus 30
Yeast
  Fermentation 313
  Fungi 114
Yellow card 524

Yellow light 318, 331
Yellow ochre 442
Yellow orpiment 271
Yellow River 265
Yellow warning arm
  330
Yellow-wort 144
Yew 123
Y.M.C.A. 532
Yolk 192
Yolk sac 192
Ytterbium 311
Yttrium 310
"Y" turret 395
Yucca 126
Yucca sp. 126

Z

Zagros Mountains 75
Zaire 265
Zap button 586
Zea mays 127
Zeami 35
Zebra 198
Zeeman 41
Zeilleria frenzlii 66
Zeppelin ipod speaker
  dock 586
Zeta Centauri 21
Zeta Sagittarii 21
Zeugen 282
Ziggurat-style step-back
  494
Zinc 281, 312
Zinc phosphating 348
Zinc plating 477
Zingiber officinale 155
Zion Canyon 276
Zirconium 310
Zona pellucida 606, 607
Zone
  Jupiter 44-45

Structure of Saturn 47
Zone defences 533
Zonular ligament 241
Zoom keys 590
Zoomorphic head 374
Zosteres 572
Zosterophyllum
  llanoveranum 64
Zubenelgenubi 18, 21
Zubeneschamali 18, 21
Zugon 373
Zygian 373
Zygomatic arch
  Bear 194
  Chimpanzee 202
  Human 215, 220
  Lion 194
  Smilodon 106
  Toxodon 107
Zygomatic bone 220-221
Zygomaticus major
  muscle 228-229
Zygote
  Bryophyte 118-119
  Fertilization 146-147
  Plant formation 146
  Primitive land plants
    120
  Seaweed 116-117

Acknowledgments

Dorling Kindersley would like to thank (in order of sections):

The Universe
(consultant editors – Sue Becklake, Gevorkyan Tatyana Alekseyevna):

John Becklake; the Memorial Museum of Cosmonautics, Moscow; The Cosmos Pavilion, Moscow; The United States Space and Rocket Centre, Alabama; Broadhurst, Clarkson and Fuller Ltd; Susannah Massey

Prehistoric Earth
(consultant editors – William Lindsay, Martyn Bramwell, Dr Ralph E. Molnar, David Lambert):

Dr Monty Reid, Andrew Neuman, and the staff of the Royal Tyrrell Museum of Palaeontology, Drumheller, Alberta; Dr Angela Milner and the staff of the Department of Palaeontology, the Natural History Museum, London; Professor W. Ziegler and the staff, in particular Michael Loderstaedt, of the Naturmuseum Senckenburg, Frankfurt; Dr Alexander Liebau, Axel Hunghrebüller, Reiner Schoch, and the staff of the Institut und Museum für Geologie und Paläontologie der Universität, Tübingen; Rupert Wild of the Institut für Paläontologie, Staatliches Museum für Naturkunde, Stuttgart; Dr Scheiber of the Stadtmuseum, Nördlingen; Professor Dr Dietrich Herm of Staatssammlung für Paläontologie und Historische Geologie, München; Dr Michael Keith-Lucas of the Department of Botany, University of Reading; Richard Walker; American Museum of Natural History, New York

Plants
(consultant editor – Richard Walker):

Diana Miller; Lawrie Springate; Karen Sidwell; Chris Thody; Michelle End; Susan Barnes and Chris Jones of the EMU Unit of the Natural History Museum, London; Jenny Evans of Kew Gardens, London; Kate Biggs of the Royal Horticultural Society Gardens, Wisley, Surrey; Spike Walker of Microworld Services; Neil Fletcher; John Bryant of Bedgebury Pinetum, Kent; Dean Franklin

Animals
(consultant editor – Richard Walker):

David Manning's Animal Ark; Intellectual Animals; Howletts Zoo, Canterbury; John Dunlop; Alexander O'Donnell; Sue Evans of the Royal Veterinary College, London; Dr Geoff Potts and Fred Frettsome of the Marine Biological Association of the United Kingdom, Plymouth; Jeremy Adams of the Booth Museum of Natural History, Brighton; Derek Telling of the Department of Anatomy, University of Bristol; the Natural History Museum, London; Andy Highfield of the Tortoise Trust; Brian Harris of the Aquarium, London Zoo; the Invertebrate Department, London Zoo; Dr Harold McClure of the Yerkes Regional Primate Research Center, Emory University, Atlanta, Georgia; Nielson Lausen of the Harvard Medical School, New England Regional Primates Research

Centre, Southborough, Massachusetts; Dr Paul Hopwood of the Department of Veterinary Anatomy, University of Sydney; Dean Franklin

The Human Body
(consultant editors – Dr Frances Williams, Dr Fiona Payne, Richard Cummins FRCS):
Derek Edwards and Dr Martin Collins, British School of Osteopathy; Dr M.C.E. Hutchinson of the Department of Anatomy, United Medical and Dental Schools of Guy's and St Thomas' Hospitals, London. Models – Barry O'Rorke (Bodyline Agency) and Pauline Swaine (MOT Model Agency)

Geology, Geography, and Meteorology
(consultant editor – Martyn Bramwell):
Dr John Nudds of the Manchester Museum, Manchester; Dr Alan Wooley and Dr Andrew Clark of the Natural History Museum, London; Graham Bartlett of the National Meteorological Library and Archive, Bracknell; Tony Drake of BP Exploration, Uxbridge; Jane Davies of the Royal Society of Chemistry, Cambridge; Dr Tony Waltham of Nottingham Trent University, Nottingham; staff of the Smithsonian Institute, Washington; staff of the United States Geological Survey, Washington; staff of the National Geographic Society, Washington; staff of Edward Lawrence Associates (Export Ltd), Midhurst; John Farndon; David Lambert

Rail and Road
Rail (consultant editor – John Coiley)
Michael Ashworth of the London Transport Museum

Road (consultant editors – David Burgess-Wise, Hugo Wilson)
The National Motor Museum, Beaulieu; Alf Newell of Renault UK Ltd; David Suter of Cheltenham Cutaway Exhibits Ltd; Francesca Riccini of the Science Museum, London. Signore Amadelli of the Museo dell' Automobile Carlo Biscaretti di Ruffia; Paul Bolton of the Mazda MCL Group; Duncan Bradford of Reg Mills Wire Wheels; John and Leslie Brewster of Autocavan; David Burgess-Wise; Trevor Cass of Garrett Turbo Service; John Corbett of The Patrick Collection; Gary Crumpler of Williams Grand Prix Engineering Ltd; Mollie Easterbrooke and Duncan Gough of Overland Ltd; Arthur Fairley of the Vauxhall Motor Company; Paul Foulkes-Halbard of Filching Manor Motor Museum; Frank Gilbert of I. Wilkinson and Son Ltd; Paolo Gratton of Gratton Museum; Colvin Gunn of Gunn and Son; Judy Hogg of Ecurie Bertelli; Milton Holman of Dream Cars; Ian Matthews of IMAT Electronics; Eric Neal of Jaguar Cars Ltd; Paul Niblett, Keith Davidson, Mark Reumel, and David Woolf of Michelin Tyre plc; Doug Nye; Kevin O'Keefe of O'Keefe Cars; Seat UK; Ian Whitley, Raj Johal and Andy Faiers of the Honda Institute; Roger Smith; Jim Stirling of Ironbridge Gorge Museum, Staffordshire; Jon Taylor; Doug Thompson; Martyn Watkins of Ford Motor Company Ltd; John Cattermole, Customer Services Manager at London Northern Buses; F. W. Evans Cycles Ltd; Trek UK Ltd (Bicycle); Sam Grimmer; Colin Uttley

Physics and Chemistry
(consultant editor – Jack Challoner)

Sea and Air
Sea (consultant editors – Geoff Hales and Harvey B. Loomis):
David Spence, Gillian Hutchinson, David Topliss, Simon Stephens, Robert Baldwin, Jonathan Betts, all of the National Maritime Museum, London; Ian Friel; Simon Turnage of Captain O.M. Watts of London Ltd; Davey and Company Ltd, Great Dunmow; Avon Inflatables Ltd, Llanelli; Musto Ltd, Benfleet; Peter Martin of Spencer Rigging Ltd, Southampton; Peter Rowson of Ratseys Sailmakers, Southampton; Swiftech Ltd, Wallingford; Colin Scattergood of the Barrow Boat Company Ltd, Colchester; Professor J.S. Morrison of the Trireme Trust, Cambridge; The Cutty Sark Maritime Trust; Adrian Daniels of Kelvin Hughes Marine Instruments, London; Arthur Credland of Hull City Council Museums and Art Galleries; The Hull Maritime Society; Gerald Clark; Peter Fitzgerald of the Science Museum, London; Alec Michael of HMB Subwork Ltd, Great Yarmouth, and Ray Ward of the OSEL Group, Great Yarmouth; Richard Bird of UWI, Weybridge; Walker Marine Instruments, Birmingham; The International Sailing Craft Association; The Exeter Maritime Museum; Jane Wilson of the Trinity Lighthouse Company, London; The Imperial War Museum Collections; Thorn Security Ltd; Michael Bach

Air (consultant editor – Bill Gunston):
Aeromega Helicopters, Stapleford; Aero Shopping, London; Avionics Mobile Services Ltd, Watford; Roy Barber and John Chapman of the RAF Museum, Hendon; Mitch Barnes Aviation, London; Mike Beach; British Caledonian Flight Training Ltd; Fred Coates of Helitech (Luton) Ltd; Michael Cuttell and CSE Aviation Ltd, Oxford; Dowty Aerospace Landing Gear, Gloucester; Guy Hartcup of the Airship Association; Anthony Hooley, Chris Walsh, and David Cord of British Aerospace Regional Aircraft Ltd; Ken Huntley of Mid-West Aero Engines Ltd; Imperial War Museum, Duxford; The London Gliding Club, Dunstable; Musée des Ballons, Calvados; Noel Penny Turbines Ltd; Andy Pavey of Aviation Scotland Ltd; Tony Pavey of Thermal Aircraft Developments, London; the Commanding Officer and personnel of RAF St Athan; the Commanding Officer and personnel of RAF Wittering; The Science Museum, London; Ross Sharp of the Science Museum, Wroughton; The Shuttleworth Collection; Skysport Engineering; Mike Smith; Solar Wings Ltd, Marlborough; Julian Temple of Brooklands Museum Trust Ltd; Kelvin Wilson of Flying Start

Architecture
(consultant editor – Alexandra Kennedy):
Stephen Cutler for advice and text; Gavin Morgan of the Museum of London, London; Chris Zeuner of the Weald and Downland Museum, Singleton, Sussex; Alan Hills and James Putnam of the British Museum, London; Dr Simon Penn and Michael Thomas of the Avoncroft Museum of Buildings, Bromsgrove,

Worcestershire; Christina Scull of Sir John Soane's Museum, London; Paul Kennedy and John Williamson of the London Door Company, London; Lou Davis of The Original Box Sash Window Company, Windsor; Goddard and Gibbs Studios Ltd, London, for access to stained glass windows; The Royal Courts of Justice, Strand, London; Charles Brooking and Peter Dalton for access to the doors and windows in the Charles Brooking Collection, University of Greenwich, Dartford, Kent; Clare O'Brien of the Shakespeare Globe Trust, Shakespeare's Globe Museum, Bear Gardens, Southwark, London; Ken Teague of the Horniman Museum, London; Canon Haliburton, Mike Payton, Ken Stones, and Anthony Webb of St Paul's Cathedral, London; Roy Spring of Salisbury Cathedral; Reverend Gillean Craig of the Church of St George in the East, London; the Science Museum, London; Dr Neil Bingham; Lin Kennedy of Historic Royal Palaces; Katy Harris of Sir Norman Foster and Partners; Production Design, Thames Television plc, London; Dominique Reynier of Le Centre Georges Pompidou, Paris; Denis Roche of Le Musée National des Monuments Français, Paris; Franck Gioria and students of Les Compagnons du Devoir, Paris, for access to construction models; Frank Folliot of Le Musée Carnavalet, Paris; Dr Martina Harms of Hessische Landesmuseums, Darmstadt; Jefferson Chapman of the University of Tennessee, Knoxville, for access to the model of the Hypostyle Hall, Temple of Amon-Re; staff of the Palazzo Strozzi, Florence; staff of the Sydney Opera House, Sydney; staff of the Empire State Building, New York; Nick Jackson; Ann Terrell

The Visual Arts
(consultant editor – Pip Seymour):
Rosemary Simmons; Michael Taylor of Paupers Press, London; Tessa Hunkin and Emma Biggs of Mosaic Workshop, London; John Tiranti, Jonathan Lyons of Alec Tiranti Ltd, London; Chris Hough; Dr Ashok Roy; Satwinder Sehmi of Alphabet Soup, London; Phillip Poole of Cornelissens, London; George Weil and Sons Ltd, London; The National Gallery, London; Chris Webster of the Tate Gallery, London; China Art Cultural Centre, London; London Graphic Centre, London; A.P. Fitzpatrick, London; Flowers Graphics, London; Intaglio Printmaker, London; Falkiner Papers, London; Edgar Udny and Co, London; John Green

Music
(consultant editor – Susan Sturrock):
Boosey and Hawkes Music Publishers Ltd, London, for permission to reproduce extract from The Prodigal Son by Arthur Sullivan; The Bass and Drum Cellar, London; Empire Drums and Percussion, London; Argents (part of World of Music), London; Bill Lewington Ltd, London; Frobenius organ at Kingston Parish Church, Surrey; Yamaha-Kemble Music (UK) Ltd, Tilbrook, Milton Keynes; Yamaha Atelier, London; Akai (UK) Ltd, Hounslow, Middlesex; Casio Electronics Co. Ltd, London; Roland (UK) Ltd, Fleet, Hampshire; Richard Schulman; Andy Brown of Musictrack

Sports
The Sports Council Information Centre, London; The British Olympic Games Committee; Brian Crennell of Black's Leisure Group (First Sport); Lillywhites of Piccadilly; London; Mitre Sports International Ltd, Huddersfield; David Bloomfield of the Football Association; Denver Athletics Ltd, Norfolk; Greg Everest and Keith Birley of the British League of Australian Rules Football; Peter McNally of the Gaelic Athletic Association; Jeremy Garman of James Gilbert Ltd.; Rex King of the Rugby Football Union, Twickenham; Neil Tunnicliffe and John Huxley of the Rugby Football League, Leeds; Wayne Patterson of the Basketball Hall of Fame, Springfield, Connecticut; Brian Coleman of the English Basketball Association; All American Imports, Northampton; George Bulman of the English Volleyball Association; Julie Longdon of Mizuno Mallory (UK) Ltd; Juliet Stanford of the All-England Netball Association; Jeff Rowland of the British Handball Association; Cally Melin of Adidas UK Ltd; Patrick Donnely of the Baseball Hall of Fame, Cooperstown, New York; Ian Lepage and Stephen Barlow of the Hockey Association, Milton Keynes; Alison Taylor and Anita Mason of the All England Women's Lacrosse Association, Birmingham; David Shuttleworth of the English Lacrosse Union; Les Barnett and Jock Bentley of the British Athletic Federation Ltd, Birmingham; Mike Gilks of the Badminton Association of England; Gurinder Purewall for advice on archery; Chris McCartney of the US Archery Association; Geoff Doe of the National Smallbore Rifle Association, Bisley, Surrey, for information and reference material on shooting; Fagan Sports Goods Distributors, Surrey; Konrad Bartelski for advice on skiing; The British Ski Federation, Edinburgh; Mike Barnett of Snow and Rock of London; Sally Spurway of Mast-Co. Ltd, Reading; Sarah Morgan for advice on equestrian sports; Steve Brown and the New York Racing Association Inc, New York; Danrho of London; Alan Skipp and James Chambers of the Amateur Fencing Association, London; Carla Richards of the US Fencing Association; Hamilton Bland and John Dryer of the Amateur Swimming Association, Loughborough; Cotswold Camping Ltd, London; Tim Spalton of Glyn Locke (Racing Shells) Ltd, Chalgrove; Terry Friel of the US Rowing Association; House of Hardy; Leeda Fishing Tackle

The Modern World
John Lewis, Brent Cross, for the loan of products for photography; Apple Computers UK; Palm Inc.; Epson UK; Naynesh Mistry of Brother UK; Nintendo; Sony UK; Nokia Mobile Phones Ltd; Sony Ericsson; Tony Broad of Garmin Europe; Dualit Ltd; Black and Decker Ltd; James Honour of the Buildings Research Establishment; Craig Anders of Cole Thompson Associates; Vestas Wind Systems; Bryan Adams of MIT; Dr Julian Heath of *Microscopy and Analysis*; Fei UK Ltd; Steve Parker; Ian Graham

PHOTOGRAPHY:
M. Alexander; Peter Anderson; Colin Bowling; Charles Brooks; Jane Burton; Peter Chadwick; Simon Clay; Gordon Clayton; John Coiley; Andy Crawford; Geoff Dann; Philip Dowell; John Downs; Mike Dunning; Torla Evans; David Exton; Paul Forrester; Robert and Anthony Fretwell of Fretwell Photography Ltd.; Philip Gatward; Steve Gorton; Anna Hodgson; Gary Kevin; J. Heseltine; Cyril Laubscher; John Lepine; Lynton Gardiner (American Museum of Natural History, New York); Steve Gorton; Michelangelo Gratton; Judith Harrington; Peter Hayman; Anna Hodgson; Colin Keates; Gary Kevin; Dave King; Bob Langrish; Brian D.Morgan; Nick Nicholls; Nick Parfitt; Tim Parmenter and Colin Keates (Natural History Museum, London); Tim Ridley; Dave Rudkin; Philippe Sebert; James Stevenson; Clive Streeter; Harry Taylor; Matthew Ward; Jerry Young

PHOTOGRAPHIC ASSISTANCE:
Kevin Zak; Gary Ombler; Govind Mittal

ILLUSTRATORS:
Julian Baum; Rick Blakeley; Kuo Rang Chen; Karen Cochrane; Simone End; Ian Fleming; Roy Flooks; Mark Franklin; David Gardner; Will Giles; Mick Gillah; David Hopkins; Selwyn Hutchinson; Mei Lim; Linden Artists; Nick Loates; Chris Lyon; Kathleen McDougall; Coral Mula; Sandra Pond; Dave Pugh; Colin Rose; Graham Rosewarne; John Temperton; Halli Verrinder; John Woodcock; Chris Woolmer

MODEL MAKERS:
Roby Braun; David Donkin; Morrison Frederick; Gordon Models; John Holmes; Graham High and Jeremy Hunt of Centaur Studios; Richard Kemp; Kelvin Thatcher; Paul Wilkinson

ADDITIONAL DESIGN ASSISTANCE:
Stefan Morris; Ulysses Santos; Suchada Smith; Niyati Gosain; Jomin Johny; Ridhi Khanna; Amit Malhotra; Payal Rosalind Malik; Anamica Roy; Ira Sharma; Balwant Singh

ADDITIONAL EDITORIAL ASSISTANCE:
Helen Castle; Colette Connolly; Camela Decaire; Nick Harris; Andrea Horth; Stewart McEwen; Damien Moore; Melanie Tham; Pragati Nagpal; Suparna Sengupta; Anita Kakar; Divya Chandhok

INDEX: Kay Wright; Lynn Bresler

Picture credits:

The publisher would like to thank the following for their kind permission to reproduce their photographs:

2011 Research In Motion Limited 589tr; Action Plus 530tc; Alamy images David Kilpatrick 581tr, 581cra; Nikreates 586ca; NordicImages 591tr; Oleksiy Maksymenko Photography 568cra; Arthur Turner 579cla; Martin Williams 569bl; Anglo Australian Telescope Board 11cl, 11cra, 11cbl, 12tr, 12bc, 13tl, 13bl, 14tl, 16b, 17tc, 17bl, 22tl/D.Malin 16tl, 26tr, 27tl; Austin Brown and the Aviation Picture Library 426tl; Baptistery, Florence/ Alison Harris 453r; Biophoto Associates 217ca, 217cra, 228cbc, 228cbc 230tr; BRE Imaging 602bl, 602r, 603tr, 603br; Paul Brierley 311bra; Bowers & Wilkins: B&W Group Ltd 586b; British Aerospace/Anthony Hooley 412tl, 415tl; British Aerospace (Commercial Aircraft) Ltd 416tl; By prmission of the British Library 432tl, 445bl; British Museum 459tl, 459tr, 460tr, 460tc, 460tb, 489b; BP Exploration 299; Duncan Brown 25tl; Frank Lloyd Wright, American, 1867-1959, Model of Midway Gardens, 1914, executed by Richard Tickner, mixed media, 1987, 41.9 x 81.3 x 76.2, 1989.48. view 1. Photography courtesy of the Art Intitute of Chicago 495t; J.A. Coiley 331cr; Bruce Coleman Ltd/Andy Price 272tl; Canon Europe 581crb; Corbis Joseph Sohm/Visions of America 494l; Paul Sounders/Terra 328b; Jon Stokes/Science Photo Library 576cl; Wu Ching-ting/Xinhua Press 568br; Haruyoshi Yamaguchi/Sygma 608r; Courtesy of the Board of Trustees of the Victoria and Albert Museum, London 454-455b; Creative Labs, Inc. 586tc; Dorling Kindersley Owen Peyton Jones 566cr, 582-583, 589; Dreamstime.com Vasimila 431b; Dyson 592tr; European Passenger Services 329tl; ESA /PLV 11bl; European Southern Observatory (ESO) 53tl; Fei Co. 610tc, 610r; French Railways 329c; FUJIFILM UK 581br; Garmin Europe 590c; Geoscience Features 311cla; Robert Harding Picture Library 62tl; Getty Images Bloomberg 569bc, 569br; Tony Cordoza 584tr; GraphicaArtis 448clb; Bill Johnson/The Denver Post 448tl; Hannah Johnston 588ca; Photodisc/Ryan McVay 577tl; Harman International Industries, Incorporated JBL 586cl; Hitachi High-Technologies Co. Ltd 61 1tr; Michael Holford/British Museum 372bl, Michael Holford 374tr; Honda 354tr, 355b; Hutchison Picture Library

60cl; iFixit Miroslav Djuric 580-581 (Nikon Coolpix S1000PJ), 587 (Components of Microsoft Zune HD); Brett Hartt 578cra; The Image Bank/Edward Bower 306tr; Jet Propulsion Laboratory 11cbr; 30bc; 31bc; 31bcr; 38tl; 42crb; 44cb; 44cbr; 44bc; 46tl; 46cr; 46cb; 46bc; 46br; 50tl; 50cra; 50cl; 50c; 50cr; 50br; Kawasaki (UK) 609bl; KeyMed Ltd 248bl, 249bl, 249bcl; Department of Prints and Drawings, Uffizi, Florence/Philip Gatward 431tc/Uffizi, Florence/Philip Gatward 433tl; Robin Kerrod/Spacecharts 615br; Dr D.N. Landon (Institute of Neurology) 228bl,br; LG Electronics 588cr; Life Science Images/Ron Boardman 244bl, 244br; The Lund Observatory 15bc; Brian Morrison 329tl, 329tr; © The Henry Moore Foundation 455tr; Used with permission from Microsoft 578tr, 587br; Musée d'Orsay, Paris/Philippe Sebert 457tc, 441tc; Musée du Louvre, Paris/Philippe Sebert 453tl, 453l; Musictrack/MOTU Digital performer 521bcl; NASA/AUI 13tr; NASA and The Hubble Heritage Team (AURA/STScl) 44tl; NASA Dr. R. Albrecht, ESA/ESO Space Telescope European Coordinating Facility 31fbr; CXC/ASU/J. Hester et al 28cra; JPL/ DLR 44br; JPL JHUAPL 44fbr; JPL-Caltech/ University of Arizona 42fbr; NASA/JPL 11 cbr, 11br, 30tl, 30bl, 30br, 30bc, 31bc, 31bcr, 31bl, 34cr, 38tl, 40tl, 40cr, 42cr, 44cb, 44cbr, 44bc, 44cr, 46crb, 46tl, 46cr, 46cb, 46bc, 46br, 48tl, 48cra, 48bca, 48bc, 48br, 50tl, 50bc, 50bc, 50cbr, 50br, 50cr, 52cr, 612cr, 612tr, 613tl, 613tcl, 613cr, 613tr, 613c, 613cr, 614tl, 614tr 614cl, 614bl, 614c, 615tr, 615cr, 615c; National Maritime Museum 373br, 392-393b; National Medical Slide Bank 217cr; Nature Photographers/Paul Sterry 286tl; Newage International 317bl; Nintendo 578tl, 578clb, 579tl, 579tr, 579cra; Olympus 610cl, 61 0bi; Oxford Scientific Films/Breck P. Kent 166tl; Planet Earth 274tr; Press Association Images AP 609cr; Quadrant 326tr; Margaret Robinson 332tl; Giotto The Expulsion of the Merchants from the Temple Scala 435tc, 435bl, 435br; RapidRepair.com Ben Levy 569ca (iPad Components); Rex Features Jonathan Hordle 609br; Roland UK 521tl; Science Photo Library 10bl, 13tr, 214bcr, 214bl, 236tr/Michael Abbey 225tc/Agema Infrared Systems 318tl/AGFA 220tl/Alex Barte 605tr/David Becker 607cr/ Biophoto Associates: 217crb/Dr Jeremy Burgess/ Science Photo Library 132tr; Dr Jeremy Burgess 235bc/CNRI 214tl, 214cl, 214c, 214cr, 214bl, 214clb, 214crb, 214blc, 214br, 217cb, 235bcr, 238tl, 249bcr, 253tr, 253cra, 256tl; Sci-

ence Photo library /Earth Satellite Corporation 288cl, 293br/Dr Brian Eyden 228cbr/Professor C. Ferlaud 245bl/Vaughan Fleming 311tl/ Simon Fraser/U.S. Dept.of Energy 214bcl, 266tl/Eric Grave 217br/Hale Observatories 32br/Max Planck Institute for Radio Astronomy 15tl/Jan Hinsch 225tc/Jodrell Bank 11tr, 13c /Manfred Kage 217c, 235br, 257br/Dr William C. Keel 13br/Keith Kent 564c/James King-Holmes 316tl, 606bl/Russ Lappa 310bra/ John Mead 605br/Astrid & Hans-Freider Michler 217tr/ Dennis Milon 52bl/NASA 11cla, 12tl, 15tr, 30c, 32tl, 35tl, 36tl, 36cl, 36cr, 36bc, 42tr, 52tl, 291tr, 300tl/National Optical Astro Observatory 52tr/NIBSC 253crb/Omikron 244bc/David Parker 63bl, 304-305, 308br/ Alfred Pasieka 606cr/Philippe Plailly 308tl/ Quest 611br/Roussel-UCLAF/CNRI 217tc/Rev Ronald Royer 32cr/Royal Observatory, Edinburgh/D Malin 11tl, 11cr, 16cr, 16cl, 17br/David Scharf 235bl/Dr Kaus Schiller 248bcl, 248bcr, 248br/Secchi-Lecaque/Koussel-UCLAF/CNRI 253br/H. Sochurek 214cb/ Stammers/Thompson 230tl/Sheila Terry 234tl/ US Department of Energy 310bc/US Geological Survey/Science Photo Library 8-9, 30bcr, 42tl, 42bl/Tom Van Sant/Geosphere Project, Santa Monica/Science Photo Library 273tr, 281tr, 296tr, 297tl/Dr Christopher B. Williams/(Saint Marks Hospital) 249br; Oxford Scientific Films/Animals/ Breck P. Kent 167tl; Pratt & Whitney Canada 418-419b, 419t; Science Museum 306bl, 306bcl; 306 bcr, 324t, 326-327b), 330tr, 331ct, 331 cb; Sony Corporation 586tr, 586cr; Sporting Pictures 524tl, 544cr; TechRepublic Bill Detwiler 578-579b; Tony Stone Worldwide 280tl; J.M.W. Turner The Burning of the Houses of Parliament Tate Gallery 439tc; Vision 26tr, 27c; Jerry Young 306tl; Dr Robert Youngson 241cr; courtesy of Vestas Wind Systems 604t; Zefa 217bc/Janicek 276tl/H. Sochurek 210tl, 250tl, 254tl/G. Steenmans 292tl

(a=above, b=below/bottom, c=centre, f=far, l-left, r=right, t=top)

All other images © Dorling Kindersley For further information see: www.dkimages.com

Every effort has been made to trace the copyright holders. Dorling Kindersley apologizes for any unintentional omissions and would be pleased, in any such cases, to add an acknowledgment in future editions.

Some pages in this book previously appeared in the Visual Dictionary series published by Dorling Kindersley. Contributors to this series include:

Project Art Editors: Duncan Brown, Ross George, Nicola Liddiard, Andrew Nash, Clare Shedden, Bryn Walls

Designers: Lesley Betts, Paul Calver, Simone End, Ellen Woodward

Additional design assistance: Sandra Archer, Christina Betts, Alexandra Brown, Nick Jackson, Susan Knight

Project Editors: Fiona Courtney-Thompson, Paul Docherty, Tim Fraser, Stephanie Jackson, Mary Lindsay

Editorial Assistant: Emily Hill

Additional editorial assistance: Susan Bosanko, Edward Bunting, Candace Burch, Deirdre Clark, Jeanette Cossar, Danièle Guitton, Jacqui Hand, David Harding, Nicholas Jackson, Edwina Johnson, David Lambert, Gail Lawther, David Learmount, Paul Jackson, Christine Murdock, Bob Ogden, Cathy Rubinstein, Louise Tucker, Dr Robert Youngson

Picture Researchers: Vere Dodds, Danièle Guitton, Anna Lord, Catherine O'Rourke, Christine Rista, Sandra Schneider, Vanessa Smith, Clive Webster

Series Editor: Martyn Page

Series Art Editor: Paul Wilkinson

Managing Art Editors: Philip Gilderdale, Steve Knowlden

Art Director: Chez Picthall

Managing Editor: Ruth Midgley

Production: Jayne Simpson